Hugh D. Young • Roger A. Freedman
Contributing Author
A. Lewis Ford

Sears and Zemansky's

University Physics
With Modern Physics

Physics & Astronomy Custom Edition for
San Jose State University
Physics 49 and Physics 50

Taken from:
*Sears and Zemansky's University Physics:
With Modern Physics,* Fourteenth Edition
by Hugh D. Young and Roger A. Freedman

Physics 50.
5:30 PM
Gary Do

Cover Art: Courtesy of Photodisc/Getty Images.

Taken from:

Sears and Zemansky's University Physics: With Modern Physics, Fourteenth Edition
by Hugh D. Young and Roger A. Freedman
Copyright © 2016, 2014, 2012 by Pearson Education, Inc.
New York, New York 10013

This special edition published in cooperation with Pearson Learning Solutions.

Pearson Learning Solutions, 330 Hudson Street, New York, New York 10013
A Pearson Education Company
www.pearsoned.com

Printed in the United States of America

4 16

000200010271971238

KM

ISBN 10: 1-323-17118-5
ISBN 13: 978-1-323-17118-9

DETAILED CONTENTS

MECHANICS

? Tornadoes are spawned by severe thunderstorms, so being able to predict the path of thunderstorms is essential. If a thunderstorm is moving at 15 km/h in a direction 37° north of east, how far north does the thunderstorm move in 2.0 h? (i) 30 km; (ii) 24 km; (iii) 18 km; (iv) 12 km; (v) 9 km.

1 UNITS, PHYSICAL QUANTITIES, AND VECTORS

LEARNING GOALS

Looking forward at ...

1.1 What a physical theory is.

1.2 The four steps you can use to solve any physics problem.

1.3 Three fundamental quantities of physics and the units physicists use to measure them.

1.4 How to work with units in your calculations.

1.5 How to keep track of significant figures in your calculations.

1.6 How to make rough, order-of-magnitude estimates.

1.7 The difference between scalars and vectors, and how to add and subtract vectors graphically.

1.8 What the components of a vector are and how to use them in calculations.

1.9 What unit vectors are and how to use them with components to describe vectors.

1.10 Two ways to multiply vectors: the scalar (dot) product and the vector (cross) product.

P hysics is one of the most fundamental of the sciences. Scientists of all disciplines use the ideas of physics, including chemists who study the structure of molecules, paleontologists who try to reconstruct how dinosaurs walked, and climatologists who study how human activities affect the atmosphere and oceans. Physics is also the foundation of all engineering and technology. No engineer could design a flat-screen TV, a prosthetic leg, or even a better mousetrap without first understanding the basic laws of physics.

The study of physics is also an adventure. You will find it challenging, sometimes frustrating, occasionally painful, and often richly rewarding. If you've ever wondered why the sky is blue, how radio waves can travel through empty space, or how a satellite stays in orbit, you can find the answers by using fundamental physics. You will come to see physics as a towering achievement of the human intellect in its quest to understand our world and ourselves.

In this opening chapter, we'll go over some important preliminaries that we'll need throughout our study. We'll discuss the nature of physical theory and the use of idealized models to represent physical systems. We'll introduce the systems of units used to describe physical quantities and discuss ways to describe the accuracy of a number. We'll look at examples of problems for which we can't (or don't want to) find a precise answer, but for which rough estimates can be useful and interesting. Finally, we'll study several aspects of vectors and vector algebra. We'll need vectors throughout our study of physics to help us describe and analyze physical quantities, such as velocity and force, that have direction as well as magnitude.

1

1.1 THE NATURE OF PHYSICS

Physics is an *experimental* science. Physicists observe the phenomena of nature and try to find patterns that relate these phenomena. These patterns are called physical theories or, when they are very well established and widely used, physical laws or principles.

CAUTION **The meaning of "theory"** A theory is *not* just a random thought or an unproven concept. Rather, a theory is an explanation of natural phenomena based on observation and accepted fundamental principles. An example is the well-established theory of biological evolution, which is the result of extensive research and observation by generations of biologists.

To develop a physical theory, a physicist has to learn to ask appropriate questions, design experiments to try to answer the questions, and draw appropriate conclusions from the results. **Figure 1.1** shows two important facilities used for physics experiments.

Legend has it that Galileo Galilei (1564–1642) dropped light and heavy objects from the top of the Leaning Tower of Pisa (Fig. 1.1a) to find out whether their rates of fall were different. From examining the results of his experiments (which were actually much more sophisticated than in the legend), he made the inductive leap to the principle, or theory, that the acceleration of a falling object is independent of its weight.

The development of physical theories such as Galileo's often takes an indirect path, with blind alleys, wrong guesses, and the discarding of unsuccessful theories in favor of more promising ones. Physics is not simply a collection of facts and principles; it is also the *process* by which we arrive at general principles that describe how the physical universe behaves.

No theory is ever regarded as the final or ultimate truth. The possibility always exists that new observations will require that a theory be revised or discarded. It is in the nature of physical theory that we can disprove a theory by finding behavior that is inconsistent with it, but we can never prove that a theory is always correct.

Getting back to Galileo, suppose we drop a feather and a cannonball. They certainly do *not* fall at the same rate. This does not mean that Galileo was wrong; it means that his theory was incomplete. If we drop the feather and the cannonball *in a vacuum* to eliminate the effects of the air, then they do fall at the same rate. Galileo's theory has a **range of validity:** It applies only to objects for which the force exerted by the air (due to air resistance and buoyancy) is much less than the weight. Objects like feathers or parachutes are clearly outside this range.

1.1 Two research laboratories.

(a) According to legend, Galileo investigated falling objects by dropping them from the Leaning Tower of Pisa, Italy, ...

... and he studied pendulum motion by observing the swinging chandelier in the adjacent cathedral.

(b) The Planck spacecraft is designed to study the faint electromagnetic radiation left over from the Big Bang 13.8 billion years ago.

These technicians are reflected in the spacecraft's light-gathering mirror during pre-launch testing.

1.2 SOLVING PHYSICS PROBLEMS

At some point in their studies, almost all physics students find themselves thinking, "I understand the concepts, but I just can't solve the problems." But in physics, truly understanding a concept *means* being able to apply it to a variety of problems. Learning how to solve problems is absolutely essential; you don't *know* physics unless you can *do* physics.

How do you learn to solve physics problems? In every chapter of this book you will find *Problem-Solving Strategies* that offer techniques for setting up and solving problems efficiently and accurately. Following each *Problem-Solving Strategy* are one or more worked *Examples* that show these techniques in action. (The *Problem-Solving Strategies* will also steer you away from some *incorrect* techniques that you may be tempted to use.) You'll also find additional examples that aren't associated with a particular *Problem-Solving Strategy*. In addition, at the end of each chapter you'll find a *Bridging Problem* that uses more than one of the key ideas from the chapter. Study these strategies and problems carefully, and work through each example for yourself on a piece of paper.

Different techniques are useful for solving different kinds of physics problems, which is why this book offers dozens of *Problem-Solving Strategies.* No matter what kind of problem you're dealing with, however, there are certain key steps that you'll always follow. (These same steps are equally useful for problems in math, engineering, chemistry, and many other fields.) In this book we've organized these steps into four stages of solving a problem.

All of the *Problem-Solving Strategies* and *Examples* in this book will follow these four steps. (In some cases we will combine the first two or three steps.) We encourage you to follow these same steps when you solve problems yourself. You may find it useful to remember the acronym *I SEE*—short for *Identify, Set up, Execute,* and *Evaluate.*

| PROBLEM-SOLVING STRATEGY 1.1 | **SOLVING PHYSICS PROBLEMS** |

IDENTIFY *the relevant concepts:* Use the physical conditions stated in the problem to help you decide which physics concepts are relevant. Identify the **target variables** of the problem—that is, the quantities whose values you're trying to find, such as the speed at which a projectile hits the ground, the intensity of a sound made by a siren, or the size of an image made by a lens. Identify the known quantities, as stated or implied in the problem. This step is essential whether the problem asks for an algebraic expression or a numerical answer.

SET UP *the problem:* Given the concepts you have identified, the known quantities, and the target variables, choose the equations that you'll use to solve the problem and decide how you'll use them. Make sure that the variables you have identified correlate exactly with those in the equations. If appropriate, draw a sketch of the situation described in the problem. (Graph paper, ruler, protractor, and compass will help you make clear, useful sketches.)

As best you can, estimate what your results will be and, as appropriate, predict what the physical behavior of a system will be. The worked examples in this book include tips on how to make these kinds of estimates and predictions. If this seems challenging, don't worry—you'll get better with practice!

EXECUTE *the solution:* This is where you "do the math." Study the worked examples to see what's involved in this step.

EVALUATE *your answer:* Compare your answer with your estimates, and reconsider things if there's a discrepancy. If your answer includes an algebraic expression, assure yourself that it correctly represents what would happen if the variables in it had very large or very small values. For future reference, make note of any answer that represents a quantity of particular significance. Ask yourself how you might answer a more general or more difficult version of the problem you have just solved.

Idealized Models

In everyday conversation we use the word "model" to mean either a small-scale replica, such as a model railroad, or a person who displays articles of clothing (or the absence thereof). In physics a **model** is a simplified version of a physical system that would be too complicated to analyze in full detail.

For example, suppose we want to analyze the motion of a thrown baseball (**Fig. 1.2a**). How complicated is this problem? The ball is not a perfect sphere (it has raised seams), and it spins as it moves through the air. Air resistance and wind influence its motion, the ball's weight varies a little as its altitude changes, and so on. If we try to include all these things, the analysis gets hopelessly complicated. Instead, we invent a simplified version of the problem. We ignore the size and shape of the ball by representing it as a point object, or **particle.** We ignore air resistance by making the ball move in a vacuum, and we make the weight constant. Now we have a problem that is simple enough to deal with (Fig. 1.2b). We will analyze this model in detail in Chapter 3.

We have to overlook quite a few minor effects to make an idealized model, but we must be careful not to neglect too much. If we ignore the effects of gravity completely, then our model predicts that when we throw the ball up, it will go in a straight line and disappear into space. A useful model simplifies a problem enough to make it manageable, yet keeps its essential features.

1.2 To simplify the analysis of (a) a baseball in flight, we use (b) an idealized model.

(a) A real baseball in flight

Baseball spins and has a complex shape.

Air resistance and wind exert forces on the ball.

Direction of motion

Gravitational force on ball depends on altitude.

(b) An idealized model of the baseball

Treat the baseball as a point object (particle).

No air resistance.

Direction of motion

Gravitational force on ball is constant.

The validity of the predictions we make using a model is limited by the validity of the model. For example, Galileo's prediction about falling objects (see Section 1.1) corresponds to an idealized model that does not include the effects of air resistance. This model works fairly well for a dropped cannonball, but not so well for a feather.

Idealized models play a crucial role throughout this book. Watch for them in discussions of physical theories and their applications to specific problems.

1.3 STANDARDS AND UNITS

As we learned in Section 1.1, physics is an experimental science. Experiments require measurements, and we generally use numbers to describe the results of measurements. Any number that is used to describe a physical phenomenon quantitatively is called a **physical quantity.** For example, two physical quantities that describe you are your weight and your height. Some physical quantities are so fundamental that we can define them only by describing how to measure them. Such a definition is called an **operational definition.** Two examples are measuring a distance by using a ruler and measuring a time interval by using a stopwatch. In other cases we define a physical quantity by describing how to calculate it from other quantities that we *can* measure. Thus we might define the average speed of a moving object as the distance traveled (measured with a ruler) divided by the time of travel (measured with a stopwatch).

When we measure a quantity, we always compare it with some reference standard. When we say that a Ferrari 458 Italia is 4.53 meters long, we mean that it is 4.53 times as long as a meter stick, which we define to be 1 meter long. Such a standard defines a **unit** of the quantity. The meter is a unit of distance, and the second is a unit of time. When we use a number to describe a physical quantity, we must always specify the unit that we are using; to describe a distance as simply "4.53" wouldn't mean anything.

To make accurate, reliable measurements, we need units of measurement that do not change and that can be duplicated by observers in various locations. The system of units used by scientists and engineers around the world is commonly called "the metric system," but since 1960 it has been known officially as the **International System,** or **SI** (the abbreviation for its French name, *Système International*). Appendix A gives a list of all SI units as well as definitions of the most fundamental units.

Time

From 1889 until 1967, the unit of time was defined as a certain fraction of the mean solar day, the average time between successive arrivals of the sun at its highest point in the sky. The present standard, adopted in 1967, is much more precise. It is based on an atomic clock, which uses the energy difference between the two lowest energy states of the cesium atom (^{133}Cs). When bombarded by microwaves of precisely the proper frequency, cesium atoms undergo a transition from one of these states to the other. One **second** (abbreviated s) is defined as the time required for 9,192,631,770 cycles of this microwave radiation (**Fig. 1.3a**).

Length

In 1960 an atomic standard for the meter was also established, using the wavelength of the orange-red light emitted by excited atoms of krypton (^{86}Kr). From this length standard, the speed of light in vacuum was measured to be 299,792,458 m/s. In November 1983, the length standard was changed again so that the speed of light in vacuum was *defined* to be precisely 299,792,458 m/s.

1.3 The measurements used to determine (a) the duration of a second and (b) the length of a meter. These measurements are useful for setting standards because they give the same results no matter where they are made.

(a) Measuring the second

Microwave radiation with a frequency of exactly 9,192,631,770 cycles per second ...

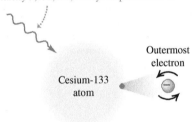

Outermost electron

Cesium-133 atom

... causes the outermost electron of a cesium-133 atom to reverse its spin direction.

Cesium-133 atom

An atomic clock uses this phenomenon to tune microwaves to this exact frequency. It then counts 1 second for each 9,192,631,770 cycles.

(b) Measuring the meter

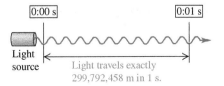

0:00 s   0:01 s

Light source

Light travels exactly 299,792,458 m in 1 s.

Hence the new definition of the **meter** (abbreviated m) is the distance that light travels in vacuum in 1/299,792,458 second (Fig. 1.3b). This modern definition provides a much more precise standard of length than the one based on a wavelength of light.

Mass

The standard of mass, the **kilogram** (abbreviated kg), is defined to be the mass of a particular cylinder of platinum–iridium alloy kept at the International Bureau of Weights and Measures at Sèvres, near Paris (**Fig. 1.4**). An atomic standard of mass would be more fundamental, but at present we cannot measure masses on an atomic scale with as much accuracy as on a macroscopic scale. The *gram* (which is not a fundamental unit) is 0.001 kilogram.

Other *derived units* can be formed from the fundamental units. For example, the units of speed are meters per second, or m/s; these are the units of length (m) divided by the units of time (s).

Unit Prefixes

Once we have defined the fundamental units, it is easy to introduce larger and smaller units for the same physical quantities. In the metric system these other units are related to the fundamental units (or, in the case of mass, to the gram) by multiples of 10 or $\frac{1}{10}$ Thus one kilometer (1 km) is 1000 meters, and one centimeter (1 cm) is $\frac{1}{100}$ meter. We usually express multiples of 10 or $\frac{1}{10}$ in exponential notation: $1000 = 10^3$, $\frac{1}{1000} = 10^{-3}$, and so on. With this notation, $1 \text{ km} = 10^3$ m and $1 \text{ cm} = 10^{-2}$ m.

The names of the additional units are derived by adding a **prefix** to the name of the fundamental unit. For example, the prefix "kilo-," abbreviated k, always means a unit larger by a factor of 1000; thus

$$1 \text{ kilometer} = 1 \text{ km} = 10^3 \text{ meters} = 10^3 \text{ m}$$

$$1 \text{ kilogram} = 1 \text{ kg} = 10^3 \text{ grams} = 10^3 \text{ g}$$

$$1 \text{ kilowatt} = 1 \text{ kW} = 10^3 \text{ watts} = 10^3 \text{ W}$$

A table in Appendix A lists the standard SI units, with their meanings and abbreviations.

Table 1.1 gives some examples of the use of multiples of 10 and their prefixes with the units of length, mass, and time. **Figure 1.5** (next page) shows how these prefixes are used to describe both large and small distances.

1.4 The international standard kilogram is the metal object carefully enclosed within these nested glass containers.

TABLE 1.1	Some Units of Length, Mass, and Time	
Length	**Mass**	**Time**
1 nanometer = 1 nm = 10^{-9} m (a few times the size of the largest atom)	1 microgram = 1 μg = 10^{-6} g = 10^{-9} kg (mass of a very small dust particle)	1 nanosecond = 1 ns = 10^{-9} s (time for light to travel 0.3 m)
1 micrometer = 1 μm = 10^{-6} m (size of some bacteria and other cells)	1 milligram = 1 mg = 10^{-3} g = 10^{-6} kg (mass of a grain of salt)	1 microsecond = 1 μs = 10^{-6} s (time for space station to move 8 mm)
1 millimeter = 1 mm = 10^{-3} m (diameter of the point of a ballpoint pen)	1 gram = 1 g = 10^{-3} kg (mass of a paper clip)	1 millisecond = 1 ms = 10^{-3} s (time for a car moving at freeway speed to travel 3 cm)
1 centimeter = 1 cm = 10^{-2} m (diameter of your little finger)		
1 kilometer = 1 km = 10^3 m (distance in a 10-minute walk)		

1.5 Some typical lengths in the universe.

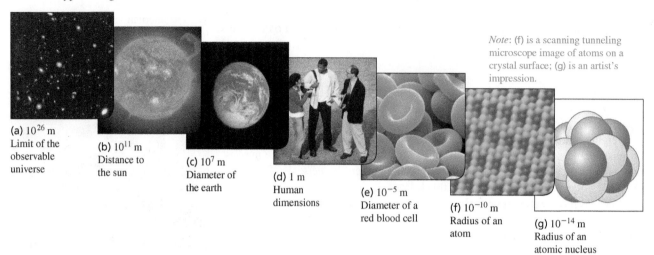

Note: (f) is a scanning tunneling microscope image of atoms on a crystal surface; (g) is an artist's impression.

(a) 10^{26} m
Limit of the observable universe

(b) 10^{11} m
Distance to the sun

(c) 10^7 m
Diameter of the earth

(d) 1 m
Human dimensions

(e) 10^{-5} m
Diameter of a red blood cell

(f) 10^{-10} m
Radius of an atom

(g) 10^{-14} m
Radius of an atomic nucleus

1.6 Many everyday items make use of both SI and British units. An example is this speedometer from a U.S.-built automobile, which shows the speed in both kilometers per hour (inner scale) and miles per hour (outer scale).

The British System

Finally, we mention the British system of units. These units are used in only the United States and a few other countries, and in most of these they are being replaced by SI units. British units are now officially defined in terms of SI units, as follows:

Length: 1 inch = 2.54 cm (exactly)

Force: 1 pound = 4.448221615260 newtons (exactly)

The newton, abbreviated N, is the SI unit of force. The British unit of time is the second, defined the same way as in SI. In physics, British units are used in mechanics and thermodynamics only; there is no British system of electrical units.

In this book we use SI units for all examples and problems, but we occasionally give approximate equivalents in British units. As you do problems using SI units, you may also wish to convert to the approximate British equivalents if they are more familiar to you (**Fig. 1.6**). But you should try to *think* in SI units as much as you can.

1.4 USING AND CONVERTING UNITS

We use equations to express relationships among physical quantities, represented by algebraic symbols. Each algebraic symbol always denotes both a number and a unit. For example, d might represent a distance of 10 m, t a time of 5 s, and v a speed of 2 m/s.

An equation must always be **dimensionally consistent.** You can't add apples and automobiles; two terms may be added or equated only if they have the same units. For example, if a body moving with constant speed v travels a distance d in a time t, these quantities are related by the equation

$$d = vt$$

If d is measured in meters, then the product vt must also be expressed in meters. Using the above numbers as an example, we may write

$$10 \text{ m} = \left(2\,\frac{\text{m}}{\cancel{\text{s}}}\right)(5\,\cancel{\text{s}})$$

Because the unit s in the denominator of m/s cancels, the product has units of meters, as it must. In calculations, units are treated just like algebraic symbols with respect to multiplication and division.

CAUTION **Always use units in calculations** Make it a habit to *always* write numbers with the correct units and carry the units through the calculation as in the example above. This provides a very useful check. If at some stage in a calculation you find that an equation or an expression has inconsistent units, you know you have made an error. In this book we will *always* carry units through all calculations, and we strongly urge you to follow this practice when you solve problems.

PROBLEM-SOLVING STRATEGY 1.2 | SOLVING PHYSICS PROBLEMS

IDENTIFY *the relevant concepts:* In most cases, it's best to use the fundamental SI units (lengths in meters, masses in kilograms, and times in seconds) in every problem. If you need the answer to be in a different set of units (such as kilometers, grams, or hours), wait until the end of the problem to make the conversion.

SET UP *the problem* and **EXECUTE** *the solution:* Units are multiplied and divided just like ordinary algebraic symbols. This gives us an easy way to convert a quantity from one set of units to another: Express the same physical quantity in two different units and form an equality.

For example, when we say that 1 min = 60 s, we don't mean that the number 1 is equal to the number 60; rather, we mean that 1 min represents the same physical time interval as 60 s. For this reason, the ratio (1 min)/(60 s) equals 1, as does its reciprocal, (60 s)/(1 min). We may multiply a quantity by either of these factors (which we call *unit multipliers*) without changing that quantity's physical meaning. For example, to find the number of seconds in 3 min, we write

$$3 \text{ min} = (3 \text{ min})\left(\frac{60 \text{ s}}{1 \text{ min}}\right) = 180 \text{ s}$$

EVALUATE *your answer:* If you do your unit conversions correctly, unwanted units will cancel, as in the example above. If, instead, you had multiplied 3 min by (1 min)/(60 s), your result would have been the nonsensical $\frac{1}{20}$ min^2/s. To be sure you convert units properly, include the units at *all* stages of the calculation.

Finally, check whether your answer is reasonable. For example, the result 3 min = 180 s is reasonable because the second is a smaller unit than the minute, so there are more seconds than minutes in the same time interval.

EXAMPLE 1.1 CONVERTING SPEED UNITS

The world land speed record of 763.0 mi/h was set on October 15, 1997, by Andy Green in the jet-engine car *Thrust SSC*. Express this speed in meters per second.

SOLUTION

IDENTIFY, SET UP, and EXECUTE: We need to convert the units of a speed from mi/h to m/s. We must therefore find unit multipliers that relate (i) miles to meters and (ii) hours to seconds. In Appendix E we find the equalities 1 mi = 1.609 km, 1 km = 1000 m, and 1 h = 3600 s. We set up the conversion as follows, which ensures that all the desired cancellations by division take place:

$$763.0 \text{ mi/h} = \left(763.0 \frac{\text{mi}}{\text{h}}\right)\left(\frac{1.609 \text{ km}}{1 \text{ mi}}\right)\left(\frac{1000 \text{ m}}{1 \text{ km}}\right)\left(\frac{1 \text{ h}}{3600 \text{ s}}\right)$$
$$= 341.0 \text{ m/s}$$

EVALUATE: This example shows a useful rule of thumb: A speed expressed in m/s is a bit less than half the value expressed in mi/h, and a bit less than one-third the value expressed in km/h. For example, a normal freeway speed is about 30 m/s = 67 mi/h = 108 km/h, and a typical walking speed is about 1.4 m/s = 3.1 mi/h = 5.0 km/h.

EXAMPLE 1.2 CONVERTING VOLUME UNITS

One of the world's largest cut diamonds is the First Star of Africa (mounted in the British Royal Sceptre and kept in the Tower of London). Its volume is 1.84 cubic inches. What is its volume in cubic centimeters? In cubic meters?

SOLUTION

IDENTIFY, SET UP, and EXECUTE: Here we are to convert the units of a volume from cubic inches (in.^{3}) to both cubic centimeters (cm^3) and cubic meters (m^3). Appendix E gives us the equality 1 in. = 2.540 cm, from which we obtain 1 in.^{3} = (2.54 cm)^3. We then have

$$1.84 \text{ in.}^3 = (1.84 \text{ in.}^3)\left(\frac{2.54 \text{ cm}}{1 \text{ in.}}\right)^3$$
$$= (1.84)(2.54)^3 \frac{\text{in.}^3 \text{ cm}^3}{\text{in.}^3} = 30.2 \text{ cm}^3$$

Appendix E also gives us 1 m = 100 cm, so

$$30.2 \text{ cm}^3 = (30.2 \text{ cm}^3)\left(\frac{1 \text{ m}}{100 \text{ cm}}\right)^3$$
$$= (30.2)\left(\frac{1}{100}\right)^3 \frac{\text{cm}^3 \text{ m}^3}{\text{cm}^3} = 30.2 \times 10^{-6} \text{ m}^3$$
$$= 3.02 \times 10^{-5} \text{ m}^3$$

EVALUATE: Following the pattern of these conversions, can you show that 1 in.$^3 \approx$ 16 cm^3 and that 1 m$^3 \approx$ 60,000 in.^{3}?

1.7 This spectacular mishap was the result of a very small percent error—traveling a few meters too far at the end of a journey of hundreds of thousands of meters.

TABLE 1.2 **Using Significant Figures**

Multiplication or division:
Result can have no more significant figures than the factor with the fewest significant figures:

$$\frac{0.745 \times 2.2}{3.885} = 0.42$$

$$1.32578 \times 10^7 \times 4.11 \times 10^{-3} = 5.45 \times 10^4$$

Addition or subtraction:
Number of significant figures is determined by the term with the largest uncertainty (i.e., fewest digits to the right of the decimal point):

$$27.153 + 138.2 - 11.74 = 153.6$$

1.8 Determining the value of π from the circumference and diameter of a circle.

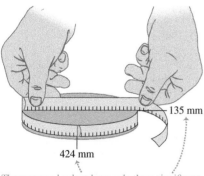

135 mm

424 mm

The measured values have only three significant figures, so their calculated ratio (π) also has only three significant figures.

1.5 UNCERTAINTY AND SIGNIFICANT FIGURES

Measurements always have uncertainties. If you measure the thickness of the cover of a hardbound version of this book using an ordinary ruler, your measurement is reliable to only the nearest millimeter, and your result will be 3 mm. It would be *wrong* to state this result as 3.00 mm; given the limitations of the measuring device, you can't tell whether the actual thickness is 3.00 mm, 2.85 mm, or 3.11 mm. But if you use a micrometer caliper, a device that measures distances reliably to the nearest 0.01 mm, the result will be 2.91 mm. The distinction between the measurements with a ruler and with a caliper is in their **uncertainty;** the measurement with a caliper has a smaller uncertainty. The uncertainty is also called the **error** because it indicates the maximum difference there is likely to be between the measured value and the true value. The uncertainty or error of a measured value depends on the measurement technique used.

We often indicate the **accuracy** of a measured value—that is, how close it is likely to be to the true value—by writing the number, the symbol $\pm$, and a second number indicating the uncertainty of the measurement. If the diameter of a steel rod is given as 56.47 $\pm$ 0.02 mm, this means that the true value is likely to be within the range from 56.45 mm to 56.49 mm. In a commonly used shorthand notation, the number 1.6454(21) means 1.6454 $\pm$ 0.0021. The numbers in parentheses show the uncertainty in the final digits of the main number.

We can also express accuracy in terms of the maximum likely **fractional error** or **percent error** (also called *fractional uncertainty* and *percent uncertainty*). A resistor labeled "47 ohms $\pm$ 10%" probably has a true resistance that differs from 47 ohms by no more than 10% of 47 ohms—that is, by about 5 ohms. The resistance is probably between 42 and 52 ohms. For the diameter of the steel rod given above, the fractional error is $(0.02 \text{ mm})/(56.47 \text{ mm})$, or about 0.0004; the percent error is $(0.0004)(100\%)$, or about 0.04%. Even small percent errors can be very significant (**Fig. 1.7**).

In many cases the uncertainty of a number is not stated explicitly. Instead, the uncertainty is indicated by the number of meaningful digits, or **significant figures,** in the measured value. We gave the thickness of the cover of the book as 2.91 mm, which has three significant figures. By this we mean that the first two digits are known to be correct, while the third digit is uncertain. The last digit is in the hundredths place, so the uncertainty is about 0.01 mm. Two values with the *same* number of significant figures may have *different* uncertainties; a distance given as 137 km also has three significant figures, but the uncertainty is about 1 km. A distance given as 0.25 km has two significant figures (the zero to the left of the decimal point doesn't count); if given as 0.250 km, it has three significant figures.

When you use numbers that have uncertainties to compute other numbers, the computed numbers are also uncertain. When numbers are multiplied or divided, the result can have no more significant figures than the factor with the fewest significant figures has. For example, $3.1416 \times 2.34 \times 0.58 = 4.3$. When we add and subtract numbers, it's the location of the decimal point that matters, not the number of significant figures. For example, $123.62 + 8.9 = 132.5$. Although 123.62 has an uncertainty of about 0.01, 8.9 has an uncertainty of about 0.1. So their sum has an uncertainty of about 0.1 and should be written as 132.5, not 132.52. **Table 1.2** summarizes these rules for significant figures.

To apply these ideas, suppose you want to verify the value of π, the ratio of the circumference of a circle to its diameter. The true value of this ratio to ten digits is 3.141592654. To test this, you draw a large circle and measure its circumference and diameter to the nearest millimeter, obtaining the values 424 mm and 135 mm (**Fig. 1.8**). You punch these into your calculator and obtain the quotient $(424 \text{ mm})/(135 \text{ mm}) = 3.140740741$. This may seem to disagree with the true value of π, but keep in mind that each of your measurements has three significant figures, so your measured value of π can have only three significant figures. It should be stated simply as 3.14. Within the limit of three significant figures, your value does agree with the true value.

In the examples and problems in this book we usually give numerical values with three significant figures, so your answers should usually have no more than three significant figures. (Many numbers in the real world have even less accuracy. An automobile speedometer, for example, usually gives only two significant figures.) Even if you do the arithmetic with a calculator that displays ten digits, a ten-digit answer would misrepresent the accuracy of the results. Always round your final answer to keep only the correct number of significant figures or, in doubtful cases, one more at most. In Example 1.1 it would have been wrong to state the answer as 341.01861 m/s. Note that when you reduce such an answer to the appropriate number of significant figures, you must *round,* not *truncate.* Your calculator will tell you that the ratio of 525 m to 311 m is 1.688102894; to three significant figures, this is 1.69, not 1.68.

When we work with very large or very small numbers, we can show significant figures much more easily by using **scientific notation,** sometimes called **powers-of-10 notation.** The distance from the earth to the moon is about 384,000,000 m, but writing the number in this form doesn't indicate the number of significant figures. Instead, we move the decimal point eight places to the left (corresponding to dividing by 10^8) and multiply by 10^8; that is,

$$384,000,000 \text{ m} = 3.84 \times 10^8 \text{ m}$$

In this form, it is clear that we have three significant figures. The number 4.00×10^{-7} also has three significant figures, even though two of them are zeros. Note that in scientific notation the usual practice is to express the quantity as a number between 1 and 10 multiplied by the appropriate power of 10.

When an integer or a fraction occurs in an algebraic equation, we treat that number as having no uncertainty at all. For example, in the equation $v_x^2 = v_{0x}^2 + 2a_x(x - x_0)$, which is Eq. (2.13) in Chapter 2, the coefficient 2 is *exactly* 2. We can consider this coefficient as having an infinite number of significant figures (2.000000 . . .). The same is true of the exponent 2 in v_x^2 and v_{0x}^2.

Finally, let's note that **precision** is not the same as *accuracy.* A cheap digital watch that gives the time as 10:35:17 A.M. is very *precise* (the time is given to the second), but if the watch runs several minutes slow, then this value isn't very *accurate.* On the other hand, a grandfather clock might be very accurate (that is, display the correct time), but if the clock has no second hand, it isn't very precise. A high-quality measurement is both precise *and* accurate.

EXAMPLE 1.3 SIGNIFICANT FIGURES IN MULTIPLICATION

The rest energy E of an object with rest mass m is given by Albert Einstein's famous equation $E = mc^2$, where c is the speed of light in vacuum. Find E for an electron for which (to three significant figures) $m = 9.11 \times 10^{-31}$ kg. The SI unit for E is the joule (J); $1 \text{ J} = 1 \text{ kg} \cdot \text{m}^2/\text{s}^2$.

SOLUTION

IDENTIFY and SET UP: Our target variable is the energy E. We are given the value of the mass m; from Section 1.3 (or Appendix F) the speed of light is $c = 2.99792458 \times 10^8$ m/s.

EXECUTE: Substituting the values of m and c into Einstein's equation, we find

$$\begin{aligned}
E &= (9.11 \times 10^{-31} \text{ kg})(2.99792458 \times 10^8 \text{ m/s})^2 \\
&= (9.11)(2.99792458)^2 (10^{-31})(10^8)^2 \text{ kg} \cdot \text{m}^2/\text{s}^2 \\
&= (81.87659678)(10^{[-31+(2\times8)]}) \text{ kg} \cdot \text{m}^2/\text{s}^2 \\
&= 8.187659678 \times 10^{-14} \text{ kg} \cdot \text{m}^2/\text{s}^2
\end{aligned}$$

Since the value of m was given to only three significant figures, we must round this to

$$E = 8.19 \times 10^{-14} \text{ kg} \cdot \text{m}^2/\text{s}^2 = 8.19 \times 10^{-14} \text{ J}$$

EVALUATE: While the rest energy contained in an electron may seem ridiculously small, on the atomic scale it is tremendous. Compare our answer to 10^{-19} J, the energy gained or lost by a single atom during a typical chemical reaction. The rest energy of an electron is about 1,000,000 times larger! (We'll discuss the significance of rest energy in Chapter 37.)

PhET: Estimation

1.6 ESTIMATES AND ORDERS OF MAGNITUDE

We have stressed the importance of knowing the accuracy of numbers that represent physical quantities. But even a very crude estimate of a quantity often gives us useful information. Sometimes we know how to calculate a certain quantity, but we have to guess at the data we need for the calculation. Or the calculation might be too complicated to carry out exactly, so we make rough approximations. In either case our result is also a guess, but such a guess can be useful even if it is uncertain by a factor of two, ten, or more. Such calculations are called **order-of-magnitude estimates.** The great Italian-American nuclear physicist Enrico Fermi (1901–1954) called them "back-of-the-envelope calculations."

Exercises 1.17 through 1.23 at the end of this chapter are of the estimating, or order-of-magnitude, variety. Most require guesswork for the needed input data. Don't try to look up a lot of data; make the best guesses you can. Even when they are off by a factor of ten, the results can be useful and interesting.

EXAMPLE 1.4   **AN ORDER-OF-MAGNITUDE ESTIMATE**

You are writing an adventure novel in which the hero escapes with a billion dollars' worth of gold in his suitcase. Could anyone carry that much gold? Would it fit in a suitcase?

SOLUTION

IDENTIFY, SET UP, and EXECUTE: Gold sells for about $1400 an ounce, or about $100 for $\frac{1}{14}$ ounce. (The price per ounce has varied between $200 and $1900 over the past twenty years or so.) An ounce is about 30 grams, so $100 worth of gold has a mass of about $\frac{1}{14}$ of 30 grams, or roughly 2 grams. A billion (10^9) dollars' worth of gold has a mass 10^7 times greater, about

2×10^7 (20 million) grams or 2×10^4 (20,000) kilograms. A thousand kilograms has a weight in British units of about a ton, so the suitcase weighs roughly 20 tons! No human could lift it.

Roughly what is the *volume* of this gold? The density of water is 10^3 kg/m^3; if gold, which is much denser than water, has a density 10 times greater, then 10^4 kg of gold fit into a volume of 1 m^3. So 10^9 dollars' worth of gold has a volume of 2 m^3, many times the volume of a suitcase.

EVALUATE: Clearly your novel needs rewriting. Try the calculation again with a suitcase full of five-carat (1-gram) diamonds, each worth $500,000. Would this work?

Application Scalar Temperature, Vector Wind   The comfort level on a wintry day depends on the temperature, a scalar quantity that can be positive or negative (say, $+5°C$ or $-20°C$) but has no direction. It also depends on the wind velocity, a vector quantity with both magnitude and direction (for example, 15 km/h from the west).

1.7 VECTORS AND VECTOR ADDITION

Some physical quantities, such as time, temperature, mass, and density, can be described completely by a single number with a unit. But many other important quantities in physics have a *direction* associated with them and cannot be described by a single number. A simple example is the motion of an airplane: We must say not only how fast the plane is moving but also in what direction. The speed of the airplane combined with its direction of motion constitute a quantity called *velocity*. Another example is *force,* which in physics means a push or pull exerted on a body. Giving a complete description of a force means describing both how hard the force pushes or pulls on the body and the direction of the push or pull.

When a physical quantity is described by a single number, we call it a **scalar quantity.** In contrast, a **vector quantity** has both a **magnitude** (the "how much" or "how big" part) and a direction in space. Calculations that combine scalar quantities use the operations of ordinary arithmetic. For example, 6 kg + 3 kg = 9 kg, or 4 × 2 s = 8 s. However, combining vectors requires a different set of operations.

To understand more about vectors and how they combine, we start with the simplest vector quantity, **displacement.** Displacement is a change in the position of an object. Displacement is a vector quantity because we must state not only how far the object moves but also in what direction. Walking 3 km north from your front door doesn't get you to the same place as walking 3 km southeast; these two displacements have the same magnitude but different directions.

We usually represent a vector quantity such as displacement by a single letter, such as $\vec{A}$ in **Fig. 1.9a.** In this book we always print vector symbols in ***boldface italic type with an arrow above them.*** We do this to remind you that vector quantities have different properties from scalar quantities; the arrow is a reminder that vectors have direction. When you handwrite a symbol for a vector, *always* write it with an arrow on top. If you don't distinguish between scalar and vector quantities in your notation, you probably won't make the distinction in your thinking either, and confusion will result.

We always *draw* a vector as a line with an arrowhead at its tip. The length of the line shows the vector's magnitude, and the direction of the arrowhead shows the vector's direction. Displacement is always a straight-line segment directed from the starting point to the ending point, even though the object's actual path may be curved (Fig. 1.9b). Note that displacement is not related directly to the total *distance* traveled. If the object were to continue past P_2 and then return to P_1, the displacement for the entire trip would be *zero* (Fig. 1.9c).

If two vectors have the same direction, they are **parallel.** If they have the same magnitude *and* the same direction, they are *equal,* no matter where they are located in space. The vector $\vec{A}'$ from point P_3 to point P_4 in **Fig. 1.10** has the same length and direction as the vector $\vec{A}$ from P_1 to P_2. These two displacements are equal, even though they start at different points. We write this as $\vec{A}' = \vec{A}$ in Fig. 1.10; the boldface equals sign emphasizes that equality of two vector quantities is not the same relationship as equality of two scalar quantities. Two vector quantities are equal only when they have the same magnitude *and* the same direction.

Vector $\vec{B}$ in Fig. 1.10, however, is not equal to $\vec{A}$ because its direction is *opposite* that of $\vec{A}$. We define the **negative of a vector** as a vector having the same magnitude as the original vector but the *opposite* direction. The negative of vector quantity $\vec{A}$ is denoted as $-\vec{A}$, and we use a boldface minus sign to emphasize the vector nature of the quantities. If $\vec{A}$ is 87 m south, then $-\vec{A}$ is 87 m north. Thus we can write the relationship between $\vec{A}$ and $\vec{B}$ in Fig. 1.10 as $\vec{A} = -\vec{B}$ or $\vec{B} = -\vec{A}$. When two vectors $\vec{A}$ and $\vec{B}$ have opposite directions, whether their magnitudes are the same or not, we say that they are **antiparallel.**

We usually represent the *magnitude* of a vector quantity by the same letter used for the vector, but in *lightface italic type* with *no* arrow on top. For example, if displacement vector $\vec{A}$ is 87 m south, then $A = 87$ m. An alternative notation is the vector symbol with vertical bars on both sides:

$$\text{(Magnitude of } \vec{A}) = A = |\vec{A}| \tag{1.1}$$

The magnitude of a vector quantity is a scalar quantity (a number) and is *always positive.* Note that a vector can never be equal to a scalar because they are different kinds of quantities. The expression "$\vec{A} = 6$ m" is just as wrong as "2 oranges = 3 apples"!

When we draw diagrams with vectors, it's best to use a scale similar to those used for maps. For example, a displacement of 5 km might be represented in a diagram by a vector 1 cm long, and a displacement of 10 km by a vector 2 cm long.

1.9 Displacement as a vector quantity.

(a) We represent a displacement by an arrow that points in the direction of displacement.

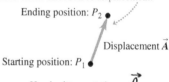

Ending position: P_2

Displacement $\vec{A}$

Starting position: P_1

Handwritten notation: $\vec{A}$

(b) A displacement is always a straight arrow directed from the starting position to the ending position. It does not depend on the path taken, even if the path is curved.

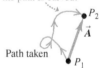

P_2

$\vec{A}$

Path taken

P_1

(c) Total displacement for a round trip is 0, regardless of the path taken or distance traveled.

P_1

1.10 The meaning of vectors that have the same magnitude and the same or opposite direction.

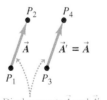

P_2 P_4 P_5

$\vec{A}$ $\vec{A}' = \vec{A}$ $\vec{B} = -\vec{A}$

P_1 P_3 P_6

Displacements $\vec{A}$ and $\vec{A}'$ are equal because they have the same length and direction.

Displacement $\vec{B}$ has the same magnitude as $\vec{A}$ but opposite direction; $\vec{B}$ is the negative of $\vec{A}$.

1.11 Three ways to add two vectors.

(a) We can add two vectors by placing them head to tail.

The vector sum $\vec{C}$
extends from the
tail of vector $\vec{A}$ ...
... to the head
of vector $\vec{B}$.

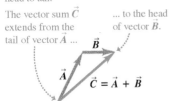

$\vec{C} = \vec{A} + \vec{B}$

(b) Adding them in reverse order gives the same result: $\vec{A} + \vec{B} = \vec{B} + \vec{A}$. The order doesn't matter in vector addition.

$\vec{C} = \vec{B} + \vec{A}$

(c) We can also add two vectors by placing them tail to tail and constructing a parallelogram.

$\vec{C} = \vec{A} + \vec{B}$

1.12 Adding vectors that are (a) parallel and (b) antiparallel.

(a) Only when vectors $\vec{A}$ and $\vec{B}$ are parallel does the magnitude of their vector sum $\vec{C}$ equal the sum of their magnitudes: $C = A + B$.

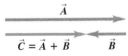

$\vec{C} = \vec{A} + \vec{B}$

(b) When $\vec{A}$ and $\vec{B}$ are antiparallel, the magnitude of their vector sum $\vec{C}$ equals the *difference* of their magnitudes: $C = |A - B|$.

$\vec{A}$

$\vec{C} = \vec{A} + \vec{B}$ $\vec{B}$

Vector Addition and Subtraction

Suppose a particle undergoes a displacement $\vec{A}$ followed by a second displacement $\vec{B}$. The final result is the same as if the particle had started at the same initial point and undergone a single displacement $\vec{C}$ (**Fig. 1.11a**). We call displacement $\vec{C}$ the **vector sum,** or **resultant,** of displacements $\vec{A}$ and $\vec{B}$. We express this relationship symbolically as

$$\vec{C} = \vec{A} + \vec{B} \tag{1.2}$$

The boldface plus sign emphasizes that adding two vector quantities requires a geometrical process and is not the same operation as adding two scalar quantities such as $2 + 3 = 5$. In vector addition we usually place the *tail* of the *second* vector at the *head*, or tip, of the *first* vector (Fig. 1.11a).

If we make the displacements $\vec{A}$ and $\vec{B}$ in reverse order, with $\vec{B}$ first and $\vec{A}$ second, the result is the same (Fig. 1.11b). Thus

$$\vec{C} = \vec{B} + \vec{A} \quad \text{and} \quad \vec{A} + \vec{B} = \vec{B} + \vec{A} \tag{1.3}$$

This shows that the order of terms in a vector sum doesn't matter. In other words, vector addition obeys the *commutative* law.

Figure 1.11c shows another way to represent the vector sum: If we draw vectors $\vec{A}$ and $\vec{B}$ with their tails at the same point, vector $\vec{C}$ is the diagonal of a parallelogram constructed with $\vec{A}$ and $\vec{B}$ as two adjacent sides.

⸻ CAUTION ⸻ **Magnitudes in vector addition** It's a common error to conclude that if $\vec{C} = \vec{A} + \vec{B}$, then magnitude C equals magnitude A plus magnitude B. In general, this conclusion is *wrong;* for the vectors shown in Fig. 1.11, $C < A + B$. The magnitude of $\vec{A} + \vec{B}$ depends on the magnitudes of $\vec{A}$ and $\vec{B}$ *and* on the angle between $\vec{A}$ and $\vec{B}$. Only in the special case in which $\vec{A}$ and $\vec{B}$ are *parallel* is the magnitude of $\vec{C} = \vec{A} + \vec{B}$ equal to the sum of the magnitudes of $\vec{A}$ and $\vec{B}$ (**Fig. 1.12a**). When the vectors are *antiparallel* (Fig. 1.12b), the magnitude of $\vec{C}$ equals the *difference* of the magnitudes of $\vec{A}$ and $\vec{B}$. Be careful to distinguish between scalar and vector quantities, and you'll avoid making errors about the magnitude of a vector sum. ▮

Figure 1.13a shows *three* vectors $\vec{A}$, $\vec{B}$, and $\vec{C}$. To find the vector sum of all three, in Fig. 1.13b we first add $\vec{A}$ and $\vec{B}$ to give a vector sum $\vec{D}$; we then add vectors $\vec{C}$ and $\vec{D}$ by the same process to obtain the vector sum $\vec{R}$:

$$\vec{R} = (\vec{A} + \vec{B}) + \vec{C} = \vec{D} + \vec{C}$$

Alternatively, we can first add $\vec{B}$ and $\vec{C}$ to obtain vector $\vec{E}$ (Fig. 1.13c), and then add $\vec{A}$ and $\vec{E}$ to obtain $\vec{R}$:

$$\vec{R} = \vec{A} + (\vec{B} + \vec{C}) = \vec{A} + \vec{E}$$

We don't even need to draw vectors $\vec{D}$ and $\vec{E}$; all we need to do is draw $\vec{A}$, $\vec{B}$, and $\vec{C}$ in succession, with the tail of each at the head of the one preceding it. The sum vector $\vec{R}$ extends from the tail of the first vector to the head of the last vector

1.13 Several constructions for finding the vector sum $\vec{A} + \vec{B} + \vec{C}$.

(a) To find the sum of these three vectors ...

(b) ... add $\vec{A}$ and $\vec{B}$ to get $\vec{D}$ and then add $\vec{C}$ to $\vec{D}$ to get the final sum (resultant) $\vec{R}$ ...

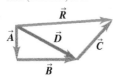

(c) ... or add $\vec{B}$ and $\vec{C}$ to get $\vec{E}$ and then add $\vec{A}$ to $\vec{E}$ to get $\vec{R}$ ...

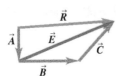

(d) ... or add $\vec{A}$, $\vec{B}$, and $\vec{C}$ to get $\vec{R}$ directly ...

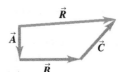

(e) ... or add $\vec{A}$, $\vec{B}$, and $\vec{C}$ in any other order and still get $\vec{R}$.

1.14 To construct the vector difference $\vec{A} - \vec{B}$, you can either place the tail of $-\vec{B}$ at the head of $\vec{A}$ or place the two vectors $\vec{A}$ and $\vec{B}$ head to head.

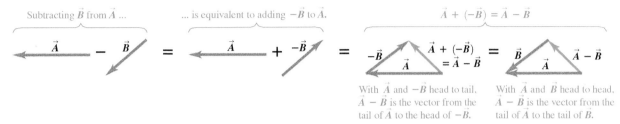

Subtracting $\vec{B}$ from $\vec{A}$ ...   ... is equivalent to adding $-\vec{B}$ to $\vec{A}$. $\vec{A} + (-\vec{B}) = \vec{A} - \vec{B}$

With $\vec{A}$ and $-\vec{B}$ head to tail, $\vec{A} - \vec{B}$ is the vector from the tail of $\vec{A}$ to the head of $-\vec{B}$.

With $\vec{A}$ and $\vec{B}$ head to head, $\vec{A} - \vec{B}$ is the vector from the tail of $\vec{A}$ to the tail of $\vec{B}$.

(Fig. 1.13d). The order makes no difference; Fig. 1.13e shows a different order, and you should try others. Vector addition obeys the *associative* law.

We can *subtract* vectors as well as add them. To see how, recall that vector $-\vec{A}$ has the same magnitude as $\vec{A}$ but the opposite direction. We define the difference $\vec{A} - \vec{B}$ of two vectors $\vec{A}$ and $\vec{B}$ to be the vector sum of $\vec{A}$ and $-\vec{B}$:

$$\vec{A} - \vec{B} = \vec{A} + (-\vec{B}) \tag{1.4}$$

Figure 1.14 shows an example of vector subtraction.

A vector quantity such as a displacement can be multiplied by a scalar quantity (an ordinary number). The displacement $2\vec{A}$ is a displacement (vector quantity) in the same direction as vector $\vec{A}$ but twice as long; this is the same as adding $\vec{A}$ to itself (**Fig. 1.15a**). In general, when we multiply a vector $\vec{A}$ by a scalar c, the result $c\vec{A}$ has magnitude $|c|A$ (the absolute value of c multiplied by the magnitude of vector $\vec{A}$). If c is positive, $c\vec{A}$ is in the same direction as $\vec{A}$; if c is negative, $c\vec{A}$ is in the direction opposite to $\vec{A}$. Thus $3\vec{A}$ is parallel to $\vec{A}$, while $-3\vec{A}$ is antiparallel to $\vec{A}$ (Fig. 1.15b).

A scalar used to multiply a vector can also be a physical quantity. For example, you may be familiar with the relationship $\vec{F} = m\vec{a}$; the net force $\vec{F}$ (a vector quantity) that acts on a body is equal to the product of the body's mass m (a scalar quantity) and its acceleration $\vec{a}$ (a vector quantity). The direction of $\vec{F}$ is the same as that of $\vec{a}$ because m is positive, and the magnitude of $\vec{F}$ is equal to the mass m multiplied by the magnitude of $\vec{a}$. The unit of force is the unit of mass multiplied by the unit of acceleration.

 MP

PhET: Vector Addition

1.15 Multiplying a vector by a scalar.

(a) Multiplying a vector by a positive scalar changes the magnitude (length) of the vector but not its direction.

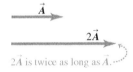

$2\vec{A}$ is twice as long as $\vec{A}$.

(b) Multiplying a vector by a negative scalar changes its magnitude and reverses its direction.

$-3\vec{A}$ is three times as long as $\vec{A}$ and points in the opposite direction.

EXAMPLE 1.5   **ADDING TWO VECTORS AT RIGHT ANGLES**

A cross-country skier skis 1.00 km north and then 2.00 km east on a horizontal snowfield. How far and in what direction is she from the starting point?

SOLUTION

IDENTIFY and SET UP: The problem involves combining two displacements at right angles to each other. This vector addition amounts to solving a right triangle, so we can use the Pythagorean theorem and simple trigonometry. The target variables are the skier's straight-line distance and direction from her starting point. **Figure 1.16** is a scale diagram of the two displacements and the resultant net displacement. We denote the direction from the starting point by the angle ϕ (the Greek letter phi). The displacement appears to be a bit more than 2 km. Measuring the angle with a protractor indicates that ϕ is about 63°.

1.16 The vector diagram, drawn to scale, for a ski trip.

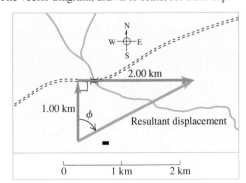

Continued

EXECUTE: The distance from the starting point to the ending point is equal to the length of the hypotenuse:

$$\sqrt{(1.00\text{ km})^2 + (2.00\text{ km})^2} = 2.24\text{ km}$$

A little trigonometry (from Appendix B) allows us to find angle ϕ:

$$\tan\phi = \frac{\text{Opposite side}}{\text{Adjacent side}} = \frac{2.00\text{ km}}{1.00\text{ km}} = 2.00$$

$$\phi = \arctan 2.00 = 63.4°$$

We can describe the direction as 63.4° east of north or $90° - 63.4° = 26.6°$ north of east.

EVALUATE: Our answers (2.24 km and $\phi = 63.4°$) are close to our predictions. In Section 1.8 we'll learn how to easily add two vectors *not* at right angles to each other.

DATA *SPEAKS*

Vector Addition and Subtraction

When students were given a problem about adding or subtracting two vectors, more than 28% gave an incorrect answer. Common errors:

- When adding vectors, drawing vectors $\vec{A}$, $\vec{B}$, and $\vec{A} + \vec{B}$ incorrectly. The head-to-tail arrangement shown in Figs. 1.11a and 1.11b is easiest.

- When subtracting vectors, drawing vectors $\vec{A}$, $\vec{B}$, and $\vec{A} - \vec{B}$ incorrectly. Remember that subtracting $\vec{B}$ from $\vec{A}$ is the same as adding $-\vec{B}$ to $\vec{A}$ (Fig. 1.14).

TEST YOUR UNDERSTANDING OF SECTION 1.7 Two displacement vectors, $\vec{S}$ and $\vec{T}$, have magnitudes $S = 3$ m and $T = 4$ m. Which of the following could be the magnitude of the difference vector $\vec{S} - \vec{T}$? (There may be more than one correct answer.) (i) 9 m; (ii) 7 m; (iii) 5 m; (iv) 1 m; (v) 0 m; (vi) −1 m. ▌

1.8 COMPONENTS OF VECTORS

In Section 1.7 we added vectors by using a scale diagram and properties of right triangles. Making measurements of a diagram offers only very limited accuracy, and calculations with right triangles work only when the two vectors are perpendicular. So we need a simple but general method for adding vectors. This is called the method of *components*.

To define what we mean by the components of a vector $\vec{A}$, we begin with a rectangular (Cartesian) coordinate system of axes (**Fig. 1.17**). If we think of $\vec{A}$ as a displacement vector, we can regard $\vec{A}$ as the sum of a displacement parallel to the x-axis and a displacement parallel to the y-axis. We use the numbers A_x and A_y to tell us how much displacement there is parallel to the x-axis and how much there is parallel to the y-axis, respectively. For example, if the $+x$-axis points east and the $+y$-axis points north, $\vec{A}$ in Figure 1.17 could be the sum of a 2.00-m displacement to the east and a 1.00-m displacement to the north. Then $A_x = +2.00$ m and $A_y = +1.00$ m. We can use the same idea for any vectors, not just displacement vectors. The two numbers A_x and A_y are called the **components** of $\vec{A}$.

1.17 Representing a vector $\vec{A}$ in terms of its components A_x and A_y.

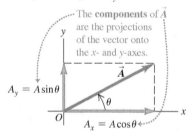

The **components** of $\vec{A}$ are the projections of the vector onto the x- and y-axes.

$A_y = A\sin\theta$

$\vec{A}$

θ

$A_x = A\cos\theta$

In this case, both A_x and A_y are positive.

CAUTION **Components are not vectors** The components A_x and A_y of a vector $\vec{A}$ are numbers; they are *not* vectors themselves. This is why we print the symbols for components in lightface italic type with *no* arrow on top instead of in boldface italic with an arrow, which is reserved for vectors. ▌

We can calculate the components of vector $\vec{A}$ if we know its magnitude A and its direction. We'll describe the direction of a vector by its angle relative to some reference direction. In Fig. 1.17 this reference direction is the positive x-axis, and the angle between vector $\vec{A}$ and the positive x-axis is θ (the Greek letter theta). Imagine that vector $\vec{A}$ originally lies along the $+x$-axis and that you then rotate it to its true direction, as indicated by the arrow in Fig. 1.17 on the arc for angle θ. If this rotation is from the $+x$-axis toward the $+y$-axis, as is the case in Fig. 1.17, then θ is *positive;* if the rotation is from the $+x$-axis toward the $-y$-axis, then θ is *negative*. Thus the $+y$-axis is at an angle of 90°, the $-x$-axis at 180°, and the $-y$-axis at 270° (or −90°). If θ is measured in this way, then from the definition of the trigonometric functions,

$$\frac{A_x}{A} = \cos\theta \qquad \text{and} \qquad \frac{A_y}{A} = \sin\theta$$

$$A_x = A\cos\theta \qquad \text{and} \qquad A_y = A\sin\theta \tag{1.5}$$

(θ measured from the $+x$-axis, rotating toward the $+y$-axis)

In Fig. 1.17 A_x and A_y are positive. This is consistent with Eqs. (1.5); θ is in the first quadrant (between $0°$ and $90°$), and both the cosine and the sine of an angle in this quadrant are positive. But in **Fig. 1.18a** the component B_x is negative and the component B_y is positive. (If the $+x$-axis points east and the $+y$-axis points north, $\vec{B}$ could represent a displacement of 2.00 m west and 1.00 m north. Since west is in the $-x$-direction and north is in the $+y$-direction, $B_x = -2.00$ m is negative and $B_y = +1.00$ m is positive.) Again, this is consistent with Eqs. (1.5); now θ is in the second quadrant, so $\cos\theta$ is negative and $\sin\theta$ is positive. In Fig. 1.18b both C_x and C_y are negative (both $\cos\theta$ and $\sin\theta$ are negative in the third quadrant).

CAUTION Relating a vector's magnitude and direction to its components Equations (1.5) are correct *only* when the angle θ is measured from the positive x-axis. If the angle of the vector is given from a different reference direction or you use a different rotation direction, the relationships are different! Example 1.6 illustrates this point. ▌

1.18 The components of a vector may be positive or negative numbers.

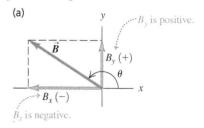

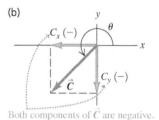

EXAMPLE 1.6   **FINDING COMPONENTS**

(a) What are the x- and y-components of vector $\vec{D}$ in **Fig. 1.19a**? The magnitude of the vector is $D = 3.00$ m, and angle $\alpha = 45°$. (b) What are the x- and y-components of vector $\vec{E}$ in Fig. 1.19b? The magnitude of the vector is $E = 4.50$ m, and angle $\beta = 37.0°$.

SOLUTION

IDENTIFY and SET UP: We can use Eqs. (1.5) to find the components of these vectors, but we must be careful: Neither angle α nor β in Fig. 1.19 is measured from the $+x$-axis toward the $+y$-axis. We estimate from the figure that the lengths of both

1.19 Calculating the x- and y-components of vectors.

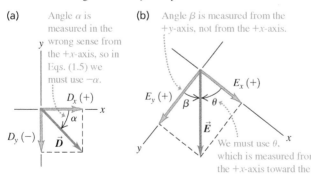

components in part (a) are roughly 2 m, and that those in part (b) are 3 m and 4 m. The figure indicates the signs of the components.

EXECUTE: (a) The angle α (the Greek letter alpha) between the positive x-axis and $\vec{D}$ is measured toward the *negative* y-axis. The angle we must use in Eqs. (1.5) is $\theta = -\alpha = -45°$. We then find

$$D_x = D\cos\theta = (3.00\text{ m})(\cos(-45°)) = +2.1\text{ m}$$
$$D_y = D\sin\theta = (3.00\text{ m})(\sin(-45°)) = -2.1\text{ m}$$

Had we carelessly substituted $+45°$ for θ in Eqs. (1.5), our result for D_y would have had the wrong sign.

(b) The x- and y-axes in Fig. 1.19b are at right angles, so it doesn't matter that they aren't horizontal and vertical, respectively. But we can't use the angle β (the Greek letter beta) in Eqs. (1.5), because β is measured from the $+y$-axis. Instead, we must use the angle $\theta = 90.0° - \beta = 90.0° - 37.0° = 53.0°$. Then we find

$$E_x = E\cos 53.0° = (4.50\text{ m})(\cos 53.0°) = +2.71\text{ m}$$
$$E_y = E\sin 53.0° = (4.50\text{ m})(\sin 53.0°) = +3.59\text{ m}$$

EVALUATE: Our answers to both parts are close to our predictions. But why do the answers in part (a) correctly have only two significant figures?

Using Components to Do Vector Calculations

Using components makes it relatively easy to do various calculations involving vectors. Let's look at three important examples: finding a vector's magnitude and direction, multiplying a vector by a scalar, and calculating the vector sum of two or more vectors.

Finding the direction of a vector from its components There's one complication in using Eqs. (1.7) to find θ: Any two angles that differ by 180° have the same tangent. Suppose $A_x = 2$ m and $A_y = -2$ m as in **Fig. 1.20**; then $\tan\theta = -1$. But both 135° and 315° (or $-45°$) have tangents of -1. To decide which is correct, we have to look at the individual components. Because A_x is positive and A_y is negative, the angle must be in the fourth quadrant; thus $\theta = 315°$ (or $-45°$) is the correct value. Most pocket calculators give $\arctan(-1) = -45°$. In this case that is correct; but if instead we have $A_x = -2$ m and $A_y = 2$ m, then the correct angle is 135°. Similarly, when both A_x and A_y are negative, the tangent is positive, but the angle is in the third quadrant. *Always draw a sketch like Fig. 1.20 to determine which of the two possibilities is correct.*

1.20 Drawing a sketch of a vector reveals the signs of its x- and y-components.

Suppose that $\tan\theta = \dfrac{A_y}{A_x} = -1$. What is θ?

Two angles have tangents of -1: 135° and 315°. The diagram shows that θ must be 315°.

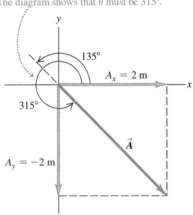

1.21 Finding the vector sum (resultant) of $\vec{A}$ and $\vec{B}$ using components.

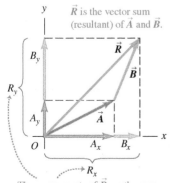

$\vec{R}$ is the vector sum (resultant) of $\vec{A}$ and $\vec{B}$.

The components of $\vec{R}$ are the sums of the components of $\vec{A}$ and $\vec{B}$:

$R_y = A_y + B_y$ $R_x = A_x + B_x$

1. **Finding a vector's magnitude and direction from its components**. We can describe a vector completely by giving either its magnitude and direction or its x- and y-components. Equations (1.5) show how to find the components if we know the magnitude and direction. We can also reverse the process: We can find the magnitude and direction if we know the components. By applying the Pythagorean theorem to Fig. 1.17, we find that the magnitude of vector $\vec{A}$ is

$$A = \sqrt{A_x^2 + A_y^2} \qquad (1.6)$$

(We always take the positive root.) Equation (1.6) is valid for any choice of x-axis and y-axis, as long as they are mutually perpendicular. The expression for the vector direction comes from the definition of the tangent of an angle. If θ is measured from the positive x-axis, and a positive angle is measured toward the positive y-axis (as in Fig. 1.17), then

$$\tan\theta = \frac{A_y}{A_x} \quad \text{and} \quad \theta = \arctan\frac{A_y}{A_x} \qquad (1.7)$$

We will always use the notation arctan for the inverse tangent function (see Example 1.5 in Section 1.7). The notation $\tan^{-1}$ is also commonly used, and your calculator may have an INV or 2ND button to be used with the TAN button.

2. **Multiplying a vector by a scalar.** If we multiply a vector $\vec{A}$ by a scalar c, each component of the product $\vec{D} = c\vec{A}$ is the product of c and the corresponding component of $\vec{A}$:

$$D_x = cA_x, \qquad D_y = cA_y \qquad \text{(components of } \vec{D} = c\vec{A}\text{)} \qquad (1.8)$$

For example, Eqs. (1.8) say that each component of the vector $2\vec{A}$ is twice as great as the corresponding component of $\vec{A}$, so $2\vec{A}$ is in the same direction as $\vec{A}$ but has twice the magnitude. Each component of the vector $-3\vec{A}$ is three times as great as the corresponding component of $\vec{A}$ but has the opposite sign, so $-3\vec{A}$ is in the opposite direction from $\vec{A}$ and has three times the magnitude. Hence Eqs. (1.8) are consistent with our discussion in Section 1.7 of multiplying a vector by a scalar (see Fig. 1.15).

3. **Using components to calculate the vector sum (resultant) of two or more vectors. Figure 1.21** shows two vectors $\vec{A}$ and $\vec{B}$ and their vector sum $\vec{R}$, along with the x- and y-components of all three vectors. The x-component R_x of the vector sum is simply the sum $(A_x + B_x)$ of the x-components of the vectors being added. The same is true for the y-components. In symbols,

Each component of $\vec{R} = \vec{A} + \vec{B}$ ...

$$R_x = A_x + B_x, \qquad R_y = A_y + B_y \qquad (1.9)$$

... is the sum of the corresponding components of $\vec{A}$ and $\vec{B}$.

Figure 1.21 shows this result for the case in which the components A_x, A_y, B_x, and B_y are all positive. Draw additional diagrams to verify for yourself that Eqs. (1.9) are valid for *any* signs of the components of $\vec{A}$ and $\vec{B}$.

If we know the components of any two vectors $\vec{A}$ and $\vec{B}$, perhaps by using Eqs. (1.5), we can compute the components of the vector sum $\vec{R}$. Then if we need the magnitude and direction of $\vec{R}$, we can obtain them from Eqs. (1.6) and (1.7) with the A's replaced by R's.

We can use the same procedure to find the sum of any number of vectors. If $\vec{R}$ is the vector sum of $\vec{A}, \vec{B}, \vec{C}, \vec{D}, \vec{E}, \ldots$, the components of $\vec{R}$ are

$$R_x = A_x + B_x + C_x + D_x + E_x + \cdots$$
$$R_y = A_y + B_y + C_y + D_y + E_y + \cdots \quad (1.10)$$

We have talked about vectors that lie in the *xy*-plane only, but the component method works just as well for vectors having any direction in space. We can introduce a *z*-axis perpendicular to the *xy*-plane; then in general a vector $\vec{A}$ has components A_x, A_y, and A_z in the three coordinate directions. Its magnitude A is

$$A = \sqrt{A_x^2 + A_y^2 + A_z^2} \quad (1.11)$$

Again, we always take the positive root (**Fig. 1.22**). Also, Eqs. (1.10) for the vector sum $\vec{R}$ have a third component:

$$R_z = A_z + B_z + C_z + D_z + E_z + \cdots$$

We've focused on adding *displacement* vectors, but the method is applicable to all vector quantities. When we study the concept of force in Chapter 4, we'll find that forces are vectors that obey the same rules of vector addition.

1.22 A vector in three dimensions.

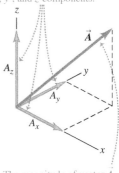

In three dimensions, a vector has *x*-, *y*-, and *z*-components.

The magnitude of vector A is $A = \sqrt{A_x^2 + A_y^2 + A_z^2}$.

PROBLEM-SOLVING STRATEGY 1.3 **VECTOR ADDITION**

IDENTIFY *the relevant concepts:* Decide what the target variable is. It may be the magnitude of the vector sum, the direction, or both.

SET UP *the problem:* Sketch the vectors being added, along with suitable coordinate axes. Place the tail of the first vector at the origin of the coordinates, place the tail of the second vector at the head of the first vector, and so on. Draw the vector sum $\vec{R}$ from the tail of the first vector (at the origin) to the head of the last vector. Use your sketch to estimate the magnitude and direction of $\vec{R}$. Select the mathematical tools you'll use for the full calculation: Eqs. (1.5) to obtain the components of the vectors given, if necessary, Eqs. (1.10) to obtain the components of the vector sum, Eq. (1.11) to obtain its magnitude, and Eqs. (1.7) to obtain its direction.

EXECUTE *the solution* as follows:
1. Find the *x*- and *y*-components of each individual vector and record your results in a table, as in Example 1.7. If a vector is described by a magnitude A and an angle θ, measured from the +*x*-axis toward the +*y*-axis, then its components are given by Eqs. 1.5:

$$A_x = A\cos\theta \qquad A_y = A\sin\theta$$

If the angles of the vectors are given in some other way, perhaps using a different reference direction, convert them to angles measured from the +*x*-axis as in Example 1.6.
2. Add the individual *x*-components algebraically (including signs) to find R_x, the *x*-component of the vector sum. Do the same for the *y*-components to find R_y. See Example 1.7.
3. Calculate the magnitude R and direction θ of the vector sum by using Eqs. (1.6) and (1.7):

$$R = \sqrt{R_x^2 + R_y^2} \qquad \theta = \arctan\frac{R_y}{R_x}$$

EVALUATE *your answer:* Confirm that your results for the magnitude and direction of the vector sum agree with the estimates you made from your sketch. The value of θ that you find with a calculator may be off by 180°; your drawing will indicate the correct value.

EXAMPLE 1.7 **USING COMPONENTS TO ADD VECTORS**

Three players on a reality TV show are brought to the center of a large, flat field. Each is given a meter stick, a compass, a calculator, a shovel, and (in a different order for each contestant) the following three displacements:

$\vec{A}$: 72.4 m, 32.0° east of north
$\vec{B}$: 57.3 m, 36.0° south of west
$\vec{C}$: 17.8 m due south

The three displacements lead to the point in the field where the keys to a new Porsche are buried. Two players start measuring immediately, but the winner first *calculates* where to go. What does she calculate?

SOLUTION

IDENTIFY and SET UP: The goal is to find the sum (resultant) of the three displacements, so this is a problem in vector addition. See **Figure 1.23.** We have chosen the +*x*-axis as east and the +*y*-axis as north. We estimate from the diagram that the vector sum $\vec{R}$ is about 10 m, 40° west of north (so θ is about 90° plus 40°, or about 130°).

Continued

1.23 Three successive displacements $\vec{A}$, $\vec{B}$, and $\vec{C}$ and the resultant (vector sum) displacement $\vec{R} = \vec{A} + \vec{B} + \vec{C}$.

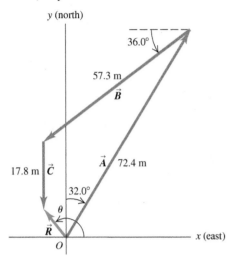

We've kept an extra significant figure in the components; we'll round to the correct number of significant figures at the end of our calculation. The table below shows the components of all the displacements, the addition of the components, and the other calculations from Eqs. (1.6) and (1.7).

Distance	Angle	x-component	y-component
A = 72.4 m	58.0°	38.37 m	61.40 m
B = 57.3 m	216.0°	−46.36 m	−33.68 m
C = 17.8 m	270.0°	0.00 m	−17.80 m
		$R_x = -7.99$ m	$R_y = 9.92$ m

$$R = \sqrt{(-7.99 \text{ m})^2 + (9.92 \text{ m})^2} = 12.7 \text{ m}$$

$$\theta = \arctan\frac{9.92 \text{ m}}{-7.99 \text{ m}} = -51°$$

Comparing to angle θ in Fig. 1.23 shows that the calculated angle is clearly off by 180°. The correct value is $\theta = 180° + (-51°) = 129°$, or 39° west of north.

EVALUATE: Our calculated answers for R and θ agree with our estimates. Notice how drawing the diagram in Fig. 1.23 made it easy to avoid a 180° error in the direction of the vector sum.

EXECUTE: The angles of the vectors, measured from the +x-axis toward the +y-axis, are $(90.0° - 32.0°) = 58.0°$, $(180.0° + 36.0°) = 216.0°$, and 270.0°, respectively. We may now use Eqs. (1.5) to find the components of $\vec{A}$:

$$A_x = A \cos \theta_A = (72.4 \text{ m})(\cos 58.0°) = 38.37 \text{ m}$$
$$A_y = A \sin \theta_A = (72.4 \text{ m})(\sin 58.0°) = 61.40 \text{ m}$$

TEST YOUR UNDERSTANDING OF SECTION 1.8 Two vectors $\vec{A}$ and $\vec{B}$ lie in the xy-plane. (a) Can $\vec{A}$ have the same magnitude as $\vec{B}$ but different components? (b) Can $\vec{A}$ have the same components as $\vec{B}$ but a different magnitude? ▮

1.9 UNIT VECTORS

A **unit vector** is a vector that has a magnitude of 1, with no units. Its only purpose is to *point*—that is, to describe a direction in space. Unit vectors provide a convenient notation for many expressions involving components of vectors. We will always include a caret, or "hat" (^), in the symbol for a unit vector to distinguish it from ordinary vectors whose magnitude may or may not be equal to 1.

In an xy-coordinate system we can define a unit vector $\hat{\imath}$ that points in the direction of the positive x-axis and a unit vector $\hat{\jmath}$ that points in the direction of the positive y-axis (**Fig. 1.24a**). Then we can write a vector $\vec{A}$ in terms of its components as

$$\vec{A} = A_x\hat{\imath} + A_y\hat{\jmath} \tag{1.12}$$

Equation (1.12) is a vector equation; each term, such as $A_x\hat{\imath}$, is a vector quantity (Fig. 1.24b).

Using unit vectors, we can express the vector sum $\vec{R}$ of two vectors $\vec{A}$ and $\vec{B}$ as follows:

$$\vec{A} = A_x\hat{\imath} + A_y\hat{\jmath}$$
$$\vec{B} = B_x\hat{\imath} + B_y\hat{\jmath}$$
$$\vec{R} = \vec{A} + \vec{B}$$
$$= (A_x\hat{\imath} + A_y\hat{\jmath}) + (B_x\hat{\imath} + B_y\hat{\jmath}) \tag{1.13}$$
$$= (A_x + B_x)\hat{\imath} + (A_y + B_y)\hat{\jmath}$$
$$= R_x\hat{\imath} + R_y\hat{\jmath}$$

1.24 (a) The unit vectors $\hat{\imath}$ and $\hat{\jmath}$. (b) Expressing a vector $\vec{A}$ in terms of its components.

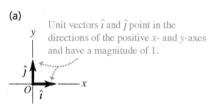

Equation (1.13) restates the content of Eqs. (1.9) in the form of a single vector equation rather than two component equations.

If not all of the vectors lie in the *xy*-plane, then we need a third component. We introduce a third unit vector $\hat{k}$ that points in the direction of the positive *z*-axis (**Fig. 1.25**). Then Eqs. (1.12) and (1.13) become

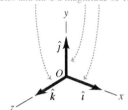

1.25 The unit vectors $\hat{\imath}$, $\hat{\jmath}$, and $\hat{k}$.

Unit vectors $\hat{\imath}$, $\hat{\jmath}$, and $\hat{k}$ point in the directions of the positive *x*-, *y*-, and *z*-axes and have a magnitude of 1.

Any vector can be expressed in terms of its *x*-, *y*-, and *z*-components ...

$$\vec{A} = A_x\hat{\imath} + A_y\hat{\jmath} + A_z\hat{k}$$
$$\vec{B} = B_x\hat{\imath} + B_y\hat{\jmath} + B_z\hat{k} \qquad (1.14)$$

... and unit vectors $\hat{\imath}$, $\hat{\jmath}$, and $\hat{k}$.

$$\vec{R} = (A_x + B_x)\hat{\imath} + (A_y + B_y)\hat{\jmath} + (A_z + B_z)\hat{k}$$
$$= R_x\hat{\imath} + R_y\hat{\jmath} + R_z\hat{k} \qquad (1.15)$$

EXAMPLE 1.8   **USING UNIT VECTORS**

Given the two displacements

$$\vec{D} = (6.00\,\hat{\imath} + 3.00\,\hat{\jmath} - 1.00\hat{k})\text{ m} \quad \text{and}$$

$$\vec{E} = (4.00\,\hat{\imath} - 5.00\,\hat{\jmath} + 8.00\hat{k})\text{ m}$$

find the magnitude of the displacement $2\vec{D} - \vec{E}$.

SOLUTION

IDENTIFY and SET UP: We are to multiply vector $\vec{D}$ by 2 (a scalar) and subtract vector $\vec{E}$ from the result, so as to obtain the vector $\vec{F} = 2\vec{D} - \vec{E}$. Equation (1.8) says that to multiply $\vec{D}$ by 2, we multiply each of its components by 2. We can use Eq. (1.15) to do the subtraction; recall from Section 1.7 that subtracting a vector is the same as adding the negative of that vector.

EXECUTE: We have

$$\vec{F} = 2(6.00\,\hat{\imath} + 3.00\,\hat{\jmath} - 1.00\hat{k})\text{ m} - (4.00\,\hat{\imath} - 5.00\,\hat{\jmath} + 8.00\hat{k})\text{ m}$$
$$= [(12.00 - 4.00)\hat{\imath} + (6.00 + 5.00)\hat{\jmath} + (-2.00 - 8.00)\hat{k}]\text{ m}$$
$$= (8.00\hat{\imath} + 11.00\,\hat{\jmath} - 10.00\hat{k})\text{ m}$$

From Eq. (1.11) the magnitude of $\vec{F}$ is

$$F = \sqrt{F_x^2 + F_y^2 + F_z^2}$$
$$= \sqrt{(8.00\text{ m})^2 + (11.00\text{ m})^2 + (-10.00\text{ m})^2}$$
$$= 16.9\text{ m}$$

EVALUATE: Our answer is of the same order of magnitude as the larger components that appear in the sum. We wouldn't expect our answer to be much larger than this, but it could be much smaller.

TEST YOUR UNDERSTANDING OF SECTION 1.9   Arrange the following vectors in order of their magnitude, with the vector of largest magnitude first. (i) $\vec{A} = (3\hat{\imath} + 5\hat{\jmath} - 2\hat{k})$ m; (ii) $\vec{B} = (-3\hat{\imath} + 5\hat{\jmath} - 2\hat{k})$ m; (iii) $\vec{C} = (3\hat{\imath} - 5\hat{\jmath} - 2\hat{k})$ m; (iv) $\vec{D} = (3\hat{\imath} + 5\hat{\jmath} + 2\hat{k})$ m. ∎

1.10 PRODUCTS OF VECTORS

We saw how vector addition develops naturally from the problem of combining displacements. It will prove useful for calculations with many other vector quantities. We can also express many physical relationships by using *products* of vectors. Vectors are not ordinary numbers, so we can't directly apply ordinary multiplication to vectors. We'll define two different kinds of products of vectors. The first, called the *scalar product,* yields a result that is a scalar quantity. The second, the *vector product,* yields another vector.

Scalar Product

We denote the **scalar product** of two vectors $\vec{A}$ and $\vec{B}$ by $\vec{A} \cdot \vec{B}$. Because of this notation, the scalar product is also called the **dot product.** Although $\vec{A}$ and $\vec{B}$ are vectors, the quantity $\vec{A} \cdot \vec{B}$ is a scalar.

1.26 Calculating the scalar product of two vectors, $\vec{A} \cdot \vec{B} = AB \cos \phi$.

(a)

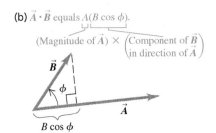

Place the vectors tail to tail.

(b) $\vec{A} \cdot \vec{B}$ equals $A(B \cos \phi)$.

(Magnitude of $\vec{A}$) $\times$ $\begin{pmatrix} \text{Component of } \vec{B} \\ \text{in direction of } \vec{A} \end{pmatrix}$

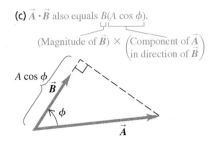

$B \cos \phi$

(c) $\vec{A} \cdot \vec{B}$ also equals $B(A \cos \phi)$.

(Magnitude of $\vec{B}$) $\times$ $\begin{pmatrix} \text{Component of } \vec{A} \\ \text{in direction of } \vec{B} \end{pmatrix}$

$A \cos \phi$

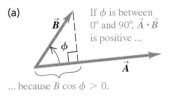

1.27 The scalar product $\vec{A} \cdot \vec{B} = AB \cos \phi$ can be positive, negative, or zero, depending on the angle between $\vec{A}$ and $\vec{B}$.

(a)

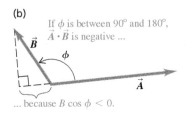

If ϕ is between 0° and 90°, $\vec{A} \cdot \vec{B}$ is positive ...

... because $B \cos \phi > 0$.

(b)

If ϕ is between 90° and 180°, $\vec{A} \cdot \vec{B}$ is negative ...

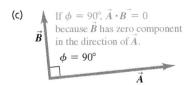

... because $B \cos \phi < 0$.

(c)

If $\phi = 90°$, $\vec{A} \cdot \vec{B} = 0$ because $\vec{B}$ has zero component in the direction of $\vec{A}$.

$\phi = 90°$

To define the scalar product $\vec{A} \cdot \vec{B}$ we draw the two vectors $\vec{A}$ and $\vec{B}$ with their tails at the same point (**Fig. 1.26a**). The angle ϕ (the Greek letter phi) between their directions ranges from 0° to 180°. Figure 1.26b shows the projection of vector $\vec{B}$ onto the direction of $\vec{A}$; this projection is the component of $\vec{B}$ in the direction of $\vec{A}$ and is equal to $B \cos \phi$. (We can take components along *any* direction that's convenient, not just the *x*- and *y*-axes.) We define $\vec{A} \cdot \vec{B}$ to be the magnitude of $\vec{A}$ multiplied by the component of $\vec{B}$ in the direction of $\vec{A}$, or

Scalar (dot) product of vectors $\vec{A}$ and $\vec{B}$ ⟶   Magnitudes of $\vec{A}$ and $\vec{B}$

$$\vec{A} \cdot \vec{B} = AB \cos \phi = |\vec{A}||\vec{B}| \cos \phi \qquad (1.16)$$

Angle between $\vec{A}$ and $\vec{B}$ when placed tail to tail

Alternatively, we can define $\vec{A} \cdot \vec{B}$ to be the magnitude of $\vec{B}$ multiplied by the component of $\vec{A}$ in the direction of $\vec{B}$, as in Fig. 1.26c. Hence $\vec{A} \cdot \vec{B} = B(A \cos \phi) = AB \cos \phi$, which is the same as Eq. (1.16).

The scalar product is a scalar quantity, not a vector, and it may be positive, negative, or zero. When ϕ is between 0° and 90°, $\cos \phi > 0$ and the scalar product is positive (**Fig. 1.27a**). When ϕ is between 90° and 180° so $\cos \phi < 0$, the component of $\vec{B}$ in the direction of $\vec{A}$ is negative, and $\vec{A} \cdot \vec{B}$ is negative (Fig. 1.27b). Finally, when $\phi = 90°$, $\vec{A} \cdot \vec{B} = 0$ (Fig. 1.27c). *The scalar product of two perpendicular vectors is always zero.*

For any two vectors $\vec{A}$ and $\vec{B}$, $AB \cos \phi = BA \cos \phi$. This means that $\vec{A} \cdot \vec{B} = \vec{B} \cdot \vec{A}$. The scalar product obeys the commutative law of multiplication; the order of the two vectors does not matter.

We'll use the scalar product in Chapter 6 to describe work done by a force. In later chapters we'll use the scalar product for a variety of purposes, from calculating electric potential to determining the effects that varying magnetic fields have on electric circuits.

Using Components to Calculate the Scalar Product

We can calculate the scalar product $\vec{A} \cdot \vec{B}$ directly if we know the *x*-, *y*-, and *z*-components of $\vec{A}$ and $\vec{B}$. To see how this is done, let's first work out the scalar products of the unit vectors $\hat{\imath}$, $\hat{\jmath}$, and $\hat{k}$. All unit vectors have magnitude 1 and are perpendicular to each other. Using Eq. (1.16), we find

$$\hat{\imath} \cdot \hat{\imath} = \hat{\jmath} \cdot \hat{\jmath} = \hat{k} \cdot \hat{k} = (1)(1) \cos 0° = 1$$

$$\hat{\imath} \cdot \hat{\jmath} = \hat{\imath} \cdot \hat{k} = \hat{\jmath} \cdot \hat{k} = (1)(1) \cos 90° = 0 \qquad (1.17)$$

Now we express $\vec{A}$ and $\vec{B}$ in terms of their components, expand the product, and use these products of unit vectors:

$$\vec{A} \cdot \vec{B} = (A_x \hat{\imath} + A_y \hat{\jmath} + A_z \hat{k}) \cdot (B_x \hat{\imath} + B_y \hat{\jmath} + B_z \hat{k})$$

$$= A_x \hat{\imath} \cdot B_x \hat{\imath} + A_x \hat{\imath} \cdot B_y \hat{\jmath} + A_x \hat{\imath} \cdot B_z \hat{k}$$

$$+ A_y \hat{\jmath} \cdot B_x \hat{\imath} + A_y \hat{\jmath} \cdot B_y \hat{\jmath} + A_y \hat{\jmath} \cdot B_z \hat{k}$$

$$+ A_z \hat{k} \cdot B_x \hat{\imath} + A_z \hat{k} \cdot B_y \hat{\jmath} + A_z \hat{k} \cdot B_z \hat{k} \qquad (1.18)$$

$$= A_x B_x \hat{\imath} \cdot \hat{\imath} + A_x B_y \hat{\imath} \cdot \hat{\jmath} + A_x B_z \hat{\imath} \cdot \hat{k}$$

$$+ A_y B_x \hat{\jmath} \cdot \hat{\imath} + A_y B_y \hat{\jmath} \cdot \hat{\jmath} + A_y B_z \hat{\jmath} \cdot \hat{k}$$

$$+ A_z B_x \hat{k} \cdot \hat{\imath} + A_z B_y \hat{k} \cdot \hat{\jmath} + A_z B_z \hat{k} \cdot \hat{k}$$

From Eqs. (1.17) you can see that six of these nine terms are zero. The three that survive give

Scalar (dot) product
of vectors $\vec{A}$ and $\vec{B}$ Components of $\vec{A}$

$$\vec{A} \cdot \vec{B} = A_x B_x + A_y B_y + A_z B_z \qquad (1.19)$$

Components of $\vec{B}$

Thus *the scalar product of two vectors is the sum of the products of their respective components.*

The scalar product gives a straightforward way to find the angle ϕ between any two vectors $\vec{A}$ and $\vec{B}$ whose components are known. In this case we can use Eq. (1.19) to find the scalar product of $\vec{A}$ and $\vec{B}$. Example 1.10 shows how to do this.

EXAMPLE 1.9   CALCULATING A SCALAR PRODUCT

Find the scalar product $\vec{A} \cdot \vec{B}$ of the two vectors in **Fig. 1.28**. The magnitudes of the vectors are $A = 4.00$ and $B = 5.00$.

SOLUTION

IDENTIFY and SET UP: We can calculate the scalar product in two ways: using the magnitudes of the vectors and the angle between them (Eq. 1.16), and using the components of the vectors (Eq. 1.19). We'll do it both ways, and the results will check each other.

1.28 Two vectors $\vec{A}$ and $\vec{B}$ in two dimensions.

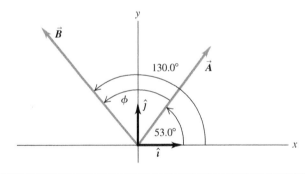

EXECUTE: The angle between the two vectors $\vec{A}$ and $\vec{B}$ is $\phi = 130.0° - 53.0° = 77.0°$, so Eq. (1.16) gives us

$$\vec{A} \cdot \vec{B} = AB \cos \phi = (4.00)(5.00) \cos 77.0° = 4.50$$

To use Eq. (1.19), we must first find the components of the vectors. The angles of $\vec{A}$ and $\vec{B}$ are given with respect to the $+x$-axis and are measured in the sense from the $+x$-axis to the $+y$-axis, so we can use Eqs. (1.5):

$$A_x = (4.00) \cos 53.0° = 2.407$$
$$A_y = (4.00) \sin 53.0° = 3.195$$
$$B_x = (5.00) \cos 130.0° = -3.214$$
$$B_y = (5.00) \sin 130.0° = 3.830$$

As in Example 1.7, we keep an extra significant figure in the components and round at the end. Equation (1.19) now gives us

$$\vec{A} \cdot \vec{B} = A_x B_x + A_y B_y + A_z B_z$$
$$= (2.407)(-3.214) + (3.195)(3.830) + (0)(0) = 4.50$$

EVALUATE: Both methods give the same result, as they should.

EXAMPLE 1.10   FINDING AN ANGLE WITH THE SCALAR PRODUCT

Find the angle between the vectors

$$\vec{A} = 2.00\hat{\imath} + 3.00\hat{\jmath} + 1.00\hat{k}$$

and

$$\vec{B} = -4.00\hat{\imath} + 2.00\hat{\jmath} - 1.00\hat{k}$$

SOLUTION

IDENTIFY and SET UP: We're given the x-, y-, and z-components of two vectors. Our target variable is the angle ϕ between them (**Fig. 1.29**). To find this, we'll solve Eq. (1.16), $\vec{A} \cdot \vec{B} = AB \cos \phi$, for ϕ in terms of the scalar product $\vec{A} \cdot \vec{B}$ and the magnitudes A and B. We can use Eq. (1.19) to evaluate the scalar product, $\vec{A} \cdot \vec{B} = A_x B_x + A_y B_y + A_z B_z$, and we can use Eq. (1.6) to find A and B.

1.29 Two vectors in three dimensions.

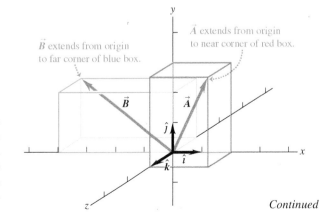

B extends from origin to far corner of blue box.

$\vec{A}$ extends from origin to near corner of red box.

Continued

EXECUTE: We solve Eq. (1.16) for cos ϕ and use Eq. (1.19) to write $\vec{A} \cdot \vec{B}$:

$$\cos\phi = \frac{\vec{A} \cdot \vec{B}}{AB} = \frac{A_x B_x + A_y B_y + A_z B_z}{AB}$$

We can use this formula to find the angle between *any* two vectors $\vec{A}$ and $\vec{B}$. Here we have $A_x = 2.00$, $A_y = 3.00$, and $A_z = 1.00$, and $B_x = -4.00$, $B_y = 2.00$, and $B_z = -1.00$. Thus

$$\vec{A} \cdot \vec{B} = A_x B_x + A_y B_y + A_z B_z$$

$$= (2.00)(-4.00) + (3.00)(2.00) + (1.00)(-1.00)$$

$$= -3.00$$

$$A = \sqrt{A_x^2 + A_y^2 + A_z^2} = \sqrt{(2.00)^2 + (3.00)^2 + (1.00)^2}$$
$$= \sqrt{14.00}$$

$$B = \sqrt{B_x^2 + B_y^2 + B_z^2} = \sqrt{(-4.00)^2 + (2.00)^2 + (-1.00)^2}$$
$$= \sqrt{21.00}$$

$$\cos\phi = \frac{A_x B_x + A_y B_y + A_z B_z}{AB} = \frac{-3.00}{\sqrt{14.00}\,\sqrt{21.00}} = -0.175$$

$$\phi = 100°$$

EVALUATE: As a check on this result, note that the scalar product $\vec{A} \cdot \vec{B}$ is negative. This means that ϕ is between 90° and 180° (see Fig. 1.27), which agrees with our answer.

1.30 The vector product of (a) $\vec{A} \times \vec{B}$ and (b) $\vec{B} \times \vec{A}$.

(a) Using the right-hand rule to find the direction of $\vec{A} \times \vec{B}$

① Place $\vec{A}$ and $\vec{B}$ tail to tail.

② Point fingers of right hand along $\vec{A}$, with palm facing $\vec{B}$.

③ Curl fingers toward $\vec{B}$.

④ Thumb points in direction of $\vec{A} \times \vec{B}$.

$\vec{A} \times \vec{B}$

$\vec{A}$

ϕ

$\vec{B}$

(b) Using the right-hand rule to find the direction of $\vec{B} \times \vec{A} = -\vec{A} \times \vec{B}$ (vector product is anticommutative)

① Place $\vec{B}$ and $\vec{A}$ tail to tail.

② Point fingers of right hand along $\vec{B}$, with palm facing $\vec{A}$.

③ Curl fingers toward $\vec{A}$.

④ Thumb points in direction of $\vec{B} \times \vec{A}$.

⑤ $\vec{B} \times \vec{A}$ has same magnitude as $\vec{A} \times \vec{B}$ but points in opposite direction.

$\vec{A}$

ϕ

$\vec{B}$

$\vec{B} \times \vec{A}$

Vector Product

We denote the **vector product** of two vectors $\vec{A}$ and $\vec{B}$, also called the **cross product,** by $\vec{A} \times \vec{B}$. As the name suggests, the vector product is itself a vector. We'll use this product in Chapter 10 to describe torque and angular momentum; in Chapters 27 and 28 we'll use it to describe magnetic fields and forces.

To define the vector product $\vec{A} \times \vec{B}$, we again draw the two vectors $\vec{A}$ and $\vec{B}$ with their tails at the same point (**Fig. 1.30a**). The two vectors then lie in a plane. We define the vector product to be a vector quantity with a direction perpendicular to this plane (that is, perpendicular to both $\vec{A}$ and $\vec{B}$) and a magnitude equal to $AB \sin\phi$. That is, if $\vec{C} = \vec{A} \times \vec{B}$, then

Magnitude of **vector (cross) product** of vectors $\vec{B}$ and $\vec{A}$

$$C = AB \sin\phi \tag{1.20}$$

Magnitudes of $\vec{A}$ and $\vec{B}$ · · · · · · Angle between $\vec{A}$ and $\vec{B}$ when placed tail to tail

We measure the angle ϕ from $\vec{A}$ toward $\vec{B}$ and take it to be the smaller of the two possible angles, so ϕ ranges from 0° to 180°. Then $\sin\phi \geq 0$ and C in Eq. (1.20) is never negative, as must be the case for a vector magnitude. Note that when $\vec{A}$ and $\vec{B}$ are parallel or antiparallel, $\phi = 0°$ or 180° and $C = 0$. That is, *the vector product of two parallel or antiparallel vectors is always zero. In particular, the vector product of any vector with itself is zero.*

CAUTION **Vector product vs. scalar product** Do not confuse the expression $AB \sin\phi$ for the magnitude of the vector product $\vec{A} \times \vec{B}$ with the similar expression $AB \cos\phi$ for the scalar product $\vec{A} \cdot \vec{B}$. To see the difference between these two expressions, imagine that we vary the angle between $\vec{A}$ and $\vec{B}$ while keeping their magnitudes constant. When $\vec{A}$ and $\vec{B}$ are parallel, the magnitude of the vector product will be zero and the scalar product will be maximum. When $\vec{A}$ and $\vec{B}$ are perpendicular, the magnitude of the vector product will be maximum and the scalar product will be zero.

There are always *two* directions perpendicular to a given plane, one on each side of the plane. We choose which of these is the direction of $\vec{A} \times \vec{B}$ as follows. Imagine rotating vector $\vec{A}$ about the perpendicular line until $\vec{A}$ is aligned with $\vec{B}$, choosing the smaller of the two possible angles between $\vec{A}$ and $\vec{B}$. Curl the fingers of your right hand around the perpendicular line so that your fingertips point in the direction of rotation; your thumb will then point in the direction of $\vec{A} \times \vec{B}$. Figure 1.30a shows this **right-hand rule** and describes a second way to think about this rule.

Similarly, we determine the direction of $\vec{B} \times \vec{A}$ by rotating $\vec{B}$ into $\vec{A}$ as in Fig. 1.30b. The result is a vector that is *opposite* to the vector $\vec{A} \times \vec{B}$. The vector product is *not* commutative but instead is *anticommutative:* For any two vectors $\vec{A}$ and $\vec{B}$,

$$\vec{A} \times \vec{B} = -\vec{B} \times \vec{A} \tag{1.21}$$

Just as we did for the scalar product, we can give a geometrical interpretation of the magnitude of the vector product. In **Fig. 1.31a,** $B \sin\phi$ is the component of vector $\vec{B}$ that is *perpendicular* to the direction of vector $\vec{A}$. From Eq. (1.20) the magnitude of $\vec{A} \times \vec{B}$ equals the magnitude of $\vec{A}$ multiplied by the component of $\vec{B}$ that is perpendicular to $\vec{A}$. Figure 1.31b shows that the magnitude of $\vec{A} \times \vec{B}$ also equals the magnitude of $\vec{B}$ multiplied by the component of $\vec{A}$ that is perpendicular to $\vec{B}$. Note that Fig. 1.31 shows the case in which ϕ is between $0°$ and $90°$; draw a similar diagram for ϕ between $90°$ and $180°$ to show that the same geometrical interpretation of the magnitude of $\vec{A} \times \vec{B}$ applies.

Using Components to Calculate the Vector Product

If we know the components of $\vec{A}$ and $\vec{B}$, we can calculate the components of the vector product by using a procedure similar to that for the scalar product. First we work out the multiplication table for unit vectors $\hat{\imath}$, $\hat{\jmath}$, and $\hat{k}$, all three of which are perpendicular to each other (**Fig. 1.32a**). The vector product of any vector with itself is zero, so

$$\hat{\imath} \times \hat{\imath} = \hat{\jmath} \times \hat{\jmath} = \hat{k} \times \hat{k} = \mathbf{0}$$

The boldface zero is a reminder that each product is a zero *vector*—that is, one with all components equal to zero and an undefined direction. Using Eqs. (1.20) and (1.21) and the right-hand rule, we find

$$\hat{\imath} \times \hat{\jmath} = -\hat{\jmath} \times \hat{\imath} = \hat{k}$$
$$\hat{\jmath} \times \hat{k} = -\hat{k} \times \hat{\jmath} = \hat{\imath} \tag{1.22}$$
$$\hat{k} \times \hat{\imath} = -\hat{\imath} \times \hat{k} = \hat{\jmath}$$

You can verify these equations by referring to Fig. 1.32a.

Next we express $\vec{A}$ and $\vec{B}$ in terms of their components and the corresponding unit vectors, and we expand the expression for the vector product:

$$\begin{aligned}
\vec{A} \times \vec{B} &= (A_x\hat{\imath} + A_y\hat{\jmath} + A_z\hat{k}) \times (B_x\hat{\imath} + B_y\hat{\jmath} + B_z\hat{k}) \\
&= A_x\hat{\imath} \times B_x\hat{\imath} + A_x\hat{\imath} \times B_y\hat{\jmath} + A_x\hat{\imath} \times B_z\hat{k} \\
&\quad + A_y\hat{\jmath} \times B_x\hat{\imath} + A_y\hat{\jmath} \times B_y\hat{\jmath} + A_y\hat{\jmath} \times B_z\hat{k} \\
&\quad + A_z\hat{k} \times B_x\hat{\imath} + A_z\hat{k} \times B_y\hat{\jmath} + A_z\hat{k} \times B_z\hat{k}
\end{aligned} \tag{1.23}$$

We can also rewrite the individual terms in Eq. (1.23) as $A_x\hat{\imath} \times B_y\hat{\jmath} = (A_xB_y)\hat{\imath} \times \hat{\jmath}$, and so on. Evaluating these by using the multiplication table for the unit vectors in Eqs. (1.22) and then grouping the terms, we get

$$\vec{A} \times \vec{B} = (A_yB_z - A_zB_y)\hat{\imath} + (A_zB_x - A_xB_z)\hat{\jmath} + (A_xB_y - A_yB_x)\hat{k} \tag{1.24}$$

If you compare Eq. (1.24) with Eq. (1.14), you'll see that the components of $\vec{C} = \vec{A} \times \vec{B}$ are

Components of vector (cross) product $\vec{A} \times \vec{B}$

$$C_x = A_yB_z - A_zB_y \qquad C_y = A_zB_x - A_xB_z \qquad C_z = A_xB_y - A_yB_x \tag{1.25}$$

$A_x, A_y, A_z =$ components of $\vec{A}$ $B_x, B_y, B_z =$ components of $\vec{B}$

1.31 Calculating the magnitude $AB\sin\phi$ of the vector product of two vectors, $\vec{A} \times \vec{B}$.

(a)

(Magnitude of $\vec{A} \times \vec{B}$) equals $A(B\sin\phi)$.

(Magnitude of $\vec{A}$) $\times$ $\left(\begin{array}{c}\text{Component of } \vec{B} \\ \text{perpendicular to } \vec{A}\end{array}\right)$

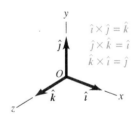

$\vec{B}$ $B\sin\phi$ ϕ $\vec{A}$

(b)

(Magnitude of $\vec{A} \times \vec{B}$) also equals $B(A\sin\phi)$.

(Magnitude of $\vec{B}$) $\times$ $\left(\begin{array}{c}\text{Component of } \vec{A} \\ \text{perpendicular to } \vec{B}\end{array}\right)$

$\vec{B}$ $A\sin\phi$ ϕ $\vec{A}$

1.32 (a) We will always use a right-handed coordinate system, like this one. (b) We will never use a left-handed coordinate system (in which $\hat{\imath} \times \hat{\jmath} = -\hat{k}$, and so on).

(a) A right-handed coordinate system

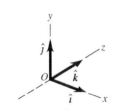

$\hat{\imath} \times \hat{\jmath} = \hat{k}$
$\hat{\jmath} \times \hat{k} = \hat{\imath}$
$\hat{k} \times \hat{\imath} = \hat{\jmath}$

(b) A left-handed coordinate system; we will not use these.

With the axis system of Fig. 1.32a, if we reverse the direction of the z-axis, we get the system shown in Fig. 1.32b. Then, as you may verify, the definition of the vector product gives $\hat{\imath} \times \hat{\jmath} = -\hat{k}$ instead of $\hat{\imath} \times \hat{\jmath} = \hat{k}$. In fact, all vector products of unit vectors $\hat{\imath}$, $\hat{\jmath}$, and $\hat{k}$ would have signs opposite to those in Eqs. (1.22). So there are two kinds of coordinate systems, which differ in the signs of the vector products of unit vectors. An axis system in which $\hat{\imath} \times \hat{\jmath} = \hat{k}$, as in Fig. 1.32a, is called a **right-handed system.** The usual practice is to use *only* right-handed systems, and we'll follow that practice throughout this book.

EXAMPLE 1.11   CALCULATING A VECTOR PRODUCT

Vector $\vec{A}$ has magnitude 6 units and is in the direction of the $+x$-axis. Vector $\vec{B}$ has magnitude 4 units and lies in the xy-plane, making an angle of 30° with the $+x$-axis (**Fig. 1.33**). Find the vector product $\vec{C} = \vec{A} \times \vec{B}$.

SOLUTION

IDENTIFY and SET UP: We'll find the vector product in two ways, which will provide a check of our calculations. First we'll use Eq. (1.20) and the right-hand rule; then we'll use Eqs. (1.25) to find the vector product by using components.

1.33 Vectors $\vec{A}$ and $\vec{B}$ and their vector product $\vec{C} = \vec{A} \times \vec{B}$. Vector $\vec{B}$ lies in the xy-plane.

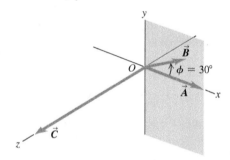

EXECUTE: From Eq. (1.20) the magnitude of the vector product is

$$AB \sin \phi = (6)(4)(\sin 30°) = 12$$

By the right-hand rule, the direction of $\vec{A} \times \vec{B}$ is along the $+z$-axis (the direction of the unit vector $\hat{k}$), so $\vec{C} = \vec{A} \times \vec{B} = 12\hat{k}$.

To use Eqs. (1.25), we first determine the components of $\vec{A}$ and $\vec{B}$. Note that $\vec{A}$ points along the x-axis, so its only nonzero component is A_x. For $\vec{B}$, Fig. 1.33 shows that $\phi = 30°$ is measured from the $+x$-axis toward the $+y$-axis, so we can use Eqs. (1.5):

$A_x = 6$	$A_y = 0$	$A_z = 0$
$B_x = 4 \cos 30° = 2\sqrt{3}$	$B_y = 4 \sin 30° = 2$	$B_z = 0$

Then Eqs. (1.25) yield

$$C_x = (0)(0) - (0)(2) = 0$$

$$C_y = (0)(2\sqrt{3}) - (6)(0) = 0$$

$$C_z = (6)(2) - (0)(2\sqrt{3}) = 12$$

Thus again we have $\vec{C} = 12\hat{k}$.

EVALUATE: Both methods give the same result. Depending on the situation, one or the other of the two approaches may be the more convenient one to use.

TEST YOUR UNDERSTANDING OF SECTION 1.10 Vector $\vec{A}$ has magnitude 2 and vector $\vec{B}$ has magnitude 3. The angle ϕ between $\vec{A}$ and $\vec{B}$ is (i) 0°, (ii) 90°, or (iii) 180°. For each of the following situations, state what the value of ϕ must be. (In each situation there may be more than one correct answer.) (a) $\vec{A} \cdot \vec{B} = 0$; (b) $\vec{A} \times \vec{B} = 0$; (c) $\vec{A} \cdot \vec{B} = 6$; (d) $\vec{A} \cdot \vec{B} = -6$; (e) (magnitude of $\vec{A} \times \vec{B}$) = 6. ▮

Physical quantities and units: Three fundamental physical quantities are mass, length, and time. The corresponding fundamental SI units are the kilogram, the meter, and the second. Derived units for other physical quantities are products or quotients of the basic units. Equations must be dimensionally consistent; two terms can be added only when they have the same units. (See Examples 1.1 and 1.2.)

Significant figures: The accuracy of a measurement can be indicated by the number of significant figures or by a stated uncertainty. The significant figures in the result of a calculation are determined by the rules summarized in Table 1.2. When only crude estimates are available for input data, we can often make useful order-of-magnitude estimates. (See Examples 1.3 and 1.4.)

Significant figures in magenta

$$\pi = \frac{C}{2r} = \frac{0.424 \text{ m}}{2(0.06750 \text{ m})} = 3.14$$

$$123.62 + 8.9 = 132.5$$

Scalars, vectors, and vector addition: Scalar quantities are numbers and combine according to the usual rules of arithmetic. Vector quantities have direction as well as magnitude and combine according to the rules of vector addition. The negative of a vector has the same magnitude but points in the opposite direction. (See Example 1.5.)

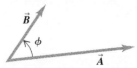

Vector components and vector addition: Vectors can be added by using components of vectors. The x-component of $\vec{R} = \vec{A} + \vec{B}$ is the sum of the x-components of $\vec{A}$ and $\vec{B}$, and likewise for the y- and z-components. (See Examples 1.6 and 1.7.)

$$R_x = A_x + B_x$$
$$R_y = A_y + B_y \quad (1.9)$$
$$R_z = A_z + B_z$$

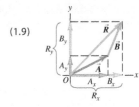

Unit vectors: Unit vectors describe directions in space. A unit vector has a magnitude of 1, with no units. The unit vectors $\hat{\imath}$, $\hat{\jmath}$, and $\hat{k}$, aligned with the x-, y-, and z-axes of a rectangular coordinate system, are especially useful. (See Example 1.8.)

$$\vec{A} = A_x\hat{\imath} + A_y\hat{\jmath} + A_z\hat{k} \quad (1.14)$$

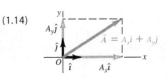

Scalar product: The scalar product $C = \vec{A} \cdot \vec{B}$ of two vectors $\vec{A}$ and $\vec{B}$ is a scalar quantity. It can be expressed in terms of the magnitudes of $\vec{A}$ and $\vec{B}$ and the angle ϕ between the two vectors, or in terms of the components of $\vec{A}$ and $\vec{B}$. The scalar product is commutative; $\vec{A} \cdot \vec{B} = \vec{B} \cdot \vec{A}$. The scalar product of two perpendicular vectors is zero. (See Examples 1.9 and 1.10.)

$$\vec{A} \cdot \vec{B} = AB\cos\phi = |\vec{A}||\vec{B}|\cos\phi \quad (1.16)$$
$$\vec{A} \cdot \vec{B} = A_xB_x + A_yB_y + A_zB_z \quad (1.19)$$

Scalar product $\vec{A} \cdot \vec{B} = AB\cos\phi$

Vector product: The vector product $\vec{C} = \vec{A} \times \vec{B}$ of two vectors $\vec{A}$ and $\vec{B}$ is a third vector $\vec{C}$. The magnitude of $\vec{A} \times \vec{B}$ depends on the magnitudes of $\vec{A}$ and $\vec{B}$ and the angle ϕ between the two vectors. The direction of $\vec{A} \times \vec{B}$ is perpendicular to the plane of the two vectors being multiplied, as given by the right-hand rule. The components of $\vec{C} = \vec{A} \times \vec{B}$ can be expressed in terms of the components of $\vec{A}$ and $\vec{B}$. The vector product is not commutative; $\vec{A} \times \vec{B} = -\vec{B} \times \vec{A}$. The vector product of two parallel or antiparallel vectors is zero. (See Example 1.11.)

$$C = AB \sin \phi \qquad (1.20)$$

$$C_x = A_y B_z - A_z B_y$$

$$C_y = A_z B_x - A_x B_z \qquad (1.25)$$

$$C_z = A_x B_y - A_y B_x$$

$\vec{A} \times \vec{B}$ is perpendicular to the plane of $\vec{A}$ and $\vec{B}$.

(Magnitude of $\vec{A} \times \vec{B}$) $= AB \sin \phi$

BRIDGING PROBLEM VECTORS ON THE ROOF

An air-conditioning unit is fastened to a roof that slopes at an angle of 35° above the horizontal (**Fig. 1.34**). Its weight is a force $\vec{F}$ on the air conditioner that is directed vertically downward. In order that the unit not crush the roof tiles, the component of the unit's weight perpendicular to the roof cannot exceed 425 N. (One newton, or 1 N, is the SI unit of force. It is equal to 0.2248 lb.) (a) What is the maximum allowed weight of the unit? (b) If the fasteners fail, the unit slides 1.50 m along the roof before it comes to a halt against a ledge. How much work does the weight force do on the unit during its slide if the unit has the weight calculated in part (a)? The work done by a force $\vec{F}$ on an object that undergoes a displacement $\vec{s}$ is $W = \vec{F} \cdot \vec{s}$.

1.34 An air-conditioning unit on a slanted roof.

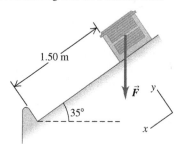

SOLUTION GUIDE

IDENTIFY and SET UP

1. This problem involves vectors and components. What are the known quantities? Which aspect(s) of the weight vector (magnitude, direction, and/or particular components) represent the target variable for part (a)? Which aspect(s) must you know to solve part (b)?
2. Make a sketch based on Fig. 1.34. Draw the x- and y-axes, choosing the positive direction for each. Your axes don't have to be horizontal and vertical, but they do have to be mutually perpendicular. Figure 1.34 shows a convenient choice of axes: The x-axis is parallel to the slope of the roof.
3. Choose the equations you'll use to determine the target variables.

EXECUTE

4. Use the relationship between the magnitude and direction of a vector and its components to solve for the target variable in

part (a). Be careful: Is 35° the correct angle to use in the equation? (*Hint:* Check your sketch.)
5. Make sure your answer has the correct number of significant figures.
6. Use the definition of the scalar product to solve for the target variable in part (b). Again, use the correct number of significant figures.

EVALUATE

7. Did your answer to part (a) include a vector component whose absolute value is greater than the magnitude of the vector? Is that possible?
8. There are two ways to find the scalar product of two vectors, one of which you used to solve part (b). Check your answer by repeating the calculation, using the other way. Do you get the same answer?

Problems

For assigned homework and other learning materials, go to MasteringPhysics®. **MP**

•, ••, •••: Difficulty levels. CP: Cumulative problems incorporating material from earlier chapters. CALC: Problems requiring calculus.
DATA: Problems involving real data, scientific evidence, experimental design, and/or statistical reasoning. BIO: Biosciences problems.

DISCUSSION QUESTIONS

Q1.1 How many correct experiments do we need to disprove a theory? How many do we need to prove a theory? Explain.

Q1.2 Suppose you are asked to compute the tangent of 5.00 meters. Is this possible? Why or why not?

Q1.3 What is your height in centimeters? What is your weight in newtons?

Q1.4 The U.S. National Institute of Standards and Technology (NIST) maintains several accurate copies of the international standard kilogram. Even after careful cleaning, these national standard kilograms are gaining mass at an average rate of about 1 μg/y (y = year) when compared every 10 years or so to the standard international kilogram. Does this apparent increase have any importance? Explain.

Q1.5 What physical phenomena (other than a pendulum or cesium clock) could you use to define a time standard?

Q1.6 Describe how you could measure the thickness of a sheet of paper with an ordinary ruler.

Q1.7 The quantity $\pi = 3.14159\ldots$ is a number with no dimensions, since it is a ratio of two lengths. Describe two or three other geometrical or physical quantities that are dimensionless.

Q1.8 What are the units of volume? Suppose another student tells you that a cylinder of radius r and height h has volume given by $\pi r^3 h$. Explain why this cannot be right.

Q1.9 Three archers each fire four arrows at a target. Joe's four arrows hit at points 10 cm above, 10 cm below, 10 cm to the left, and 10 cm to the right of the center of the target. All four of Moe's arrows hit within 1 cm of a point 20 cm from the center, and Flo's four arrows hit within 1 cm of the center. The contest judge says that one of the archers is precise but not accurate, another archer is accurate but not precise, and the third archer is both accurate and precise. Which description applies to which archer? Explain.

Q1.10 Is the vector $(\hat{\imath} + \hat{\jmath} + \hat{k})$ a unit vector? Is the vector $(3.0\hat{\imath} - 2.0\hat{\jmath})$ a unit vector? Justify your answers.

Q1.11 A circular racetrack has a radius of 500 m. What is the displacement of a bicyclist when she travels around the track from the north side to the south side? When she makes one complete circle around the track? Explain.

Q1.12 Can you find two vectors with different lengths that have a vector sum of zero? What length restrictions are required for three vectors to have a vector sum of zero? Explain.

Q1.13 The "direction of time" is said to proceed from past to future. Does this mean that time is a vector quantity? Explain.

Q1.14 Air traffic controllers give instructions called "vectors" to tell airline pilots in which direction they are to fly. If these are the only instructions given, is the name "vector" used correctly? Why or why not?

Q1.15 Can you find a vector quantity that has a magnitude of zero but components that are not zero? Explain. Can the magnitude of a vector be less than the magnitude of any of its components? Explain.

Q1.16 (a) Does it make sense to say that a vector is *negative*? Why? (b) Does it make sense to say that one vector is the negative of another? Why? Does your answer here contradict what you said in part (a)?

Q1.17 If $\vec{C} = \vec{A} + \vec{B}$, what must be true about the directions and magnitudes of $\vec{A}$ and $\vec{B}$ if $C = A + B$? What must be true about the directions and magnitudes of $\vec{A}$ and $\vec{B}$ if $C = 0$?

Q1.18 If $\vec{A}$ and $\vec{B}$ are nonzero vectors, is it possible for *both* $\vec{A} \cdot \vec{B}$ and $\vec{A} \times \vec{B}$ to be zero? Explain.

Q1.19 What does $\vec{A} \cdot \vec{A}$, the scalar product of a vector with itself, give? What about $\vec{A} \times \vec{A}$, the vector product of a vector with itself?

Q1.20 Let $\vec{A}$ represent any nonzero vector. Why is $\vec{A}/A$ a unit vector, and what is its direction? If θ is the angle that $\vec{A}$ makes with the $+x$-axis, explain why $(\vec{A}/A) \cdot \hat{\imath}$ is called the *direction cosine* for that axis.

Q1.21 Figure 1.7 shows the result of an unacceptable error in the stopping position of a train. If a train travels 890 km from Berlin to Paris and then overshoots the end of the track by 10.0 m, what is the percent error in the total distance covered? Is it correct to write the total distance covered by the train as 890,010 m? Explain.

Q1.22 Which of the following are legitimate mathematical operations: (a) $\vec{A} \cdot (\vec{B} - \vec{C})$; (b) $(\vec{A} - \vec{B}) \times \vec{C}$; (c) $\vec{A} \cdot (\vec{B} \times \vec{C})$; (d) $\vec{A} \times (\vec{B} \times \vec{C})$; (e) $\vec{A} \times (\vec{B} \cdot \vec{C})$? In each case, give the reason for your answer.

Q1.23 Consider the vector products $\vec{A} \times (\vec{B} \times \vec{C})$ and $(\vec{A} \times \vec{B}) \times \vec{C}$. Give an example that illustrates the general rule that these two vector products do not have the same magnitude or direction. Can you choose vectors $\vec{A}$, $\vec{B}$, and $\vec{C}$ such that these two vector products *are* equal? If so, give an example.

Q1.24 Show that, no matter what $\vec{A}$ and $\vec{B}$ are, $\vec{A} \cdot (\vec{A} \times \vec{B}) = 0$. (*Hint:* Do not look for an elaborate mathematical proof. Consider the definition of the direction of the cross product.)

Q1.25 (a) If $\vec{A} \cdot \vec{B} = 0$, does it necessarily follow that $A = 0$ or $B = 0$? Explain. (b) If $\vec{A} \times \vec{B} = \mathbf{0}$, does it necessarily follow that $A = 0$ or $B = 0$? Explain.

Q1.26 If $\vec{A} = \mathbf{0}$ for a vector in the xy-plane, does it follow that $A_x = -A_y$? What *can* you say about A_x and A_y?

EXERCISES

Section 1.3 Standards and Units
Section 1.4 Using and Converting Units

1.1 • Starting with the definition 1 in. = 2.54 cm, find the number of (a) kilometers in 1.00 mile and (b) feet in 1.00 km.

1.2 •• According to the label on a bottle of salad dressing, the volume of the contents is 0.473 liter (L). Using only the conversions 1 L = 1000 cm^3 and 1 in. = 2.54 cm, express this volume in cubic inches.

1.3 •• How many nanoseconds does it take light to travel 1.00 ft in vacuum? (This result is a useful quantity to remember.)

1.4 •• The density of gold is 19.3 g/cm^3. What is this value in kilograms per cubic meter?

1.5 • The most powerful engine available for the classic 1963 Chevrolet Corvette Sting Ray developed 360 horsepower and had a displacement of 327 cubic inches. Express this displacement in liters (L) by using only the conversions 1 L = 1000 cm^3 and 1 in. = 2.54 cm.

1.6 •• A square field measuring 100.0 m by 100.0 m has an area of 1.00 hectare. An acre has an area of 43,600 ft². If a lot has an area of 12.0 acres, what is its area in hectares?

1.7 • How many years older will you be 1.00 gigasecond from now? (Assume a 365-day year.)

1.8 • While driving in an exotic foreign land, you see a speed limit sign that reads 180,000 furlongs per fortnight. How many miles per hour is this? (One furlong is $\frac{1}{8}$ mile, and a fortnight is 14 days. A furlong originally referred to the length of a plowed furrow.)

1.9 • A certain fuel-efficient hybrid car gets gasoline mileage of 55.0 mpg (miles per gallon). (a) If you are driving this car in Europe and want to compare its mileage with that of other European cars, express this mileage in km/L (L = liter). Use the conversion factors in Appendix E. (b) If this car's gas tank holds 45 L, how many tanks of gas will you use to drive 1500 km?

1.10 • The following conversions occur frequently in physics and are very useful. (a) Use 1 mi = 5280 ft and 1 h = 3600 s to convert 60 mph to units of ft/s. (b) The acceleration of a freely falling object is 32 ft/s². Use 1 ft = 30.48 cm to express this acceleration in units of m/s². (c) The density of water is 1.0 g/cm³. Convert this density to units of kg/m³.

1.11 •• **Neptunium.** In the fall of 2002, scientists at Los Alamos National Laboratory determined that the critical mass of neptunium-237 is about 60 kg. The critical mass of a fissionable material is the minimum amount that must be brought together to start a nuclear chain reaction. Neptunium-237 has a density of 19.5 g/cm³. What would be the radius of a sphere of this material that has a critical mass?

1.12 • BIO (a) The recommended daily allowance (RDA) of the trace metal magnesium is 410 mg/day for males. Express this quantity in μg/day. (b) For adults, the RDA of the amino acid lysine is 12 mg per kg of body weight. How many grams per day should a 75-kg adult receive? (c) A typical multivitamin tablet can contain 2.0 mg of vitamin B_2 (riboflavin), and the RDA is 0.0030 g/day. How many such tablets should a person take each day to get the proper amount of this vitamin, if he gets none from other sources? (d) The RDA for the trace element selenium is 0.000070 g/day. Express this dose in mg/day.

1.13 •• BIO **Bacteria.** Bacteria vary in size, but a diameter of 2.0 μm is not unusual. What are the volume (in cubic centimeters) and surface area (in square millimeters) of a spherical bacterium of that size? (Consult Appendix B for relevant formulas.)

Section 1.5 Uncertainty and Significant Figures

1.14 • With a wooden ruler, you measure the length of a rectangular piece of sheet metal to be 12 mm. With micrometer calipers, you measure the width of the rectangle to be 5.98 mm. Use the correct number of significant figures: What is (a) the area of the rectangle; (b) the ratio of the rectangle's width to its length; (c) the perimeter of the rectangle; (d) the difference between the length and the width; and (e) the ratio of the length to the width?

1.15 •• A useful and easy-to-remember approximate value for the number of seconds in a year is $\pi \times 10^7$. Determine the percent error in this approximate value. (There are 365.24 days in one year.)

1.16 • Express each approximation of π to six significant figures: (a) 22/7 and (b) 355/113. (c) Are these approximations accurate to that precision?

Section 1.6 Estimates and Orders of Magnitude

1.17 •• BIO A rather ordinary middle-aged man is in the hospital for a routine checkup. The nurse writes "200" on the patient's medical chart but forgets to include the units. Which of these quantities could the 200 plausibly represent? The patient's (a) mass in kilograms; (b) height in meters; (c) height in centimeters; (d) height in millimeters; (e) age in months.

1.18 • How many gallons of gasoline are used in the United States in one day? Assume that there are two cars for every three people, that each car is driven an average of 10,000 miles per year, and that the average car gets 20 miles per gallon.

1.19 • BIO How many times does a typical person blink her eyes in a lifetime?

1.20 • BIO Four astronauts are in a spherical space station. (a) If, as is typical, each of them breathes about 500 cm³ of air with each breath, approximately what volume of air (in cubic meters) do these astronauts breathe in a year? (b) What would the diameter (in meters) of the space station have to be to contain all this air?

1.21 • In Wagner's opera *Das Rheingold*, the goddess Freia is ransomed for a pile of gold just tall enough and wide enough to hide her from sight. Estimate the monetary value of this pile. The density of gold is 19.3 g/cm³, and take its value to be about $10 per gram.

1.22 • BIO How many times does a human heart beat during a person's lifetime? How many gallons of blood does it pump? (Estimate that the heart pumps 50 cm³ of blood with each beat.)

1.23 • You are using water to dilute small amounts of chemicals in the laboratory, drop by drop. How many drops of water are in a 1.0-L bottle? (*Hint:* Start by estimating the diameter of a drop of water.)

Section 1.7 Vectors and Vector Addition

1.24 •• For the vectors $\vec{A}$ and $\vec{B}$ in **Fig. E1.24**, use a scale drawing to find the magnitude and direction of (a) the vector sum $\vec{A} + \vec{B}$ and (b) the vector difference $\vec{A} - \vec{B}$. Use your answers to find the magnitude and direction of (c) $-\vec{A} - \vec{B}$ and (d) $\vec{B} - \vec{A}$. (See also Exercise 1.31 for a different approach.)

Figure **E1.24**

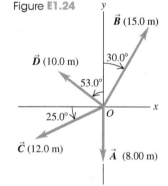

1.25 •• A postal employee drives a delivery truck along the route shown in **Fig. E1.25**. Determine the magnitude and direction of the resultant displacement by drawing a scale diagram. (See also Exercise 1.32 for a different approach.)

Figure **E1.25**

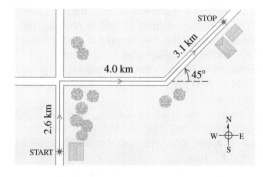

1.26 •• A spelunker is surveying a cave. She follows a passage 180 m straight west, then 210 m in a direction 45° east of south, and then 280 m at 30° east of north. After a fourth displacement, she finds herself back where she started. Use a scale drawing to determine the magnitude and direction of the fourth displacement. (See also Problem 1.61 for a different approach.)

Section 1.8 Components of Vectors

1.27 • Compute the x- and y-components of the vectors $\vec{A}, \vec{B}, \vec{C},$ and $\vec{D}$ in Fig. E1.24.

1.28 •• Let θ be the angle that the vector $\vec{A}$ makes with the $+x$-axis, measured counterclockwise from that axis. Find angle θ for a vector that has these components: (a) $A_x = 2.00$ m, $A_y = -1.00$ m; (b) $A_x = 2.00$ m, $A_y = 1.00$ m; (c) $A_x = -2.00$ m, $A_y = 1.00$ m; (d) $A_x = -2.00$ m, $A_y = -1.00$ m.

1.29 • Vector $\vec{A}$ has y-component $A_y = +9.60$ m. $\vec{A}$ makes an angle of $32.0°$ counterclockwise from the $+y$-axis. (a) What is the x-component of $\vec{A}$? (b) What is the magnitude of $\vec{A}$?

1.30 • Vector $\vec{A}$ is in the direction $34.0°$ clockwise from the $-y$-axis. The x-component of $\vec{A}$ is $A_x = -16.0$ m. (a) What is the y-component of $\vec{A}$? (b) What is the magnitude of $\vec{A}$?

1.31 • For the vectors $\vec{A}$ and $\vec{B}$ in Fig. E1.24, use the method of components to find the magnitude and direction of (a) the vector sum $\vec{A} + \vec{B}$; (b) the vector sum $\vec{B} + \vec{A}$; (c) the vector difference $\vec{A} - \vec{B}$; (d) the vector difference $\vec{B} - \vec{A}$.

1.32 •• A postal employee drives a delivery truck over the route shown in Fig. E1.25. Use the method of components to determine the magnitude and direction of her resultant displacement. In a vector-addition diagram (roughly to scale), show that the resultant displacement found from your diagram is in qualitative agreement with the result you obtained by using the method of components.

1.33 •• A disoriented physics professor drives 3.25 km north, then 2.20 km west, and then 1.50 km south. Find the magnitude and direction of the resultant displacement, using the method of components. In a vector-addition diagram (roughly to scale), show that the resultant displacement found from your diagram is in qualitative agreement with the result you obtained by using the method of components.

1.34 • Find the magnitude and direction of the vector represented by the following pairs of components: (a) $A_x = -8.60$ cm, $A_y = 5.20$ cm; (b) $A_x = -9.70$ m, $A_y = -2.45$ m; (c) $A_x = 7.75$ km, $A_y = -2.70$ km.

1.35 •• Vector $\vec{A}$ is 2.80 cm long and is $60.0°$ above the x-axis in the first quadrant. Vector $\vec{B}$ is 1.90 cm long and is $60.0°$ below the x-axis in the fourth quadrant (**Fig. E1.35**). Use components to find the magnitude and direction of (a) $\vec{A} + \vec{B}$; (b) $\vec{A} - \vec{B}$; (c) $\vec{B} - \vec{A}$. In each case, sketch the vector addition or subtraction and show that your numerical answers are in qualitative agreement with your sketch.

Figure **E1.35**

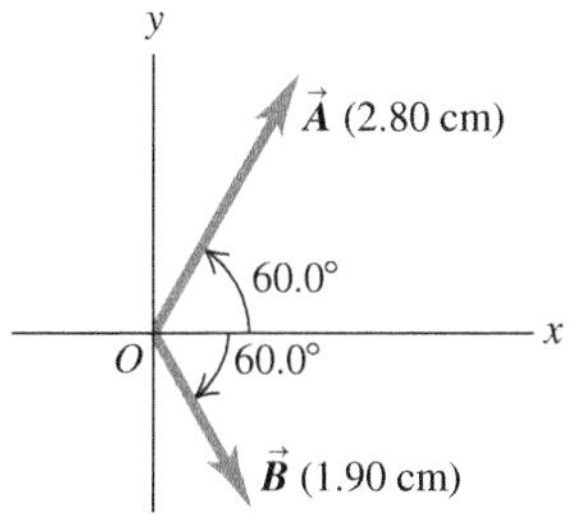

Section 1.9 Unit Vectors

1.36 • In each case, find the x- and y-components of vector $\vec{A}$: (a) $\vec{A} = 5.0\hat{i} - 6.3\hat{j}$; (b) $\vec{A} = 11.2\hat{j} - 9.91\hat{i}$; (c) $\vec{A} = -15.0\hat{i} + 22.4\hat{j}$; (d) $\vec{A} = 5.0\vec{B}$, where $\vec{B} = 4\hat{i} - 6\hat{j}$.

1.37 •• Write each vector in Fig. E1.24 in terms of the unit vectors $\hat{i}$ and $\hat{j}$.

1.38 •• Given two vectors $\vec{A} = 4.00\hat{i} + 7.00\hat{j}$ and $\vec{B} = 5.00\hat{i} - 2.00\hat{j}$, (a) find the magnitude of each vector; (b) use unit vectors

to write an expression for the vector difference $\vec{A} - \vec{B}$; and (c) find the magnitude and direction of the vector difference $\vec{A} - \vec{B}$. (d) In a vector diagram show $\vec{A}, \vec{B},$ and $\vec{A} - \vec{B}$, and show that your diagram agrees qualitatively with your answer to part (c).

1.39 •• (a) Write each vector in Fig. E1.39 in terms of the unit vectors $\hat{i}$ and $\hat{j}$. (b) Use unit vectors to express vector $\vec{C}$, where $\vec{C} = 3.00\,\vec{A} - 4.00\,\vec{B}$. (c) Find the magnitude and direction of $\vec{C}$.

Figure **E1.39**

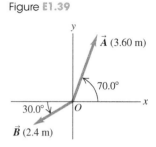

1.40 • You are given two vectors $\vec{A} = -3.00\hat{i} + 6.00\hat{j}$ and $\vec{B} = 7.00\hat{i} + 2.00\hat{j}$. Let counterclockwise angles be positive. (a) What angle does $\vec{A}$ make with the $+x$-axis? (b) What angle does $\vec{B}$ make with the $+x$-axis? (c) Vector $\vec{C}$ is the sum of $\vec{A}$ and $\vec{B}$, so $\vec{C} = \vec{A} + \vec{B}$. What angle does $\vec{C}$ make with the $+x$-axis?

1.41 • Given two vectors $\vec{A} = -2.00\hat{i} + 3.00\hat{j} + 4.00\hat{k}$ and $\vec{B} = 3.00\hat{i} + 1.00\hat{j} - 3.00\hat{k}$, (a) find the magnitude of each vector; (b) use unit vectors to write an expression for the vector difference $\vec{A} - \vec{B}$; and (c) find the magnitude of the vector difference $\vec{A} - \vec{B}$. Is this the same as the magnitude of $\vec{B} - \vec{A}$? Explain.

Section 1.10 Products of Vectors

1.42 •• (a) Find the scalar product of the vectors $\vec{A}$ and $\vec{B}$ given in Exercise 1.38. (b) Find the angle between these two vectors.

1.43 • For the vectors $\vec{A}, \vec{B},$ and $\vec{C}$ in Fig. E1.24, find the scalar products (a) $\vec{A} \cdot \vec{B}$; (b) $\vec{B} \cdot \vec{C}$; (c) $\vec{A} \cdot \vec{C}$.

1.44 •• Find the vector product $\vec{A} \times \vec{B}$ (expressed in unit vectors) of the two vectors given in Exercise 1.38. What is the magnitude of the vector product?

1.45 •• Find the angle between each of these pairs of vectors:

(a) $\vec{A} = -2.00\hat{i} + 6.00\hat{j}$ and $\vec{B} = 2.00\hat{i} - 3.00\hat{j}$

(b) $\vec{A} = 3.00\hat{i} + 5.00\hat{j}$ and $\vec{B} = 10.00\hat{i} + 6.00\hat{j}$

(c) $\vec{A} = -4.00\hat{i} + 2.00\hat{j}$ and $\vec{B} = 7.00\hat{i} + 14.00\hat{j}$

1.46 • For the two vectors in Fig. E1.35, find the magnitude and direction of (a) the vector product $\vec{A} \times \vec{B}$; (b) the vector product $\vec{B} \times \vec{A}$.

1.47 • For the two vectors $\vec{A}$ and $\vec{D}$ in Fig. E1.24, find the magnitude and direction of (a) the vector product $\vec{A} \times \vec{D}$; (b) the vector product $\vec{D} \times \vec{A}$.

1.48 • For the two vectors $\vec{A}$ and $\vec{B}$ in Fig. E1.39, find (a) the scalar product $\vec{A} \cdot \vec{B}$; (b) the magnitude and direction of the vector product $\vec{A} \times \vec{B}$.

PROBLEMS

1.49 •• **White Dwarfs and Neutron Stars.** Recall that density is mass divided by volume, and consult Appendix B as needed. (a) Calculate the average density of the earth in g/cm^3, assuming our planet is a perfect sphere. (b) In about 5 billion years, at the end of its lifetime, our sun will end up as a white dwarf that has about the same mass as it does now but is reduced to about 15,000 km in diameter. What will be its density at that stage? (c) A neutron star is the remnant of certain supernovae (explosions of giant stars). Typically, neutron stars are about 20 km in diameter and have about the same mass as our sun. What is a typical neutron star density in g/cm^3?

1.50 • An acre has a length of one furlong ($\frac{1}{8}$ mi) and a width one-tenth of its length. (a) How many acres are in a square mile? (b) How many square feet are in an acre? See Appendix E. (c) An acre-foot is the volume of water that would cover 1 acre of flat land to a depth of 1 foot. How many gallons are in 1 acre-foot?

1.51 •• **An Earthlike Planet.** In January 2006 astronomers reported the discovery of a planet, comparable in size to the earth, orbiting another star and having a mass about 5.5 times the earth's mass. It is believed to consist of a mixture of rock and ice, similar to Neptune. If this planet has the same density as Neptune (1.76 g/cm^3), what is its radius expressed (a) in kilometers and (b) as a multiple of earth's radius? Consult Appendix F for astronomical data.

1.52 •• **The Hydrogen Maser.** A maser is a laser-type device that produces electromagnetic waves with frequencies in the microwave and radio-wave bands of the electromagnetic spectrum. You can use the radio waves generated by a hydrogen maser as a standard of frequency. The frequency of these waves is 1,420,405,751.786 hertz. (A hertz is another name for one cycle per second.) A clock controlled by a hydrogen maser is off by only 1 s in 100,000 years. For the following questions, use only three significant figures. (The large number of significant figures given for the frequency simply illustrates the remarkable accuracy to which it has been measured.) (a) What is the time for one cycle of the radio wave? (b) How many cycles occur in 1 h? (c) How many cycles would have occurred during the age of the earth, which is estimated to be 4.6×10^9 years? (d) By how many seconds would a hydrogen maser clock be off after a time interval equal to the age of the earth?

1.53 • BIO **Breathing Oxygen.** The density of air under standard laboratory conditions is 1.29 kg/m^3, and about 20% of that air consists of oxygen. Typically, people breathe about $\frac{1}{2}$ L of air per breath. (a) How many grams of oxygen does a person breathe in a day? (b) If this air is stored uncompressed in a cubical tank, how long is each side of the tank?

1.54 ••• A rectangular piece of aluminum is 7.60 ± 0.01 cm long and 1.90 ± 0.01 cm wide. (a) Find the area of the rectangle and the uncertainty in the area. (b) Verify that the fractional uncertainty in the area is equal to the sum of the fractional uncertainties in the length and in the width. (This is a general result.)

1.55 ••• As you eat your way through a bag of chocolate chip cookies, you observe that each cookie is a circular disk with a diameter of 8.50 ± 0.02 cm and a thickness of 0.050 ± 0.005 cm. (a) Find the average volume of a cookie and the uncertainty in the volume. (b) Find the ratio of the diameter to the thickness and the uncertainty in this ratio.

1.56 • BIO Biological tissues are typically made up of 98% water. Given that the density of water is $1.0 \times 10^3 \text{ kg/m}^3$, estimate the mass of (a) the heart of an adult human; (b) a cell with a diameter of 0.5 μm; (c) a honeybee.

1.57 • BIO Estimate the number of atoms in your body. (*Hint:* Based on what you know about biology and chemistry, what are the most common types of atom in your body? What is the mass of each type of atom? Appendix D gives the atomic masses of different elements, measured in atomic mass units; you can find the value of an atomic mass unit, or 1 u, in Appendix E.)

1.58 •• Two ropes in a vertical plane exert equal-magnitude forces on a hanging weight but pull with an angle of 72.0° between them. What pull does each rope exert if their resultant pull is 372 N directly upward?

1.59 ••• Two workers pull horizontally on a heavy box, but one pulls twice as hard as the other. The larger pull is directed at 21.0° west of north, and the resultant of these two pulls is 460.0 N directly northward. Use vector components to find the magnitude of each of these pulls and the direction of the smaller pull.

1.60 •• Three horizontal ropes pull on a large stone stuck in the ground, producing the vector forces $\vec{A}$, $\vec{B}$, and $\vec{C}$ shown in **Fig. P1.60.** Find the magnitude and direction of a fourth force on the stone that will make the vector sum of the four forces zero.

Figure **P1.60**

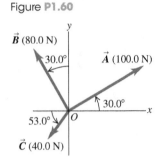

1.61 ••• As noted in Exercise 1.26, a spelunker is surveying a cave. She follows a passage 180 m straight west, then 210 m in a direction 45° east of south, and then 280 m at 30° east of north. After a fourth displacement, she finds herself back where she started. Use the method of components to determine the magnitude and direction of the fourth displacement. Draw the vector-addition diagram and show that it is in qualitative agreement with your numerical solution.

1.62 ••• **Emergency Landing.** A plane leaves the airport in Galisteo and flies 170 km at 68.0° east of north; then it changes direction to fly 230 km at 36.0° south of east, after which it makes an immediate emergency landing in a pasture. When the airport sends out a rescue crew, in which direction and how far should this crew fly to go directly to this plane?

1.63 ••• BIO **Dislocated Shoulder.** A patient with a dislocated shoulder is put into a traction apparatus as shown in **Fig. P1.63.** The pulls $\vec{A}$ and $\vec{B}$ have equal magnitudes and must combine to produce an outward traction force of 12.8 N on the patient's arm. How large should these pulls be?

Figure **P1.63**

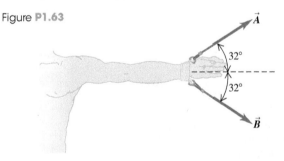

1.64 •• A sailor in a small sailboat encounters shifting winds. She sails 2.00 km east, next 3.50 km southeast, and then an additional distance in an unknown direction. Her final position is 5.80 km directly east of the starting point (**Fig. P1.64**). Find the magnitude and direction of the third leg of the journey. Draw the vector-addition diagram and show that it is in qualitative agreement with your numerical solution.

Figure **P1.64**

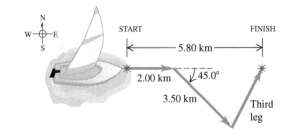

1.65 ·· You leave the airport in College Station and fly 23.0 km in a direction 34.0° south of east. You then fly 46.0 km due north. How far and in what direction must you then fly to reach a private landing strip that is 32.0 km due west of the College Station airport?

1.66 ··· On a training flight, a student pilot flies from Lincoln, Nebraska, to Clarinda, Iowa, next to St. Joseph, Missouri, and then to Manhattan, Kansas (**Fig. P1.66**). The directions are shown relative to north: 0° is north, 90° is east, 180° is south, and 270° is west. Use the method of components to find (a) the distance she has to fly from Manhattan to get back to Lincoln, and (b) the direction (relative to north) she must fly to get there. Illustrate your solutions with a vector diagram.

Figure **P1.66**

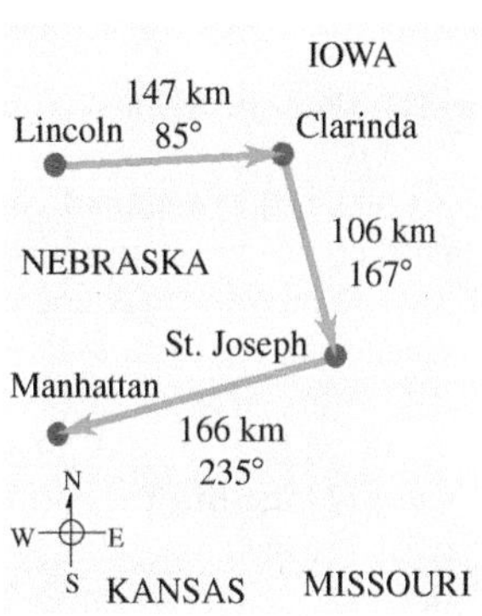

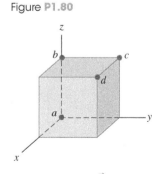

1.67 ·· As a test of orienteering skills, your physics class holds a contest in a large, open field. Each contestant is told to travel 20.8 m due north from the starting point, then 38.0 m due east, and finally 18.0 m in the direction 33.0° west of south. After the specified displacements, a contestant will find a silver dollar hidden under a rock. The winner is the person who takes the shortest time to reach the location of the silver dollar. Remembering what you learned in class, you run on a straight line from the starting point to the hidden coin. How far and in what direction do you run?

1.68 ··· **Getting Back.** An explorer in Antarctica leaves his shelter during a whiteout. He takes 40 steps northeast, next 80 steps at 60° north of west, and then 50 steps due south. Assume all of his steps are equal in length. (a) Sketch, roughly to scale, the three vectors and their resultant. (b) Save the explorer from becoming hopelessly lost by giving him the displacement, calculated by using the method of components, that will return him to his shelter.

1.69 ·· You are lost at night in a large, open field. Your GPS tells you that you are 122.0 m from your truck, in a direction 58.0° east of south. You walk 72.0 m due west along a ditch. How much farther, and in what direction, must you walk to reach your truck?

1.70 ··· A ship leaves the island of Guam and sails 285 km at 62.0° north of west. In which direction must it now head and how far must it sail so that its resultant displacement will be 115 km directly east of Guam?

1.71 ·· BIO **Bones and Muscles.** A physical therapy patient has a forearm that weighs 20.5 N and lifts a 112.0-N weight. These two forces are directed vertically downward. The only other significant forces on this forearm come from the biceps muscle (which acts perpendicular to the forearm) and the force at the elbow. If the biceps produces a pull of 232 N when the forearm is raised 43.0° above the horizontal, find the magnitude and direction of the force that the elbow exerts on the forearm. (The sum of the elbow force and the biceps force must balance the weight of the arm and the weight it is carrying, so their vector sum must be 132.5 N, upward.)

1.72 ··· You decide to go to your favorite neighborhood restaurant. You leave your apartment, take the elevator 10 flights down (each flight is 3.0 m), and then walk 15 m south to the apartment exit. You then proceed 0.200 km east, turn north, and walk 0.100 km to the entrance of the restaurant. (a) Determine the displacement from your apartment to the restaurant. Use unit vector notation for your answer, clearly indicating your choice of coordinates. (b) How far did you travel along the path you took from your apartment to the restaurant, and what is the magnitude of the displacement you calculated in part (a)?

1.73 ·· While following a treasure map, you start at an old oak tree. You first walk 825 m directly south, then turn and walk 1.25 km at 30.0° west of north, and finally walk 1.00 km at 32.0° north of east, where you find the treasure: a biography of Isaac Newton! (a) To return to the old oak tree, in what direction should you head and how far will you walk? Use components to solve this problem. (b) To see whether your calculation in part (a) is reasonable, compare it with a graphical solution drawn roughly to scale.

1.74 ·· A fence post is 52.0 m from where you are standing, in a direction 37.0° north of east. A second fence post is due south from you. How far are you from the second post if the distance between the two posts is 68.0 m?

1.75 ·· A dog in an open field runs 12.0 m east and then 28.0 m in a direction 50.0° west of north. In what direction and how far must the dog then run to end up 10.0 m south of her original starting point?

1.76 ··· Ricardo and Jane are standing under a tree in the middle of a pasture. An argument ensues, and they walk away in different directions. Ricardo walks 26.0 m in a direction 60.0° west of north. Jane walks 16.0 m in a direction 30.0° south of west. They then stop and turn to face each other. (a) What is the distance between them? (b) In what direction should Ricardo walk to go directly toward Jane?

1.77 ··· You are camping with Joe and Karl. Since all three of you like your privacy, you don't pitch your tents close together. Joe's tent is 21.0 m from yours, in the direction 23.0° south of east. Karl's tent is 32.0 m from yours, in the direction 37.0° north of east. What is the distance between Karl's tent and Joe's tent?

1.78 ·· **Bond Angle in Methane.** In the methane molecule, CH_4, each hydrogen atom is at a corner of a regular tetrahedron with the carbon atom at the center. In coordinates for which one of the C—H bonds is in the direction of $\hat{i} + \hat{j} + \hat{k}$, an adjacent C—H bond is in the $\hat{i} - \hat{j} - \hat{k}$ direction. Calculate the angle between these two bonds.

1.79 ·· Vectors $\vec{A}$ and $\vec{B}$ have scalar product −6.00, and their vector product has magnitude +9.00. What is the angle between these two vectors?

1.80 ·· A cube is placed so that one corner is at the origin and three edges are along the x-, y-, and z-axes of a coordinate system (**Fig. P1.80**). Use vectors to compute (a) the angle between the edge along the z-axis (line ab) and the diagonal from the origin to the opposite corner (line ad), and (b) the angle between line ac (the diagonal of a face) and line ad.

Figure **P1.80**

1.81 ·· Vector $\vec{A}$ has magnitude 12.0 m, and vector $\vec{B}$ has magnitude 16.0 m. The scalar product $\vec{A} \cdot \vec{B}$ is 112.0 m². What is the magnitude of the vector product between these two vectors?

1.82 ··· Obtain a *unit vector* perpendicular to the two vectors given in Exercise 1.41.

1.83 ·· The scalar product of vectors $\vec{A}$ and $\vec{B}$ is +48.0 m². Vector $\vec{A}$ has magnitude 9.00 m and direction 28.0° west of south. If vector $\vec{B}$ has direction 39.0° south of east, what is the magnitude of $\vec{B}$?

1.84 •• Two vectors $\vec{A}$ and $\vec{B}$ have magnitudes $A = 3.00$ and $B = 3.00$. Their vector product is $\vec{A} \times \vec{B} = -5.00\hat{k} + 2.00\hat{i}$. What is the angle between $\vec{A}$ and $\vec{B}$?

1.85 •• You are given vectors $\vec{A} = 5.0\hat{i} - 6.5\hat{j}$ and $\vec{B} = 3.5\hat{i} - 7.0\hat{j}$. A third vector, $\vec{C}$, lies in the xy-plane. Vector $\vec{C}$ is perpendicular to vector $\vec{A}$, and the scalar product of $\vec{C}$ with $\vec{B}$ is 15.0. From this information, find the components of vector $\vec{C}$.

1.86 •• Later in our study of physics we will encounter quantities represented by $(\vec{A} \times \vec{B}) \cdot \vec{C}$. (a) Prove that for any three vectors $\vec{A}$, $\vec{B}$, and $\vec{C}$, $\vec{A} \cdot (\vec{B} \times \vec{C}) = (\vec{A} \times \vec{B}) \cdot \vec{C}$. (b) Calculate $(\vec{A} \times \vec{B}) \cdot \vec{C}$ for vector $\vec{A}$ with magnitude $A = 5.00$ and angle $\theta_A = 26.0°$ (measured from the $+x$-axis toward the $+y$-axis), vector $\vec{B}$ with $B = 4.00$ and $\theta_B = 63.0°$, and vector $\vec{C}$ with magnitude 6.00 and in the $+z$-direction. Vectors $\vec{A}$ and $\vec{B}$ are in the xy-plane.

1.87 ••• DATA You are a team leader at a pharmaceutical company. Several technicians are preparing samples, and you want to compare the densities of the samples (density = mass/volume) by using the mass and volume values they have reported. Unfortunately, you did not specify what units to use. The technicians used a variety of units in reporting their values, as shown in the following table.

Sample ID	Mass	Volume
A	8.00 g	1.67×10^{-6} m^3
B	6.00 μg	9.38×10^{6} μm^3
C	8.00 mg	2.50×10^{-3} cm^3
D	9.00×10^{-4} kg	2.81×10^{3} mm^3
E	9.00×10^{4} ng	1.41×10^{-2} mm^3
F	6.00×10^{-2} mg	1.25×10^{8} μm^3

List the sample IDs in order of increasing density of the sample.

1.88 ••• DATA You are a mechanical engineer working for a manufacturing company. Two forces, $\vec{F}_1$ and $\vec{F}_2$, act on a component part of a piece of equipment. Your boss asked you to find the magnitude of the larger of these two forces. You can vary the angle between $\vec{F}_1$ and $\vec{F}_2$ from 0° to 90° while the magnitude of each force stays constant. And, you can measure the magnitude of the resultant force they produce (their vector sum), but you cannot directly measure the magnitude of each separate force. You measure the magnitude of the resultant force for four angles θ between the directions of the two forces as follows:

θ	Resultant force (N)
0.0°	8.00
45.0°	7.43
60.0°	7.00
90.0°	5.83

(a) What is the magnitude of the larger of the two forces? (b) When the equipment is used on the production line, the angle between the two forces is 30.0°. What is the magnitude of the resultant force in this case?

1.89 ••• DATA **Navigating in the Solar System.** The *Mars Polar Lander* spacecraft was launched on January 3, 1999. On December 3, 1999, the day *Mars Polar Lander* impacted the Martian surface at high velocity and probably disintegrated, the positions of the earth and Mars were given by these coordinates:

	x	y	z
Earth	0.3182 AU	0.9329 AU	0.0000 AU
Mars	1.3087 AU	-0.4423 AU	-0.0414 AU

With these coordinates, the sun is at the origin and the earth's orbit is in the xy-plane. The earth passes through the $+x$-axis once a year on the autumnal equinox, the first day of autumn in the northern hemisphere (on or about September 22). One AU, or *astronomical unit,* is equal to 1.496×10^8 km, the average distance from the earth to the sun. (a) Draw the positions of the sun, the earth, and Mars on December 3, 1999. (b) Find these distances in AU on December 3, 1999: from (i) the sun to the earth; (ii) the sun to Mars; (iii) the earth to Mars. (c) As seen from the earth, what was the angle between the direction to the sun and the direction to Mars on December 3, 1999? (d) Explain whether Mars was visible from your current location at midnight on December 3, 1999. (When it is midnight, the sun is on the opposite side of the earth from you.)

CHALLENGE PROBLEMS

1.90 ••• **Completed Pass.** The football team at Enormous State University (ESU) uses vector displacements to record its plays, with the origin taken to be the position of the ball before the play starts. In a certain pass play, the receiver starts at $+1.0\hat{i} - 5.0\hat{j}$, where the units are yards, $\hat{i}$ is to the right, and $\hat{j}$ is downfield. Subsequent displacements of the receiver are $+9.0\hat{i}$ (he is in motion before the snap), $+11.0\hat{j}$ (breaks downfield), $-6.0\hat{i} + 4.0\hat{j}$ (zigs), and $+12.0\hat{i} + 18.0\hat{j}$ (zags). Meanwhile, the quarterback has dropped straight back to a position $-7.0\hat{j}$. How far and in which direction must the quarterback throw the ball? (Like the coach, you will be well advised to diagram the situation before solving this numerically.)

1.91 ••• **Navigating in the Big Dipper.** All of the stars of the Big Dipper (part of the constellation Ursa Major) may appear to be the same distance from the earth, but in fact they are very far from each other. **Figure P1.91** shows the distances from the earth to each of these stars. The distances are given in light-years (ly), the distance that light travels in one year. One light-year equals 9.461×10^{15} m. (a) Alkaid and Merak are 25.6° apart in the earth's sky. In a diagram, show the relative positions of Alkaid, Merak, and our sun. Find the distance in light-years from Alkaid to Merak. (b) To an inhabitant of a planet orbiting Merak, how many degrees apart in the sky would Alkaid and our sun be?

Figure **P1.91**

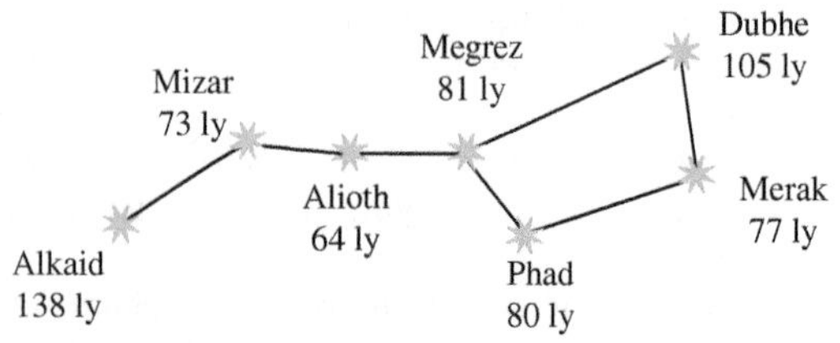

BIO **CALCULATING LUNG VOLUME IN HUMANS.** In humans, oxygen and carbon dioxide are exchanged in the blood within many small sacs called alveoli in the lungs. Alveoli provide a large surface area for gas exchange. Recent careful measurements show that the total number of alveoli in a typical pair of lungs is about 480×10^6 and that the average volume of a single alveolus is $4.2 \times 10^6 \ \mu\text{m}^3$. (The volume of a sphere is $V = \frac{4}{3}\pi r^3$, and the area of a sphere is $A = 4\pi r^2$.)

1.92 What is total volume of the gas-exchanging region of the lungs? (a) 2000 μm^3; (b) 2 m^3; (c) 2.0 L; (d) 120 L.

1.93 If we assume that alveoli are spherical, what is the diameter of a typical alveolus? (a) 0.20 mm; (b) 2 mm; (c) 20 mm; (d) 200 mm.

1.94 Individuals vary considerably in total lung volume. **Figure P1.94** shows the results of measuring the total lung volume and average alveolar volume of six individuals. From these data, what can you infer about the relationship among alveolar

size, total lung volume, and number of alveoli per individual? As the total volume of the lungs increases, (a) the number and volume of individual alveoli increase; (b) the number of alveoli increases and the volume of individual alveoli decreases; (c) the volume of the individual alveoli remains constant and the number of alveoli increases; (d) both the number of alveoli and the volume of individual alveoli remain constant.

Figure **P1.94**

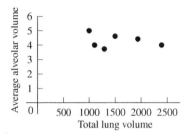

Answers

Chapter Opening Question ?

(iii) Take the $+x$-axis to point east and the $+y$-axis to point north. Then we need to find the y-component of the velocity vector, which has magnitude $v = 15$ km/h and is at an angle $\theta = 37°$ measured from the $+x$-axis toward the $+y$-axis. From Eqs. (1.5) we have $v_y = v \sin\theta = (15 \text{ km/h}) \sin 37° = 9.0$ km/h. So the thunderstorm moves 9.0 km north in 1 h and 18 km north in 2 h.

Test Your Understanding Questions

1.5 (ii) Density $= (1.80 \text{ kg})/(6.0 \times 10^{-4} \text{ m}^3) = 3.0 \times 10^3 \text{ kg/m}^3$. When we multiply or divide, the number with the fewest significant figures controls the number of significant figures in the result.

1.6 The answer depends on how many students are enrolled at your campus.

1.7 (ii), (iii), and (iv) Vector $-\vec{T}$ has the same magnitude as vector $\vec{T}$, so $\vec{S} - \vec{T} = \vec{S} + (-\vec{T})$ is the *sum* of one vector of magnitude 3 m and one of magnitude 4 m. This sum has magnitude 7 m if $\vec{S}$ and $-\vec{T}$ are parallel and magnitude 1 m if $\vec{S}$ and $-\vec{T}$ are antiparallel. The magnitude of $\vec{S} - \vec{T}$ is 5 m if $\vec{S}$ and $-\vec{T}$ are perpendicular, when vectors $\vec{S}$, $\vec{T}$, and $\vec{S} - \vec{T}$ form a 3–4–5 right triangle. Answer (i) is impossible because the magnitude of the sum of two vectors cannot be greater than the sum of the magnitudes; answer (v) is impossible because the sum of two vectors can be zero only if the two vectors are antiparallel and have the same magnitude; and answer (vi) is impossible because the magnitude of a vector cannot be negative.

1.8 (a) yes, (b) no Vectors $\vec{A}$ and $\vec{B}$ can have the same magnitude but different components if they point in different directions. If they have the same components, however, they are the same vector ($\vec{A} = \vec{B}$) and so must have the same magnitude.

1.9 All have the same magnitude. Vectors $\vec{A}$, $\vec{B}$, $\vec{C}$, and $\vec{D}$ point in different directions but have the same magnitude:

$$A = B = C = D = \sqrt{(\pm 3 \text{ m})^2 + (\pm 5 \text{ m})^2 + (\pm 2 \text{ m})^2}$$
$$= \sqrt{9 \text{ m}^2 + 25 \text{ m}^2 + 4 \text{ m}^2} = \sqrt{38 \text{ m}^2} = 6.2 \text{ m}$$

1.10 (a) (ii) $\phi = 90°$, **(b) (i)** $\phi = 0°$ or **(iii)** $\phi = 180°$, **(c) (i)** $\phi = 0°$, **(d) (iii)** $\phi = 180°$, **(e) (ii)** $\phi = 90°$ (a) The scalar product is zero only if $\vec{A}$ and $\vec{B}$ are perpendicular. (b) The vector product is zero only if $\vec{A}$ and $\vec{B}$ are parallel or antiparallel. (c) The scalar product is equal to the product of the magnitudes ($\vec{A} \cdot \vec{B} = AB$) only if $\vec{A}$ and $\vec{B}$ are parallel. (d) The scalar product is equal to the negative of the product of the magnitudes ($\vec{A} \cdot \vec{B} = -AB$) only if $\vec{A}$ and $\vec{B}$ are antiparallel. (e) The magnitude of the vector product is equal to the product of the magnitudes $[(\text{magnitude of } \vec{A} \times \vec{B}) = AB]$ only if $\vec{A}$ and $\vec{B}$ are perpendicular.

Bridging Problem

(a) 5.2×10^2 N
(b) 4.5×10^2 N $\cdot$ m

? A typical runner gains speed gradually during the course of a sprinting foot race and then slows down after crossing the finish line. In which part of the motion is it accurate to say that the runner is accelerating? (i) During the race; (ii) after the runner crosses the finish line; (iii) both (i) and (ii); (iv) neither (i) nor (ii); (v) answer depends on how rapidly the runner gains speed during the race.

2 MOTION ALONG A STRAIGHT LINE

LEARNING GOALS

Looking forward at …

2.1 How the ideas of displacement and average velocity help us describe straight-line motion.

2.2 The meaning of instantaneous velocity; the difference between velocity and speed.

2.3 How to use average acceleration and instantaneous acceleration to describe changes in velocity.

2.4 How to use equations and graphs to solve problems that involve straight-line motion with constant acceleration.

2.5 How to solve problems in which an object is falling freely under the influence of gravity alone.

2.6 How to analyze straight-line motion when the acceleration is not constant.

Looking back at …

1.7 The displacement vector.

1.8 Components of a vector.

What distance must an airliner travel down a runway before it reaches takeoff speed? When you throw a baseball straight up in the air, how high does it go? When a glass slips from your hand, how much time do you have to catch it before it hits the floor? These are the kinds of questions you will learn to answer in this chapter. We begin our study of physics with *mechanics,* the study of the relationships among force, matter, and motion. In this chapter and the next we will study *kinematics,* the part of mechanics that enables us to describe motion. Later we will study *dynamics,* which helps us understand why objects move in different ways.

In this chapter we'll concentrate on the simplest kind of motion: a body moving along a straight line. To describe this motion, we introduce the physical quantities *velocity* and *acceleration.* In physics these quantities have definitions that are more precise and slightly different from the ones used in everyday language. Both velocity and acceleration are *vectors:* As you learned in Chapter 1, this means that they have both magnitude and direction. Our concern in this chapter is with motion along a straight line only, so we won't need the full mathematics of vectors just yet. But using vectors will be essential in Chapter 3 when we consider motion in two or three dimensions.

We'll develop simple equations to describe straight-line motion in the important special case when acceleration is constant. An example is the motion of a freely falling body. We'll also consider situations in which acceleration varies during the motion; in this case, it's necessary to use integration to describe the motion. (If you haven't studied integration yet, Section 2.6 is optional.)

2.1 DISPLACEMENT, TIME, AND AVERAGE VELOCITY

Suppose a drag racer drives her dragster along a straight track (**Fig. 2.1**). To study the dragster's motion, we need a coordinate system. We choose the *x*-axis to lie along the dragster's straight-line path, with the origin *O* at the starting line.

2.1 Positions of a dragster at two times during its run.

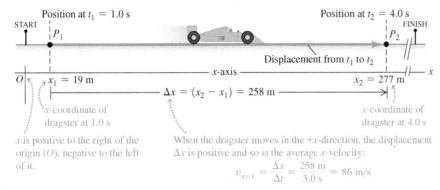

We also choose a point on the dragster, such as its front end, and represent the entire dragster by that point. Hence we treat the dragster as a **particle.**

A useful way to describe the motion of this particle is in terms of the change in its coordinate x over a time interval. Suppose that 1.0 s after the start the front of the dragster is at point P_1, 19 m from the origin, and 4.0 s after the start it is at point P_2, 277 m from the origin. The *displacement* of the particle is a vector that points from P_1 to P_2 (see Section 1.7). Figure 2.1 shows that this vector points along the x-axis. The x-component (see Section 1.8) of the displacement is the change in the value of x, (277 m − 19 m) = 258 m, that took place during the time interval of (4.0 s − 1.0 s) = 3.0 s. We define the dragster's **average velocity** during this time interval as a *vector* whose x-component is the change in x divided by the time interval: (258 m)/(3.0 s) = 86 m/s.

In general, the average velocity depends on the particular time interval chosen. For a 3.0-s time interval *before* the start of the race, the dragster is at rest at the starting line and has zero displacement, so its average velocity for this time interval is zero.

Let's generalize the concept of average velocity. At time t_1 the dragster is at point P_1, with coordinate x_1, and at time t_2 it is at point P_2, with coordinate x_2. The displacement of the dragster during the time interval from t_1 to t_2 is the vector from P_1 to P_2. The x-component of the displacement, denoted Δx, is the change in the coordinate x:

$$\Delta x = x_2 - x_1 \qquad (2.1)$$

The dragster moves along the x-axis only, so the y- and z-components of the displacement are equal to zero.

CAUTION **The meaning of Δx** Note that Δx is *not* the product of Δ and x; it is a single symbol that means "the change in quantity x." We use the Greek capital letter Δ (delta) to represent a *change* in a quantity, equal to the *final* value of the quantity minus the *initial* value—never the reverse. Likewise, the time interval from t_1 to t_2 is Δt, the change in t: $\Delta t = t_2 - t_1$ (final time minus initial time). ▌

The x-component of average velocity, or the **average x-velocity,** is the x-component of displacement, Δx, divided by the time interval Δt during which the displacement occurs. We use the symbol $v_{\text{av-}x}$ for average x-velocity (the subscript "av" signifies average value, and the subscript x indicates that this is the x-component):

Average x-velocity of a particle in **straight-line motion** during time interval from t_1 to t_2 $\qquad$ x-component of the particle's displacement

$$v_{\text{av-}x} = \frac{\Delta x}{\Delta t} = \frac{x_2 - x_1}{t_2 - t_1} \qquad (2.2)$$

Final x-coordinate minus initial x-coordinate

Time interval $\qquad$ Final time minus initial time

2.2 Positions of an official's truck at two times during its motion. The points P_1 and P_2 now indicate the positions of the truck, not the dragster, and so are the reverse of Fig. 2.1.

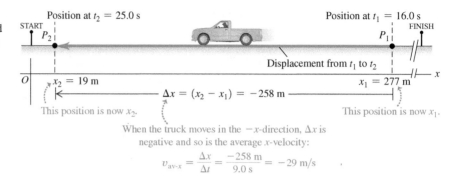

When the truck moves in the $-x$-direction, Δx is negative and so is the average x-velocity:

$$v_{\text{av-}x} = \frac{\Delta x}{\Delta t} = \frac{-258 \text{ m}}{9.0 \text{ s}} = -29 \text{ m/s}$$

As an example, for the dragster in Fig. 2.1, $x_1 = 19$ m, $x_2 = 277$ m, $t_1 = 1.0$ s, and $t_2 = 4.0$ s. So Eq. (2.2) gives

$$v_{\text{av-}x} = \frac{277 \text{ m} - 19 \text{ m}}{4.0 \text{ s} - 1.0 \text{ s}} = \frac{258 \text{ m}}{3.0 \text{ s}} = 86 \text{ m/s}$$

The average x-velocity of the dragster is positive. This means that during the time interval, the coordinate x increased and the dragster moved in the positive x-direction (to the right in Fig. 2.1).

If a particle moves in the *negative* x-direction during a time interval, its average velocity for that time interval is negative. For example, suppose an official's truck moves to the left along the track (**Fig. 2.2**). The truck is at $x_1 = 277$ m at $t_1 = 16.0$ s and is at $x_2 = 19$ m at $t_2 = 25.0$ s. Then $\Delta x = (19 \text{ m} - 277 \text{ m}) = -258$ m and $\Delta t = (25.0 \text{ s} - 16.0 \text{ s}) = 9.0$ s. The x-component of average velocity is $v_{\text{av-}x} = \Delta x / \Delta t = (-258 \text{ m})/(9.0 \text{ s}) = -29$ m/s. **Table 2.1** lists some simple rules for deciding whether the x-velocity is positive or negative.

CAUTION **The sign of average x-velocity** In our example positive $v_{\text{av-}x}$ means motion to the right, as in Fig. 2.1, and negative $v_{\text{av-}x}$ means motion to the left, as in Fig. 2.2. But that's *only* because we chose the $+x$-direction to be to the right. Had we chosen the $+x$-direction to be to the left, the average x-velocity $v_{\text{av-}x}$ would have been negative for the dragster moving to the right and positive for the truck moving to the left. In most problems the direction of the coordinate axis is yours to choose. Once you've made your choice, you *must* take it into account when interpreting the signs of $v_{\text{av-}x}$ and other quantities that describe motion! ▌

With straight-line motion we sometimes call Δx simply the displacement and $v_{\text{av-}x}$ simply the average velocity. But remember that these are the x-components of vector quantities that, in this special case, have *only* x-components. In Chapter 3, displacement, velocity, and acceleration vectors will have two or three nonzero components.

Figure 2.3 is a graph of the dragster's position as a function of time—that is, an **x-t graph.** The curve in the figure *does not* represent the dragster's path;

TABLE 2.1 Rules for the Sign of x-Velocity

If x-coordinate is:	. . . x-velocity is:
Positive & increasing (getting more positive)	Positive: Particle is moving in $+x$-direction
Positive & decreasing (getting less positive)	Negative: Particle is moving in $-x$-direction
Negative & increasing (getting less negative)	Positive: Particle is moving in $+x$-direction
Negative & decreasing (getting more negative)	Negative: Particle is moving in $-x$-direction

Note: These rules apply to both the average x-velocity $v_{\text{av-}x}$ and the instantaneous x-velocity v_x (to be discussed in Section 2.2).

2.3 A graph of the position of a dragster as a function of time.

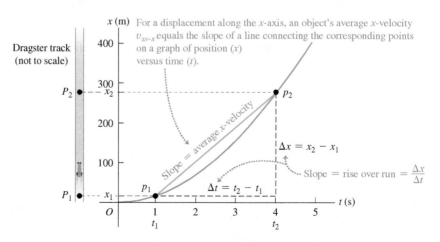

as Fig. 2.1 shows, the path is a straight line. Rather, the graph represents how the dragster's position changes with time. The points p_1 and p_2 on the graph correspond to the points P_1 and P_2 along the dragster's path. Line p_1p_2 is the hypotenuse of a right triangle with vertical side $\Delta x = x_2 - x_1$ and horizontal side $\Delta t = t_2 - t_1$. The average x-velocity $v_{\text{av-}x} = \Delta x/\Delta t$ of the dragster equals the *slope* of the line p_1p_2—that is, the ratio of the triangle's vertical side Δx to its horizontal side Δt. (The slope has units of meters divided by seconds, or m/s, the correct units for average x-velocity.)

The average x-velocity depends on only the total displacement $\Delta x = x_2 - x_1$ that occurs during the time interval $\Delta t = t_2 - t_1$, not on what happens during the time interval. At time t_1 a motorcycle might have raced past the dragster at point P_1 in Fig. 2.1, then slowed down to pass through point P_2 at the same time t_2 as the dragster. Both vehicles have the same displacement during the same time interval and so have the same average x-velocity.

If distance is given in meters and time in seconds, average velocity is measured in meters per second, or m/s (**Table 2.2**). Other common units of velocity are kilometers per hour (km/h), feet per second (ft/s), miles per hour (mi/h), and knots (1 knot = 1 nautical mile/h = 6080 ft/h).

TABLE 2.2	Typical Velocity Magnitudes
A snail's pace	10^{-3} m/s
A brisk walk	2 m/s
Fastest human	11 m/s
Freeway speeds	30 m/s
Fastest car	341 m/s
Random motion of air molecules	500 m/s
Fastest airplane	1000 m/s
Orbiting communications satellite	3000 m/s
Electron orbiting in a hydrogen atom	2×10^6 m/s
Light traveling in vacuum	3×10^8 m/s

TEST YOUR UNDERSTANDING OF SECTION 2.1   Each of the following five trips takes one hour. The positive x-direction is to the east. (i) Automobile A travels 50 km due east. (ii) Automobile B travels 50 km due west. (iii) Automobile C travels 60 km due east, then turns around and travels 10 km due west. (iv) Automobile D travels 70 km due east. (v) Automobile E travels 20 km due west, then turns around and travels 20 km due east. (a) Rank the five trips in order of average x-velocity from most positive to most negative. (b) Which trips, if any, have the same average x-velocity? (c) For which trip, if any, is the average x-velocity equal to zero? ∎

2.2 INSTANTANEOUS VELOCITY

Sometimes average velocity is all you need to know about a particle's motion. For example, a race along a straight line is really a competition to see whose average velocity, $v_{\text{av-}x}$, has the greatest magnitude. The prize goes to the competitor who can travel the displacement Δx from the start to the finish line in the shortest time interval, Δt (**Fig. 2.4**).

But the average velocity of a particle during a time interval can't tell us how fast, or in what direction, the particle was moving at any given time during the interval. For that we need to know the **instantaneous velocity,** or the velocity at a specific instant of time or specific point along the path.

_____
CAUTION   **How long is an instant?**   You might use the phrase "It lasted just an instant" to refer to something that spanned a very short time interval. But in physics an instant has no duration at all; it refers to a single value of time. ▌

To find the instantaneous velocity of the dragster in Fig. 2.1 at point P_1, we move point P_2 closer and closer to point P_1 and compute the average velocity $v_{\text{av-}x} = \Delta x/\Delta t$ over the ever-shorter displacement and time interval. Both Δx and Δt become very small, but their ratio does not necessarily become small. In the language of calculus, the limit of $\Delta x/\Delta t$ as Δt approaches zero is called the **derivative** of x with respect to t and is written dx/dt. We use the symbol v_x, with no "av" subscript, for the instantaneous velocity along the x-axis, or the **instantaneous x-velocity:**

2.4 The winner of a 50-m swimming race is the swimmer whose average velocity has the greatest magnitude—that is, the swimmer who traverses a displacement Δx of 50 m in the shortest elapsed time Δt.

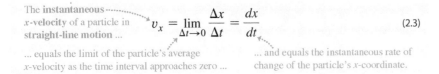

The **instantaneous x-velocity** of a particle in straight-line motion ...

$$v_x = \lim_{\Delta t \to 0} \frac{\Delta x}{\Delta t} = \frac{dx}{dt} \qquad (2.3)$$

... equals the limit of the particle's average x-velocity as the time interval approaches zero ...

... and equals the instantaneous rate of change of the particle's x-coordinate.

2.5 In any problem involving straight-line motion, the choice of which direction is positive and which is negative is entirely up to you.

······ A bicyclist moving to the left ...

O ⟶ x

... has a negative x-velocity v_x if we choose the positive x-direction to the right ...

x ⟶ O

... but has a positive x-velocity v_x if we choose the positive x-direction to the left.

The time interval Δt is always positive, so v_x has the same algebraic sign as Δx. A positive value of v_x means that x is increasing and the motion is in the positive x-direction; a negative value of v_x means that x is decreasing and the motion is in the negative x-direction. A body can have positive x and negative v_x, or the reverse; x tells us where the body is, while v_x tells us how it's moving (**Fig. 2.5**). The rules that we presented in Table 2.1 (Section 2.1) for the sign of average x-velocity $v_{\text{av-}x}$ also apply to the sign of instantaneous x-velocity v_x.

Instantaneous velocity, like average velocity, is a vector; Eq. (2.3) defines its x-component. In straight-line motion, all other components of instantaneous velocity are zero. In this case we often call v_x simply the instantaneous velocity. (In Chapter 3 we'll deal with the general case in which the instantaneous velocity can have nonzero x-, y-, and z-components.) When we use the term "velocity," we will always mean instantaneous rather than average velocity.

"Velocity" and "speed" are used interchangeably in everyday language, but they have distinct definitions in physics. We use the term **speed** to denote distance traveled divided by time, on either an average or an instantaneous basis. Instantaneous *speed,* for which we use the symbol v with *no* subscripts, measures how fast a particle is moving; instantaneous *velocity* measures how fast *and* in what direction it's moving. Instantaneous speed is the magnitude of instantaneous velocity and so can never be negative. For example, a particle with instantaneous velocity $v_x = 25$ m/s and a second particle with $v_x = -25$ m/s are moving in opposite directions at the same instantaneous speed 25 m/s.

CAUTION **Average speed and average velocity** Average speed is *not* the magnitude of average velocity. When César Cielo set a world record in 2009 by swimming 100.0 m in 46.91 s, his average speed was $(100.0 \text{ m})/(46.91 \text{ s}) = 2.132$ m/s. But because he swam two lengths in a 50-m pool, he started and ended at the same point and so had zero total displacement and zero average *velocity!* Both average speed and instantaneous speed are scalars, not vectors, because these quantities contain no information about direction. ▮

 SOLUTION

EXAMPLE 2.1 **AVERAGE AND INSTANTANEOUS VELOCITIES**

A cheetah is crouched 20 m to the east of a vehicle (**Fig. 2.6a**). At time $t = 0$ the cheetah begins to run due east toward an antelope that is 50 m to the east of the vehicle. During the first 2.0 s of the chase, the cheetah's x-coordinate varies with time according to the equation $x = 20 \text{ m} + (5.0 \text{ m/s}^2)t^2$. (a) Find the cheetah's displacement between $t_1 = 1.0$ s and $t_2 = 2.0$ s. (b) Find its average velocity during that interval. (c) Find its instantaneous velocity at $t_1 = 1.0$ s by taking $\Delta t = 0.1$ s, then 0.01 s, then 0.001 s. (d) Derive an expression for the cheetah's instantaneous velocity as a function of time, and use it to find v_x at $t = 1.0$ s and $t = 2.0$ s.

2.6 A cheetah attacking an antelope from ambush. The animals are not drawn to the same scale as the axis.

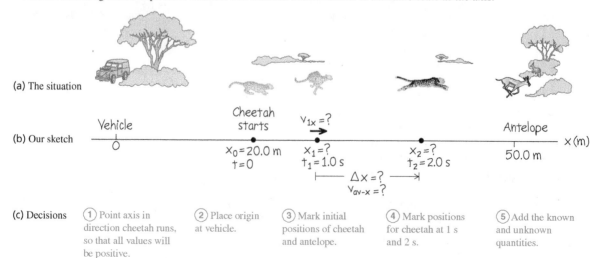

(a) The situation

(b) Our sketch

Vehicle
O

Cheetah starts
$x_0 = 20.0$ m
$t = 0$

$v_{1x} = ?$
$x_1 = ?$
$t_1 = 1.0$ s

$x_2 = ?$
$t_2 = 2.0$ s

Antelope
50.0 m

x (m)

$\Delta x = ?$
$v_{\text{av-}x} = ?$

(c) Decisions

① Point axis in direction cheetah runs, so that all values will be positive.

② Place origin at vehicle.

③ Mark initial positions of cheetah and antelope.

④ Mark positions for cheetah at 1 s and 2 s.

⑤ Add the known and unknown quantities.

SOLUTION

IDENTIFY and SET UP: Figure 2.6b shows our sketch of the cheetah's motion. We use Eq. (2.1) for displacement, Eq. (2.2) for average velocity, and Eq. (2.3) for instantaneous velocity.

EXECUTE: (a) At $t_1 = 1.0$ s and $t_2 = 2.0$ s the cheetah's positions x_1 and x_2 are

$$x_1 = 20 \text{ m} + (5.0 \text{ m/s}^2)(1.0 \text{ s})^2 = 25 \text{ m}$$

$$x_2 = 20 \text{ m} + (5.0 \text{ m/s}^2)(2.0 \text{ s})^2 = 40 \text{ m}$$

The displacement during this 1.0-s interval is

$$\Delta x = x_2 - x_1 = 40 \text{ m} - 25 \text{ m} = 15 \text{ m}$$

(b) The average x-velocity during this interval is

$$v_{\text{av-}x} = \frac{x_2 - x_1}{t_2 - t_1} = \frac{40 \text{ m} - 25 \text{ m}}{2.0 \text{ s} - 1.0 \text{ s}} = \frac{15 \text{ m}}{1.0 \text{ s}}$$

$$= 15 \text{ m/s}$$

(c) With $\Delta t = 0.1$ s the time interval is from $t_1 = 1.0$ s to a new $t_2 = 1.1$ s. At t_2 the position is

$$x_2 = 20 \text{ m} + (5.0 \text{ m/s}^2)(1.1 \text{ s})^2 = 26.05 \text{ m}$$

The average x-velocity during this 0.1-s interval is

$$v_{\text{av-}x} = \frac{26.05 \text{ m} - 25 \text{ m}}{1.1 \text{ s} - 1.0 \text{ s}} = 10.5 \text{ m/s}$$

Following this pattern, you can calculate the average x-velocities for 0.01-s and 0.001-s intervals: The results are 10.05 m/s and 10.005 m/s. As Δt gets smaller, the average x-velocity gets closer to 10.0 m/s, so we conclude that the instantaneous x-velocity at $t = 1.0$ s is 10.0 m/s. (We suspended the rules for significant-figure counting in these calculations.)

(d) From Eq. (2.3) the instantaneous x-velocity is $v_x = dx/dt$. The derivative of a constant is zero and the derivative of t^2 is $2t$, so

$$v_x = \frac{dx}{dt} = \frac{d}{dt}[20 \text{ m} + (5.0 \text{ m/s}^2)t^2]$$

$$= 0 + (5.0 \text{ m/s}^2)(2t) = (10 \text{ m/s}^2)t$$

At $t = 1.0$ s, this yields $v_x = 10$ m/s, as we found in part (c); at $t = 2.0$ s, $v_x = 20$ m/s.

EVALUATE: Our results show that the cheetah picked up speed from $t = 0$ (when it was at rest) to $t = 1.0$ s ($v_x = 10$ m/s) to $t = 2.0$ s ($v_x = 20$ m/s). This makes sense; the cheetah covered only 5 m during the interval $t = 0$ to $t = 1.0$ s, but it covered 15 m during the interval $t = 1.0$ s to $t = 2.0$ s.

Finding Velocity on an *x-t* Graph

We can also find the x-velocity of a particle from the graph of its position as a function of time. Suppose we want to find the x-velocity of the dragster in Fig. 2.1 at point P_1. As point P_2 in Fig. 2.1 approaches point P_1, point p_2 in the x-t graphs of **Figs. 2.7a** and 2.7b approaches point p_1 and the average x-velocity is calculated over shorter time intervals Δt. In the limit that $\Delta t \rightarrow 0$, shown in Fig. 2.7c, the slope of the line p_1p_2 equals the slope of the line tangent to the curve at point p_1. Thus, *on a graph of position as a function of time for straight-line motion, the instantaneous x-velocity at any point is equal to the slope of the tangent to the curve at that point.*

If the tangent to the x-t curve slopes upward to the right, as in Fig. 2.7c, then its slope is positive, the x-velocity is positive, and the motion is in the positive x-direction. If the tangent slopes downward to the right, the slope of the x-t graph and the x-velocity are negative, and the motion is in the negative x-direction. When the tangent is horizontal, the slope and the x-velocity are zero. **Figure 2.8** (next page) illustrates these three possibilities.

2.7 Using an x-t graph to go from (a), (b) average x-velocity to (c) instantaneous x-velocity v_x. In (c) we find the slope of the tangent to the x-t curve by dividing any vertical interval (with distance units) along the tangent by the corresponding horizontal interval (with time units).

(a)

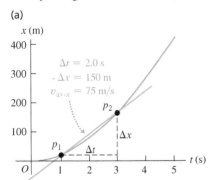

As the average x-velocity $v_{\text{av-}x}$ is calculated over shorter and shorter time intervals ...

(b)

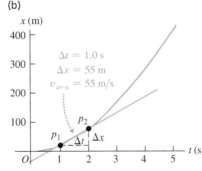

... its value $v_{\text{av-}x} = \Delta x/\Delta t$ approaches the instantaneous x-velocity.

(c)

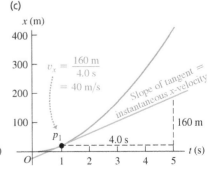

The instantaneous x-velocity v_x at any given point equals the slope of the tangent to the x-t curve at that point.

2.8 (a) The *x-t* graph of the motion of a particular particle. (b) A motion diagram showing the position and velocity of the particle at each of the times labeled on the *x-t* graph.

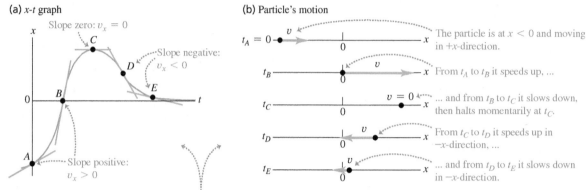

- On an *x-t* graph, the slope of the tangent at any point equals the particle's velocity at that point.
- The steeper the slope (positive or negative), the greater the particle's speed in the positive or negative *x*-direction.

Figure 2.8 depicts the motion of a particle in two ways: as (a) an *x-t* graph and (b) a **motion diagram** that shows the particle's position at various instants (like frames from a video of the particle's motion) as well as arrows to represent the particle's velocity at each instant. We will use both *x-t* graphs and motion diagrams in this chapter to represent motion. You will find it helpful to draw *both* an *x-t* graph and a motion diagram when you solve any problem involving motion.

2.9 An *x-t* graph for a particle.

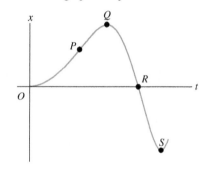

TEST YOUR UNDERSTANDING OF SECTION 2.2 **Figure 2.9** is an *x-t* graph of the motion of a particle. (a) Rank the values of the particle's *x*-velocity v_x at points *P*, *Q*, *R*, and *S* from most positive to most negative. (b) At which points is v_x positive? (c) At which points is v_x negative? (d) At which points is v_x zero? (e) Rank the values of the particle's *speed* at points *P*, *Q*, *R*, and *S* from fastest to slowest. ▌

2.3 AVERAGE AND INSTANTANEOUS ACCELERATION

Just as velocity describes the rate of change of position with time, *acceleration* describes the rate of change of velocity with time. Like velocity, acceleration is a vector quantity. When the motion is along a straight line, its only nonzero component is along that line. As we'll see, acceleration in straight-line motion can refer to either speeding up or slowing down.

Average Acceleration

Let's consider again a particle moving along the *x*-axis. Suppose that at time t_1 the particle is at point P_1 and has *x*-component of (instantaneous) velocity v_{1x}, and at a later time t_2 it is at point P_2 and has *x*-component of velocity v_{2x}. So the *x*-component of velocity changes by an amount $\Delta v_x = v_{2x} - v_{1x}$ during the time interval $\Delta t = t_2 - t_1$. As the particle moves from P_1 to P_2, its **average acceleration** is a vector quantity whose *x*-component $a_{\text{av-}x}$ (called the **average *x*-acceleration**) equals Δv_x, the change in the *x*-component of velocity, divided by the time interval Δt:

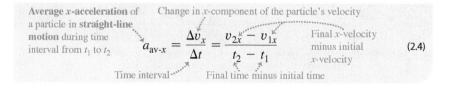

Average *x*-acceleration of a particle in **straight-line motion** during time interval from t_1 to t_2

$$a_{\text{av-}x} = \frac{\Delta v_x}{\Delta t} = \frac{v_{2x} - v_{1x}}{t_2 - t_1}$$

Change in *x*-component of the particle's velocity

Final *x*-velocity minus initial *x*-velocity

Time interval — Final time minus initial time

(2.4)

For straight-line motion along the x-axis we will often call $a_{\text{av-}x}$ simply the average acceleration. (We'll encounter the other components of the average acceleration vector in Chapter 3.)

If we express velocity in meters per second and time in seconds, then average acceleration is in meters per second per second. This is usually written as m/s^2 and is read "meters per second squared."

***

CAUTION **Don't confuse velocity and acceleration** Velocity describes how a body's position changes with time; it tells us how fast and in what direction the body moves. Acceleration describes how the velocity changes with time; it tells us how the speed and direction of motion change. To see the difference, imagine you are riding along with the moving body. If the body accelerates forward and gains speed, you feel pushed backward in your seat; if it accelerates backward and loses speed, you feel pushed forward. If the velocity is constant and there's no acceleration, you feel neither sensation. (We'll explain these sensations in Chapter 4.)

SOLUTION

EXAMPLE 2.2 AVERAGE ACCELERATION

An astronaut has left an orbiting spacecraft to test a new personal maneuvering unit. As she moves along a straight line, her partner on the spacecraft measures her velocity every 2.0 s, starting at time $t = 1.0$ s:

t	v_x	t	v_x
1.0 s	0.8 m/s	9.0 s	−0.4 m/s
3.0 s	1.2 m/s	11.0 s	−1.0 m/s
5.0 s	1.6 m/s	13.0 s	−1.6 m/s
7.0 s	1.2 m/s	15.0 s	−0.8 m/s

Find the average x-acceleration, and state whether the speed of the astronaut increases or decreases over each of these 2.0-s time intervals: (a) $t_1 = 1.0$ s to $t_2 = 3.0$ s; (b) $t_1 = 5.0$ s to $t_2 = 7.0$ s; (c) $t_1 = 9.0$ s to $t_2 = 11.0$ s; (d) $t_1 = 13.0$ s to $t_2 = 15.0$ s.

SOLUTION

IDENTIFY and SET UP: We'll use Eq. (2.4) to determine the average acceleration $a_{\text{av-}x}$ from the change in velocity over each time interval. To find the changes in speed, we'll use the idea that speed v is the magnitude of the instantaneous velocity v_x.

The upper part of **Fig. 2.10** is our graph of the x-velocity as a function of time. On this v_x-t graph, the slope of the line connecting the endpoints of each interval is the average x-acceleration $a_{\text{av-}x} = \Delta v_x/\Delta t$ for that interval. The four slopes (and thus the *signs* of the average accelerations) are, from left to right, positive, negative, negative, and positive. The third and fourth slopes (and thus the average accelerations themselves) have greater magnitude than the first and second.

EXECUTE: Using Eq. (2.4), we find:

(a) $a_{\text{av-}x} = (1.2 \text{ m/s} - 0.8 \text{ m/s})/(3.0 \text{ s} - 1.0 \text{ s}) = 0.2 \text{ m/s}^2$. The speed (magnitude of instantaneous x-velocity) increases from 0.8 m/s to 1.2 m/s.

(b) $a_{\text{av-}x} = (1.2 \text{ m/s} - 1.6 \text{ m/s})/(7.0 \text{ s} - 5.0 \text{ s}) = -0.2 \text{ m/s}^2$. The speed decreases from 1.6 m/s to 1.2 m/s.

(c) $a_{\text{av-}x} = [-1.0 \text{ m/s} - (-0.4 \text{ m/s})]/(11.0 \text{ s} - 9.0 \text{ s}) = -0.3 \text{ m/s}^2$. The speed increases from 0.4 m/s to 1.0 m/s.

2.10 Our graphs of x-velocity versus time (top) and average x-acceleration versus time (bottom) for the astronaut.

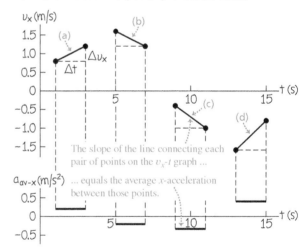

(d) $a_{\text{av-}x} = [-0.8 \text{ m/s} - (-1.6 \text{ m/s})]/(15.0 \text{ s} - 13.0 \text{ s}) = 0.4 \text{ m/s}^2$. The speed decreases from 1.6 m/s to 0.8 m/s.

In the lower part of Fig. 2.10, we graph the values of $a_{\text{av-}x}$.

EVALUATE: The signs and relative magnitudes of the average accelerations agree with our qualitative predictions. Notice that when the average x-acceleration has the *same* algebraic sign as the initial velocity, as in intervals (a) and (c), the astronaut goes faster. When $a_{\text{av-}x}$ has the *opposite* algebraic sign from the initial velocity, as in intervals (b) and (d), she slows down. Thus positive x-acceleration means speeding up if the x-velocity is positive [interval (a)] but slowing down if the x-velocity is negative [interval (d)]. Similarly, negative x-acceleration means speeding up if the x-velocity is negative [interval (c)] but slowing down if the x-velocity is positive [interval (b)].

2.11 A Grand Prix car at two points on the straightaway.

Speed v_1
x-velocity v_{1x}

Speed v_2
x-velocity v_{2x}

O P_1 P_2 x

Instantaneous Acceleration

We can now define **instantaneous acceleration** by following the same procedure that we used to define instantaneous velocity. Suppose a race car driver is driving along a straightaway as shown in **Fig. 2.11**. To define the instantaneous acceleration at point P_1, we take point P_2 in Fig. 2.11 to be closer and closer to P_1 so that the average acceleration is computed over shorter and shorter time intervals. Thus

The **instantaneous**
x-acceleration of a particle
in **straight-line motion** ...

$$a_x = \lim_{\Delta t \to 0} \frac{\Delta v_x}{\Delta t} = \frac{dv_x}{dt} \qquad (2.5)$$

... equals the limit of the particle's average
x-acceleration as the time interval approaches zero ...

... and equals the instantaneous rate
of change of the particle's x-velocity.

In Eq. (2.5) a_x is the x-component of the acceleration vector, which we call the **instantaneous x-acceleration;** in straight-line motion, all other components of this vector are zero. From now on, when we use the term "acceleration," we will always mean instantaneous acceleration, not average acceleration.

SOLUTION

EXAMPLE 2.3   AVERAGE AND INSTANTANEOUS ACCELERATIONS

Suppose the x-velocity v_x of the car in Fig. 2.11 at any time t is given by the equation

$$v_x = 60 \text{ m/s} + (0.50 \text{ m/s}^3)t^2$$

(a) Find the change in x-velocity of the car in the time interval $t_1 = 1.0$ s to $t_2 = 3.0$ s. (b) Find the average x-acceleration in this time interval. (c) Find the instantaneous x-acceleration at time $t_1 = 1.0$ s by taking Δt to be first 0.1 s, then 0.01 s, then 0.001 s. (d) Derive an expression for the instantaneous x-acceleration as a function of time, and use it to find a_x at $t = 1.0$ s and $t = 3.0$ s.

SOLUTION

IDENTIFY and SET UP: This example is analogous to Example 2.1 in Section 2.2. In that example we found the average x-velocity from the change in position over shorter and shorter time intervals, and we obtained an expression for the instantaneous x-velocity by differentiating the position as a function of time. In this example we have an exact parallel. Using Eq. (2.4), we'll find the average *x-acceleration* from the change in *x-velocity* over a time interval. Likewise, using Eq. (2.5), we'll obtain an expression for the instantaneous *x-acceleration* by differentiating the *x-velocity* as a function of time.

EXECUTE: (a) Before we can apply Eq. (2.4), we must find the x-velocity at each time from the given equation. At $t_1 = 1.0$ s and $t_2 = 3.0$ s, the velocities are

$$v_{1x} = 60 \text{ m/s} + (0.50 \text{ m/s}^3)(1.0 \text{ s})^2 = 60.5 \text{ m/s}$$

$$v_{2x} = 60 \text{ m/s} + (0.50 \text{ m/s}^3)(3.0 \text{ s})^2 = 64.5 \text{ m/s}$$

The change in x-velocity Δv_x between $t_1 = 1.0$ s and $t_2 = 3.0$ s is

$$\Delta v_x = v_{2x} - v_{1x} = 64.5 \text{ m/s} - 60.5 \text{ m/s} = 4.0 \text{ m/s}$$

(b) The average x-acceleration during this time interval of duration $t_2 - t_1 = 2.0$ s is

$$a_{\text{av-}x} = \frac{v_{2x} - v_{1x}}{t_2 - t_1} = \frac{4.0 \text{ m/s}}{2.0 \text{ s}} = 2.0 \text{ m/s}^2$$

During this time interval the x-velocity and average x-acceleration have the same algebraic sign (in this case, positive), and the car speeds up.

(c) When $\Delta t = 0.1$ s, we have $t_2 = 1.1$ s. Proceeding as before, we find

$$v_{2x} = 60 \text{ m/s} + (0.50 \text{ m/s}^3)(1.1 \text{ s})^2 = 60.605 \text{ m/s}$$

$$\Delta v_x = 0.105 \text{ m/s}$$

$$a_{\text{av-}x} = \frac{\Delta v_x}{\Delta t} = \frac{0.105 \text{ m/s}}{0.1 \text{ s}} = 1.05 \text{ m/s}^2$$

You should follow this pattern to calculate $a_{\text{av-}x}$ for $\Delta t = 0.01$ s and $\Delta t = 0.001$ s; the results are $a_{\text{av-}x} = 1.005 \text{ m/s}^2$ and $a_{\text{av-}x} = 1.0005 \text{ m/s}^2$, respectively. As Δt gets smaller, the average x-acceleration gets closer to 1.0 m/s^2, so the instantaneous x-acceleration at $t = 1.0$ s is 1.0 m/s^2.

(d) By Eq. (2.5) the instantaneous x-acceleration is $a_x = dv_x/dt$. The derivative of a constant is zero and the derivative of t^2 is $2t$, so

$$a_x = \frac{dv_x}{dt} = \frac{d}{dt}\left[60 \text{ m/s} + (0.50 \text{ m/s}^3)t^2\right]$$

$$= (0.50 \text{ m/s}^3)(2t) = (1.0 \text{ m/s}^3)t$$

When $t = 1.0$ s,

$$a_x = (1.0 \text{ m/s}^3)(1.0 \text{ s}) = 1.0 \text{ m/s}^2$$

When $t = 3.0$ s,

$$a_x = (1.0 \text{ m/s}^3)(3.0 \text{ s}) = 3.0 \text{ m/s}^2$$

EVALUATE: Neither of the values we found in part (d) is equal to the average x-acceleration found in part (b). That's because the car's instantaneous x-acceleration varies with time. The rate of change of acceleration with time is sometimes called the "jerk."

Finding Acceleration on a v_x-t Graph or an x-t Graph

In Section 2.2 we interpreted average and instantaneous x-velocity in terms of the slope of a graph of position versus time. In the same way, we can interpret average and instantaneous x-acceleration by using a graph of instantaneous velocity v_x versus time t—that is, a **v_x-t graph** (**Fig. 2.12**). Points p_1 and p_2 on the graph correspond to points P_1 and P_2 in Fig. 2.11. The average x-acceleration $a_{\text{av-}x} = \Delta v_x / \Delta t$ during this interval is the slope of the line $p_1 p_2$.

As point P_2 in Fig. 2.11 approaches point P_1, point p_2 in the v_x-t graph of Fig. 2.12 approaches point p_1, and the slope of the line $p_1 p_2$ approaches the slope of the line tangent to the curve at point p_1. Thus, *on a graph of x-velocity as a function of time, the instantaneous x-acceleration at any point is equal to the slope of the tangent to the curve at that point.* Tangents drawn at different points along the curve in Fig. 2.12 have different slopes, so the instantaneous x-acceleration varies with time.

CAUTION Signs of x-acceleration and x-velocity The algebraic sign of the x-acceleration does *not* tell you whether a body is speeding up or slowing down. **?** You must compare the signs of the x-velocity and the x-acceleration. When v_x and a_x have the *same* sign, the body is speeding up. If both are positive, the body is moving in the positive direction with increasing speed. If both are negative, the body is moving in the negative direction with an x-velocity that is becoming more negative, and again the speed is increasing. When v_x and a_x have *opposite* signs, the body is slowing down. If v_x is positive and a_x is negative, the body is moving in the positive direction with decreasing speed; if v_x is negative and a_x is positive, the body is moving in the negative direction with an x-velocity that is becoming less negative, and again the body is slowing down. **Table 2.3** summarizes these rules, and **Fig. 2.13** (next page) illustrates some of them.

The term "deceleration" is sometimes used for a decrease in speed. Because it may mean positive or negative a_x, depending on the sign of v_x, we avoid this term.

We can also learn about the acceleration of a body from a graph of its *position* versus time. Because $a_x = dv_x/dt$ and $v_x = dx/dt$, we can write

$$a_x = \frac{dv_x}{dt} = \frac{d}{dt}\left(\frac{dx}{dt}\right) = \frac{d^2x}{dt^2} \tag{2.6}$$

Rules for the Sign of

TABLE 2.3	x-Acceleration
If x-velocity is:	**... x-acceleration is:**
Positive & increasing (getting more positive)	Positive: Particle is moving in $+x$-direction & speeding up
Positive & decreasing (getting less positive)	Negative: Particle is moving in $+x$-direction & slowing down
Negative & increasing (getting less negative)	Positive: Particle is moving in $-x$-direction & slowing down
Negative & decreasing (getting more negative)	Negative: Particle is moving in $-x$-direction & speeding up

Note: These rules apply to both the average x-acceleration $a_{\text{av-}x}$ and the instantaneous x-acceleration a_x.

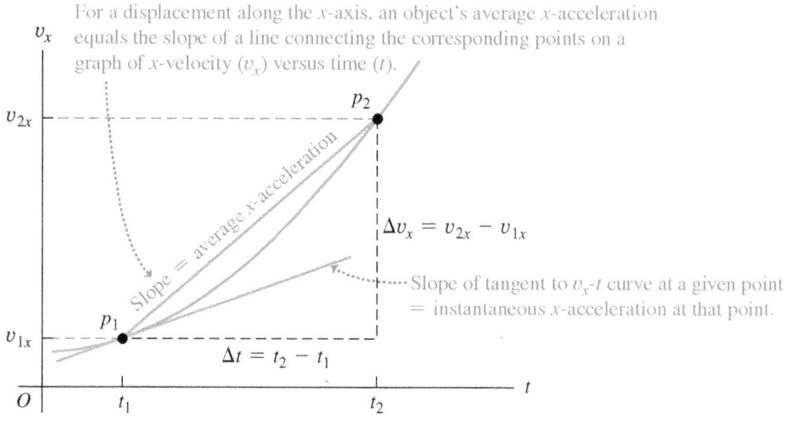

2.12 A v_x-t graph of the motion in Fig. 2.11.

For a displacement along the x-axis, an object's average x-acceleration equals the slope of a line connecting the corresponding points on a graph of x-velocity (v_x) versus time (t).

Slope = average x-acceleration

$\Delta v_x = v_{2x} - v_{1x}$

Slope of tangent to v_x-t curve at a given point = instantaneous x-acceleration at that point.

$\Delta t = t_2 - t_1$

2.13 (a) The v_x-t graph of the motion of a different particle from that shown in Fig. 2.8. (b) A motion diagram showing the position, velocity, and acceleration of the particle at each of the times labeled on the v_x-t graph.

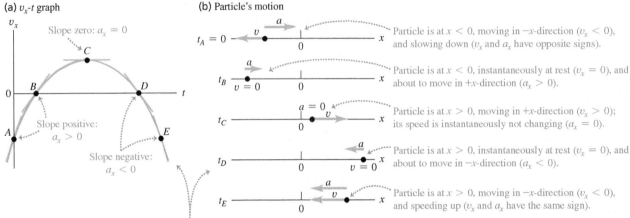

(a) v_x-t graph

Slope zero: $a_x = 0$

C

B D

0 t

Slope positive:
$a_x > 0$

A E

Slope negative:
$a_x < 0$

(b) Particle's motion

a
v
$t_A = 0$ ———•———|———— x
                 0

Particle is at $x < 0$, moving in $-x$-direction ($v_x < 0$), and slowing down (v_x and a_x have opposite signs).

a
$v = 0$
t_B ———•———|———— x
                 0

Particle is at $x < 0$, instantaneously at rest ($v_x = 0$), and about to move in $+x$-direction ($a_x > 0$).

$a = 0$
v
t_C ——————|———•—— x
                 0

Particle is at $x > 0$, moving in $+x$-direction ($v_x > 0$); its speed is instantaneously not changing ($a_x = 0$).

a
t_D ——————|———•—— x
                 0 $v = 0$

Particle is at $x > 0$, instantaneously at rest ($v_x = 0$), and about to move in $-x$-direction ($a_x < 0$).

a
v
t_E ——————|——•——— x
                 0

Particle is at $x > 0$, moving in $-x$-direction ($v_x < 0$), and speeding up (v_x and a_x have the same sign).

• On a v_x-t graph, the slope of the tangent at any point equals the particle's acceleration at that point.
• The steeper the slope (positive or negative), the greater the particle's acceleration in the positive or negative x-direction.

That is, a_x is the second derivative of x with respect to t. The second derivative of any function is directly related to the *concavity* or *curvature* of the graph of that function (**Fig. 2.14**). At a point where the x-t graph is concave up (curved upward), such as point A or E in Fig. 2.14a, the x-acceleration is positive and v_x is increasing. At a point where the x-t graph is concave down (curved downward), such as point C in Fig. 2.14a, the x-acceleration is negative and v_x is decreasing. At a point where the x-t graph has no curvature, such as the inflection points B and D in Fig. 2.14a, the x-acceleration is zero and the velocity is not changing.

Examining the curvature of an x-t graph is an easy way to identify the *sign* of acceleration. This technique is less helpful for determining numerical values of acceleration because the curvature of a graph is hard to measure accurately.

TEST YOUR UNDERSTANDING OF SECTION 2.3   Look again at the x-t graph in Fig. 2.9 at the end of Section 2.2. (a) At which of the points P, Q, R, and S is the x-acceleration a_x positive? (b) At which points is the x-acceleration negative? (c) At which points does the x-acceleration appear to be zero? (d) At each point state whether the velocity is increasing, decreasing, or not changing. ▮

2.14 (a) The same x-t graph as shown in Fig. 2.8a. (b) A motion diagram showing the position, velocity, and acceleration of the particle at each of the times labeled on the x-t graph.

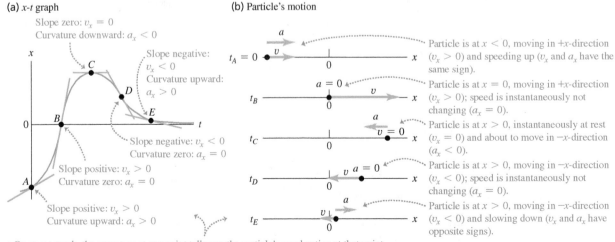

(a) x-t graph

Slope zero: $v_x = 0$
Curvature downward: $a_x < 0$

x
                 C
                        Slope negative:
                        $v_x < 0$
                        Curvature upward:
                     D $a_x > 0$
                        E
0 B ——————————————— t

Slope negative: $v_x < 0$
Curvature zero: $a_x = 0$

Slope positive: $v_x > 0$
Curvature zero: $a_x = 0$

A

Slope positive: $v_x > 0$
Curvature upward: $a_x > 0$

(b) Particle's motion

a
v
$t_A = 0$ •————————|———— x
                     0

Particle is at $x < 0$, moving in $+x$-direction ($v_x > 0$) and speeding up (v_x and a_x have the same sign).

$a = 0$
v
t_B ————————•———→ x
                 0

Particle is at $x = 0$, moving in $+x$-direction ($v_x > 0$); speed is instantaneously not changing ($a_x = 0$).

a
$v = 0$
t_C ——————|———•—— x
                 0

Particle is at $x > 0$, instantaneously at rest ($v_x = 0$) and about to move in $-x$-direction ($a_x < 0$).

v $a = 0$
t_D ——————|——•——— x
                 0

Particle is at $x > 0$, moving in $-x$-direction ($v_x < 0$); speed is instantaneously not changing ($a_x = 0$).

a
v
t_E ——————•|———— x
                 0

Particle is at $x > 0$, moving in $-x$-direction ($v_x < 0$) and slowing down (v_x and a_x have opposite signs).

• On an x-t graph, the curvature at any point tells you the particle's acceleration at that point.
• The greater the curvature (positive or negative), the greater the particle's acceleration in the positive or negative x-direction.

2.4 MOTION WITH CONSTANT ACCELERATION

The simplest kind of accelerated motion is straight-line motion with *constant* acceleration. In this case the velocity changes at the same rate throughout the motion. As an example, a falling body has a constant acceleration if the effects of the air are not important. The same is true for a body sliding on an incline or along a rough horizontal surface, or for an airplane being catapulted from the deck of an aircraft carrier.

Figure 2.15 is a motion diagram showing the position, velocity, and acceleration of a particle moving with constant acceleration. **Figures 2.16** and **2.17** depict this same motion in the form of graphs. Since the x-acceleration is constant, the a_x-t **graph** (graph of x-acceleration versus time) in Figure 2.16 is a horizontal line. The graph of x-velocity versus time, or v_x-t graph, has a constant *slope* because the acceleration is constant, so this graph is a straight line (Fig. 2.17).

When the x-acceleration a_x is constant, the average x-acceleration $a_{\text{av-}x}$ for any time interval is the same as a_x. This makes it easy to derive equations for the position x and the x-velocity v_x as functions of time. To find an expression for v_x, we first replace $a_{\text{av-}x}$ in Eq. (2.4) by a_x:

$$a_x = \frac{v_{2x} - v_{1x}}{t_2 - t_1} \qquad (2.7)$$

Now we let $t_1 = 0$ and let t_2 be any later time t. We use the symbol v_{0x} for the initial x-velocity at time $t = 0$; the x-velocity at the later time t is v_x. Then Eq. (2.7) becomes

$$a_x = \frac{v_x - v_{0x}}{t - 0} \qquad \text{or}$$

x-velocity at time t of ⋯⋯ x-velocity of the particle at time 0
a particle with
constant x-acceleration $v_x = v_{0x} + a_x t$ (2.8)
      Constant x-acceleration of the particle   Time

In Eq. (2.8) the term $a_x t$ is the product of the constant rate of change of x-velocity, a_x, and the time interval t. Therefore it equals the *total* change in x-velocity from $t = 0$ to time t. The x-velocity v_x at any time t then equals the initial x-velocity v_{0x} (at $t = 0$) plus the change in x-velocity $a_x t$ (Fig. 2.17).

Equation (2.8) also says that the change in x-velocity $v_x - v_{0x}$ of the particle between $t = 0$ and any later time t equals the *area* under the a_x-t graph between those two times. You can verify this from Fig. 2.16: Under this graph is a rectangle of vertical side a_x, horizontal side t, and area $a_x t$. From Eq. (2.8) the area $a_x t$ is indeed equal to the change in velocity $v_x - v_{0x}$. In Section 2.6 we'll show that even if the x-acceleration is not constant, the change in x-velocity during a time interval is still equal to the area under the a_x-t curve, although then Eq. (2.8) does not apply.

Next we'll derive an equation for the position x as a function of time when the x-acceleration is constant. To do this, we use two different expressions for the average x-velocity $v_{\text{av-}x}$ during the interval from $t = 0$ to any later time t. The first expression comes from the definition of $v_{\text{av-}x}$, Eq. (2.2), which is true whether or not the acceleration is constant. We call the position at time $t = 0$ the *initial position*, denoted by x_0. The position at time t is simply x. Thus for the time interval $\Delta t = t - 0$ the displacement is $\Delta x = x - x_0$, and Eq. (2.2) gives

$$v_{\text{av-}x} = \frac{x - x_0}{t} \qquad (2.9)$$

To find a second expression for $v_{\text{av-}x}$, note that the x-velocity changes at a constant rate if the x-acceleration is constant. In this case the average x-velocity

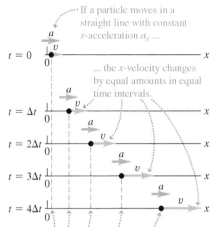

2.15 A motion diagram for a particle moving in a straight line in the positive x-direction with constant positive x-acceleration a_x.

If a particle moves in a straight line with constant x-acceleration a_x ...

... the x-velocity changes by equal amounts in equal time intervals.

However, the position changes by *different* amounts in equal time intervals because the velocity is changing.

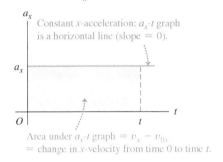

2.16 An acceleration-time $(a_x\text{-}t)$ graph of straight-line motion with constant positive x-acceleration a_x.

Constant x-acceleration: a_x-t graph is a horizontal line (slope = 0).

Area under a_x-t graph = $v_x - v_{0x}$ = change in x-velocity from time 0 to time t.

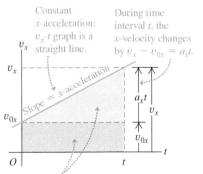

2.17 A velocity-time $(v_x\text{-}t)$ graph of straight-line motion with constant positive x-acceleration a_x. The initial x-velocity v_{0x} is also positive in this case.

Constant x-acceleration: v_x-t graph is a straight line.

During time interval t, the x-velocity changes by $v_x - v_{0x} = a_x t$.

Slope = x-acceleration

Total area under v_x-t graph = $x - x_0$ = change in x-coordinate from time 0 to time t.

BIO Application Testing Humans at High Accelerations In experiments carried out by the U.S. Air Force in the 1940s and 1950s, humans riding a rocket sled could withstand accelerations as great as 440 m/s². The first three photos in this sequence show Air Force physician John Stapp speeding up from rest to 188 m/s (678 km/h = 421 mi/h) in just 5 s. Photos 4–6 show the even greater magnitude of acceleration as the rocket sled braked to a halt.

for the time interval from 0 to t is simply the average of the x-velocities at the beginning and end of the interval:

$$v_{\text{av-}x} = \tfrac{1}{2}(v_{0x} + v_x) \quad \text{(constant } x\text{-acceleration only)} \tag{2.10}$$

[Equation (2.10) is *not* true if the x-acceleration varies during the time interval.] We also know that with constant x-acceleration, the x-velocity v_x at any time t is given by Eq. (2.8). Substituting that expression for v_x into Eq. (2.10), we find

$$v_{\text{av-}x} = \tfrac{1}{2}(v_{0x} + v_{0x} + a_xt) \quad \text{(constant}$$
$$= v_{0x} + \tfrac{1}{2}a_xt \qquad\qquad x\text{-acceleration only)} \tag{2.11}$$

Finally, we set Eqs. (2.9) and (2.11) equal to each other and simplify:

$$v_{0x} + \tfrac{1}{2}a_xt = \frac{x - x_0}{t} \qquad \text{or}$$

Position of the particle at time 0

Position at time t of a particle with constant x-acceleration ⟶ Time

$$x = x_0 + v_{0x}t + \tfrac{1}{2}a_xt^2 \tag{2.12}$$

x-velocity of the particle at time 0   Constant x-acceleration of the particle

Equation (2.12) tells us that the particle's position at time t is the sum of three terms: its initial position at $t = 0$, x_0, plus the displacement $v_{0x}t$ it would have if its x-velocity remained equal to its initial value, plus an additional displacement $\tfrac{1}{2}a_xt^2$ caused by the change in x-velocity.

A graph of Eq. (2.12)—that is, an x-t graph for motion with constant x-acceleration (**Fig. 2.18a**)—is always a *parabola*. Figure 2.18b shows such a graph. The curve intercepts the vertical axis (x-axis) at x_0, the position at $t = 0$. The slope of the tangent at $t = 0$ equals v_{0x}, the initial x-velocity, and the slope of the tangent at any time t equals the x-velocity v_x at that time. The slope and x-velocity are continuously increasing, so the x-acceleration a_x is positive and the graph in Fig. 2.18b is concave up (it curves upward). If a_x is negative, the x-t graph is a parabola that is concave down (has a downward curvature).

If there is zero x-acceleration, the x-t graph is a straight line; if there is a constant x-acceleration, the additional $\tfrac{1}{2}a_xt^2$ term in Eq. (2.12) for x as a function of t curves the graph into a parabola (**Fig. 2.19a**). Similarly, if there is zero x-acceleration, the v_x-t graph is a horizontal line (the x-velocity is constant). Adding a constant x-acceleration in Eq. (2.8) gives a slope to the graph (Fig. 2.19b).

Here's another way to derive Eq. (2.12). Just as the change in x-velocity of the particle equals the area under the a_x-t graph, the displacement (change in position) equals the area under the v_x-t graph. So the displacement $x - x_0$ of the particle between $t = 0$ and any later time t equals the area under the v_x-t graph between

2.18 (a) Straight-line motion with constant acceleration. (b) A position-time (x-t) graph for this motion (the same motion as is shown in Figs. 2.15, 2.16, and 2.17). For this motion the initial position x_0, the initial velocity v_{0x}, and the acceleration a_x are all positive.

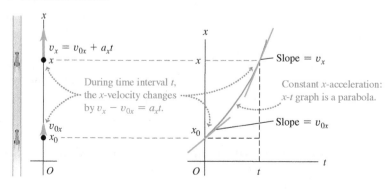

(a) A race car moves in the x-direction with constant acceleration.

(b) The x-t graph

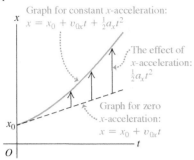

(a) An x-t graph for a particle moving with positive constant x-acceleration

Graph for constant x-acceleration:
$x = x_0 + v_{0x}t + \frac{1}{2}a_x t^2$

The effect of x-acceleration: $\frac{1}{2}a_x t^2$

Graph for zero x-acceleration: $x = x_0 + v_{0x}t$

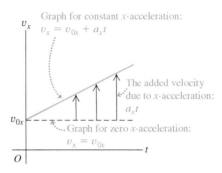

(b) The v_x-t graph for the same particle

Graph for constant x-acceleration:
$v_x = v_{0x} + a_x t$

The added velocity due to x-acceleration: $a_x t$

Graph for zero x-acceleration: $v_x = v_{0x}$

2.19 (a) How a constant x-acceleration affects a particle's (a) x-t graph and (b) v_x-t graph.

those times. In Fig. 2.17 we divide the area under the graph into a dark-colored rectangle (vertical side v_{0x}, horizontal side t, and area $v_{0x}t$) and a light-colored right triangle (vertical side $a_x t$, horizontal side t, and area $\frac{1}{2}(a_x t)(t) = \frac{1}{2}a_x t^2$). The total area under the v_x-t graph is $x - x_0 = v_{0x}t + \frac{1}{2}a_x t^2$, in accord with Eq. (2.12).

The displacement during a time interval is always equal to the area under the v_x-t curve. This is true even if the acceleration is *not* constant, although in that case Eq. (2.12) does not apply. (We'll show this in Section 2.6.)

It's often useful to have a relationship for position, x-velocity, and (constant) x-acceleration that does not involve time. To obtain this, we first solve Eq. (2.8) for t and then substitute the resulting expression into Eq. (2.12):

$$t = \frac{v_x - v_{0x}}{a_x}$$

$$x = x_0 + v_{0x}\left(\frac{v_x - v_{0x}}{a_x}\right) + \frac{1}{2}a_x\left(\frac{v_x - v_{0x}}{a_x}\right)^2$$

We transfer the term x_0 to the left side, multiply through by $2a_x$, and simplify:

$$2a_x(x - x_0) = 2v_{0x}v_x - 2v_{0x}{}^2 + v_x{}^2 - 2v_{0x}v_x + v_{0x}{}^2$$

Finally,

x-**velocity** at time t of a particle with **constant x-acceleration**

x-velocity of the particle at time 0

$$v_x{}^2 = v_{0x}{}^2 + 2a_x(x - x_0) \qquad (2.13)$$

Constant x-acceleration of the particle

Position of the particle at time t

Position of the particle at time 0

We can get one more useful relationship by equating the two expressions for $v_{\text{av-}x}$, Eqs. (2.9) and (2.10), and multiplying through by t:

Position at time t of a particle with **constant x-acceleration**

Position of the particle at time 0   Time

$$x - x_0 = \frac{1}{2}(v_{0x} + v_x)t \qquad (2.14)$$

x-velocity of the particle at time 0 x-velocity of the particle at time t

Note that Eq. (2.14) does not contain the x-acceleration a_x. This equation can be handy when a_x is constant but its value is unknown.

Equations (2.8), (2.12), (2.13), and (2.14) are the *equations of motion with constant acceleration* (**Table 2.4**). By using these equations, we can solve *any* problem involving straight-line motion of a particle with constant acceleration.

For the particular case of motion with constant x-acceleration depicted in Fig. 2.15 and graphed in Figs. 2.16, 2.17, and 2.18, the values of x_0, v_{0x}, and a_x are all positive. We recommend that you redraw these figures for cases in which one, two, or all three of these quantities are negative.

Equations of Motion with Constant Acceleration

TABLE 2.4		

Equation		Includes Quantities
$v_x = v_{0x} + a_x t$ (2.8)	t	v_x a_x
$x = x_0 + v_{0x}t + \frac{1}{2}a_x t^2$ (2.12)	t x	a_x
$v_x{}^2 = v_{0x}{}^2 + 2a_x(x - x_0)$ (2.13)	x v_x	a_x
$x - x_0 = \frac{1}{2}(v_{0x} + v_x)t$ (2.14)	t x	v_x

PROBLEM-SOLVING STRATEGY 2.1 **MOTION WITH CONSTANT ACCELERATION**

IDENTIFY *the relevant concepts:* In most straight-line motion problems, you can use the constant-acceleration equations (2.8), (2.12), (2.13), and (2.14). If you encounter a situation in which the acceleration *isn't* constant, you'll need a different approach (see Section 2.6).

SET UP *the problem* using the following steps:
1. Read the problem carefully. Make a motion diagram showing the location of the particle at the times of interest. Decide where to place the origin of coordinates and which axis direction is positive. It's often helpful to place the particle at the origin at time $t = 0$; then $x_0 = 0$. Your choice of the positive axis direction automatically determines the positive directions for x-velocity and x-acceleration. If x is positive to the right of the origin, then v_x and a_x are also positive toward the right.
2. Identify the physical quantities (times, positions, velocities, and accelerations) that appear in Eqs. (2.8), (2.12), (2.13), and (2.14) and assign them appropriate symbols: x, x_0, v_x, v_{0x}, and a_x, or symbols related to those. Translate the prose into physics: "*When* does the particle arrive at its highest point" means "What is the value of t when x has its maximum value?" In Example 2.4, "Where is he when his speed is 25 m/s?" means "What is the value of x when $v_x = 25$ m/s?" Be alert for implicit information. For example, "A car sits at a stop light" usually means $v_{0x} = 0$.
3. List the quantities such as x, x_0, v_x, v_{0x}, a_x, and t. Some of them will be known and some will be unknown. Write down the values

of the known quantities, and decide which of the unknowns are the target variables. Make note of the *absence* of any of the quantities that appear in the four constant-acceleration equations.
4. Use Table 2.4 to identify the applicable equations. (These are often the equations that don't include any of the absent quantities that you identified in step 3.) Usually you'll find a single equation that contains only one of the target variables. Sometimes you must find two equations, each containing the same two unknowns.
5. Sketch graphs corresponding to the applicable equations. The v_x-t graph of Eq. (2.8) is a straight line with slope a_x. The x-t graph of Eq. (2.12) is a parabola that's concave up if a_x is positive and concave down if a_x is negative.
6. On the basis of your experience with such problems, and taking account of what your sketched graphs tell you, make any qualitative and quantitative predictions you can about the solution.

EXECUTE *the solution:* If a single equation applies, solve it for the target variable, *using symbols only*; then substitute the known values and calculate the value of the target variable. If you have two equations in two unknowns, solve them simultaneously for the target variables.

EVALUATE *your answer:* Take a hard look at your results to see whether they make sense. Are they within the general range of values that you expected?

EXAMPLE 2.4 **CONSTANT-ACCELERATION CALCULATIONS**

SOLUTION

A motorcyclist heading east through a small town accelerates at a constant 4.0 m/s² after he leaves the city limits (**Fig. 2.20**). At time $t = 0$ he is 5.0 m east of the city-limits signpost while he moves east at 15 m/s. (a) Find his position and velocity at $t = 2.0$ s. (b) Where is he when his speed is 25 m/s?

SOLUTION

IDENTIFY and SET UP: The x-acceleration is constant, so we can use the constant-acceleration equations. We take the signpost as the origin of coordinates ($x = 0$) and choose the positive x-axis to point east (see Fig. 2.20, which is also a motion diagram). The known variables are the initial position and velocity, $x_0 = 5.0$ m and $v_{0x} = 15$ m/s, and the acceleration, $a_x = 4.0$ m/s². The unknown target variables in part (a) are the values of the position x and the x-velocity v_x at $t = 2.0$ s; the target variable in part (b) is the value of x when $v_x = 25$ m/s.

EXECUTE: (a) Since we know the values of x_0, v_{0x}, and a_x, Table 2.4 tells us that we can find the position x at $t = 2.0$ s by using

2.20 A motorcyclist traveling with constant acceleration.

$a_x = 4.0 \text{ m/s}^2$

$v_{0x} = 15$ m/s $v_x = ?$

OSAGE

O $x_0 = 5.0$ m $x = ?$ x (east)
           $t = 0$ $t = 2.0$ s

Eq. (2.12) and the x-velocity v_x at this time by using Eq. (2.8):

$$x = x_0 + v_{0x}t + \tfrac{1}{2}a_xt^2$$
$$= 5.0 \text{ m} + (15 \text{ m/s})(2.0 \text{ s}) + \tfrac{1}{2}(4.0 \text{ m/s}^2)(2.0 \text{ s})^2$$
$$= 43 \text{ m}$$
$$v_x = v_{0x} + a_xt$$
$$= 15 \text{ m/s} + (4.0 \text{ m/s}^2)(2.0 \text{ s}) = 23 \text{ m/s}$$

(b) We want to find the value of x when $v_x = 25$ m/s, but we don't know the time when the motorcycle has this velocity. Table 2.4 tells us that we should use Eq. (2.13), which involves x, v_x, and a_x but does *not* involve t:

$$v_x^2 = v_{0x}^2 + 2a_x(x - x_0)$$

Solving for x and substituting the known values, we find

$$x = x_0 + \frac{v_x^2 - v_{0x}^2}{2a_x}$$

$$= 5.0 \text{ m} + \frac{(25 \text{ m/s})^2 - (15 \text{ m/s})^2}{2(4.0 \text{ m/s}^2)} = 55 \text{ m}$$

EVALUATE: You can check the result in part (b) by first using Eq. (2.8), $v_x = v_{0x} + a_xt$, to find the time at which $v_x = 25$ m/s, which turns out to be $t = 2.5$ s. You can then use Eq. (2.12), $x = x_0 + v_{0x}t + \tfrac{1}{2}a_xt^2$, to solve for x. You should find $x = 55$ m, the same answer as above. That's the long way to solve the problem, though. The method we used in part (b) is much more efficient.

EXAMPLE 2.5 TWO BODIES WITH DIFFERENT ACCELERATIONS

A motorist traveling at a constant 15 m/s (about 34 mi/h) passes a school crossing where the speed limit is 10 m/s (about 22 mi/h). Just as the motorist passes the school-crossing sign, a police officer on a motorcycle stopped there starts in pursuit with constant acceleration 3.0 m/s² (**Fig. 2.21a**). (a) How much time elapses before the officer passes the motorist? At that time, (b) what is the officer's speed and (c) how far has each vehicle traveled?

SOLUTION

IDENTIFY and SET UP: Both the officer and the motorist move with constant acceleration (equal to zero for the motorist), so we can use the constant-acceleration formulas. We take the origin at the sign, so $x_0 = 0$ for both, and we take the positive direction to the right. Let x_P and x_M represent the positions of the police officer and the motorist at any time. Their initial velocities are $v_{P0x} = 0$ and $v_{M0x} = 15$ m/s, and their accelerations are $a_{Px} = 3.0$ m/s² and $a_{Mx} = 0$. Our target variable in part (a) is the time when the officer and motorist are at the same position x; Table 2.4 tells us that Eq. (2.12) is useful for this part. In part (b) we'll use Eq. (2.8) to find the officer's speed v (the magnitude of her velocity) at the time found in part (a). In part (c) we'll use Eq. (2.12) again to find the position of either vehicle at this same time.

Figure 2.21b shows an x-t graph for both vehicles. The straight line represents the motorist's motion, $x_M = x_{M0} + v_{M0x}t = v_{M0x}t$. The graph for the officer's motion is the right half of a parabola with upward curvature:

$$x_P = x_{P0} + v_{P0x}t + \tfrac{1}{2}a_{Px}t^2 = \tfrac{1}{2}a_{Px}t^2$$

A good sketch shows that the officer and motorist are at the same position ($x_P = x_M$) at about $t = 10$ s, at which time both have traveled about 150 m from the sign.

EXECUTE: (a) To find the value of the time t at which the motorist and police officer are at the same position, we set $x_P = x_M$ by equating the expressions above and solving that equation for t:

$$v_{M0x}t = \tfrac{1}{2}a_{Px}t^2$$

$$t = 0 \quad \text{or} \quad t = \frac{2v_{M0x}}{a_{Px}} = \frac{2(15 \text{ m/s})}{3.0 \text{ m/s}^2} = 10 \text{ s}$$

Both vehicles have the same x-coordinate at *two* times, as Fig. 2.21b indicates. At $t = 0$ the motorist passes the officer; at $t = 10$ s the officer passes the motorist.

(b) We want the magnitude of the officer's x-velocity v_{Px} at the time t found in part (a). Substituting the values of v_{P0x} and a_{Px} into Eq. (2.8) along with $t = 10$ s from part (a), we find

$$v_{Px} = v_{P0x} + a_{Px}t = 0 + (3.0 \text{ m/s}^2)(10 \text{ s}) = 30 \text{ m/s}$$

The officer's speed is the absolute value of this, which is also 30 m/s.

(c) In 10 s the motorist travels a distance

$$x_M = v_{M0x}t = (15 \text{ m/s})(10 \text{ s}) = 150 \text{ m}$$

and the officer travels

$$x_P = \tfrac{1}{2}a_{Px}t^2 = \tfrac{1}{2}(3.0 \text{ m/s}^2)(10 \text{ s})^2 = 150 \text{ m}$$

This verifies that they have gone equal distances after 10 s.

EVALUATE: Our results in parts (a) and (c) agree with our estimates from our sketch. Note that when the officer passes the motorist, they do *not* have the same velocity: The motorist is moving at 15 m/s and the officer is moving at 30 m/s. You can also see this from Fig. 2.21b. Where the two x-t curves cross, their slopes (equal to the values of v_x for the two vehicles) are different.

Is it just coincidence that when the two vehicles are at the same position, the officer is going twice the speed of the motorist? Equation (2.14), $x - x_0 = \tfrac{1}{2}(v_{0x} + v_x)t$, gives the answer. The motorist has constant velocity, so $v_{M0x} = v_{Mx}$, and the motorist's displacement $x - x_0$ in time t is $v_{M0x}t$. Because $v_{P0x} = 0$, in the same time t the officer's displacement is $\tfrac{1}{2}v_{Px}t$. The two vehicles have the same displacement in the same amount of time, so $v_{M0x}t = \tfrac{1}{2}v_{Px}t$ and $v_{Px} = 2v_{M0x}$—that is, the officer has exactly twice the motorist's velocity. This is true no matter what the value of the officer's acceleration.

2.21 (a) Motion with constant acceleration overtaking motion with constant velocity. (b) A graph of x versus t for each vehicle.

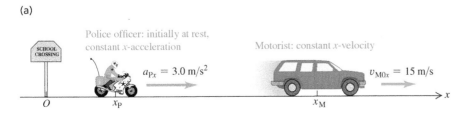

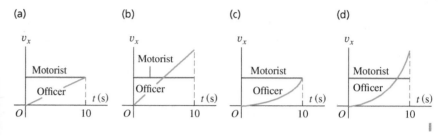

2.22 Multiflash photo of a freely falling ball.

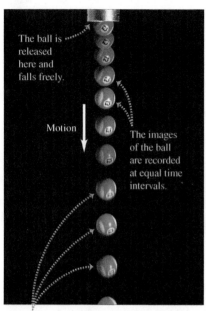

The ball is released here and falls freely.

Motion

The images of the ball are recorded at equal time intervals.

• The average velocity in each time interval is proportional to the distance between images.
• This distance continuously increases, so the ball's velocity is continuously changing; the ball is accelerating downward.

PhET: Lunar Lander

DATA *SPEAKS*

Free Fall

When students were given a problem about free fall, more than 20% gave an incorrect answer. Common errors:

• Confusing speed, velocity, and acceleration. Speed can never be negative; velocity can be positive or negative, depending on the direction of motion. In free fall, speed and velocity change continuously but acceleration (rate of change of velocity) is constant and downward.

• Not realizing that a freely falling body that moves upward at a certain speed past a point will pass that same point at the same speed as it moves downward (see Example 2.7).

2.5 FREELY FALLING BODIES

The most familiar example of motion with (nearly) constant acceleration is a body falling under the influence of the earth's gravitational attraction. Such motion has held the attention of philosophers and scientists since ancient times. In the fourth century B.C., Aristotle thought (erroneously) that heavy bodies fall faster than light bodies, in proportion to their weight. Nineteen centuries later, Galileo (see Section 1.1) argued that a body should fall with a downward acceleration that is constant and independent of its weight.

Experiment shows that if the effects of the air can be ignored, Galileo is right; all bodies at a particular location fall with the same downward acceleration, regardless of their size or weight. If in addition the distance of the fall is small compared with the radius of the earth, and if we ignore small effects due to the earth's rotation, the acceleration is constant. The idealized motion that results under all of these assumptions is called **free fall,** although it includes rising as well as falling motion. (In Chapter 3 we will extend the discussion of free fall to include the motion of projectiles, which move both vertically and horizontally.)

Figure 2.22 is a photograph of a falling ball made with a stroboscopic light source that produces a series of short, intense flashes at equal time intervals. As each flash occurs, an image of the ball at that instant is recorded on the photograph. The increasing spacing between successive images in Fig. 2.22 indicates that the ball is accelerating downward. Careful measurement shows that the velocity change is the same in each time interval, so the acceleration of the freely falling ball is constant.

The constant acceleration of a freely falling body is called the **acceleration due to gravity,** and we denote its magnitude with the letter g. We will frequently use the approximate value of g at or near the earth's surface:

$$g = 9.80 \text{ m/s}^2 = 980 \text{ cm/s}^2 = 32.2 \text{ ft/s}^2 \quad \text{(approximate value near the earth's surface)}$$

The exact value varies with location, so we will often give the value of g at the earth's surface to only two significant figures as 9.8 m/s^2. On the moon's surface, the acceleration due to gravity is caused by the attractive force of the moon rather than the earth, and $g = 1.6 \text{ m/s}^2$. Near the surface of the sun, $g = 270 \text{ m/s}^2$.

⸻

CAUTION **g is always a positive number** Because g is the *magnitude* of a vector quantity, it is always a *positive* number. If you take the positive direction to be upward, as we do in most situations involving free fall, the acceleration is negative (downward) and equal to $-g$. Be careful with the sign of g, or you'll have trouble with free-fall problems. ▌

In the following examples we use the constant-acceleration equations developed in Section 2.4. Review Problem-Solving Strategy 2.1 in that section before you study the next examples.

EXAMPLE 2.6 A FREELY FALLING COIN

A one-euro coin is dropped from the Leaning Tower of Pisa and falls freely from rest. What are its position and velocity after 1.0 s, 2.0 s, and 3.0 s?

SOLUTION

IDENTIFY and SET UP: "Falls freely" means "falls with constant acceleration due to gravity," so we can use the constant-acceleration equations. The right side of **Fig. 2.23** shows our motion diagram

2.23 A coin freely falling from rest.

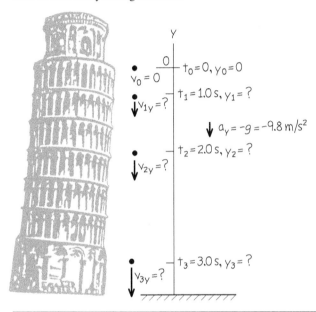

for the coin. The motion is vertical, so we use a vertical coordinate axis and call the coordinate y instead of x. We take the origin O at the starting point and the *upward* direction as positive. Both the initial coordinate y_0 and initial y-velocity v_{0y} are zero. The y-acceleration is downward (in the negative y-direction), so $a_y = -g = -9.8 \text{ m/s}^2$. (Remember that, by definition, g is a positive quantity.) Our target variables are the values of y and v_y at the three given times. To find these, we use Eqs. (2.12) and (2.8) with x replaced by y. Our choice of the upward direction as positive means that all positions and velocities we calculate will be negative.

EXECUTE: At a time t after the coin is dropped, its position and y-velocity are

$$y = y_0 + v_{0y}t + \tfrac{1}{2}a_y t^2 = 0 + 0 + \tfrac{1}{2}(-g)t^2 = (-4.9 \text{ m/s}^2)t^2$$

$$v_y = v_{0y} + a_y t = 0 + (-g)t = (-9.8 \text{ m/s}^2)t$$

When $t = 1.0 \text{ s}$, $y = (-4.9 \text{ m/s}^2)(1.0 \text{ s})^2 = -4.9 \text{ m}$ and $v_y = (-9.8 \text{ m/s}^2)(1.0 \text{ s}) = -9.8 \text{ m/s}$; after 1.0 s, the coin is 4.9 m below the origin (y is negative) and has a downward velocity (v_y is negative) with magnitude 9.8 m/s.

We can find the positions and y-velocities at 2.0 s and 3.0 s in the same way. The results are $y = -20 \text{ m}$ and $v_y = -20 \text{ m/s}$ at $t = 2.0 \text{ s}$, and $y = -44 \text{ m}$ and $v_y = -29 \text{ m/s}$ at $t = 3.0 \text{ s}$.

EVALUATE: All our answers are negative, as we expected. If we had chosen the positive y-axis to point downward, the acceleration would have been $a_y = +g$ and all our answers would have been positive.

EXAMPLE 2.7 UP-AND-DOWN MOTION IN FREE FALL

You throw a ball vertically upward from the roof of a tall building. The ball leaves your hand at a point even with the roof railing with an upward speed of 15.0 m/s; the ball is then in free fall. On its way back down, it just misses the railing. Find (a) the ball's position and velocity 1.00 s and 4.00 s after leaving your hand; (b) the ball's velocity when it is 5.00 m above the railing; (c) the maximum height reached; (d) the ball's acceleration when it is at its maximum height.

SOLUTION

IDENTIFY and SET UP: The words "in free fall" mean that the acceleration is due to gravity, which is constant. Our target variables are position [in parts (a) and (c)], velocity [in parts (a) and (b)], and acceleration [in part (d)]. We take the origin at the point where the ball leaves your hand, and take the positive direction to be upward (**Fig. 2.24**). The initial position y_0 is zero, the initial y-velocity v_{0y} is $+15.0 \text{ m/s}$, and the y-acceleration is $a_y = -g = -9.80 \text{ m/s}^2$. In part (a), as in Example 2.6, we'll use Eqs. (2.12) and (2.8) to find the position and velocity as functions of time. In part (b) we must find the velocity at a given *position* (no time is given), so we'll use Eq. (2.13).

2.24 Position and velocity of a ball thrown vertically upward.

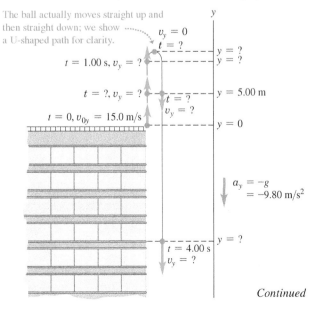

Continued

2.25 (a) Position and (b) velocity as functions of time for a ball thrown upward with an initial speed of 15.0 m/s.

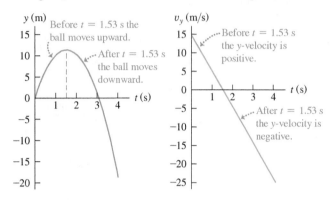

(a) y-t graph (curvature is downward because $a_y = -g$ is negative)

(b) v_y-t graph (straight line with negative slope because $a_y = -g$ is constant and negative)

Figure 2.25 shows the y-t and v_y-t graphs for the ball. The y-t graph is a concave-down parabola that rises and then falls, and the v_y-t graph is a downward-sloping straight line. Note that the ball's velocity is zero when it is at its highest point.

EXECUTE: (a) The position and y-velocity at time t are given by Eqs. (2.12) and (2.8) with x's replaced by y's:

$$y = y_0 + v_{0y}t + \tfrac{1}{2}a_yt^2 = y_0 + v_{0y}t + \tfrac{1}{2}(-g)t^2$$
$$= (0) + (15.0 \text{ m/s})t + \tfrac{1}{2}(-9.80 \text{ m/s}^2)t^2$$
$$v_y = v_{0y} + a_yt = v_{0y} + (-g)t$$
$$= 15.0 \text{ m/s} + (-9.80 \text{ m/s}^2)t$$

When $t = 1.00$ s, these equations give $y = +10.1$ m and $v_y = +5.2$ m/s. That is, the ball is 10.1 m above the origin (y is positive) and moving upward (v_y is positive) with a speed of 5.2 m/s. This is less than the initial speed because the ball slows as it ascends. When $t = 4.00$ s, those equations give $y = -18.4$ m and $v_y = -24.2$ m/s. The ball has passed its highest point and is 18.4 m *below* the origin (y is negative). It is moving *downward*

(v_y is negative) with a speed of 24.2 m/s. Equation (2.13) tells us that the ball is moving at the initial 15.0-m/s speed as it moves downward past the launching point and continues to gain speed as it descends further.

(b) The y-velocity at any position y is given by Eq. (2.13) with x's replaced by y's:

$$v_y^2 = v_{0y}^2 + 2a_y(y - y_0) = v_{0y}^2 + 2(-g)(y - 0)$$
$$= (15.0 \text{ m/s})^2 + 2(-9.80 \text{ m/s}^2)y$$

When the ball is 5.00 m above the origin we have $y = +5.00$ m, so

$$v_y^2 = (15.0 \text{ m/s})^2 + 2(-9.80 \text{ m/s}^2)(5.00 \text{ m}) = 127 \text{ m}^2/\text{s}^2$$
$$v_y = \pm 11.3 \text{ m/s}$$

We get *two* values of v_y because the ball passes through the point $y = +5.00$ m twice, once on the way up (so v_y is positive) and once on the way down (so v_y is negative) (see Figs. 2.24 and 2.25a).

(c) At the instant at which the ball reaches its maximum height y_1, its y-velocity is momentarily zero: $v_y = 0$. We use Eq. (2.13) to find y_1. With $v_y = 0$, $y_0 = 0$, and $a_y = -g$, we get

$$0 = v_{0y}^2 + 2(-g)(y_1 - 0)$$
$$y_1 = \frac{v_{0y}^2}{2g} = \frac{(15.0 \text{ m/s})^2}{2(9.80 \text{ m/s}^2)} = +11.5 \text{ m}$$

(d) <u>CAUTION</u> **A free-fall misconception** It's a common misconception that at the highest point of free-fall motion, where the velocity is zero, the acceleration is also zero. If this were so, once the ball reached the highest point it would hang there suspended in midair! Remember that acceleration is the rate of change of velocity, and the ball's velocity is continuously changing. At every point, including the highest point, and at any velocity, including zero, the acceleration in free fall is always $a_y = -g = -9.80 \text{ m/s}^2$. ∎

EVALUATE: A useful way to check any free-fall problem is to draw the y-t and v_y-t graphs, as we did in Fig. 2.25. Note that these are graphs of Eqs. (2.12) and (2.8), respectively. Given the initial position, initial velocity, and acceleration, you can easily create these graphs by using a graphing calculator or an online mathematics program.

EXAMPLE 2.8 **TWO SOLUTIONS OR ONE?**

At what time after being released has the ball in Example 2.7 fallen 5.00 m below the roof railing?

SOLUTION

IDENTIFY and SET UP: We treat this as in Example 2.7, so y_0, v_{0y}, and $a_y = -g$ have the same values as there. Now, however, the target variable is the time at which the ball is at $y = -5.00$ m. The best equation to use is Eq. (2.12), which gives the position y as a function of time t:

$$y = y_0 + v_{0y}t + \tfrac{1}{2}a_yt^2$$
$$= y_0 + v_{0y}t + \tfrac{1}{2}(-g)t^2$$

This is a *quadratic* equation for t, which we want to solve for the value of t when $y = -5.00$ m.

EXECUTE: We rearrange the equation so that it has the standard form of a quadratic equation for an unknown x, $Ax^2 + Bx + C = 0$:

$$\left(\tfrac{1}{2}g\right)t^2 + (-v_{0y})t + (y - y_0) = At^2 + Bt + C = 0$$

By comparison, we identify $A = \tfrac{1}{2}g$, $B = -v_{0y}$, and $C = y - y_0$. The quadratic formula (see Appendix B) tells us that this equation has *two* solutions:

$$t = \frac{-B \pm \sqrt{B^2 - 4AC}}{2A}$$
$$= \frac{-(-v_{0y}) \pm \sqrt{(-v_{0y})^2 - 4\left(\tfrac{1}{2}g\right)(y - y_0)}}{2\left(\tfrac{1}{2}g\right)}$$
$$= \frac{v_{0y} \pm \sqrt{v_{0y}^2 - 2g(y - y_0)}}{g}$$

Substituting the values $y_0 = 0$, $v_{0y} = +15.0$ m/s, $g = 9.80$ m/s^2, and $y = -5.00$ m, we find

$$t = \frac{(15.0 \text{ m/s}) \pm \sqrt{(15.0 \text{ m/s})^2 - 2(9.80 \text{ m/s}^2)(-5.00 \text{ m} - 0)}}{9.80 \text{ m/s}^2}$$

You can confirm that the numerical answers are $t = +3.36$ s and $t = -0.30$ s. The answer $t = -0.30$ s doesn't make physical sense, since it refers to a time *before* the ball left your hand at $t = 0$. So the correct answer is $t = +3.36$ s.

EVALUATE: Why did we get a second, fictitious solution? The explanation is that constant-acceleration equations like Eq. (2.12) are based on the assumption that the acceleration is constant for *all* values of time, whether positive, negative, or zero. Hence the solution $t = -0.30$ s refers to an imaginary moment when a freely falling ball was 5.00 m below the roof railing and rising to meet your hand. Since the ball didn't leave your hand and go into free fall until $t = 0$, this result is pure fiction.

Repeat these calculations to find the times when the ball is 5.00 m *above* the origin ($y = +5.00$ m). The two answers are $t = +0.38$ s and $t = +2.68$ s. Both are positive values of t, and both refer to the real motion of the ball after leaving your hand. At the earlier time the ball passes through $y = +5.00$ m moving upward; at the later time it passes through this point moving downward. [Compare this with part (b) of Example 2.7, and again refer to Fig. 2.25a.]

You should also solve for the times when $y = +15.0$ m. In this case, both solutions involve the square root of a negative number, so there are *no* real solutions. Again Fig. 2.25a shows why; we found in part (c) of Example 2.7 that the ball's maximum height is $y = +11.5$ m, so it *never* reaches $y = +15.0$ m. While a quadratic equation such as Eq. (2.12) always has two solutions, in some situations one or both of the solutions aren't physically reasonable.

TEST YOUR UNDERSTANDING OF SECTION 2.5 If you toss a ball upward with a certain initial speed, it falls freely and reaches a maximum height h a time t after it leaves your hand. (a) If you throw the ball upward with double the initial speed, what new maximum height does the ball reach? (i) $h\sqrt{2}$; (ii) $2h$; (iii) $4h$; (iv) $8h$; (v) $16h$. (b) If you throw the ball upward with double the initial speed, how long does it take to reach its new maximum height? (i) $t/2$; (ii) $t/\sqrt{2}$; (iii) t; (iv) $t\sqrt{2}$; (v) $2t$. ▮

2.6 VELOCITY AND POSITION BY INTEGRATION

This section is intended for students who have already learned a little integral calculus. In Section 2.4 we analyzed the special case of straight-line motion with constant acceleration. When a_x is not constant, as is frequently the case, the equations that we derived in that section are no longer valid (**Fig. 2.26**). But even when a_x varies with time, we can still use the relationship $v_x = dx/dt$ to find the x-velocity v_x as a function of time if the position x is a known function of time. And we can still use $a_x = dv_x/dt$ to find the x-acceleration a_x as a function of time if the x-velocity v_x is a known function of time.

In many situations, however, position and velocity are not known functions of time, while acceleration is (**Fig. 2.27**). How can we find the position and velocity in straight-line motion from the acceleration function $a_x(t)$?

2.26 When you push a car's accelerator pedal to the floorboard, the resulting acceleration is *not* constant: The greater the car's speed, the more slowly it gains additional speed. A typical car takes twice as long to accelerate from 50 km/h to 100 km/h as it does to accelerate from 0 to 50 km/h.

2.27 The inertial navigation system (INS) on board a long-range airliner keeps track of the airliner's acceleration. Given the airliner's initial position and velocity before takeoff, the INS uses the acceleration data to calculate the airliner's position and velocity throughout the flight.

2.28 An a_x-t graph for a body whose x-acceleration is not constant.

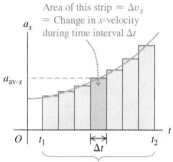

Area of this strip = Δv_x
= Change in x-velocity
during time interval Δt

Total area under the x-t graph from t_1 to t_2
= Net change in x-velocity from t_1 to t_2

Figure 2.28 is a graph of x-acceleration versus time for a body whose acceleration is not constant. We can divide the time interval between times t_1 and t_2 into many smaller subintervals, calling a typical one Δt. Let the average x-acceleration during Δt be $a_{av\text{-}x}$. From Eq. (2.4) the change in x-velocity Δv_x during Δt is

$$\Delta v_x = a_{av\text{-}x}\,\Delta t$$

Graphically, Δv_x equals the area of the shaded strip with height $a_{av\text{-}x}$ and width Δt—that is, the area under the curve between the left and right sides of Δt. The total change in x-velocity from t_1 to t_2 is the sum of the x-velocity changes Δv_x in the small subintervals. So the total x-velocity change is represented graphically by the *total* area under the a_x-t curve between the vertical lines t_1 and t_2. (In Section 2.4 we showed this for the special case in which a_x is constant.)

In the limit that all the Δt's become very small and they become very large in number, the value of $a_{av\text{-}x}$ for the interval from any time t to $t + \Delta t$ approaches the instantaneous x-acceleration a_x at time t. In this limit, the area under the a_x-t curve is the *integral* of a_x (which is in general a function of t) from t_1 to t_2. If v_{1x} is the x-velocity of the body at time t_1 and v_{2x} is the velocity at time t_2, then

$$v_{2x} - v_{1x} = \int_{v_{1x}}^{v_{2x}} dv_x = \int_{t_1}^{t_2} a_x\,dt \qquad (2.15)$$

The change in the x-velocity v_x is the time integral of the x-acceleration a_x.

We can carry out exactly the same procedure with the curve of x-velocity versus time. If x_1 is a body's position at time t_1 and x_2 is its position at time t_2, from Eq. (2.2) the displacement Δx during a small time interval Δt is equal to $v_{av\text{-}x}\,\Delta t$, where $v_{av\text{-}x}$ is the average x-velocity during Δt. The total displacement $x_2 - x_1$ during the interval $t_2 - t_1$ is given by

$$x_2 - x_1 = \int_{x_1}^{x_2} dx = \int_{t_1}^{t_2} v_x\,dt \qquad (2.16)$$

The change in position x—that is, the displacement—is the time integral of x-velocity v_x. Graphically, the displacement between times t_1 and t_2 is the area under the v_x-t curve between those two times. [This is the same result that we obtained in Section 2.4 for the special case in which v_x is given by Eq. (2.8).]

If $t_1 = 0$ and t_2 is any later time t, and if x_0 and v_{0x} are the position and velocity, respectively, at time $t = 0$, then we can rewrite Eqs. (2.15) and (2.16) as

x-velocity of a particle at time t $\cdots$ x-velocity of the particle at time 0

$$v_x = v_{0x} + \int_0^t a_x\,dt \qquad (2.17)$$

Integral of the x-acceleration of the particle from time 0 to time t

Position of a particle at time t $\cdots$ Position of the particle at time 0

$$x = x_0 + \int_0^t v_x\,dt \qquad (2.18)$$

Integral of the x-velocity of the particle from time 0 to time t

If we know the x-acceleration a_x as a function of time and we know the initial velocity v_{0x}, we can use Eq. (2.17) to find the x-velocity v_x at any time; in other words, we can find v_x as a function of time. Once we know this function, and given the initial position x_0, we can use Eq. (2.18) to find the position x at any time.

EXAMPLE 2.9 MOTION WITH CHANGING ACCELERATION

Sally is driving along a straight highway in her 1965 Mustang. At $t = 0$, when she is moving at 10 m/s in the positive x-direction, she passes a signpost at $x = 50$ m. Her x-acceleration as a function of time is

$$a_x = 2.0 \text{ m/s}^2 - (0.10 \text{ m/s}^3)t$$

(a) Find her x-velocity v_x and position x as functions of time. (b) When is her x-velocity greatest? (c) What is that maximum x-velocity? (d) Where is the car when it reaches that maximum x-velocity?

SOLUTION

IDENTIFY and SET UP: The x-acceleration is a function of time, so we *cannot* use the constant-acceleration formulas of Section 2.4. Instead, we use Eq. (2.17) to obtain an expression for v_x as a function of time, and then use that result in Eq. (2.18) to find an expression for x as a function of t. We'll then be able to answer a variety of questions about the motion.

EXECUTE: (a) At $t = 0$, Sally's position is $x_0 = 50$ m and her x-velocity is $v_{0x} = 10$ m/s. To use Eq. (2.17), we note that the integral of t^n (except for $n = -1$) is $\int t^n \, dt = \frac{1}{n+1} t^{n+1}$. Hence

$$v_x = 10 \text{ m/s} + \int_0^t [2.0 \text{ m/s}^2 - (0.10 \text{ m/s}^3)t] \, dt$$

$$= 10 \text{ m/s} + (2.0 \text{ m/s}^2)t - \frac{1}{2}(0.10 \text{ m/s}^3)t^2$$

Now we use Eq. (2.18) to find x as a function of t:

$$x = 50 \text{ m} + \int_0^t \left[10 \text{ m/s} + (2.0 \text{ m/s}^2)t - \frac{1}{2}(0.10 \text{ m/s}^3)t^2\right] dt$$

$$= 50 \text{ m} + (10 \text{ m/s})t + \frac{1}{2}(2.0 \text{ m/s}^2)t^2 - \frac{1}{6}(0.10 \text{ m/s}^3)t^3$$

Figure 2.29 shows graphs of a_x, v_x, and x as functions of time as given by the previous equations. Note that for any time t, the slope of the v_x-t graph equals the value of a_x and the slope of the x-t graph equals the value of v_x.

(b) The maximum value of v_x occurs when the x-velocity stops increasing and begins to decrease. At that instant, $dv_x/dt = a_x = 0$. So we set the expression for a_x equal to zero and solve for t:

$$0 = 2.0 \text{ m/s}^2 - (0.10 \text{ m/s}^3)t$$

$$t = \frac{2.0 \text{ m/s}^2}{0.10 \text{ m/s}^3} = 20 \text{ s}$$

(c) We find the maximum x-velocity by substituting $t = 20$ s, the time from part (b) when velocity is maximum, into the equation for v_x from part (a):

$$v_{\text{max-}x} = 10 \text{ m/s} + (2.0 \text{ m/s}^2)(20 \text{ s}) - \frac{1}{2}(0.10 \text{ m/s}^3)(20 \text{ s})^2$$

$$= 30 \text{ m/s}$$

(d) To find the car's position at the time that we found in part (b), we substitute $t = 20$ s into the expression for x from part (a):

$$x = 50 \text{ m} + (10 \text{ m/s})(20 \text{ s}) + \frac{1}{2}(2.0 \text{ m/s}^2)(20 \text{ s})^2$$

$$- \frac{1}{6}(0.10 \text{ m/s}^3)(20 \text{ s})^3$$

$$= 517 \text{ m}$$

EVALUATE: Figure 2.29 helps us interpret our results. The left-hand graph shows that a_x is positive between $t = 0$ and $t = 20$ s and negative after that. It is zero at $t = 20$ s, the time at which v_x is maximum (the high point in the middle graph). The car speeds up until $t = 20$ s (because v_x and a_x have the same sign) and slows down after $t = 20$ s (because v_x and a_x have opposite signs).

Since v_x is maximum at $t = 20$ s, the x-t graph (the right-hand graph in Fig. 2.29) has its maximum positive slope at this time. Note that the x-t graph is concave up (curved upward) from $t = 0$ to $t = 20$ s, when a_x is positive. The graph is concave down (curved downward) after $t = 20$ s, when a_x is negative.

2.29 The position, velocity, and acceleration of the car in Example 2.9 as functions of time. Can you show that if this motion continues, the car will stop at $t = 44.5$ s?

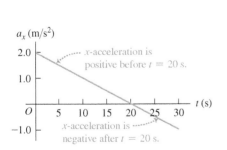

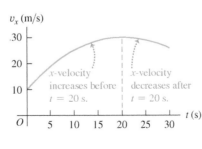

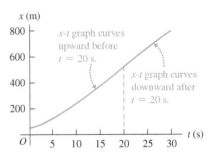

TEST YOUR UNDERSTANDING OF SECTION 2.6 If the x-acceleration a_x of an object moving in straight-line motion is increasing with time, will the v_x-t graph be (i) a straight line, (ii) concave up (i.e., with an upward curvature), or (iii) concave down (i.e., with a downward curvature)? ▮

CHAPTER 2 SUMMARY

SOLUTIONS TO ALL EXAMPLES

Straight-line motion, average and instantaneous x-velocity: When a particle moves along a straight line, we describe its position with respect to an origin O by means of a coordinate such as x. The particle's average x-velocity v_{av-x} during a time interval $\Delta t = t_2 - t_1$ is equal to its displacement $\Delta x = x_2 - x_1$ divided by Δt. The instantaneous x-velocity v_x at any time t is equal to the average x-velocity over the time interval from t to $t + \Delta t$ in the limit that Δt goes to zero. Equivalently, v_x is the derivative of the position function with respect to time. (See Example 2.1.)

$$v_{av-x} = \frac{\Delta x}{\Delta t} = \frac{x_2 - x_1}{t_2 - t_1} \quad (2.2)$$

$$v_x = \lim_{\Delta t \to 0} \frac{\Delta x}{\Delta t} = \frac{dx}{dt} \quad (2.3)$$

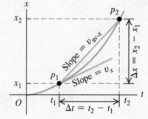

Average and instantaneous x-acceleration: The average x-acceleration a_{av-x} during a time interval Δt is equal to the change in velocity $\Delta v_x = v_{2x} - v_{1x}$ during that time interval divided by Δt. The instantaneous x-acceleration a_x is the limit of a_{av-x} as Δt goes to zero, or the derivative of v_x with respect to t. (See Examples 2.2 and 2.3.)

$$a_{av-x} = \frac{\Delta v_x}{\Delta t} = \frac{v_{2x} - v_{1x}}{t_2 - t_1} \quad (2.4)$$

$$a_x = \lim_{\Delta t \to 0} \frac{\Delta v_x}{\Delta t} = \frac{dv_x}{dt} \quad (2.5)$$

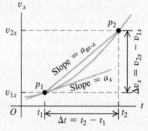

Straight-line motion with constant acceleration: When the x-acceleration is constant, four equations relate the position x and the x-velocity v_x at any time t to the initial position x_0, the initial x-velocity v_{0x} (both measured at time $t = 0$), and the x-acceleration a_x. (See Examples 2.4 and 2.5.)

Constant x-acceleration only:

$$v_x = v_{0x} + a_x t \quad (2.8)$$

$$x = x_0 + v_{0x}t + \tfrac{1}{2}a_x t^2 \quad (2.12)$$

$$v_x^2 = v_{0x}^2 + 2a_x(x - x_0) \quad (2.13)$$

$$x - x_0 = \tfrac{1}{2}(v_{0x} + v_x)t \quad (2.14)$$

Freely falling bodies: Free fall is a case of motion with constant acceleration. The magnitude of the acceleration due to gravity is a positive quantity, g. The acceleration of a body in free fall is always downward. (See Examples 2.6–2.8.)

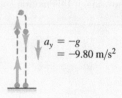

Straight-line motion with varying acceleration: When the acceleration is not constant but is a known function of time, we can find the velocity and position as functions of time by integrating the acceleration function. (See Example 2.9.)

$$v_x = v_{0x} + \int_0^t a_x \, dt \quad (2.17)$$

$$x = x_0 + \int_0^t v_x \, dt \quad (2.18)$$

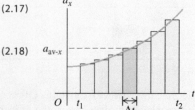

SOLUTION

BRIDGING PROBLEM THE FALL OF A SUPERHERO

The superhero Green Lantern steps from the top of a tall building. He falls freely from rest to the ground, falling half the total distance to the ground during the last 1.00 s of his fall (**Fig. 2.30**). What is the height *h* of the building?

SOLUTION GUIDE

IDENTIFY and SET UP
1. You're told that Green Lantern falls freely from rest. What does this imply about his acceleration? About his initial velocity?
2. Choose the direction of the positive *y*-axis. It's easiest to make the same choice we used for freely falling objects in Section 2.5.
3. You can divide Green Lantern's fall into two parts: from the top of the building to the halfway point and from the halfway point to the ground. You know that the second part of the fall lasts 1.00 s. Decide what you would need to know about Green Lantern's motion at the halfway point in order to solve for the target variable *h*. Then choose two equations, one for the first part of the fall and one for the second part, that you'll use together to find an expression for *h*. (There are several pairs of equations that you could choose.)

EXECUTE
4. Use your two equations to solve for the height *h*. Heights are always positive numbers, so your answer should be positive.

2.30 Our sketch for this problem.

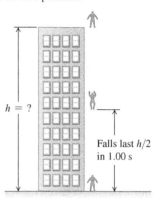

$h = ?$

Falls last *h*/2 in 1.00 s

EVALUATE
5. To check your answer for *h*, use one of the free-fall equations to find how long it takes Green Lantern to fall (i) from the top of the building to half the height and (ii) from the top of the building to the ground. If your answer for *h* is correct, time (ii) should be 1.00 s greater than time (i). If it isn't, go back and look for errors in how you found *h*.

Problems

For assigned homework and other learning materials, go to MasteringPhysics®. **MP**

•, ••, •••: Difficulty levels. CP: Cumulative problems incorporating material from earlier chapters. CALC: Problems requiring calculus. DATA: Problems involving real data, scientific evidence, experimental design, and/or statistical reasoning. BIO: Biosciences problems.

DISCUSSION QUESTIONS

Q2.1 Does the speedometer of a car measure speed or velocity? Explain.

Q2.2 The black dots at the top of **Fig. Q2.2** represent a series of high-speed photographs of an insect flying in a straight line from left to right (in the positive *x*-direction). Which of the graphs in Fig. Q2.2 most plausibly depicts this insect's motion?

Figure Q2.2

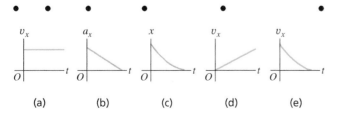

Q2.3 Can an object with constant acceleration reverse its direction of travel? Can it reverse its direction *twice*? In both cases, explain your reasoning.

Q2.4 Under what conditions is average velocity equal to instantaneous velocity?

Q2.5 Is it possible for an object to be (a) slowing down while its acceleration is increasing in magnitude; (b) speeding up while its acceleration is decreasing? In both cases, explain your reasoning.

Q2.6 Under what conditions does the magnitude of the average velocity equal the average speed?

Q2.7 When a Dodge Viper is at Elwood's Car Wash, a BMW Z3 is at Elm and Main. Later, when the Dodge reaches Elm and Main, the BMW reaches Elwood's Car Wash. How are the cars' average velocities between these two times related?

Q2.8 A driver in Massachusetts was sent to traffic court for speeding. The evidence against the driver was that a policewoman observed the driver's car alongside a second car at a certain moment, and the policewoman had already clocked the second car going faster than the speed limit. The driver argued, "The second car was passing me. I was not speeding." The judge ruled against the driver because, in the judge's words, "If two cars were side by side, both of you were speeding." If you were a lawyer representing the accused driver, how would you argue this case?

Q2.9 Can you have zero displacement and nonzero average velocity? Zero displacement and nonzero velocity? Illustrate your answers on an *x-t* graph.

Q2.10 Can you have zero acceleration and nonzero velocity? Use a v_x-*t* graph to explain.

Q2.11 Can you have zero velocity and nonzero average acceleration? Zero velocity and nonzero acceleration? Use a v_x-*t* graph to explain, and give an example of such motion.

Q2.12 An automobile is traveling west. Can it have a velocity toward the west and at the same time have an acceleration toward the east? Under what circumstances?

Q2.13 The official's truck in Fig. 2.2 is at $x_1 = 277$ m at $t_1 = 16.0$ s and is at $x_2 = 19$ m at $t_2 = 25.0$ s. (a) Sketch *two* different possible x-t graphs for the motion of the truck. (b) Does the average velocity $v_{av\text{-}x}$ during the time interval from t_1 to t_2 have the same value for both of your graphs? Why or why not?

Q2.14 Under constant acceleration the average velocity of a particle is half the sum of its initial and final velocities. Is this still true if the acceleration is *not* constant? Explain.

Q2.15 You throw a baseball straight up in the air so that it rises to a maximum height much greater than your height. Is the magnitude of the ball's acceleration greater while it is being thrown or after it leaves your hand? Explain.

Q2.16 Prove these statements: (a) As long as you can ignore the effects of the air, if you throw anything vertically upward, it will have the same speed when it returns to the release point as when it was released. (b) The time of flight will be twice the time it takes to get to its highest point.

Q2.17 A dripping water faucet steadily releases drops 1.0 s apart. As these drops fall, does the distance between them increase, decrease, or remain the same? Prove your answer.

Q2.18 If you know the initial position and initial velocity of a vehicle and have a record of the acceleration at each instant, can you compute the vehicle's position after a certain time? If so, explain how this might be done.

Q2.19 From the top of a tall building, you throw one ball straight up with speed v_0 and one ball straight down with speed v_0. (a) Which ball has the greater speed when it reaches the ground? (b) Which ball gets to the ground first? (c) Which ball has a greater displacement when it reaches the ground? (d) Which ball has traveled the greater distance when it hits the ground?

Q2.20 You run due east at a constant speed of 3.00 m/s for a distance of 120.0 m and then continue running east at a constant speed of 5.00 m/s for another 120.0 m. For the total 240.0-m run, is your average velocity 4.00 m/s, greater than 4.00 m/s, or less than 4.00 m/s? Explain.

Q2.21 An object is thrown straight up into the air and feels no air resistance. How can the object have an acceleration when it has stopped moving at its highest point?

Q2.22 When you drop an object from a certain height, it takes time T to reach the ground with no air resistance. If you dropped it from three times that height, how long (in terms of T) would it take to reach the ground?

EXERCISES

Section 2.1 Displacement, Time, and Average Velocity

2.1 • A car travels in the $+x$-direction on a straight and level road. For the first 4.00 s of its motion, the average velocity of the car is $v_{av\text{-}x} = 6.25$ m/s. How far does the car travel in 4.00 s?

2.2 •• In an experiment, a shearwater (a seabird) was taken from its nest, flown 5150 km away, and released. The bird found its way back to its nest 13.5 days after release. If we place the origin at the nest and extend the $+x$-axis to the release point, what was the bird's average velocity in m/s (a) for the return flight and (b) for the whole episode, from leaving the nest to returning?

2.3 •• **Trip Home.** You normally drive on the freeway between San Diego and Los Angeles at an average speed of 105 km/h (65 mi/h), and the trip takes 1 h and 50 min. On a Friday afternoon, however, heavy traffic slows you down and you drive the same distance at an average speed of only 70 km/h (43 mi/h). How much longer does the trip take?

2.4 •• **From Pillar to Post.** Starting from a pillar, you run 200 m east (the $+x$-direction) at an average speed of 5.0 m/s and then run 280 m west at an average speed of 4.0 m/s to a post. Calculate (a) your average speed from pillar to post and (b) your average velocity from pillar to post.

2.5 • Starting from the front door of a ranch house, you walk 60.0 m due east to a windmill, turn around, and then slowly walk 40.0 m west to a bench, where you sit and watch the sunrise. It takes you 28.0 s to walk from the house to the windmill and then 36.0 s to walk from the windmill to the bench. For the entire trip from the front door to the bench, what are your (a) average velocity and (b) average speed?

2.6 •• A Honda Civic travels in a straight line along a road. The car's distance x from a stop sign is given as a function of time t by the equation $x(t) = \alpha t^2 - \beta t^3$, where $\alpha = 1.50$ m/s^2 and $\beta = 0.0500$ m/s^3. Calculate the average velocity of the car for each time interval: (a) $t = 0$ to $t = 2.00$ s; (b) $t = 0$ to $t = 4.00$ s; (c) $t = 2.00$ s to $t = 4.00$ s.

Section 2.2 Instantaneous Velocity

2.7 • CALC A car is stopped at a traffic light. It then travels along a straight road such that its distance from the light is given by $x(t) = bt^2 - ct^3$, where $b = 2.40$ m/s^2 and $c = 0.120$ m/s^3. (a) Calculate the average velocity of the car for the time interval $t = 0$ to $t = 10.0$ s. (b) Calculate the instantaneous velocity of the car at $t = 0$, $t = 5.0$ s, and $t = 10.0$ s. (c) How long after starting from rest is the car again at rest?

2.8 • CALC A bird is flying due east. Its distance from a tall building is given by $x(t) = 28.0$ m $+ (12.4$ m/s$)t - (0.0450$ m/s$^3)t^3$. What is the instantaneous velocity of the bird when $t = 8.00$ s?

2.9 •• A ball moves in a straight line (the x-axis). The graph in **Fig. E2.9** shows this ball's velocity as a function of time. (a) What are the ball's average speed and average velocity during the first 3.0 s? (b) Suppose that the ball moved in such a way that the graph segment after 2.0 s was -3.0 m/s instead of $+3.0$ m/s. Find the ball's average speed and average velocity in this case.

Figure **E2.9**

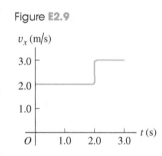

2.10 •• A physics professor leaves her house and walks along the sidewalk toward campus. After 5 min it starts to rain, and she returns home. Her distance from her house as a function of time is shown in **Fig. E2.10**. At which of the labeled points is her velocity (a) zero? (b) constant and positive? (c) constant and negative? (d) increasing in magnitude? (e) decreasing in magnitude?

Figure **E2.10**

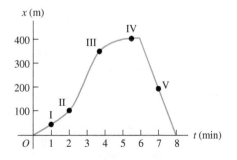

2.11 •• A test car travels in a straight line along the *x*-axis. The graph in **Fig. E2.11** shows the car's position *x* as a function of time. Find its instantaneous velocity at points *A* through *G*.

Figure **E2.11**

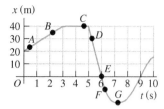

Section 2.3 Average and Instantaneous Acceleration

2.12 • **Figure E2.12** shows the velocity of a solar-powered car as a function of time. The driver accelerates from a stop sign, cruises for 20 s at a constant speed of 60 km/h, and then brakes to come to a stop 40 s after leaving the stop sign. (a) Compute the average acceleration during these time intervals: (i) $t = 0$ to $t = 10$ s; (ii) $t = 30$ s to $t = 40$ s; (iii) $t = 10$ s to $t = 30$ s; (iv) $t = 0$ to $t = 40$ s. (b) What is the instantaneous acceleration at $t = 20$ s and at $t = 35$ s?

Figure **E2.12**

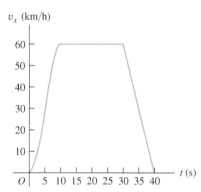

2.13 • **The Fastest (and Most Expensive) Car!** The table shows test data for the Bugatti Veyron Super Sport, the fastest street car made. The car is moving in a straight line (the *x*-axis).

Time (s)	0	2.1	20.0	53
Speed (mi/h)	0	60	200	253

(a) Sketch a v_x-*t* graph of this car's velocity (in mi/h) as a function of time. Is its acceleration constant? (b) Calculate the car's average acceleration (in m/s²) between (i) 0 and 2.1 s; (ii) 2.1 s and 20.0 s; (iii) 20.0 s and 53 s. Are these results consistent with your graph in part (a)? (Before you decide to buy this car, it might be helpful to know that only 300 will be built, it runs out of gas in 12 minutes at top speed, and it costs more than $1.5 million!)

2.14 •• CALC A race car starts from rest and travels east along a straight and level track. For the first 5.0 s of the car's motion, the eastward component of the car's velocity is given by $v_x(t) = (0.860 \text{ m/s}^3)t^2$. What is the acceleration of the car when $v_x = 12.0$ m/s?

2.15 • CALC A turtle crawls along a straight line, which we will call the *x*-axis with the positive direction to the right. The equation for the turtle's position as a function of time is $x(t) = 50.0 \text{ cm} + (2.00 \text{ cm/s})t - (0.0625 \text{ cm/s}^2)t^2$. (a) Find the turtle's initial velocity, initial position, and initial acceleration. (b) At what time *t* is the velocity of the turtle zero? (c) How long after

starting does it take the turtle to return to its starting point? (d) At what times *t* is the turtle a distance of 10.0 cm from its starting point? What is the velocity (magnitude and direction) of the turtle at each of those times? (e) Sketch graphs of *x* versus *t*, v_x versus *t*, and a_x versus *t*, for the time interval $t = 0$ to $t = 40$ s.

2.16 • An astronaut has left the International Space Station to test a new space scooter. Her partner measures the following velocity changes, each taking place in a 10-s interval. What are the magnitude, the algebraic sign, and the direction of the average acceleration in each interval? Assume that the positive direction is to the right. (a) At the beginning of the interval, the astronaut is moving toward the right along the *x*-axis at 15.0 m/s, and at the end of the interval she is moving toward the right at 5.0 m/s. (b) At the beginning she is moving toward the left at 5.0 m/s, and at the end she is moving toward the left at 15.0 m/s. (c) At the beginning she is moving toward the right at 15.0 m/s, and at the end she is moving toward the left at 15.0 m/s.

2.17 • CALC A car's velocity as a function of time is given by $v_x(t) = \alpha + \beta t^2$, where $\alpha = 3.00 \text{ m/s}$ and $\beta = 0.100 \text{ m/s}^3$. (a) Calculate the average acceleration for the time interval $t = 0$ to $t = 5.00$ s. (b) Calculate the instantaneous acceleration for $t = 0$ and $t = 5.00$ s. (c) Draw v_x-*t* and a_x-*t* graphs for the car's motion between $t = 0$ and $t = 5.00$ s.

2.18 •• CALC The position of the front bumper of a test car under microprocessor control is given by $x(t) = 2.17 \text{ m} + (4.80 \text{ m/s}^2)t^2 - (0.100 \text{ m/s}^6)t^6$. (a) Find its position and acceleration at the instants when the car has zero velocity. (b) Draw *x*-*t*, v_x-*t*, and a_x-*t* graphs for the motion of the bumper between $t = 0$ and $t = 2.00$ s.

Section 2.4 Motion with Constant Acceleration

2.19 •• An antelope moving with constant acceleration covers the distance between two points 70.0 m apart in 6.00 s. Its speed as it passes the second point is 15.0 m/s. What are (a) its speed at the first point and (b) its acceleration?

2.20 •• BIO **Blackout?** A jet fighter pilot wishes to accelerate from rest at a constant acceleration of 5*g* to reach Mach 3 (three times the speed of sound) as quickly as possible. Experimental tests reveal that he will black out if this acceleration lasts for more than 5.0 s. Use 331 m/s for the speed of sound. (a) Will the period of acceleration last long enough to cause him to black out? (b) What is the greatest speed he can reach with an acceleration of 5*g* before he blacks out?

2.21 • **A Fast Pitch.** The fastest measured pitched baseball left the pitcher's hand at a speed of 45.0 m/s. If the pitcher was in contact with the ball over a distance of 1.50 m and produced constant acceleration, (a) what acceleration did he give the ball, and (b) how much time did it take him to pitch it?

2.22 •• **A Tennis Serve.** In the fastest measured tennis serve, the ball left the racquet at 73.14 m/s. A served tennis ball is typically in contact with the racquet for 30.0 ms and starts from rest. Assume constant acceleration. (a) What was the ball's acceleration during this serve? (b) How far did the ball travel during the serve?

2.23 •• BIO **Automobile Air Bags.** The human body can survive an acceleration trauma incident (sudden stop) if the magnitude of the acceleration is less than 250 m/s². If you are in an automobile accident with an initial speed of 105 km/h (65 mi/h) and are stopped by an airbag that inflates from the dashboard, over what distance must the airbag stop you for you to survive the crash?

2.24 • BIO A pilot who accelerates at more than $4g$ begins to "gray out" but doesn't completely lose consciousness. (a) Assuming constant acceleration, what is the shortest time that a jet pilot starting from rest can take to reach Mach 4 (four times the speed of sound) without graying out? (b) How far would the plane travel during this period of acceleration? (Use 331 m/s for the speed of sound in cold air.)

2.25 • BIO **Air-Bag Injuries.** During an auto accident, the vehicle's air bags deploy and slow down the passengers more gently than if they had hit the windshield or steering wheel. According to safety standards, air bags produce a maximum acceleration of $60g$ that lasts for only 36 ms (or less). How far (in meters) does a person travel in coming to a complete stop in 36 ms at a constant acceleration of $60g$?

2.26 • BIO **Prevention of Hip Fractures.** Falls resulting in hip fractures are a major cause of injury and even death to the elderly. Typically, the hip's speed at impact is about 2.0 m/s. If this can be reduced to 1.3 m/s or less, the hip will usually not fracture. One way to do this is by wearing elastic hip pads. (a) If a typical pad is 5.0 cm thick and compresses by 2.0 cm during the impact of a fall, what constant acceleration (in m/s^2 and in g's) does the hip undergo to reduce its speed from 2.0 m/s to 1.3 m/s? (b) The acceleration you found in part (a) may seem rather large, but to assess its effects on the hip, calculate how long it lasts.

2.27 • BIO **Are We Martians?** It has been suggested, and not facetiously, that life might have originated on Mars and been carried to the earth when a meteor hit Mars and blasted pieces of rock (perhaps containing primitive life) free of the Martian surface. Astronomers know that many Martian rocks have come to the earth this way. (For instance, search the Internet for "ALH 84001.") One objection to this idea is that microbes would have had to undergo an enormous lethal acceleration during the impact. Let us investigate how large such an acceleration might be. To escape Mars, rock fragments would have to reach its escape velocity of 5.0 km/s, and that would most likely happen over a distance of about 4.0 m during the meteor impact. (a) What would be the acceleration (in m/s^2 and g's) of such a rock fragment, if the acceleration is constant? (b) How long would this acceleration last? (c) In tests, scientists have found that over 40% of *Bacillus subtilis* bacteria survived after an acceleration of $450,000g$. In light of your answer to part (a), can we rule out the hypothesis that life might have been blasted from Mars to the earth?

2.28 • **Entering the Freeway.** A car sits on an entrance ramp to a freeway, waiting for a break in the traffic. Then the driver accelerates with constant acceleration along the ramp and onto the freeway. The car starts from rest, moves in a straight line, and has a speed of 20 m/s (45 mi/h) when it reaches the end of the 120-m-long ramp. (a) What is the acceleration of the car? (b) How much time does it take the car to travel the length of the ramp? (c) The traffic on the freeway is moving at a constant speed of 20 m/s. What distance does the traffic travel while the car is moving the length of the ramp?

2.29 •• At launch a rocket ship weighs 4.5 million pounds. When it is launched from rest, it takes 8.00 s to reach 161 km/h; at the end of the first 1.00 min, its speed is 1610 km/h. (a) What is the average acceleration (in m/s^2) of the rocket (i) during the first 8.00 s and (ii) between 8.00 s and the end of the first 1.00 min? (b) Assuming the acceleration is constant during each time interval (but not necessarily the same in both intervals), what distance does the rocket travel (i) during the first 8.00 s and (ii) during the interval from 8.00 s to 1.00 min?

2.30 •• A cat walks in a straight line, which we shall call the x-axis, with the positive direction to the right. As an observant physicist, you make measurements of this cat's motion and construct a graph of the feline's velocity as a function of time (**Fig. E2.30**). (a) Find the cat's velocity at $t = 4.0$ s and at $t = 7.0$ s. (b) What is the cat's acceleration at $t = 3.0$ s? At $t = 6.0$ s? At $t = 7.0$ s? (c) What distance does the cat move during the first 4.5 s? From $t = 0$ to $t = 7.5$ s? (d) Assuming that the cat started at the origin, sketch clear graphs of the cat's acceleration and position as functions of time.

Figure **E2.30**

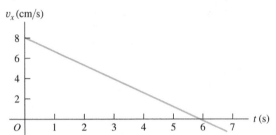

2.31 •• The graph in **Fig. E2.31** shows the velocity of a motorcycle police officer plotted as a function of time. (a) Find the instantaneous acceleration at $t = 3$ s, $t = 7$ s, and $t = 11$ s. (b) How far does the officer go in the first 5 s? The first 9 s? The first 13 s?

Figure **E2.31**

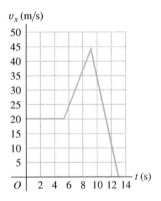

2.32 • Two cars, A and B, move along the x-axis. **Figure E2.32** is a graph of the positions of A and B versus time. (a) In motion diagrams (like Figs. 2.13b and 2.14b), show the position, velocity, and acceleration of each of the two cars at $t = 0$, $t = 1$ s, and $t = 3$ s. (b) At what time(s), if any, do A and B have the same position? (c) Graph velocity versus time for both A and B. (d) At what time(s), if any, do A and B have the same velocity? (e) At what time(s), if any, does car A pass car B? (f) At what time(s), if any, does car B pass car A?

Figure **E2.32**

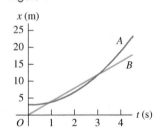

2.33 •• A small block has constant acceleration as it slides down a frictionless incline. The block is released from rest at the top of the incline, and its speed after it has traveled 6.80 m to the bottom of the incline is 3.80 m/s. What is the speed of the block when it is 3.40 m from the top of the incline?

2.34 • At the instant the traffic light turns green, a car that has been waiting at an intersection starts ahead with a constant acceleration of 2.80 m/s^2. At the same instant a truck, traveling with a constant speed of 20.0 m/s, overtakes and passes the car. (a) How far beyond its starting point does the car overtake the truck? (b) How fast is the car traveling when it overtakes the truck? (c) Sketch an x-t graph of the motion of both vehicles. Take $x = 0$ at the intersection. (d) Sketch a v_x-t graph of the motion of both vehicles.

Section 2.5 Freely Falling Bodies

2.35 •• (a) If a flea can jump straight up to a height of 0.440 m, what is its initial speed as it leaves the ground? (b) How long is it in the air?

2.36 •• A small rock is thrown vertically upward with a speed of 22.0 m/s from the edge of the roof of a 30.0-m-tall building. The rock doesn't hit the building on its way back down and lands on the street below. Ignore air resistance. (a) What is the speed of the rock just before it hits the street? (b) How much time elapses from when the rock is thrown until it hits the street?

2.37 • A juggler throws a bowling pin straight up with an initial speed of 8.20 m/s. How much time elapses until the bowling pin returns to the juggler's hand?

2.38 •• You throw a glob of putty straight up toward the ceiling, which is 3.60 m above the point where the putty leaves your hand. The initial speed of the putty as it leaves your hand is 9.50 m/s. (a) What is the speed of the putty just before it strikes the ceiling? (b) How much time from when it leaves your hand does it take the putty to reach the ceiling?

2.39 •• A tennis ball on Mars, where the acceleration due to gravity is $0.379g$ and air resistance is negligible, is hit directly upward and returns to the same level 8.5 s later. (a) How high above its original point did the ball go? (b) How fast was it moving just after it was hit? (c) Sketch graphs of the ball's vertical position, vertical velocity, and vertical acceleration as functions of time while it's in the Martian air.

2.40 •• **Touchdown on the Moon.** A lunar lander is making its descent to Moon Base I (**Fig. E2.40**). The lander descends slowly under the retro-thrust of its descent engine. The engine is cut off when the lander is 5.0 m above the surface and has a downward speed of 0.8 m/s. With the engine off, the lander is in free fall. What is the speed of the lander just before it touches the surface? The acceleration due to gravity on the moon is 1.6 m/s^2.

Figure **E2.40**

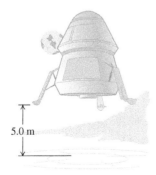

5.0 m

2.41 •• **A Simple Reaction-Time Test.** A meter stick is held vertically above your hand, with the lower end between your thumb and first finger. When you see the meter stick released, you grab it with those two fingers. You can calculate your reaction time from the distance the meter stick falls, read directly from the point where your fingers grabbed it. (a) Derive a relationship for your reaction time in terms of this measured distance, d. (b) If the measured distance is 17.6 cm, what is your reaction time?

2.42 •• A brick is dropped (zero initial speed) from the roof of a building. The brick strikes the ground in 1.90 s. You may ignore air resistance, so the brick is in free fall. (a) How tall, in meters, is the building? (b) What is the magnitude of the brick's velocity just before it reaches the ground? (c) Sketch a_y-t, v_y-t, and y-t graphs for the motion of the brick.

2.43 •• **Launch Failure.** A 7500-kg rocket blasts off vertically from the launch pad with a constant upward acceleration of 2.25 m/s^2 and feels no appreciable air resistance. When it has reached a height of 525 m, its engines suddenly fail; the only force acting on it is now gravity. (a) What is the maximum height this rocket will reach above the launch pad? (b) How much time will elapse after engine failure before the rocket comes crashing down to the launch pad, and how fast will it be moving just before it crashes? (c) Sketch a_y-t, v_y-t, and y-t graphs of the rocket's motion from the instant of blast-off to the instant just before it strikes the launch pad.

2.44 •• A hot-air balloonist, rising vertically with a constant velocity of magnitude 5.00 m/s, releases a sandbag at an instant when the balloon is 40.0 m above the ground (**Fig. E2.44**). After the sandbag is released, it is in free fall. (a) Compute the position and velocity of the sandbag at 0.250 s and 1.00 s after its release. (b) How many seconds after its release does the bag strike the ground? (c) With what magnitude of velocity does it strike the ground? (d) What is the greatest height above the ground that the sandbag reaches? (e) Sketch a_y-t, v_y-t, and y-t graphs for the motion.

Figure **E2.44**

$v = 5.00 \text{ m/s}$

40.0 m to ground

2.45 • BIO The rocket-driven sled *Sonic Wind No. 2,* used for investigating the physiological effects of large accelerations, runs on a straight, level track 1070 m (3500 ft) long. Starting from rest, it can reach a speed of 224 m/s (500 mi/h) in 0.900 s. (a) Compute the acceleration in m/s^2, assuming that it is constant. (b) What is the ratio of this acceleration to that of a freely falling body (g)? (c) What distance is covered in 0.900 s? (d) A magazine article states that at the end of a certain run, the speed of the sled decreased from 283 m/s (632 mi/h) to zero in 1.40 s and that during this time the magnitude of the acceleration was greater than $40g$. Are these figures consistent?

2.46 • An egg is thrown nearly vertically upward from a point near the cornice of a tall building. The egg just misses the cornice on the way down and passes a point 30.0 m below its starting point 5.00 s after it leaves the thrower's hand. Ignore air resistance. (a) What is the initial speed of the egg? (b) How high does it rise above its starting point? (c) What is the magnitude of its velocity at the highest point? (d) What are the magnitude and direction of its acceleration at the highest point? (e) Sketch a_y-t, v_y-t, and y-t graphs for the motion of the egg.

2.47 •• A 15-kg rock is dropped from rest on the earth and reaches the ground in 1.75 s. When it is dropped from the same height on Saturn's satellite Enceladus, the rock reaches the ground in 18.6 s. What is the acceleration due to gravity on Enceladus?

2.48 • A large boulder is ejected vertically upward from a volcano with an initial speed of 40.0 m/s. Ignore air resistance. (a) At what time after being ejected is the boulder moving at 20.0 m/s upward? (b) At what time is it moving at 20.0 m/s downward? (c) When is the displacement of the boulder from its initial position zero? (d) When is the velocity of the boulder zero? (e) What are the magnitude and direction of the acceleration while the boulder is (i) moving upward? (ii) Moving downward? (iii) At the highest point? (f) Sketch a_y-t, v_y-t, and y-t graphs for the motion.

2.49 •• You throw a small rock straight up from the edge of a highway bridge that crosses a river. The rock passes you on its way down, 6.00 s after it was thrown. What is the speed of the rock just before it reaches the water 28.0 m below the point where the rock left your hand? Ignore air resistance.

2.50 •• CALC A small object moves along the x-axis with acceleration $a_x(t) = -(0.0320 \text{ m/s}^3)(15.0 \text{ s} - t)$. At $t = 0$ the object is at $x = -14.0$ m and has velocity $v_{0x} = 8.00$ m/s. What is the x-coordinate of the object when $t = 10.0$ s?

Section 2.6 Velocity and Position by Integration

2.51 • CALC A rocket starts from rest and moves upward from the surface of the earth. For the first 10.0 s of its motion, the vertical acceleration of the rocket is given by $a_y = (2.80 \text{ m/s}^3)t$, where the $+y$-direction is upward. (a) What is the height of the rocket above the surface of the earth at $t = 10.0$ s? (b) What is the speed of the rocket when it is 325 m above the surface of the earth?

2.52 •• CALC The acceleration of a bus is given by $a_x(t) = \alpha t$, where $\alpha = 1.2 \text{ m/s}^3$. (a) If the bus's velocity at time $t = 1.0$ s is 5.0 m/s, what is its velocity at time $t = 2.0$ s? (b) If the bus's position at time $t = 1.0$ s is 6.0 m, what is its position at time $t = 2.0$ s? (c) Sketch a_y-t, v_y-t, and x-t graphs for the motion.

2.53 •• CALC The acceleration of a motorcycle is given by $a_x(t) = At - Bt^2$, where $A = 1.50 \text{ m/s}^3$ and $B = 0.120 \text{ m/s}^4$. The motorcycle is at rest at the origin at time $t = 0$. (a) Find its position and velocity as functions of time. (b) Calculate the maximum velocity it attains.

2.54 •• BIO **Flying Leap of the Flea.** High-speed motion pictures (3500 frames/second) of a jumping, 210-μg flea yielded the data used to plot the graph in **Fig. E2.54**. (See "The Flying Leap of the Flea" by M. Rothschild, Y. Schlein, K. Parker, C. Neville, and S. Sternberg in the November 1973 *Scientific American*.) This flea was about 2 mm long and jumped at a nearly vertical takeoff angle. Use the graph to answer these questions: (a) Is the acceleration of the flea ever zero? If so, when? Justify your answer. (b) Find the maximum height the flea reached in the first 2.5 ms. (c) Find the flea's acceleration at 0.5 ms, 1.0 ms, and 1.5 ms. (d) Find the flea's height at 0.5 ms, 1.0 ms, and 1.5 ms.

Figure **E2.54**

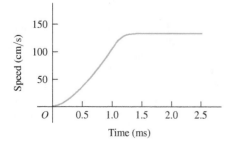

PROBLEMS

2.55 • BIO A typical male sprinter can maintain his maximum acceleration for 2.0 s, and his maximum speed is 10 m/s. After he reaches this maximum speed, his acceleration becomes zero, and then he runs at constant speed. Assume that his acceleration is constant during the first 2.0 s of the race, that he starts from rest, and that he runs in a straight line. (a) How far has the sprinter run when he reaches his maximum speed? (b) What is the magnitude of his average velocity for a race of these lengths: (i) 50.0 m; (ii) 100.0 m; (iii) 200.0 m?

2.56 • CALC A lunar lander is descending toward the moon's surface. Until the lander reaches the surface, its height above the surface of the moon is given by $y(t) = b - ct + dt^2$, where $b = 800$ m is the initial height of the lander above the surface, $c = 60.0$ m/s, and $d = 1.05 \text{ m/s}^2$. (a) What is the initial velocity of the lander, at $t = 0$? (b) What is the velocity of the lander just before it reaches the lunar surface?

2.57 ••• **Earthquake Analysis.** Earthquakes produce several types of shock waves. The most well known are the P-waves (P for *primary* or *pressure*) and the S-waves (S for *secondary* or *shear*). In the earth's crust, P-waves travel at about 6.5 km/s and S-waves move at about 3.5 km/s. The time delay between the arrival of these two waves at a seismic recording station tells geologists how far away an earthquake occurred. If the time delay is 33 s, how far from the seismic station did the earthquake occur?

2.58 •• A brick is dropped from the roof of a tall building. After it has been falling for a few seconds, it falls 40.0 m in a 1.00-s time interval. What distance will it fall during the next 1.00 s? Ignore air resistance.

2.59 ••• A rocket carrying a satellite is accelerating straight up from the earth's surface. At 1.15 s after liftoff, the rocket clears the top of its launch platform, 63 m above the ground. After an additional 4.75 s, it is 1.00 km above the ground. Calculate the magnitude of the average velocity of the rocket for (a) the 4.75-s part of its flight and (b) the first 5.90 s of its flight.

2.60 ••• A subway train starts from rest at a station and accelerates at a rate of 1.60 m/s^2 for 14.0 s. It runs at constant speed for 70.0 s and slows down at a rate of 3.50 m/s^2 until it stops at the next station. Find the *total* distance covered.

2.61 • A gazelle is running in a straight line (the x-axis). The graph in **Fig. P2.61** shows this animal's velocity as a function of time. During the first 12.0 s, find (a) the total distance moved and (b) the displacement of the gazelle. (c) Sketch an a_x-t graph showing this gazelle's acceleration as a function of time for the first 12.0 s.

Figure **P2.61**

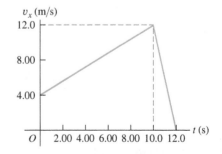

2.62 •• **Collision.** The engineer of a passenger train traveling at 25.0 m/s sights a freight train whose caboose is 200 m ahead on the same track (**Fig. P2.62**). The freight train is traveling at 15.0 m/s in the same direction as the passenger train. The engineer of the passenger train immediately applies the brakes,

Figure P2.62

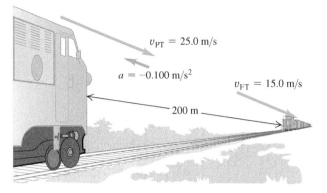

causing a constant acceleration of 0.100 m/s² in a direction opposite to the train's velocity, while the freight train continues with constant speed. Take $x = 0$ at the location of the front of the passenger train when the engineer applies the brakes. (a) Will the cows nearby witness a collision? (b) If so, where will it take place? (c) On a single graph, sketch the positions of the front of the passenger train and the back of the freight train.

2.63 ••• A ball starts from rest and rolls down a hill with uniform acceleration, traveling 200 m during the second 5.0 s of its motion. How far did it roll during the first 5.0 s of motion?

2.64 •• Two cars start 200 m apart and drive toward each other at a steady 10 m/s. On the front of one of them, an energetic grasshopper jumps back and forth between the cars (he has strong legs!) with a constant horizontal velocity of 15 m/s relative to the ground. The insect jumps the instant he lands, so he spends no time resting on either car. What total distance does the grasshopper travel before the cars hit?

2.65 • A car and a truck start from rest at the same instant, with the car initially at some distance behind the truck. The truck has a constant acceleration of 2.10 m/s², and the car has an acceleration of 3.40 m/s². The car overtakes the truck after the truck has moved 60.0 m. (a) How much time does it take the car to overtake the truck? (b) How far was the car behind the truck initially? (c) What is the speed of each when they are abreast? (d) On a single graph, sketch the position of each vehicle as a function of time. Take $x = 0$ at the initial location of the truck.

2.66 •• You are standing at rest at a bus stop. A bus moving at a constant speed of 5.00 m/s passes you. When the rear of the bus is 12.0 m past you, you realize that it is your bus, so you start to run toward it with a constant acceleration of 0.960 m/s². How far would you have to run before you catch up with the rear of the bus, and how fast must you be running then? Would an average college student be physically able to accomplish this?

2.67 •• **Passing.** The driver of a car wishes to pass a truck that is traveling at a constant speed of 20.0 m/s (about 45 mi/h). Initially, the car is also traveling at 20.0 m/s, and its front bumper is 24.0 m behind the truck's rear bumper. The car accelerates at a constant 0.600 m/s², then pulls back into the truck's lane when the rear of the car is 26.0 m ahead of the front of the truck. The car is 4.5 m long, and the truck is 21.0 m long. (a) How much time is required for the car to pass the truck? (b) What distance does the car travel during this time? (c) What is the final speed of the car?

2.68 •• CALC An object's velocity is measured to be $v_x(t) = \alpha - \beta t^2$, where $\alpha = 4.00$ m/s and $\beta = 2.00$ m/s³. At $t = 0$ the object is at $x = 0$. (a) Calculate the object's position and acceleration as functions of time. (b) What is the object's maximum *positive* displacement from the origin?

2.69 ••• CALC The acceleration of a particle is given by $a_x(t) = -2.00$ m/s² $+ (3.00$ m/s³$)t$. (a) Find the initial velocity v_{0x} such that the particle will have the same x-coordinate at $t = 4.00$ s as it had at $t = 0$. (b) What will be the velocity at $t = 4.00$ s?

2.70 • **Egg Drop.** You are on the roof of the physics building, 46.0 m above the ground (**Fig. P2.70**). Your physics professor, who is 1.80 m tall, is walking alongside the building at a constant speed of 1.20 m/s. If you wish to drop an egg on your professor's head, where should the professor be when you release the egg? Assume that the egg is in free fall.

Figure **P2.70**

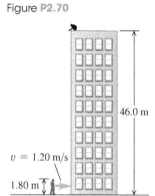

2.71 • A certain volcano on earth can eject rocks vertically to a maximum height H. (a) How high (in terms of H) would these rocks go if a volcano on Mars ejected them with the same initial velocity? The acceleration due to gravity on Mars is 3.71 m/s²; ignore air resistance on both planets. (b) If the rocks are in the air for a time T on earth, for how long (in terms of T) would they be in the air on Mars?

2.72 •• An entertainer juggles balls while doing other activities. In one act, she throws a ball vertically upward, and while it is in the air, she runs to and from a table 5.50 m away at an average speed of 3.00 m/s, returning just in time to catch the falling ball. (a) With what minimum initial speed must she throw the ball upward to accomplish this feat? (b) How high above its initial position is the ball just as she reaches the table?

2.73 ••• **Look Out Below.** Sam heaves a 16-lb shot straight up, giving it a constant upward acceleration from rest of 35.0 m/s² for 64.0 cm. He releases it 2.20 m above the ground. Ignore air resistance. (a) What is the speed of the shot when Sam releases it? (b) How high above the ground does it go? (c) How much time does he have to get out of its way before it returns to the height of the top of his head, 1.83 m above the ground?

2.74 ••• A flowerpot falls off a windowsill and passes the window of the story below. Ignore air resistance. It takes the pot 0.380 s to pass from the top to the bottom of this window, which is 1.90 m high. How far is the top of the window below the windowsill from which the flowerpot fell?

2.75 •• Two stones are thrown vertically upward from the ground, one with three times the initial speed of the other. (a) If the faster stone takes 10 s to return to the ground, how long will it take the slower stone to return? (b) If the slower stone reaches a maximum height of H, how high (in terms of H) will the faster stone go? Assume free fall.

2.76 ••• **A Multistage Rocket.** In the first stage of a two-stage rocket, the rocket is fired from the launch pad starting from rest but with a constant acceleration of 3.50 m/s² upward. At 25.0 s after launch, the second stage fires for 10.0 s, which boosts the rocket's velocity to 132.5 m/s upward at 35.0 s after launch. This firing uses up all of the fuel, however, so after the second stage has finished firing, the only force acting on the rocket is gravity. Ignore air resistance. (a) Find the maximum height that the stage-two rocket reaches above the launch pad. (b) How much time after the end of the stage-two firing will it take for the rocket to fall back to the launch pad? (c) How fast will the stage-two rocket be moving just as it reaches the launch pad?

2.77 ••• During your summer internship for an aerospace company, you are asked to design a small research rocket. The rocket is to be launched from rest from the earth's surface and is to reach a maximum height of 960 m above the earth's surface. The rocket's engines give the rocket an upward acceleration of 16.0 m/s^2 during the time T that they fire. After the engines shut off, the rocket is in free fall. Ignore air resistance. What must be the value of T in order for the rocket to reach the required altitude?

2.78 •• A physics teacher performing an outdoor demonstration suddenly falls from rest off a high cliff and simultaneously shouts "Help." When she has fallen for 3.0 s, she hears the echo of her shout from the valley floor below. The speed of sound is 340 m/s. (a) How tall is the cliff? (b) If we ignore air resistance, how fast will she be moving just before she hits the ground? (Her actual speed will be less than this, due to air resistance.)

2.79 ••• A helicopter carrying Dr. Evil takes off with a constant upward acceleration of 5.0 m/s^2. Secret agent Austin Powers jumps on just as the helicopter lifts off the ground. After the two men struggle for 10.0 s, Powers shuts off the engine and steps out of the helicopter. Assume that the helicopter is in free fall after its engine is shut off, and ignore the effects of air resistance. (a) What is the maximum height above ground reached by the helicopter? (b) Powers deploys a jet pack strapped on his back 7.0 s after leaving the helicopter, and then he has a constant downward acceleration with magnitude 2.0 m/s^2. How far is Powers above the ground when the helicopter crashes into the ground?

2.80 •• **Cliff Height.** You are climbing in the High Sierra when you suddenly find yourself at the edge of a fog-shrouded cliff. To find the height of this cliff, you drop a rock from the top; 8.00 s later you hear the sound of the rock hitting the ground at the foot of the cliff. (a) If you ignore air resistance, how high is the cliff if the speed of sound is 330 m/s? (b) Suppose you had ignored the time it takes the sound to reach you. In that case, would you have overestimated or underestimated the height of the cliff? Explain.

2.81 •• **CALC** An object is moving along the x-axis. At $t = 0$ it has velocity $v_{0x} = 20.0 \text{ m/s}$. Starting at time $t = 0$ it has acceleration $a_x = -Ct$, where C has units of m/s^3. (a) What is the value of C if the object stops in 8.00 s after $t = 0$? (b) For the value of C calculated in part (a), how far does the object travel during the 8.00 s?

2.82 •• A ball is thrown straight up from the ground with speed v_0. At the same instant, a second ball is dropped from rest from a height H, directly above the point where the first ball was thrown upward. There is no air resistance. (a) Find the time at which the two balls collide. (b) Find the value of H in terms of v_0 and g such that at the instant when the balls collide, the first ball is at the highest point of its motion.

2.83 • **CALC** Cars A and B travel in a straight line. The distance of A from the starting point is given as a function of time by $x_A(t) = \alpha t + \beta t^2$, with $\alpha = 2.60 \text{ m/s}$ and $\beta = 1.20 \text{ m/s}^2$. The distance of B from the starting point is $x_B(t) = \gamma t^2 - \delta t^3$, with $\gamma = 2.80 \text{ m/s}^2$ and $\delta = 0.20 \text{ m/s}^3$. (a) Which car is ahead just after the two cars leave the starting point? (b) At what time(s) are the cars at the same point? (c) At what time(s) is the distance from A to B neither increasing nor decreasing? (d) At what time(s) do A and B have the same acceleration?

2.84 •• **DATA** In your physics lab you release a small glider from rest at various points on a long, frictionless air track that is inclined at an angle θ above the horizontal. With an electronic photocell, you measure the time t it takes the glider to slide a distance x from the release point to the bottom of the track. Your measurements are given in **Fig. P2.84,** which shows a

Figure **P2.84**

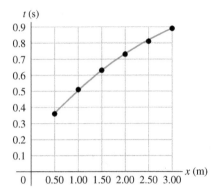

second-order polynomial (quadratic) fit to the plotted data. You are asked to find the glider's acceleration, which is assumed to be constant. There is some error in each measurement, so instead of using a single set of x and t values, you can be more accurate if you use graphical methods and obtain your measured value of the acceleration from the graph. (a) How can you re-graph the data so that the data points fall close to a straight line? (*Hint:* You might want to plot x or t, or both, raised to some power.) (b) Construct the graph you described in part (a) and find the equation for the straight line that is the best fit to the data points. (c) Use the straight-line fit from part (b) to calculate the acceleration of the glider. (d) The glider is released at a distance $x = 1.35 \text{ m}$ from the bottom of the track. Use the acceleration value you obtained in part (c) to calculate the speed of the glider when it reaches the bottom of the track.

2.85 •• **DATA** In a physics lab experiment, you release a small steel ball at various heights above the ground and measure the ball's speed just before it strikes the ground. You plot your data on a graph that has the release height (in meters) on the vertical axis and the square of the final speed (in m^2/s^2) on the horizontal axis. In this graph your data points lie close to a straight line. (a) Using $g = 9.80 \text{ m/s}^2$ and ignoring the effect of air resistance, what is the numerical value of the slope of this straight line? (Include the correct units.) The presence of air resistance reduces the magnitude of the downward acceleration, and the effect of air resistance increases as the speed of the object increases. You repeat the experiment, but this time with a tennis ball as the object being dropped. Air resistance now has a noticeable effect on the data. (b) Is the final speed for a given release height higher than, lower than, or the same as when you ignored air resistance? (c) Is the graph of the release height versus the square of the final speed still a straight line? Sketch the qualitative shape of the graph when air resistance is present.

2.86 ••• **DATA** A model car starts from rest and travels in a straight line. A smartphone mounted on the car has an app that transmits the magnitude of the car's acceleration (measured by an accelerometer) every second. The results are given in the table:

Time (s)	Acceleration (m/s²)
0	5.95
1.00	5.52
2.00	5.08
3.00	4.55
4.00	3.96
5.00	3.40

Each measured value has some experimental error. (a) Plot acceleration versus time and find the equation for the straight line that gives the best fit to the data. (b) Use the equation for $a(t)$ that you found in part (a) to calculate $v(t)$, the speed of the car as a function of time. Sketch the graph of v versus t. Is this graph a straight line? (c) Use your result from part (b) to calculate the speed of the car at $t = 5.00$ s. (d) Calculate the distance the car travels between $t = 0$ and $t = 5.00$ s.

CHALLENGE PROBLEMS

2.87 ••• In the vertical jump, an athlete starts from a crouch and jumps upward as high as possible. Even the best athletes spend little more than 1.00 s in the air (their "hang time"). Treat the athlete as a particle and let y_{max} be his maximum height above the floor. To explain why he seems to hang in the air, calculate the ratio of the time he is above $y_{max}/2$ to the time it takes him to go from the floor to that height. Ignore air resistance.

2.88 ••• **Catching the Bus.** A student is running at her top speed of 5.0 m/s to catch a bus, which is stopped at the bus stop. When the student is still 40.0 m from the bus, it starts to pull away, moving with a constant acceleration of 0.170 m/s². (a) For how much time and what distance does the student have to run at 5.0 m/s before she overtakes the bus? (b) When she reaches the bus, how fast is the bus traveling? (c) Sketch an x-t graph for both the student and the bus. Take $x = 0$ at the initial position of the student. (d) The equations you used in part (a) to find the time have a second solution, corresponding to a later time for which the student and bus are again at the same place if they continue their specified motions. Explain the significance of this second solution. How fast is the bus traveling at this point? (e) If the student's top speed is 3.5 m/s, will she catch the bus? (f) What is the *minimum* speed the student must have to just catch up with the bus? For what time and what distance does she have to run in that case?

2.89 ••• A ball is thrown straight up from the edge of the roof of a building. A second ball is dropped from the roof 1.00 s later. Ignore air resistance. (a) If the height of the building is 20.0 m, what must the initial speed of the first ball be if both are to hit the ground at the same time? On the same graph, sketch the positions of both balls as a function of time, measured from when the first ball is thrown. Consider the same situation, but now let the initial speed v_0 of the first ball be given and treat the height h of the building as an unknown. (b) What must the height of the building be for both balls to reach the ground at the same time if (i) v_0 is 6.0 m/s and (ii) v_0 is 9.5 m/s? (c) If v_0 is greater than some value v_{max}, no value of h exists that allows both balls to hit the ground at the same time. Solve for v_{max}. The value v_{max} has a simple physical interpretation. What is it? (d) If v_0 is less than some value v_{min}, no value of h exists that allows both balls to hit the ground at the same time. Solve for v_{min}. The value v_{min} also has a simple physical interpretation. What is it?

BIO **BLOOD FLOW IN THE HEART.** The human circulatory system is closed—that is, the blood pumped out of the left ventricle of the heart into the arteries is constrained to a series of continuous, branching vessels as it passes through the capillaries and then into the veins as it returns to the heart. The blood in each of the heart's four chambers comes briefly to rest before it is ejected by contraction of the heart muscle.

2.90 If the contraction of the left ventricle lasts 250 ms and the speed of blood flow in the aorta (the large artery leaving the heart) is 0.80 m/s at the end of the contraction, what is the average acceleration of a red blood cell as it leaves the heart? (a) 310 m/s²; (b) 31 m/s²; (c) 3.2 m/s²; (d) 0.32 m/s².

2.91 If the aorta (diameter d_a) branches into two equal-sized arteries with a combined area equal to that of the aorta, what is the diameter of one of the branches? (a) $\sqrt{d_a}$; (b) $d_a/\sqrt{2}$; (c) $2d_a$; (d) $d_a/2$.

2.92 The velocity of blood in the aorta can be measured directly with ultrasound techniques. A typical graph of blood velocity versus time during a single heartbeat is shown in **Fig. P2.92**. Which statement is the best interpretation of this graph? (a) The blood flow changes direction at about 0.25 s; (b) the speed of the blood flow begins to decrease at about 0.10 s; (c) the acceleration of the blood is greatest in magnitude at about 0.25 s; (d) the acceleration of the blood is greatest in magnitude at about 0.10 s.

Figure **P2.92**

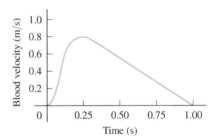

Answers

Chapter Opening Question ?

(iii) Acceleration refers to *any* change in velocity, including both speeding up and slowing down.

Test Your Understanding Questions

2.1 (a): (iv), (i) and (iii) (tie), (v), (ii); (b): (i) and (iii); (c): (v) In (a) the average x-velocity is $v_{\text{av-}x} = \Delta x/\Delta t$. For all five trips, $\Delta t = 1$ h. For the individual trips, (i) $\Delta x = +50$ km, $v_{\text{av-}x} = +50$ km/h; (ii) $\Delta x = -50$ km, $v_{\text{av-}x} = -50$ km/h; (iii) $\Delta x = 60$ km $- 10$ km $= +50$ km, $v_{\text{av-}x} = +50$ km/h; (iv) $\Delta x = +70$ km, $v_{\text{av-}x} = +70$ km/h; (v) $\Delta x = -20$ km $+ 20$ km $= 0$, $v_{\text{av-}x} = 0$. In (b) both have $v_{\text{av-}x} = +50$ km/h.

2.2 (a) P, Q and S (tie), R The x-velocity is **(b)** positive when the slope of the x-t graph is positive (**P**), **(c)** negative when the slope is negative (**R**), and **(d)** zero when the slope is zero (**Q and S**). **(e) R, P, Q and S (tie)** The speed is greatest when the slope of the x-t graph is steepest (either positive or negative) and zero when the slope is zero.

2.3 (a) S, where the x-t graph is curved upward (concave up). **(b) Q,** where the x-t graph is curved downward (concave down). **(c) P and R,** where the x-t graph is not curved either up or down. **(d)** At P, $a_x = 0$ (velocity is **not changing**); at Q, $a_x < 0$ (velocity is **decreasing,** i.e., changing from positive to zero to negative); at R, $a_x = 0$ (velocity is **not changing**); and at S, $a_x > 0$ (velocity is **increasing,** i.e., changing from negative to zero to positive).

2.4 (b) The officer's x-acceleration is constant, so her v_x-t graph is a straight line. The motorcycle is moving faster than the car when the two vehicles meet at $t = 10$ s.

2.5 (a) (iii) Use Eq. (2.13) with x replaced by y and $a_y = -g$; $v_y^2 = v_{0y}^2 - 2g(y - y_0)$. The starting height is $y_0 = 0$ and the y-velocity at the maximum height $y = h$ is $v_y = 0$, so $0 = v_{0y}^2 - 2gh$ and $h = v_{0y}^2/2g$. If the initial y-velocity is increased by a factor of 2, the maximum height increases by a factor of $2^2 = 4$ and the ball goes to height $4h$. **(b) (v)** Use Eq. (2.8) with x replaced by y and $a_y = -g$; $v_y = v_{0y} - gt$. The y-velocity at the maximum height is $v_y = 0$, so $0 = v_{0y} - gt$ and $t = v_{0y}/g$. If the initial y-velocity is increased by a factor of 2, the time to reach the maximum height increases by a factor of 2 and becomes $2t$.

2.6 (ii) The acceleration a_x is equal to the slope of the v_x-t graph. If a_x is increasing, the slope of the v_x-t graph is also increasing and the graph is concave up.

Bridging Problem

$h = 57.1$ m

? If a cyclist is going around a curve at constant speed, is he accelerating? If so, what is the direction of his acceleration? (i) No; (ii) yes, in the direction of his motion; (iii) yes, toward the inside of the curve; (iv) yes, toward the outside of the curve; (v) yes, but in some other direction.

3 MOTION IN TWO OR THREE DIMENSIONS

What determines where a batted baseball lands? How do you describe the motion of a roller coaster car along a curved track or the flight of a circling hawk? Which hits the ground first: a baseball that you simply drop or one that you throw horizontally?

We can't answer these kinds of questions by using the techniques of Chapter 2, in which particles moved only along a straight line. Instead, we need to extend our descriptions of motion to two- and three-dimensional situations. We'll still use the vector quantities displacement, velocity, and acceleration, but now these quantities will no longer lie along a single line. We'll find that several important kinds of motion take place in two dimensions only—that is, in a *plane*.

We also need to consider how the motion of a particle is described by different observers who are moving relative to each other. The concept of *relative velocity* will play an important role later in the book when we explore electromagnetic phenomena and when we introduce Einstein's special theory of relativity.

This chapter merges the vector mathematics of Chapter 1 with the kinematic language of Chapter 2. As before, we're concerned with describing motion, not with analyzing its causes. But the language you learn here will be an essential tool in later chapters when we study the relationship between force and motion.

3.1 POSITION AND VELOCITY VECTORS

Let's see how to describe a particle's motion in space. If the particle is at a point P at a certain instant, the **position vector** $\vec{r}$ of the particle at this instant is a vector that goes from the origin of the coordinate system to point P (**Fig. 3.1** on next page). The Cartesian coordinates x, y, and z of point P are the x-, y-, and z-components of vector $\vec{r}$. Using the unit vectors we introduced in Section 1.9, we can write

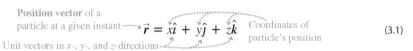

Position vector of a particle at a given instant

$$\vec{r} = x\hat{\imath} + y\hat{\jmath} + z\hat{k}$$

Unit vectors in x-, y-, and z-directions

Coordinates of particle's position

(3.1)

3.1 The position vector $\vec{r}$ from origin O to point P has components x, y, and z.

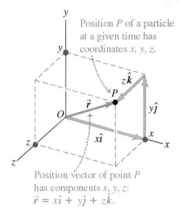

Position P of a particle at a given time has coordinates x, y, z.

Position vector of point P has components x, y, z:
$\vec{r} = x\hat{\imath} + y\hat{\jmath} + z\hat{k}$.

3.2 The average velocity $\vec{v}_{av}$ between points P_1 and P_2 has the same direction as the displacement $\Delta\vec{r}$.

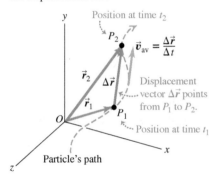

Position at time t_2

$\vec{v}_{av} = \dfrac{\Delta\vec{r}}{\Delta t}$

Displacement vector $\Delta\vec{r}$ points from P_1 to P_2.

Position at time t_1

Particle's path

3.3 The vectors $\vec{v}_1$ and $\vec{v}_2$ are the instantaneous velocities at the points P_1 and P_2 shown in Fig. 3.2.

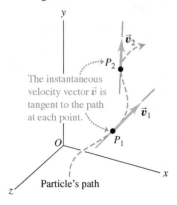

The instantaneous velocity vector $\vec{v}$ is tangent to the path at each point.

Particle's path

During a time interval Δt the particle moves from P_1, where its position vector is $\vec{r}_1$, to P_2, where its position vector is $\vec{r}_2$. The change in position (the displacement) during this interval is $\Delta\vec{r} = \vec{r}_2 - \vec{r}_1 = (x_2 - x_1)\hat{\imath} + (y_2 - y_1)\hat{\jmath} + (z_2 - z_1)\hat{k}$. We define the **average velocity** $\vec{v}_{av}$ during this interval in the same way we did in Chapter 2 for straight-line motion, as the displacement divided by the time interval (**Fig. 3.2**):

Change in the particle's position vector

Average velocity vector of a particle during time interval from t_1 to t_2

$$\vec{v}_{av} = \frac{\Delta\vec{r}}{\Delta t} = \frac{\vec{r}_2 - \vec{r}_1}{t_2 - t_1} \qquad (3.2)$$

Final position minus initial position

Time interval   Final time minus initial time

Dividing a vector by a scalar is a special case of *multiplying* a vector by a scalar, described in Section 1.7; the average velocity $\vec{v}_{av}$ is equal to the displacement vector $\Delta\vec{r}$ multiplied by $1/\Delta t$. Note that the x-component of Eq. (3.2) is $v_{av-x} = (x_2 - x_1)/(t_2 - t_1) = \Delta x/\Delta t$. This is just Eq. (2.2), the expression for average x-velocity that we found in Section 2.1 for one-dimensional motion.

We now define **instantaneous velocity** just as we did in Chapter 2: It equals the instantaneous rate of change of position with time. The key difference is that both position $\vec{r}$ and instantaneous velocity $\vec{v}$ are now vectors:

The **instantaneous velocity** vector of a particle ...

$$\vec{v} = \lim_{\Delta t \to 0} \frac{\Delta\vec{r}}{\Delta t} = \frac{d\vec{r}}{dt} \qquad (3.3)$$

... equals the limit of its average velocity vector as the time interval approaches zero ...   ... and equals the instantaneous rate of change of its position vector.

At any instant, the *magnitude* of $\vec{v}$ is the *speed* v of the particle at that instant, and the *direction* of $\vec{v}$ is the direction in which the particle is moving at that instant.

As $\Delta t \to 0$, points P_1 and P_2 in Fig. 3.2 move closer and closer together. In this limit, the vector $\Delta\vec{r}$ becomes tangent to the path. The direction of $\Delta\vec{r}$ in this limit is also the direction of $\vec{v}$. So *at every point along the path, the instantaneous velocity vector is tangent to the path at that point* (**Fig. 3.3**).

It's often easiest to calculate the instantaneous velocity vector by using components. During any displacement $\Delta\vec{r}$, the changes Δx, Δy, and Δz in the three coordinates of the particle are the *components* of $\Delta\vec{r}$. It follows that the components v_x, v_y, and v_z of the instantaneous velocity $\vec{v} = v_x\hat{\imath} + v_y\hat{\jmath} + v_z\hat{k}$ are simply the time derivatives of the coordinates x, y, and z:

Each **component of** a particle's **instantaneous velocity vector** ...

$$v_x = \frac{dx}{dt} \qquad v_y = \frac{dy}{dt} \qquad v_z = \frac{dz}{dt} \qquad (3.4)$$

... equals the instantaneous rate of change of its corresponding coordinate.

The x-component of $\vec{v}$ is $v_x = dx/dt$, which is the same as Eq. (2.3) for straight-line motion (see Section 2.2). Hence Eq. (3.4) is a direct extension of instantaneous velocity to motion in three dimensions.

We can also get Eq. (3.4) by taking the derivative of Eq. (3.1). The unit vectors $\hat{\imath}$, $\hat{\jmath}$, and $\hat{k}$ don't depend on time, so their derivatives are zero and we find

$$\vec{v} = \frac{d\vec{r}}{dt} = \frac{dx}{dt}\hat{\imath} + \frac{dy}{dt}\hat{\jmath} + \frac{dz}{dt}\hat{k} \qquad (3.5)$$

This shows again that the components of $\vec{v}$ are dx/dt, dy/dt, and dz/dt.

The magnitude of the instantaneous velocity vector $\vec{v}$—that is, the speed—is given in terms of the components v_x, v_y, and v_z by the Pythagorean relation:

$$|\vec{v}| = v = \sqrt{v_x^2 + v_y^2 + v_z^2} \qquad (3.6)$$

Figure 3.4 shows the situation when the particle moves in the *xy*-plane. In this case, *z* and v_z are zero. Then the speed (the magnitude of $\vec{v}$) is

$$v = \sqrt{v_x{}^2 + v_y{}^2}$$

and the direction of the instantaneous velocity $\vec{v}$ is given by angle α (the Greek letter alpha) in the figure. We see that

$$\tan \alpha = \frac{v_y}{v_x} \tag{3.7}$$

(We use α for the direction of the instantaneous velocity vector to avoid confusion with the direction θ of the *position* vector of the particle.)

From now on, when we use the word "velocity," we will always mean the *instantaneous* velocity vector $\vec{v}$ (rather than the average velocity vector). Usually, we won't even bother to call $\vec{v}$ a vector; it's up to you to remember that velocity is a vector quantity with both magnitude and direction.

3.4 The two velocity components for motion in the *xy*-plane.

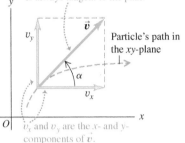

The instantaneous velocity vector $\vec{v}$ is always tangent to the path.

Particle's path in the *xy*-plane

v_x and v_y are the *x*- and *y*-components of $\vec{v}$.

EXAMPLE 3.1 CALCULATING AVERAGE AND INSTANTANEOUS VELOCITY

A robotic vehicle, or rover, is exploring the surface of Mars. The stationary Mars lander is the origin of coordinates, and the surrounding Martian surface lies in the *xy*-plane. The rover, which we represent as a point, has *x*- and *y*-coordinates that vary with time:

$$x = 2.0 \text{ m} - (0.25 \text{ m/s}^2)t^2$$
$$y = (1.0 \text{ m/s})t + (0.025 \text{ m/s}^3)t^3$$

(a) Find the rover's coordinates and distance from the lander at $t = 2.0$ s. (b) Find the rover's displacement and average velocity vectors for the interval $t = 0.0$ s to $t = 2.0$ s. (c) Find a general expression for the rover's instantaneous velocity vector $\vec{v}$. Express $\vec{v}$ at $t = 2.0$ s in component form and in terms of magnitude and direction.

SOLUTION

IDENTIFY and SET UP: This problem involves motion in two dimensions, so we must use the vector equations obtained in this section. **Figure 3.5** shows the rover's path (dashed line). We'll use Eq. (3.1) for position $\vec{r}$, the expression $\Delta \vec{r} = \vec{r}_2 - \vec{r}_1$ for displacement, Eq. (3.2) for average velocity, and Eqs. (3.5), (3.6), and (3.7) for instantaneous velocity and its magnitude and direction.

3.5 At $t = 0.0$ s the rover has position vector $\vec{r}_0$ and instantaneous velocity vector $\vec{v}_0$. Likewise, $\vec{r}_1$ and $\vec{v}_1$ are the vectors at $t = 1.0$ s; $\vec{r}_2$ and $\vec{v}_2$ are the vectors at $t = 2.0$ s.

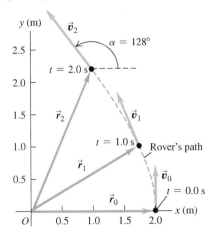

EXECUTE: (a) At $t = 2.0$ s the rover's coordinates are

$$x = 2.0 \text{ m} - (0.25 \text{ m/s}^2)(2.0 \text{ s})^2 = 1.0 \text{ m}$$
$$y = (1.0 \text{ m/s})(2.0 \text{ s}) + (0.025 \text{ m/s}^3)(2.0 \text{ s})^3 = 2.2 \text{ m}$$

The rover's distance from the origin at this time is

$$r = \sqrt{x^2 + y^2} = \sqrt{(1.0 \text{ m})^2 + (2.2 \text{ m})^2} = 2.4 \text{ m}$$

(b) To find the displacement and average velocity over the given time interval, we first express the position vector $\vec{r}$ as a function of time *t*. From Eq. (3.1) this is

$$\vec{r} = x\hat{\imath} + y\hat{\jmath}$$
$$= [2.0 \text{ m} - (0.25 \text{ m/s}^2)t^2]\hat{\imath}$$
$$+ [(1.0 \text{ m/s})t + (0.025 \text{ m/s}^3)t^3]\hat{\jmath}$$

At $t = 0.0$ s the position vector $\vec{r}_0$ is

$$\vec{r}_0 = (2.0 \text{ m})\hat{\imath} + (0.0 \text{ m})\hat{\jmath}$$

From part (a), the position vector $\vec{r}_2$ at $t = 2.0$ s is

$$\vec{r}_2 = (1.0 \text{ m})\hat{\imath} + (2.2 \text{ m})\hat{\jmath}$$

The displacement from $t = 0.0$ s to $t = 2.0$ s is therefore

$$\Delta \vec{r} = \vec{r}_2 - \vec{r}_0 = (1.0 \text{ m})\hat{\imath} + (2.2 \text{ m})\hat{\jmath} - (2.0 \text{ m})\hat{\imath}$$
$$= (-1.0 \text{ m})\hat{\imath} + (2.2 \text{ m})\hat{\jmath}$$

During this interval the rover moves 1.0 m in the negative *x*-direction and 2.2 m in the positive *y*-direction. From Eq. (3.2), the average velocity over this interval is the displacement divided by the elapsed time:

$$\vec{v}_{av} = \frac{\Delta \vec{r}}{\Delta t} = \frac{(-1.0 \text{ m})\hat{\imath} + (2.2 \text{ m})\hat{\jmath}}{2.0 \text{ s} - 0.0 \text{ s}}$$
$$= (-0.50 \text{ m/s})\hat{\imath} + (1.1 \text{ m/s})\hat{\jmath}$$

The components of this average velocity are $v_{av\text{-}x} = -0.50$ m/s and $v_{av\text{-}y} = 1.1$ m/s.

Continued

(c) From Eq. (3.4) the components of *instantaneous* velocity are the time derivatives of the coordinates:

$$v_x = \frac{dx}{dt} = (-0.25 \text{ m/s}^2)(2t)$$

$$v_y = \frac{dy}{dt} = 1.0 \text{ m/s} + (0.025 \text{ m/s}^3)(3t^2)$$

Hence the instantaneous velocity vector is

$$\vec{v} = v_x\hat{i} + v_y\hat{j}$$

$$= (-0.50 \text{ m/s}^2)t\hat{i} + [1.0 \text{ m/s} + (0.075 \text{ m/s}^3)t^2]\hat{j}$$

At $t = 2.0$ s the velocity vector $\vec{v}_2$ has components

$$v_{2x} = (-0.50 \text{ m/s}^2)(2.0 \text{ s}) = -1.0 \text{ m/s}$$

$$v_{2y} = 1.0 \text{ m/s} + (0.075 \text{ m/s}^3)(2.0 \text{ s})^2 = 1.3 \text{ m/s}$$

The magnitude of the instantaneous velocity (that is, the speed) at $t = 2.0$ s is

$$v_2 = \sqrt{v_{2x}^2 + v_{2y}^2} = \sqrt{(-1.0 \text{ m/s})^2 + (1.3 \text{ m/s})^2}$$

$$= 1.6 \text{ m/s}$$

Figure 3.5 shows the direction of velocity vector $\vec{v}_2$, which is at an angle α between $90°$ and $180°$ with respect to the positive x-axis. From Eq. (3.7) we have

$$\arctan\frac{v_y}{v_x} = \arctan\frac{1.3 \text{ m/s}}{-1.0 \text{ m/s}} = -52°$$

This is off by $180°$; the correct value is $\alpha = 180° - 52° = 128°$, or $38°$ west of north.

EVALUATE: Compare the components of *average* velocity from part (b) for the interval from $t = 0.0$ s to $t = 2.0$ s ($v_{\text{av-}x} = -0.50$ m/s, $v_{\text{av-}y} = 1.1$ m/s) with the components of *instantaneous* velocity at $t = 2.0$ s from part (c) ($v_{2x} = -1.0$ m/s, $v_{2y} = 1.3$ m/s). Just as in one dimension, the average velocity vector $\vec{v}_{\text{av}}$ over an interval is in general *not* equal to the instantaneous velocity $\vec{v}$ at the end of the interval (see Example 2.1).

Figure 3.5 shows the position vectors $\vec{r}$ and instantaneous velocity vectors $\vec{v}$ at $t = 0.0$ s, 1.0 s, and 2.0 s. (Calculate these quantities for $t = 0.0$ s and $t = 1.0$ s.) Notice that $\vec{v}$ is tangent to the path at every point. The magnitude of $\vec{v}$ increases as the rover moves, which means that its speed is increasing.

TEST YOUR UNDERSTANDING OF SECTION 3.1 In which of these situations *would* the average velocity vector $\vec{v}_{\text{av}}$ over an interval be equal to the instantaneous velocity $\vec{v}$ at the end of the interval? (i) A body moving along a curved path at constant speed; (ii) a body moving along a curved path and speeding up; (iii) a body moving along a straight line at constant speed; (iv) a body moving along a straight line and speeding up. ❙

3.2 THE ACCELERATION VECTOR

Now let's consider the *acceleration* of a particle moving in space. Just as for motion in a straight line, acceleration describes how the velocity of the particle changes. But since we now treat velocity as a vector, acceleration will describe changes in the velocity magnitude (that is, the speed) *and* changes in the direction of velocity (that is, the direction in which the particle is moving).

In **Fig. 3.6a**, a car (treated as a particle) is moving along a curved road. Vectors $\vec{v}_1$ and $\vec{v}_2$ represent the car's instantaneous velocities at time t_1, when the car is

3.6 (a) A car moving along a curved road from P_1 to P_2. (b) How to obtain the change in velocity $\Delta\vec{v} = \vec{v}_2 - \vec{v}_1$ by vector subtraction. (c) The vector $\vec{a}_{\text{av}} = \Delta\vec{v}/\Delta t$ represents the average acceleration between P_1 and P_2.

(a)

(b)

(c)

This car accelerates by slowing while rounding a curve. (Its instantaneous velocity changes in both magnitude and direction.)

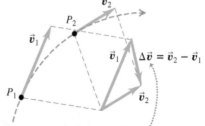

To find the car's average acceleration between P_1 and P_2, we first find the change in velocity $\Delta\vec{v}$ by subtracting $\vec{v}_1$ from $\vec{v}_2$. (Notice that $\vec{v}_1 + \Delta\vec{v} = \vec{v}_2$.)

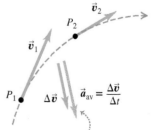

The average acceleration has the same direction as the change in velocity, $\Delta\vec{v}$.

at point P_1, and at time t_2, when the car is at point P_2. During the time interval from t_1 to t_2, the *vector change in velocity* is $\vec{v}_2 - \vec{v}_1 = \Delta\vec{v}$, so $\vec{v}_2 = \vec{v}_1 + \Delta\vec{v}$ (Fig. 3.6b). The **average acceleration** $\vec{a}_{av}$ of the car during this time interval is the velocity change divided by the time interval $t_2 - t_1 = \Delta t$:

DEMO

$$\underset{\substack{\text{Average acceleration} \\ \text{vector of a particle} \\ \text{during time interval} \\ \text{from } t_1 \text{ to } t_2}}{}\quad \vec{a}_{av} = \frac{\Delta\vec{v}}{\Delta t} = \frac{\vec{v}_2 - \vec{v}_1}{t_2 - t_1} \quad \underset{}{\substack{\text{Final velocity} \\ \text{minus initial} \\ \text{velocity}}} \tag{3.8}$$

Change in the particle's velocity — $\Delta\vec{v}$

Time interval — Δt Final time minus initial time

Average acceleration is a *vector* quantity in the same direction as $\Delta\vec{v}$ (Fig. 3.6c). The x-component of Eq. (3.8) is $a_{av-x} = (v_{2x} - v_{1x})/(t_2 - t_1) = \Delta v_x/\Delta t$, which is just Eq. (2.4) for average acceleration in straight-line motion.

As in Chapter 2, we define the **instantaneous acceleration** $\vec{a}$ (a *vector* quantity) at point P_1 as the limit of the average acceleration vector when point P_2 approaches point P_1, so both $\Delta\vec{v}$ and Δt approach zero (**Fig. 3.7**):

$$\underset{\substack{\text{The instantaneous} \\ \text{acceleration vector} \\ \text{of a particle ...}}}{}\quad \vec{a} = \lim_{\Delta t \to 0} \frac{\Delta\vec{v}}{\Delta t} = \frac{d\vec{v}}{dt} \tag{3.9}$$

... equals the limit of its average acceleration vector as the time interval approaches zero ...   ... and equals the instantaneous rate of change of its velocity vector.

The velocity vector $\vec{v}$ is always tangent to the particle's path, but the instantaneous acceleration vector $\vec{a}$ does *not* have to be tangent to the path. If the path is curved, $\vec{a}$ points toward the concave side of the path—that is, toward the inside of any turn that the particle is making (Fig. 3.7a). The acceleration is tangent to the path only if the particle moves in a straight line (Fig. 3.7b).

> CAUTION **Any particle following a curved path is accelerating** When a particle is moving in a curved path, it always has nonzero acceleration, even when it moves with constant speed. This conclusion is contrary to the everyday use of the word "acceleration" to mean that speed is increasing. The more precise definition given in Eq. (3.9) shows that there is a nonzero acceleration whenever the velocity vector changes in *any* way, whether there is a change of speed, direction, or both. ▌

To convince yourself that a particle is accelerating as it moves on a curved path with constant speed, think of your sensations when you ride in a car. When the car accelerates, you tend to move inside the car in a direction *opposite* to the car's acceleration. (In Chapter 4 we'll learn why this is so.) Thus you tend to slide toward the back of the car when it accelerates forward (speeds up) and toward the front of the car when it accelerates backward (slows down). If the car makes a turn on a level road, you tend to slide toward the outside of the turn; hence the car is accelerating toward the inside of the turn.

We'll usually be interested in instantaneous acceleration, not average acceleration. From now on, we'll use the term "acceleration" to mean the instantaneous acceleration vector $\vec{a}$.

Each component of the acceleration vector $\vec{a} = a_x\hat{\imath} + a_y\hat{\jmath} + a_z\hat{k}$ is the derivative of the corresponding component of velocity:

Each **component of** a particle's **instantaneous acceleration vector** ...

$$a_x = \frac{dv_x}{dt} \qquad a_y = \frac{dv_y}{dt} \qquad a_z = \frac{dv_z}{dt} \tag{3.10}$$

... equals the instantaneous rate of change of its corresponding velocity component.

3.7 (a) Instantaneous acceleration $\vec{a}$ at point P_1 in Fig. 3.6. (b) Instantaneous acceleration for motion along a straight line.

(a) Acceleration: curved trajectory

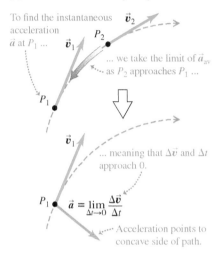

To find the instantaneous acceleration $\vec{a}$ at P_1 ... we take the limit of $\vec{a}_{av}$ as P_2 approaches P_1 ... meaning that $\Delta\vec{v}$ and Δt approach 0.

$$\vec{a} = \lim_{\Delta t \to 0} \frac{\Delta\vec{v}}{\Delta t}$$

Acceleration points to concave side of path.

(b) Acceleration: straight-line trajectory

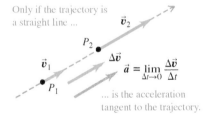

Only if the trajectory is a straight line ...

$$\vec{a} = \lim_{\Delta t \to 0} \frac{\Delta\vec{v}}{\Delta t}$$

... is the acceleration tangent to the trajectory.

BIO **Application Horses on a Curved Path** By leaning to the side and hitting the ground with their hooves at an angle, these horses give themselves the sideways acceleration necessary to make a sharp change in direction.

3.8 When the fingers release the arrow, its acceleration vector has a horizontal component (a_x) and a vertical component (a_y).

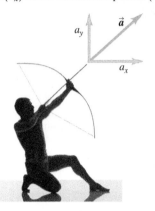

In terms of unit vectors,

$$\vec{a} = \frac{d\vec{v}}{dt} = \frac{dv_x}{dt}\hat{i} + \frac{dv_y}{dt}\hat{j} + \frac{dv_z}{dt}\hat{k} \qquad (3.11)$$

The x-component of Eqs. (3.10) and (3.11), $a_x = dv_x/dt$, is just Eq. (2.5) for instantaneous acceleration in one dimension. **Figure 3.8** shows an example of an acceleration vector that has both x- and y-components.

Since each component of velocity is the derivative of the corresponding coordinate, we can express the components a_x, a_y, and a_z of the acceleration vector $\vec{a}$ as

$$a_x = \frac{d^2x}{dt^2} \qquad a_y = \frac{d^2y}{dt^2} \qquad a_z = \frac{d^2z}{dt^2} \qquad (3.12)$$

SOLUTION

EXAMPLE 3.2 CALCULATING AVERAGE AND INSTANTANEOUS ACCELERATION

Let's return to the motions of the Mars rover in Example 3.1. (a) Find the components of the average acceleration for the interval $t = 0.0$ s to $t = 2.0$ s. (b) Find the instantaneous acceleration at $t = 2.0$ s.

SOLUTION

IDENTIFY and SET UP: In Example 3.1 we found the components of the rover's instantaneous velocity at any time t:

$$v_x = \frac{dx}{dt} = (-0.25 \text{ m/s}^2)(2t) = (-0.50 \text{ m/s}^2)t$$

$$v_y = \frac{dy}{dt} = 1.0 \text{ m/s} + (0.025 \text{ m/s}^3)(3t^2)$$

$$= 1.0 \text{ m/s} + (0.075 \text{ m/s}^3)t^2$$

We'll use the vector relationships among velocity, average acceleration, and instantaneous acceleration. In part (a) we determine the values of v_x and v_y at the beginning and end of the interval and then use Eq. (3.8) to calculate the components of the average acceleration. In part (b) we obtain expressions for the instantaneous acceleration components at any time t by taking the time derivatives of the velocity components as in Eqs. (3.10).

EXECUTE: (a) In Example 3.1 we found that at $t = 0.0$ s the velocity components are

$$v_x = 0.0 \text{ m/s} \qquad v_y = 1.0 \text{ m/s}$$

and that at $t = 2.0$ s the components are

$$v_x = -1.0 \text{ m/s} \qquad v_y = 1.3 \text{ m/s}$$

Thus the components of average acceleration in the interval $t = 0.0$ s to $t = 2.0$ s are

$$a_{\text{av-}x} = \frac{\Delta v_x}{\Delta t} = \frac{-1.0 \text{ m/s} - 0.0 \text{ m/s}}{2.0 \text{ s} - 0.0 \text{ s}} = -0.50 \text{ m/s}^2$$

$$a_{\text{av-}y} = \frac{\Delta v_y}{\Delta t} = \frac{1.3 \text{ m/s} - 1.0 \text{ m/s}}{2.0 \text{ s} - 0.0 \text{ s}} = 0.15 \text{ m/s}^2$$

(b) Using Eqs. (3.10), we find

$$a_x = \frac{dv_x}{dt} = -0.50 \text{ m/s}^2 \qquad a_y = \frac{dv_y}{dt} = (0.075 \text{ m/s}^3)(2t)$$

Hence the instantaneous acceleration vector $\vec{a}$ at time t is

$$\vec{a} = a_x\hat{i} + a_y\hat{j} = (-0.50 \text{ m/s}^2)\hat{i} + (0.15 \text{ m/s}^3)t\hat{j}$$

At $t = 2.0$ s the components of acceleration and the acceleration vector are

$$a_x = -0.50 \text{ m/s}^2 \qquad a_y = (0.15 \text{ m/s}^3)(2.0 \text{ s}) = 0.30 \text{ m/s}^2$$

$$\vec{a} = (-0.50 \text{ m/s}^2)\hat{i} + (0.30 \text{ m/s}^2)\hat{j}$$

The magnitude of acceleration at this time is

$$a = \sqrt{a_x^2 + a_y^2}$$

$$= \sqrt{(-0.50 \text{ m/s}^2)^2 + (0.30 \text{ m/s}^2)^2} = 0.58 \text{ m/s}^2$$

A sketch of this vector (**Fig. 3.9**) shows that the direction angle β of $\vec{a}$ with respect to the positive x-axis is between $90°$ and $180°$. From Eq. (3.7) we have

$$\arctan\frac{a_y}{a_x} = \arctan\frac{0.30 \text{ m/s}^2}{-0.50 \text{ m/s}^2} = -31°$$

Hence $\beta = 180° + (-31°) = 149°$.

3.9 The path of the robotic rover, showing the velocity and acceleration at $t = 0.0$ s ($\vec{v}_0$ and $\vec{a}_0$), $t = 1.0$ s ($\vec{v}_1$ and $\vec{a}_1$), and $t = 2.0$ s ($\vec{v}_2$ and $\vec{a}_2$).

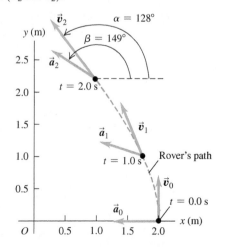

EVALUATE: Figure 3.9 shows the rover's path and the velocity and acceleration vectors at $t = 0.0$ s, 1.0 s, and 2.0 s. (Use the results of part (b) to calculate the instantaneous acceleration at $t = 0.0$ s and $t = 1.0$ s for yourself.) Note that $\vec{v}$ and $\vec{a}$ are *not* in the same direction at any of these times. The velocity vector $\vec{v}$ is tangent to the path at each point (as is always the case), and the acceleration vector $\vec{a}$ points toward the concave side of the path.

Parallel and Perpendicular Components of Acceleration

Equations (3.10) tell us about the components of a particle's instantaneous acceleration vector $\vec{a}$ along the x-, y-, and z-axes. Another useful way to think about $\vec{a}$ is in terms of one component *parallel* to the particle's path and to its velocity $\vec{v}$, and one component *perpendicular* to the path and to $\vec{v}$ (**Fig. 3.10**). That's because the parallel component $a_\parallel$ tells us about changes in the particle's *speed*, while the perpendicular component $a_\perp$ tells us about changes in the particle's *direction of motion*. To see why the parallel and perpendicular components of $\vec{a}$ have these properties, let's consider two special cases.

In **Fig. 3.11a** the acceleration vector is in the same direction as the velocity $\vec{v}_1$, so $\vec{a}$ has only a parallel component $a_\parallel$ (that is, $a_\perp = 0$). The velocity change $\Delta\vec{v}$ during a small time interval Δt is in the same direction as $\vec{a}$ and hence in the same direction as $\vec{v}_1$. The velocity $\vec{v}_2$ at the end of Δt is in the same direction as $\vec{v}_1$ but has greater magnitude. Hence during the time interval Δt the particle in Fig. 3.11a moved in a straight line with increasing speed (compare Fig. 3.7b).

In Fig. 3.11b the acceleration is *perpendicular* to the velocity, so $\vec{a}$ has only a perpendicular component $a_\perp$ (that is, $a_\parallel = 0$). In a small time interval Δt, the velocity change $\Delta\vec{v}$ is very nearly perpendicular to $\vec{v}_1$, and so $\vec{v}_1$ and $\vec{v}_2$ have different directions. As the time interval Δt approaches zero, the angle ϕ in the figure also approaches zero, $\Delta\vec{v}$ becomes perpendicular to *both* $\vec{v}_1$ and $\vec{v}_2$, and $\vec{v}_1$ and $\vec{v}_2$ have the same magnitude. In other words, the speed of the particle stays the same, but the direction of motion changes and the path of the particle curves.

In the most general case, the acceleration $\vec{a}$ has *both* components parallel and perpendicular to the velocity $\vec{v}$, as in Fig. 3.10. Then the particle's speed will change (described by the parallel component $a_\parallel$) *and* its direction of motion will change (described by the perpendicular component $a_\perp$).

Figure 3.12 shows a particle moving along a curved path for three situations: constant speed, increasing speed, and decreasing speed. If the speed is constant, $\vec{a}$ is perpendicular, or *normal*, to the path and to $\vec{v}$ and points toward the concave side of the path (Fig. 3.12a). If the speed is increasing, there is still a perpendicular component of $\vec{a}$, but there is also a parallel component with the same direction as $\vec{v}$ (Fig. 3.12b). Then $\vec{a}$ points ahead of the normal to the path. (This was the case in Example 3.2.) If the speed is decreasing, the parallel component has the direction opposite to $\vec{v}$, and $\vec{a}$ points behind the normal to the path (Fig. 3.12c; compare Fig. 3.7a). We will use these ideas again in Section 3.4 when we study the special case of motion in a circle.

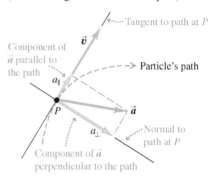

3.10 The acceleration can be resolved into a component $a_\parallel$ parallel to the path (that is, along the tangent to the path) and a component $a_\perp$ perpendicular to the path (that is, along the normal to the path).

3.11 The effect of acceleration directed (a) parallel to and (b) perpendicular to a particle's velocity.

(a) Acceleration parallel to velocity

Changes only *magnitude* of velocity: speed changes; direction doesn't.

(b) Acceleration perpendicular to velocity

Changes only *direction* of velocity: particle follows curved path at constant speed.

PhET: Maze Game

3.12 Velocity and acceleration vectors for a particle moving through a point P on a curved path with (a) constant speed, (b) increasing speed, and (c) decreasing speed.

(a) When speed is constant along a curved path ...

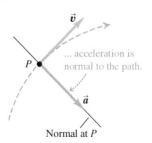

... acceleration is normal to the path.

Normal at P

(b) When speed is increasing along a curved path ...

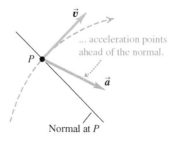

... acceleration points ahead of the normal.

Normal at P

(c) When speed is decreasing along a curved path ...

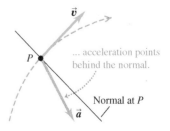

... acceleration points behind the normal.

Normal at P

EXAMPLE 3.3   CALCULATING PARALLEL AND PERPENDICULAR COMPONENTS OF ACCELERATION

For the rover of Examples 3.1 and 3.2, find the parallel and per-pendicular components of the acceleration at $t = 2.0$ s.

3.13 The parallel and perpendicular components of the accelera-tion of the rover at $t = 2.0$ s.

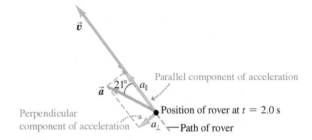

SOLUTION

IDENTIFY and SET UP: We want to find the components of the ac-celeration vector $\vec{a}$ that are parallel and perpendicular to velocity vector $\vec{v}$. We found the directions of $\vec{v}$ and $\vec{a}$ in Examples 3.1 and 3.2, respectively; Fig. 3.9 shows the results. From these directions we can find the angle between the two vectors and the compo-nents of $\vec{a}$ with respect to the direction of $\vec{v}$.

EXECUTE: From Example 3.2, at $t = 2.0$ s the particle has an ac-celeration of magnitude 0.58 m/s^2 at an angle of 149° with respect to the positive x-axis. In Example 3.1 we found that at this time the velocity vector is at an angle of 128° with respect to the positive x-axis. The angle between $\vec{a}$ and $\vec{v}$ is therefore $149° - 128° = 21°$ (**Fig. 3.13**). Hence the components of acceleration parallel and perpendicular to $\vec{v}$ are

$$a_\parallel = a \cos 21° = (0.58 \text{ m/s}^2)\cos 21° = 0.54 \text{ m/s}^2$$

$$a_\perp = a \sin 21° = (0.58 \text{ m/s}^2)\sin 21° = 0.21 \text{ m/s}^2$$

EVALUATE: The parallel component $a_\parallel$ is positive (in the same direction as $\vec{v}$), which means that the speed is increasing at this instant. The value $a_\parallel = +0.54$ m/s^2 tells us that the speed is increasing at this instant at a rate of 0.54 m/s per second. The perpendicular component $a_\perp$ is not zero, which means that at this instant the rover is turning—that is, it is changing direction and following a curved path.

CONCEPTUAL EXAMPLE 3.4   ACCELERATION OF A SKIER

A skier moves along a ski-jump ramp (**Fig. 3.14a**). The ramp is straight from point A to point C and curved from point C onward. The skier speeds up as she moves downhill from point A to point E, where her speed is maximum. She slows down after pass-ing point E. Draw the direction of the acceleration vector at each of the points B, D, E, and F.

3.14 (a) The skier's path. (b) Our solution.

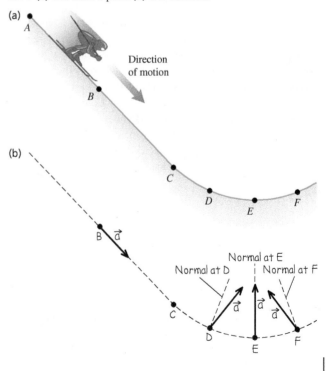

SOLUTION

Figure 3.14b shows our solution. At point B the skier is moving in a straight line with increasing speed, so her acceleration points downhill, in the same direction as her velocity. At points D, E, and F the skier is moving along a curved path, so her acceleration has a component perpendicular to the path (toward the concave side of the path) at each of these points. At point D there is also an acceleration component in the direction of her motion because she is speeding up. So the acceleration vector points *ahead* of the normal to her path at point D. At point E, the skier's speed is instantaneously not changing; her speed is maximum at this point, so its derivative is zero. There is therefore no parallel component of $\vec{a}$, and the acceleration is perpendicular to her motion. At point F there is an acceleration component *opposite to* the direction of her motion because she's slowing down. The acceleration vector therefore points *behind* the normal to her path.

In the next section we'll consider the skier's acceleration after she flies off the ramp.

TEST YOUR UNDERSTANDING OF SECTION 3.2 A sled travels over the crest of a snow-covered hill. The sled slows down as it climbs up one side of the hill and gains speed as it descends on the other side. Which of the vectors (1 through 9) in the figure correctly shows the direction of the sled's acceleration at the crest? (Choice 9 is that the acceleration is zero.) ▌

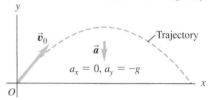

3.3 PROJECTILE MOTION

A **projectile** is any body that is given an initial velocity and then follows a path determined entirely by the effects of gravitational acceleration and air resistance. A batted baseball, a thrown football, and a bullet shot from a rifle are all projectiles. The path followed by a projectile is called its **trajectory.**

To analyze the motion of a projectile, we'll use an idealized model. We'll represent the projectile as a particle with an acceleration (due to gravity) that is constant in both magnitude and direction. We'll ignore the effects of air resistance and the curvature and rotation of the earth. This model has limitations, however: We have to consider the earth's curvature when we study the flight of long-range missiles, and air resistance is of crucial importance to a sky diver. Nevertheless, we can learn a lot from analysis of this simple model. For the remainder of this chapter the phrase "projectile motion" will imply that we're ignoring air resistance. In Chapter 5 we'll see what happens when air resistance cannot be ignored.

Projectile motion is always confined to a vertical plane determined by the direction of the initial velocity (**Fig. 3.15**). This is because the acceleration due to gravity is purely vertical; gravity can't accelerate the projectile sideways. Thus projectile motion is *two-dimensional.* We will call the plane of motion the *xy*-coordinate plane, with the *x*-axis horizontal and the *y*-axis vertically upward.

The key to analyzing projectile motion is that we can treat the *x*- and *y*-coordinates separately. **Figure 3.16** illustrates this for two projectiles: a red ball dropped from rest and a yellow ball projected horizontally from the same height. The figure shows that the horizontal motion of the yellow projectile has *no* effect on its vertical motion. For both projectiles, the *x*-component of acceleration is zero and the *y*-component is constant and equal to $-g$. (By definition, g is always positive; with our choice of coordinate directions, a_y is negative.) So *we can analyze projectile motion as a combination of horizontal motion with constant velocity and vertical motion with constant acceleration.*

We can then express all the vector relationships for the projectile's position, velocity, and acceleration by separate equations for the horizontal and vertical components. The components of $\vec{a}$ are

$$a_x = 0 \qquad a_y = -g \qquad \text{(projectile motion, no air resistance)} \qquad (3.13)$$

Since both the *x*-acceleration and *y*-acceleration are constant, we can use Eqs. (2.8), (2.12), (2.13), and (2.14) directly. Suppose that at time $t = 0$ our particle is at the point (x_0, y_0) and its initial velocity at this time has components v_{0x} and v_{0y}. The components of acceleration are $a_x = 0$, $a_y = -g$. Considering the *x*-motion first, we substitute 0 for a_x in Eqs. (2.8) and (2.12). We find

$$v_x = v_{0x} \qquad (3.14)$$

$$x = x_0 + v_{0x}t \qquad (3.15)$$

For the *y*-motion we substitute *y* for *x*, v_y for v_x, v_{0y} for v_{0x}, and $a_y = -g$ for a_x:

$$v_y = v_{0y} - gt \qquad (3.16)$$

$$y = y_0 + v_{0y}t - \tfrac{1}{2}gt^2 \qquad (3.17)$$

DEMO

3.15 The trajectory of an idealized projectile.

- A projectile moves in a vertical plane that contains the initial velocity vector $\vec{v}_0$.
- Its trajectory depends only on $\vec{v}_0$ and on the downward acceleration due to gravity.

$a_x = 0, a_y = -g$

3.16 The red ball is dropped from rest, and the yellow ball is simultaneously projected horizontally.

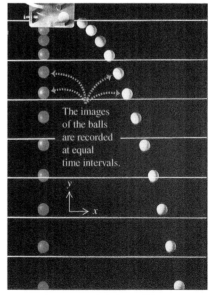

The images of the balls are recorded at equal time intervals.

- At any time the two balls have different *x*-coordinates and *x*-velocities but the same *y*-coordinate, *y*-velocity, and *y*-acceleration.
- The horizontal motion of the yellow ball has no effect on its vertical motion.

3.17 If air resistance is negligible, the trajectory of a projectile is a combination of horizontal motion with constant velocity and vertical motion with constant acceleration.

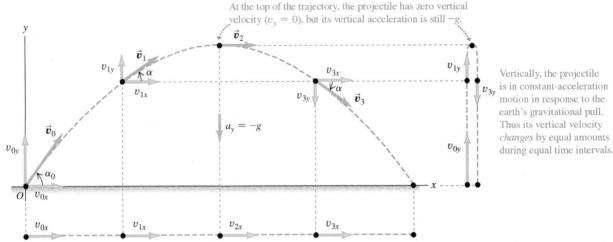

At the top of the trajectory, the projectile has zero vertical velocity ($v_y = 0$), but its vertical acceleration is still $-g$.

Vertically, the projectile is in constant-acceleration motion in response to the earth's gravitational pull. Thus its vertical velocity *changes* by equal amounts during equal time intervals.

Horizontally, the projectile is in constant-velocity motion: Its horizontal acceleration is zero, so it moves equal x-distances in equal time intervals.

3.18 The initial velocity components v_{0x} and v_{0y} of a projectile (such as a kicked soccer ball) are related to the initial speed v_0 and initial angle α_0.

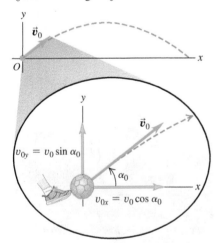

It's usually simplest to take the initial position (at $t = 0$) as the origin; then $x_0 = y_0 = 0$. This might be the position of a ball at the instant it leaves the hand of the person who throws it or the position of a bullet at the instant it leaves the gun barrel.

Figure 3.17 shows the trajectory of a projectile that starts at (or passes through) the origin at time $t = 0$, along with its position, velocity, and velocity components at equal time intervals. The x-velocity v_x is constant; the y-velocity v_y changes by equal amounts in equal times, just as if the projectile were launched vertically with the same initial y-velocity.

We can also represent the initial velocity $\vec{v}_0$ by its magnitude v_0 (the initial speed) and its angle α_0 with the positive x-axis (**Fig. 3.18**). In terms of these quantities, the components v_{0x} and v_{0y} of the initial velocity are

$$v_{0x} = v_0 \cos \alpha_0 \qquad v_{0y} = v_0 \sin \alpha_0 \tag{3.18}$$

If we substitute Eqs. (3.18) into Eqs. (3.14) through (3.17) and set $x_0 = y_0 = 0$, we get the following equations. They describe the position and velocity of the projectile in Fig. 3.17 at any time t:

DEMO   **DEMO**   **DEMO**

PhET: Projectile Motion

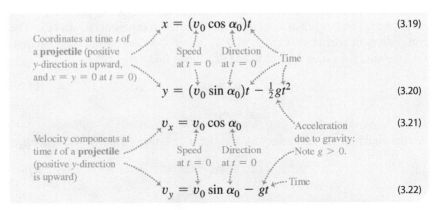

Coordinates at time t of a **projectile** (positive y-direction is upward, and $x = y = 0$ at $t = 0$)

$$x = (v_0 \cos \alpha_0)t \tag{3.19}$$

Speed at $t = 0$ Direction at $t = 0$ Time

$$y = (v_0 \sin \alpha_0)t - \tfrac{1}{2}gt^2 \tag{3.20}$$

$$v_x = v_0 \cos \alpha_0 \tag{3.21}$$

Acceleration due to gravity: Note $g > 0$.

Velocity components at time t of a **projectile** (positive y-direction is upward)

Speed at $t = 0$ Direction at $t = 0$ Time

$$v_y = v_0 \sin \alpha_0 - gt \tag{3.22}$$

We can get a lot of information from Eqs. (3.19) through (3.22). For example, the distance r from the origin to the projectile at any time t is

$$r = \sqrt{x^2 + y^2} \qquad (3.23)$$

The projectile's speed (the magnitude of its velocity) at any time is

$$v = \sqrt{v_x^2 + v_y^2} \qquad (3.24)$$

The *direction* of the velocity, in terms of the angle α it makes with the positive x-direction (see Fig. 3.17), is

$$\tan \alpha = \frac{v_y}{v_x} \qquad (3.25)$$

The velocity vector $\vec{v}$ is tangent to the trajectory at each point.

We can derive an equation for the trajectory's shape in terms of x and y by eliminating t. From Eqs. (3.19) and (3.20), we find $t = x/(v_0 \cos \alpha_0)$ and

$$y = (\tan \alpha_0)x - \frac{g}{2v_0^2 \cos^2 \alpha_0}x^2 \qquad (3.26)$$

Don't worry about the details of this equation; the important point is its general form. Since v_0, $\tan \alpha_0$, $\cos \alpha_0$, and g are constants, Eq. (3.26) has the form

$$y = bx - cx^2$$

where b and c are constants. This is the equation of a *parabola*. In our simple model of projectile motion, the trajectory is always a parabola (**Fig. 3.19**).

When air resistance *isn't* negligible and has to be included, calculating the trajectory becomes a lot more complicated; the effects of air resistance depend on velocity, so the acceleration is no longer constant. **Figure 3.20** shows a computer simulation of the trajectory of a baseball both without air resistance and with air resistance proportional to the square of the baseball's speed. We see that air resistance has a very large effect; the projectile does not travel as far or as high, and the trajectory is no longer a parabola.

DEMO

3.19 The nearly parabolic trajectories of a bouncing ball.

Successive images of the ball are separated by equal time intervals.

Successive peaks decrease in height because the ball loses energy with each bounce.

3.20 Air resistance has a large cumulative effect on the motion of a baseball. In this simulation we allow the baseball to fall below the height from which it was thrown (for example, the baseball could have been thrown from a cliff).

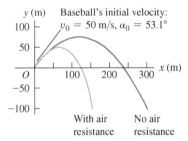

CONCEPTUAL EXAMPLE 3.5   ACCELERATION OF A SKIER, CONTINUED

SOLUTION

Let's consider again the skier in Conceptual Example 3.4. What is her acceleration at each of the points G, H, and I in **Fig. 3.21a** *after* she flies off the ramp? Neglect air resistance.

SOLUTION

Figure 3.21b shows our answer. The skier's acceleration changed from point to point while she was on the ramp. But as soon as she leaves the ramp, she becomes a projectile. So at points G, H, and I, and indeed at *all* points after she leaves the ramp, the skier's acceleration points vertically downward and has magnitude g. No matter how complicated the acceleration of a particle before it becomes a projectile, its acceleration as a projectile is given by $a_x = 0$, $a_y = -g$.

3.21 (a) The skier's path during the jump. (b) Our solution.

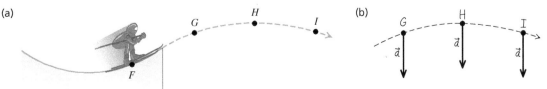

| PROBLEM-SOLVING STRATEGY 3.1 | **PROJECTILE MOTION**

NOTE: The strategies we used in Sections 2.4 and 2.5 for straight-line, constant-acceleration problems are also useful here.

IDENTIFY *the relevant concepts:* The key concept is that throughout projectile motion, the acceleration is downward and has a constant magnitude g. Projectile-motion equations don't apply to *throwing* a ball, because during the throw the ball is acted on by both the thrower's hand and gravity. These equations apply only *after* the ball leaves the thrower's hand.

SET UP *the problem* using the following steps:
1. Define your coordinate system and make a sketch showing your axes. It's almost always best to make the x-axis horizontal and the y-axis vertical, and to choose the origin to be where the body first becomes a projectile (for example, where a ball leaves the thrower's hand). Then the components of acceleration are $a_x = 0$ and $a_y = -g$, as in Eq. (3.13); the initial position is $x_0 = y_0 = 0$; and you can use Eqs. (3.19) through (3.22). (If you choose a different origin or axes, you'll have to modify these equations.)
2. List the unknown and known quantities, and decide which unknowns are your target variables. For example, you might be given the initial velocity (either the components or the magnitude and direction) and asked to find the coordinates and velocity components at some later time. Make sure that

you have as many equations as there are target variables to be found. In addition to Eqs. (3.19) through (3.22), Eqs. (3.23) through (3.26) may be useful.
3. State the problem in words and then translate those words into symbols. For example, *when* does the particle arrive at a certain point? (That is, at what value of *t*?) *Where* is the particle when its velocity has a certain value? (That is, what are the values of *x* and *y* when v_x or v_y has the specified value?) Since $v_y = 0$ at the highest point in a trajectory, the question "When does the projectile reach its highest point?" translates into "What is the value of *t* when $v_y = 0$?" Similarly, "When does the projectile return to its initial elevation?" translates into "What is the value of *t* when $y = y_0$?"

EXECUTE *the solution:* Find the target variables using the equations you chose. Resist the temptation to break the trajectory into segments and analyze each segment separately. You don't have to start all over when the projectile reaches its highest point! It's almost always easier to use the same axes and time scale throughout the problem. If you need numerical values, use $g = 9.80 \text{ m/s}^2$. Remember that g is positive!

EVALUATE *your answer:* Do your results make sense? Do the numerical values seem reasonable?

EXAMPLE 3.6 **A BODY PROJECTED HORIZONTALLY**

A motorcycle stunt rider rides off the edge of a cliff. Just at the edge his velocity is horizontal, with magnitude 9.0 m/s. Find the motorcycle's position, distance from the edge of the cliff, and velocity 0.50 s after it leaves the edge of the cliff.

SOLUTION

IDENTIFY and SET UP: Figure 3.22 shows our sketch of the trajectory of motorcycle and rider. He is in projectile motion as soon as he leaves the edge of the cliff, which we take to be the origin (so $x_0 = y_0 = 0$). His initial velocity $\vec{v}_0$ at the edge of the cliff is horizontal (that is, $\alpha_0 = 0$), so its components are $v_{0x} = v_0 \cos \alpha_0 = 9.0$ m/s and $v_{0y} = v_0 \sin \alpha_0 = 0$. To find the motorcycle's position

at $t = 0.50$ s, we use Eqs. (3.19) and (3.20); we then find the distance from the origin using Eq. (3.23). Finally, we use Eqs. (3.21) and (3.22) to find the velocity components at $t = 0.50$ s.

EXECUTE: From Eqs. (3.19) and (3.20), the motorcycle's x- and y-coordinates at $t = 0.50$ s are

$$x = v_{0x}t = (9.0 \text{ m/s})(0.50 \text{ s}) = 4.5 \text{ m}$$

$$y = -\tfrac{1}{2}gt^2 = -\tfrac{1}{2}(9.80 \text{ m/s}^2)(0.50 \text{ s})^2 = -1.2 \text{ m}$$

The negative value of y shows that the motorcycle is below its starting point.

From Eq. (3.23), the motorcycle's distance from the origin at $t = 0.50$ s is

$$r = \sqrt{x^2 + y^2} = \sqrt{(4.5 \text{ m})^2 + (-1.2 \text{ m})^2} = 4.7 \text{ m}$$

From Eqs. (3.21) and (3.22), the velocity components at $t = 0.50$ s are

$$v_x = v_{0x} = 9.0 \text{ m/s}$$

$$v_y = -gt = (-9.80 \text{ m/s}^2)(0.50 \text{ s}) = -4.9 \text{ m/s}$$

The motorcycle has the same horizontal velocity v_x as when it left the cliff at $t = 0$, but in addition there is a downward (negative) vertical velocity v_y. The velocity vector at $t = 0.50$ s is

$$\vec{v} = v_x\hat{i} + v_y\hat{j} = (9.0 \text{ m/s})\hat{i} + (-4.9 \text{ m/s})\hat{j}$$

3.22 Our sketch for this problem.

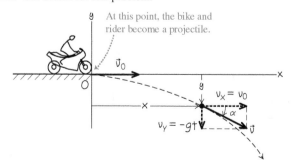

From Eqs. (3.24) and (3.25), at $t = 0.50$ s the velocity has magnitude v and angle α given by

$$v = \sqrt{v_x^2 + v_y^2} = \sqrt{(9.0 \text{ m/s})^2 + (-4.9 \text{ m/s})^2} = 10.2 \text{ m/s}$$

$$\alpha = \arctan \frac{v_y}{v_x} = \arctan\left(\frac{-4.9 \text{ m/s}}{9.0 \text{ m/s}}\right) = -29°$$

The motorcycle is moving at 10.2 m/s in a direction 29° below the horizontal.

EVALUATE: Just as in Fig. 3.17, the motorcycle's horizontal motion is unchanged by gravity; the motorcycle continues to move horizontally at 9.0 m/s, covering 4.5 m in 0.50 s. The motorcycle initially has zero vertical velocity, so it falls vertically just like a body released from rest and descends a distance $\frac{1}{2}gt^2 = 1.2$ m in 0.50 s.

EXAMPLE 3.7 **HEIGHT AND RANGE OF A PROJECTILE I: A BATTED BASEBALL**

A batter hits a baseball so that it leaves the bat at speed $v_0 = 37.0$ m/s at an angle $\alpha_0 = 53.1°$. (a) Find the position of the ball and its velocity (magnitude and direction) at $t = 2.00$ s. (b) Find the time when the ball reaches the highest point of its flight, and its height h at this time. (c) Find the *horizontal range* R—that is, the horizontal distance from the starting point to where the ball hits the ground—and the ball's velocity just before it hits.

___

SOLUTION

IDENTIFY and SET UP: As Fig. 3.20 shows, air resistance strongly affects the motion of a baseball. For simplicity, however, we'll ignore air resistance here and use the projectile-motion equations to describe the motion. The ball leaves the bat at $t = 0$ a meter or so above ground level, but we'll ignore this distance and assume that it starts at ground level ($y_0 = 0$). **Figure 3.23** shows our sketch of the ball's trajectory. We'll use the same coordinate system as in Figs. 3.17 and 3.18, so we can use Eqs. (3.19) through (3.22). Our target variables are (a) the position and velocity of the ball 2.00 s after it leaves the bat, (b) the time t when the ball is at its maximum height (that is, when $v_y = 0$) and the y-coordinate at this time, and (c) the x-coordinate when the ball returns to ground level ($y = 0$) and the ball's vertical component of velocity then.

EXECUTE: (a) We want to find x, y, v_x, and v_y at $t = 2.00$ s. The initial velocity of the ball has components

$$v_{0x} = v_0\cos\alpha_0 = (37.0 \text{ m/s})\cos 53.1° = 22.2 \text{ m/s}$$

$$v_{0y} = v_0\sin\alpha_0 = (37.0 \text{ m/s})\sin 53.1° = 29.6 \text{ m/s}$$

From Eqs. (3.19) through (3.22),

$$x = v_{0x}t = (22.2 \text{ m/s})(2.00 \text{ s}) = 44.4 \text{ m}$$

$$y = v_{0y}t - \tfrac{1}{2}gt^2$$
$$= (29.6 \text{ m/s})(2.00 \text{ s}) - \tfrac{1}{2}(9.80 \text{ m/s}^2)(2.00 \text{ s})^2 = 39.6 \text{ m}$$

3.23 Our sketch for this problem.

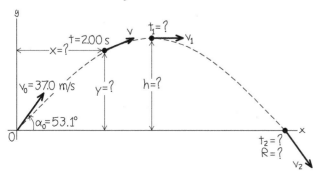

$$v_x = v_{0x} = 22.2 \text{ m/s}$$

$$v_y = v_{0y} - gt = 29.6 \text{ m/s} - (9.80 \text{ m/s}^2)(2.00 \text{ s}) = 10.0 \text{ m/s}$$

The y-component of velocity is positive at $t = 2.00$ s, so the ball is still moving upward (Fig. 3.23). From Eqs. (3.24) and (3.25), the magnitude and direction of the velocity are

$$v = \sqrt{v_x^2 + v_y^2} = \sqrt{(22.2 \text{ m/s})^2 + (10.0 \text{ m/s})^2} = 24.4 \text{ m/s}$$

$$\alpha = \arctan\left(\frac{10.0 \text{ m/s}}{22.2 \text{ m/s}}\right) = \arctan 0.450 = 24.2°$$

The ball is moving at 24.4 m/s in a direction 24.2° above the horizontal.

(b) At the highest point, the vertical velocity v_y is zero. Call the time when this happens t_1; then

$$v_y = v_{0y} - gt_1 = 0$$

$$t_1 = \frac{v_{0y}}{g} = \frac{29.6 \text{ m/s}}{9.80 \text{ m/s}^2} = 3.02 \text{ s}$$

The height h at the highest point is the value of y at time t_1:

$$h = v_{0y}t_1 - \tfrac{1}{2}gt_1^2$$
$$= (29.6 \text{ m/s})(3.02 \text{ s}) - \tfrac{1}{2}(9.80 \text{ m/s}^2)(3.02 \text{ s})^2 = 44.7 \text{ m}$$

(c) We'll find the horizontal range in two steps. First, we find the time t_2 when $y = 0$ (the ball is at ground level):

$$y = 0 = v_{0y}t_2 - \tfrac{1}{2}gt_2^2 = t_2\left(v_{0y} - \tfrac{1}{2}gt_2\right)$$

This is a quadratic equation for t_2. It has two roots:

$$t_2 = 0 \quad \text{and} \quad t_2 = \frac{2v_{0y}}{g} = \frac{2(29.6 \text{ m/s})}{9.80 \text{ m/s}^2} = 6.04 \text{ s}$$

The ball is at $y = 0$ at both times. The ball *leaves* the ground at $t_2 = 0$, and it hits the ground at $t_2 = 2v_{0y}/g = 6.04$ s.

The horizontal range R is the value of x when the ball returns to the ground at $t_2 = 6.04$ s:

$$R = v_{0x}t_2 = (22.2 \text{ m/s})(6.04 \text{ s}) = 134 \text{ m}$$

The vertical component of velocity when the ball hits the ground is

$$v_y = v_{0y} - gt_2 = 29.6 \text{ m/s} - (9.80 \text{ m/s}^2)(6.04 \text{ s})$$
$$= -29.6 \text{ m/s}$$

Continued

That is, v_y has the same magnitude as the initial vertical velocity v_{0y} but the opposite direction (down). Since v_x is constant, the angle $\alpha = -53.1°$ (below the horizontal) at this point is the negative of the initial angle $\alpha_0 = 53.1°$.

EVALUATE: It's often useful to check results by getting them in a different way. For example, we can also find the maximum height in part (b) by applying the constant-acceleration formula Eq. (2.13) to the y-motion:

$$v_y^2 = v_{0y}^2 + 2a_y(y - y_0) = v_{0y}^2 - 2g(y - y_0)$$

At the highest point, $v_y = 0$ and $y = h$. Solve this equation for h; you should get the answer that we obtained in part (b). (Do you?)

Note that the time to hit the ground, $t_2 = 6.04\ \text{s}$, is exactly twice the time to reach the highest point, $t_1 = 3.02\ \text{s}$. Hence the time of descent equals the time of ascent. This is *always* true if the starting point and endpoint are at the same elevation and if air resistance can be ignored.

Note also that $h = 44.7\ \text{m}$ in part (b) is comparable to the 61.0-m height above second base of the roof at Marlins Park in Miami, and the horizontal range $R = 134\ \text{m}$ in part (c) is greater than the 99.7-m distance from home plate to the right-field fence at Safeco Field in Seattle. In reality, due to air resistance (which we have ignored) a batted ball with the initial speed and angle we've used here won't go as high or as far as we've calculated (see Fig. 3.20).

EXAMPLE 3.8   **HEIGHT AND RANGE OF A PROJECTILE II: MAXIMUM HEIGHT, MAXIMUM RANGE**

Find the maximum height h and horizontal range R (see Fig. 3.23) of a projectile launched with speed v_0 at an initial angle α_0 between 0 and 90°. For a given v_0, what value of α_0 gives maximum height? What value gives maximum horizontal range?

SOLUTION

IDENTIFY and SET UP: This is almost the same as parts (b) and (c) of Example 3.7, except that now we want general expressions for h and R. We also want the values of α_0 that give the maximum values of h and R. In part (b) of Example 3.7 we found that the projectile reaches the high point of its trajectory (so that $v_y = 0$) at time $t_1 = v_{0y}/g$, and in part (c) we found that the projectile returns to its starting height (so that $y = y_0$) at time $t_2 = 2v_{0y}/g = 2t_1$. We'll use Eq. (3.20) to find the y-coordinate h at t_1 and Eq. (3.19) to find the x-coordinate R at time t_2. We'll express our answers in terms of the launch speed v_0 and launch angle α_0 by using Eqs. (3.18).

EXECUTE: From Eqs. (3.18), $v_{0x} = v_0\cos\alpha_0$ and $v_{0y} = v_0\sin\alpha_0$. Hence we can write the time t_1 when $v_y = 0$ as

$$t_1 = \frac{v_{0y}}{g} = \frac{v_0\sin\alpha_0}{g}$$

Equation (3.20) gives the height $y = h$ at this time:

$$h = (v_0\sin\alpha_0)\left(\frac{v_0\sin\alpha_0}{g}\right) - \tfrac{1}{2}g\left(\frac{v_0\sin\alpha_0}{g}\right)^2 = \frac{v_0^2\sin^2\alpha_0}{2g}$$

For a given launch speed v_0, the maximum value of h occurs for $\sin\alpha_0 = 1$ and $\alpha_0 = 90°$—that is, when the projectile is launched straight up. (If it is launched horizontally, as in Example 3.6, $\alpha_0 = 0$ and the maximum height is zero!)

The time t_2 when the projectile hits the ground is

$$t_2 = \frac{2v_{0y}}{g} = \frac{2v_0\sin\alpha_0}{g}$$

The horizontal range R is the value of x at this time. From Eq. (3.19), this is

$$R = (v_0\cos\alpha_0)t_2 = (v_0\cos\alpha_0)\frac{2v_0\sin\alpha_0}{g} = \frac{v_0^2\sin2\alpha_0}{g}$$

(We used the trigonometric identity $2\sin\alpha_0\cos\alpha_0 = \sin2\alpha_0$, found in Appendix B.) The maximum value of $\sin2\alpha_0$ is 1; this occurs when $2\alpha_0 = 90°$, or $\alpha_0 = 45°$. This angle gives the maximum range for a given initial speed if air resistance can be ignored.

EVALUATE: Figure 3.24 is based on a composite photograph of three trajectories of a ball projected from a small spring gun at angles of 30°, 45°, and 60°. The initial speed v_0 is approximately the same in all three cases. The horizontal range is greatest for the 45° angle. The ranges are nearly the same for the 30° and 60° angles: Can you prove that for a given value of v_0 the range is the same for both an initial angle α_0 and an initial angle $90° - \alpha_0$? (This is not the case in Fig. 3.24 due to air resistance.)

CAUTION   **Height and range of a projectile** We don't recommend memorizing the above expressions for h and R. They are applicable only in the special circumstances we've described. In particular, you can use the expression for the range R *only* when launch and landing heights are equal. There are many end-of-chapter problems to which these equations do *not* apply. ▮

3.24 A launch angle of 45° gives the maximum horizontal range. The range is shorter with launch angles of 30° and 60°.

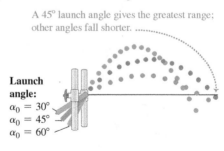

A 45° launch angle gives the greatest range; other angles fall shorter.

Launch angle:
$\alpha_0 = 30°$
$\alpha_0 = 45°$
$\alpha_0 = 60°$

EXAMPLE 3.9 DIFFERENT INITIAL AND FINAL HEIGHTS

You throw a ball from your window 8.0 m above the ground. When the ball leaves your hand, it is moving at 10.0 m/s at an angle of 20° below the horizontal. How far horizontally from your window will the ball hit the ground? Ignore air resistance.

SOLUTION

IDENTIFY and SET UP: As in Examples 3.7 and 3.8, we want to find the horizontal coordinate of a projectile when it is at a given y-value. The difference here is that this value of y is *not* the same as the initial value. We again choose the x-axis to be horizontal and the y-axis to be upward, and place the origin of coordinates at the point where the ball leaves your hand (**Fig. 3.25**). We have $v_0 = 10.0$ m/s and $\alpha_0 = -20°$ (the angle is negative because the initial velocity is below the horizontal). Our target variable is the value of x when the ball reaches the ground at $y = -8.0$ m. We'll use Eq. (3.20) to find the time t when this happens and then use Eq. (3.19) to find the value of x at this time.

3.25 Our sketch for this problem.

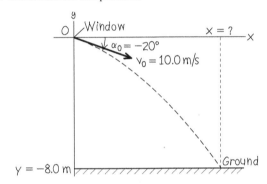

EXECUTE: To determine t, we rewrite Eq. (3.20) in the standard form for a quadratic equation for t:

$$\tfrac{1}{2}gt^2 - (v_0\sin\alpha_0)t + y = 0$$

The roots of this equation are

$$t = \frac{v_0\sin\alpha_0 \pm \sqrt{(-v_0\sin\alpha_0)^2 - 4\left(\tfrac{1}{2}g\right)y}}{2\left(\tfrac{1}{2}g\right)}$$

$$= \frac{v_0\sin\alpha_0 \pm \sqrt{v_0^2\sin^2\alpha_0 - 2gy}}{g}$$

$$= \frac{\left[\begin{array}{l}(10.0 \text{ m/s})\sin(-20°) \\ \pm \sqrt{(10.0 \text{ m/s})^2 \sin^2(-20°) - 2(9.80 \text{ m/s}^2)(-8.0 \text{ m})}\end{array}\right]}{9.80 \text{ m/s}^2}$$

$$= -1.7 \text{ s} \quad \text{or} \quad 0.98 \text{ s}$$

We discard the negative root, since it refers to a time before the ball left your hand. The positive root tells us that the ball reaches the ground at $t = 0.98$ s. From Eq. (3.19), the ball's x-coordinate at that time is

$$x = (v_0\cos\alpha_0)t = (10.0 \text{ m/s})\left[\cos(-20°)\right](0.98 \text{ s}) = 9.2 \text{ m}$$

The ball hits the ground a horizontal distance of 9.2 m from your window.

EVALUATE: The root $t = -1.7$ s is an example of a "fictional" solution to a quadratic equation. We discussed these in Example 2.8 in Section 2.5; review that discussion.

EXAMPLE 3.10 THE ZOOKEEPER AND THE MONKEY

A monkey escapes from the zoo and climbs a tree. After failing to entice the monkey down, the zookeeper fires a tranquilizer dart directly at the monkey (**Fig. 3.26**). The monkey lets go at the instant the dart leaves the gun. Show that the dart will *always* hit the monkey, provided that the dart reaches the monkey before he hits the ground and runs away.

SOLUTION

IDENTIFY and SET UP: We have *two* bodies in projectile motion: the dart and the monkey. They have different initial positions and initial velocities, but they go into projectile motion at the same time $t = 0$. We'll first use Eq. (3.19) to find an expression for the time t when the x-coordinates x_{monkey} and x_{dart} are equal. Then we'll use that expression in Eq. (3.20) to see whether y_{monkey} and y_{dart} are also equal at this time; if they are, the dart hits the monkey. We make the usual choice for the x- and y-directions, and place the origin of coordinates at the muzzle of the tranquilizer gun (Fig. 3.26).

EXECUTE: The monkey drops straight down, so $x_{\text{monkey}} = d$ at all times. From Eq. (3.19), $x_{\text{dart}} = (v_0\cos\alpha_0)t$. We solve for the time t when these x-coordinates are equal:

$$d = (v_0\cos\alpha_0)t \quad \text{so} \quad t = \frac{d}{v_0\cos\alpha_0}$$

We must now show that $y_{\text{monkey}} = y_{\text{dart}}$ at this time. The monkey is in one-dimensional free fall; its position at any time is given by Eq. (2.12), with appropriate symbol changes. Figure 3.26 shows that the monkey's initial height above the dart-gun's muzzle is $y_{\text{monkey}-0} = d\tan\alpha_0$, so

$$y_{\text{monkey}} = d\tan\alpha_0 - \tfrac{1}{2}gt^2$$

From Eq. (3.20),

$$y_{\text{dart}} = (v_0\sin\alpha_0)t - \tfrac{1}{2}gt^2$$

Continued

3.26 The tranquilizer dart hits the falling monkey.

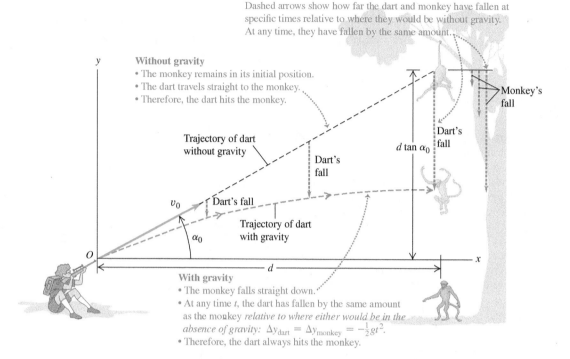

Dashed arrows show how far the dart and monkey have fallen at specific times relative to where they would be without gravity. At any time, they have fallen by the same amount.

Without gravity
• The monkey remains in its initial position.
• The dart travels straight to the monkey.
• Therefore, the dart hits the monkey.

Trajectory of dart without gravity

Dart's fall

v_0

α_0

Dart's fall

Trajectory of dart with gravity

$d \tan \alpha_0$

Dart's fall

Monkey's fall

d

With gravity
• The monkey falls straight down.
• At any time t, the dart has fallen by the same amount as the monkey *relative to where either would be in the absence of gravity*: $\Delta y_{\text{dart}} = \Delta y_{\text{monkey}} = -\frac{1}{2}gt^2$.
• Therefore, the dart always hits the monkey.

Comparing these two equations, we see that we'll have $y_{\text{monkey}} = y_{\text{dart}}$ (and a hit) if $d \tan \alpha_0 = (v_0 \sin \alpha_0)t$ when the two x-coordinates are equal. To show that this happens, we replace t with $d/(v_0 \cos \alpha_0)$, the time when $x_{\text{monkey}} = x_{\text{dart}}$. Sure enough,

$$(v_0 \sin \alpha_0)t = (v_0 \sin \alpha_0)\frac{d}{v_0 \cos \alpha_0} = d \tan \alpha_0$$

EVALUATE: We've proved that the y-coordinates of the dart and the monkey are equal at the same time that their x-coordinates are

equal; a dart aimed at the monkey *always* hits it, no matter what v_0 is (provided the monkey doesn't hit the ground first). This result is independent of the value of g, the acceleration due to gravity. With no gravity ($g = 0$), the monkey would remain motionless, and the dart would travel in a straight line to hit him. With gravity, both fall the same distance $gt^2/2$ below their $t = 0$ positions, and the dart still hits the monkey (Fig. 3.26).

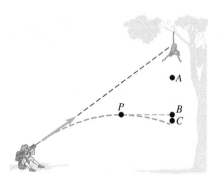

TEST YOUR UNDERSTANDING OF SECTION 3.3 In Example 3.10, suppose the tranquilizer dart has a relatively low muzzle velocity so that the dart reaches a maximum height at a point P before striking the monkey, as shown in the figure. When the dart is at point P, will the monkey be (i) at point A (higher than P), (ii) at point B (at the same height as P), or (iii) at point C (lower than P)? Ignore air resistance. ▌

3.4 MOTION IN A CIRCLE

When a particle moves along a curved path, the direction of its velocity changes. As we saw in Section 3.2, this means that the particle *must* have a component of acceleration perpendicular to the path, even if its speed is constant (see Fig. 3.11b). In this section we'll calculate the acceleration for the important special case of motion in a circle.

Uniform Circular Motion

When a particle moves in a circle with *constant speed,* the motion is called **uniform circular motion.** A car rounding a curve with constant radius at constant speed, a satellite moving in a circular orbit, and an ice skater skating in a circle

3.27 A car moving along a circular path. If the car is in uniform circular motion as in (a), the speed is constant and the acceleration is directed toward the center of the circular path (compare Fig. 3.12).

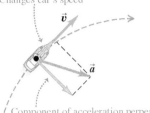

(a) **Uniform circular motion:** Constant speed along a circular path

Acceleration is exactly perpendicular to velocity; no parallel component

To center of circle

(b) **Car speeding up along a circular path**

Component of acceleration parallel to velocity: Changes car's speed

Component of acceleration perpendicular to velocity: Changes car's direction

(c) **Car slowing down along a circular path**

Component of acceleration perpendicular to velocity: Changes car's direction

Component of acceleration parallel to velocity: Changes car's speed

with constant speed are all examples of uniform circular motion (**Fig. 3.27a**; compare Fig. 3.12a). There is no component of acceleration parallel (tangent) to the path; otherwise, the speed would change. The acceleration vector is perpendicular (normal) to the path and hence directed inward (never outward!) toward the center of the circular path. This causes the direction of the velocity to change without changing the speed.

We can find a simple expression for the magnitude of the acceleration in uniform circular motion. We begin with **Fig. 3.28a**, which shows a particle moving with constant speed in a circular path of radius R with center at O. The particle moves a distance Δs from P_1 to P_2 in a time interval Δt. Figure 3.28b shows the vector change in velocity $\Delta \vec{v}$ during this interval.

The angles labeled $\Delta \phi$ in Figs. 3.28a and 3.28b are the same because $\vec{v}_1$ is perpendicular to the line OP_1 and $\vec{v}_2$ is perpendicular to the line OP_2. Hence the triangles in Figs. 3.28a and 3.28b are *similar*. The ratios of corresponding sides of similar triangles are equal, so

$$\frac{|\Delta \vec{v}|}{v_1} = \frac{\Delta s}{R} \qquad \text{or} \qquad |\Delta \vec{v}| = \frac{v_1}{R} \Delta s$$

The magnitude a_{av} of the average acceleration during Δt is therefore

$$a_{av} = \frac{|\Delta \vec{v}|}{\Delta t} = \frac{v_1}{R} \frac{\Delta s}{\Delta t}$$

The magnitude a of the *instantaneous* acceleration $\vec{a}$ at point P_1 is the limit of this expression as we take point P_2 closer and closer to point P_1:

$$a = \lim_{\Delta t \to 0} \frac{v_1}{R} \frac{\Delta s}{\Delta t} = \frac{v_1}{R} \lim_{\Delta t \to 0} \frac{\Delta s}{\Delta t}$$

If the time interval Δt is short, Δs is the distance the particle moves along its curved path. So the limit of $\Delta s/\Delta t$ is the speed v_1 at point P_1. Also, P_1 can be any point on the path, so we can drop the subscript and let v represent the speed at any point. Then

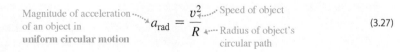

Magnitude of acceleration of an object in **uniform circular motion** $a_{rad} = \dfrac{v^2}{R}$ Speed of object / Radius of object's circular path (3.27)

The subscript "rad" is a reminder that the direction of the instantaneous acceleration at each point is always along a radius of the circle (toward the center of the circle; see Figs. 3.27a and 3.28c). So *in uniform circular motion, the magnitude*

3.28 Finding the velocity change $\Delta \vec{v}$, average acceleration $\vec{a}_{av}$, and instantaneous acceleration $\vec{a}_{rad}$ for a particle moving in a circle with constant speed.

(a) A particle moves a distance Δs at constant speed along a circular path.

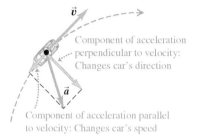

(b) The corresponding change in velocity and average acceleration

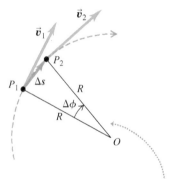

These two triangles are similar.

(c) The instantaneous acceleration

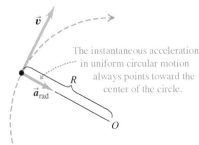

The instantaneous acceleration in uniform circular motion always points toward the center of the circle.

3.29 Acceleration and velocity (a) for a particle in uniform circular motion and (b) for a projectile with no air resistance.

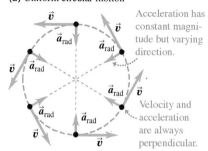

(a) Uniform circular motion

Acceleration has constant magnitude but varying direction.

Velocity and acceleration are always perpendicular.

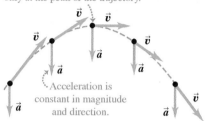

(b) Projectile motion

Velocity and acceleration are perpendicular only at the peak of the trajectory.

Acceleration is constant in magnitude and direction.

DATA *SPEAKS*

Acceleration on a Curved Path

When students were given a problem about an object following a curved path (not necessarily the parabolic path of a projectile), more than 46% gave an incorrect answer. Common errors:

- Confusion between the acceleration vector $\vec{a}$ and the velocity vector $\vec{v}$. Remember that $\vec{a}$ is the rate of change of $\vec{v}$, and on a curved path $\vec{a}$ and $\vec{v}$ cannot be in the same direction (see Fig. 3.12).

- Confusion about the direction of $\vec{a}$. If the path is curved, $\vec{a}$ always has a component toward the inside of the curve (see Fig. 3.12).

PhET: Ladybug Revolution
PhET: Motion in 2D

a_rad of the instantaneous acceleration is equal to the square of the speed v divided by the radius R of the circle. Its direction is perpendicular to $\vec{v}$ and inward along the radius (**Fig. 3.29a**).

Because the acceleration in uniform circular motion is always directed toward the center of the circle, it is sometimes called **centripetal acceleration.** The word "centripetal" is derived from two Greek words meaning "seeking the center."

CAUTION **Uniform circular motion vs. projectile motion** Notice the differences between acceleration in uniform circular motion (Fig. 3.29a) and acceleration in projectile motion (Fig. 3.29b). It's true that in both kinds of motion the *magnitude* of acceleration is the same at all times. However, in uniform circular motion the *direction* of $\vec{a}$ changes continuously—it always points toward the center of the circle. In projectile motion, the direction of $\vec{a}$ remains the same at all times. ▌

We can also express the magnitude of the acceleration in uniform circular motion in terms of the **period** T of the motion, the time for one revolution (one complete trip around the circle). In a time T the particle travels a distance equal to the circumference $2\pi R$ of the circle, so its speed is

$$v = \frac{2\pi R}{T} \tag{3.28}$$

When we substitute this into Eq. (3.27), we obtain the alternative expression

Magnitude of acceleration of an object in **uniform circular motion** $\quad a_\text{rad} = \dfrac{4\pi^2 R}{T^2}$ ◄···· Radius of object's circular path

····· Period of motion $\tag{3.29}$

EXAMPLE 3.11 CENTRIPETAL ACCELERATION ON A CURVED ROAD

An Aston Martin V8 Vantage sports car has a "lateral acceleration" of $0.96g = (0.96)(9.8 \text{ m/s}^2) = 9.4 \text{ m/s}^2$. This is the maximum centripetal acceleration the car can sustain without skidding out of a curved path. If the car is traveling at a constant 40 m/s (about 89 mi/h, or 144 km/h) on level ground, what is the radius R of the tightest unbanked curve it can negotiate?

SOLUTION

IDENTIFY, SET UP, and EXECUTE: The car is in uniform circular motion because it's moving at a constant speed along a curve that is a segment of a circle. Hence we can use Eq. (3.27) to solve for the target variable R in terms of the given centripetal accelera-

ion a_rad and speed v:

$$R = \frac{v^2}{a_\text{rad}} = \frac{(40 \text{ m/s})^2}{9.4 \text{ m/s}^2} = 170 \text{ m (about 560 ft)}$$

This is the *minimum* turning radius because a_rad is the *maximum* centripetal acceleration.

EVALUATE: The minimum turning radius R is proportional to the *square* of the speed, so even a small reduction in speed can make R substantially smaller. For example, reducing v by 20% (from 40 m/s to 32 m/s) would decrease R by 36% (from 170 m to 109 m).

Another way to make the minimum turning radius smaller is to *bank* the curve. We'll investigate this option in Chapter 5.

EXAMPLE 3.12 CENTRIPETAL ACCELERATION ON A CARNIVAL RIDE

Passengers on a carnival ride move at constant speed in a horizontal circle of radius 5.0 m, making a complete circle in 4.0 s. What is their acceleration?

SOLUTION

IDENTIFY and SET UP: The speed is constant, so this is uniform circular motion. We are given the radius $R = 5.0$ m and the period $T = 4.0$ s, so we can use Eq. (3.29) to calculate the acceleration directly, or we can calculate the speed v by using Eq. (3.28) and then find the acceleration by using Eq. (3.27).

EXECUTE: From Eq. (3.29),

$$a_{\text{rad}} = \frac{4\pi^2(5.0 \text{ m})}{(4.0 \text{ s})^2} = 12 \text{ m/s}^2 = 1.3g$$

EVALUATE: We can check this answer by using the second, roundabout approach. From Eq. (3.28), the speed is

$$v = \frac{2\pi R}{T} = \frac{2\pi(5.0 \text{ m})}{4.0 \text{ s}} = 7.9 \text{ m/s}$$

The centripetal acceleration is then

$$a_{\text{rad}} = \frac{v^2}{R} = \frac{(7.9 \text{ m/s})^2}{5.0 \text{ m}} = 12 \text{ m/s}^2$$

As in Fig. 3.29a, the direction of $\vec{a}$ is always toward the center of the circle. The magnitude of $\vec{a}$ is relatively mild as carnival rides go; some roller coasters subject their passengers to accelerations as great as $4g$.

Nonuniform Circular Motion

We have assumed throughout this section that the particle's speed is constant as it goes around the circle. If the speed varies, we call the motion **nonuniform circular motion.** In nonuniform circular motion, Eq. (3.27) still gives the *radial* component of acceleration $a_{\text{rad}} = v^2/R$, which is always *perpendicular* to the instantaneous velocity and directed toward the center of the circle. But since the speed v has different values at different points in the motion, the value of a_{rad} is not constant. The radial (centripetal) acceleration is greatest at the point in the circle where the speed is greatest.

In nonuniform circular motion there is also a component of acceleration that is *parallel* to the instantaneous velocity (see Figs. 3.27b and 3.27c). This is the component $a_{\parallel}$ that we discussed in Section 3.2; here we call this component a_{tan} to emphasize that it is *tangent* to the circle. The tangential component of acceleration a_{tan} is equal to the rate of change of *speed*. Thus

$$a_{\text{rad}} = \frac{v^2}{R} \quad \text{and} \quad a_{\text{tan}} = \frac{d|\vec{v}|}{dt} \qquad \text{(nonuniform circular motion)} \quad (3.30)$$

The tangential component is in the same direction as the velocity if the particle is speeding up, and in the opposite direction if the particle is slowing down (**Fig. 3.30**). If the particle's speed is constant, $a_{\text{tan}} = 0$.

CAUTION **Uniform vs. nonuniform circular motion** The two quantities

$$\frac{d|\vec{v}|}{dt} \quad \text{and} \quad \left|\frac{d\vec{v}}{dt}\right|$$

are *not* the same. The first, equal to the tangential acceleration, is the rate of change of speed; it is zero whenever a particle moves with constant speed, even when its direction of motion changes (such as in *uniform* circular motion). The second is the magnitude of the vector acceleration; it is zero only when the particle's acceleration *vector* is zero—that is, when the particle moves in a straight line with constant speed. In *uniform* circular motion $|d\vec{v}/dt| = a_{\text{rad}} = v^2/r$; in *nonuniform* circular motion there is also a tangential component of acceleration, so $|d\vec{v}/dt| = \sqrt{a_{\text{rad}}^2 + a_{\text{tan}}^2}$.

TEST YOUR UNDERSTANDING OF SECTION 3.4 Suppose that the particle in Fig. 3.30 experiences four times the acceleration at the bottom of the loop as it does at the top of the loop. Compared to its speed at the top of the loop, is its speed at the bottom of the loop (i) $\sqrt{2}$ times as great; (ii) 2 times as great; (iii) $2\sqrt{2}$ times as great; (iv) 4 times as great; or (v) 16 times as great?

Application Watch Out: Tight Curves Ahead! These roller coaster cars are in nonuniform circular motion: They slow down and speed up as they move around a vertical loop. The large accelerations involved in traveling at high speed around a tight loop mean extra stress on the passengers' circulatory systems, which is why people with cardiac conditions are cautioned against going on such rides.

3.30 A particle moving in a vertical loop with a varying speed, like a roller coaster car.

3.31 Airshow pilots face a complicated problem involving relative velocities. They must keep track of their motion relative to the air (to maintain enough airflow over the wings to sustain lift), relative to each other (to keep a tight formation without colliding), and relative to their audience (to remain in sight of the spectators).

3.32 (a) A passenger walking in a train. (b) The position of the passenger relative to the cyclist's frame of reference and the train's frame of reference.

(a)

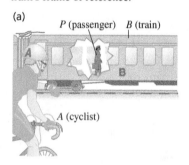

(b)

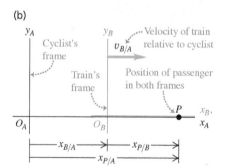

3.5 RELATIVE VELOCITY

If you stand next to a one-way highway, all the cars appear to be moving forward. But if you're driving in the fast lane on that highway, slower cars appear to be moving backward. In general, when two observers measure the velocity of the same body, they get different results if one observer is moving relative to the other. The velocity seen by a particular observer is called the velocity *relative* to that observer, or simply **relative velocity.** In many situations relative velocity is extremely important (**Fig. 3.31**).

We'll first consider relative velocity along a straight line and then generalize to relative velocity in a plane.

Relative Velocity in One Dimension

A passenger walks with a velocity of 1.0 m/s along the aisle of a train that is moving with a velocity of 3.0 m/s (**Fig. 3.32a**). What is the passenger's velocity? It's a simple enough question, but it has no single answer. As seen by a second passenger sitting in the train, she is moving at 1.0 m/s. A person on a bicycle standing beside the train sees the walking passenger moving at 1.0 m/s + 3.0 m/s = 4.0 m/s. An observer in another train going in the opposite direction would give still another answer. We have to specify which observer we mean, and we speak of the velocity *relative* to a particular observer. The walking passenger's velocity relative to the train is 1.0 m/s, her velocity relative to the cyclist is 4.0 m/s, and so on. Each observer, equipped in principle with a meter stick and a stopwatch, forms what we call a **frame of reference.** Thus a frame of reference is a coordinate system plus a time scale.

Let's use the symbol A for the cyclist's frame of reference (at rest with respect to the ground) and the symbol B for the frame of reference of the moving train. In straight-line motion the position of a point P relative to frame A is given by $x_{P/A}$ (the position of P with respect to A), and the position of P relative to frame B is given by $x_{P/B}$ (Fig. 3.32b). The position of the origin of B with respect to the origin of A is $x_{B/A}$. Figure 3.32b shows that

$$x_{P/A} = x_{P/B} + x_{B/A} \qquad (3.31)$$

In words, the coordinate of P relative to A equals the coordinate of P relative to B plus the coordinate of B relative to A.

The x-velocity of P relative to frame A, denoted by $v_{P/A\text{-}x}$, is the derivative of $x_{P/A}$ with respect to time. We can find the other velocities in the same way. So the time derivative of Eq. (3.31) gives us a relationship among the various velocities:

$$\frac{dx_{P/A}}{dt} = \frac{dx_{P/B}}{dt} + \frac{dx_{B/A}}{dt} \qquad \text{or}$$

Relative velocity along a line:
$$v_{P/A\text{-}x} = v_{P/B\text{-}x} + v_{B/A\text{-}x} \qquad (3.32)$$

x-velocity of P relative to A x-velocity of P relative to B x-velocity of B relative to A

Getting back to the passenger on the train in Fig. 3.32a, we see that A is the cyclist's frame of reference, B is the frame of reference of the train, and point P represents the passenger. Using the above notation, we have

$$v_{P/B\text{-}x} = +1.0 \text{ m/s} \qquad v_{B/A\text{-}x} = +3.0 \text{ m/s}$$

From Eq. (3.32) the passenger's velocity $v_{P/A\text{-}x}$ relative to the cyclist is

$$v_{P/A\text{-}x} = +1.0 \text{ m/s} + 3.0 \text{ m/s} = +4.0 \text{ m/s}$$

as we already knew.

In this example, both velocities are toward the right, and we have taken this as the positive *x*-direction. If the passenger walks toward the *left* relative to the train, then $v_{P/B\text{-}x} = -1.0$ m/s, and her *x*-velocity relative to the cyclist is $v_{P/A\text{-}x} = -1.0$ m/s $+ 3.0$ m/s $= +2.0$ m/s. The sum in Eq. (3.32) is always an algebraic sum, and any or all of the *x*-velocities may be negative.

When the passenger looks out the window, the stationary cyclist on the ground appears to her to be moving backward; we call the cyclist's velocity relative to her $v_{A/P\text{-}x}$. This is just the negative of the *passenger's* velocity relative to the cyclist, $v_{P/A\text{-}x}$. In general, if *A* and *B* are any two points or frames of reference,

$$v_{A/B\text{-}x} = -v_{B/A\text{-}x} \qquad (3.33)$$

PROBLEM-SOLVING STRATEGY 3.2) **RELATIVE VELOCITY**

IDENTIFY *the relevant concepts:* Whenever you see the phrase "velocity relative to" or "velocity with respect to," it's likely that the concepts of relative velocity will be helpful.

SET UP *the problem:* Sketch and label each frame of reference in the problem. Each moving body has its own frame of reference; in addition, you'll almost always have to include the frame of reference of the earth's surface. (Statements such as "The car is traveling north at 90 km/h" implicitly refer to the car's velocity relative to the surface of the earth.) Use the labels to help identify the target variable. For example, if you want to find the *x*-velocity of a car (*C*) with respect to a bus (*B*), your target variable is $v_{C/B\text{-}x}$.

EXECUTE *the solution:* Solve for the target variable using Eq. (3.32). (If the velocities aren't along the same direction, you'll need to use

the vector form of this equation, derived later in this section.) It's important to note the order of the double subscripts in Eq. (3.32): $v_{B/A\text{-}x}$ means "*x*-velocity of *B* relative to *A*." These subscripts obey a kind of algebra. If we regard each one as a fraction, then the fraction on the left side is the *product* of the fractions on the right side: $P/A = (P/B)(B/A)$. You can apply this rule to any number of frames of reference. For example, if there are three frames of reference *A*, *B*, and *C*, Eq. (3.32) becomes

$$v_{P/A\text{-}x} = v_{P/C\text{-}x} + v_{C/B\text{-}x} + v_{B/A\text{-}x}$$

EVALUATE *your answer:* Be on the lookout for stray minus signs in your answer. If the target variable is the *x*-velocity of a car relative to a bus ($v_{C/B\text{-}x}$), make sure that you haven't accidentally calculated the *x*-velocity of the *bus* relative to the *car* ($v_{B/C\text{-}x}$). If you've made this mistake, you can recover by using Eq. (3.33).

EXAMPLE 3.13 **RELATIVE VELOCITY ON A STRAIGHT ROAD**

You drive north on a straight two-lane road at a constant 88 km/h. A truck in the other lane approaches you at a constant 104 km/h (**Fig. 3.33**). Find (a) the truck's velocity relative to you and (b) your velocity relative to the truck. (c) How do the relative velocities change after you and the truck pass each other? Treat this as a one-dimensional problem.

3.33 Reference frames for you and the truck.

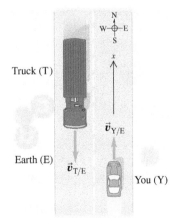

Truck (T)

Earth (E) $\vec{v}_{T/E}$

You (Y)

SOLUTION

IDENTIFY and **SET UP**: In this problem about relative velocities along a line, there are three reference frames: you (Y), the truck (T), and the earth's surface (E). Let the positive *x*-direction be north (Fig. 3.33). Then your *x*-velocity relative to the earth is $v_{Y/E\text{-}x} = +88$ km/h. The truck is initially approaching you, so it is moving south and its *x*-velocity with respect to the earth is $v_{T/E\text{-}x} = -104$ km/h. The target variables in parts (a) and (b) are $v_{T/Y\text{-}x}$ and $v_{Y/T\text{-}x}$, respectively. We'll use Eq. (3.32) to find the first target variable and Eq. (3.33) to find the second.

EXECUTE: (a) To find $v_{T/Y\text{-}x}$, we write Eq. (3.32) for the known $v_{T/E\text{-}x}$ and rearrange:

$$v_{T/E\text{-}x} = v_{T/Y\text{-}x} + v_{Y/E\text{-}x}$$
$$v_{T/Y\text{-}x} = v_{T/E\text{-}x} - v_{Y/E\text{-}x}$$
$$= -104 \text{ km/h} - 88 \text{ km/h} = -192 \text{ km/h}$$

The truck is moving at 192 km/h in the negative *x*-direction (south) relative to you.

Continued

(b) From Eq. (3.33),

$$v_{Y/T\text{-}x} = -v_{T/Y\text{-}x} = -(-192 \text{ km/h}) = +192 \text{ km/h}$$

You are moving at 192 km/h in the positive x-direction (north) relative to the truck.

(c) The relative velocities do *not* change after you and the truck pass each other. The relative *positions* of the bodies don't matter. After it passes you the truck is still moving at 192 km/h toward

the south relative to you, even though it is now moving away from you instead of toward you.

EVALUATE: To check your answer in part (b), use Eq. (3.32) directly in the form $v_{Y/T\text{-}x} = v_{Y/E\text{-}x} + v_{E/T\text{-}x}$. (The x-velocity of the earth with respect to the truck is the opposite of the x-velocity of the truck with respect to the earth: $v_{E/T\text{-}x} = -v_{T/E\text{-}x}$.) Do you get the same result?

Relative Velocity in Two or Three Dimensions

Let's extend the concept of relative velocity to include motion in a plane or in space. Suppose that the passenger in Fig. 3.32a is walking not down the aisle of the railroad car but from one side of the car to the other, with a speed of 1.0 m/s (**Fig. 3.34a**). We can again describe the passenger's position P in two frames of reference: A for the stationary ground observer and B for the moving train. But instead of coordinates x, we use position vectors $\vec{r}$ because the problem is now two-dimensional. Then, as Fig. 3.34b shows,

$$\vec{r}_{P/A} = \vec{r}_{P/B} + \vec{r}_{B/A} \tag{3.34}$$

Just as we did before, we take the time derivative of this equation to get a relationship among the various velocities; the velocity of P relative to A is $\vec{v}_{P/A} = d\vec{r}_{P/A}/dt$ and so on for the other velocities. We get

Relative velocity in space:
$$\vec{v}_{P/A} = \vec{v}_{P/B} + \vec{v}_{B/A} \tag{3.35}$$

Velocity of P relative to A Velocity of P relative to B Velocity of B relative to A

Equation (3.35) is known as the *Galilean velocity transformation*. It relates the velocity of a body P with respect to frame A and its velocity with respect to frame B ($\vec{v}_{P/A}$ and $\vec{v}_{P/B}$, respectively) to the velocity of frame B with respect to frame A ($\vec{v}_{B/A}$). If all three of these velocities lie along the same line, then Eq. (3.35) reduces to Eq. (3.32) for the components of the velocities along that line.

If the train is moving at $v_{B/A} = 3.0$ m/s relative to the ground and the passenger is moving at $v_{P/B} = 1.0$ m/s relative to the train, then the passenger's velocity

3.34 (a) A passenger walking across a railroad car. (b) Position of the passenger relative to the cyclist's frame and the train's frame. (c) Vector diagram for the velocity of the passenger relative to the ground (the cyclist's frame), $\vec{v}_{P/A}$.

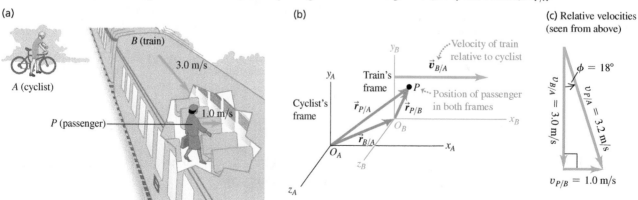

vector $\vec{v}_{P/A}$ relative to the ground is as shown in Fig. 3.34c. The Pythagorean theorem then gives us

$$v_{P/A} = \sqrt{(3.0 \text{ m/s})^2 + (1.0 \text{ m/s})^2} = \sqrt{10 \text{ m}^2/\text{s}^2} = 3.2 \text{ m/s}$$

Figure 3.34c also shows that the *direction* of the passenger's velocity vector relative to the ground makes an angle ϕ with the train's velocity vector $\vec{v}_{B/A}$, where

$$\tan \phi = \frac{v_{P/B}}{v_{B/A}} = \frac{1.0 \text{ m/s}}{3.0 \text{ m/s}} \quad \text{and} \quad \phi = 18°$$

As in the case of motion along a straight line, we have the general rule that if A and B are *any* two points or frames of reference,

$$\vec{v}_{A/B} = -\vec{v}_{B/A} \tag{3.36}$$

The velocity of the passenger relative to the train is the negative of the velocity of the train relative to the passenger, and so on.

In the early 20th century Albert Einstein showed that Eq. (3.35) has to be modified when speeds approach the speed of light, denoted by c. It turns out that if the passenger in Fig. 3.32a could walk down the aisle at $0.30c$ and the train could move at $0.90c$, then her speed relative to the ground would be not $1.20c$ but $0.94c$; nothing can travel faster than light! We'll return to Einstein and his *special theory of relativity* in Chapter 37.

SOLUTION

EXAMPLE 3.14   FLYING IN A CROSSWIND

An airplane's compass indicates that it is headed due north, and its airspeed indicator shows that it is moving through the air at 240 km/h. If there is a 100-km/h wind from west to east, what is the velocity of the airplane relative to the earth?

SOLUTION

IDENTIFY and SET UP: This problem involves velocities in two dimensions (northward and eastward), so it is a relative velocity problem using vectors. We are given the magnitude and direction of the velocity of the plane (P) relative to the air (A). We are also given the magnitude and direction of the wind velocity, which is the velocity of the air A with respect to the earth (E):

$$\vec{v}_{P/A} = 240 \text{ km/h} \quad \text{due north}$$

$$\vec{v}_{A/E} = 100 \text{ km/h} \quad \text{due east}$$

We'll use Eq. (3.35) to find our target variables: the magnitude and direction of velocity $\vec{v}_{P/E}$ of the plane relative to the earth.

EXECUTE: From Eq. (3.35) we have

$$\vec{v}_{P/E} = \vec{v}_{P/A} + \vec{v}_{A/E}$$

Figure 3.35 shows that the three relative velocities constitute a right-triangle vector addition; the unknowns are the speed $v_{P/E}$ and the angle α. We find

$$v_{P/E} = \sqrt{(240 \text{ km/h})^2 + (100 \text{ km/h})^2} = 260 \text{ km/h}$$

$$\alpha = \arctan\left(\frac{100 \text{ km/h}}{240 \text{ km/h}}\right) = 23° \text{ E of N}$$

3.35 The plane is pointed north, but the wind blows east, giving the resultant velocity $\vec{v}_{P/E}$ relative to the earth.

$\vec{v}_{A/E} = 100 \text{ km/h}$, east

$\vec{v}_{P/A} = 240 \text{ km/h}$, north

$\vec{v}_{P/E}$

α

N
W—⊕—E
S

EVALUATE: You can check the results by taking measurements on the scale drawing in Fig. 3.35. The crosswind increases the speed of the airplane relative to the earth, but pushes the airplane off course.

EXAMPLE 3.15 CORRECTING FOR A CROSSWIND

With wind and airspeed as in Example 3.14, in what direction should the pilot head to travel due north? What will be her velocity relative to the earth?

SOLUTION

IDENTIFY and SET UP: Like Example 3.14, this is a relative velocity problem with vectors. **Figure 3.36** is a scale drawing of the situation. Again the vectors add in accordance with Eq. (3.35) and form a right triangle:

$$\vec{v}_{P/E} = \vec{v}_{P/A} + \vec{v}_{A/E}$$

As Fig. 3.36 shows, the pilot points the nose of the airplane at an angle β into the wind to compensate for the crosswind. This angle, which tells us the direction of the vector $\vec{v}_{P/A}$ (the velocity of the airplane relative to the air), is one of our target variables. The other target variable is the speed of the airplane over the ground, which is the magnitude of the vector $\vec{v}_{P/E}$ (the velocity of the airplane relative to the earth). The known and unknown quantities are

$\vec{v}_{P/E}$ = magnitude unknown   due north
$\vec{v}_{P/A}$ = 240 km/h   direction unknown
$\vec{v}_{A/E}$ = 100 km/h   due east

We'll solve for the target variables by using Fig. 3.36 and trigonometry.

EXECUTE: From Fig. 3.36 the speed $v_{P/E}$ and the angle β are

$$v_{P/E} = \sqrt{(240 \text{ km/h})^2 - (100 \text{ km/h})^2} = 218 \text{ km/h}$$

$$\beta = \arcsin\left(\frac{100 \text{ km/h}}{240 \text{ km/h}}\right) = 25°$$

3.36 The pilot must point the plane in the direction of the vector $\vec{v}_{P/A}$ to travel due north relative to the earth.

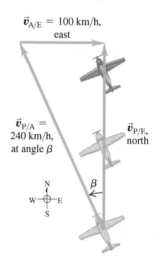

The pilot should point the airplane 25° west of north, and her ground speed is then 218 km/h.

EVALUATE: There were two target variables—the magnitude of a vector and the direction of a vector—in both this example and Example 3.14. In Example 3.14 the magnitude and direction referred to the *same* vector ($\vec{v}_{P/E}$); here they refer to *different* vectors ($\vec{v}_{P/E}$ and $\vec{v}_{P/A}$).

While we expect a *headwind* to reduce an airplane's speed relative to the ground, this example shows that a *crosswind* does, too. That's an unfortunate fact of aeronautical life.

TEST YOUR UNDERSTANDING OF SECTION 3.5 Suppose the nose of an airplane is pointed due east and the airplane has an airspeed of 150 km/h. Due to the wind, the airplane is moving due *north* relative to the ground and its speed relative to the ground is 150 km/h. What is the velocity of the air relative to the earth? (i) 150 km/h from east to west; (ii) 150 km/h from south to north; (iii) 150 km/h from southeast to northwest; (iv) 212 km/h from east to west; (v) 212 km/h from south to north; (vi) 212 km/h from southeast to northwest; (vii) there is no possible wind velocity that could cause this. ∎

Position, velocity, and acceleration vectors: The position vector $\vec{r}$ of a point P in space is the vector from the origin to P. Its components are the coordinates x, y, and z.

The average velocity vector $\vec{v}_{av}$ during the time interval Δt is the displacement $\Delta \vec{r}$ (the change in position vector $\vec{r}$) divided by Δt. The instantaneous velocity vector $\vec{v}$ is the time derivative of $\vec{r}$, and its components are the time derivatives of x, y, and z. The instantaneous speed is the magnitude of $\vec{v}$. The velocity $\vec{v}$ of a particle is always tangent to the particle's path. (See Example 3.1.)

The average acceleration vector $\vec{a}_{av}$ during the time interval Δt equals $\Delta \vec{v}$ (the change in velocity vector $\vec{v}$) divided by Δt. The instantaneous acceleration vector $\vec{a}$ is the time derivative of $\vec{v}$, and its components are the time derivatives of v_x, v_y, and v_z. (See Example 3.2.)

The component of acceleration parallel to the direction of the instantaneous velocity affects the speed, while the component of $\vec{a}$ perpendicular to $\vec{v}$ affects the direction of motion. (See Examples 3.3 and 3.4.)

$$\vec{r} = x\hat{i} + y\hat{j} + z\hat{k} \quad (3.1)$$

$$\vec{v}_{av} = \frac{\vec{r}_2 - \vec{r}_1}{t_2 - t_1} = \frac{\Delta \vec{r}}{\Delta t} \quad (3.2)$$

$$\vec{v} = \lim_{\Delta t \to 0} \frac{\Delta \vec{r}}{\Delta t} = \frac{d\vec{r}}{dt} \quad (3.3)$$

$$v_x = \frac{dx}{dt} \quad v_y = \frac{dy}{dt} \quad v_z = \frac{dz}{dt} \quad (3.4)$$

$$\vec{a}_{av} = \frac{\vec{v}_2 - \vec{v}_1}{t_2 - t_1} = \frac{\Delta \vec{v}}{\Delta t} \quad (3.8)$$

$$\vec{a} = \lim_{\Delta t \to 0} \frac{\Delta \vec{v}}{\Delta t} = \frac{d\vec{v}}{dt} \quad (3.9)$$

$$a_x = \frac{dv_x}{dt}$$

$$a_y = \frac{dv_y}{dt} \quad (3.10)$$

$$a_z = \frac{dv_z}{dt}$$

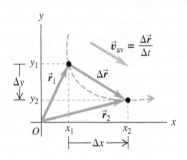

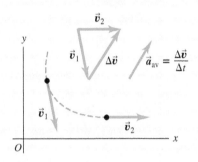

Projectile motion: In projectile motion with no air resistance, $a_x = 0$ and $a_y = -g$. The coordinates and velocity components are simple functions of time, and the shape of the path is always a parabola. We usually choose the origin to be at the initial position of the projectile. (See Examples 3.5–3.10.)

$$x = (v_0 \cos \alpha_0)t \quad (3.19)$$

$$y = (v_0 \sin \alpha_0)t - \frac{1}{2}gt^2 \quad (3.20)$$

$$v_x = v_0 \cos \alpha_0 \quad (3.21)$$

$$v_y = v_0 \sin \alpha_0 - gt \quad (3.22)$$

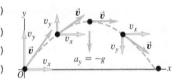

Uniform and nonuniform circular motion: When a particle moves in a circular path of radius R with constant speed v (uniform circular motion), its acceleration $\vec{a}$ is directed toward the center of the circle and perpendicular to $\vec{v}$. The magnitude a_{rad} of the acceleration can be expressed in terms of v and R or in terms of R and the period T (the time for one revolution), where $v = 2\pi R/T$. (See Examples 3.11 and 3.12.)

If the speed is not constant in circular motion (nonuniform circular motion), there is still a radial component of $\vec{a}$ given by Eq. (3.27) or (3.29), but there is also a component of $\vec{a}$ parallel (tangential) to the path. This tangential component is equal to the rate of change of speed, dv/dt.

$$a_{rad} = \frac{v^2}{R} \quad (3.27)$$

$$a_{rad} = \frac{4\pi^2 R}{T^2} \quad (3.29)$$

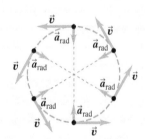

Relative velocity: When a body P moves relative to a body (or reference frame) B, and B moves relative to a body (or reference frame) A, we denote the velocity of P relative to B by $\vec{v}_{P/B}$, the velocity of P relative to A by $\vec{v}_{P/A}$, and the velocity of B relative to A by $\vec{v}_{B/A}$. If these velocities are all along the same line, their components along that line are related by Eq. (3.32). More generally, these velocities are related by Eq. (3.35). (See Examples 3.13–3.15.)

$$v_{P/A\text{-}x} = v_{P/B\text{-}x} + v_{B/A\text{-}x} \quad (3.32)$$
(relative velocity along a line)

$$\vec{v}_{P/A} = \vec{v}_{P/B} + \vec{v}_{B/A} \quad (3.35)$$
(relative velocity in space)

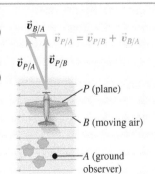

BRIDGING PROBLEM LAUNCHING UP AN INCLINE

You fire a ball with an initial speed v_0 at an angle ϕ above the surface of an incline, which is itself inclined at an angle θ above the horizontal (**Fig. 3.37**). (a) Find the distance, measured along the incline, from the launch point to the point when the ball strikes the incline. (b) What angle ϕ gives the maximum range, measured along the incline? Ignore air resistance.

SOLUTION GUIDE

IDENTIFY and SET UP

1. Since there's no air resistance, this is a problem in projectile motion. The goal is to find the point where the ball's parabolic trajectory intersects the incline.
2. Choose the x- and y-axes and the position of the origin. When in doubt, use the suggestions given in Problem-Solving Strategy 3.1 in Section 3.3.

3.37 Launching a ball from an inclined ramp.

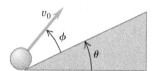

3. In the projectile equations in Section 3.3, the launch angle α_0 is measured from the horizontal. What is this angle in terms of θ and ϕ? What are the initial x- and y-components of the ball's initial velocity?
4. You'll need to write an equation that relates x and y for points along the incline. What is this equation? (This takes just geometry and trigonometry, not physics.)

EXECUTE

5. Write the equations for the x-coordinate and y-coordinate of the ball as functions of time t.
6. When the ball hits the incline, x and y are related by the equation that you found in step 4. Based on this, at what time t does the ball hit the incline?
7. Based on your answer from step 6, at what coordinates x and y does the ball land on the incline? How far is this point from the launch point?
8. What value of ϕ gives the *maximum* distance from the launch point to the landing point? (Use your knowledge of calculus.)

EVALUATE

9. Check your answers for the case $\theta = 0$, which corresponds to the incline being horizontal rather than tilted. (You already know the answers for this case. Do you know why?)

Problems

For assigned homework and other learning materials, go to MasteringPhysics®.

°, °°, °°°: Difficulty levels. CP: Cumulative problems incorporating material from earlier chapters. CALC: Problems requiring calculus. DATA: Problems involving real data, scientific evidence, experimental design, and/or statistical reasoning. BIO: Biosciences problems.

DISCUSSION QUESTIONS

Q3.1 A simple pendulum (a mass swinging at the end of a string) swings back and forth in a circular arc. What is the direction of the acceleration of the mass when it is at the ends of the swing? At the midpoint? In each case, explain how you obtained your answer.

Q3.2 Redraw Fig. 3.11a if $\vec{a}$ is antiparallel to $\vec{v}_1$. Does the particle move in a straight line? What happens to its speed?

Q3.3 A projectile moves in a parabolic path without air resistance. Is there any point at which $\vec{a}$ is parallel to $\vec{v}$? Perpendicular to $\vec{v}$? Explain.

Q3.4 A book slides off a horizontal tabletop. As it leaves the table's edge, the book has a horizontal velocity of magnitude v_0. The book strikes the floor in time t. If the initial velocity of the book is doubled to $2v_0$, what happens to (a) the time the book is in the air, (b) the horizontal distance the book travels while it is in the air, and (c) the speed of the book just before it reaches the floor? In particular, does each of these quantities stay the same, double, or change in another way? Explain.

Q3.5 At the instant that you fire a bullet horizontally from a rifle, you drop a bullet from the height of the gun barrel. If there is no air resistance, which bullet hits the level ground first? Explain.

Q3.6 A package falls out of an airplane that is flying in a straight line at a constant altitude and speed. If you ignore air resistance, what would be the path of the package as observed by the pilot? As observed by a person on the ground?

Q3.7 Sketch the six graphs of the x- and y-components of position, velocity, and acceleration versus time for projectile motion with $x_0 = y_0 = 0$ and $0 < \alpha_0 < 90°$.

Q3.8 If a jumping frog can give itself the same initial speed regardless of the direction in which it jumps (forward or straight up), how is the maximum vertical height to which it can jump related to its maximum horizontal range $R_{max} = v_0^2/g$?

Q3.9 A projectile is fired upward at an angle θ above the horizontal with an initial speed v_0. At its maximum height, what are its velocity vector, its speed, and its acceleration vector?

Q3.10 In uniform circular motion, what are the *average* velocity and *average* acceleration for one revolution? Explain.

Q3.11 In uniform circular motion, how does the acceleration change when the speed is increased by a factor of 3? When the radius is decreased by a factor of 2?

Q3.12 In uniform circular motion, the acceleration is perpendicular to the velocity at every instant. Is this true when the motion is not uniform—that is, when the speed is not constant?

Q3.13 Raindrops hitting the side windows of a car in motion often leave diagonal streaks even if there is no wind. Why? Is the explanation the same or different for diagonal streaks on the windshield?

Q3.14 In a rainstorm with a strong wind, what determines the best position in which to hold an umbrella?

Q3.15 You are on the west bank of a river that is flowing north with a speed of 1.2 m/s. Your swimming speed relative to the water is 1.5 m/s, and the river is 60 m wide. What is your path relative to the earth that allows you to cross the river in the shortest time? Explain your reasoning.

Q3.16 A stone is thrown into the air at an angle above the horizontal and feels negligible air resistance. Which graph in **Fig. Q3.16** best depicts the stone's *speed v* as a function of time *t* while it is in the air?

Figure **Q3.16**

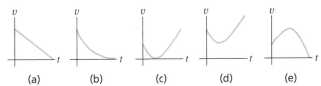

(a)   (b)   (c)   (d)   (e)

EXERCISES

Section 3.1 Position and Velocity Vectors

3.1 • A squirrel has x- and y-coordinates $(1.1 \text{ m}, 3.4 \text{ m})$ at time $t_1 = 0$ and coordinates $(5.3 \text{ m}, -0.5 \text{ m})$ at time $t_2 = 3.0$ s. For this time interval, find (a) the components of the average velocity, and (b) the magnitude and direction of the average velocity.

3.2 • A rhinoceros is at the origin of coordinates at time $t_1 = 0$. For the time interval from $t_1 = 0$ to $t_2 = 12.0$ s, the rhino's average velocity has x-component -3.8 m/s and y-component 4.9 m/s. At time $t_2 = 12.0$ s, (a) what are the x- and y-coordinates of the rhino? (b) How far is the rhino from the origin?

3.3 •• **CALC** A web page designer creates an animation in which a dot on a computer screen has position

$$\vec{r} = [4.0 \text{ cm} + (2.5 \text{ cm/s}^2)t^2]\hat{\imath} + (5.0 \text{ cm/s})t\,\hat{\jmath}.$$

(a) Find the magnitude and direction of the dot's average velocity between $t = 0$ and $t = 2.0$ s. (b) Find the magnitude and direction of the instantaneous velocity at $t = 0$, $t = 1.0$ s, and $t = 2.0$ s. (c) Sketch the dot's trajectory from $t = 0$ to $t = 2.0$ s, and show the velocities calculated in part (b).

3.4 • **CALC** The position of a squirrel running in a park is given by $\vec{r} = [(0.280 \text{ m/s})t + (0.0360 \text{ m/s}^2)t^2]\hat{\imath} + (0.0190 \text{ m/s}^3)t^3\hat{\jmath}$. (a) What are $v_x(t)$ and $v_y(t)$, the x- and y-components of the velocity of the squirrel, as functions of time? (b) At $t = 5.00$ s, how far is the squirrel from its initial position? (c) At $t = 5.00$ s, what are the magnitude and direction of the squirrel's velocity?

Section 3.2 The Acceleration Vector

3.5 • A jet plane is flying at a constant altitude. At time $t_1 = 0$, it has components of velocity $v_x = 90$ m/s, $v_y = 110$ m/s. At time $t_2 = 30.0$ s, the components are $v_x = -170$ m/s, $v_y = 40$ m/s. (a) Sketch the velocity vectors at t_1 and t_2. How do these two vectors differ? For this time interval calculate (b) the components of the average acceleration, and (c) the magnitude and direction of the average acceleration.

3.6 •• A dog running in an open field has components of velocity $v_x = 2.6$ m/s and $v_y = -1.8$ m/s at $t_1 = 10.0$ s. For the time interval from $t_1 = 10.0$ s to $t_2 = 20.0$ s, the average acceleration of the dog has magnitude 0.45 m/s^2 and direction $31.0°$ measured from the $+x$-axis toward the $+y$-axis. At $t_2 = 20.0$ s, (a) what are the x- and y-components of the dog's velocity? (b) What are the magnitude and direction of the dog's velocity? (c) Sketch the velocity vectors at t_1 and t_2. How do these two vectors differ?

3.7 •• **CALC** The coordinates of a bird flying in the xy-plane are given by $x(t) = \alpha t$ and $y(t) = 3.0 \text{ m} - \beta t^2$, where $\alpha = 2.4$ m/s and $\beta = 1.2$ m/s^2. (a) Sketch the path of the bird between $t = 0$ and $t = 2.0$ s. (b) Calculate the velocity and acceleration vectors of the bird as functions of time. (c) Calculate the magnitude and direction of the bird's velocity and acceleration at $t = 2.0$ s. (d) Sketch the velocity and acceleration vectors at $t = 2.0$ s. At this instant, is the bird's speed increasing, decreasing, or not changing? Is the bird turning? If so, in what direction?

3.8 • **CALC** A remote-controlled car is moving in a vacant parking lot. The velocity of the car as a function of time is given by $\vec{v} = [5.00 \text{ m/s} - (0.0180 \text{ m/s}^3)t^2]\hat{\imath} + [2.00 \text{ m/s} + (0.550 \text{ m/s}^2)t]\hat{\jmath}$. (a) What are $a_x(t)$ and $a_y(t)$, the x- and y-components of the car's velocity as functions of time? (b) What are the magnitude and direction of the car's velocity at $t = 8.00$ s? (b) What are the magnitude and direction of the car's acceleration at $t = 8.00$ s?

Section 3.3 Projectile Motion

3.9 • A physics book slides off a horizontal tabletop with a speed of 1.10 m/s. It strikes the floor in 0.480 s. Ignore air resistance. Find (a) the height of the tabletop above the floor; (b) the horizontal distance from the edge of the table to the point where the book strikes the floor; (c) the horizontal and vertical components of the book's velocity, and the magnitude and direction of its velocity, just before the book reaches the floor. (d) Draw x-t, y-t, v_x-t, and v_y-t graphs for the motion.

3.10 •• A daring 510-N swimmer dives off a cliff with a running horizontal leap, as shown in **Fig. E3.10**. What must her minimum speed be just as she leaves the top of the cliff so that she will miss the ledge at the bottom, which is 1.75 m wide and 9.00 m below the top of the cliff?

Figure **E3.10**

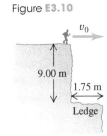

9.00 m

1.75 m

Ledge

v_0

3.11 • Crickets Chirpy and Milada jump from the top of a vertical cliff. Chirpy drops downward and reaches the ground in 2.70 s, while Milada jumps horizontally with an initial speed of 95.0 cm/s. How far from the base of the cliff will Milada hit the ground? Ignore air resistance.

3.12 • A rookie quarterback throws a football with an initial upward velocity component of 12.0 m/s and a horizontal velocity component of 20.0 m/s. Ignore air resistance. (a) How much time is required for the football to reach the highest point of the trajectory? (b) How high is this point? (c) How much time (after it is thrown) is required for the football to return to its original level? How does this compare with the time calculated in part (a)? (d) How far has the football traveled horizontally during this time? (e) Draw x-t, y-t, v_x-t, and v_y-t graphs for the motion.

3.13 •• **Leaping the River I.** During a storm, a car traveling on a level horizontal road comes upon a bridge that has washed out. The driver must get to the other side, so he decides to try leaping the river with his car. The side of the road the car is on is 21.3 m above the river, while the opposite side is only 1.8 m above the river. The river itself is a raging torrent 48.0 m wide. (a) How fast should the car be traveling at the time it leaves the road in order just to clear the river and land safely on the opposite side? (b) What is the speed of the car just before it lands on the other side?

3.14 • BIO **The Champion Jumper of the Insect World.** The froghopper, *Philaenus spumarius,* holds the world record for insect jumps. When leaping at an angle of 58.0° above the horizontal, some of the tiny critters have reached a maximum height of 58.7 cm above the level ground. (See *Nature,* Vol. 424, July 31, 2003, p. 509.) (a) What was the takeoff speed for such a leap? (b) What horizontal distance did the froghopper cover for this world-record leap?

3.15 •• Inside a starship at rest on the earth, a ball rolls off the top of a horizontal table and lands a distance D from the foot of the table. This starship now lands on the unexplored Planet X. The commander, Captain Curious, rolls the same ball off the same table with the same initial speed as on earth and finds that it lands a distance $2.76D$ from the foot of the table. What is the acceleration due to gravity on Planet X?

3.16 • On level ground a shell is fired with an initial velocity of 40.0 m/s at 60.0° above the horizontal and feels no appreciable air resistance. (a) Find the horizontal and vertical components of the shell's initial velocity. (b) How long does it take the shell to reach its highest point? (c) Find its maximum height above the ground. (d) How far from its firing point does the shell land? (e) At its highest point, find the horizontal and vertical components of its acceleration and velocity.

3.17 • A major leaguer hits a baseball so that it leaves the bat at a speed of 30.0 m/s and at an angle of 36.9° above the horizontal. Ignore air resistance. (a) At what *two* times is the baseball at a height of 10.0 m above the point at which it left the bat? (b) Calculate the horizontal and vertical components of the baseball's velocity at each of the two times calculated in part (a). (c) What are the magnitude and direction of the baseball's velocity when it returns to the level at which it left the bat?

3.18 • A shot putter releases the shot some distance above the level ground with a velocity of 12.0 m/s, 51.0° above the horizontal. The shot hits the ground 2.08 s later. Ignore air resistance. (a) What are the components of the shot's acceleration while in flight? (b) What are the components of the shot's velocity at the beginning and at the end of its trajectory? (c) How far did she throw the shot horizontally? (d) Why does the expression for R in Example 3.8 *not* give the correct answer for part (c)? (e) How high was the shot above the ground when she released it? (f) Draw *x-t, y-t, v_x-t,* and *v_y-t* graphs for the motion.

3.19 •• **Win the Prize.** In a carnival booth, you can win a stuffed giraffe if you toss a quarter into a small dish. The dish is on a shelf above the point where the quarter leaves your hand and is a horizontal distance of 2.1 m from this point (**Fig. E3.19**). If you toss the coin with a velocity of 6.4 m/s at an angle of 60° above the horizontal, the coin will land in the dish. Ignore air resistance.

Figure **E3.19**

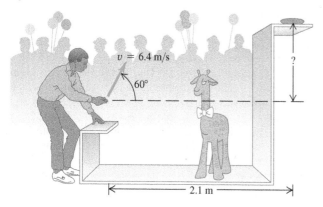

(a) What is the height of the shelf above the point where the quarter leaves your hand? (b) What is the vertical component of the velocity of the quarter just before it lands in the dish?

3.20 • Firemen use a high-pressure hose to shoot a stream of water at a burning building. The water has a speed of 25.0 m/s as it leaves the end of the hose and then exhibits projectile motion. The firemen adjust the angle of elevation α of the hose until the water takes 3.00 s to reach a building 45.0 m away. Ignore air resistance; assume that the end of the hose is at ground level. (a) Find α. (b) Find the speed and acceleration of the water at the highest point in its trajectory. (c) How high above the ground does the water strike the building, and how fast is it moving just before it hits the building?

3.21 •• A man stands on the roof of a 15.0-m-tall building and throws a rock with a speed of 30.0 m/s at an angle of 33.0° above the horizontal. Ignore air resistance. Calculate (a) the maximum height above the roof that the rock reaches; (b) the speed of the rock just before it strikes the ground; and (c) the horizontal range from the base of the building to the point where the rock strikes the ground. (d) Draw *x-t, y-t, v_x-t,* and *v_y-t* graphs for the motion.

3.22 •• A 124-kg balloon carrying a 22-kg basket is descending with a constant downward velocity of 20.0 m/s. A 1.0-kg stone is thrown from the basket with an initial velocity of 15.0 m/s perpendicular to the path of the descending balloon, as measured relative to a person at rest in the basket. That person sees the stone hit the ground 5.00 s after it was thrown. Assume that the balloon continues its downward descent with the same constant speed of 20.0 m/s. (a) How high is the balloon when the rock is thrown? (b) How high is the balloon when the rock hits the ground? (c) At the instant the rock hits the ground, how far is it from the basket? (d) Just before the rock hits the ground, find its horizontal and vertical velocity components as measured by an observer (i) at rest in the basket and (ii) at rest on the ground.

Section 3.4 Motion in a Circle

3.23 •• The earth has a radius of 6380 km and turns around once on its axis in 24 h. (a) What is the radial acceleration of an object at the earth's equator? Give your answer in m/s² and as a fraction of g. (b) If a_{rad} at the equator is greater than g, objects will fly off the earth's surface and into space. (We will see the reason for this in Chapter 5.) What would the period of the earth's rotation have to be for this to occur?

3.24 •• BIO **Dizziness.** Our balance is maintained, at least in part, by the endolymph fluid in the inner ear. Spinning displaces this fluid, causing dizziness. Suppose that a skater is spinning very fast at 3.0 revolutions per second about a vertical axis through the center of his head. Take the inner ear to be approximately 7.0 cm from the axis of spin. (The distance varies from person to person.) What is the radial acceleration (in m/s² and in g's) of the endolymph fluid?

3.25 • BIO **Pilot Blackout in a Power Dive.** A jet plane comes in for a downward dive as shown in **Fig. E3.25.** The bottom part of the path is a quarter circle with a radius of curvature of 280 m. According to medical tests, pilots will lose consciousness when they pull out of a dive at an upward acceleration greater than 5.5g. At what speed (in m/s and in mph) will the pilot black out during this dive?

Figure **E3.25**

3.26 •• A model of a helicopter rotor has four blades, each 3.40 m long from the central shaft to the blade tip. The model is rotated in a wind tunnel at 550 rev/min. (a) What is the linear speed of the blade tip, in m/s? (b) What is the radial acceleration of the blade tip expressed as a multiple of *g*?

3.27 • A Ferris wheel with radius 14.0 m is turning about a horizontal axis through its center (**Fig. E3.27**). The linear speed of a passenger on the rim is constant and equal to 6.00 m/s. What are the magnitude and direction of the passenger's acceleration as she passes through (a) the lowest point in her circular motion and (b) the highest point in her circular motion? (c) How much time does it take the Ferris wheel to make one revolution?

Figure **E3.27**

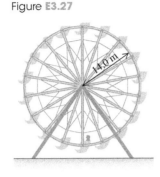

3.28 • The radius of the earth's orbit around the sun (assumed to be circular) is 1.50×10^8 km, and the earth travels around this orbit in 365 days. (a) What is the magnitude of the orbital velocity of the earth, in m/s? (b) What is the radial acceleration of the earth toward the sun, in m/s²? (c) Repeat parts (a) and (b) for the motion of the planet Mercury (orbit radius = 5.79×10^7 km, orbital period = 88.0 days).

3.29 •• BIO **Hypergravity.** At its Ames Research Center, NASA uses its large "20-G" centrifuge to test the effects of very large accelerations ("hypergravity") on test pilots and astronauts. In this device, an arm 8.84 m long rotates about one end in a horizontal plane, and an astronaut is strapped in at the other end. Suppose that he is aligned along the centrifuge's arm with his head at the outermost end. The maximum sustained acceleration to which humans are subjected in this device is typically 12.5*g*. (a) How fast must the astronaut's head be moving to experience this maximum acceleration? (b) What is the *difference* between the acceleration of his head and feet if the astronaut is 2.00 m tall? (c) How fast in rpm (rev/min) is the arm turning to produce the maximum sustained acceleration?

Section 3.5 Relative Velocity

3.30 • A railroad flatcar is traveling to the right at a speed of 13.0 m/s relative to an observer standing on the ground. Someone is riding a motor scooter on the flatcar (**Fig. E3.30**). What is the velocity (magnitude and direction) of the scooter relative to the flatcar if the scooter's velocity relative to the observer on the ground is (a) 18.0 m/s to the right? (b) 3.0 m/s to the left? (c) zero?

Figure **E3.30**

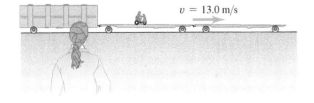

$v = 13.0$ m/s

3.31 • A "moving sidewalk" in an airport terminal moves at 1.0 m/s and is 35.0 m long. If a woman steps on at one end and walks at 1.5 m/s relative to the moving sidewalk, how much time does it take her to reach the opposite end if she walks (a) in the same direction the sidewalk is moving? (b) In the opposite direction?

3.32 • Two piers, *A* and *B*, are located on a river; *B* is 1500 m downstream from *A* (**Fig. E3.32**). Two friends must make round trips from pier *A* to pier *B* and return. One rows a boat at a constant speed of 4.00 km/h relative to the water; the other walks on the shore at a constant speed of 4.00 km/h. The velocity of the river is 2.80 km/h in the direction from *A* to *B*. How much time does it take each person to make the round trip?

Figure **E3.32**

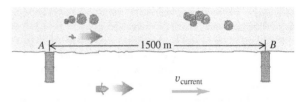

A ← —————— 1500 m —————— → B

v_{current}

3.33 •• A canoe has a velocity of 0.40 m/s southeast relative to the earth. The canoe is on a river that is flowing 0.50 m/s east relative to the earth. Find the velocity (magnitude and direction) of the canoe relative to the river.

3.34 •• The nose of an ultralight plane is pointed due south, and its airspeed indicator shows 35 m/s. The plane is in a 10-m/s wind blowing toward the southwest relative to the earth. (a) In a vector-addition diagram, show the relationship of $\vec{v}_{\text{P/E}}$ (the velocity of the plane relative to the earth) to the two given vectors. (b) Let *x* be east and *y* be north, and find the components of $\vec{v}_{\text{P/E}}$. (c) Find the magnitude and direction of $\vec{v}_{\text{P/E}}$.

3.35 • **Crossing the River I.** A river flows due south with a speed of 2.0 m/s. You steer a motorboat across the river; your velocity relative to the water is 4.2 m/s due east. The river is 500 m wide. (a) What is your velocity (magnitude and direction) relative to the earth? (b) How much time is required to cross the river? (c) How far south of your starting point will you reach the opposite bank?

3.36 • **Crossing the River II.** (a) In which direction should the motorboat in Exercise 3.35 head to reach a point on the opposite bank directly east from your starting point? (The boat's speed relative to the water remains 4.2 m/s.) (b) What is the velocity of the boat relative to the earth? (c) How much time is required to cross the river?

3.37 •• BIO **Bird Migration.** Canada geese migrate essentially along a north–south direction for well over a thousand kilometers in some cases, traveling at speeds up to about 100 km/h. If one goose is flying at 100 km/h relative to the air but a 40-km/h wind is blowing from west to east, (a) at what angle relative to the north–south direction should this bird head to travel directly southward relative to the ground? (b) How long will it take the goose to cover a ground distance of 500 km from north to south? (*Note:* Even on cloudy nights, many birds can navigate by using the earth's magnetic field to fix the north–south direction.)

3.38 •• An airplane pilot wishes to fly due west. A wind of 80.0 km/h (about 50 mi/h) is blowing toward the south. (a) If the airspeed of the plane (its speed in still air) is 320.0 km/h (about 200 mi/h), in which direction should the pilot head? (b) What is the speed of the plane over the ground? Draw a vector diagram.

PROBLEMS

3.39 • **CALC** A rocket is fired at an angle from the top of a tower of height $h_0 = 50.0$ m. Because of the design of the engines, its position coordinates are of the form $x(t) = A + Bt^2$ and $y(t) = C + Dt^3$, where A, B, C, and D are constants. The acceleration of the rocket 1.00 s after firing is $\vec{a} = (4.00\hat{\imath} + 3.00\hat{\jmath})$ m/s^2. Take the origin of coordinates to be at the base of the tower. (a) Find the constants A, B, C, and D, including their SI units. (b) At the instant after the rocket is fired, what are its acceleration vector and its velocity? (c) What are the x- and y-components of the rocket's velocity 10.0 s after it is fired, and how fast is it moving? (d) What is the position vector of the rocket 10.0 s after it is fired?

3.40 ••• **CALC** A faulty model rocket moves in the xy-plane (the positive y-direction is vertically upward). The rocket's acceleration has components $a_x(t) = \alpha t^2$ and $a_y(t) = \beta - \gamma t$, where $\alpha = 2.50$ m/s^4, $\beta = 9.00$ m/s^2, and $\gamma = 1.40$ m/s^3. At $t = 0$ the rocket is at the origin and has velocity $\vec{v}_0 = v_{0x}\hat{\imath} + v_{0y}\hat{\jmath}$ with $v_{0x} = 1.00$ m/s and $v_{0y} = 7.00$ m/s. (a) Calculate the velocity and position vectors as functions of time. (b) What is the maximum height reached by the rocket? (c) What is the horizontal displacement of the rocket when it returns to $y = 0$?

3.41 •• **CALC** If $\vec{r} = bt^2\hat{\imath} + ct^3\hat{\jmath}$, where b and c are positive constants, when does the velocity vector make an angle of 45.0° with the x- and y-axes?

3.42 •• **CALC** The position of a dragonfly that is flying parallel to the ground is given as a function of time by $\vec{r} = [2.90 \text{ m} + (0.0900 \text{ m/s}^2)t^2]\hat{\imath} - (0.0150 \text{ m/s}^3)t^3\hat{\jmath}$. (a) At what value of t does the velocity vector of the dragonfly make an angle of 30.0° clockwise from the $+x$-axis? (b) At the time calculated in part (a), what are the magnitude and direction of the dragonfly's acceleration vector?

3.43 ••• **CP** A test rocket starting from rest at point A is launched by accelerating it along a 200.0-m incline at 1.90 m/s^2 (**Fig. P3.43**). The incline rises at 35.0° above the horizontal, and at the instant the rocket leaves it, the engines turn off and the rocket is subject to gravity only (ignore air resistance). Find (a) the maximum height above the ground that the rocket reaches, and (b) the rocket's greatest horizontal range beyond point A.

Figure **P3.43**

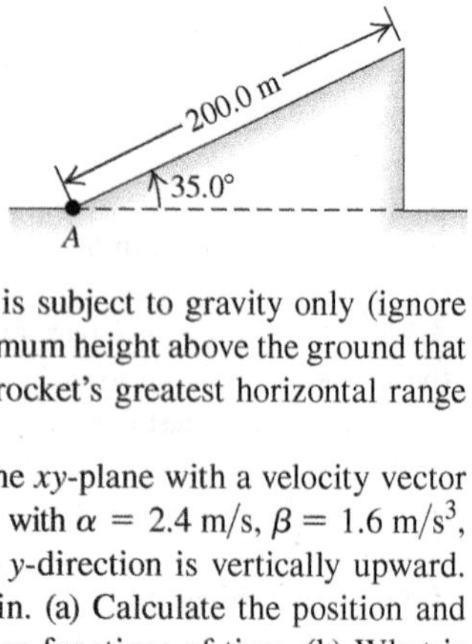

200.0 m
35.0°
A

3.44 •• **CALC** A bird flies in the xy-plane with a velocity vector given by $\vec{v} = (\alpha - \beta t^2)\hat{\imath} + \gamma t\hat{\jmath}$, with $\alpha = 2.4$ m/s, $\beta = 1.6$ m/s^3, and $\gamma = 4.0$ m/s^2. The positive y-direction is vertically upward. At $t = 0$ the bird is at the origin. (a) Calculate the position and acceleration vectors of the bird as functions of time. (b) What is the bird's altitude (y-coordinate) as it flies over $x = 0$ for the first time after $t = 0$?

3.45 •• A sly 1.5-kg monkey and a jungle veterinarian with a blow-gun loaded with a tranquilizer dart are 25 m above the ground in trees 70 m apart. Just as the veterinarian shoots horizontally at the monkey, the monkey drops from the tree in a vain attempt to escape being hit. What must the minimum muzzle velocity of the dart be for the dart to hit the monkey before the monkey reaches the ground?

3.46 ••• **BIO** **Spiraling Up.** Birds of prey typically rise upward on thermals. The paths these birds take may be spiral-like. You can model the spiral motion as uniform circular motion combined with a constant upward velocity. Assume that a bird completes a circle of radius 6.00 m every 5.00 s and rises vertically at a constant rate of 3.00 m/s. Determine (a) the bird's speed relative to the ground; (b) the bird's acceleration (magnitude and direction); and (c) the angle between the bird's velocity vector and the horizontal.

3.47 •• In fighting forest fires, airplanes work in support of ground crews by dropping water on the fires. For practice, a pilot drops a canister of red dye, hoping to hit a target on the ground below. If the plane is flying in a horizontal path 90.0 m above the ground and has a speed of 64.0 m/s (143 mi/h), at what horizontal distance from the target should the pilot release the canister? Ignore air resistance.

3.48 ••• A movie stuntwoman drops from a helicopter that is 30.0 m above the ground and moving with a constant velocity whose components are 10.0 m/s upward and 15.0 m/s horizontal and toward the south. Ignore air resistance. (a) Where on the ground (relative to the position of the helicopter when she drops) should the stuntwoman have placed foam mats to break her fall? (b) Draw x-t, y-t, v_x-t, and v_y-t graphs of her motion.

3.49 •• An airplane is flying with a velocity of 90.0 m/s at an angle of 23.0° above the horizontal. When the plane is 114 m directly above a dog that is standing on level ground, a suitcase drops out of the luggage compartment. How far from the dog will the suitcase land? Ignore air resistance.

3.50 •• A cannon, located 60.0 m from the base of a vertical 25.0-m-tall cliff, shoots a 15-kg shell at 43.0° above the horizontal toward the cliff. (a) What must the minimum muzzle velocity be for the shell to clear the top of the cliff? (b) The ground at the top of the cliff is level, with a constant elevation of 25.0 m above the cannon. Under the conditions of part (a), how far does the shell land past the edge of the cliff?

3.51 • **CP CALC** A toy rocket is launched with an initial velocity of 12.0 m/s in the horizontal direction from the roof of a 30.0-m-tall building. The rocket's engine produces a horizontal acceleration of $(1.60 \text{ m/s}^3)t$, in the same direction as the initial velocity, but in the vertical direction the acceleration is g, downward. Ignore air resistance. What horizontal distance does the rocket travel before reaching the ground?

3.52 ••• An important piece of landing equipment must be thrown to a ship, which is moving at 45.0 cm/s, before the ship can dock. This equipment is thrown at 15.0 m/s at 60.0° above the horizontal from the top of a tower at the edge of the water, 8.75 m above the ship's deck (**Fig. P3.52**). For this equipment to land at the front of the ship, at what distance D from the dock should the ship be when the equipment is thrown? Ignore air resistance.

Figure **P3.52**

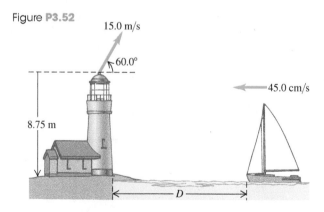

15.0 m/s
60.0°
45.0 cm/s
8.75 m
D

3.53 ••• **The Longest Home Run.** According to *Guinness World Records*, the longest home run ever measured was hit by Roy "Dizzy" Carlyle in a minor league game. The ball traveled 188 m (618 ft) before landing on the ground outside the ballpark. (a) If the ball's initial velocity was in a direction 45° above the horizontal, what did the initial speed of the ball need to be to produce such a home run if the ball was hit at a point 0.9 m (3.0 ft) above ground level? Ignore air resistance, and assume that the ground was perfectly flat. (b) How far would the ball be above a fence 3.0 m (10 ft) high if the fence was 116 m (380 ft) from home plate?

3.54 •• **An Errand of Mercy.** An airplane is dropping bales of hay to cattle stranded in a blizzard on the Great Plains. The pilot releases the bales at 150 m above the level ground when the plane is flying at 75 m/s in a direction 55° above the horizontal. How far in front of the cattle should the pilot release the hay so that the bales land at the point where the cattle are stranded?

3.55 •• A baseball thrown at an angle of 60.0° above the horizontal strikes a building 18.0 m away at a point 8.00 m above the point from which it is thrown. Ignore air resistance. (a) Find the magnitude of the ball's initial velocity (the velocity with which the ball is thrown). (b) Find the magnitude and direction of the velocity of the ball just before it strikes the building.

3.56 ••• A water hose is used to fill a large cylindrical storage tank of diameter D and height $2D$. The hose shoots the water at 45° above the horizontal from the same level as the base of the tank and is a distance $6D$ away (**Fig. P3.56**). For what *range* of launch speeds (v_0) will the water enter the tank? Ignore air resistance, and express your answer in terms of D and g.

Figure **P3.56**

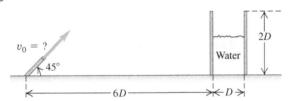

3.57 •• A grasshopper leaps into the air from the edge of a vertical cliff, as shown in **Fig. P3.57**. Find (a) the initial speed of the grasshopper and (b) the height of the cliff.

Figure **P3.57**

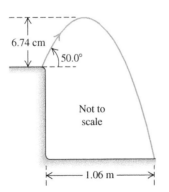

Not to scale

3.58 •• **Kicking an Extra Point.** In Canadian football, after a touchdown the team has the opportunity to earn one more point by kicking the ball over the bar between the goal posts. The bar is 10.0 ft above the ground, and the ball is kicked from ground level, 36.0 ft horizontally from the bar (**Fig. P3.58**). Football regulations are stated in English units, but convert them to SI units for this problem. (a) There is a minimum angle above the ground such that if the ball is launched below this angle, it can never clear the bar, no matter how fast it is kicked. What is this angle? (b) If the ball is kicked at 45.0° above the horizontal, what must its initial speed be if it is just to clear the bar? Express your answer in m/s and in km/h.

Figure **P3.58**

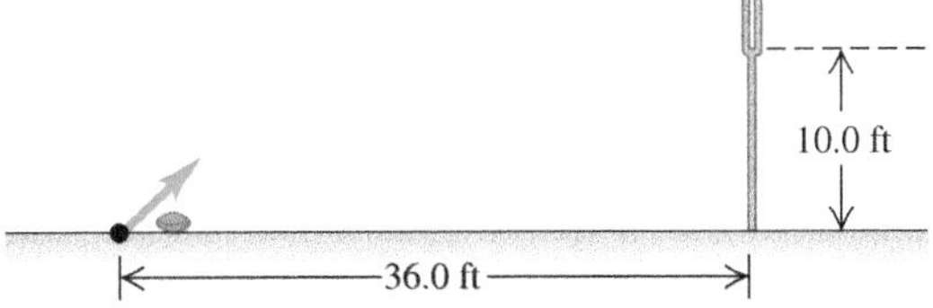

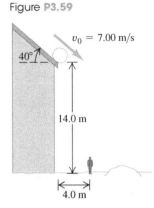

3.59 ••• **Look Out!** A snowball rolls off a barn roof that slopes downward at an angle of 40° (**Fig. P3.59**). The edge of the roof is 14.0 m above the ground, and the snowball has a speed of 7.00 m/s as it rolls off the roof. Ignore air resistance. (a) How far from the edge of the barn does the snowball strike the ground if it doesn't strike anything else while falling? (b) Draw x-t, y-t, v_x-t, and v_y-t graphs for the motion in part (a). (c) A man 1.9 m tall is standing 4.0 m from the edge of the barn. Will the snowball hit him?

Figure **P3.59**

3.60 •• A boy 12.0 m above the ground in a tree throws a ball for his dog, who is standing right below the tree and starts running the instant the ball is thrown. If the boy throws the ball horizontally at 8.50 m/s, (a) how fast must the dog run to catch the ball just as it reaches the ground, and (b) how far from the tree will the dog catch the ball?

3.61 •• Suppose that the boy in Problem 3.60 throws the ball upward at 60.0° above the horizontal, but all else is the same. Repeat parts (a) and (b) of that problem.

3.62 •• A rock is thrown with a velocity v_0, at an angle of α_0 from the horizontal, from the roof of a building of height h. Ignore air resistance. Calculate the speed of the rock just before it strikes the ground, and show that this speed is independent of α_0.

3.63 •• **Leaping the River II.** A physics professor did daredevil stunts in his spare time. His last stunt was an attempt to jump across a river on a motorcycle (**Fig. P3.63**). The takeoff ramp was inclined at 53.0°, the river was 40.0 m wide, and the far bank was 15.0 m lower than the top of the ramp. The river itself was 100 m below the ramp. Ignore air resistance. (a) What should his speed have been at the top of the ramp to have just made it to the edge of the far bank? (b) If his speed was only half the value found in part (a), where did he land?

Figure **P3.63**

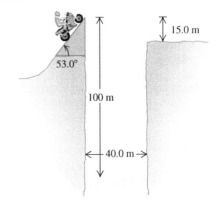

3.64 • A 2.7-kg ball is thrown upward with an initial speed of 20.0 m/s from the edge of a 45.0-m-high cliff. At the instant the ball is thrown, a woman starts running away from the base of the cliff with a constant speed of 6.00 m/s. The woman runs in a straight line on level ground. Ignore air resistance on the ball. (a) At what angle above the horizontal should the ball be thrown so that the runner will catch it just before it hits the ground, and how far does she run before she catches the ball? (b) Carefully sketch the ball's trajectory as viewed by (i) a person at rest on the ground and (ii) the runner.

3.65 • A 76.0-kg rock is rolling horizontally at the top of a vertical cliff that is 20 m above the surface of a lake (**Fig. P3.65**). The top of the vertical face of a dam is located 100 m from the foot of the cliff, with the top of the dam level with the surface of the water in the lake. A level plain is 25 m below the top of the dam. (a) What must be the minimum speed of the rock just as it leaves the cliff so that it will reach the plain without striking the dam? (b) How far from the foot of the dam does the rock hit the plain?

Figure **P3.65**

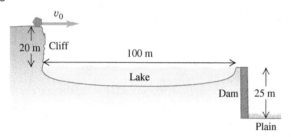

3.66 •• **Tossing Your Lunch.** Henrietta is jogging on the sidewalk at 3.05 m/s on the way to her physics class. Bruce realizes that she forgot her bag of bagels, so he runs to the window, which is 38.0 m above the street level and directly above the sidewalk, to throw the bag to her. He throws it horizontally 9.00 s after she has passed below the window, and she catches it on the run. Ignore air resistance. (a) With what initial speed must Bruce throw the bagels so that Henrietta can catch the bag just before it hits the ground? (b) Where is Henrietta when she catches the bagels?

3.67 •• A cart carrying a vertical missile launcher moves horizontally at a constant velocity of 30.0 m/s to the right. It launches a rocket vertically upward. The missile has an initial vertical velocity of 40.0 m/s relative to the cart. (a) How high does the rocket go? (b) How far does the cart travel while the rocket is in the air? (c) Where does the rocket land relative to the cart?

3.68 •• A firefighting crew uses a water cannon that shoots water at 25.0 m/s at a fixed angle of 53.0° above the horizontal. The firefighters want to direct the water at a blaze that is 10.0 m above ground level. How far from the building should they position their cannon? There are *two* possibilities; can you get them both? (*Hint:* Start with a sketch showing the trajectory of the water.)

3.69 ••• In the middle of the night you are standing a horizontal distance of 14.0 m from the high fence that surrounds the estate of your rich uncle. The top of the fence is 5.00 m above the ground. You have taped an important message to a rock that you want to throw over the fence. The ground is level, and the width of the fence is small enough to be ignored. You throw the rock from a height of 1.60 m above the ground and at an angle of 56.0° above the horizontal. (a) What minimum initial speed must the rock have as it leaves your hand to clear the top of the fence? (b) For the initial velocity calculated in part (a), what horizontal distance beyond the fence will the rock land on the ground?

3.70 ••• **CP Bang!** A student sits atop a platform a distance h above the ground. He throws a large firecracker horizontally with a speed v. However, a wind blowing parallel to the ground gives the firecracker a constant horizontal acceleration with magnitude a. As a result, the firecracker reaches the ground directly below the student. Determine the height h in terms of v, a, and g. Ignore the effect of air resistance on the vertical motion.

3.71 •• An airplane pilot sets a compass course due west and maintains an airspeed of 220 km/h. After flying for 0.500 h, she finds herself over a town 120 km west and 20 km south of her starting point. (a) Find the wind velocity (magnitude and direction). (b) If the wind velocity is 40 km/h due south, in what direction should the pilot set her course to travel due west? Use the same airspeed of 220 km/h.

3.72 •• **Raindrops.** When a train's velocity is 12.0 m/s eastward, raindrops that are falling vertically with respect to the earth make traces that are inclined 30.0° to the vertical on the windows of the train. (a) What is the horizontal component of a drop's velocity with respect to the earth? With respect to the train? (b) What is the magnitude of the velocity of the raindrop with respect to the earth? With respect to the train?

3.73 ••• In a World Cup soccer match, Juan is running due north toward the goal with a speed of 8.00 m/s relative to the ground. A teammate passes the ball to him. The ball has a speed of 12.0 m/s and is moving in a direction 37.0° east of north, relative to the ground. What are the magnitude and direction of the ball's velocity relative to Juan?

3.74 •• An elevator is moving upward at a constant speed of 2.50 m/s. A bolt in the elevator ceiling 3.00 m above the elevator floor works loose and falls. (a) How long does it take for the bolt to fall to the elevator floor? What is the speed of the bolt just as it hits the elevator floor (b) according to an observer in the elevator? (c) According to an observer standing on one of the floor landings of the building? (d) According to the observer in part (c), what distance did the bolt travel between the ceiling and the floor of the elevator?

3.75 •• Two soccer players, Mia and Alice, are running as Alice passes the ball to Mia. Mia is running due north with a speed of 6.00 m/s. The velocity of the ball relative to Mia is 5.00 m/s in a direction 30.0° east of south. What are the magnitude and direction of the velocity of the ball relative to the ground?

3.76 •• **DATA** A spring-gun projects a small rock from the ground with speed v_0 at an angle θ_0 above the ground. You have been asked to determine v_0. From the way the spring-gun is constructed, you know that to a good approximation v_0 is independent of the launch angle. You go to a level, open field, select a launch angle, and measure the horizontal distance the rock travels. You use $g = 9.80 \text{ m/s}^2$ and ignore the small height of the end of the spring-gun's barrel above the ground. Since your measurement includes some uncertainty in values measured for the launch angle and for the horizontal range, you repeat the measurement for several launch angles and obtain the results given in **Fig. 3.76**. You

Figure **P3.76**

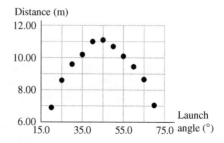

ignore air resistance because there is no wind and the rock is small and heavy. (a) Select a way to represent the data well as a straight line. (b) Use the slope of the best straight-line fit to your data from part (a) to calculate v_0. (c) When the launch angle is 36.9°, what maximum height above the ground does the rock reach?

3.77 •• DATA You have constructed a hair-spray-powered potato gun and want to find the muzzle speed v_0 of the potatoes, the speed they have as they leave the end of the gun barrel. You use the same amount of hair spray each time you fire the gun, and you have confirmed by repeated firings at the same height that the muzzle speed is approximately the same for each firing. You climb on a microwave relay tower (with permission, of course) to launch the potatoes horizontally from different heights above the ground. Your friend measures the height of the gun barrel above the ground and the range R of each potato. You obtain the following data:

Launch height h	Horizontal range R
2.00 m	10.4 m
6.00 m	17.1 m
9.00 m	21.3 m
12.00 m	25.8 m

Each of the values of h and R has some measurement error: The muzzle speed is not precisely the same each time, and the barrel isn't precisely horizontal. So you use all of the measurements to get the best estimate of v_0. No wind is blowing, so you decide to ignore air resistance. You use $g = 9.80 \text{ m/s}^2$ in your analysis. (a) Select a way to represent the data well as a straight line. (b) Use the slope of the best-fit line from part (a) to calculate the average value of v_0. (c) What would be the horizontal range of a potato that is fired from ground level at an angle of 30.0° above the horizontal? Use the value of v_0 that you calculated in part (b).

3.78 ••• DATA You are a member of a geological team in Central Africa. Your team comes upon a wide river that is flowing east. You must determine the width of the river and the current speed (the speed of the water relative to the earth). You have a small boat with an outboard motor. By measuring the time it takes to cross a pond where the water isn't flowing, you have calibrated the throttle settings to the speed of the boat in still water. You set the throttle so that the speed of the boat relative to the river is a constant 6.00 m/s. Traveling due north across the river, you reach the opposite bank in 20.1 s. For the return trip, you change the throttle setting so that the speed of the boat relative to the water is 9.00 m/s. You travel due south from one bank to the other and cross the river in 11.2 s. (a) How wide is the river, and what is the current speed? (b) With the throttle set so that the speed of the boat relative to the water is 6.00 m/s, what is the shortest time in which you could cross the river, and where on the far bank would you land?

CHALLENGE PROBLEMS

3.79 ••• CALC A projectile thrown from a point P moves in such a way that its distance from P is always increasing. Find the maximum angle above the horizontal with which the projectile could have been thrown. Ignore air resistance.

3.80 ••• Two students are canoeing on a river. While heading upstream, they accidentally drop an empty bottle overboard. They then continue paddling for 60 minutes, reaching a point 2.0 km farther upstream. At this point they realize that the bottle is missing and, driven by ecological awareness, they turn around and head downstream. They catch up with and retrieve the bottle (which has been moving along with the current) 5.0 km downstream from the turnaround point. (a) Assuming a constant paddling effort throughout, how fast is the river flowing? (b) What would the canoe speed in a still lake be for the same paddling effort?

3.81 ••• CP A rocket designed to place small payloads into orbit is carried to an altitude of 12.0 km above sea level by a converted airliner. When the airliner is flying in a straight line at a constant speed of 850 km/h, the rocket is dropped. After the drop, the airliner maintains the same altitude and speed and continues to fly in a straight line. The rocket falls for a brief time, after which its rocket motor turns on. Once that motor is on, the combined effects of thrust and gravity give the rocket a constant acceleration of magnitude $3.00g$ directed at an angle of 30.0° above the horizontal. For safety, the rocket should be at least 1.00 km in front of the airliner when it climbs through the airliner's altitude. Your job is to determine the minimum time that the rocket must fall before its engine starts. Ignore air resistance. Your answer should include (i) a diagram showing the flight paths of both the rocket and the airliner, labeled at several points with vectors for their velocities and accelerations; (ii) an x-t graph showing the motions of both the rocket and the airliner; and (iii) a y-t graph showing the motions of both the rocket and the airliner. In the diagram and the graphs, indicate when the rocket is dropped, when the rocket motor turns on, and when the rocket climbs through the altitude of the airliner.

PASSAGE PROBLEMS

BIO **BALLISTIC SEED DISPERSAL.** Some plants disperse their seeds when the fruit splits and contracts, propelling the seeds through the air. The trajectory of these seeds can be determined with a high-speed camera. In an experiment on one type of plant, seeds are projected at 20 cm above ground level with initial speeds between 2.3 m/s and 4.6 m/s. The launch angle is measured from the horizontal, with +90° corresponding to an initial velocity straight up and −90° straight down.

3.82 The experiment is designed so that the seeds move no more than 0.20 mm between photographic frames. What minimum frame rate for the high-speed camera is needed to achieve this? (a) 250 frames/s; (b) 2500 frames/s; (c) 25,000 frames/s; (d) 250,000 frames/s.

3.83 About how long does it take a seed launched at 90° at the highest possible initial speed to reach its maximum height? Ignore air resistance. (a) 0.23 s; (b) 0.47 s; (c) 1.0 s; (d) 2.3 s.

3.84 If a seed is launched at an angle of 0° with the maximum initial speed, how far from the plant will it land? Ignore air resistance, and assume that the ground is flat. (a) 20 cm; (b) 93 cm; (c) 2.2 m; (d) 4.6 m.

3.85 A large number of seeds are observed, and their initial launch angles are recorded. The range of projection angles is found to be −51° to 75°, with a mean of 31°. Approximately 65% of the seeds are launched between 6° and 56°. (See W. J. Garrison et al., "Ballistic seed projection in two herbaceous species," *Amer. J. Bot.,* Sept. 2000, 87:9, 1257–64.) Which of these hypotheses is best supported by the data? Seeds are preferentially launched (a) at angles that maximize the height they travel above the plant; (b) at angles below the horizontal in order to drive the seeds into the ground with more force; (c) at angles that maximize the horizontal distance the seeds travel from the plant; (d) at angles that minimize the time the seeds spend exposed to the air.

Answers

Chapter Opening Question ?

(iii) A cyclist going around a curve at constant speed has an acceleration directed toward the inside of the curve (see Section 3.2, especially Fig. 3.12a).

Test Your Understanding Questions

3.1 (iii) If the instantaneous velocity $\vec{v}$ is constant over an interval, its value at any point (including the end of the interval) is the same as the average velocity $\vec{v}_{av}$ over the interval. In (i) and (ii) the direction of $\vec{v}$ at the end of the interval is tangent to the path at that point, while the direction of $\vec{v}_{av}$ points from the beginning of the path to its end (in the direction of the net displacement). In (iv) both $\vec{v}$ and $\vec{v}_{av}$ are directed along the straight line, but $\vec{v}$ has a greater magnitude because the speed has been increasing.

3.2 Vector 7 At the high point of the sled's path, the speed is minimum. At that point the speed is neither increasing nor decreasing, and the parallel component of the acceleration (that is, the horizontal component) is zero. The acceleration has only a perpendicular component toward the inside of the sled's curved path. In other words, the acceleration is downward.

3.3 (i) If there were no gravity ($g = 0$), the monkey would not fall and the dart would follow a straight-line path (shown as a dashed line). The effect of gravity is to make both the monkey and the dart fall the same distance $\frac{1}{2}gt^2$ below their $g = 0$ positions. Point A is the same distance below the monkey's initial position as point P is below the dashed straight line, so point A is where we would find the monkey at the time in question.

3.4 (ii) At both the top and bottom of the loop, the acceleration is purely radial and is given by Eq. (3.27). Radius R is the same at both points, so the difference in acceleration is due purely to differences in speed. Since a_{rad} is proportional to the square of v, the speed must be twice as great at the bottom of the loop as at the top.

3.5 (vi) The effect of the wind is to cancel the airplane's eastward motion and give it a northward motion. So the velocity of the air relative to the ground (the wind velocity) must have one 150-km/h component to the west and one 150-km/h component to the north. The combination of these is a vector of magnitude $\sqrt{(150 \text{ km/h})^2 + (150 \text{ km/h})^2} = 212$ km/h that points to the northwest.

Bridging Problem

(a) $R = \dfrac{2v_0^2}{g} \dfrac{\cos(\theta + \phi)\sin\phi}{\cos^2\theta}$ (b) $\phi = 45° - \dfrac{\theta}{2}$

? Under what circumstances does the barbell push on the weightlifter just as hard as he pushes on the barbell? (i) When he holds the barbell stationary; (ii) when he raises the barbell; (iii) when he lowers the barbell; (iv) two of (i), (ii), and (iii); (v) all of (i), (ii), and (iii); (vi) none of these.

4 NEWTON'S LAWS OF MOTION

LEARNING GOALS

Looking forward at …

4.1 What the concept of force means in physics, why forces are vectors, and the significance of the net force on an object.

4.2 What happens when the net force on an object is zero, and the significance of inertial frames of reference.

4.3 How the acceleration of an object is determined by the net force on the object and the object's mass.

4.4 The difference between the mass of an object and its weight.

4.5 How the forces that two objects exert on each other are related.

4.6 How to use a free-body diagram to help analyze the forces on an object.

Looking back at …

2.4 Straight-line motion with constant acceleration.

2.5 The motion of freely falling bodies.

3.2 Acceleration as a vector.

3.4 Uniform circular motion.

3.5 Relative velocity.

W e've seen in the last two chapters how to use *kinematics* to describe motion in one, two, or three dimensions. But what *causes* bodies to move the way that they do? For example, why does a dropped feather fall more slowly than a dropped baseball? Why do you feel pushed backward in a car that accelerates forward? The answers to such questions take us into the subject of **dynamics,** the relationship of motion to the forces that cause it.

The principles of dynamics were clearly stated for the first time by Sir Isaac Newton (1642–1727); today we call them **Newton's laws of motion.** The first law states that when the net force on a body is zero, its motion doesn't change. The second law tells us that a body accelerates when the net force is *not* zero. The third law relates the forces that two interacting bodies exert on each other.

Newton did not *derive* the three laws of motion, but rather *deduced* them from a multitude of experiments performed by other scientists, especially Galileo Galilei (who died the year Newton was born). Newton's laws are the foundation of **classical mechanics** (also called **Newtonian mechanics**); using them, we can understand most familiar kinds of motion. Newton's laws need modification only for situations involving extremely high speeds (near the speed of light) or very small sizes (such as within the atom).

Newton's laws are very simple to state, yet many students find these laws difficult to grasp and to work with. The reason is that before studying physics, you've spent years walking, throwing balls, pushing boxes, and doing dozens of things that involve motion. Along the way, you've developed a set of "common sense" ideas about motion and its causes. But many of these "common sense" ideas don't stand up to logical analysis. A big part of the job of this chapter—and of the rest of our study of physics—is helping you recognize how "common sense" ideas can sometimes lead you astray, and how to adjust your understanding of the physical world to make it consistent with what experiments tell us.

4.1 Some properties of forces.

- A force is a push or a pull.
- A force is an interaction between two objects or between an object and its environment.
- A force is a vector quantity, with magnitude and direction.

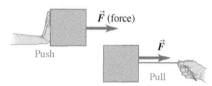

Push $\vec{F}$ (force)

$\vec{F}$

Pull

4.2 Four common types of forces.

(a) Normal force $\vec{n}$: When an object rests or pushes on a surface, the surface exerts a push on it that is directed perpendicular to the surface.

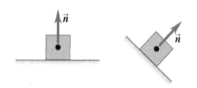

$\vec{n}$

$\vec{n}$

(b) Friction force $\vec{f}$: In addition to the normal force, a surface may exert a friction force on an object, directed parallel to the surface.

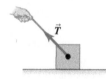

$\vec{n}$

$\vec{f}$

(c) Tension force $\vec{T}$: A pulling force exerted on an object by a rope, cord, etc.

$\vec{T}$

(d) Weight $\vec{w}$: The pull of gravity on an object is a long-range force (a force that acts over a distance).

$\vec{w}$

4.1 FORCE AND INTERACTIONS

In everyday language, a **force** is a push or a pull. A better definition is that a force is an *interaction* between two bodies or between a body and its environment (**Fig. 4.1**). That's why we always refer to the force that one body *exerts* on a second body. When you push on a car that is stuck in the snow, you exert a force on the car; a steel cable exerts a force on the beam it is hoisting at a construction site; and so on. As Fig. 4.1 shows, force is a *vector* quantity; you can push or pull a body in different directions.

When a force involves direct contact between two bodies, such as a push or pull that you exert on an object with your hand, we call it a **contact force**. **Figures 4.2a**, 4.2b, and 4.2c show three common types of contact forces. The **normal force** (Fig. 4.2a) is exerted on an object by any surface with which it is in contact. The adjective *normal* means that the force always acts perpendicular to the surface of contact, no matter what the angle of that surface. By contrast, the **friction force** (Fig. 4.2b) exerted on an object by a surface acts *parallel* to the surface, in the direction that opposes sliding. The pulling force exerted by a stretched rope or cord on an object to which it's attached is called a **tension force** (Fig. 4.2c). When you tug on your dog's leash, the force that pulls on her collar is a tension force.

In addition to contact forces, there are **long-range forces** that act even when the bodies are separated by empty space. The force between two magnets is an example of a long-range force, as is the force of gravity (Fig. 4.2d); the earth pulls a dropped object toward it even though there is no direct contact between the object and the earth. The gravitational force that the earth exerts on your body is called your **weight.**

To describe a force vector $\vec{F}$, we need to describe the *direction* in which it acts as well as its *magnitude,* the quantity that describes "how much" or "how hard" the force pushes or pulls. The SI unit of the magnitude of force is the *newton,* abbreviated N. (We'll give a precise definition of the newton in Section 4.3.) **Table 4.1** lists some typical force magnitudes.

A common instrument for measuring force magnitudes is the *spring balance.* It consists of a coil spring enclosed in a case with a pointer attached to one end. When forces are applied to the ends of the spring, it stretches by an amount that depends on the force. We can make a scale for the pointer by using a number of identical bodies with weights of exactly 1 N each. When one, two, or more of these are suspended simultaneously from the balance, the total force stretching the spring is 1 N, 2 N, and so on, and we can label the corresponding positions of the pointer 1 N, 2 N, and so on. Then we can use this instrument to measure the magnitude of an unknown force. We can also make a similar instrument that measures pushes instead of pulls.

TABLE 4.1 Typical Force Magnitudes

Sun's gravitational force on the earth	3.5×10^{22} N
Weight of a large blue whale	1.9×10^{6} N
Maximum pulling force of a locomotive	8.9×10^{5} N
Weight of a 250-lb linebacker	1.1×10^{3} N
Weight of a medium apple	1 N
Weight of the smallest insect eggs	2×10^{-6} N
Electric attraction between the proton and the electron in a hydrogen atom	8.2×10^{-8} N
Weight of a very small bacterium	1×10^{-18} N
Weight of a hydrogen atom	1.6×10^{-26} N
Weight of an electron	8.9×10^{-30} N
Gravitational attraction between the proton and the electron in a hydrogen atom	3.6×10^{-47} N

4.3 Using a vector arrow to denote the force that we exert when (a) pulling a block with a string or (b) pushing a block with a stick.

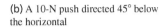

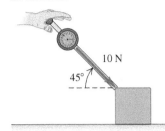

(a) A 10-N pull directed 30° above the horizontal

10 N

30°

(b) A 10-N push directed 45° below the horizontal

10 N

45°

Figure 4.3 shows a spring balance being used to measure a pull or push that we apply to a box. In each case we draw a vector to represent the applied force. The length of the vector shows the magnitude; the longer the vector, the greater the force magnitude.

Superposition of Forces

When you throw a ball, at least two forces act on it: the push of your hand and the downward pull of gravity. Experiment shows that when two forces $\vec{F}_1$ and $\vec{F}_2$ act at the same time at the same point on a body (**Fig. 4.4**), the effect on the body's motion is the same as if a single force $\vec{R}$ were acting equal to the vector sum, or resultant, of the original forces: $\vec{R} = \vec{F}_1 + \vec{F}_2$. More generally, *any number of forces applied at a point on a body have the same effect as a single force equal to the vector sum of the forces.* This important principle is called **superposition of forces.**

Since forces are vector quantities and add like vectors, we can use all of the rules of vector mathematics that we learned in Chapter 1 to solve problems that involve vectors. This would be a good time to review the rules for vector addition presented in Sections 1.7 and 1.8.

We learned in Section 1.8 that it's easiest to add vectors by using components. That's why we often describe a force $\vec{F}$ in terms of its x- and y-components F_x and F_y. Note that the x- and y-coordinate axes do *not* have to be horizontal and vertical, respectively. As an example, **Fig. 4.5** shows a crate being pulled up a ramp by a force $\vec{F}$. In this situation it's most convenient to choose one axis to be parallel to the ramp and the other to be perpendicular to the ramp. For the case shown in Fig. 4.5, both F_x and F_y are positive; in other situations, depending on your choice of axes and the orientation of the force $\vec{F}$, either F_x or F_y may be negative or zero.

_____ CAUTION **Using a wiggly line in force diagrams** In Fig. 4.5 we draw a wiggly line through the force vector $\vec{F}$ to show that we have replaced it by its x- and y-components. Otherwise, the diagram would include the same force twice. We will draw such a wiggly line in any force diagram where a force is replaced by its components. Look for this wiggly line in other figures in this and subsequent chapters. ▮

We will often need to find the vector sum (resultant) of *all* forces acting on a body. We call this the **net force** acting on the body. We will use the Greek letter Σ (capital sigma, equivalent to the Roman S) as a shorthand notation for a sum. If the forces are labeled $\vec{F}_1$, $\vec{F}_2$, $\vec{F}_3$, and so on, we can write

The net force ········▸ $\vec{R} = \Sigma\vec{F} = \vec{F}_1 + \vec{F}_2 + \vec{F}_3 + \cdots$ (4.1)
acting on a body ...

    ... is the vector sum, or resultant, of all individual forces acting on that body.

4.4 Superposition of forces.

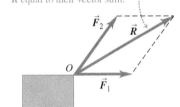

Two forces $\vec{F}_1$ and $\vec{F}_2$ acting on a body at point O have the same effect as a single force R equal to their vector sum.

4.5 F_x and F_y are the components of $\vec{F}$ parallel and perpendicular to the sloping surface of the inclined plane.

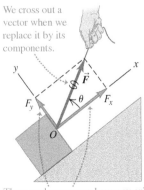

We cross out a vector when we replace it by its components.

The x- and y-axes can have any orientation, just so they're mutually perpendicular.

4.6 Finding the components of the vector sum (resultant) $\vec{R}$ of two forces $\vec{F}_1$ and $\vec{F}_2$.

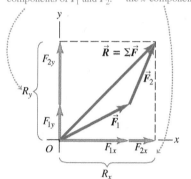

The y-component of $\vec{R}$ equals the sum of the y-components of $\vec{F}_1$ and $\vec{F}_2$.

The same goes for the x-components.

We read $\sum \vec{F}$ as "the vector sum of the forces" or "the net force." The x-component of the net force is the sum of the x-components of the individual forces, and likewise for the y-component (**Fig. 4.6**):

$$R_x = \sum F_x \qquad R_y = \sum F_y \qquad (4.2)$$

Each component may be positive or negative, so be careful with signs when you evaluate these sums.

Once we have R_x and R_y we can find the magnitude and direction of the net force $\vec{R} = \sum \vec{F}$ acting on the body. The magnitude is

$$R = \sqrt{R_x^2 + R_y^2}$$

and the angle θ between $\vec{R}$ and the +x-axis can be found from the relationship $\tan \theta = R_y/R_x$. The components R_x and R_y may be positive, negative, or zero, and the angle θ may be in any of the four quadrants.

In three-dimensional problems, forces may also have z-components; then we add the equation $R_z = \sum F_z$ to Eq. (4.2). The magnitude of the net force is then

$$R = \sqrt{R_x^2 + R_y^2 + R_z^2}$$

EXAMPLE 4.1   SUPERPOSITION OF FORCES

Three professional wrestlers are fighting over a champion's belt. **Figure 4.7a** shows the horizontal force each wrestler applies to the belt, as viewed from above. The forces have magnitudes $F_1 = 250\ N$, $F_2 = 50\ N$, and $F_3 = 120\ N$. Find the x- and y-components of the net force on the belt, and find its magnitude and direction.

SOLUTION

IDENTIFY and SET UP: This is a problem in vector addition in which the vectors happen to represent forces. We want to find the x- and y-components of the net force $\vec{R}$, so we'll use the component method of vector addition expressed by Eqs. (4.2). Once we know the components of $\vec{R}$, we can find its magnitude and direction.

EXECUTE: From Fig. 4.7a the angles between the three forces $\vec{F}_1$, $\vec{F}_2$, and $\vec{F}_3$ and the +x-axis are $\theta_1 = 180° - 53° = 127°$, $\theta_2 = 0°$, and $\theta_3 = 270°$. The x- and y-components of the three forces are

$$F_{1x} = (250\ N)\cos 127° = -150\ N$$

$$F_{1y} = (250\ N)\sin 127° = 200\ N$$

$$F_{2x} = (50\ N)\cos 0° = 50\ N$$

$$F_{2y} = (50\ N)\sin 0° = 0\ N$$

$$F_{3x} = (120\ N)\cos 270° = 0\ N$$

$$F_{3y} = (120\ N)\sin 270° = -120\ N$$

From Eqs. (4.2) the net force $\vec{R} = \sum \vec{F}$ has components

$$R_x = F_{1x} + F_{2x} + F_{3x} = (-150\ N) + 50\ N + 0\ N = -100\ N$$

$$R_y = F_{1y} + F_{2y} + F_{3y} = 200\ N + 0\ N + (-120\ N) = 80\ N$$

The net force has a negative x-component and a positive y-component, as Fig. 4.7b shows.

The magnitude of $\vec{R}$ is

$$R = \sqrt{R_x^2 + R_y^2} = \sqrt{(-100\ N)^2 + (80\ N)^2} = 128\ N$$

To find the angle between the net force and the +x-axis, we use Eq. (1.7):

$$\theta = \arctan\frac{R_y}{R_x} = \arctan\left(\frac{80\ N}{-100\ N}\right) = \arctan(-0.80)$$

The arctangent of -0.80 is $-39°$, but Fig. 4.7b shows that the net force lies in the second quadrant. Hence the correct solution is $\theta = -39° + 180° = 141°$.

EVALUATE: The net force is *not* zero. Your intuition should suggest that wrestler 1 (who exerts the greatest force on the belt, $F_1 = 250\ N$) will walk away with it when the struggle ends.

You should check the direction of $\vec{R}$ by adding the vectors $\vec{F}_1$, $\vec{F}_2$, and $\vec{F}_3$ graphically. Does your drawing show that $\vec{R} = \vec{F}_1 + \vec{F}_2 + \vec{F}_3$ points in the second quadrant as we found?

4.7 (a) Three forces acting on a belt. (b) The net force $\vec{R} = \sum \vec{F}$ and its components.

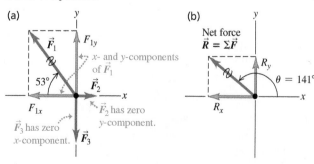

TEST YOUR UNDERSTANDING OF SECTION 4.1   Figure 4.5 shows a force $\vec{F}$ acting on a crate. With the *x*- and *y*-axes shown in the figure, which statement about the components of the *gravitational* force that the earth exerts on the crate (the crate's weight) is *correct*? (i) Both the *x*- and *y*-components are positive. (ii) The *x*-component is zero and the *y*-component is positive. (iii) The *x*-component is negative and the *y*-component is positive. (iv) Both the *x*- and *y*-components are negative. (v) The *x*-component is zero and the *y*-component is negative. (vi) The *x*-component is positive and the *y*-component is negative. ▮

4.2 NEWTON'S FIRST LAW

How do the forces that act on a body affect its motion? To begin to answer this question, let's first consider what happens when the net force on a body is *zero*. You would almost certainly agree that if a body is at rest, and if no net force acts on it (that is, no net push or pull), that body will remain at rest. But what if there is zero net force acting on a body in *motion*?

To see what happens in this case, suppose you slide a hockey puck along a horizontal tabletop, applying a horizontal force to it with your hand (**Fig. 4.8a**). After you stop pushing, the puck *does not* continue to move indefinitely; it slows down and stops. To keep it moving, you have to keep pushing (that is, applying a force). You might come to the "common sense" conclusion that bodies in motion naturally come to rest and that a force is required to sustain motion.

But now imagine pushing the puck across a smooth surface of ice (Fig. 4.8b). After you quit pushing, the puck will slide a lot farther before it stops. Put it on an air-hockey table, where it floats on a thin cushion of air, and it moves still farther (Fig. 4.8c). In each case, what slows the puck down is *friction*, an interaction between the lower surface of the puck and the surface on which it slides. Each surface exerts a friction force on the puck that resists the puck's motion; the difference in the three cases is the magnitude of the friction force. The ice exerts less friction than the tabletop, so the puck travels farther. The gas molecules of the air-hockey table exert the least friction of all. If we could eliminate friction completely, the puck would never slow down, and we would need no force at all to keep the puck moving once it had been started. Thus the "common sense" idea that a force is required to sustain motion is *incorrect*.

Experiments like the ones we've just described show that when *no* net force acts on a body, the body either remains at rest *or* moves with constant velocity in a straight line. Once a body has been set in motion, no net force is needed to keep it moving. We call this observation *Newton's first law of motion:*

NEWTON'S FIRST LAW OF MOTION: A body acted on by no net force has a constant velocity (which may be zero) and zero acceleration.

The tendency of a body to keep moving once it is set in motion is called **inertia.** You use inertia when you try to get ketchup out of a bottle by shaking it. First you start the bottle (and the ketchup inside) moving forward; when you jerk the bottle back, the ketchup tends to keep moving forward and, you hope, ends up on your burger. Inertia is also the tendency of a body at rest to remain at rest. You may have seen a tablecloth yanked out from under the china without breaking anything. The force on the china isn't great enough to make it move appreciably during the short time it takes to pull the tablecloth away.

It's important to note that the *net* force is what matters in Newton's first law. For example, a physics book at rest on a horizontal tabletop has two forces acting on it: an upward supporting force, or normal force, exerted by the tabletop (see Fig. 4.2a) and the downward force of the earth's gravity (which acts even if the tabletop is elevated above the ground; see Fig. 4.2d). The upward push of the surface is just as great as the downward pull of gravity, so the *net* force acting

4.8 The slicker the surface, the farther a puck slides after being given an initial velocity. On an air-hockey table (c) the friction force is practically zero, so the puck continues with almost constant velocity.

(a) Table: puck stops short.

(b) Ice: puck slides farther.

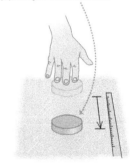

(c) Air-hockey table: puck slides even farther.

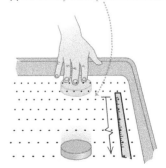

4.9 (a) A hockey puck accelerates in the direction of a net applied force $\vec{F}_1$. (b) When the net force is zero, the acceleration is zero, and the puck is in equilibrium.

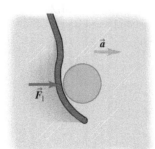

(a) A puck on a frictionless surface accelerates when acted on by a single horizontal force.

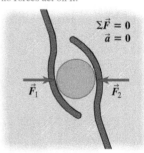

(b) This puck is acted on by two horizontal forces whose vector sum is zero. The puck behaves as though no forces act on it.

$$\Sigma \vec{F} = 0$$
$$\vec{a} = 0$$

Application Sledding with Newton's First Law The downward force of gravity acting on the child and sled is balanced by an upward normal force exerted by the ground. The adult's foot exerts a forward force that balances the backward force of friction on the sled. Hence there is no net force on the child and sled, and they slide with a constant velocity.

on the book (that is, the vector sum of the two forces) is zero. In agreement with Newton's first law, if the book is at rest on the tabletop, it remains at rest. The same principle applies to a hockey puck sliding on a horizontal, frictionless surface: The vector sum of the upward push of the surface and the downward pull of gravity is zero. Once the puck is in motion, it continues to move with constant velocity because the *net* force acting on it is zero.

Here's another example. Suppose a hockey puck rests on a horizontal surface with negligible friction, such as an air-hockey table or a slab of wet ice. If the puck is initially at rest and a single horizontal force $\vec{F}_1$ acts on it (**Fig. 4.9a**), the puck starts to move. If the puck is in motion to begin with, the force changes its speed, its direction, or both, depending on the direction of the force. In this case the net force is equal to $\vec{F}_1$, which is *not* zero. (There are also two vertical forces: the earth's gravitational attraction and the upward normal force exerted by the surface. But as we mentioned earlier, these two forces cancel.)

Now suppose we apply a second force, $\vec{F}_2$ (Fig. 4.9b), equal in magnitude to $\vec{F}_1$ but opposite in direction. The two forces are negatives of each other, $\vec{F}_2 = -\vec{F}_1$, and their vector sum is zero:

$$\Sigma \vec{F} = \vec{F}_1 + \vec{F}_2 = \vec{F}_1 + (-\vec{F}_1) = 0$$

Again, we find that if the body is at rest at the start, it remains at rest; if it is initially moving, it continues to move in the same direction with constant speed. These results show that in Newton's first law, *zero net force is equivalent to no force at all.* This is just the principle of superposition of forces that we saw in Section 4.1.

When a body is either at rest or moving with constant velocity (in a straight line with constant speed), we say that the body is in **equilibrium.** For a body to be in equilibrium, it must be acted on by no forces, or by several forces such that their vector sum—that is, the net force—is zero:

Newton's first law: Net force on a body ... $\cdots\!\!\rightarrow \Sigma \vec{F} = 0 \leftarrow\!\cdots$ ... must be zero if body is in **equilibrium.**   (4.3)

We're assuming that the body can be represented adequately as a point particle. When the body has finite size, we also have to consider *where* on the body the forces are applied. We'll return to this point in Chapter 11.

CONCEPTUAL EXAMPLE 4.2   **ZERO NET FORCE MEANS CONSTANT VELOCITY**

In the classic 1950 science-fiction film *Rocketship X-M*, a spaceship is moving in the vacuum of outer space, far from any star or planet, when its engine dies. As a result, the spaceship slows down and stops. What does Newton's first law say about this scene?

SOLUTION

No forces act on the spaceship after the engine dies, so according to Newton's first law it will *not* stop but will continue to move in a straight line with constant speed. Some science-fiction movies are based on accurate science; this is not one of them.

CONCEPTUAL EXAMPLE 4.3 CONSTANT VELOCITY MEANS ZERO NET FORCE

You are driving a Maserati GranTurismo S on a straight testing track at a constant speed of 250 km/h. You pass a 1971 Volkswagen Beetle doing a constant 75 km/h. On which car is the net force greater?

SOLUTION

The key word in this question is "net." Both cars are in equilibrium because their velocities are constant; Newton's first law therefore says that the *net* force on each car is *zero*.

This seems to contradict the "common sense" idea that the faster car must have a greater force pushing it. Thanks to your Maserati's high-power engine, it's true that the track exerts a greater forward force on your Maserati than it does on the Volkswagen. But a *backward* force also acts on each car due to road friction and air resistance. When the car is traveling with constant velocity, the vector sum of the forward and backward forces is zero. There is more air resistance on the fast-moving Maserati than on the slow-moving Volkswagen, which is why the Maserati's engine must be more powerful than that of the Volkswagen.

Inertial Frames of Reference

In discussing relative velocity in Section 3.5, we introduced the concept of *frame of reference.* This concept is central to Newton's laws of motion. Suppose you are in a bus that is traveling on a straight road and speeding up. If you could stand in the aisle on roller skates, you would start moving *backward* relative to the bus as the bus gains speed. If instead the bus was slowing to a stop, you would start moving forward down the aisle. In either case, it looks as though Newton's first law is not obeyed; there is no net force acting on you, yet your velocity changes. What's wrong?

The point is that the bus is accelerating with respect to the earth and is *not* a suitable frame of reference for Newton's first law. This law is valid in some frames of reference and not valid in others. A frame of reference in which Newton's first law *is* valid is called an **inertial frame of reference.** The earth is at least approximately an inertial frame of reference, but the bus is not. (The earth is not a completely inertial frame, owing to the acceleration associated with its rotation and its motion around the sun. These effects are quite small, however; see Exercises 3.23 and 3.28.) Because Newton's first law is used to define what we mean by an inertial frame of reference, it is sometimes called the *law of inertia.*

Figure 4.10 helps us understand what you experience when riding in a vehicle that's accelerating. In Fig. 4.10a, a vehicle is initially at rest and then begins to

4.10 Riding in an accelerating vehicle.

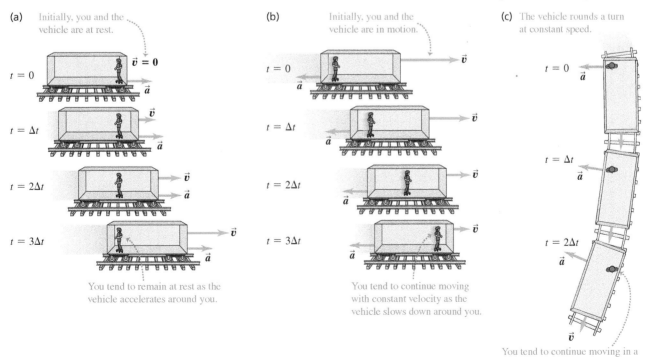

(a) Initially, you and the vehicle are at rest.

You tend to remain at rest as the vehicle accelerates around you.

(b) Initially, you and the vehicle are in motion.

You tend to continue moving with constant velocity as the vehicle slows down around you.

(c) The vehicle rounds a turn at constant speed.

You tend to continue moving in a straight line as the vehicle turns.

accelerate to the right. A passenger standing on roller skates (which nearly eliminate the effects of friction) has virtually no net force acting on her, so she tends to remain at rest relative to the inertial frame of the earth. As the vehicle accelerates around her, she moves backward relative to the vehicle. In the same way, a passenger in a vehicle that is slowing down tends to continue moving with constant velocity relative to the earth, and so moves forward relative to the vehicle (Fig. 4.10b). A vehicle is also accelerating if it moves at a constant speed but is turning (Fig. 4.10c). In this case a passenger tends to continue moving relative to the earth at constant speed in a straight line; relative to the vehicle, the passenger moves to the side of the vehicle on the outside of the turn.

In each case shown in Fig. 4.10, an observer in the vehicle's frame of reference might be tempted to conclude that there *is* a net force acting on the passenger, since the passenger's velocity *relative to the vehicle* changes in each case. This conclusion is simply wrong; the net force on the passenger is indeed zero. The vehicle observer's mistake is in trying to apply Newton's first law in the vehicle's frame of reference, which is *not* an inertial frame and in which Newton's first law isn't valid (**Fig. 4.11**). In this book we will use *only* inertial frames of reference.

We've mentioned only one (approximately) inertial frame of reference: the earth's surface. But there are many inertial frames. If we have an inertial frame of reference A, in which Newton's first law is obeyed, then *any* second frame of reference B will also be inertial if it moves relative to A with constant velocity $\vec{v}_{B/A}$. We can prove this by using the relative-velocity relationship Eq. (3.35) from Section 3.5:

$$\vec{v}_{P/A} = \vec{v}_{P/B} + \vec{v}_{B/A}$$

Suppose that P is a body that moves with constant velocity $\vec{v}_{P/A}$ with respect to an inertial frame A. By Newton's first law the net force on this body is zero. The velocity of P relative to another frame B has a different value, $\vec{v}_{P/B} = \vec{v}_{P/A} - \vec{v}_{B/A}$. But if the relative velocity $\vec{v}_{B/A}$ of the two frames is constant, then $\vec{v}_{P/B}$ is constant as well. Thus B is also an inertial frame; the velocity of P in this frame is constant, and the net force on P is zero, so Newton's first law is obeyed in B. Observers in frames A and B will disagree about the velocity of P, but they will agree that P has a constant velocity (zero acceleration) and has zero net force acting on it.

There is no single inertial frame of reference that is preferred over all others for formulating Newton's laws. If one frame is inertial, then every other frame moving relative to it with constant velocity is also inertial. Viewed in this light, the state of rest and the state of motion with constant velocity are not very different; both occur when the vector sum of forces acting on the body is zero.

TEST YOUR UNDERSTANDING OF SECTION 4.2 In which of the following situations is there zero net force on the body? (i) An airplane flying due north at a steady 120 m/s and at a constant altitude; (ii) a car driving straight up a hill with a 3° slope at a constant 90 km/h; (iii) a hawk circling at a constant 20 km/h at a constant height of 15 m above an open field; (iv) a box with slick, frictionless surfaces in the back of a truck as the truck accelerates forward on a level road at 5 m/s². ∎

4.3 NEWTON'S SECOND LAW

Newton's first law tells us that when a body is acted on by zero net force, the body moves with constant velocity and zero acceleration. In **Fig. 4.12a**, a hockey puck is sliding to the right on wet ice. There is negligible friction, so there are no horizontal forces acting on the puck; the downward force of gravity and the upward normal force exerted by the ice surface sum to zero. So the net force $\Sigma \vec{F}$ acting on the puck is zero, the puck has zero acceleration, and its velocity is constant.

4.11 From the frame of reference of the car, it seems as though a force is pushing the crash test dummies forward as the car comes to a sudden stop. But there is really no such force: As the car stops, the dummies keep moving forward as a consequence of Newton's first law.

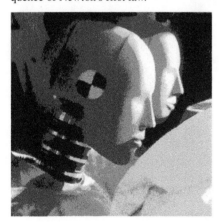

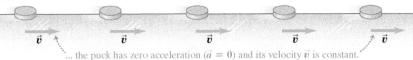

(a) If there is zero net force on the puck, so $\sum \vec{F} = 0$, ...

... the puck has zero acceleration ($\vec{a} = 0$) and its velocity $\vec{v}$ is constant.

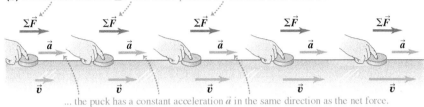

(b) If a constant net force $\sum \vec{F}$ acts on the puck in the direction of its motion ...

... the puck has a constant acceleration $\vec{a}$ in the same direction as the net force.

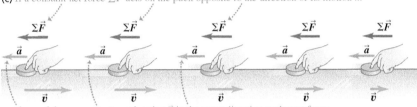

(c) If a constant net force $\sum \vec{F}$ acts on the puck opposite to the direction of its motion ...

... the puck has a constant acceleration $\vec{a}$ in the same direction as the net force.

4.12 Using a hockey puck on a frictionless surface to explore the relationship between the net force $\sum \vec{F}$ on a body and the resulting acceleration $\vec{a}$ of the body.

But what happens when the net force is *not* zero? In Fig. 4.12b we apply a constant horizontal force to a sliding puck in the same direction that the puck is moving. Then $\sum \vec{F}$ is constant and in the same horizontal direction as $\vec{v}$. We find that during the time the force is acting, the velocity of the puck changes at a constant rate; that is, the puck moves with constant acceleration. The speed of the puck increases, so the acceleration $\vec{a}$ is in the same direction as $\vec{v}$ and $\sum \vec{F}$.

In Fig. 4.12c we reverse the direction of the force on the puck so that $\sum \vec{F}$ acts opposite to $\vec{v}$. In this case as well, the puck has an acceleration; the puck moves more and more slowly to the right. The acceleration $\vec{a}$ in this case is to the left, in the same direction as $\sum \vec{F}$. As in the previous case, experiment shows that the acceleration is constant if $\sum \vec{F}$ is constant.

We conclude that *a net force acting on a body causes the body to accelerate in the same direction as the net force.* If the magnitude of the net force is constant, as in Figs. 4.12b and 4.12c, then so is the magnitude of the acceleration.

These conclusions about net force and acceleration also apply to a body moving along a curved path. For example, **Fig. 4.13** shows a hockey puck moving in a horizontal circle on an ice surface of negligible friction. A rope is attached to the puck and to a stick in the ice, and this rope exerts an inward tension force of constant magnitude on the puck. The net force and acceleration are both constant in magnitude and directed toward the center of the circle. The speed of the puck is constant, so this is uniform circular motion, as discussed in Section 3.4.

Figure 4.14a shows another experiment to explore the relationship between acceleration and net force. We apply a constant horizontal force to a puck on a frictionless horizontal surface, using the spring balance described in Section 4.1 with the spring stretched a constant amount. As in Figs. 4.12b and 4.12c, this horizontal force equals the net force on the puck. If we change the magnitude of the net force, the acceleration changes in the same proportion. Doubling the net force doubles the acceleration (Fig. 4.14b), halving the net force halves the acceleration (Fig. 4.14c), and so on. Many such experiments show that *for any given body, the magnitude of the acceleration is directly proportional to the magnitude of the net force acting on the body.*

4.13 A top view of a hockey puck in uniform circular motion on a frictionless horizontal surface.

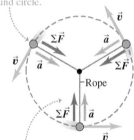

Puck moves at constant speed around circle.

At all points, the acceleration $\vec{a}$ and the net force $\sum \vec{F}$ point in the same direction—always toward the center of the circle.

4.14 The magnitude of a body's acceleration $\vec{a}$ is directly proportional to the magnitude of the net force $\sum \vec{F}$ acting on the body of mass m.

(a) A constant net force $\sum \vec{F}$ causes a constant acceleration $\vec{a}$.

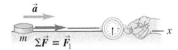

(b) Doubling the net force doubles the acceleration.

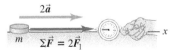

(c) Halving the force halves the acceleration.

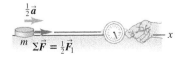

Mass and Force

Our results mean that for a given body, the *ratio* of the magnitude $|\Sigma\vec{F}|$ of the net force to the magnitude $a = |\vec{a}|$ of the acceleration is constant, regardless of the magnitude of the net force. We call this ratio the *inertial mass,* or simply the **mass,** of the body and denote it by m. That is,

$$m = \frac{|\Sigma\vec{F}|}{a} \qquad \text{or} \qquad |\Sigma\vec{F}| = ma \qquad \text{or} \qquad a = \frac{|\Sigma\vec{F}|}{m} \qquad (4.4)$$

Mass is a quantitative measure of inertia, which we discussed in Section 4.2. The last of the equations in Eqs. (4.4) says that the greater a body's mass, the more the body "resists" being accelerated. When you hold a piece of fruit in your hand at the supermarket and move it slightly up and down to estimate its heft, you're applying a force and seeing how much the fruit accelerates up and down in response. If a force causes a large acceleration, the fruit has a small mass; if the same force causes only a small acceleration, the fruit has a large mass. In the same way, if you hit a table-tennis ball and then a basketball with the same force, the basketball has much smaller acceleration because it has much greater mass.

The SI unit of mass is the **kilogram.** We mentioned in Section 1.3 that the kilogram is officially defined to be the mass of a cylinder of platinum–iridium alloy kept in a vault near Paris (Fig. 1.4). We can use this standard kilogram, along with Eqs. (4.4), to define the **newton:**

> **One newton is the amount of net force that gives an acceleration of 1 meter per second squared to a body with a mass of 1 kilogram.**

This definition allows us to calibrate the spring balances and other instruments used to measure forces. Because of the way we have defined the newton, it is related to the units of mass, length, and time. For Eqs. (4.4) to be dimensionally consistent, it must be true that

$$1 \text{ newton} = (1 \text{ kilogram})(1 \text{ meter per second squared})$$

or

$$1 \text{ N} = 1 \text{ kg} \cdot \text{m/s}^2$$

We will use this relationship many times in the next few chapters, so keep it in mind.

We can also use Eqs. (4.4) to compare a mass with the standard mass and thus to *measure* masses. Suppose we apply a constant net force $\Sigma\vec{F}$ to a body having a known mass m_1 and we find an acceleration of magnitude a_1 (**Fig. 4.15a**). We then apply the same force to another body having an unknown mass m_2, and we find an acceleration of magnitude a_2 (Fig. 4.15b). Then, according to Eqs. (4.4),

$$m_1 a_1 = m_2 a_2$$

$$\frac{m_2}{m_1} = \frac{a_1}{a_2} \qquad \text{(same net force)} \qquad (4.5)$$

For the same net force, the ratio of the masses of two bodies is the inverse of the ratio of their accelerations. In principle we could use Eq. (4.5) to measure an unknown mass m_2, but it is usually easier to determine mass indirectly by measuring the body's *weight.* We'll return to this point in Section 4.4.

When two bodies with masses m_1 and m_2 are fastened together, we find that the mass of the composite body is always $m_1 + m_2$ (Fig. 4.15c). This additive property of mass may seem obvious, but it has to be verified experimentally. Ultimately, the mass of a body is related to the number of protons, electrons, and neutrons it contains. This wouldn't be a good way to *define* mass because there is no practical way to count these particles. But the concept of mass is the most fundamental way to characterize the quantity of matter in a body.

4.15 For a given net force $\Sigma\vec{F}$ acting on a body, the acceleration is inversely proportional to the mass of the body. Masses add like ordinary scalars.

(a) A known force $\Sigma\vec{F}$ causes an object with mass m_1 to have an acceleration $\vec{a}_1$.

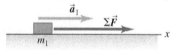

(b) Applying the same force $\Sigma\vec{F}$ to a second object and noting the acceleration allow us to measure the mass.

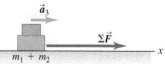

(c) When the two objects are fastened together, the same method shows that their composite mass is the sum of their individual masses.

Stating Newton's Second Law

Experiment shows that the *net* force on a body is what causes that body to accelerate. If a combination of forces $\vec{F}_1$, $\vec{F}_2$, $\vec{F}_3$, and so on is applied to a body, the body will have the same acceleration vector $\vec{a}$ as when only a single force is applied, if that single force is equal to the vector sum $\vec{F}_1 + \vec{F}_2 + \vec{F}_3 + \cdots$. In other words, the principle of superposition of forces (see Fig. 4.4) also holds true when the net force is not zero and the body is accelerating.

Equations (4.4) relate the magnitude of the net force on a body to the magnitude of the acceleration that it produces. We have also seen that the direction of the net force is the same as the direction of the acceleration, whether the body's path is straight or curved. What's more, the forces that affect a body's motion are *external* forces, those exerted on the body by other bodies in its environment. Newton wrapped up all these results into a single concise statement that we now call *Newton's second law of motion:*

NEWTON'S SECOND LAW OF MOTION: **If a net external force acts on a body, the body accelerates. The direction of acceleration is the same as the direction of the net force. The mass of the body times the acceleration vector of the body equals the net force vector.**

In symbols,

Newton's second law:
If there is a net force on a body ... $\qquad$ ... the body accelerates in same direction as the net force.

$$\sum \vec{F} = m\vec{a} \qquad (4.6)$$

Mass of body

An alternative statement is that the acceleration of a body is equal to the net force acting on the body divided by the body's mass:

$$\vec{a} = \frac{\sum \vec{F}}{m}$$

Newton's second law is a fundamental law of nature, the basic relationship between force and motion. Most of the remainder of this chapter and all of the next are devoted to learning how to apply this principle in various situations.

Equation (4.6) has many practical applications (**Fig. 4.16**). You've actually been using it all your life to measure your body's acceleration. In your inner ear, microscopic hair cells sense the magnitude and direction of the force that they must exert to cause small membranes to accelerate along with the rest of your body. By Newton's second law, the acceleration of the membranes—and hence that of your body as a whole—is proportional to this force and has the same direction. In this way, you can sense the magnitude and direction of your acceleration even with your eyes closed!

Using Newton's Second Law

There are at least four aspects of Newton's second law that deserve special attention. First, Eq. (4.6) is a *vector* equation. Usually we will use it in component form, with a separate equation for each component of force and the corresponding component of acceleration:

Newton's second law: $\qquad$ Each component of net force on a body ...

$$\sum F_x = ma_x \qquad \sum F_y = ma_y \qquad \sum F_z = ma_z \qquad (4.7)$$

... equals body's mass times the corresponding acceleration component.

This set of component equations is equivalent to the single vector Eq. (4.6).

Second, the statement of Newton's second law refers to *external* forces. It's impossible for a body to affect its own motion by exerting a force on itself; if it were possible, you could lift yourself to the ceiling by pulling up on your belt! That's why only external forces are included in the sum $\sum \vec{F}$ in Eqs. (4.6) and (4.7).

4.16 The design of high-performance motorcycles depends fundamentally on Newton's second law. To maximize the forward acceleration, the designer makes the motorcycle as light as possible (that is, minimizes the mass) and uses the most powerful engine possible (thus maximizing the forward force).

Lightweight body (small m)

Powerful engine (large F)

Application Blame Newton's Second Law This car stopped because of Newton's second law: The tree exerted an external force on the car, giving the car an acceleration that changed its velocity to zero.

Third, Eqs. (4.6) and (4.7) are valid only when the mass m is *constant*. It's easy to think of systems whose masses change, such as a leaking tank truck, a rocket ship, or a moving railroad car being loaded with coal. Such systems are better handled by using the concept of momentum; we'll get to that in Chapter 8.

Finally, Newton's second law is valid in inertial frames of reference only, just like the first law. Thus it is not valid in the reference frame of any of the accelerating vehicles in Fig. 4.10; relative to any of these frames, the passenger accelerates even though the net force on the passenger is zero. We will usually assume that the earth is an adequate approximation to an inertial frame, although because of its rotation and orbital motion it is not precisely inertial.

DEMO

CAUTION *$m\vec{a}$ is not a force* Even though the vector $m\vec{a}$ is equal to the vector sum $\sum \vec{F}$ of all the forces acting on the body, the vector $m\vec{a}$ is *not* a force. Acceleration is a *result* of a nonzero net force; it is not a force itself. It's "common sense" to think that there is a "force of acceleration" that pushes you back into your seat when your car accelerates forward from rest. But *there is no such force;* instead, your inertia causes you to tend to stay at rest relative to the earth, and the car accelerates around you (see Fig. 4.10a). The "common sense" confusion arises from trying to apply Newton's second law where it isn't valid—in the noninertial reference frame of an accelerating car. We will always examine motion relative to *inertial* frames of reference only. ▮

In learning how to use Newton's second law, we will begin in this chapter with examples of straight-line motion. Then in Chapter 5 we will consider more general cases and develop more detailed problem-solving strategies.

EXAMPLE 4.4   DETERMINING ACCELERATION FROM FORCE

A worker applies a constant horizontal force with magnitude 20 N to a box with mass 40 kg resting on a level floor with negligible friction. What is the acceleration of the box?

SOLUTION

IDENTIFY and SET UP: This problem involves force and acceleration, so we'll use Newton's second law. In *any* problem involving forces, the first steps are to choose a coordinate system and to identify all of the forces acting on the body in question. It's usually convenient to take one axis either along or opposite the direction of the body's acceleration, which in this case is horizontal. Hence we take the $+x$-axis to be in the direction of the applied horizontal force (which is the direction in which the box accelerates) and the $+y$-axis to be upward (**Fig. 4.17**). In most force problems that you'll encounter (including this one), the force vectors all lie in a plane, so the z-axis isn't used.

4.17 Our sketch for this problem. The tiles under the box are freshly waxed, so we assume that friction is negligible.

The box has no vertical acceleration, so the vertical components of the net force sum to zero. Nevertheless, for completeness, we show the vertical forces acting on the box.

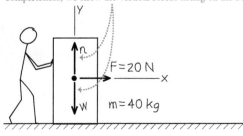

The forces acting on the box are (i) the horizontal force $\vec{F}$ exerted by the worker, of magnitude 20 N; (ii) the weight $\vec{w}$ of the box—that is, the downward gravitational force exerted by the earth; and (iii) the upward supporting force $\vec{n}$ exerted by the floor. As in Section 4.2, we call $\vec{n}$ a *normal* force because it is normal (perpendicular) to the surface of contact. (We use an italic letter n to avoid confusion with the abbreviation N for newton.) Friction is negligible, so no friction force is present.

The box doesn't move vertically, so the y-acceleration is zero: $a_y = 0$. Our target variable is the x-acceleration, a_x. We'll find it by using Newton's second law in component form, Eqs. (4.7).

EXECUTE: From Fig. 4.17 only the 20-N force exerted by the worker has a nonzero x-component. Hence the first of Eqs. (4.7) tells us that

$$\sum F_x = F = 20\,\text{N} = ma_x$$

The x-component of acceleration is therefore

$$a_x = \frac{\sum F_x}{m} = \frac{20\,\text{N}}{40\,\text{kg}} = \frac{20\,\text{kg} \cdot \text{m/s}^2}{40\,\text{kg}} = 0.50\,\text{m/s}^2$$

EVALUATE: The acceleration is in the $+x$-direction, the same direction as the net force. The net force is constant, so the acceleration is also constant. If we know the initial position and velocity of the box, we can find its position and velocity at any later time from the constant-acceleration equations of Chapter 2.

To determine a_x, we didn't need the y-component of Newton's second law from Eqs. (4.7), $\sum F_y = ma_y$. Can you use this equation to show that the magnitude n of the normal force in this situation is equal to the weight of the box?

EXAMPLE 4.5 DETERMINING FORCE FROM ACCELERATION

A waitress shoves a ketchup bottle with mass 0.45 kg to her right along a smooth, level lunch counter. The bottle leaves her hand moving at 2.8 m/s, then slows down as it slides because of a constant horizontal friction force exerted on it by the countertop. It slides for 1.0 m before coming to rest. What are the magnitude and direction of the friction force acting on the bottle?

SOLUTION

IDENTIFY and SET UP: This problem involves forces and acceleration (the slowing of the ketchup bottle), so we'll use Newton's second law to solve it. As in Example 4.4, we choose a coordinate system and identify the forces acting on the bottle (**Fig. 4.18**). We choose the $+x$-axis to be in the direction that the bottle slides, and take the origin to be where the bottle leaves the waitress's hand. The friction force $\vec{f}$ slows the bottle down, so its direction must be opposite the direction of the bottle's velocity (see Fig. 4.12c).

Our target variable is the magnitude f of the friction force. We'll find it by using the x-component of Newton's second law from Eqs. (4.7). We aren't told the x-component of the bottle's acceleration, a_x, but we know that it's constant because the friction force that causes the acceleration is constant. Hence we can use a constant-acceleration formula from Section 2.4 to calculate a_x. We know the bottle's initial and final x-coordinates ($x_0 = 0$ and $x = 1.0$ m) and its initial and final x-velocity ($v_{0x} = 2.8$ m/s and $v_x = 0$), so the easiest equation to use is Eq. (2.13), $v_x^2 = v_{0x}^2 + 2a_x(x - x_0)$.

EXECUTE: We solve Eq. (2.13) for a_x:

$$a_x = \frac{v_x^2 - v_{0x}^2}{2(x - x_0)} = \frac{(0 \text{ m/s})^2 - (2.8 \text{ m/s})^2}{2(1.0 \text{ m} - 0 \text{ m})} = -3.9 \text{ m/s}^2$$

The negative sign means that the bottle's acceleration is toward the *left* in Fig. 4.18, opposite to its velocity; this is as it must be, because the bottle is slowing down. The net force in the x-direction is the x-component $-f$ of the friction force, so

$$\Sigma F_x = -f = ma_x = (0.45 \text{ kg})(-3.9 \text{ m/s}^2)$$
$$= -1.8 \text{ kg} \cdot \text{m/s}^2 = -1.8 \text{ N}$$

The negative sign shows that the net force on the bottle is toward the left. The *magnitude* of the friction force is $f = 1.8$ N.

EVALUATE: As a check on the result, try repeating the calculation with the $+x$-axis to the *left* in Fig. 4.18. You'll find that ΣF_x is equal to $+f = +1.8$ N (because the friction force is now in the $+x$-direction), and again you'll find $f = 1.8$ N. The answers for the *magnitudes* of forces don't depend on the choice of coordinate axes!

4.18 Our sketch for this problem.

We draw one diagram for the bottle's motion and one showing the forces on the bottle.

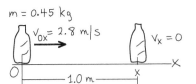
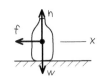

Some Notes on Units

A few words about units are in order. In the cgs metric system (not used in this book), the unit of mass is the gram, equal to 10^{-3} kg, and the unit of distance is the centimeter, equal to 10^{-2} m. The cgs unit of force is called the *dyne:*

$$1 \text{ dyne} = 1 \text{ g} \cdot \text{cm/s}^2 = 10^{-5} \text{ N}$$

In the British system, the unit of force is the *pound* (or pound-force) and the unit of mass is the *slug* (**Fig. 4.19**). The unit of acceleration is 1 foot per second squared, so

$$1 \text{ pound} = 1 \text{ slug} \cdot \text{ft/s}^2$$

The official definition of the pound is

$$1 \text{ pound} = 4.448221615260 \text{ newtons}$$

It is handy to remember that a pound is about 4.4 N and a newton is about 0.22 pound. Another useful fact: A body with a mass of 1 kg has a weight of about 2.2 lb at the earth's surface.

Table 4.2 lists the units of force, mass, and acceleration in the three systems.

4.19 Despite its name, the English unit of mass has nothing to do with the type of slug shown here. A common garden slug has a mass of about 15 grams, or about 10^{-3} slug.

System of Units	Force	Mass	Acceleration
SI	newton (N)	kilogram (kg)	m/s^2
cgs	dyne (dyn)	gram (g)	cm/s^2
British	pound (lb)	slug	ft/s^2

TABLE 4.2 Units of Force, Mass, and Acceleration

TEST YOUR UNDERSTANDING OF SECTION 4.3 Rank the following situations in order of the magnitude of the object's acceleration, from lowest to highest. Are there any cases that have the same magnitude of acceleration? (i) A 2.0-kg object acted on by a 2.0-N net force; (ii) a 2.0-kg object acted on by an 8.0-N net force; (iii) an 8.0-kg object acted on by a 2.0-N net force; (iv) an 8.0-kg object acted on by a 8.0-N net force.

4.4 MASS AND WEIGHT

One of the most familiar forces is the *weight* of a body, which is the gravitational force that the earth exerts on the body. (If you are on another planet, your weight is the gravitational force that planet exerts on you.) Unfortunately, the terms *mass* and *weight* are often misused and interchanged in everyday conversation. It is absolutely essential for you to understand clearly the distinctions between these two physical quantities.

Mass characterizes the *inertial* properties of a body. Mass is what keeps the china on the table when you yank the tablecloth out from under it. The greater the mass, the greater the force needed to cause a given acceleration; this is reflected in Newton's second law, $\sum \vec{F} = m\vec{a}$.

Weight, on the other hand, is a *force* exerted on a body by the pull of the earth. Mass and weight are related: Bodies that have large mass also have large weight. A large stone is hard to throw because of its large *mass,* and hard to lift off the ground because of its large *weight.*

To understand the relationship between mass and weight, note that a freely falling body has an acceleration of magnitude g (see Section 2.5). Newton's second law tells us that a force must act to produce this acceleration. If a 1-kg body falls with an acceleration of 9.8 m/s², the required force has magnitude

$$F = ma = (1\text{ kg})(9.8\text{ m/s}^2) = 9.8\text{ kg} \cdot \text{m/s}^2 = 9.8\text{ N}$$

The force that makes the body accelerate downward is its weight. Any body near the surface of the earth that has a mass of 1 kg *must* have a weight of 9.8 N to give it the acceleration we observe when it is in free fall. More generally,

$$\underset{\text{weight of a body}}{\text{Magnitude of}} \cdots\!\!\rightarrow w = mg \xleftarrow{\;\;} \underset{\text{Magnitude of acceleration}}{\overset{\text{Mass of body}}{}} \qquad (4.8)$$
$$\text{due to gravity}$$

Hence the magnitude w of a body's weight is directly proportional to its mass m. The weight of a body is a force, a vector quantity, and we can write Eq. (4.8) as a vector equation (**Fig. 4.20**):

$$\vec{w} = m\vec{g} \qquad (4.9)$$

Remember that g is the *magnitude* of $\vec{g}$, the acceleration due to gravity, so g is always a positive number, by definition. Thus w, given by Eq. (4.8), is the *magnitude* of the weight and is also always positive.

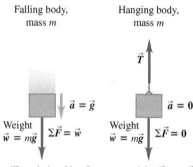

4.20 Relating the mass and weight of a body.

Falling body, mass *m*   Hanging body, mass *m*

$\vec{a} = \vec{g}$ $\vec{a} = 0$

Weight $\vec{w} = m\vec{g}$ $\sum\vec{F} = \vec{w}$ Weight $\vec{w} = m\vec{g}$ $\sum\vec{F} = 0$

- The relationship of mass to weight: $\vec{w} = m\vec{g}$.
- This relationship is the same whether a body is falling or stationary.

CAUTION **A body's weight acts at all times** The weight of a body acts on the body *all the time,* whether it is in free fall or not. If we suspend an object from a rope, it is in equilibrium and its acceleration is zero. But its weight, given by Eq. (4.9), is still pulling down on it (Fig. 4.20). In this case the rope pulls up on the object, applying an upward force. The *vector sum* of the forces is zero, but the weight still acts. ▮

CONCEPTUAL EXAMPLE 4.6   **NET FORCE AND ACCELERATION IN FREE FALL**

In Example 2.6 of Section 2.5, a one-euro coin was dropped from rest from the Leaning Tower of Pisa. If the coin falls freely, so that the effects of the air are negligible, how does the net force on the coin vary as it falls?

SOLUTION

In free fall, the acceleration $\vec{a}$ of the coin is constant and equal to $\vec{g}$. Hence by Newton's second law the net force $\sum \vec{F} = m\vec{a}$ is also constant and equal to $m\vec{g}$, which is the coin's weight $\vec{w}$ (**Fig. 4.21**). The coin's velocity changes as it falls, but the net force acting on it is constant. (If this surprises you, reread Conceptual Example 4.3.)

The net force on a freely falling coin is constant even if you initially toss it upward. The force that your hand exerts on the coin to toss it is a contact force, and it disappears the instant the coin

leaves your hand. From then on, the only force acting on the coin is its weight $\vec{w}$.

4.21 The acceleration of a freely falling object is constant, and so is the net force acting on the object.

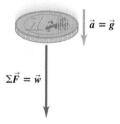

$\vec{a} = \vec{g}$

$\sum \vec{F} = \vec{w}$

Variation of *g* with Location

We will use $g = 9.80 \text{ m/s}^2$ for problems set on the earth (or, if the other data in the problem are given to only two significant figures, $g = 9.8 \text{ m/s}^2$). In fact, the value of g varies somewhat from point to point on the earth's surface—from about 9.78 to 9.82 m/s^2—because the earth is not perfectly spherical and because of effects due to its rotation and orbital motion. At a point where $g = 9.80 \text{ m/s}^2$, the weight of a standard kilogram is $w = 9.80$ N. At a different point, where $g = 9.78 \text{ m/s}^2$, the weight is $w = 9.78$ N but the mass is still 1 kg. The weight of a body varies from one location to another; the mass does not.

If we take a standard kilogram to the surface of the moon, where the acceleration of free fall (equal to the value of g at the moon's surface) is 1.62 m/s^2, its weight is 1.62 N but its mass is still 1 kg (**Fig. 4.22**). An 80.0-kg astronaut has a weight on earth of $(80.0 \text{ kg})(9.80 \text{ m/s}^2) = 784$ N, but on the moon the astronaut's weight would be only $(80.0 \text{ kg})(1.62 \text{ m/s}^2) = 130$ N. In Chapter 13 we'll see how to calculate the value of g at the surface of the moon or on other worlds.

Measuring Mass and Weight

In Section 4.3 we described a way to compare masses by comparing their accelerations when they are subjected to the same net force. Usually, however, the easiest way to measure the mass of a body is to measure its weight, often by comparing with a standard. Equation (4.8) says that two bodies that have the same weight at a particular location also have the same mass. We can compare weights very precisely; the familiar equal-arm balance (**Fig. 4.23**) can determine with great precision (up to 1 part in 10^6) when the weights of two bodies are equal and hence when their masses are equal.

The concept of mass plays two rather different roles in mechanics. The weight of a body (the gravitational force acting on it) is proportional to its mass; we call the property related to gravitational interactions *gravitational mass*. On the other hand, we call the inertial property that appears in Newton's second law the *inertial mass*. If these two quantities were different, the acceleration due to gravity might well be different for different bodies. However, extraordinarily precise experiments have established that in fact the two *are* the same to a precision of better than one part in 10^{12}.

CAUTION **Don't confuse mass and weight** The SI units for mass and weight are often misused in everyday life. For example, it's incorrect to say "This box weighs 6 kg"; what this really means is that the *mass* of the box, probably determined indirectly by *weighing*, is 6 kg. Avoid this sloppy usage in your own work! In SI units, weight (a force) is measured in newtons, while mass is measured in kilograms. ▌

4.22 The weight of a 1-kilogram mass (a) on earth and (b) on the moon.

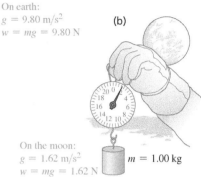

(a)

On earth:
$g = 9.80 \text{ m/s}^2$
$w = mg = 9.80$ N

(b)

On the moon:
$g = 1.62 \text{ m/s}^2$
$w = mg = 1.62$ N
$m = 1.00$ kg

4.23 An equal-arm balance determines the mass of a body (such as an apple) by comparing its weight to a known weight.

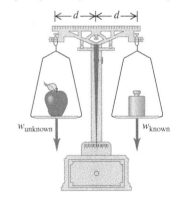

w_{unknown} w_{known}

EXAMPLE 4.7 MASS AND WEIGHT

A 2.49×10^4 N Rolls-Royce Phantom traveling in the $+x$-direction makes an emergency stop; the x-component of the net force acting on it is -1.83×10^4 N. What is its acceleration?

SOLUTION

IDENTIFY and SET UP: Our target variable is the x-component of the car's acceleration, a_x. We use the x-component portion of Newton's second law, Eqs. (4.7), to relate force and acceleration. To do this, we need to know the car's mass. The newton is a unit for force, however, so 2.49×10^4 N is the car's *weight*, not its mass. Hence we'll first use Eq. (4.8) to determine the car's mass from its weight. The car has a positive x-velocity and is slowing down, so its x-acceleration will be negative.

EXECUTE: The mass of the car is

$$m = \frac{w}{g} = \frac{2.49 \times 10^4 \text{ N}}{9.80 \text{ m/s}^2} = \frac{2.49 \times 10^4 \text{ kg} \cdot \text{m/s}^2}{9.80 \text{ m/s}^2}$$
$$= 2540 \text{ kg}$$

Continued

Then $\sum F_x = ma_x$ gives

$$a_x = \frac{\sum F_x}{m} = \frac{-1.83 \times 10^4 \text{ N}}{2540 \text{ kg}} = \frac{-1.83 \times 10^4 \text{ kg} \cdot \text{m/s}^2}{2540 \text{ kg}}$$

$$= -7.20 \text{ m/s}^2$$

EVALUATE: The negative sign means that the acceleration vector points in the negative x-direction, as we expected. The magnitude

of this acceleration is pretty high; passengers in this car will experience a lot of rearward force from their shoulder belts.

This acceleration equals $-0.735g$. The number -0.735 is also the ratio of -1.83×10^4 N (the x-component of the net force) to 2.49×10^4 N (the weight). In fact, the acceleration of a body, expressed as a multiple of g, is *always* equal to the ratio of the net force on the body to its weight. Can you see why?

TEST YOUR UNDERSTANDING OF SECTION 4.4 Suppose an astronaut landed on a planet where $g = 19.6$ m/s². Compared to earth, would it be easier, harder, or just as easy for her to walk around? Would it be easier, harder, or just as easy for her to catch a ball that is moving horizontally at 12 m/s? (Assume that the astronaut's spacesuit is a lightweight model that doesn't impede her movements in any way.) ▌

4.5 NEWTON'S THIRD LAW

A force acting on a body is always the result of its interaction with another body, so forces always come in pairs. You can't pull on a doorknob without the doorknob pulling back on you. When you kick a football, the forward force that your foot exerts on the ball launches it into its trajectory, but you also feel the force the ball exerts back on your foot.

In each of these cases, the force that you exert on the other body is in the opposite direction to the force that body exerts on you. Experiments show that whenever two bodies interact, the two forces that they exert on each other are always *equal in magnitude* and *opposite in direction*. This fact is called *Newton's third law of motion:*

> **NEWTON'S THIRD LAW OF MOTION:** If body A exerts a force on body B (an "action"), then body B exerts a force on body A (a "reaction"). These two forces have the same magnitude but are opposite in direction. These two forces act on *different* bodies.

For example, in **Fig. 4.24** $\vec{F}_{A \text{ on } B}$ is the force applied *by* body A (first subscript) *on* body B (second subscript), and $\vec{F}_{B \text{ on } A}$ is the force applied *by* body B (first subscript) *on* body A (second subscript). In equation form,

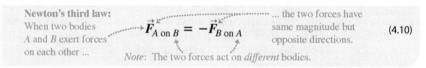

Newton's third law:
When two bodies
A and B exert forces
on each other ...

$$\vec{F}_{A \text{ on } B} = -\vec{F}_{B \text{ on } A}$$

... the two forces have
same magnitude but
opposite directions.

(4.10)

Note: The two forces act on *different* bodies.

It doesn't matter whether one body is inanimate (like the soccer ball in Fig. 4.24) and the other is not (like the kicker's foot): They necessarily exert forces on each other that obey Eq. (4.10).

In the statement of Newton's third law, "action" and "reaction" are the two opposite forces (in Fig. 4.24, $\vec{F}_{A \text{ on } B}$ and $\vec{F}_{B \text{ on } A}$); we sometimes refer to them as an **action–reaction pair.** This is *not* meant to imply any cause-and-effect relationship; we can consider either force as the "action" and the other as the "reaction." We often say simply that the forces are "equal and opposite," meaning that they have equal magnitudes and opposite directions.

CAUTION **The two forces in an action–reaction pair act on different bodies** We stress that the two forces described in Newton's third law act on *different* bodies. This is important in problems involving Newton's first or second law, which involve the forces that act on a single body. For instance, the net force on the soccer ball in Fig. 4.24 is the vector sum of the weight of the ball and the force $\vec{F}_{A \text{ on } B}$ exerted by the kicker. You wouldn't include the force $\vec{F}_{B \text{ on } A}$ because this force acts on the kicker, not on the ball. ▌

4.24 Newton's third law of motion.

If body A exerts force $\vec{F}_{A \text{ on } B}$ on body B (for example, a foot kicks a ball) ...

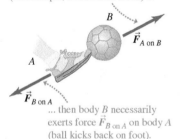

... then body B necessarily exerts force $\vec{F}_{B \text{ on } A}$ on body A (ball kicks back on foot).

The two forces have same magnitude but opposite directions: $\vec{F}_{A \text{ on } B} = -\vec{F}_{B \text{ on } A}$.

DEMO

In Fig. 4.24 the action and reaction forces are *contact* forces that are present only when the two bodies are touching. But Newton's third law also applies to *long-range* forces that do not require physical contact, such as the force of gravitational attraction. A table-tennis ball exerts an upward gravitational force on the earth that's equal in magnitude to the downward gravitational force the earth exerts on the ball. When you drop the ball, both the ball and the earth accelerate toward each other. The net force on each body has the same magnitude, but the earth's acceleration is microscopically small because its mass is so great. Nevertheless, it does move!

CONCEPTUAL EXAMPLE 4.8   WHICH FORCE IS GREATER?

After your sports car breaks down, you start to push it to the nearest repair shop. While the car is starting to move, how does the force you exert on the car compare to the force the car exerts on you? How do these forces compare when you are pushing the car along at a constant speed?

SOLUTION

Newton's third law says that in *both* cases, the force you exert on the car is equal in magnitude and opposite in direction to the force the car exerts on you. It's true that you have to push harder to get the car going than to keep it going. But no matter how hard you push on the car, the car pushes just as hard back on you. Newton's third law gives the same result whether the two bodies are at rest, moving with constant velocity, or accelerating.

You may wonder how the car "knows" to push back on you with the same magnitude of force that you exert on it. It may help to visualize the forces you and the car exert on each other as interactions between the atoms at the surface of your hand and the atoms at the surface of the car. These interactions are analogous to miniature springs between adjacent atoms, and a compressed spring exerts equally strong forces on both of its ends.

Fundamentally, though, the reason we know that objects of different masses exert equally strong forces on each other is that experiment tells us so. Physics isn't merely a collection of rules and equations; rather, it's a systematic description of the natural world based on experiment and observation.

CONCEPTUAL EXAMPLE 4.9   APPLYING NEWTON'S THIRD LAW: OBJECTS AT REST

An apple sits at rest on a table, in equilibrium. What forces act on the apple? What is the reaction force to each of the forces acting on the apple? What are the action–reaction pairs?

SOLUTION

Figure 4.25a shows the forces acting on the apple. $\vec{F}_{\text{earth on apple}}$ is the weight of the apple—that is, the downward gravitational force exerted *by* the earth *on* the apple. Similarly, $\vec{F}_{\text{table on apple}}$ is the upward normal force exerted *by* the table *on* the apple.

Figure 4.25b shows one of the action–reaction pairs involving the apple. As the earth pulls down on the apple, with force $\vec{F}_{\text{earth on apple}}$, the apple exerts an equally strong upward pull on the earth $\vec{F}_{\text{apple on earth}}$. By Newton's third law (Eq. 4.10) we have

$$\vec{F}_{\text{apple on earth}} = -\vec{F}_{\text{earth on apple}}$$

Also, as the table pushes up on the apple with force $\vec{F}_{\text{table on apple}}$, the corresponding reaction is the downward force $\vec{F}_{\text{apple on table}}$

4.25 The two forces in an action–reaction pair always act on different bodies.

(a) The forces acting on the apple

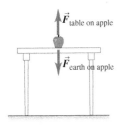

(b) The action–reaction pair for the interaction between the apple and the earth

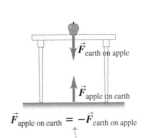

$\vec{F}_{\text{apple on earth}} = -\vec{F}_{\text{earth on apple}}$

Action–reaction pairs always represent a mutual interaction of two different objects.

(c) The action–reaction pair for the interaction between the apple and the table

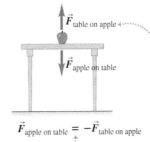

$\vec{F}_{\text{apple on table}} = -\vec{F}_{\text{table on apple}}$

(d) We eliminate one of the forces acting on the apple.

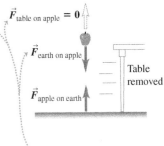

Table removed

The two forces on the apple *cannot* be an action–reaction pair, because they act on the same object.

Continued

exerted by the apple on the table (Fig. 4.25c). For this action–reaction pair we have

$$\vec{F}_{\text{apple on table}} = -\vec{F}_{\text{table on apple}}$$

The two forces acting on the apple, $\vec{F}_{\text{table on apple}}$ and $\vec{F}_{\text{earth on apple}}$, are *not* an action–reaction pair, despite being equal in magnitude and opposite in direction. They do not represent the mutual interaction of two bodies; they are two different forces acting on the *same* body. Figure 4.25d shows another way to see this. If we suddenly yank the table out from under the apple, the forces $\vec{F}_{\text{apple on table}}$ and $\vec{F}_{\text{table on apple}}$ suddenly become zero, but $\vec{F}_{\text{apple on earth}}$ and $\vec{F}_{\text{earth on apple}}$ are unchanged (the gravitational interaction is still present). Because $\vec{F}_{\text{table on apple}}$ is now zero, it can't be the negative of the nonzero $\vec{F}_{\text{earth on apple}}$, and these two forces can't be an action–reaction pair. *The two forces in an action–reaction pair **never** act on the same body.*

CONCEPTUAL EXAMPLE 4.10   APPLYING NEWTON'S THIRD LAW: OBJECTS IN MOTION

A stonemason drags a marble block across a floor by pulling on a rope attached to the block (**Fig. 4.26a**). The block is not necessarily in equilibrium. How are the various forces related? What are the action–reaction pairs?

SOLUTION

We'll use the subscripts B for the block, R for the rope, and M for the mason. In Fig. 4.26b the vector $\vec{F}_{\text{M on R}}$ represents the force exerted by the *mason* on the *rope*. The corresponding reaction is the force $\vec{F}_{\text{R on M}}$ exerted by the *rope* on the *mason*. Similarly, $\vec{F}_{\text{R on B}}$ represents the force exerted by the *rope* on the *block,* and the corresponding reaction is the force $\vec{F}_{\text{B on R}}$ exerted by the *block* on the *rope*. The forces in each action–reaction pair are equal and opposite:

$$\vec{F}_{\text{R on M}} = -\vec{F}_{\text{M on R}} \quad \text{and} \quad \vec{F}_{\text{B on R}} = -\vec{F}_{\text{R on B}}$$

Forces $\vec{F}_{\text{M on R}}$ and $\vec{F}_{\text{B on R}}$ (Fig. 4.26c) are *not* an action–reaction pair, because both of these forces act on the *same* body (the rope); an action and its reaction *must* always act on *different* bodies. Furthermore, the forces $\vec{F}_{\text{M on R}}$ and $\vec{F}_{\text{B on R}}$ are not necessarily equal in magnitude. Applying Newton's second law to the rope, we get

$$\Sigma \vec{F} = \vec{F}_{\text{M on R}} + \vec{F}_{\text{B on R}} = m_{\text{rope}}\vec{a}_{\text{rope}}$$

If the block and rope are accelerating (speeding up or slowing down), the rope is not in equilibrium, and $\vec{F}_{\text{M on R}}$ must have a different magnitude than $\vec{F}_{\text{B on R}}$. By contrast, the action–reaction forces $\vec{F}_{\text{M on R}}$ and $\vec{F}_{\text{R on M}}$ are always equal in magnitude, as are $\vec{F}_{\text{R on B}}$ and $\vec{F}_{\text{B on R}}$. Newton's third law holds whether or not the bodies are accelerating.

In the special case in which the rope is in equilibrium, the forces $\vec{F}_{\text{M on R}}$ and $\vec{F}_{\text{B on R}}$ are equal in magnitude, and they are opposite in direction. But this is an example of Newton's *first* law, not his third; these are two forces on the same body, not forces of two bodies on each other. Another way to look at this is that in equilibrium, $\vec{a}_{\text{rope}} = 0$ in the previous equation. Then $\vec{F}_{\text{B on R}} = -\vec{F}_{\text{M on R}}$ because of Newton's first or second law.

Another special case is if the rope is accelerating but has negligibly small mass compared to that of the block or the mason. In this case, $m_{\text{rope}} = 0$ in the previous equation, so again $\vec{F}_{\text{B on R}} = -\vec{F}_{\text{M on R}}$. Since Newton's third law says that $\vec{F}_{\text{B on R}}$ *always* equals $-\vec{F}_{\text{R on B}}$ (they are an action–reaction pair), in this "massless-rope" case $\vec{F}_{\text{R on B}}$ also equals $\vec{F}_{\text{M on R}}$.

For both the "massless-rope" case and the case of the rope in equilibrium, the force of the rope on the block is equal in magnitude and direction to the force of the mason on the rope (Fig. 4.26d). Hence we can think of the rope as "transmitting" to the block the force the mason exerts on the rope. This is a useful point of view, but remember that it is valid *only* when the rope has negligibly small mass or is in equilibrium.

4.26 Identifying the forces that act when a mason pulls on a rope attached to a block.

(a) The block, the rope, and the mason

(b) The action–reaction pairs

$\vec{F}_{\text{R on M}}$ $\vec{F}_{\text{M on R}}$

$\vec{F}_{\text{B on R}}$ $\vec{F}_{\text{R on B}}$

(c) *Not* an action–reaction pair

$\vec{F}_{\text{B on R}}$ $\vec{F}_{\text{M on R}}$

These forces cannot be an action–reaction pair because they act on the same object (the rope).

(d) Not necessarily equal

$\vec{F}_{\text{R on B}}$ $\vec{F}_{\text{M on R}}$

These forces are equal only if the rope is in equilibrium (or can be treated as massless).

CONCEPTUAL EXAMPLE 4.11   A NEWTON'S THIRD LAW PARADOX?

We saw in Conceptual Example 4.10 that the stonemason pulls as hard on the rope–block combination as that combination pulls back on him. Why, then, does the block move while the stonemason remains stationary?

SOLUTION

To resolve this seeming paradox, keep in mind the difference between Newton's *second* and *third* laws. The only forces involved in Newton's second law are those that act *on* a given body. The vector sum of these forces determines the body's acceleration, if any. By contrast, Newton's third law relates the forces that two *different* bodies exert on *each other*. The third law alone tells you nothing about the motion of either body.

If the rope–block combination is initially at rest, it begins to slide if the stonemason exerts a force $\vec{F}_{\text{M on R}}$ that is *greater* in magnitude than the friction force that the floor exerts on the block (**Fig. 4.27**). (The block has a smooth underside, which minimizes friction.) Then there is a net force to the right on the rope–block combination, and it accelerates to the right. By contrast, the stonemason *doesn't* move because the net force acting on him is *zero*. His shoes have nonskid soles that don't slip on the floor, so the friction force that the floor exerts on him is strong enough to balance the pull of the rope on him, $\vec{F}_{\text{R on M}}$. (Both the block and the stonemason also experience a downward force of gravity and an upward normal force exerted by the floor. These forces balance each other, so we haven't included them in Fig. 4.27.)

Once the block is moving, the stonemason doesn't need to pull as hard; he must exert only enough force to balance the friction force on the block. Then the net force on the moving block is zero, and by Newton's first law the block continues to move toward the mason at a constant velocity.

4.27 The horizontal forces acting on the block–rope combination (left) and the mason (right). (The vertical forces are not shown.)

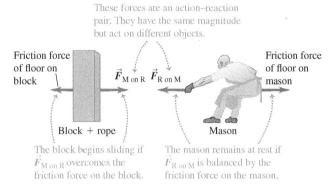

These forces are an action–reaction pair. They have the same magnitude but act on different objects.

Friction force of floor on block

$\vec{F}_{\text{M on R}}$ $\vec{F}_{\text{R on M}}$

Friction force of floor on mason

Block + rope

The block begins sliding if $\vec{F}_{\text{M on R}}$ overcomes the friction force on the block.

Mason

The mason remains at rest if $\vec{F}_{\text{R on M}}$ is balanced by the friction force on the mason.

So the block accelerates but the stonemason doesn't because different amounts of friction act on them. If the floor were freshly waxed, so that there was little friction between the floor and the stonemason's shoes, pulling on the rope might start the block sliding to the right *and* start him sliding to the left.

The moral of this example is that when analyzing the motion of a body, you must remember that only the forces acting *on* a body determine its motion. From this perspective, Newton's third law is merely a tool that can help you determine what those forces are.

A body that has pulling forces applied at its ends, such as the rope in Fig. 4.26, is said to be in *tension*. The **tension** at any point along the rope is the magnitude of the force acting at that point (see Fig. 4.2c). In Fig. 4.26b the tension at the right end of the rope is the magnitude of $\vec{F}_{\text{M on R}}$ (or of $\vec{F}_{\text{R on M}}$), and the tension at the left end equals the magnitude of $\vec{F}_{\text{B on R}}$ (or of $\vec{F}_{\text{R on B}}$). If the rope is in equilibrium and if no forces act except at its ends, the tension is the *same* at both ends and throughout the rope. Thus, if the magnitudes of $\vec{F}_{\text{B on R}}$ and $\vec{F}_{\text{M on R}}$ are 50 N each, the tension in the rope is 50 N (*not* 100 N). The *total* force vector $\vec{F}_{\text{B on R}} + \vec{F}_{\text{M on R}}$ acting on the rope in this case is zero!

We emphasize once again that the two forces in an action–reaction pair *never* act on the same body. Remembering this fact can help you avoid confusion about action–reaction pairs and Newton's third law.

TEST YOUR UNDERSTANDING OF SECTION 4.5   You are driving a car on a country road when a mosquito splatters on the windshield. Which has the greater magnitude: the force that the car exerted on the mosquito or the force that the mosquito exerted on the car? Or are the magnitudes the same? If they are different, how can you reconcile this fact with Newton's third law? If they are equal, why is the mosquito splattered while the car is undamaged? ▌

DATA *SPEAKS*

Force and Motion

When students were given a problem about forces acting on an object and how they affect the object's motion, more than 20% gave an incorrect answer. Common errors:

- Confusion about contact forces. If your fingers push on an object, the force you exert acts only when your fingers and the object are in contact. Once contact is broken, the force is no longer present even if the object is still moving.

- Confusion about Newton's third law. The third law relates the forces that two objects exert on each other. By itself, this law can't tell you anything about two forces that act on the same object.

4.6 FREE-BODY DIAGRAMS

DEMO   DEMO

4.28 The simple act of walking depends crucially on Newton's third law. To start moving forward, you push backward on the ground with your foot. As a reaction, the ground pushes forward on your foot (and hence on your body as a whole) with a force of the same magnitude. This *external* force provided by the ground is what accelerates your body forward.

CAUTION Forces in free-body diagrams For a free-body diagram to be complete, you *must* be able to answer this question for each force: What other body is applying this force? If you can't answer that question, you may be dealing with a nonexistent force. Avoid nonexistent forces such as "the force of acceleration" or "the $m\vec{a}$ force," discussed in Section 4.3.

Newton's three laws of motion contain all the basic principles we need to solve a wide variety of problems in mechanics. These laws are very simple in form, but the process of applying them to specific situations can pose real challenges. In this brief section we'll point out three key ideas and techniques to use in any problems involving Newton's laws. You'll learn others in Chapter 5, which also extends the use of Newton's laws to cover more complex situations.

1. *Newton's first and second laws apply to a specific body.* Whenever you use Newton's first law, $\sum \vec{F} = 0$, for an equilibrium situation or Newton's second law, $\sum \vec{F} = m\vec{a}$, for a nonequilibrium situation, you must decide at the beginning to which body you are referring. This decision may sound trivial, but it isn't.

2. *Only forces acting on the body matter.* The sum $\sum \vec{F}$ includes all the forces that act *on* the body in question. Hence, once you've chosen the body to analyze, you have to identify all the forces acting on it. Don't confuse the forces acting on a body with the forces exerted by that body on some other body. For example, to analyze a person walking, you would include in $\sum \vec{F}$ the force that the ground exerts on the person as he walks, but *not* the force that the person exerts on the ground (**Fig. 4.28**). These forces form an action–reaction pair and are related by Newton's third law, but only the member of the pair that acts on the body you're working with goes into $\sum \vec{F}$.

3. *Free-body diagrams are essential to help identify the relevant forces.* A **free-body diagram** shows the chosen body by itself, "free" of its surroundings, with vectors drawn to show the magnitudes and directions of all the forces that act on the body. We've already shown free-body diagrams in Figs. 4.17, 4.18, 4.20, and 4.25a. Be careful to include all the forces acting *on* the body, but be equally careful *not* to include any forces that the body exerts on any other body. In particular, the two forces in an action–reaction pair must *never* appear in the same free-body diagram because they never act on the same body. Furthermore, never include forces that a body exerts on itself, since these can't affect the body's motion.

When a problem involves more than one body, you have to take the problem apart and draw a separate free-body diagram for each body. For example, Fig. 4.26c shows a separate free-body diagram for the rope in the case in which the rope is considered massless (so that no gravitational force acts on it). Figure 4.27 also shows diagrams for the block and the mason, but these are *not* complete free-body diagrams because they don't show all the forces acting on each body. (We left out the vertical forces—the weight force exerted by the earth and the upward normal force exerted by the floor.)

In **Fig. 4.29** we present three real-life situations and the corresponding complete free-body diagrams. Note that in each situation a person exerts a force on something in his or her surroundings, but the force that shows up in the person's free-body diagram is the surroundings pushing back *on* the person.

TEST YOUR UNDERSTANDING OF SECTION 4.6   The buoyancy force shown in Fig. 4.29c is one half of an action–reaction pair. What force is the other half of this pair? (i) The weight of the swimmer; (ii) the forward thrust force; (iii) the backward drag force; (iv) the downward force that the swimmer exerts on the water; (v) the backward force that the swimmer exerts on the water by kicking.

4.29 Examples of free-body diagrams. Each free-body diagram shows all of the external forces that act on the object in question.

(a)

The force of the starting block on the runner has a vertical component that counteracts her weight and a large horizontal component that accelerates her.

(b)

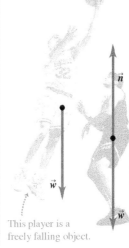

This player is a freely falling object.

To jump up, this player will push down against the floor, increasing the upward reaction force $\vec{n}$ of the floor on him.

(c)

The water exerts a buoyancy force that counters the swimmer's weight.

$\vec{F}_{\text{buoyancy}}$

$\vec{F}_{\text{thrust}}$ $\vec{F}_{\text{drag}}$

$\vec{w}$

Kicking causes the water to exert a forward reaction force, or thrust, on the swimmer.

Thrust is countered by drag forces exerted by the water on the moving swimmer.

CHAPTER 4 SUMMARY

SOLUTIONS TO ALL EXAMPLES

Force as a vector: Force is a quantitative measure of the interaction between two bodies. It is a vector quantity. When several forces act on a body, the effect on its motion is the same as when a single force, equal to the vector sum (resultant) of the forces, acts on the body. (See Example 4.1.)

$$\vec{R} = \sum \vec{F} = \vec{F}_1 + \vec{F}_2 + \vec{F}_3 + \cdots \quad (4.1)$$

$\vec{F}_1$

$\vec{R} = \sum \vec{F} = \vec{F}_1 + \vec{F}_2$

$\vec{F}_2$

The net force on a body and Newton's first law: Newton's first law states that when the vector sum of all forces acting on a body (the *net force*) is zero, the body is in equilibrium and has zero acceleration. If the body is initially at rest, it remains at rest; if it is initially in motion, it continues to move with constant velocity. This law is valid in inertial frames of reference only. (See Examples 4.2 and 4.3.)

$$\sum \vec{F} = 0 \quad (4.3)$$

$\vec{v}$ = constant

$\vec{F}_1$ $\vec{F}_2 = -\vec{F}_1$

$\sum \vec{F} = 0$

Mass, acceleration, and Newton's second law: The inertial properties of a body are characterized by its *mass*. The acceleration of a body under the action of a given set of forces is directly proportional to the vector sum of the forces (the *net force*) and inversely proportional to the mass of the body. This relationship is Newton's second law. Like Newton's first law, this law is valid in inertial frames of reference only. The unit of force is defined in terms of the units of mass and acceleration. In SI units, the unit of force is the newton (N), equal to 1 kg · m/s². (See Examples 4.4 and 4.5.)

$$\sum \vec{F} = m\vec{a} \tag{4.6}$$

$$\sum F_x = ma_x$$
$$\sum F_y = ma_y \tag{4.7}$$
$$\sum F_z = ma_z$$

Weight: The weight $\vec{w}$ of a body is the gravitational force exerted on it by the earth. Weight is a vector quantity. The magnitude of the weight of a body at any specific location is equal to the product of its mass m and the magnitude of the acceleration due to gravity g at that location. While the weight of a body depends on its location, the mass is independent of location. (See Examples 4.6 and 4.7.)

$$w = mg \tag{4.8}$$

$$\vec{w} = m\vec{g}$$

Newton's third law and action–reaction pairs: Newton's third law states that when two bodies interact, they exert forces on each other that are equal in magnitude and opposite in direction. These forces are called action and reaction forces. Each of these two forces acts on only one of the two bodies; they never act on the same body. (See Examples 4.8–4.11.)

$$\vec{F}_{A \text{ on } B} = -\vec{F}_{B \text{ on } A} \tag{4.10}$$

BRIDGING PROBLEM   LINKS IN A CHAIN

A student suspends a chain consisting of three links, each of mass $m = 0.250$ kg, from a light rope. The rope is attached to the top link of the chain, which does not swing. She pulls upward on the rope, so that the rope applies an upward force of 9.00 N to the chain. (a) Draw a free-body diagram for the entire chain, considered as a body, and one for each of the three links. (b) Use the diagrams of part (a) and Newton's laws to find (i) the acceleration of the chain, (ii) the force exerted by the top link on the middle link, and (iii) the force exerted by the middle link on the bottom link. Treat the rope as massless.

SOLUTION GUIDE

IDENTIFY and SET UP

1. There are four objects of interest in this problem: the chain as a whole and the three individual links. For each of these four objects, make a list of the external forces that act on it. Besides the force of gravity, your list should include only forces exerted by other objects that *touch* the object in question.
2. Some of the forces in your lists form action–reaction pairs (one pair is the force of the top link on the middle link and the force of the middle link on the top link). Identify all such pairs.
3. Use your lists to help you draw a free-body diagram for each of the four objects. Choose the coordinate axes.

4. Use your lists to decide how many unknowns there are in this problem. Which of these are target variables?

EXECUTE

5. Write a Newton's second law equation for each of the four objects, and write a Newton's third law equation for each action–reaction pair. You should have at least as many equations as there are unknowns (see step 4). Do you?
6. Solve the equations for the target variables.

EVALUATE

7. You can check your results by substituting them back into the equations from step 6. This is especially important to do if you ended up with more equations in step 5 than you used in step 6.
8. Rank the force of the rope on the chain, the force of the top link on the middle link, and the force of the middle link on the bottom link in order from smallest to largest magnitude. Does this ranking make sense? Explain.
9. Repeat the problem for the case in which the upward force that the rope exerts on the chain is only 7.35 N. Is the ranking in step 8 the same? Does this make sense?

Problems

For assigned homework and other learning materials, go to MasteringPhysics®.

•, ••, •••: Difficulty levels. CP: Cumulative problems incorporating material from earlier chapters. CALC: Problems requiring calculus.
DATA: Problems involving real data, scientific evidence, experimental design, and/or statistical reasoning. BIO: Biosciences problems.

DISCUSSION QUESTIONS

Q4.1 Can a body be in equilibrium when only one force acts on it? Explain.

Q4.2 A ball thrown straight up has zero velocity at its highest point. Is the ball in equilibrium at this point? Why or why not?

Q4.3 A helium balloon hovers in midair, neither ascending nor descending. Is it in equilibrium? What forces act on it?

Q4.4 When you fly in an airplane at night in smooth air, you have no sensation of motion, even though the plane may be moving at 800 km/h (500 mi/h). Why?

Q4.5 If the two ends of a rope in equilibrium are pulled with forces of equal magnitude and opposite directions, why isn't the total tension in the rope zero?

Q4.6 You tie a brick to the end of a rope and whirl the brick around you in a horizontal circle. Describe the path of the brick after you suddenly let go of the rope.

Q4.7 When a car stops suddenly, the passengers tend to move forward relative to their seats. Why? When a car makes a sharp turn, the passengers tend to slide to one side of the car. Why?

Q4.8 Some people say that the "force of inertia" (or "force of momentum") throws the passengers forward when a car brakes sharply. What is wrong with this explanation?

Q4.9 A passenger in a moving bus with no windows notices that a ball that has been at rest in the aisle suddenly starts to move toward the rear of the bus. Think of two possible explanations, and devise a way to decide which is correct.

Q4.10 Suppose you chose the fundamental physical quantities to be force, length, and time instead of mass, length, and time. What would be the units of mass in terms of those fundamental quantities?

Q4.11 Why is the earth only approximately an inertial reference frame?

Q4.12 Does Newton's second law hold true for an observer in a van as it speeds up, slows down, or rounds a corner? Explain.

Q4.13 Some students refer to the quantity $m\vec{a}$ as "the force of acceleration." Is it correct to refer to this quantity as a force? If so, what exerts this force? If not, what is a better description of this quantity?

Q4.14 The acceleration of a falling body is measured in an elevator that is traveling upward at a constant speed of 9.8 m/s. What value is obtained?

Q4.15 You can play catch with a softball in a bus moving with constant speed on a straight road, just as though the bus were at rest. Is this still possible when the bus is making a turn at constant speed on a level road? Why or why not?

Q4.16 Students sometimes say that the force of gravity on an object is 9.8 m/s². What is wrong with this view?

Q4.17 Why can it hurt your foot more to kick a big rock than a small pebble? *Must* the big rock hurt more? Explain.

Q4.18 "It's not the fall that hurts you; it's the sudden stop at the bottom." Translate this saying into the language of Newton's laws of motion.

Q4.19 A person can dive into water from a height of 10 m without injury, but a person who jumps off the roof of a 10-m-tall building and lands on a concrete street is likely to be seriously injured. Why is there a difference?

Q4.20 Why are cars designed to crumple in front and back for safety? Why not for side collisions and rollovers?

Q4.21 When a string barely strong enough lifts a heavy weight, it can lift the weight by a steady pull; but if you jerk the string, it will break. Explain in terms of Newton's laws of motion.

Q4.22 A large crate is suspended from the end of a vertical rope. Is the tension in the rope greater when the crate is at rest or when it is moving upward at constant speed? If the crate is traveling upward, is the tension in the rope greater when the crate is speeding up or when it is slowing down? In each case, explain in terms of Newton's laws of motion.

Q4.23 Which feels a greater pull due to the earth's gravity: a 10-kg stone or a 20-kg stone? If you drop the two stones, why doesn't the 20-kg stone fall with twice the acceleration of the 10-kg stone? Explain.

Q4.24 Why is it incorrect to say that 1.0 kg *equals* 2.2 lb?

Q4.25 A horse is hitched to a wagon. Since the wagon pulls back on the horse just as hard as the horse pulls on the wagon, why doesn't the wagon remain in equilibrium, no matter how hard the horse pulls?

Q4.26 True or false? You exert a push P on an object and it pushes back on you with a force F. If the object is moving at constant velocity, then F is equal to P, but if the object is being accelerated, then P must be greater than F.

Q4.27 A large truck and a small compact car have a head-on collision. During the collision, the truck exerts a force $\vec{F}_{\text{T on C}}$ on the car, and the car exerts a force $\vec{F}_{\text{C on T}}$ on the truck. Which force has the larger magnitude, or are they the same? Does your answer depend on how fast each vehicle was moving before the collision? Why or why not?

Q4.28 When a car comes to a stop on a level highway, what force causes it to slow down? When the car increases its speed on the same highway, what force causes it to speed up? Explain.

Q4.29 A small compact car is pushing a large van that has broken down, and they travel along the road with equal velocities and accelerations. While the car is speeding up, is the force it exerts on the van larger than, smaller than, or the same magnitude as the force the van exerts on it? Which vehicle has the larger net force on it, or are the net forces the same? Explain.

Q4.30 Consider a tug-of-war between two people who pull in opposite directions on the ends of a rope. By Newton's third law, the force that A exerts on B is just as great as the force that B exerts on A. So what determines who wins? (*Hint:* Draw a free-body diagram showing all the forces that act on each person.)

Q4.31 Boxes A and B are in contact on a horizontal, frictionless surface. You push on box A with a horizontal 100-N force (**Fig. Q4.31**). Box A weighs 150 N, and box B weighs 50 N. Is the force that box A exerts on box B equal to 100 N, greater than 100 N, or less than 100 N? Explain.

Figure Q4.31

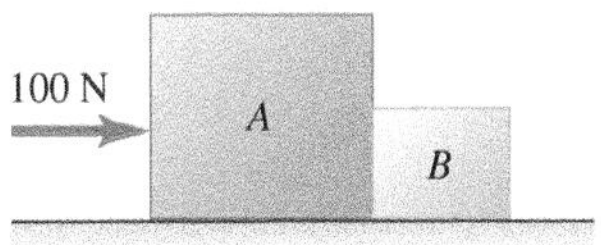

100 N   A   B

Q4.32 A manual for student pilots contains this passage: "When an airplane flies at a steady altitude, neither climbing nor descending, the upward lift force from the wings equals the plane's weight. When the plane is climbing at a steady rate, the upward lift is greater than the weight; when the plane is descending at a steady rate, the upward lift is less than the weight." Are these statements correct? Explain.

Q4.33 If your hands are wet and no towel is handy, you can remove some of the excess water by shaking them. Why does this work?

Q4.34 If you squat down (such as when you examine the books on a bottom shelf) and then suddenly get up, you may temporarily feel light-headed. What do Newton's laws of motion have to say about why this happens?

Q4.35 When a car is hit from behind, the occupants may experience whiplash. Use Newton's laws of motion to explain what causes this result.

Q4.36 In a head-on auto collision, passengers who are not wearing seat belts may be thrown through the windshield. Use Newton's laws of motion to explain why this happens.

Q4.37 In a head-on collision between a compact 1000-kg car and a large 2500-kg car, which one experiences the greater force? Explain. Which one experiences the greater acceleration? Explain why. Why are passengers in the small car more likely to be injured than those in the large car, even when the two car bodies are equally strong?

Q4.38 Suppose you are in a rocket with no windows, traveling in deep space far from other objects. Without looking outside the rocket or making any contact with the outside world, explain how you could determine whether the rocket is (a) moving forward at a constant 80% of the speed of light and (b) accelerating in the forward direction.

EXERCISES

Section 4.1 Force and Interactions

4.1 •• Two dogs pull horizontally on ropes attached to a post; the angle between the ropes is 60.0°. If Rover exerts a force of 270 N and Fido exerts a force of 300 N, find the magnitude of the resultant force and the angle it makes with Rover's rope.

4.2 • To extricate an SUV stuck in the mud, workmen use three horizontal ropes, producing the force vectors shown in **Fig. E4.2**. (a) Find the x- and y-components of each of the three pulls. (b) Use the components to find the magnitude and direction of the resultant of the three pulls.

Figure **E4.2**

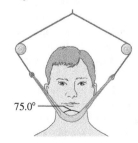

4.3 • BIO **Jaw Injury.** Due to a jaw injury, a patient must wear a strap (**Fig. E4.3**) that produces a net upward force of 5.00 N on his chin. The tension is the same throughout the strap. To what tension must the strap be adjusted to provide the necessary upward force?

Figure **E4.3**

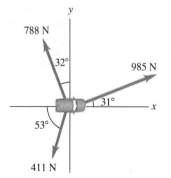

4.4 • A man is dragging a trunk up the loading ramp of a mover's truck. The ramp has a slope angle of 20.0°, and the man pulls upward with a force $\vec{F}$ whose direction makes an angle of 30.0° with the ramp (**Fig. E4.4**). (a) How large a force $\vec{F}$ is necessary for the component F_x parallel to the ramp to be 90.0 N? (b) How large will the component F_y perpendicular to the ramp be then?

Figure **E4.4**

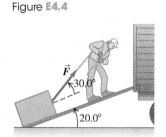

4.5 • Forces $\vec{F}_1$ and $\vec{F}_2$ act at a point. The magnitude of $\vec{F}_1$ is 9.00 N, and its direction is 60.0° above the x-axis in the second quadrant. The magnitude of $\vec{F}_2$ is 6.00 N, and its direction is 53.1° below the x-axis in the third quadrant. (a) What are the x- and y-components of the resultant force? (b) What is the magnitude of the resultant force?

Section 4.3 Newton's Second Law

4.6 • An electron (mass $= 9.11 \times 10^{-31}$ kg) leaves one end of a TV picture tube with zero initial speed and travels in a straight line to the accelerating grid, which is 1.80 cm away. It reaches the grid with a speed of 3.00×10^6 m/s. If the accelerating force is constant, compute (a) the acceleration; (b) the time to reach the grid; and (c) the net force, in newtons. Ignore the gravitational force on the electron.

4.7 •• A 68.5-kg skater moving initially at 2.40 m/s on rough horizontal ice comes to rest uniformly in 3.52 s due to friction from the ice. What force does friction exert on the skater?

4.8 •• You walk into an elevator, step onto a scale, and push the "up" button. You recall that your normal weight is 625 N. Draw a free-body diagram. (a) When the elevator has an upward acceleration of magnitude 2.50 m/s², what does the scale read? (b) If you hold a 3.85-kg package by a light vertical string, what will be the tension in this string when the elevator accelerates as in part (a)?

4.9 • A box rests on a frozen pond, which serves as a frictionless horizontal surface. If a fisherman applies a horizontal force with magnitude 48.0 N to the box and produces an acceleration of magnitude 2.20 m/s², what is the mass of the box?

4.10 •• A dockworker applies a constant horizontal force of 80.0 N to a block of ice on a smooth horizontal floor. The frictional force is negligible. The block starts from rest and moves 11.0 m in 5.00 s. (a) What is the mass of the block of ice? (b) If the worker stops pushing at the end of 5.00 s, how far does the block move in the next 5.00 s?

4.11 • A hockey puck with mass 0.160 kg is at rest at the origin ($x = 0$) on the horizontal, frictionless surface of the rink. At time $t = 0$ a player applies a force of 0.250 N to the puck, parallel to the x-axis; she continues to apply this force until $t = 2.00$ s. (a) What are the position and speed of the puck at $t = 2.00$ s? (b) If the same force is again applied at $t = 5.00$ s, what are the position and speed of the puck at $t = 7.00$ s?

4.12 • A crate with mass 32.5 kg initially at rest on a warehouse floor is acted on by a net horizontal force of 14.0 N. (a) What acceleration is produced? (b) How far does the crate travel in 10.0 s? (c) What is its speed at the end of 10.0 s?

4.13 • A 4.50-kg experimental cart undergoes an acceleration in a straight line (the x-axis). The graph in **Fig. E4.13** shows this acceleration as a function of time. (a) Find the maximum net force on this cart. When does this maximum force occur? (b) During what times is the net force on the cart a constant? (c) When is the net force equal to zero?

Figure **E4.13**

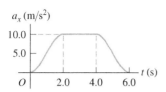

4.14 • A 2.75-kg cat moves in a straight line (the *x*-axis). **Figure E4.14** shows a graph of the *x*-component of this cat's velocity as a function of time. (a) Find the maximum net force on this cat. When does this force occur? (b) When is the net force on the cat equal to zero? (c) What is the net force at time 8.5 s?

Figure **E4.14**

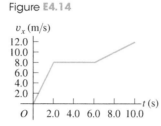

4.15 • A small 8.00-kg rocket burns fuel that exerts a time-varying upward force on the rocket (assume constant mass) as the rocket moves upward from the launch pad. This force obeys the equation $F = A + Bt^2$. Measurements show that at $t = 0$, the force is 100.0 N, and at the end of the first 2.00 s, it is 150.0 N. (a) Find the constants A and B, including their SI units. (b) Find the *net* force on this rocket and its acceleration (i) the instant after the fuel ignites and (ii) 3.00 s after the fuel ignites. (c) Suppose that you were using this rocket in outer space, far from all gravity. What would its acceleration be 3.00 s after fuel ignition?

Section 4.4 Mass and Weight

4.16 • An astronaut's pack weighs 17.5 N when she is on the earth but only 3.24 N when she is at the surface of a moon. (a) What is the acceleration due to gravity on this moon? (b) What is the mass of the pack on this moon?

4.17 • Superman throws a 2400-N boulder at an adversary. What horizontal force must Superman apply to the boulder to give it a horizontal acceleration of 12.0 m/s²?

4.18 • BIO (a) An ordinary flea has a mass of 210 μg. How many newtons does it weigh? (b) The mass of a typical froghopper is 12.3 mg. How many newtons does it weigh? (c) A house cat typically weighs 45 N. How many pounds does it weigh, and what is its mass in kilograms?

4.19 • At the surface of Jupiter's moon Io, the acceleration due to gravity is $g = 1.81$ m/s². A watermelon weighs 44.0 N at the surface of the earth. (a) What is the watermelon's mass on the earth's surface? (b) What would be its mass and weight on the surface of Io?

Section 4.5 Newton's Third Law

4.20 • A small car of mass 380 kg is pushing a large truck of mass 900 kg due east on a level road. The car exerts a horizontal force of 1600 N on the truck. What is the magnitude of the force that the truck exerts on the car?

4.21 • BIO World-class sprinters can accelerate out of the starting blocks with an acceleration that is nearly horizontal and has magnitude 15 m/s². How much horizontal force must a 55-kg sprinter exert on the starting blocks to produce this acceleration? Which body exerts the force that propels the sprinter: the blocks or the sprinter herself?

4.22 •• The upward normal force exerted by the floor is 620 N on an elevator passenger who weighs 650 N. What are the reaction forces to these two forces? Is the passenger accelerating? If so, what are the magnitude and direction of the acceleration?

4.23 •• Boxes *A* and *B* are in contact on a horizontal, frictionless surface (**Fig. E4.23**). Box *A* has mass 20.0 kg and box *B* has mass 5.0 kg. A horizontal force of 250 N is exerted on box *A*. What is the magnitude of the force that box *A* exerts on box *B*?

Figure **E4.23**

4.24 •• A student of mass 45 kg jumps off a high diving board. What is the acceleration of the earth toward her as she accelerates toward the earth with an acceleration of 9.8 m/s²? Use 6.0×10^{24} kg for the mass of the earth, and assume that the net force on the earth is the force of gravity she exerts on it.

Section 4.6 Free-Body Diagrams

4.25 •• Crates *A* and *B* sit at rest side by side on a frictionless horizontal surface. They have masses m_A and m_B, respectively. When a horizontal force $\vec{F}$ is applied to crate *A*, the two crates move off to the right. (a) Draw clearly labeled free-body diagrams for crate *A* and for crate *B*. Indicate which pairs of forces, if any, are third-law action–reaction pairs. (b) If the magnitude of $\vec{F}$ is less than the total weight of the two crates, will it cause the crates to move? Explain.

4.26 •• You pull horizontally on block *B* in **Fig. E4.26,** causing both blocks to move together as a unit. For this moving system, make a carefully labeled free-body diagram of block *A* if (a) the table is frictionless and (b) there is friction between block *B* and the table and the pull is equal in magnitude to the friction force on block *B* due to the table.

Figure **E4.26**

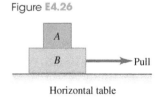

Horizontal table

4.27 • A ball is hanging from a long string that is tied to the ceiling of a train car traveling eastward on horizontal tracks. An observer inside the train car sees the ball hang motionless. Draw a clearly labeled free-body diagram for the ball if (a) the train has a uniform velocity and (b) the train is speeding up uniformly. Is the net force on the ball zero in either case? Explain.

4.28 •• CP A .22-caliber rifle bullet traveling at 350 m/s strikes a large tree and penetrates it to a depth of 0.130 m. The mass of the bullet is 1.80 g. Assume a constant retarding force. (a) How much time is required for the bullet to stop? (b) What force, in newtons, does the tree exert on the bullet?

4.29 •• A chair of mass 12.0 kg is sitting on the horizontal floor; the floor is not frictionless. You push on the chair with a force $F = 40.0$ N that is directed at an angle of 37.0° below the horizontal, and the chair slides along the floor. (a) Draw a clearly labeled free-body diagram for the chair. (b) Use your diagram and Newton's laws to calculate the normal force that the floor exerts on the chair.

PROBLEMS

4.30 ••• A large box containing your new computer sits on the bed of your pickup truck. You are stopped at a red light. When the light turns green, you stomp on the gas and the truck accelerates. To your horror, the box starts to slide toward the back of the truck. Draw clearly labeled free-body diagrams for the truck and for the box. Indicate pairs of forces, if any, that are third-law action–reaction pairs. (The horizontal truck bed is *not* frictionless.)

4.31 •• CP A 5.60-kg bucket of water is accelerated upward by a cord of negligible mass whose breaking strength is 75.0 N. If the bucket starts from rest, what is the minimum time required to raise the bucket a vertical distance of 12.0 m without breaking the cord?

4.32 •• CP You have just landed on Planet X. You release a 100-g ball from rest from a height of 10.0 m and measure that it takes 3.40 s to reach the ground. Ignore any force on the ball from the atmosphere of the planet. How much does the 100-g ball weigh on the surface of Planet X?

4.33 •• Two adults and a child want to push a wheeled cart in the direction marked *x* in **Fig. P4.33**. The two adults push with horizontal forces $\vec{F}_1$ and $\vec{F}_2$ as shown. (a) Find the magnitude and direction of the *smallest* force that the child should exert. Ignore the effects of friction. (b) If the child exerts the minimum force found in part (a), the cart accelerates at 2.0 m/s² in the +x-direction. What is the weight of the cart?

Figure **P4.33**

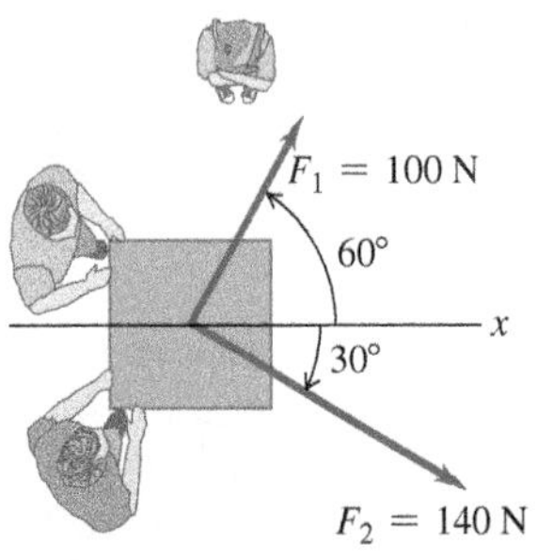

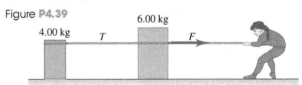

$F_1 = 100$ N

$60°$

$30°$

x

$F_2 = 140$ N

4.34 • CP An oil tanker's engines have broken down, and the wind is blowing the tanker straight toward a reef at a constant speed of 1.5 m/s (**Fig. P4.34**). When the tanker is 500 m from the reef, the wind dies down just as the engineer gets the engines going again. The rudder is stuck, so the only choice is to try to accelerate straight backward away from the reef. The mass of the tanker and cargo is 3.6×10^7 kg, and the engines produce a net horizontal force of 8.0×10^4 N on the tanker. Will the ship hit the reef? If it does, will the oil be safe? The hull can withstand an impact at a speed of 0.2 m/s or less. Ignore the retarding force of the water on the tanker's hull.

Figure **P4.34**

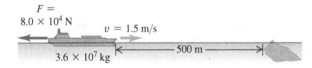

$F = 8.0 \times 10^4$ N

$v = 1.5$ m/s

500 m

3.6×10^7 kg

4.35 •• CP BIO **A Standing Vertical Jump.** Basketball player Darrell Griffith is on record as attaining a standing vertical jump of 1.2 m (4 ft). (This means that he moved upward by 1.2 m after his feet left the floor.) Griffith weighed 890 N (200 lb). (a) What was his speed as he left the floor? (b) If the time of the part of the jump before his feet left the floor was 0.300 s, what was his average acceleration (magnitude and direction) while he pushed against the floor? (c) Draw his free-body diagram. In terms of the forces on the diagram, what was the net force on him? Use Newton's laws and the results of part (b) to calculate the average force he applied to the ground.

4.36 ••• CP An advertisement claims that a particular automobile can "stop on a dime." What net force would be necessary to stop a 850-kg automobile traveling initially at 45.0 km/h in a distance equal to the diameter of a dime, 1.8 cm?

4.37 •• BIO **Human Biomechanics.** The fastest pitched baseball was measured at 46 m/s. A typical baseball has a mass of 145 g. If the pitcher exerted his force (assumed to be horizontal and constant) over a distance of 1.0 m, (a) what force did he produce on the ball during this record-setting pitch? (b) Draw free-body diagrams of the ball during the pitch and just *after* it left the pitcher's hand.

4.38 •• BIO **Human Biomechanics.** The fastest served tennis ball, served by "Big Bill" Tilden in 1931, was measured at 73.14 m/s. The mass of a tennis ball is 57 g, and the ball, which starts from rest, is typically in contact with the tennis racquet for 30.0 ms. Assuming constant acceleration, (a) what force did Big Bill's tennis racquet exert on the ball if he hit it essentially horizontally? (b) Draw free-body diagrams of the ball during the serve and just after it moved free of the racquet.

4.39 • Two crates, one with mass 4.00 kg and the other with mass 6.00 kg, sit on the frictionless surface of a frozen pond, connected by a light rope (**Fig. P4.39**). A woman wearing golf shoes (for traction) pulls horizontally on the 6.00-kg crate with a force F that gives the crate an acceleration of 2.50 m/s². (a) What is the acceleration of the 4.00-kg crate? (b) Draw a free-body diagram for the 4.00-kg crate. Use that diagram and Newton's second law to find the tension T in the rope that connects the two crates. (c) Draw a free-body diagram for the 6.00-kg crate. What is the direction of the net force on the 6.00-kg crate? Which is larger in magnitude, T or F? (d) Use part (c) and Newton's second law to calculate the magnitude of F.

Figure **P4.39**

4.00 kg

6.00 kg

T

F

4.40 •• CP Two blocks connected by a light horizontal rope sit at rest on a horizontal, frictionless surface. Block A has mass 15.0 kg, and block B has mass m. A constant horizontal force $F = 60.0$ N is applied to block A (**Fig. P4.40**). In the first 5.00 s after the force is applied, block A moves 18.0 m to the right. (a) While the blocks are moving, what is the tension T in the rope that connects the two blocks? (b) What is the mass of block B?

Figure **P4.40**

B

A

F

4.41 • CALC To study damage to aircraft that collide with large birds, you design a test gun that will accelerate chicken-sized objects so that their displacement along the gun barrel is given by $x = (9.0 \times 10^3 \text{ m/s}^2)t^2 - (8.0 \times 10^4 \text{ m/s}^3)t^3$. The object leaves the end of the barrel at $t = 0.025$ s. (a) How long must the gun barrel be? (b) What will be the speed of the objects as they leave the end of the barrel? (c) What net force must be exerted on a 1.50-kg object at (i) $t = 0$ and (ii) $t = 0.025$ s?

4.42 •• CP A 6.50-kg instrument is hanging by a vertical wire inside a spaceship that is blasting off from rest at the earth's surface. This spaceship reaches an altitude of 276 m in 15.0 s with constant acceleration. (a) Draw a free-body diagram for the instrument during this time. Indicate which force is greater. (b) Find the force that the wire exerts on the instrument.

4.43 •• BIO **Insect Dynamics.** The froghopper (*Philaenus spumarius*), the champion leaper of the insect world, has a mass of 12.3 mg and leaves the ground (in the most energetic jumps) at 4.0 m/s from a vertical start. The jump itself lasts a mere 1.0 ms before the insect is clear of the ground. Assuming constant acceleration, (a) draw a free-body diagram of this mighty leaper during the jump; (b) find the force that the ground exerts on the froghopper during the jump; and (c) express the force in part (b) in terms of the froghopper's weight.

4.44 • A loaded elevator with very worn cables has a total mass of 2200 kg, and the cables can withstand a maximum tension of 28,000 N. (a) Draw the free-body force diagram for the elevator. In terms of the forces on your diagram, what is the net force on the elevator? Apply Newton's second law to the elevator and find the maximum upward acceleration for the elevator if the cables are not to break. (b) What would be the answer to part (a) if the elevator were on the moon, where $g = 1.62 \text{ m/s}^2$?

4.45 •• CP After an annual checkup, you leave your physician's office, where you weighed 683 N. You then get into an elevator that, conveniently, has a scale. Find the magnitude and direction of the elevator's acceleration if the scale reads (a) 725 N and (b) 595 N.

4.46 ••• CP A nail in a pine board stops a 4.9-N hammer head from an initial downward velocity of 3.2 m/s in a distance of 0.45 cm. In addition, the person using the hammer exerts a 15-N downward force on it. Assume that the acceleration of the hammer head is constant while it is in contact with the nail and moving downward. (a) Draw a free-body diagram for the hammer head. Identify the reaction force for each action force in the diagram. (b) Calculate the downward force $\vec{F}$ exerted by the hammer head on the nail while the hammer head is in contact with the nail and moving downward. (c) Suppose that the nail is in hardwood and the distance the hammer head travels in coming to rest is only 0.12 cm. The downward forces on the hammer head are the same as in part (b). What then is the force $\vec{F}$ exerted by the hammer head on the nail while the hammer head is in contact with the nail and moving downward?

4.47 •• CP **Jumping to the Ground.** A 75.0-kg man steps off a platform 3.10 m above the ground. He keeps his legs straight as he falls, but his knees begin to bend at the moment his feet touch the ground; treated as a particle, he moves an additional 0.60 m before coming to rest. (a) What is his speed at the instant his feet touch the ground? (b) If we treat the man as a particle, what is his acceleration (magnitude and direction) as he slows down, if the acceleration is assumed to be constant? (c) Draw his free-body diagram. In terms of the forces on the diagram, what is the net force on him? Use Newton's laws and the results of part (b) to calculate the average force his feet exert on the ground while he slows down. Express this force both in newtons and as a multiple of his weight.

4.48 •• The two blocks in **Fig. P4.48** are connected by a heavy uniform rope with a mass of 4.00 kg. An upward force of 200 N is applied as shown. (a) Draw three free-body diagrams: one for the 6.00-kg block, one for the 4.00-kg rope, and another one for the 5.00-kg block. For each force, indicate what body exerts that force. (b) What is the acceleration of the system? (c) What is the tension at the top of the heavy rope? (d) What is the tension at the midpoint of the rope?

Figure **P4.48**

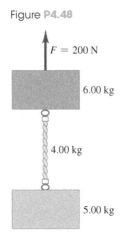

4.49 •• CP Boxes *A* and *B* are connected to each end of a light vertical rope (**Fig. P4.49**). A constant upward force $F = 80.0$ N is applied to box *A*. Starting from rest, box *B* descends 12.0 m in 4.00 s. The tension in the rope connecting the two boxes is 36.0 N. What are the masses of (a) box *B*, (b) box *A*?

Figure **P4.49**

4.50 •• CP **Extraterrestrial Physics.** You have landed on an unknown planet, Newtonia, and want to know what objects weigh there. When you push a certain tool, starting from rest, on a frictionless horizontal surface with a 12.0-N force, the tool moves 16.0 m in the first 2.00 s. You next observe that if you release this tool from rest at 10.0 m above the ground, it takes 2.58 s to reach the ground. What does the tool weigh on Newtonia, and what does it weigh on Earth?

4.51 •• CP CALC A mysterious rocket-propelled object of mass 45.0 kg is initially at rest in the middle of the horizontal, frictionless surface of an ice-covered lake. Then a force directed east and with magnitude $F(t) = (16.8 \text{ N/s})t$ is applied. How far does the object travel in the first 5.00 s after the force is applied?

4.52 ••• CALC The position of a training helicopter (weight 2.75×10^5 N) in a test is given by $\vec{r} = (0.020 \text{ m/s}^3)t^3\hat{i} + (2.2 \text{ m/s})t\hat{j} - (0.060 \text{ m/s}^2)t^2\hat{k}$. Find the net force on the helicopter at $t = 5.0$ s.

4.53 •• DATA The table* gives automobile performance data for a few types of cars:

Make and Model (Year)	Mass (kg)	Time (s) to go from 0 to 60 mph
Alpha Romeo 4C (2013)	895	4.4
Honda Civic 2.0i (2011)	1320	6.4
Ferrari F430 (2004)	1435	3.9
Ford Focus RS500 (2010)	1468	5.4
Volvo S60 (2013)	1650	7.2

*Source: www.autosnout.com

(a) During an acceleration of 0 to 60 mph, which car has the largest average net force acting on it? The smallest? (b) During this acceleration, for which car would the average net force on a 72.0-kg passenger be the largest? The smallest? (c) When the Ferrari F430 accelerates from 0 to 100 mph in 8.6 s, what is the average net force acting on it? How does this net force compare with the average net force during the acceleration from 0 to 60 mph? Explain why these average net forces might differ. (d) Discuss why a car has a top speed. What is the net force on the Ferrari F430 when it is traveling at its top speed, 196 mph?

4.54 •• DATA An 8.00-kg box sits on a level floor. You give the box a sharp push and find that it travels 8.22 m in 2.8 s before coming to rest again. (a) You measure that with a different push the box traveled 4.20 m in 2.0 s. Do you think the box has a constant acceleration as it slows down? Explain your reasoning. (b) You add books to the box to increase its mass. Repeating the experiment, you give the box a push and measure how long it takes the box to come to rest and how far the box travels. The

? Each of the seeds being blown off the head of a dandelion (genus *Taraxacum*) has a feathery structure called a pappus. The pappus acts like a parachute and enables the seed to be borne by the wind and drift gently to the ground. If a seed with its pappus descends straight down at a steady speed, which force acting on the seed has a greater magnitude? (i) The force of gravity; (ii) the upward force exerted by the air; (iii) both forces have the same magnitude; (iv) it depends on the speed at which the seed descends.

5 APPLYING NEWTON'S LAWS

We saw in Chapter 4 that Newton's three laws of motion, the foundation of classical mechanics, can be stated very simply. But *applying* these laws to situations such as an iceboat skating across a frozen lake, a toboggan sliding down a hill, or an airplane making a steep turn requires analytical skills and problem-solving technique. In this chapter we'll help you extend the problem-solving skills you began to develop in Chapter 4.

We'll begin with equilibrium problems, in which we analyze the forces that act on a body that is at rest or moving with constant velocity. We'll then consider bodies that are not in equilibrium, for which we'll have to deal with the relationship between forces and motion. We'll learn how to describe and analyze the contact force that acts on a body when it rests on or slides over a surface. We'll also analyze the forces that act on a body that moves in a circle with constant speed. We close the chapter with a brief look at the fundamental nature of force and the classes of forces found in our physical universe.

5.1 USING NEWTON'S FIRST LAW: PARTICLES IN EQUILIBRIUM

We learned in Chapter 4 that a body is in *equilibrium* when it is at rest or moving with constant velocity in an inertial frame of reference. A hanging lamp, a kitchen table, an airplane flying straight and level at a constant speed—all are examples of equilibrium situations. In this section we consider only the equilibrium of a body that can be modeled as a particle. (In Chapter 11 we'll see how to analyze a body in equilibrium that can't be represented adequately as a particle, such as a bridge that's supported at various points along its span.) The essential physical principle is Newton's first law:

Newton's first law: ⋯⋯→ $\sum \vec{F} = 0$ ←⋯ ... must be *zero* for a
Net force on a body ...   body in equilibrium.

Sum of *x*-components of force   Sum of *y*-components of force   (5.1)
on body must be zero.   on body must be zero.

$$\sum F_x = 0 \qquad \sum F_y = 0$$

This section is about using Newton's first law to solve problems dealing with bodies in equilibrium. Some of these problems may seem complicated, but remember that *all* problems involving particles in equilibrium are done in the same way. Problem-Solving Strategy 5.1 details the steps you need to follow for any and all such problems. Study this strategy carefully, look at how it's applied in the worked-out examples, and try to apply it when you solve assigned problems.

| PROBLEM-SOLVING STRATEGY 5.1 | NEWTON'S FIRST LAW: EQUILIBRIUM OF A PARTICLE |

IDENTIFY *the relevant concepts:* You must use Newton's *first* law, Eqs. (5.1), for any problem that involves forces acting on a body in equilibrium—that is, either at rest or moving with constant velocity. A car is in equilibrium when it's parked, but also when it's traveling down a straight road at a steady speed.

If the problem involves more than one body and the bodies interact with each other, you'll also need to use Newton's *third* law. This law allows you to relate the force that one body exerts on a second body to the force that the second body exerts on the first one.

Identify the target variable(s). Common target variables in equilibrium problems include the magnitude and direction (angle) of one of the forces, or the components of a force.

SET UP *the problem* by using the following steps:
1. Draw a very simple sketch of the physical situation, showing dimensions and angles. You don't have to be an artist!
2. Draw a free-body diagram for each body that is in equilibrium. For now, we consider the body as a particle, so you can represent it as a large dot. In your free-body diagram, *do not* include the other bodies that interact with it, such as a surface it may be resting on or a rope pulling on it.
3. Ask yourself what is interacting with the body by contact or in any other way. On your free-body diagram, draw a force vector for each interaction. Label each force with a symbol for the *magnitude* of the force. If you know the angle at which a force is directed, draw the angle accurately and label it. Include the body's weight, unless the body has negligible mass. If the mass is given, use $w = mg$ to find the weight. A surface in contact with the body exerts a normal force perpendicular to the surface and possibly a friction force parallel to the surface. A rope or chain exerts a pull (never a push) in a direction along its length.

4. *Do not* show in the free-body diagram any forces exerted *by* the body on any other body. The sums in Eqs. (5.1) include only forces that act *on* the body. For each force on the body, ask yourself "What other body causes that force?" If you can't answer that question, you may be imagining a force that isn't there.
5. Choose a set of coordinate axes and include them in your free-body diagram. (If there is more than one body in the problem, choose axes for each body separately.) Label the positive direction for each axis. If a body rests or slides on a plane surface, for simplicity choose axes that are parallel and perpendicular to this surface, even when the plane is tilted.

EXECUTE *the solution* as follows:
1. Find the components of each force along each of the body's coordinate axes. Draw a wiggly line through each force vector that has been replaced by its components, so you don't count it twice. The *magnitude* of a force is always positive, but its *components* may be positive or negative.
2. Set the sum of all *x*-components of force equal to zero. In a separate equation, set the sum of all *y*-components equal to zero. (*Never* add *x*- and *y*-components in a single equation.)
3. If there are two or more bodies, repeat all of the above steps for each body. If the bodies interact with each other, use Newton's third law to relate the forces they exert on each other.
4. Make sure that you have as many independent equations as the number of unknown quantities. Then solve these equations to obtain the target variables.

EVALUATE *your answer:* Look at your results and ask whether they make sense. When the result is a symbolic expression or formula, check to see that your formula works for any special cases (particular values or extreme cases for the various quantities) for which you can guess what the results ought to be.

| **EXAMPLE 5.1** | ONE-DIMENSIONAL EQUILIBRIUM: TENSION IN A MASSLESS ROPE |

A gymnast with mass $m_G = 50.0 \text{ kg}$ suspends herself from the lower end of a hanging rope of negligible mass. The upper end of the rope is attached to the gymnasium ceiling. (a) What is the gymnast's weight? (b) What force (magnitude and direction) does the rope exert on her? (c) What is the tension at the top of the rope?

SOLUTION

IDENTIFY and SET UP: The gymnast and the rope are in equilibrium, so we can apply Newton's first law to both bodies. We'll use Newton's third law to relate the forces that they exert on each

Continued

other. The target variables are the gymnast's weight, w_G; the force that the bottom of the rope exerts on the gymnast (call it $T_{R \text{ on } G}$); and the force that the ceiling exerts on the top of the rope (call it $T_{C \text{ on } R}$). **Figure 5.1** shows our sketch of the situation and free-body diagrams for the gymnast and for the rope. We take the positive y-axis to be upward in each diagram. Each force acts in the vertical direction and so has only a y-component.

The forces $T_{R \text{ on } G}$ (the upward force of the rope on the gymnast, Fig. 5.1b) and $T_{G \text{ on } R}$ (the downward force of the gymnast on the rope, Fig. 5.1c) form an action–reaction pair. By Newton's third law, they must have the same magnitude.

Note that Fig. 5.1c includes only the forces that act *on* the rope. In particular, it doesn't include the force that the *rope* exerts on the *ceiling* (compare the discussion of the apple in Conceptual Example 4.9 in Section 4.5).

5.1 Our sketches for this problem.

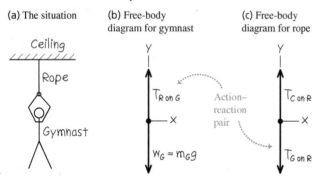

(a) The situation
(b) Free-body diagram for gymnast
(c) Free-body diagram for rope

EXECUTE: (a) The magnitude of the gymnast's weight is the product of her mass and the acceleration due to gravity, g:

$$w_G = m_G g = (50.0 \text{ kg})(9.80 \text{ m/s}^2) = 490 \text{ N}$$

(b) The gravitational force on the gymnast (her weight) points in the negative y-direction, so its y-component is $-w_G$. The upward force of the rope on the gymnast has unknown magnitude $T_{R \text{ on } G}$ and positive y-component $+T_{R \text{ on } G}$. We find this by using Newton's first law from Eqs. (5.1):

$$\text{Gymnast:} \quad \Sigma F_y = T_{R \text{ on } G} + (-w_G) = 0 \quad \text{so}$$
$$T_{R \text{ on } G} = w_G = 490 \text{ N}$$

The rope pulls *up* on the gymnast with a force $T_{R \text{ on } G}$ of magnitude 490 N. (By Newton's third law, the gymnast pulls *down* on the rope with a force of the same magnitude, $T_{G \text{ on } R} = 490$ N.)

(c) We have assumed that the rope is weightless, so the only forces on it are those exerted by the ceiling (upward force of unknown magnitude $T_{C \text{ on } R}$) and by the gymnast (downward force of magnitude $T_{G \text{ on } R} = 490$ N). From Newton's first law, the *net* vertical force on the rope in equilibrium must be zero:

$$\text{Rope:} \quad \Sigma F_y = T_{C \text{ on } R} + (-T_{G \text{ on } R}) = 0 \quad \text{so}$$
$$T_{C \text{ on } R} = T_{G \text{ on } R} = 490 \text{ N}$$

EVALUATE: The *tension* at any point in the rope is the magnitude of the force that acts at that point. For this weightless rope, the tension $T_{G \text{ on } R}$ at the lower end has the same value as the tension $T_{C \text{ on } R}$ at the upper end. For such an ideal weightless rope, the tension has the same value at any point along the rope's length. (See the discussion in Conceptual Example 4.10 in Section 4.5.)

EXAMPLE 5.2 **ONE-DIMENSIONAL EQUILIBRIUM: TENSION IN A ROPE WITH MASS**

Find the tension at each end of the rope in Example 5.1 if the weight of the rope is 120 N.

SOLUTION

IDENTIFY and SET UP: As in Example 5.1, the target variables are the magnitudes $T_{G \text{ on } R}$ and $T_{C \text{ on } R}$ of the forces that act at the bottom and top of the rope, respectively. Once again, we'll apply Newton's first law to the gymnast and to the rope, and use Newton's third law to relate the forces that the gymnast and rope exert on each other. Again we draw separate free-body diagrams for the gymnast (**Fig. 5.2a**) and the rope (Fig. 5.2b). There is now a *third* force acting on the rope, however: the weight of the rope, of magnitude $w_R = 120$ N.

EXECUTE: The gymnast's free-body diagram is the same as in Example 5.1, so her equilibrium condition is also the same. From Newton's third law, $T_{R \text{ on } G} = T_{G \text{ on } R}$, and we again have

$$\text{Gymnast:} \quad \Sigma F_y = T_{R \text{ on } G} + (-w_G) = 0 \quad \text{so}$$
$$T_{R \text{ on } G} = T_{G \text{ on } R} = w_G = 490 \text{ N}$$

The equilibrium condition $\Sigma F_y = 0$ for the rope is now

$$\text{Rope:} \quad \Sigma F_y = T_{C \text{ on } R} + (-T_{G \text{ on } R}) + (-w_R) = 0$$

Note that the y-component of $T_{C \text{ on } R}$ is positive because it points in the $+y$-direction, but the y-components of both $T_{G \text{ on } R}$ and w_R are negative. We solve for $T_{C \text{ on } R}$ and substitute the values $T_{G \text{ on } R} = T_{R \text{ on } G} = 490$ N and $w_R = 120$ N:

$$T_{C \text{ on } R} = T_{G \text{ on } R} + w_R = 490 \text{ N} + 120 \text{ N} = 610 \text{ N}$$

5.2 Our sketches for this problem, including the weight of the rope.

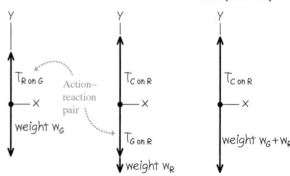

(a) Free-body diagram for gymnast
(b) Free-body diagram for rope
(c) Free-body diagram for gymnast and rope as a composite body

EVALUATE: When we include the weight of the rope, the tension is *different* at the rope's two ends: 610 N at the top and 490 N at the bottom. The force $T_{C \text{ on } R} = 610$ N exerted by the ceiling has to hold up both the 490-N weight of the gymnast and the 120-N weight of the rope.

To see this more clearly, we draw a free-body diagram for a composite body consisting of the gymnast and rope together (Fig. 5.2c). Only two external forces act on this composite body: the force $T_{C \text{ on } R}$ exerted by the ceiling and the total weight

$w_G + w_R = 490 \text{ N} + 120 \text{ N} = 610 \text{ N}$. (The forces $T_{\text{G on R}}$ and $T_{\text{R on G}}$ are *internal* to the composite body. Newton's first law applies only to *external* forces, so these internal forces play no role.) Hence Newton's first law applied to this composite body is

Composite body: $\quad \Sigma F_y = T_{\text{C on R}} + [-(w_G + w_R)] = 0$

and so $T_{\text{C on R}} = w_G + w_R = 610 \text{ N}$.

Treating the gymnast and rope as a composite body is simpler, but we can't find the tension $T_{\text{G on R}}$ at the bottom of the rope by this method. *Moral: Whenever you have more than one body in a problem involving Newton's laws, the safest approach is to treat each body separately.*

EXAMPLE 5.3   TWO-DIMENSIONAL EQUILIBRIUM

In **Fig. 5.3a**, a car engine with weight w hangs from a chain that is linked at ring O to two other chains, one fastened to the ceiling and the other to the wall. Find expressions for the tension in each of the three chains in terms of w. The weights of the ring and chains are negligible compared with the weight of the engine.

SOLUTION

IDENTIFY and SET UP: The target variables are the tension magnitudes T_1, T_2, and T_3 in the three chains (Fig. 5.3a). All the bodies are in equilibrium, so we'll use Newton's first law. We need three independent equations, one for each target variable. However, applying Newton's first law in component form to just one body gives only *two* equations [the x- and y-equations in Eqs. (5.1)]. So we'll have to consider more than one body in equilibrium. We'll look at the engine (which is acted on by T_1) and the ring (which is attached to all three chains and so is acted on by all three tensions).

Figures 5.3b and 5.3c show our free-body diagrams and choice of coordinate axes. Two forces act on the engine: its weight w and the upward force T_1 exerted by the vertical chain. Three forces act on the ring: the tensions from the vertical chain (T_1), the horizontal chain (T_2), and the slanted chain (T_3). Because the vertical chain has negligible weight, it exerts forces of the same magnitude T_1 at both of its ends (see Example 5.1). (If the weight of this chain were not negligible, these two forces would have different magnitudes; see Example 5.2.) The weight of the ring is also negligible, so it isn't included in Fig. 5.3c.

EXECUTE: The forces acting on the engine are along the y-axis only, so Newton's first law [Eqs. (5.1)] says

Engine: $\quad \Sigma F_y = T_1 + (-w) = 0 \quad$ and $\quad T_1 = w$

The horizontal and slanted chains don't exert forces on the engine itself because they are not attached to it. These forces do appear when we apply Newton's first law to the ring, however. In the free-body diagram for the ring (Fig. 5.3c), remember that T_1, T_2, and T_3 are the *magnitudes* of the forces. We resolve the force with magnitude T_3 into its x- and y-components. Applying Newton's first law in component form to the ring gives us the two equations

Ring: $\quad \Sigma F_x = T_3 \cos 60° + (-T_2) = 0$

Ring: $\quad \Sigma F_y = T_3 \sin 60° + (-T_1) = 0$

Because $T_1 = w$ (from the engine equation), we can rewrite the second ring equation as

$$T_3 = \frac{T_1}{\sin 60°} = \frac{w}{\sin 60°} = 1.2w$$

We can now use this result in the first ring equation:

$$T_2 = T_3 \cos 60° = w\frac{\cos 60°}{\sin 60°} = 0.58w$$

EVALUATE: The chain attached to the ceiling exerts a force on the ring with a *vertical* component equal to T_1, which in turn is equal to w. But this force also has a horizontal component, so its magnitude T_3 is somewhat greater than w. This chain is under the greatest tension and is the one most susceptible to breaking.

To get enough equations to solve this problem, we had to consider not only the forces on the engine but also the forces acting on a second body (the ring connecting the chains). Situations like this are fairly common in equilibrium problems, so keep this technique in mind.

5.3 Our sketches for this problem.

(a) Engine, chains, and ring

(b) Free-body diagram for engine

(c) Free-body diagram for ring O

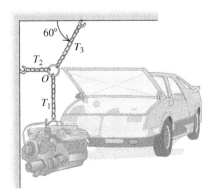

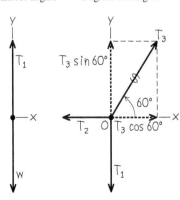

EXAMPLE 5.4 AN INCLINED PLANE

A car of weight w rests on a slanted ramp attached to a trailer (**Fig. 5.4a**). Only a cable running from the trailer to the car prevents the car from rolling off the ramp. (The car's brakes are off and its transmission is in neutral.) Find the tension in the cable and the force that the ramp exerts on the car's tires.

SOLUTION

IDENTIFY: The car is in equilibrium, so we use Newton's first law. The ramp exerts a separate force on each of the car's tires, but for simplicity we lump these forces into a single force. For a further simplification, we'll neglect any friction force the ramp exerts on the tires (see Fig. 4.2b). Hence the ramp exerts only a force on the car that is *perpendicular* to the ramp. As in Section 4.1, we call this force the *normal* force (see Fig. 4.2a). The two target variables are the magnitude T of the tension in the cable and the magnitude n of the normal force.

SET UP: Figure 5.4 shows the situation and a free-body diagram for the car. The three forces acting on the car are its weight (magnitude w), the tension in the cable (magnitude T), and the normal force (magnitude n). Note that the angle α between the ramp and the horizontal is equal to the angle α between the weight vector $\vec{w}$ and the downward normal to the plane of the ramp. Note also that we choose the x- and y-axes to be parallel and perpendicular to the ramp so that we need to resolve only one force (the weight) into x- and y-components. If we had chosen axes that were horizontal and vertical, we'd have to resolve both the normal force and the tension into components.

EXECUTE: To write down the x- and y-components of Newton's first law, we must first find the components of the weight. One complication is that the angle α in Fig. 5.4b is *not* measured from the $+x$-axis toward the $+y$-axis. Hence we *cannot* use Eqs. (1.5) directly to find the components. (You may want to review Section 1.8 to make sure that you understand this important point.)

5.4 A cable holds a car at rest on a ramp.

(a) Car on ramp

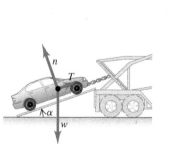

(b) Free-body diagram for car

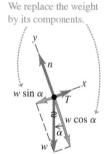

We replace the weight by its components.

One way to find the components of $\vec{w}$ is to consider the right triangles in Fig. 5.4b. The sine of α is the magnitude of the x-component of $\vec{w}$ (that is, the side of the triangle opposite α) divided by the magnitude w (the hypotenuse of the triangle). Similarly, the cosine of α is the magnitude of the y-component (the side of the triangle adjacent to α) divided by w. Both components are negative, so $w_x = -w\sin\alpha$ and $w_y = -w\cos\alpha$.

Another approach is to recognize that one component of $\vec{w}$ must involve $\sin\alpha$ while the other component involves $\cos\alpha$. To decide which is which, draw the free-body diagram so that the angle α is noticeably smaller or larger than 45°. (You'll have to fight the natural tendency to draw such angles as being close to 45°.) We've drawn Fig. 5.4b so that α is smaller than 45°, so $\sin\alpha$ is less than $\cos\alpha$. The figure shows that the x-component of $\vec{w}$ is smaller than the y-component, so the x-component must involve $\sin\alpha$ and the y-component must involve $\cos\alpha$. We again find $w_x = -w\sin\alpha$ and $w_y = -w\cos\alpha$.

In Fig. 5.4b we draw a wiggly line through the original vector representing the weight to remind us not to count it twice. Newton's first law gives us

$$\sum F_x = T + (-w\sin\alpha) = 0$$
$$\sum F_y = n + (-w\cos\alpha) = 0$$

(Remember that T, w, and n are all *magnitudes* of vectors and are therefore all positive.) Solving these equations for T and n, we find

$$T = w\sin\alpha$$
$$n = w\cos\alpha$$

EVALUATE: Our answers for T and n depend on the value of α. To check this dependence, let's look at some special cases. If the ramp is horizontal ($\alpha = 0$), we get $T = 0$ and $n = w$: No cable tension T is needed to hold the car, and the normal force n is equal in magnitude to the weight. If the ramp is vertical ($\alpha = 90°$), we get $T = w$ and $n = 0$: The cable tension T supports all of the car's weight, and there's nothing pushing the car against the ramp.

CAUTION **Normal force and weight may not be equal** It's a common error to assume that the normal-force magnitude n equals the weight w. Our result shows that this is *not* always the case. Always treat n as a variable and solve for its value, as we've done here. ▌

How would the answers for T and n be affected if the car were being pulled up the ramp at a constant speed? This, too, is an equilibrium situation, since the car's velocity is constant. So the calculation is the same, and T and n have the same values as when the car is at rest. (It's true that T must be greater than $w\sin\alpha$ to *start* the car moving up the ramp, but that's not what we asked.)

EXAMPLE 5.5 EQUILIBRIUM OF BODIES CONNECTED BY CABLE AND PULLEY

Your firm needs to haul granite blocks up a 15° slope out of a quarry and to lower dirt into the quarry to fill the holes. You design a system in which a granite block on a cart with steel wheels (weight w_1, including both block and cart) is pulled uphill on steel rails by a dirt-filled bucket (weight w_2, including both dirt and bucket) that descends vertically into the quarry (**Fig. 5.5a**). How must the weights w_1 and w_2 be related in order for the system to move with constant speed? Ignore friction in the pulley and wheels, and ignore the weight of the cable.

5.5 Our sketches for this problem.

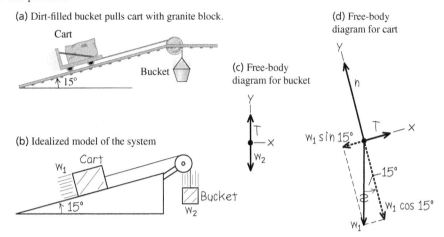

(a) Dirt-filled bucket pulls cart with granite block.

Cart

Bucket

15°

(b) Idealized model of the system

w_1 Cart

15°   Bucket w_2

(c) Free-body diagram for bucket

Y

T

x

w_2

(d) Free-body diagram for cart

Y

n

$w_1 \sin 15°$ T x

15°

$w_1 \cos 15°$

w_1

SOLUTION

IDENTIFY and SET UP: The cart and bucket each move with a constant velocity (in a straight line at constant speed). Hence each body is in equilibrium, and we can apply Newton's first law to each. Our target is an expression relating the weights w_1 and w_2.

Figure 5.5b shows our idealized model for the system, and Figs. 5.5c and 5.5d show our free-body diagrams. The two forces on the bucket are its weight w_2 and an upward tension exerted by the cable. As for the car on the ramp in Example 5.4, three forces act on the cart: its weight w_1, a normal force of magnitude n exerted by the rails, and a tension force from the cable. Since we're assuming that the cable has negligible weight, the tension forces that the cable exerts on the cart and on the bucket have the same magnitude T. (We're ignoring friction, so we assume that the rails exert no force on the cart parallel to the incline.) Note that we orient the axes differently for each body; the choices shown are the most convenient ones. We find the components of the weight force in the same way that we did in Example 5.4. (Compare Fig. 5.5d with Fig. 5.4b.)

EXECUTE: Applying $\Sigma F_y = 0$ to the bucket in Fig. 5.5c, we find

$$\Sigma F_y = T + (-w_2) = 0 \qquad \text{so} \qquad T = w_2$$

Applying $\Sigma F_x = 0$ to the cart (and block) in Fig. 5.5d, we get

$$\Sigma F_x = T + (-w_1 \sin 15°) = 0 \qquad \text{so} \qquad T = w_1 \sin 15°$$

Equating the two expressions for T, we find

$$w_2 = w_1 \sin 15° = 0.26w_1$$

EVALUATE: Our analysis doesn't depend at all on the direction in which the cart and bucket move. Hence the system can move with constant speed in *either* direction if the weight of the dirt and bucket is 26% of the weight of the granite block and cart. What would happen if w_2 were greater than $0.26w_1$? If it were less than $0.26w_1$?

Notice that we didn't need the equation $\Sigma F_y = 0$ for the cart and block. Can you use this to show that $n = w_1 \cos 15°$?

TEST YOUR UNDERSTANDING OF SECTION 5.1   A traffic light of weight w hangs from two lightweight cables, one on each side of the light. Each cable hangs at a 45° angle from the horizontal. What is the tension in each cable? (i) $w/2$; (ii) $w/\sqrt{2}$; (iii) w; (iv) $w\sqrt{2}$; (v) $2w$. ▮

5.2 USING NEWTON'S SECOND LAW: DYNAMICS OF PARTICLES

We are now ready to discuss *dynamics* problems. In these problems, we apply Newton's second law to bodies on which the net force is *not* zero. These bodies are *not* in equilibrium and hence are accelerating:

Newton's second law: $\Sigma \vec{F} = m\vec{a}$ ... body has *acceleration* in
If *net* force on a body   same direction as net force.
is not zero ...   Mass of body

(5.2)

Each component of $\Sigma F_x = ma_x$ $\Sigma F_y = ma_y$ ... equals body's mass
net force on body ...   times corresponding
                                                            acceleration component.

5.6 Correct and incorrect free-body diagrams for a falling body.

(a)

Only the force of gravity acts on this falling fruit.

(b) Correct free-body diagram

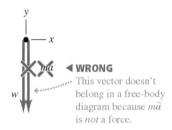

w a_y ◄ **RIGHT!**
... You can safely draw the acceleration vector to one side of the diagram.

(c) Incorrect free-body diagram

$m\vec{a}$ ◄ **WRONG**
... This vector doesn't belong in a free-body diagram because $m\vec{a}$ is *not* a force.
w

The following problem-solving strategy is very similar to Problem-Solving Strategy 5.1 for equilibrium problems in Section 5.1. Study it carefully, watch how we apply it in our examples, and use it when you tackle the end-of-chapter problems. You can use this strategy to solve *any* dynamics problem.

> CAUTION $m\vec{a}$ **doesn't belong in free-body diagrams** Remember that the quantity $m\vec{a}$ is the *result* of forces acting on a body, *not* a force itself. When you draw the free-body diagram for an accelerating body (like the fruit in **Fig. 5.6a**), *never* include the "$m\vec{a}$ force" because *there is no such force* (Fig. 5.6c). Review Section 4.3 if you're not clear on this point. Sometimes we draw the acceleration vector $\vec{a}$ *alongside* a free-body diagram, as in Fig. 5.6b. But we *never* draw the acceleration vector with its tail touching the body (a position reserved exclusively for forces that act on the body). ▮

PROBLEM-SOLVING STRATEGY 5.2 NEWTON'S SECOND LAW: DYNAMICS OF PARTICLES

IDENTIFY *the relevant concepts:* You have to use Newton's second law, Eqs. (5.2), for *any* problem that involves forces acting on an accelerating body.

Identify the target variable—usually an acceleration or a force. If the target variable is something else, you'll need to select another concept to use. For example, suppose the target variable is how fast a sled is moving when it reaches the bottom of a hill. Newton's second law will let you find the sled's acceleration; you'll then use the constant-acceleration relationships from Section 2.4 to find velocity from acceleration.

SET UP *the problem* by using the following steps:
1. Draw a simple sketch of the situation that shows each moving body. For each body, draw a free-body diagram that shows all the forces acting *on* the body. [The sums in Eqs. (5.2) include the forces that act on the body, *not* the forces that it exerts on anything else.] Make sure you can answer the question "What other body is applying this force?" for each force in your diagram. Never include the quantity $m\vec{a}$ in your free-body diagram; it's not a force!
2. Label each force with an algebraic symbol for the force's *magnitude.* Usually, one of the forces will be the body's weight; it's usually best to label this as $w = mg$.
3. Choose your x- and y-coordinate axes for each body, and show them in its free-body diagram. Indicate the positive direction for each axis. If you know the direction of the acceleration, it usually simplifies things to take one positive axis along that direction. If your problem involves two or more bodies that accelerate in different directions, you can use a different set of axes for each body.

4. In addition to Newton's second law, $\sum \vec{F} = m\vec{a}$, identify any other equations you might need. For example, you might need one or more of the equations for motion with constant acceleration. If more than one body is involved, there may be relationships among their motions; for example, they may be connected by a rope. Express any such relationships as equations relating the accelerations of the various bodies.

EXECUTE *the solution* as follows:
1. For each body, determine the components of the forces along each of the body's coordinate axes. When you represent a force in terms of its components, draw a wiggly line through the original force vector to remind you not to include it twice.
2. List all of the known and unknown quantities. In your list, identify the target variable or variables.
3. For each body, write a separate equation for each component of Newton's second law, as in Eqs. (5.2). Write any additional equations that you identified in step 4 of "Set Up." (You need as many equations as there are target variables.)
4. Do the easy part—the math! Solve the equations to find the target variable(s).

EVALUATE *your answer:* Does your answer have the correct units? (When appropriate, use the conversion $1 \text{ N} = 1 \text{ kg} \cdot \text{m/s}^2$.) Does it have the correct algebraic sign? When possible, consider particular values or extreme cases of quantities and compare the results with your intuitive expectations. Ask, "Does this result make sense?"

EXAMPLE 5.6 STRAIGHT-LINE MOTION WITH A CONSTANT FORCE

An iceboat is at rest on a frictionless horizontal surface (**Fig. 5.7a**). Due to the blowing wind, 4.0 s after the iceboat is released, it is moving to the right at 6.0 m/s (about 22 km/h, or 13 mi/h). What constant horizontal force F_W does the wind exert on the iceboat? The combined mass of iceboat and rider is 200 kg.

___

SOLUTION

IDENTIFY and SET UP: Our target variable is one of the forces (F_W) acting on the accelerating iceboat, so we need to use Newton's second law. The forces acting on the iceboat and rider (considered as a unit) are the weight w, the normal force n exerted by the surface, and the horizontal force F_W. Figure 5.7b shows the free-body diagram. The net force and hence the acceleration are to the right, so we chose the positive x-axis in this direction. The acceleration isn't given; we'll need to find it. Since the wind is assumed to exert a constant force, the resulting acceleration is constant and we can use one of the constant-acceleration formulas from Section 2.4.

5.7 Our sketches for this problem.

(a) Iceboat and rider on frictionless ice

(b) Free-body diagram for iceboat and rider

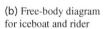

The iceboat starts at rest (its initial x-velocity is $v_{0x} = 0$) and it attains an x-velocity $v_x = 6.0$ m/s after an elapsed time $t = 4.0$ s. To relate the x-acceleration a_x to these quantities we use Eq. (2.8), $v_x = v_{0x} + a_x t$. There is no vertical acceleration, so we expect that the normal force on the iceboat is equal in magnitude to the iceboat's weight.

EXECUTE: The *known* quantities are the mass $m = 200$ kg, the initial and final x-velocities $v_{0x} = 0$ and $v_x = 6.0$ m/s, and the elapsed time $t = 4.0$ s. There are three *unknown* quantities: the acceleration a_x, the normal force n, and the horizontal force F_W. Hence we need three equations.

The first two equations are the x- and y-equations for Newton's second law, Eqs. (5.2). The force F_W is in the positive x-direction, while the forces n and $w = mg$ are in the positive and negative y-directions, respectively. Hence we have

$$\sum F_x = F_W = ma_x$$
$$\sum F_y = n + (-mg) = 0 \quad \text{so} \quad n = mg$$

The third equation is Eq. (2.8) for constant acceleration:

$$v_x = v_{0x} + a_x t$$

To find F_W, we first solve this third equation for a_x and then substitute the result into the $\sum F_x$ equation:

$$a_x = \frac{v_x - v_{0x}}{t} = \frac{6.0 \text{ m/s} - 0 \text{ m/s}}{4.0 \text{ s}} = 1.5 \text{ m/s}^2$$
$$F_W = ma_x = (200 \text{ kg})(1.5 \text{ m/s}^2) = 300 \text{ kg} \cdot \text{m/s}^2$$

Since $1 \text{ kg} \cdot \text{m/s}^2 = 1 \text{ N}$, the final answer is

$$F_W = 300 \text{ N (about 67 lb)}$$

EVALUATE: Our answers for F_W and n have the correct units for a force, and (as expected) the magnitude n of the normal force is equal to mg. Does it seem reasonable that the force F_W is substantially *less* than mg?

___

EXAMPLE 5.7 STRAIGHT-LINE MOTION WITH FRICTION

Suppose a constant horizontal friction force with magnitude 100 N opposes the motion of the iceboat in Example 5.6. In this case, what constant force F_W must the wind exert on the iceboat to cause the same constant x-acceleration $a_x = 1.5$ m/s^2?

___

SOLUTION

IDENTIFY and SET UP: Again the target variable is F_W. We are given the x-acceleration, so to find F_W all we need is Newton's second law. **Figure 5.8** shows our new free-body diagram. The only difference from Fig. 5.7b is the addition of the friction force $\vec{f}$, which points in the negative x-direction (opposite the motion). Because the wind must now overcome the friction force to yield the same acceleration as in Example 5.6, we expect our answer for F_W to be greater than the 300 N we found there.

5.8 Our free-body diagram for the iceboat and rider with friction force $\vec{f}$ opposing the motion.

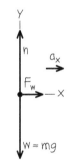

Continued

EXECUTE: Two forces now have *x*-components: the force of the wind (*x*-component $+F_W$) and the friction force (*x*-component $-f$). The *x*-component of Newton's second law gives

$$\Sigma F_x = F_W + (-f) = ma_x$$

$$F_W = ma_x + f = (200 \text{ kg})(1.5 \text{ m/s}^2) + (100 \text{ N}) = 400 \text{ N}$$

EVALUATE: The required value of F_W is 100 N greater than in Example 5.6 because the wind must now push against an additional 100-N friction force.

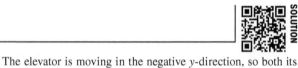

EXAMPLE 5.8   **TENSION IN AN ELEVATOR CABLE**

An elevator and its load have a combined mass of 800 kg (**Fig. 5.9a**). The elevator is initially moving downward at 10.0 m/s; it slows to a stop with constant acceleration in a distance of 25.0 m. What is the tension *T* in the supporting cable while the elevator is being brought to rest?

___

SOLUTION

IDENTIFY and SET UP: The target variable is the tension *T*, which we'll find by using Newton's second law. As in Example 5.6, we'll use a constant-acceleration formula to determine the acceleration. Our free-body diagram (Fig. 5.9b) shows two forces acting on the elevator: its weight *w* and the tension force *T* of the cable. The elevator is moving downward with decreasing speed, so its acceleration is upward; we chose the positive *y*-axis to be upward.

5.9 Our sketches for this problem.

(a) Descending elevator

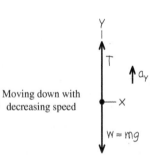

Moving down with
decreasing speed

(b) Free-body diagram
for elevator

The elevator is moving in the negative *y*-direction, so both its initial *y*-velocity v_{0y} and its *y*-displacement $y - y_0$ are negative: $v_{0y} = -10.0$ m/s and $y - y_0 = -25.0$ m. The final *y*-velocity is $v_y = 0$. To find the *y*-acceleration a_y from this information, we'll use Eq. (2.13) in the form $v_y^2 = v_{0y}^2 + 2a_y(y - y_0)$. Once we have a_y, we'll substitute it into the *y*-component of Newton's second law from Eqs. (5.2) and solve for *T*. The net force must be upward to give an upward acceleration, so we expect *T* to be greater than the weight $w = mg = (800 \text{ kg})(9.80 \text{ m/s}^2) = 7840$ N.

EXECUTE: First let's write out Newton's second law. The tension force acts upward and the weight acts downward, so

$$\Sigma F_y = T + (-w) = ma_y$$

We solve for the target variable *T*:

$$T = w + ma_y = mg + ma_y = m(g + a_y)$$

To determine a_y, we rewrite the constant-acceleration equation $v_y^2 = v_{0y}^2 + 2a_y(y - y_0)$:

$$a_y = \frac{v_y^2 - v_{0y}^2}{2(y - y_0)} = \frac{(0)^2 - (-10.0 \text{ m/s})^2}{2(-25.0 \text{ m})} = +2.00 \text{ m/s}^2$$

The acceleration is upward (positive), just as it should be.

Now we can substitute the acceleration into the equation for the tension:

$$T = m(g + a_y) = (800 \text{ kg})(9.80 \text{ m/s}^2 + 2.00 \text{ m/s}^2) = 9440 \text{ N}$$

EVALUATE: The tension is greater than the weight, as expected. Can you see that we would get the same answers for a_y and *T* if the elevator were moving *upward* and *gaining* speed at a rate of 2.00 m/s²?

EXAMPLE 5.9   **APPARENT WEIGHT IN AN ACCELERATING ELEVATOR**

A 50.0-kg woman stands on a bathroom scale while riding in the elevator in Example 5.8. What is the reading on the scale?

___

SOLUTION

IDENTIFY and SET UP: The scale (**Fig. 5.10a**) reads the magnitude of the downward force exerted *by* the woman *on* the scale. By Newton's third law, this equals the magnitude of the upward normal force exerted *by* the scale *on* the woman. Hence our target variable is the magnitude *n* of the normal force. We'll find *n* by applying Newton's second law to the woman. We already know her acceleration; it's the same as the acceleration of the elevator, which we calculated in Example 5.8.

Figure 5.10b shows our free-body diagram for the woman. The forces acting on her are the normal force *n* exerted by the

5.10 Our sketches for this problem.

(a) Woman in a
descending elevator

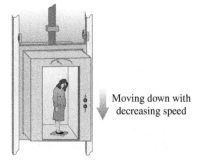

Moving down with
decreasing speed

(b) Free-body diagram
for woman

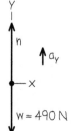

scale and her weight $w = mg = (50.0 \text{ kg})(9.80 \text{ m/s}^2) = 490$ N. (The tension force, which played a major role in Example 5.8, doesn't appear here because it doesn't act on the woman.) From Example 5.8, the y-acceleration of the elevator and of the woman is $a_y = +2.00 \text{ m/s}^2$. As in Example 5.8, the upward force on the body accelerating upward (in this case, the normal force on the woman) will have to be greater than the body's weight to produce the upward acceleration.

EXECUTE: Newton's second law gives

$$\sum F_y = n + (-mg) = ma_y$$

$$n = mg + ma_y = m(g + a_y)$$

$$= (50.0 \text{ kg})(9.80 \text{ m/s}^2 + 2.00 \text{ m/s}^2) = 590 \text{ N}$$

EVALUATE: Our answer for n means that while the elevator is stopping, the scale pushes up on the woman with a force of 590 N. By Newton's third law, she pushes down on the scale with the same force. So the scale reads 590 N, which is 100 N more than her actual weight. The scale reading is called the passenger's **apparent weight.** The woman *feels* the floor pushing up harder on her feet than when the elevator is stationary or moving with constant velocity.

What would the woman feel if the elevator were accelerating *downward*, so that $a_y = -2.00 \text{ m/s}^2$? This would be the case if the elevator were moving upward with decreasing speed or moving downward with increasing speed. To find the answer for this situation, we just insert the new value of a_y in our equation for n:

$$n = m(g + a_y) = (50.0 \text{ kg})[9.80 \text{ m/s}^2 + (-2.00 \text{ m/s}^2)]$$

$$= 390 \text{ N}$$

Now the woman would feel as though she weighs only 390 N, or 100 N *less* than her actual weight w.

You can feel these effects yourself; try taking a few steps in an elevator that is coming to a stop after descending (when your apparent weight is greater than w) or coming to a stop after ascending (when your apparent weight is less than w).

Apparent Weight and Apparent Weightlessness

Let's generalize the result of Example 5.9. When a passenger with mass m rides in an elevator with y-acceleration a_y, a scale shows the passenger's apparent weight to be

$$n = m(g + a_y)$$

When the elevator is accelerating upward, a_y is positive and n is greater than the passenger's weight $w = mg$. When the elevator is accelerating downward, a_y is negative and n is less than the weight. If the passenger doesn't know the elevator is accelerating, she may feel as though her weight is changing; indeed, this is just what the scale shows.

The extreme case occurs when the elevator has a downward acceleration $a_y = -g$—that is, when it is in free fall. In that case $n = 0$ and the passenger *seems* to be weightless. Similarly, an astronaut orbiting the earth with a spacecraft experiences *apparent weightlessness* (**Fig. 5.11**). In each case, the person is not truly weightless because a gravitational force still acts. But the person's *sensations* in this free-fall condition are exactly the same as though the person were in outer space with no gravitational force at all. In both cases the person and the vehicle (elevator or spacecraft) fall together with the same acceleration g, so nothing pushes the person against the floor or walls of the vehicle.

5.11 Astronauts in orbit feel "weightless" because they have the same acceleration as their spacecraft. They are *not* outside the pull of the earth's gravity. (We'll discuss the motions of orbiting bodies in detail in Chapter 12.)

EXAMPLE 5.10   ACCELERATION DOWN A HILL

A toboggan loaded with students (total weight w) slides down a snow-covered hill that slopes at a constant angle α. The toboggan is well waxed, so there is virtually no friction. What is its acceleration?

SOLUTION

IDENTIFY and SET UP: Our target variable is the acceleration, which we'll find by using Newton's second law. There is no friction, so only two forces act on the toboggan: its weight w and the normal force n exerted by the hill.

Figure 5.12 shows our sketch and free-body diagram. We take axes parallel and perpendicular to the surface of the hill, so that the acceleration (which is parallel to the hill) is along the positive x-direction.

5.12 Our sketches for this problem.

(a) The situation

(b) Free-body diagram for toboggan

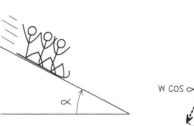

Continued

EXECUTE: The normal force has only a y-component, but the weight has both x- and y-components: $w_x = w \sin \alpha$ and $w_y = -w \cos \alpha$. (In Example 5.4 we had $w_x = -w \sin \alpha$. The difference is that the positive x-axis was uphill in Example 5.4 but is downhill in Fig. 5.12b.) The wiggly line in Fig. 5.12b reminds us that we have resolved the weight into its components. The acceleration is purely in the $+x$-direction, so $a_y = 0$. Newton's second law in component form from Eqs. (5.2) then tells us that

$$\sum F_x = w \sin \alpha = ma_x$$

$$\sum F_y = n - w \cos \alpha = ma_y = 0$$

Since $w = mg$, the x-component equation gives $mg \sin \alpha = ma_x$, or

$$a_x = g \sin \alpha$$

Note that we didn't need the y-component equation to find the acceleration. That's part of the beauty of choosing the x-axis to lie along the acceleration direction! The y-equation tells us the magnitude of the normal force exerted by the hill on the toboggan:

$$n = w \cos \alpha = mg \cos \alpha$$

EVALUATE: Notice that the normal force n is not equal to the toboggan's weight (compare Example 5.4). Notice also that the mass m does not appear in our result for the acceleration. That's because the downhill force on the toboggan (a component of the weight) is proportional to m, so the mass cancels out when we use $\sum F_x = ma_x$ to calculate a_x. Hence *any* toboggan, regardless of its mass, slides down a frictionless hill with acceleration $g \sin \alpha$.

If the plane is horizontal, $\alpha = 0$ and $a_x = 0$ (the toboggan does not accelerate); if the plane is vertical, $\alpha = 90°$ and $a_x = g$ (the toboggan is in free fall).

CAUTION   Common free-body diagram errors   Figure 5.13 shows both the correct way (Fig. 5.13a) and a common *incorrect* way (Fig. 5.13b) to draw the free-body diagram for the toboggan. The diagram in Fig. 5.13b is wrong for two reasons: The normal force must be drawn perpendicular to the surface (remember, "normal" means perpendicular), and there's no such thing as the "$m\vec{a}$ force." ∎

5.13 Correct and incorrect free-body diagrams for a toboggan on a frictionless hill.

(a) Correct free-body diagram for the sled

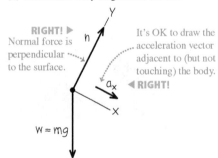

(b) Incorrect free-body diagram for the sled

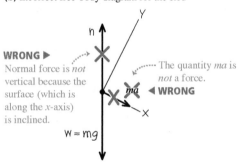

EXAMPLE 5.11   TWO BODIES WITH THE SAME ACCELERATION

You push a 1.00-kg food tray through the cafeteria line with a constant 9.0-N force. The tray pushes a 0.50-kg milk carton (**Fig. 5.14a**). The tray and carton slide on a horizontal surface so greasy that friction can be ignored. Find the acceleration of the tray and carton and the horizontal force that the tray exerts on the carton.

SOLUTION

IDENTIFY and SET UP: Our *two* target variables are the acceleration of the tray–carton system and the force of the tray on the carton. We'll use Newton's second law to get two equations, one for each target variable. We set up and solve the problem in two ways.

Method 1: We treat the carton (mass m_C) and tray (mass m_T) as separate bodies, each with its own free-body diagram (Figs. 5.14b and 5.14c). The force F that you exert on the tray doesn't appear in the free-body diagram for the carton, which is accelerated by the force (of magnitude $F_{T \text{ on } C}$) exerted on it by the tray. By Newton's third law, the carton exerts a force of equal magnitude on the tray: $F_{C \text{ on } T} = F_{T \text{ on } C}$. We take the acceleration to be in the positive x-direction; both the tray and milk carton move with the same x-acceleration a_x.

Method 2: We treat the tray and milk carton as a composite body of mass $m = m_T + m_C = 1.50 \text{ kg}$ (Fig. 5.14d). The only horizontal force acting on this body is the force F that you exert. The forces $F_{T \text{ on } C}$ and $F_{C \text{ on } T}$ don't come into play because they're *internal* to this composite body, and Newton's second law tells us that only *external* forces affect a body's acceleration (see Section 4.3). To find the magnitude $F_{T \text{ on } C}$ we'll again apply Newton's second law to the carton, as in Method 1.

EXECUTE: *Method 1:* The x-component equations of Newton's second law are

Tray: $\sum F_x = F - F_{C \text{ on } T} = F - F_{T \text{ on } C} = m_T a_x$

Carton: $\sum F_x = F_{T \text{ on } C} = m_C a_x$

These are two simultaneous equations for the two target variables a_x and $F_{T \text{ on } C}$. (Two equations are all we need, which means that the y-components don't play a role in this example.) An easy way to solve the two equations for a_x is to add them; this eliminates $F_{T \text{ on } C}$, giving

$$F = m_T a_x + m_C a_x = (m_T + m_C) a_x$$

5.14 Pushing a food tray and milk carton in the cafeteria line.

(a) A milk carton and a food tray

(b) Free-body diagram for milk carton

(c) Free-body diagram for food tray

(d) Free-body diagram for carton and tray as a composite body

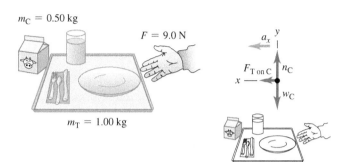

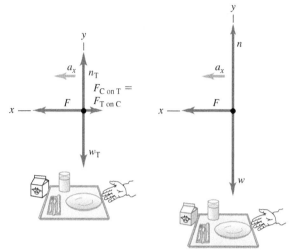

We solve this equation for a_x:

$$a_x = \frac{F}{m_T + m_C} = \frac{9.0\ \text{N}}{1.00\ \text{kg} + 0.50\ \text{kg}} = 6.0\ \text{m/s}^2 = 0.61g$$

Substituting this value into the carton equation gives

$$F_{T\ \text{on}\ C} = m_C a_x = (0.50\ \text{kg})(6.0\ \text{m/s}^2) = 3.0\ \text{N}$$

Method 2: The x-component of Newton's second law for the composite body of mass m is

$$\sum F_x = F = ma_x$$

The acceleration of this composite body is

$$a_x = \frac{F}{m} = \frac{9.0\ \text{N}}{1.50\ \text{kg}} = 6.0\ \text{m/s}^2$$

Then, looking at the milk carton by itself, we see that to give it an acceleration of $6.0\ \text{m/s}^2$ requires that the tray exert a force

$$F_{T\ \text{on}\ C} = m_C a_x = (0.50\ \text{kg})(6.0\ \text{m/s}^2) = 3.0\ \text{N}$$

EVALUATE: The answers are the same with both methods. To check the answers, note that there are different forces on the two sides of the tray: $F = 9.0\ \text{N}$ on the right and $F_{C\ \text{on}\ T} = 3.0\ \text{N}$ on the left. The net horizontal force on the tray is $F - F_{C\ \text{on}\ T} = 6.0\ \text{N}$, exactly enough to accelerate a 1.00-kg tray at $6.0\ \text{m/s}^2$.

Treating two bodies as a single, composite body works *only* if the two bodies have the same magnitude *and* direction of acceleration. If the accelerations are different we must treat the two bodies separately, as in the next example.

EXAMPLE 5.12   **TWO BODIES WITH THE SAME MAGNITUDE OF ACCELERATION**

Figure 5.15a shows an air-track glider with mass m_1 moving on a level, frictionless air track in the physics lab. The glider is connected to a lab weight with mass m_2 by a light, flexible, non-stretching string that passes over a stationary, frictionless pulley. Find the acceleration of each body and the tension in the string.

SOLUTION

IDENTIFY and SET UP: The glider and weight are accelerating, so again we must use Newton's second law. Our three target variables are the tension T in the string and the accelerations of the two bodies.

The two bodies move in different directions—one horizontal, one vertical—so we can't consider them to be a single unit as we did the bodies in Example 5.11. Figures 5.15b and 5.15c show our free-body diagrams and coordinate systems. It's convenient to have both bodies accelerate in the positive axis directions, so we chose the positive y-direction for the lab weight to be downward.

We consider the string to be massless and to slide over the pulley without friction, so the tension T in the string is the same throughout and it applies a force of the same magnitude T to each

5.15 Our sketches for this problem.

(a) Apparatus

(b) Free-body diagram for glider

(c) Free-body diagram for weight

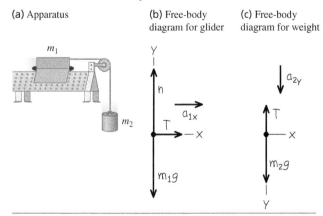

body. (You may want to review Conceptual Example 4.10, in which we discussed the tension force exerted by a massless rope.) The weights are $m_1 g$ and $m_2 g$.

Continued

While the *directions* of the two accelerations are different, their *magnitudes* are the same. (That's because the string doesn't stretch, so the two bodies must move equal distances in equal times and their speeds at any instant must be equal. When the speeds change, they change at the same rate, so the accelerations of the two bodies must have the same magnitude a.) We can express this relationship as $a_{1x} = a_{2y} = a$, which means that we have only *two* target variables: a and the tension T.

What results do we expect? If $m_1 = 0$ (or, approximately, for m_1 much less than m_2) the lab weight will fall freely with acceleration g, and the tension in the string will be zero. For $m_2 = 0$ (or, approximately, for m_2 much less than m_1) we expect zero acceleration and zero tension.

EXECUTE: Newton's second law gives

Glider: $\sum F_x = T = m_1 a_{1x} = m_1 a$

Glider: $\sum F_y = n + (-m_1 g) = m_1 a_{1y} = 0$

Lab weight: $\sum F_y = m_2 g + (-T) = m_2 a_{2y} = m_2 a$

(There are no forces on the lab weight in the x-direction.) In these equations we've used $a_{1y} = 0$ (the glider doesn't accelerate vertically) and $a_{1x} = a_{2y} = a$.

The x-equation for the glider and the equation for the lab weight give us two simultaneous equations for T and a:

Glider: $T = m_1 a$

Lab weight: $m_2 g - T = m_2 a$

We add the two equations to eliminate T, giving

$$m_2 g = m_1 a + m_2 a = (m_1 + m_2)a$$

and so the magnitude of each body's acceleration is

$$a = \frac{m_2}{m_1 + m_2} g$$

Substituting this back into the glider equation $T = m_1 a$, we get

$$T = \frac{m_1 m_2}{m_1 + m_2} g$$

EVALUATE: The acceleration is in general less than g, as you might expect; the string tension keeps the lab weight from falling freely. The tension T is *not* equal to the weight $m_2 g$ of the lab weight, but is *less* by a factor of $m_1/(m_1 + m_2)$. If T *were* equal to $m_2 g$, then the lab weight would be in equilibrium, and it isn't.

As predicted, the acceleration is equal to g for $m_1 = 0$ and equal to zero for $m_2 = 0$, and $T = 0$ for either $m_1 = 0$ or $m_2 = 0$.

CAUTION **Tension and weight may not be equal** It's a common mistake to assume that if an object is attached to a vertical string, the string tension must be equal to the object's weight. That was the case in Example 5.5, where the acceleration was zero, but it's not the case in this example! The only safe approach is *always* to treat the tension as a variable, as we did here. ▌

PhET: Lunar Lander

TEST YOUR UNDERSTANDING OF SECTION 5.2   Suppose you hold the glider in Example 5.12 so that it and the weight are initially at rest. You give the glider a push to the left in Fig. 5.15a and then release it. The string remains taut as the glider moves to the left, comes instantaneously to rest, then moves to the right. At the instant the glider has zero velocity, what is the tension in the string? (i) Greater than in Example 5.12; (ii) the same as in Example 5.12; (iii) less than in Example 5.12 but greater than zero; (iv) zero. ▌

5.3 FRICTION FORCES

We've seen several problems in which a body rests or slides on a surface that exerts forces on the body. Whenever two bodies interact by direct contact (touching) of their surfaces, we describe the interaction in terms of *contact forces*. The normal force is one example of a contact force; in this section we'll look in detail at another contact force, the force of friction.

Friction is important in many aspects of everyday life. The oil in a car engine minimizes friction between moving parts, but without friction between the tires and the road we couldn't drive or turn the car. Air drag—the friction force exerted by the air on a body moving through it—decreases automotive fuel economy but makes parachutes work. Without friction, nails would pull out and most forms of animal locomotion would be impossible (**Fig. 5.16**).

Kinetic and Static Friction

When you try to slide a heavy box of books across the floor, the box doesn't move at all unless you push with a certain minimum force. Once the box starts moving, you can usually keep it moving with less force than you needed to get it started. If you take some of the books out, you need less force to get it started or keep it moving. What can we say in general about this behavior?

5.16 There is friction between the feet of this caterpillar (the larval stage of a butterfly of the family Papilionidae) and the surfaces over which it walks. Without friction, the caterpillar could not move forward or climb over obstacles.

First, when a body rests or slides on a surface, we can think of the surface as exerting a single contact force on the body, with force components perpendicular and parallel to the surface (**Fig. 5.17**). The perpendicular component vector is the normal force, denoted by $\vec{n}$. The component vector parallel to the surface (and perpendicular to $\vec{n}$) is the **friction force,** denoted by $\vec{f}$. If the surface is frictionless, then $\vec{f}$ is zero but there is still a normal force. (Frictionless surfaces are an unattainable idealization, like a massless rope. But we can approximate a surface as frictionless if the effects of friction are negligibly small.) The direction of the friction force is always such as to oppose relative motion of the two surfaces.

The kind of friction that acts when a body slides over a surface is called a **kinetic friction force** $\vec{f}_k$. The adjective "kinetic" and the subscript "k" remind us that the two surfaces are moving relative to each other. The *magnitude* of the kinetic friction force usually increases when the normal force increases. This is why it takes more force to slide a full box of books across the floor than an empty one. Automotive brakes use the same principle: The harder the brake pads are squeezed against the rotating brake discs, the greater the braking effect. In many cases the magnitude of the kinetic friction force f_k is found experimentally to be approximately *proportional* to the magnitude n of the normal force:

$$\underset{\text{friction force}}{\text{Magnitude of kinetic}} \cdots\!\rightarrow f_k = \mu_k n \overset{\longleftarrow \text{Coefficient of kinetic friction}}{\underset{\cdots \text{Magnitude of normal force}}{}} \quad (5.3)$$

Here μ_k (pronounced "mu-sub-k") is a constant called the **coefficient of kinetic friction.** The more slippery the surface, the smaller this coefficient. Because it is a quotient of two force magnitudes, μ_k is a pure number without units.

CAUTION **Friction and normal forces are always perpendicular** Remember that Eq. (5.3) is *not* a vector equation because $\vec{f}_k$ and $\vec{n}$ are always perpendicular. Rather, it is a scalar relationship between the magnitudes of the two forces. ▌

Equation (5.3) is only an approximate representation of a complex phenomenon. On a microscopic level, friction and normal forces result from the intermolecular forces (electrical in nature) between two rough surfaces at points where they come into contact (**Fig. 5.18**). As a box slides over the floor, bonds between the two surfaces form and break, and the total number of such bonds varies. Hence the kinetic friction force is not perfectly constant. Smoothing the surfaces can actually increase friction, since more molecules can interact and bond; bringing two smooth surfaces of the same metal together can cause a "cold weld." Lubricating oils work because an oil film between two surfaces (such as the pistons and cylinder walls in a car engine) prevents them from coming into actual contact.

Table 5.1 lists some representative values of μ_k. Although these values are given with two significant figures, they are only approximate, since friction forces can also depend on the speed of the body relative to the surface. For now we'll ignore this effect and assume that μ_k and f_k are independent of speed, in order to concentrate on the simplest cases. Table 5.1 also lists coefficients of static friction; we'll define these shortly.

Friction forces may also act when there is *no* relative motion. If you try to slide a box across the floor, the box may not move at all because the floor exerts an equal and opposite friction force on the box. This is called a **static friction force** $\vec{f}_s$.

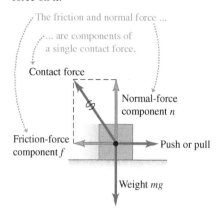

5.17 When a block is pushed or pulled over a surface, the surface exerts a contact force on it.

The friction and normal force ...
... are components of a single contact force.

Contact force

Normal-force component n

Friction-force component f

Push or pull

Weight mg

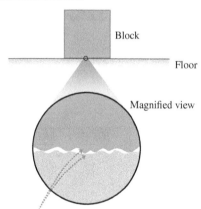

5.18 A microscopic view of the friction and normal forces.

Block

Floor

Magnified view

The friction and normal forces result from interactions between molecules in the block and in the floor where the two rough surfaces touch.

	Approximate **Coefficients of Friction**	
TABLE 5.1		
Materials	Coefficient of Static Friction, μ_s	Coefficient of Kinetic Friction, μ_k
Steel on steel	0.74	0.57
Aluminum on steel	0.61	0.47
Copper on steel	0.53	0.36
Brass on steel	0.51	0.44
Zinc on cast iron	0.85	0.21
Copper on cast iron	1.05	0.29
Glass on glass	0.94	0.40
Copper on glass	0.68	0.53
Teflon on Teflon	0.04	0.04
Teflon on steel	0.04	0.04
Rubber on concrete (dry)	1.0	0.8
Rubber on concrete (wet)	0.30	0.25

5.19 When there is no relative motion, the magnitude of the static friction force f_s is less than or equal to $\mu_s n$. When there is relative motion, the magnitude of the kinetic friction force f_k equals $\mu_k n$.

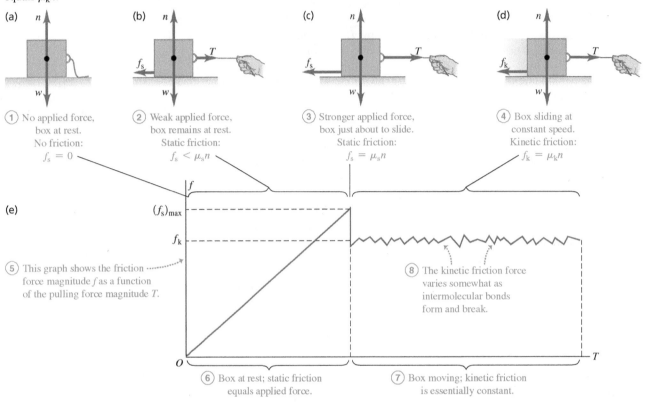

(a)
① No applied force, box at rest.
No friction:
$$f_s = 0$$

(b)
② Weak applied force, box remains at rest.
Static friction:
$$f_s < \mu_s n$$

(c)
③ Stronger applied force, box just about to slide.
Static friction:
$$f_s = \mu_s n$$

(d)
④ Box sliding at constant speed.
Kinetic friction:
$$f_k = \mu_k n$$

(e)
⑤ This graph shows the friction force magnitude f as a function of the pulling force magnitude T.

⑧ The kinetic friction force varies somewhat as intermolecular bonds form and break.

⑥ Box at rest; static friction equals applied force.

⑦ Box moving; kinetic friction is essentially constant.

Application Static Friction and Windshield Wipers The squeak of windshield wipers on dry glass is a stick-slip phenomenon. The moving wiper blade sticks to the glass momentarily, then slides when the force applied to the blade by the wiper motor overcomes the maximum force of static friction. When the glass is wet from rain or windshield cleaning solution, friction is reduced and the wiper blade doesn't stick.

In **Fig. 5.19a**, the box is at rest, in equilibrium, under the action of its weight $\vec{w}$ and the upward normal force $\vec{n}$. The normal force is equal in magnitude to the weight ($n = w$) and is exerted on the box by the floor. Now we tie a rope to the box (Fig. 5.19b) and gradually increase the tension T in the rope. At first the box remains at rest because the force of static friction f_s also increases and stays equal in magnitude to T.

At some point T becomes greater than the maximum static friction force f_s the surface can exert. Then the box "breaks loose" and starts to slide. Figure 5.19c shows the forces when T is at this critical value. For a given pair of surfaces the maximum value of f_s depends on the normal force. Experiment shows that in many cases this maximum value, called $(f_s)_{\max}$, is approximately *proportional* to n; we call the proportionality factor μ_s the **coefficient of static friction.** Table 5.1 lists some representative values of μ_s. In a particular situation, the actual force of static friction can have any magnitude between zero (when there is no other force parallel to the surface) and a maximum value given by $\mu_s n$:

Magnitude of static friction force ⟶ $f_s \leq (f_s)_{\max} = \mu_s n$ ⟵ Coefficient of static friction

Maximum static friction force ⟶   ⟵ Magnitude of normal force

(5.4)

Like Eq. (5.3), this is a relationship between magnitudes, *not* a vector relationship. The equality sign holds only when the applied force T has reached the critical value at which motion is about to start (Fig. 5.19c). When T is less than this value (Fig. 5.19b), the inequality sign holds. In that case we have to use the equilibrium conditions ($\Sigma \vec{F} = 0$) to find f_s. If there is no applied force ($T = 0$) as in Fig. 5.19a, then there is no static friction force either ($f_s = 0$).

As soon as the box starts to slide (Fig. 5.19d), the friction force usually *decreases* (Fig. 5.19e); it's easier to keep the box moving than to start it moving.

Hence the coefficient of kinetic friction is usually *less* than the coefficient of static friction for any given pair of surfaces, as Table 5.1 shows.

In some situations the surfaces will alternately stick (static friction) and slip (kinetic friction). This what causes the horrible sound made by chalk held at the wrong angle on a blackboard and the shriek of tires sliding on asphalt pavement. A more positive example is the motion of a violin bow against the string.

In the linear air tracks used in physics laboratories, gliders move with very little friction because they are supported on a layer of air. The friction force is velocity dependent, but at typical speeds the effective coefficient of friction is of the order of 0.001.

PhET: Forces in 1 Dimension
PhET: Friction
PhET: The Ramp

EXAMPLE 5.13 FRICTION IN HORIZONTAL MOTION

You want to move a 500-N crate across a level floor. To start the crate moving, you have to pull with a 230-N horizontal force. Once the crate starts to move, you can keep it moving at constant velocity with only 200 N. What are the coefficients of static and kinetic friction?

SOLUTION

IDENTIFY and SET UP: The crate is in equilibrium both when it is at rest and when it is moving at constant velocity, so we use Newton's first law, as expressed by Eqs. (5.1). We use Eqs. (5.3) and (5.4) to find the target variables μ_s and μ_k.

Figures 5.20a and 5.20b show our sketch and free-body diagram for the instant just before the crate starts to move, when the static friction force has its maximum possible value $(f_s)_{max} = \mu_s n$.

5.20 Our sketches for this problem.

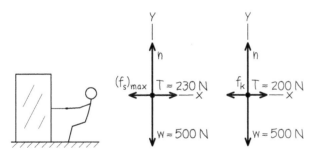

(a) Pulling a crate

(b) Free-body diagram for crate just before it starts to move

(c) Free-body diagram for crate moving at constant speed

Once the crate is moving, the friction force changes to its kinetic form (Fig. 5.20c). In both situations, four forces act on the crate: the downward weight (magnitude $w = 500$ N), the upward normal force (magnitude n) exerted by the floor, a tension force (magnitude T) to the right exerted by the rope, and a friction force to the left exerted by the floor. Because the rope in Fig. 5.20a is in equilibrium, the tension is the same at both ends. Hence the tension force that the rope exerts on the crate has the same magnitude as the force you exert on the rope. Since it's easier to keep the crate moving than to start it moving, we expect that $\mu_k < \mu_s$.

EXECUTE: Just before the crate starts to move (Fig. 5.20b), we have from Eqs. (5.1)

$$\Sigma F_x = T + (-(f_s)_{max}) = 0 \quad so \quad (f_s)_{max} = T = 230 \text{ N}$$
$$\Sigma F_y = n + (-w) = 0 \quad so \quad n = w = 500 \text{ N}$$

Now we solve Eq. (5.4), $(f_s)_{max} = \mu_s n$, for the value of μ_s:

$$\mu_s = \frac{(f_s)_{max}}{n} = \frac{230 \text{ N}}{500 \text{ N}} = 0.46$$

After the crate starts to move (Fig. 5.20c) we have

$$\Sigma F_x = T + (-f_k) = 0 \quad so \quad f_k = T = 200 \text{ N}$$
$$\Sigma F_y = n + (-w) = 0 \quad so \quad n = w = 500 \text{ N}$$

Using $f_k = \mu_k n$ from Eq. (5.3), we find

$$\mu_k = \frac{f_k}{n} = \frac{200 \text{ N}}{500 \text{ N}} = 0.40$$

EVALUATE: As expected, the coefficient of kinetic friction is less than the coefficient of static friction.

EXAMPLE 5.14 STATIC FRICTION CAN BE LESS THAN THE MAXIMUM

In Example 5.13, what is the friction force if the crate is at rest on the surface and a horizontal force of 50 N is applied to it?

SOLUTION

IDENTIFY and SET UP: The applied force is less than the maximum force of static friction, $(f_s)_{max} = 230$ N. Hence the crate remains at rest and the net force acting on it is zero. The target variable is the magnitude f_s of the friction force. The free-body

diagram is the same as in Fig. 5.20b, but with $(f_s)_{max}$ replaced by f_s and $T = 230$ N replaced by $T = 50$ N.

EXECUTE: From the equilibrium conditions, Eqs. (5.1), we have

$$\Sigma F_x = T + (-f_s) = 0 \quad so \quad f_s = T = 50 \text{ N}$$

EVALUATE: The friction force can prevent motion for any horizontal applied force up to $(f_s)_{max} = \mu_s n = 230$ N. Below that value, f_s has the same magnitude as the applied force.

EXAMPLE 5.15 MINIMIZING KINETIC FRICTION

In Example 5.13, suppose you move the crate by pulling upward on the rope at an angle of 30° above the horizontal. How hard must you pull to keep it moving with constant velocity? Assume that $\mu_k = 0.40$.

SOLUTION

IDENTIFY and SET UP: The crate is in equilibrium because its velocity is constant, so we again apply Newton's first law. Since the crate is in motion, the floor exerts a *kinetic* friction force. The target variable is the magnitude T of the tension force.

Figure 5.21 shows our sketch and free-body diagram. The kinetic friction force f_k is still equal to $\mu_k n$, but now the normal

5.21 Our sketches for this problem.

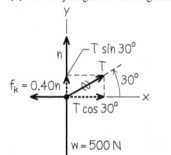

(a) Pulling a crate at an angle

(b) Free-body diagram for moving crate

force n is *not* equal in magnitude to the crate's weight. The force exerted by the rope has a vertical component that tends to lift the crate off the floor; this *reduces* n and so reduces f_k.

EXECUTE: From the equilibrium conditions and Eq. (5.3), $f_k = \mu_k n$, we have

$$\Sigma F_x = T\cos 30° + (-f_k) = 0 \quad \text{so} \quad T\cos 30° = \mu_k n$$
$$\Sigma F_y = T\sin 30° + n + (-w) = 0 \quad \text{so} \quad n = w - T\sin 30°$$

These are two equations for the two unknown quantities T and n. One way to find T is to substitute the expression for n in the second equation into the first equation and then solve the resulting equation for T:

$$T\cos 30° = \mu_k(w - T\sin 30°)$$
$$T = \frac{\mu_k w}{\cos 30° + \mu_k \sin 30°} = 188 \text{ N}$$

We can substitute this result into either of the original equations to obtain n. If we use the second equation, we get

$$n = w - T\sin 30° = (500 \text{ N}) - (188 \text{ N})\sin 30° = 406 \text{ N}$$

EVALUATE: As expected, the normal force is less than the 500-N weight of the box. It turns out that the tension required to keep the crate moving at constant speed is a little less than the 200-N force needed when you pulled horizontally in Example 5.13. Can you find an angle where the required pull is *minimum*?

EXAMPLE 5.16 TOBOGGAN RIDE WITH FRICTION I

Let's go back to the toboggan we studied in Example 5.10. The wax has worn off, so there is now a nonzero coefficient of kinetic friction μ_k. The slope has just the right angle to make the toboggan slide with constant velocity. Find this angle in terms of w and μ_k.

SOLUTION

IDENTIFY and SET UP: Our target variable is the slope angle α. The toboggan is in equilibrium because its velocity is constant, so we use Newton's first law in the form of Eqs. (5.1).

Three forces act on the toboggan: its weight, the normal force, and the kinetic friction force. The motion is downhill, so the friction force (which opposes the motion) is directed uphill. **Figure 5.22** shows our sketch and free-body diagram (compare Fig. 5.12b in Example 5.10). From Eq. (5.3), the magnitude of the kinetic friction force is $f_k = \mu_k n$. We expect that the greater the value of μ_k, the steeper will be the required slope.

EXECUTE: The equilibrium conditions are

$$\Sigma F_x = w\sin\alpha + (-f_k) = w\sin\alpha - \mu_k n = 0$$
$$\Sigma F_y = n + (-w\cos\alpha) = 0$$

Rearranging these two equations, we get

$$\mu_k n = w\sin\alpha \quad \text{and} \quad n = w\cos\alpha$$

As in Example 5.10, the normal force is *not* equal to the weight. We eliminate n by dividing the first of these equations by the

5.22 Our sketches for this problem.

(a) The situation

(b) Free-body diagram for toboggan

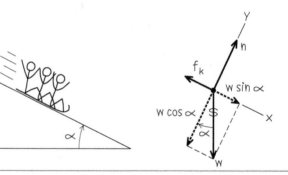

second, with the result

$$\mu_k = \frac{\sin\alpha}{\cos\alpha} = \tan\alpha \quad \text{so} \quad \alpha = \arctan\mu_k$$

EVALUATE: The weight w doesn't appear in this expression. *Any* toboggan, regardless of its weight, slides down an incline with constant speed if the coefficient of kinetic friction equals the tangent of the slope angle of the incline. The arctangent function increases as its argument increases, so it's indeed true that the slope angle α increases as μ_k increases.

EXAMPLE 5.17 TOBOGGAN RIDE WITH FRICTION II

The same toboggan with the same coefficient of friction as in Example 5.16 *accelerates* down a steeper hill. Derive an expression for the acceleration in terms of g, α, μ_k, and w.

SOLUTION

IDENTIFY and SET UP: The toboggan is accelerating, so we must use Newton's second law as given in Eqs. (5.2). Our target variable is the downhill acceleration.

Our sketch and free-body diagram (**Fig. 5.23**) are almost the same as for Example 5.16. The toboggan's y-component of acceleration a_y is still zero but the x-component a_x is not, so we've drawn $w \sin \alpha$, the downhill component of weight, as a longer vector than the (uphill) friction force.

EXECUTE: It's convenient to express the weight as $w = mg$. Then Newton's second law in component form says

$$\Sigma F_x = mg \sin \alpha + (-f_k) = ma_x$$
$$\Sigma F_y = n + (-mg \cos \alpha) = 0$$

5.23 Our sketches for this problem.

(a) The situation

(b) Free-body diagram for toboggan

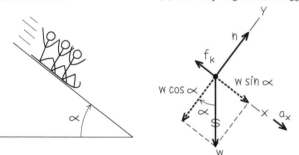

From the second equation and Eq. (5.3) we get an expression for f_k:

$$n = mg \cos \alpha$$
$$f_k = \mu_k n = \mu_k mg \cos \alpha$$

We substitute this into the x-component equation and solve for a_x:

$$mg \sin \alpha + (-\mu_k mg \cos \alpha) = ma_x$$
$$a_x = g(\sin \alpha - \mu_k \cos \alpha)$$

EVALUATE: As for the frictionless toboggan in Example 5.10, the acceleration doesn't depend on the mass m of the toboggan. That's because all of the forces that act on the toboggan (weight, normal force, and kinetic friction force) are proportional to m.

Let's check some special cases. If the hill is vertical ($\alpha = 90°$) so that $\sin \alpha = 1$ and $\cos \alpha = 0$, we have $a_x = g$ (the toboggan falls freely). For a certain value of α the acceleration is zero; this happens if

$$\sin \alpha = \mu_k \cos \alpha \qquad \text{and} \qquad \mu_k = \tan \alpha$$

This agrees with our result for the constant-velocity toboggan in Example 5.16. If the angle is even smaller, $\mu_k \cos \alpha$ is greater than $\sin \alpha$ and a_x is *negative;* if we give the toboggan an initial downhill push to start it moving, it will slow down and stop. Finally, if the hill is frictionless so that $\mu_k = 0$, we retrieve the result of Example 5.10: $a_x = g \sin \alpha$.

Notice that we started with a simple problem (Example 5.10) and extended it to more and more general situations. The general result we found in this example includes *all* the previous ones as special cases. Don't memorize this result, but do make sure you understand how we obtained it and what it means.

Suppose instead we give the toboggan an initial push *up* the hill. The direction of the kinetic friction force is now reversed, so the acceleration is different from the downhill value. It turns out that the expression for a_x is the same as for downhill motion except that the minus sign becomes plus. Can you show this?

Rolling Friction

It's a lot easier to move a loaded filing cabinet across a horizontal floor by using a cart with wheels than by sliding it. How much easier? We can define a **coefficient of rolling friction** μ_r, which is the horizontal force needed for constant speed on a flat surface divided by the upward normal force exerted by the surface. Transportation engineers call μ_r the *tractive resistance*. Typical values of μ_r are 0.002 to 0.003 for steel wheels on steel rails and 0.01 to 0.02 for rubber tires on concrete. These values show one reason railroad trains are generally much more fuel efficient than highway trucks.

Fluid Resistance and Terminal Speed

Sticking your hand out the window of a fast-moving car will convince you of the existence of **fluid resistance,** the force that a fluid (a gas or liquid) exerts on a body moving through it. The moving body exerts a force on the fluid to push it out of the way. By Newton's third law, the fluid pushes back on the body with an equal and opposite force.

The *direction* of the fluid resistance force acting on a body is always opposite the direction of the body's velocity relative to the fluid. The *magnitude* of the fluid resistance force usually increases with the speed of the body through the fluid.

DATA *SPEAKS*

Static Friction

When students were given a problem about the magnitude f_s of the static friction force acting on an object at rest, more than 36% gave an incorrect answer. Common errors:

- Assuming that f_s is always equal to $\mu_s n$ (coefficient of static friction × normal force on object). This is the *maximum* value of f_s; the actual value can be anything between zero and this maximum.

- Forgetting to apply Newton's first law to the object at rest. This is the only correct way to find the value of f_s required to keep the object from accelerating.

5.24 Motion with fluid resistance.

(a) Metal ball falling through oil

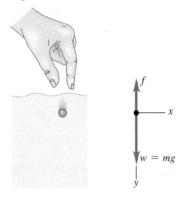

(b) Free-body diagram for ball in oil

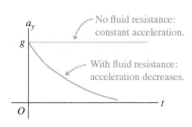

This is very different from the kinetic friction force between two surfaces in contact, which we can usually regard as independent of speed. For small objects moving at very low speeds, the magnitude f of the fluid resistance force is approximately proportional to the body's speed v:

$$f = kv \qquad \text{(fluid resistance at low speed)} \qquad (5.5)$$

where k is a proportionality constant that depends on the shape and size of the body and the properties of the fluid. Equation (5.5) is appropriate for dust particles falling in air or a ball bearing falling in oil. For larger objects moving through air at the speed of a tossed tennis ball or faster, the resisting force is approximately proportional to v^2 rather than to v. It is then called **air drag** or simply *drag*. Airplanes, falling raindrops, and bicyclists all experience air drag. In this case we replace Eq. (5.5) by

$$f = Dv^2 \qquad \text{(fluid resistance at high speed)} \qquad (5.6)$$

Because of the v^2 dependence, air drag increases rapidly with increasing speed. The air drag on a typical car is negligible at low speeds but comparable to or greater than rolling resistance at highway speeds. The value of D depends on the shape and size of the body and on the density of the air. You should verify that the units of the constant k in Eq. (5.5) are N·s/m or kg/s, and that the units of the constant D in Eq. (5.6) are N·s²/m² or kg/m.

Because of the effects of fluid resistance, an object falling in a fluid does *not* have a constant acceleration. To describe its motion, we can't use the constant-acceleration relationships from Chapter 2; instead, we have to start over with Newton's second law. As an example, suppose you drop a metal ball at the surface of a bucket of oil and let it fall to the bottom (**Fig. 5.24a**). The fluid resistance force in this situation is given by Eq. (5.5). What are the acceleration, velocity, and position of the metal ball as functions of time?

Figure 5.24b shows the free-body diagram. We take the positive y-direction to be downward and neglect any force associated with buoyancy in the oil. Since the ball is moving downward, its speed v is equal to its y-velocity v_y and the fluid resistance force is in the $-y$-direction. There are no x-components, so Newton's second law gives

$$\sum F_y = mg + (-kv_y) = ma_y \qquad (5.7)$$

When the ball first starts to move, $v_y = 0$, the resisting force is zero and the initial acceleration is $a_y = g$. As the speed increases, the resisting force also increases, until finally it is equal in magnitude to the weight. At this time $mg - kv_y = 0$, the acceleration is zero, and there is no further increase in speed. The final speed v_{t}, called the **terminal speed,** is given by $mg - kv_{\mathrm{t}} = 0$, or

$$v_{\mathrm{t}} = \frac{mg}{k} \qquad \text{(terminal speed, fluid resistance } f = kv) \qquad (5.8)$$

Figure 5.25 shows how the acceleration, velocity, and position vary with time. As time goes by, the acceleration approaches zero and the velocity approaches v_{t}

5.25 Graphs of the motion of a body falling without fluid resistance and with fluid resistance proportional to the speed.

Acceleration versus time

Velocity versus time

Position versus time

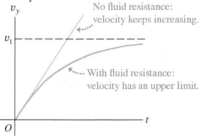

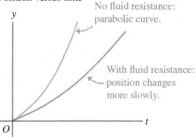

(remember that we chose the positive y-direction to be down). The slope of the graph of y versus t becomes constant as the velocity becomes constant.

To see how the graphs in Fig. 5.25 are derived, we must find the relationship between velocity and time during the interval before the terminal speed is reached. We go back to Newton's second law for the falling ball, Eq. (5.7), which we rewrite with $a_y = dv_y/dt$:

$$m\frac{dv_y}{dt} = mg - kv_y$$

After rearranging terms and replacing mg/k by v_t, we integrate both sides, noting that $v_y = 0$ when $t = 0$:

$$\int_0^v \frac{dv_y}{v_y - v_t} = -\frac{k}{m}\int_0^t dt$$

which integrates to

$$\ln\frac{v_t - v_y}{v_t} = -\frac{k}{m}t \quad \text{or} \quad 1 - \frac{v_y}{v_t} = e^{-(k/m)t}$$

and finally

$$v_y = v_t\left[1 - e^{-(k/m)t}\right] \tag{5.9}$$

Note that v_y becomes equal to the terminal speed v_t only in the limit that $t \to \infty$; the ball cannot attain terminal speed in any finite length of time.

The derivative of v_y in Eq. (5.9) gives a_y as a function of time, and the integral of v_y gives y as a function of time. We leave the derivations for you to complete; the results are

$$a_y = ge^{-(k/m)t} \tag{5.10}$$

$$y = v_t\left[t - \frac{m}{k}(1 - e^{-(k/m)t})\right] \tag{5.11}$$

Now look again at Fig. 5.25, which shows graphs of these three relationships.

In deriving the terminal speed in Eq. (5.8), we assumed that the fluid resistance force is proportional to the speed. For an object falling through the air at high speeds, so that the fluid resistance is equal to Dv^2 as in Eq. (5.6), the terminal speed is reached when Dv^2 equals the weight mg (**Fig. 5.26a**). You can show that the terminal speed v_t is given by

$$v_t = \sqrt{\frac{mg}{D}} \quad \text{(terminal speed, fluid resistance } f = Dv^2\text{)} \tag{5.12}$$

This expression for terminal speed explains why heavy objects in air tend to fall faster than light objects. Two objects that have the same physical size but different mass (say, a table-tennis ball and a lead ball with the same radius) have the same value of D but different values of m. The more massive object has a higher terminal speed and falls faster. The same idea explains why a sheet of paper falls faster if you first crumple it into a ball; the mass m is the same, but the smaller size makes D smaller (less air drag for a given speed) and v_t larger. Skydivers use the same principle to control their descent (Fig. 5.26b).

Figure 5.27 shows the trajectories of a baseball with and without air drag, assuming a coefficient $D = 1.3 \times 10^{-3}$ kg/m (appropriate for a batted ball at sea level). Both the range of the baseball and the maximum height reached are substantially smaller than the zero-drag calculation would lead you to believe. Hence the baseball trajectory we calculated in Example 3.7 (Section 3.3) by ignoring air drag is unrealistic. Air drag is an important part of the game of baseball!

5.26 (a) Air drag and terminal speed. (b) By changing the positions of their arms and legs while falling, skydivers can change the value of the constant D in Eq. (5.6) and hence adjust the terminal speed of their fall [Eq. (5.12)].

(a) Free-body diagrams for falling with air drag

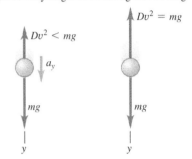

Before terminal speed: Object accelerating, drag force less than weight.

At terminal speed v_t: Object in equilibrium, drag force equals weight.

(b) A skydiver falling at terminal speed

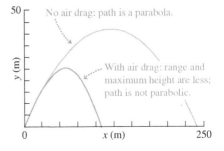

5.27 Computer-generated trajectories of a baseball launched at 50 m/s at 35° above the horizontal. Note that the scales are different on the horizontal and vertical axes.

No air drag: path is a parabola.

With air drag: range and maximum height are less; path is not parabolic.

EXAMPLE 5.18 TERMINAL SPEED OF A SKYDIVER

For a human body falling through air in a spread-eagle position (Fig. 5.26b), the numerical value of the constant D in Eq. (5.6) is about 0.25 kg/m. Find the terminal speed for a 50-kg skydiver.

SOLUTION

IDENTIFY and SET UP: This example uses the relationship among terminal speed, mass, and drag coefficient. We use Eq. (5.12) to find the target variable v_t.

EXECUTE: We find for $m = 50$ kg:

$$v_t = \sqrt{\frac{mg}{D}} = \sqrt{\frac{(50\text{ kg})(9.8\text{ m/s}^2)}{0.25\text{ kg/m}}}$$

$$= 44\text{ m/s (about 160 km/h, or 99 mi/h)}$$

EVALUATE: The terminal speed is proportional to the square root of the skydiver's mass. A skydiver with the same drag coefficient D but twice the mass would have a terminal speed $\sqrt{2} = 1.41$ times greater, or 63 m/s. (A more massive skydiver would also have more frontal area and hence a larger drag coefficient, so his terminal speed would be a bit less than 63 m/s.) Even the 50-kg skydiver's terminal speed is quite high, so skydives don't last very long. A drop from 2800 m (9200 ft) to the surface at the terminal speed takes only $(2800\text{ m})/(44\text{ m/s}) = 64$ s.

When the skydiver deploys the parachute, the value of D increases greatly. Hence the terminal speed of the skydiver and parachute decreases dramatically to a much lower value.

5.28 Net force, acceleration, and velocity in uniform circular motion.

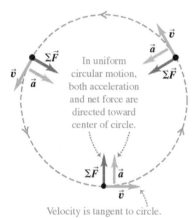

In uniform circular motion, both acceleration and net force are directed toward center of circle.

Velocity is tangent to circle.

TEST YOUR UNDERSTANDING OF SECTION 5.3 Consider a box that is placed on different surfaces. (a) In which situation(s) is *no* friction force acting on the box? (b) In which situation(s) is a *static* friction force acting on the box? (c) In which situation(s) is a *kinetic* friction force acting on the box? (i) The box is at rest on a rough horizontal surface. (ii) The box is at rest on a rough tilted surface. (iii) The box is on the rough-surfaced flat bed of a truck that is moving at a constant velocity on a straight, level road, and the box remains in place in the middle of the truck bed. (iv) The box is on the rough-surfaced flat bed of a truck that is speeding up on a straight, level road, and the box remains in place in the middle of the truck bed. (v) The box is on the rough-surfaced flat bed of a truck that is climbing a hill, and the box is sliding toward the back of the truck. ❚

5.4 DYNAMICS OF CIRCULAR MOTION

We talked about uniform circular motion in Section 3.4. We showed that when a particle moves in a circular path with constant speed, the particle's acceleration has a constant magnitude a_{rad} given by

$$\text{Magnitude of acceleration of an object in uniform circular motion} \quad a_{rad} = \frac{v^2}{R} \quad \begin{matrix}\text{Speed of object}\\\text{Radius of object's circular path}\end{matrix} \quad (5.13)$$

The subscript "rad" is a reminder that at each point the acceleration points radially inward toward the center of the circle, perpendicular to the instantaneous velocity. We explained in Section 3.4 why this acceleration is often called *centripetal acceleration* or *radial acceleration*.

We can also express the centripetal acceleration a_{rad} in terms of the *period T*, the time for one revolution:

$$T = \frac{2\pi R}{v} \quad (5.14)$$

In terms of the period, a_{rad} is

$$\text{Magnitude of acceleration of an object in uniform circular motion} \quad a_{rad} = \frac{4\pi^2 R}{T^2} \quad \begin{matrix}\text{Radius of object's circular path}\\\text{Period of motion}\end{matrix} \quad (5.15)$$

Uniform circular motion, like all other motion of a particle, is governed by Newton's second law. To make the particle accelerate toward the center of the circle, the net force $\Sigma\vec{F}$ on the particle must always be directed toward the center (**Fig. 5.28**). The magnitude of the acceleration is constant, so the magnitude F_{net} of the net force must also be constant. If the inward net force stops acting, the particle flies off in a straight line tangent to the circle (**Fig. 5.29**).

5.29 What happens if the inward radial force suddenly ceases to act on a body in circular motion?

A ball attached to a string whirls in a circle on a frictionless surface.

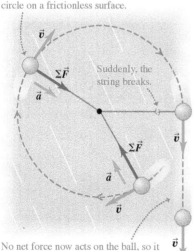

Suddenly, the string breaks.

No net force now acts on the ball, so it obeys Newton's first law—it moves in a straight line at constant velocity.

The magnitude of the radial acceleration is given by $a_{rad} = v^2/R$, so the magnitude F_{net} of the net force on a particle with mass m in uniform circular motion must be

$$F_{net} = ma_{rad} = m\frac{v^2}{R} \quad \text{(uniform circular motion)} \quad (5.16)$$

Uniform circular motion can result from *any* combination of forces, just so the net force $\Sigma\vec{F}$ is always directed toward the center of the circle and has a constant magnitude. Note that the body need not move around a complete circle: Equation (5.16) is valid for *any* path that can be regarded as part of a circular arc.

CAUTION **Avoid using "centrifugal force"** **Figure 5.30** shows a correct free-body diagram for uniform circular motion (Fig. 5.30a) and an *incorrect* diagram (Fig. 5.30b). Figure 5.30b is incorrect because it includes an extra outward force of magnitude $m(v^2/R)$ to "keep the body out there" or to "keep it in equilibrium." There are three reasons not to include such an outward force, called *centrifugal force* ("centrifugal" means "fleeing from the center"). First, the body does *not* "stay out there": It is in constant motion around its circular path. Because its velocity is constantly changing in direction, the body accelerates and is *not* in equilibrium. Second, if there *were* an outward force that balanced the inward force, the net force would be zero and the body would move in a straight line, not a circle (Fig. 5.29). Third, the quantity $m(v^2/R)$ is *not* a force; it corresponds to the $m\vec{a}$ side of $\Sigma\vec{F} = m\vec{a}$ and does not appear in $\Sigma\vec{F}$ (Fig. 5.30a). It's true that when you ride in a car that goes around a circular path, you tend to slide to the outside of the turn as though there was a "centrifugal force." But we saw in Section 4.2 that what happens is that you tend to keep moving in a straight line, and the outer side of the car "runs into" you as the car turns (Fig. 4.10c). *In an inertial frame of reference there is no such thing as "centrifugal force."* We won't mention this term again, and we strongly advise you to avoid it. ❚

5.30 Right and wrong ways to depict uniform circular motion.

(a) Correct free-body diagram

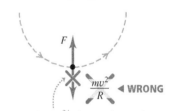

If you include the acceleration, draw it to one side of the body to show that it's not a force.

(b) Incorrect free-body diagram

The quantity mv^2/R is *not* a force—it doesn't belong in a free-body diagram.

DEMO

EXAMPLE 5.19   **FORCE IN UNIFORM CIRCULAR MOTION**

A sled with a mass of 25.0 kg rests on a horizontal sheet of essentially frictionless ice. It is attached by a 5.00-m rope to a post set in the ice. Once given a push, the sled revolves uniformly in a circle around the post (**Fig. 5.31a**). If the sled makes five complete revolutions every minute, find the force F exerted on it by the rope.

SOLUTION

IDENTIFY and SET UP: The sled is in uniform circular motion, so it has a constant radial acceleration. We'll apply Newton's second law to the sled to find the magnitude F of the force exerted by the rope (our target variable).

5.31 (a) The situation. (b) Our free-body diagram.

(a) A sled in uniform circular motion

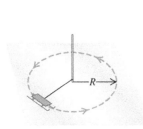

(b) Free-body diagram for sled

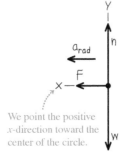

We point the positive *x*-direction toward the center of the circle.

Figure 5.31b shows our free-body diagram for the sled. The acceleration has only an *x*-component; this is toward the center of the circle, so we denote it as a_{rad}. The acceleration isn't given, so we'll need to determine its value by using Eq. (5.13) or Eq. (5.15).

EXECUTE: The force F appears in Newton's second law for the *x*-direction:

$$\Sigma F_x = F = ma_{rad}$$

We can find the centripetal acceleration a_{rad} by using Eq. (5.15). The sled moves in a circle of radius $R = 5.00$ m with a period $T = (60.0\text{ s})/(5\text{ rev}) = 12.0$ s, so

$$a_{rad} = \frac{4\pi^2 R}{T^2} = \frac{4\pi^2(5.00\text{ m})}{(12.0\text{ s})^2} = 1.37\text{ m/s}^2$$

The magnitude F of the force exerted by the rope is then

$$F = ma_{rad} = (25.0\text{ kg})(1.37\text{ m/s}^2)$$
$$= 34.3\text{ kg} \cdot \text{m/s}^2 = 34.3\text{ N}$$

EVALUATE: You can check our value for a_{rad} by first using Eq. (5.14), $v = 2\pi R/T$, to find the speed and then using $a_{rad} = v^2/R$ from Eq. (5.13). Do you get the same result?

A greater force would be needed if the sled moved around the circle at a higher speed v. In fact, if v were doubled while R remained the same, F would be four times greater. Can you show this? How would F change if v remained the same but the radius R were doubled?

EXAMPLE 5.20 A CONICAL PENDULUM

An inventor designs a pendulum clock using a bob with mass m at the end of a thin wire of length L. Instead of swinging back and forth, the bob is to move in a horizontal circle at constant speed v, with the wire making a fixed angle β with the vertical direction (**Fig. 5.32a**). This is called a *conical pendulum* because the suspending wire traces out a cone. Find the tension F in the wire and the period T (the time for one revolution of the bob).

SOLUTION

IDENTIFY and SET UP: To find our target variables, the tension F and period T, we need two equations. These will be the horizontal and vertical components of Newton's second law applied to the bob. We'll find the radial acceleration of the bob from one of the circular motion equations.

Figure 5.32b shows our free-body diagram and coordinate system for the bob at a particular instant. There are just two forces on the bob: the weight mg and the tension F in the wire. Note that the

center of the circular path is in the same horizontal plane as the bob, *not* at the top end of the wire. The horizontal component of tension is the force that produces the radial acceleration a_{rad}.

EXECUTE: The bob has zero vertical acceleration; the horizontal acceleration is toward the center of the circle, which is why we use the symbol a_{rad}. Newton's second law, Eqs. (5.2), says

$$\Sigma F_x = F\sin\beta = ma_{rad}$$
$$\Sigma F_y = F\cos\beta + (-mg) = 0$$

These are two equations for the two unknowns F and β. The equation for ΣF_y gives $F = mg/\cos\beta$; that's our target expression for F in terms of β. Substituting this result into the equation for ΣF_x and using $\sin\beta/\cos\beta = \tan\beta$, we find

$$a_{rad} = g\tan\beta$$

To relate β to the period T, we use Eq. (5.15) for a_{rad}, solve for T, and insert $a_{rad} = g\tan\beta$:

$$a_{rad} = \frac{4\pi^2 R}{T^2} \quad\text{so}\quad T^2 = \frac{4\pi^2 R}{a_{rad}}$$

$$T = 2\pi\sqrt{\frac{R}{g\tan\beta}}$$

Figure 5.32a shows that $R = L\sin\beta$. We substitute this and use $\sin\beta/\tan\beta = \cos\beta$:

$$T = 2\pi\sqrt{\frac{L\cos\beta}{g}}$$

5.32 (a) The situation. (b) Our free-body diagram.

(a) The situation

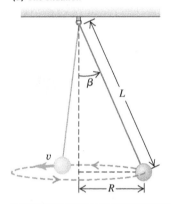

(b) Free-body diagram for pendulum bob

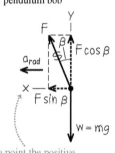

We point the positive x-direction toward the center of the circle.

EVALUATE: For a given length L, as the angle β increases, $\cos\beta$ decreases, the period T becomes smaller, and the tension $F = mg/\cos\beta$ increases. The angle can never be 90°, however; this would require that $T = 0$, $F = \infty$, and $v = \infty$. A conical pendulum would not make a very good clock because the period depends on the angle β in such a direct way.

EXAMPLE 5.21 ROUNDING A FLAT CURVE

The sports car in Example 3.11 (Section 3.4) is rounding a flat, unbanked curve with radius R (**Fig. 5.33a**). If the coefficient of static friction between tires and road is μ_s, what is the maximum speed v_{max} at which the driver can take the curve without sliding?

SOLUTION

IDENTIFY and SET UP: The car's acceleration as it rounds the curve has magnitude $a_{rad} = v^2/R$. Hence the maximum speed v_{max} (our target variable) corresponds to the maximum acceleration a_{rad} and to the maximum horizontal force on the car toward the center of its circular path. The only horizontal force acting on the car is the friction force exerted by the road. So to solve this problem we'll need Newton's second law, the equations of uniform circular motion, and our knowledge of the friction force from Section 5.3.

The free-body diagram in Fig. 5.33b includes the car's weight $w = mg$ and the two forces exerted by the road: the normal force n and the horizontal friction force f. The friction force must point toward the center of the circular path in order to cause the radial

5.33 (a) The situation. (b) Our free-body diagram.

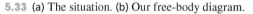

(a) Car rounding flat curve

(b) Free-body diagram for car

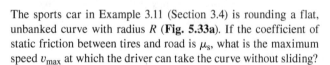

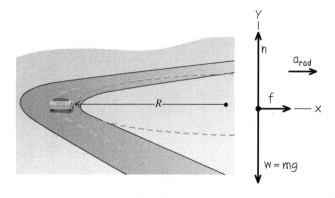

acceleration. The car doesn't slide toward or away from the center of the circle, so the friction force is *static* friction, with a maximum magnitude $f_{max} = \mu_s n$ [see Eq. (5.4)].

EXECUTE: The acceleration toward the center of the circular path is $a_{rad} = v^2/R$. There is no vertical acceleration. Thus

$$\sum F_x = f = ma_{rad} = m\frac{v^2}{R}$$

$$\sum F_y = n + (-mg) = 0$$

The second equation shows that $n = mg$. The first equation shows that the friction force *needed* to keep the car moving in its circular path increases with the car's speed. But the maximum friction force *available* is $f_{max} = \mu_s n = \mu_s mg$, and this determines the car's maximum speed. Substituting $\mu_s mg$ for f and v_{max} for v in the first equation, we find

$$\mu_s mg = m\frac{v_{max}^2}{R} \quad \text{so} \quad v_{max} = \sqrt{\mu_s gR}$$

As an example, if $\mu_s = 0.96$ and $R = 230$ m, we have

$$v_{max} = \sqrt{(0.96)(9.8 \text{ m/s}^2)(230 \text{ m})} = 47 \text{ m/s}$$

or about 170 km/h (100 mi/h). This is the maximum speed for this radius.

EVALUATE: If the car's speed is slower than $v_{max} = \sqrt{\mu_s gR}$, the required friction force is less than the maximum value $f_{max} = \mu_s mg$, and the car can easily make the curve. If we try to take the curve going *faster* than v_{max}, we will skid. We could still go in a circle without skidding at this higher speed, but the radius would have to be larger.

The maximum centripetal acceleration (called the "lateral acceleration" in Example 3.11) is equal to $\mu_s g$. That's why it's best to take curves at less than the posted speed limit if the road is wet or icy, either of which can reduce the value of μ_s and hence $\mu_s g$.

EXAMPLE 5.22   ROUNDING A BANKED CURVE

For a car traveling at a certain speed, it is possible to bank a curve at just the right angle so that no friction is needed to maintain the car's turning radius. Then a car can safely round the curve even on wet ice. (Bobsled racing depends on this idea.) Your engineering firm plans to rebuild the curve in Example 5.21 so that a car moving at a chosen speed v can safely make the turn even with no friction (**Fig. 5.34a**). At what angle β should the curve be banked?

SOLUTION

IDENTIFY and SET UP: With no friction, the only forces acting on the car are its weight and the normal force. Because the road is banked, the normal force (which acts perpendicular to the road surface) has a horizontal component. This component causes the car's horizontal acceleration toward the center of the car's circular path. We'll use Newton's second law to find the target variable β.

Our free-body diagram (Fig. 5.34b) is very similar to the diagram for the conical pendulum in Example 5.20 (Fig. 5.32b). The normal force acting on the car plays the role of the tension force exerted by the wire on the pendulum bob.

EXECUTE: The normal force $\vec{n}$ is perpendicular to the roadway and is at an angle β with the vertical (Fig. 5.34b). Thus it has a

vertical component $n\cos\beta$ and a horizontal component $n\sin\beta$. The acceleration in the x-direction is the centripetal acceleration $a_{rad} = v^2/R$; there is no acceleration in the y-direction. Thus the equations of Newton's second law are

$$\sum F_x = n\sin\beta = ma_{rad}$$

$$\sum F_y = n\cos\beta + (-mg) = 0$$

From the $\sum F_y$ equation, $n = mg/\cos\beta$. Substituting this into the $\sum F_x$ equation and using $a_{rad} = v^2/R$, we get an expression for the bank angle:

$$\tan\beta = \frac{a_{rad}}{g} = \frac{v^2}{gR} \quad \text{so} \quad \beta = \arctan\frac{v^2}{gR}$$

EVALUATE: The bank angle depends on both the speed and the radius. For a given radius, no one angle is correct for all speeds. In the design of highways and railroads, curves are often banked for the average speed of the traffic over them. If $R = 230$ m and $v = 25$ m/s (equal to a highway speed of 88 km/h, or 55 mi/h), then

$$\beta = \arctan\frac{(25 \text{ m/s})^2}{(9.8 \text{ m/s}^2)(230 \text{ m})} = 15°$$

This is within the range of bank angles actually used in highways.

5.34 (a) The situation. (b) Our free-body diagram.

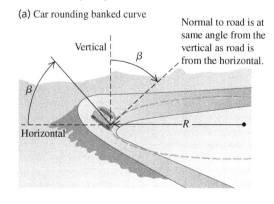

(a) Car rounding banked curve

Normal to road is at same angle from the vertical as road is from the horizontal.

Vertical

β

Horizontal

R

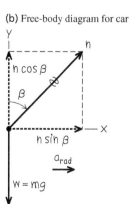

(b) Free-body diagram for car

y

n

$n\cos\beta$

β

x

$n\sin\beta$

a_{rad}

$w = mg$

5.35 An airplane banks to one side in order to turn in that direction. The vertical component of the lift force $\vec{L}$ balances the force of gravity; the horizontal component of $\vec{L}$ causes the acceleration v^2/R.

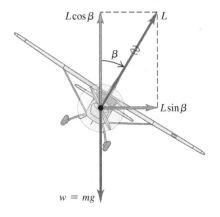

Banked Curves and the Flight of Airplanes

The results of Example 5.22 also apply to an airplane when it makes a turn in level flight (**Fig. 5.35**). When an airplane is flying in a straight line at a constant speed and at a steady altitude, the airplane's weight is exactly balanced by the lift force $\vec{L}$ exerted by the air. (The upward lift force that the air exerts on the wings is a reaction to the downward push the wings exert on the air as they move through it.) To make the airplane turn, the pilot banks the airplane to one side so that the lift force has a horizontal component, as Fig. 5.35 shows. (The pilot also changes the angle at which the wings "bite" into the air so that the vertical component of lift continues to balance the weight.) The bank angle is related to the airplane's speed v and the radius R of the turn by the same expression as in Example 5.22: $\tan\beta = v^2/gR$. For an airplane to make a tight turn (small R) at high speed (large v), $\tan\beta$ must be large and the required bank angle β must approach 90°.

We can also apply the results of Example 5.22 to the *pilot* of an airplane. The free-body diagram for the pilot of the airplane is exactly as shown in Fig. 5.34b; the normal force $n = mg/\cos\beta$ is exerted on the pilot by the seat. As in Example 5.9, n is equal to the apparent weight of the pilot, which is greater than the pilot's true weight mg. In a tight turn with a large bank angle β, the pilot's apparent weight can be tremendous: $n = 5.8mg$ at $\beta = 80°$ and $n = 9.6mg$ at $\beta = 84°$. Pilots black out in such tight turns because the apparent weight of their blood increases by the same factor, and the human heart isn't strong enough to pump such apparently "heavy" blood to the brain.

Motion in a Vertical Circle

In Examples 5.19, 5.20, 5.21, and 5.22 the body moved in a horizontal circle. Motion in a *vertical* circle is no different in principle, but the weight of the body has to be treated carefully. The following example shows what we mean.

EXAMPLE 5.23   UNIFORM CIRCULAR MOTION IN A VERTICAL CIRCLE

A passenger on a carnival Ferris wheel moves in a vertical circle of radius R with constant speed v. The seat remains upright during the motion. Find expressions for the force the seat exerts on the passenger when at the top of the circle and when at the bottom.

5.36 Our sketches for this problem.

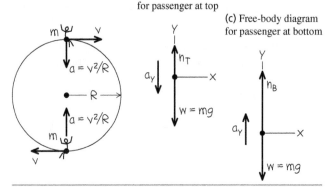

SOLUTION

IDENTIFY and SET UP: The target variables are n_T, the upward normal force the seat applies to the passenger at the top of the circle, and n_B, the normal force at the bottom. We'll find these by using Newton's second law and the uniform circular motion equations.

Figure 5.36a shows the passenger's velocity and acceleration at the two positions. The acceleration always points toward the center of the circle—downward at the top of the circle and upward at the bottom of the circle. At each position the only forces acting are vertical: the upward normal force and the downward force of gravity. Hence we need only the vertical component of Newton's second law. Figures 5.36b and 5.36c show free-body diagrams for the two positions. We take the positive y-direction as upward in both cases (that is, *opposite* the direction of the acceleration at the top of the circle).

EXECUTE: At the top the acceleration has magnitude v^2/R, but its vertical component is negative because its direction is downward.

Hence $a_y = -v^2/R$ and Newton's second law tells us that

$$\text{Top:} \quad \sum F_y = n_T + (-mg) = -m\frac{v^2}{R} \quad \text{or}$$

$$n_T = mg\left(1 - \frac{v^2}{gR}\right)$$

At the bottom the acceleration is upward, so $a_y = +v^2/R$ and Newton's second law says

Bottom: $\sum F_y = n_B + (-mg) = +m\dfrac{v^2}{R}$ or

$$n_B = mg\left(1 + \frac{v^2}{gR}\right)$$

EVALUATE: Our result for n_T tells us that at the top of the Ferris wheel, the upward force the seat applies to the passenger is *smaller*

in magnitude than the passenger's weight $w = mg$. If the ride goes fast enough that $g - v^2/R$ becomes zero, the seat applies *no* force, and the passenger is about to become airborne. If v becomes still larger, n_T becomes negative; this means that a *downward* force (such as from a seat belt) is needed to keep the passenger in the seat. By contrast, the normal force n_B at the bottom is always *greater* than the passenger's weight. You feel the seat pushing up on you more firmly than when you are at rest. You can see that n_T and n_B are the values of the passenger's *apparent weight* at the top and bottom of the circle (see Section 5.2).

When we tie a string to an object and whirl it in a vertical circle, the analysis in Example 5.23 isn't directly applicable. The reason is that v is *not* constant in this case; except at the top and bottom of the circle, the net force (and hence the acceleration) does *not* point toward the center of the circle (**Fig. 5.37**). So both $\sum \vec{F}$ and $\vec{a}$ have a component tangent to the circle, which means that the speed changes. Hence this is a case of *nonuniform* circular motion (see Section 3.4). Even worse, we can't use the constant-acceleration formulas to relate the speeds at various points because *neither* the magnitude nor the direction of the acceleration is constant. The speed relationships we need are best obtained by using the concept of energy. We'll consider such problems in Chapter 7.

5.37 A ball moving in a vertical circle.

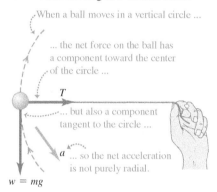

When a ball moves in a vertical circle ...

... the net force on the ball has a component toward the center of the circle ...

T

... but also a component tangent to the circle ...

a ... so the net acceleration is not purely radial.

$w = mg$

TEST YOUR UNDERSTANDING OF SECTION 5.4 Satellites are held in orbit by the force of our planet's gravitational attraction. A satellite in a small-radius orbit moves at a higher speed than a satellite in an orbit of large radius. Based on this information, what can you conclude about the earth's gravitational attraction for the satellite? (i) It increases with increasing distance from the earth. (ii) It is the same at all distances from the earth. (iii) It decreases with increasing distance from the earth. (iv) This information by itself isn't enough to answer the question. ∎

5.5 THE FUNDAMENTAL FORCES OF NATURE

We have discussed several kinds of forces—including weight, tension, friction, fluid resistance, and the normal force—and we will encounter others as we continue our study of physics. How many kinds of forces are there? Our best understanding is that all forces are expressions of just four distinct classes of *fundamental* forces, or interactions between particles (**Fig. 5.38**, next page). Two are familiar in everyday experience. The other two involve interactions between subatomic particles that we cannot observe with the unaided senses.

Gravitational interactions include the familiar force of your *weight*, which results from the earth's gravitational attraction acting on you. The mutual gravitational attraction of various parts of the earth for each other holds our planet together, and likewise for the other planets (Fig. 5.38a). Newton recognized that the sun's gravitational attraction for the earth keeps our planet in its nearly circular orbit around the sun. In Chapter 13 we'll study gravitational interactions in more detail, including their vital role in the motions of planets and satellites.

The second familiar class of forces, **electromagnetic interactions,** includes electric and magnetic forces. If you run a comb through your hair, the comb ends up with an electric charge; you can use the electric force exerted by this charge to pick up bits of paper. All atoms contain positive and negative electric charge, so atoms and molecules can exert electric forces on one another. Contact forces, including the normal force, friction, and fluid resistance, are the result of electrical interactions between atoms on the surface of an object and atoms in its surroundings (Fig. 5.38b). *Magnetic* forces, such as those between magnets or between a magnet and a piece of iron, are actually the result of electric charges in motion. For example, an electromagnet causes magnetic interactions because

BIO Application Circular Motion in a Centrifuge An important tool in medicine and biological research is the ultracentrifuge, a device that makes use of the dynamics of circular motion. A tube is filled with a solvent that contains various small particles (for example, blood containing platelets and white and red blood cells). The tube is inserted into the centrifuge, which then spins at thousands of revolutions per minute. The solvent provides the inward force that keeps the particles in circular motion. The particles slowly drift away from the rotation axis within the solvent. Because the drift rate depends on the particle size and density, particles of different types become separated in the tube, making analysis much easier.

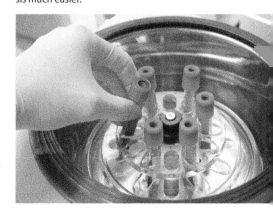

5.38 Examples of the fundamental interactions in nature.

(a) The gravitational interaction

Saturn is held together by the mutual gravitional attraction of all of its parts.

The particles that make up the rings are held in orbit by Saturn's gravitational force.

(b) The electromagnetic interaction

The contact forces between the microphone and the singer's hand are electrical in nature.

This microphone uses electric and magnetic effects to convert sound into an electrical signal that can be amplified and recorded.

(c) The strong interaction

The nucleus of a gold atom has 79 protons and 118 neutrons.

The strong interaction holds the protons and neutrons together and overcomes the electric repulsion of the protons.

(d) The weak interaction

Scientists find the age of this ancient skull by measuring its carbon-14—a form of carbon that is radioactive thanks to the weak interaction.

electric charges move through its wires. We will study electromagnetic interactions in detail in the second half of this book.

On the atomic or molecular scale, gravitational forces play no role because electric forces are enormously stronger: The electrical repulsion between two protons is stronger than their gravitational attraction by a factor of about 10^{35}. But in bodies of astronomical size, positive and negative charges are usually present in nearly equal amounts, and the resulting electrical interactions nearly cancel out. Gravitational interactions are thus the dominant influence in the motion of planets and in the internal structure of stars.

The other two classes of interactions are less familiar. One, the **strong interaction,** is responsible for holding the nucleus of an atom together (Fig. 5.38c). Nuclei contain electrically neutral neutrons and positively charged protons. The electric force between charged protons tries to push them apart; the strong attractive force between nuclear particles counteracts this repulsion and makes the nucleus stable. In this context the strong interaction is also called the *strong nuclear force*. It has much shorter range than electrical interactions, but within its range it is much stronger. Without the strong interaction, the nuclei of atoms essential to life, such as carbon (six protons, six neutrons) and oxygen (eight protons, eight neutrons), would not exist and you would not be reading these words!

Finally, there is the **weak interaction.** Its range is so short that it plays a role only on the scale of the nucleus or smaller. The weak interaction is responsible for a common form of radioactivity called beta decay, in which a neutron in a radioactive nucleus is transformed into a proton while ejecting an electron and a nearly massless particle called an antineutrino. The weak interaction between the antineutrino and ordinary matter is so feeble that an antineutrino could easily penetrate a wall of lead a million kilometers thick!

An important application of the weak interaction is *radiocarbon dating,* a technique that enables scientists to determine the ages of many biological specimens (Fig. 5.38d). Naturally occurring carbon includes atoms of both carbon-12 (with six protons and six neutrons in the nucleus) and carbon-14 (with two additional neutrons). Living organisms take in carbon atoms of both kinds from their environment but stop doing so when they die. The weak interaction makes carbon-14 nuclei unstable—one of the neutrons changes to a proton, an electron, and an antineutrino—and these nuclei decay at a known rate. By measuring the fraction of carbon-14 that is left in an organism's remains, scientists can determine how long ago the organism died.

In the 1960s physicists developed a theory that described the electromagnetic and weak interactions as aspects of a single *electroweak* interaction. This theory has passed every experimental test to which it has been put. Encouraged by this success, physicists have made similar attempts to describe the strong, electromagnetic, and weak interactions in terms of a single *grand unified theory* (GUT) and have taken steps toward a possible unification of all interactions into a *theory of everything* (TOE). Such theories are still speculative, and there are many unanswered questions in this very active field of current research.

CHAPTER 5 SUMMARY

SOLUTIONS TO ALL EXAMPLES

Using Newton's first law: When a body is in equilibrium in an inertial frame of reference—that is, either at rest or moving with constant velocity—the vector sum of forces acting on it must be zero (Newton's first law). Free-body diagrams are essential in identifying the forces that act on the body being considered.

Newton's third law (action and reaction) is also frequently needed in equilibrium problems. The two forces in an action–reaction pair *never* act on the same body. (See Examples 5.1–5.5.)

The normal force exerted on a body by a surface is *not* always equal to the body's weight. (See Example 5.4.)

Vector form:

$$\sum \vec{F} = 0$$

Component form:

$$\sum F_x = 0 \qquad \sum F_y = 0$$

(5.1)

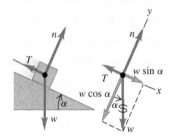

Using Newton's second law: If the vector sum of forces on a body is *not* zero, the body accelerates. The acceleration is related to the net force by Newton's second law.

Just as for equilibrium problems, free-body diagrams are essential for solving problems involving Newton's second law, and the normal force exerted on a body is not always equal to its weight. (See Examples 5.6–5.12.)

Vector form:

$$\sum \vec{F} = m\vec{a}$$

Component form:

$$\sum F_x = ma_x \qquad \sum F_y = ma_y$$

(5.2)

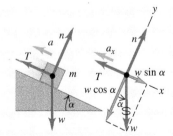

Friction and fluid resistance: The contact force between two bodies can always be represented in terms of a normal force $\vec{n}$ perpendicular to the surface of contact and a friction force $\vec{f}$ parallel to the surface.

When a body is sliding over the surface, the friction force is called *kinetic* friction. Its magnitude f_k is approximately equal to the normal force magnitude n multiplied by the coefficient of kinetic friction μ_k.

When a body is *not* moving relative to a surface, the friction force is called *static* friction. The *maximum* possible static friction force is approximately equal to the magnitude n of the normal force multiplied by the coefficient of static friction μ_s. The *actual* static friction force may be anything from zero to this maximum value, depending on the situation. Usually μ_s is greater than μ_k for a given pair of surfaces in contact. (See Examples 5.13–5.17.)

Rolling friction is similar to kinetic friction, but the force of fluid resistance depends on the speed of an object through a fluid. (See Example 5.18.)

Magnitude of kinetic friction force:

$$f_k = \mu_k n \tag{5.3}$$

Magnitude of static friction force:

$$f_s \le (f_s)_{\max} = \mu_s n \tag{5.4}$$

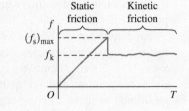

Forces in circular motion: In uniform circular motion, the acceleration vector is directed toward the center of the circle. The motion is governed by Newton's second law, $\sum \vec{F} = m\vec{a}$. (See Examples 5.19–5.23.)

Acceleration in uniform circular motion:

$$a_{\text{rad}} = \frac{v^2}{R} = \frac{4\pi^2 R}{T^2} \tag{5.13), (5.15}$$

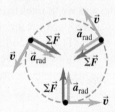

BRIDGING PROBLEM | IN A ROTATING CONE

A small block with mass m is placed inside an inverted cone that is rotating about a vertical axis such that the time for one revolution of the cone is T (**Fig. 5.39**). The walls of the cone make an angle β with the horizontal. The coefficient of static friction between the block and the cone is μ_s. If the block is to remain at a constant height h above the apex of the cone, what are (a) the maximum value of T and (b) the minimum value of T? (That is, find expressions for $T_{\max}$ and $T_{\min}$ in terms of β and h.)

SOLUTION GUIDE

IDENTIFY and SET UP

1. Although we want the block not to slide up or down on the inside of the cone, this is *not* an equilibrium problem. The block rotates with the cone and is in uniform circular motion, so it has an acceleration directed toward the center of its circular path.
2. Identify the forces on the block. What is the direction of the friction force when the cone is rotating as slowly as possible, so T

has its maximum value $T_{\max}$? What is the direction of the friction force when the cone is rotating as rapidly as possible, so T has its minimum value $T_{\min}$? In these situations does the static friction force have its *maximum* magnitude? Why or why not?

3. Draw a free-body diagram for the block when the cone is rotating with $T = T_{\max}$ and a free-body diagram when the cone is rotating with $T = T_{\min}$. Choose coordinate axes, and remember that it's usually easiest to choose one of the axes to be in the direction of the acceleration.
4. What is the radius of the circular path that the block follows? Express this in terms of β and h.
5. List the unknown quantities, and decide which of these are the target variables.

EXECUTE

6. Write Newton's second law in component form for the case in which the cone is rotating with $T = T_{\max}$. Write the acceleration in terms of $T_{\max}$, β, and h, and write the static friction force in terms of the normal force n.
7. Solve these equations for the target variable $T_{\max}$.
8. Repeat steps 6 and 7 for the case in which the cone is rotating with $T = T_{\min}$, and solve for the target variable $T_{\min}$.

EVALUATE

9. You'll end up with some fairly complicated expressions for $T_{\max}$ and $T_{\min}$, so check them over carefully. Do they have the correct units? Is the minimum time $T_{\min}$ less than the maximum time $T_{\max}$, as it must be?
10. What do your expressions for $T_{\max}$ and $T_{\min}$ become if $\mu_s = 0$? Check your results by comparing them with Example 5.22 in Section 5.4.

5.39 A block inside a spinning cone.

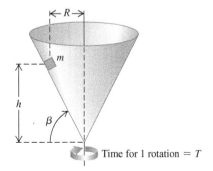

Time for 1 rotation $= T$

Problems

For assigned homework and other learning materials, go to MasteringPhysics®. MP

•, ••, •••: Difficulty levels. CP: Cumulative problems incorporating material from earlier chapters. CALC: Problems requiring calculus. DATA: Problems involving real data, scientific evidence, experimental design, and/or statistical reasoning. BIO: Biosciences problems.

[Always assume that pulleys are frictionless and massless and that strings and cords are massless, unless otherwise noted.]

DISCUSSION QUESTIONS

Q5.1 A man sits in a seat that is hanging from a rope. The rope passes over a pulley suspended from the ceiling, and the man holds the other end of the rope in his hands. What is the tension in the rope, and what force does the seat exert on him? Draw a free-body force diagram for the man.

Q5.2 "In general, the normal force is not equal to the weight." Give an example in which these two forces are equal in magnitude, and at least two examples in which they are not.

Q5.3 A clothesline hangs between two poles. No matter how tightly the line is stretched, it sags a little at the center. Explain why.

Q5.4 You drive a car up a steep hill at constant speed. Discuss all of the forces that act on the car. What pushes it up the hill?

Q5.5 For medical reasons, astronauts in outer space must determine their body mass at regular intervals. Devise a scheme for measuring body mass in an apparently weightless environment.

Q5.6 To push a box up a ramp, which requires less force: pushing horizontally or pushing parallel to the ramp? Why?

Q5.7 A woman in an elevator lets go of her briefcase, but it does not fall to the floor. How is the elevator moving?

Q5.8 A block rests on an inclined plane with enough friction to prevent it from sliding down. To start the block moving, is it easier to push it up the plane or down the plane? Why?

Q5.9 A crate slides up an inclined ramp and then slides down the ramp after momentarily stopping near the top. There is kinetic friction between the surface of the ramp and the crate. Which is greater? (i) The crate's acceleration going up the ramp; (ii) the crate's acceleration going down the ramp; (iii) both are the same. Explain.

Q5.10 A crate of books rests on a level floor. To move it along the floor at a constant velocity, why do you exert less force if you pull it at an angle θ above the horizontal than if you push it at the same angle below the horizontal?

Q5.11 In a world without friction, which of the following activities could you do (or not do)? Explain your reasoning. (a) Drive around an unbanked highway curve; (b) jump into the air; (c) start walking on a horizontal sidewalk; (d) climb a vertical ladder; (e) change lanes while you drive.

Q5.12 When you stand with bare feet in a wet bathtub, the grip feels fairly secure, and yet a catastrophic slip is quite possible. Explain this in terms of the two coefficients of friction.

Q5.13 You are pushing a large crate from the back of a freight elevator to the front as the elevator is moving to the next floor. In which situation is the force you must apply to move the crate the least, and in which is it the greatest: when the elevator is accelerating upward, when it is accelerating downward, or when it is traveling at constant speed? Explain.

Q5.14 It is often said that "friction always opposes motion." Give at least one example in which (a) static friction *causes* motion, and (b) kinetic friction *causes* motion.

Q5.15 If there is a net force on a particle in uniform circular motion, why doesn't the particle's speed change?

Q5.16 A curve in a road has a bank angle calculated and posted for 80 km/h. However, the road is covered with ice, so you cautiously plan to drive slower than this limit. What might happen to your car? Why?

Q5.17 You swing a ball on the end of a lightweight string in a horizontal circle at constant speed. Can the string ever be truly horizontal? If not, would it slope above the horizontal or below the horizontal? Why?

Q5.18 The centrifugal force is not included in the free-body diagrams of Figs. 5.34b and 5.35. Explain why not.

Q5.19 A professor swings a rubber stopper in a horizontal circle on the end of a string in front of his class. He tells Caroline, in the front row, that he is going to let the string go when the stopper is directly in front of her face. Should Caroline worry?

Q5.20 To keep the forces on the riders within allowable limits, many loop-the-loop roller coaster rides are designed so that the loop is not a perfect circle but instead has a larger radius of curvature at the bottom than at the top. Explain.

Q5.21 A tennis ball drops from rest at the top of a tall glass cylinder—first with the air pumped out of the cylinder so that there is no air resistance, and again after the air has been readmitted to the cylinder. You examine multiflash photographs of the two drops. Can you tell which photo belongs to which drop? If so, how?

Q5.22 You throw a baseball straight upward with speed v_0. When the ball returns to the point from where you threw it, how does its speed compare to v_0 (a) in the absence of air resistance and (b) in the presence of air resistance? Explain.

Q5.23 You throw a baseball straight upward. If you do *not* ignore air resistance, how does the time required for the ball to reach its maximum height compare to the time required for it to fall from its maximum height back down to the height from which you threw it? Explain.

Q5.24 You have two identical tennis balls and fill one with water. You release both balls simultaneously from the top of a tall building. If air resistance is negligible, which ball will strike the ground first? Explain. What if air resistance is *not* negligible?

Q5.25 A ball is dropped from rest and feels air resistance as it falls. Which of the graphs in **Fig. Q5.25** best represents its acceleration as a function of time?

Figure Q5.25

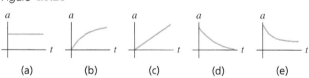

Q5.26 A ball is dropped from rest and feels air resistance as it falls. Which of the graphs in **Fig. Q5.26** best represents its vertical velocity component as a function of time?

Figure Q5.26

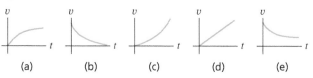

Q5.27 When a batted baseball moves with air drag, when does the ball travel a greater horizontal distance? (i) While climbing to its maximum height; (ii) while descending from its maximum height back to the ground; (iii) the same for both? Explain in terms of the forces acting on the ball.

Q5.28 "A ball is thrown from the edge of a high cliff. Regardless of the angle at which it is thrown, due to air resistance, the ball will eventually end up moving vertically downward." Justify this statement.

EXERCISES

Section 5.1 Using Newton's First Law: Particles in Equilibrium

5.1 • Two 25.0-N weights are suspended at opposite ends of a rope that passes over a light, frictionless pulley. The pulley is attached to a chain from the ceiling. (a) What is the tension in the rope? (b) What is the tension in the chain?

5.2 • In **Fig. E5.2** each of the suspended blocks has weight w. The pulleys are frictionless, and the ropes have negligible weight. In each case, draw a free-body diagram and calculate the tension T in the rope in terms of w.

Figure **E5.2**

(a)   (b)   (c)

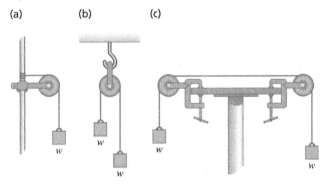

5.3 • A 75.0-kg wrecking ball hangs from a uniform, heavy-duty chain of mass 26.0 kg. (a) Find the maximum and minimum tensions in the chain. (b) What is the tension at a point three-fourths of the way up from the bottom of the chain?

5.4 •• BIO **Injuries to the Spinal Column.** In the treatment of spine injuries, it is often necessary to provide tension along the spinal column to stretch the backbone. One device for doing this is the Stryker frame (**Fig. E5.4a**). A weight W is attached to the patient (sometimes around a neck collar, Fig. E5.4b), and friction between the person's body and the bed prevents sliding. (a) If the coefficient of static friction between a 78.5-kg patient's body and the bed is 0.75, what is the maximum traction force along the spinal column that W can provide without causing the patient to slide? (b) Under the conditions of maximum traction, what is the tension in each cable attached to the neck collar?

Figure **E5.4**

(a)   (b)

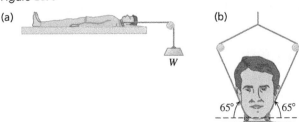

5.5 •• A picture frame hung against a wall is suspended by two wires attached to its upper corners. If the two wires make the same angle with the vertical, what must this angle be if the tension in each wire is equal to 0.75 of the weight of the frame? (Ignore any friction between the wall and the picture frame.)

5.6 •• A large wrecking ball is held in place by two light steel cables (**Fig. E5.6**). If the mass m of the wrecking ball is 3620 kg, what are (a) the tension T_B in the cable that makes an angle of 40° with the vertical and (b) the tension T_A in the horizontal cable?

Figure **E5.6**

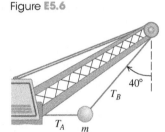

5.7 •• Find the tension in each cord in **Fig. E5.7** if the weight of the suspended object is w.

Figure **E5.7**

(a)   (b)

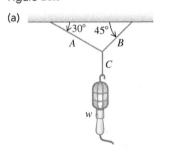 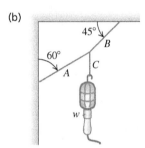

5.8 •• A 1130-kg car is held in place by a light cable on a very smooth (frictionless) ramp (**Fig. E5.8**). The cable makes an angle of 31.0° above the surface of the ramp, and the ramp itself rises at 25.0° above the horizontal. (a) Draw a free-body diagram for the car. (b) Find the tension in the cable. (c) How hard does the surface of the ramp push on the car?

Figure **E5.8**

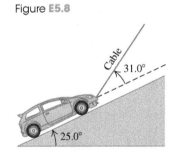

5.9 •• A man pushes on a piano with mass 180 kg; it slides at constant velocity down a ramp that is inclined at 19.0° above the horizontal floor. Neglect any friction acting on the piano. Calculate the magnitude of the force applied by the man if he pushes (a) parallel to the incline and (b) parallel to the floor.

5.10 •• In **Fig. E5.10** the weight w is 60.0 N. (a) What is the tension in the diagonal string? (b) Find the magnitudes of the horizontal forces $\vec{F}_1$ and $\vec{F}_2$ that must be applied to hold the system in the position shown.

Figure **E5.10**

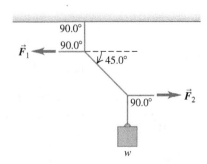

Section 5.2 Using Newton's Second Law: Dynamics of Particles

5.11 •• BIO **Stay Awake!** An astronaut is inside a 2.25×10^6 kg rocket that is blasting off vertically from the launch pad. You want this rocket to reach the speed of sound (331 m/s) as quickly as possible, but astronauts are in danger of blacking out at an acceleration greater than $4g$. (a) What is the maximum initial thrust this rocket's engines can have but just barely avoid blackout? Start with a free-body diagram of the rocket. (b) What force, in terms of the astronaut's weight w, does the rocket exert on her? Start with a free-body diagram of the astronaut. (c) What is the shortest time it can take the rocket to reach the speed of sound?

5.12 •• A rocket of initial mass 125 kg (including all the contents) has an engine that produces a constant vertical force (the *thrust*) of 1720 N. Inside this rocket, a 15.5-N electrical power supply rests on the floor. (a) Find the initial acceleration of the rocket. (b) When the rocket initially accelerates, how hard does the floor push on the power supply? (*Hint:* Start with a free-body diagram for the power supply.)

5.13 •• CP *Genesis* **Crash.** On September 8, 2004, the *Genesis* spacecraft crashed in the Utah desert because its parachute did not open. The 210-kg capsule hit the ground at 311 km/h and penetrated the soil to a depth of 81.0 cm. (a) What was its acceleration (in m/s² and in g's), assumed to be constant, during the crash? (b) What force did the ground exert on the capsule during the crash? Express the force in newtons and as a multiple of the capsule's weight. (c) How long did this force last?

5.14 • Three sleds are being pulled horizontally on frictionless horizontal ice using horizontal ropes (**Fig. E5.14**). The pull is of magnitude 190 N. Find (a) the acceleration of the system and (b) the tension in ropes A and B.

Figure **E5.14**

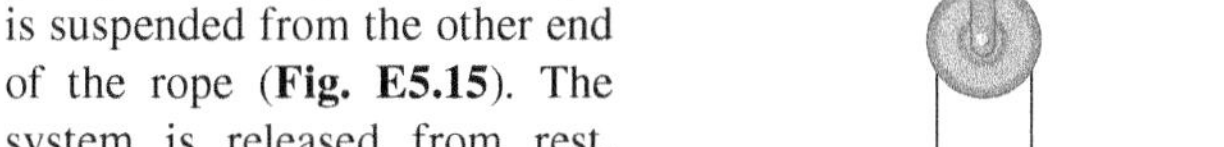

30.0 kg   20.0 kg   10.0 kg   Pull

B   A

5.15 •• **Atwood's Machine.** A 15.0-kg load of bricks hangs from one end of a rope that passes over a small, frictionless pulley. A 28.0-kg counterweight is suspended from the other end of the rope (**Fig. E5.15**). The system is released from rest. (a) Draw two free-body diagrams, one for the load of bricks and one for the counterweight. (b) What is the magnitude of the upward acceleration of the load of bricks? (c) What is the tension in the rope while the load is moving? How does the tension compare to the weight of the load of bricks? To the weight of the counterweight?

Figure **E5.15**

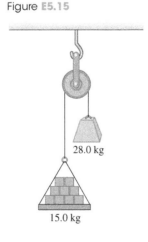

28.0 kg

15.0 kg

5.16 •• CP An 8.00-kg block of ice, released from rest at the top of a 1.50-m-long frictionless ramp, slides downhill, reaching a speed of 2.50 m/s at the bottom. (a) What is the angle between the ramp and the horizontal? (b) What would be the speed of the ice at the bottom if the motion were opposed by a constant friction force of 10.0 N parallel to the surface of the ramp?

5.17 •• A light rope is attached to a block with mass 4.00 kg that rests on a frictionless, horizontal surface. The horizontal rope passes over a frictionless, massless pulley, and a block with mass m is suspended from the other end. When the blocks are released, the tension in the rope is 15.0 N. (a) Draw two free-body diagrams: one for each block. (b) What is the acceleration of either block? (c) Find m. (d) How does the tension compare to the weight of the hanging block?

5.18 •• CP **Runway Design.** A transport plane takes off from a level landing field with two gliders in tow, one behind the other. The mass of each glider is 700 kg, and the total resistance (air drag plus friction with the runway) on each may be assumed constant and equal to 2500 N. The tension in the towrope between the transport plane and the first glider is not to exceed 12,000 N. (a) If a speed of 40 m/s is required for takeoff, what minimum length of runway is needed? (b) What is the tension in the towrope between the two gliders while they are accelerating for the takeoff?

5.19 •• CP A 750.0-kg boulder is raised from a quarry 125 m deep by a long uniform chain having a mass of 575 kg. This chain is of uniform strength, but at any point it can support a maximum tension no greater than 2.50 times its weight without breaking. (a) What is the maximum acceleration the boulder can have and still get out of the quarry, and (b) how long does it take to be lifted out at maximum acceleration if it started from rest?

5.20 •• **Apparent Weight.** A 550-N physics student stands on a bathroom scale in an elevator that is supported by a cable. The combined mass of student plus elevator is 850 kg. As the elevator starts moving, the scale reads 450 N. (a) Find the acceleration of the elevator (magnitude and direction). (b) What is the acceleration if the scale reads 670 N? (c) If the scale reads zero, should the student worry? Explain. (d) What is the tension in the cable in parts (a) and (c)?

5.21 •• CP BIO **Force During a Jump.** When jumping straight up from a crouched position, an average person can reach a maximum height of about 60 cm. During the jump, the person's body from the knees up typically rises a distance of around 50 cm. To keep the calculations simple and yet get a reasonable result, assume that the *entire body* rises this much during the jump. (a) With what initial speed does the person leave the ground to reach a height of 60 cm? (b) Draw a free-body diagram of the person during the jump. (c) In terms of this jumper's weight w, what force does the ground exert on him or her during the jump?

5.22 CP CALC A 2540-kg test rocket is launched vertically from the launch pad. Its fuel (of negligible mass) provides a thrust force such that its vertical velocity as a function of time is given by $v(t) = At + Bt^2$, where A and B are constants and time is measured from the instant the fuel is ignited. The rocket has an upward acceleration of 1.50 m/s² at the instant of ignition and, 1.00 s later, an upward velocity of 2.00 m/s. (a) Determine A and B, including their SI units. (b) At 4.00 s after fuel ignition, what is the acceleration of the rocket, and (c) what thrust force does the burning fuel exert on it, assuming no air resistance? Express the thrust in newtons and as a multiple of the rocket's weight. (d) What was the initial thrust due to the fuel?

5.23 •• CP CALC A 2.00-kg box is moving to the right with speed 9.00 m/s on a horizontal, frictionless surface. At $t = 0$ a horizontal force is applied to the box. The force is directed to the left and has magnitude $F(t) = (6.00 \text{ N/s}^2)t^2$. (a) What distance does the box move from its position at $t = 0$ before its speed is reduced to zero? (b) If the force continues to be applied, what is the speed of the box at $t = 3.00$ s?

5.24 •• CP CALC A 5.00-kg crate is suspended from the end of a short vertical rope of negligible mass. An upward force $F(t)$ is applied to the end of the rope, and the height of the crate above its initial position is given by $y(t) = (2.80 \text{ m/s})t + (0.610 \text{ m/s}^3)t^3$. What is the magnitude of F when $t = 4.00$ s?

Section 5.3 Friction Forces

5.25 • BIO **The Trendelenburg Position.** After emergencies with major blood loss, a patient is placed in the Trendelenburg position, in which the foot of the bed is raised to get maximum blood flow to the brain. If the coefficient of static friction between a typical patient and the bedsheets is 1.20, what is the maximum angle at which the bed can be tilted with respect to the floor before the patient begins to slide?

5.26 • In a laboratory experiment on friction, a 135-N block resting on a rough horizontal table is pulled by a horizontal wire. The pull gradually increases until the block begins to move and continues to increase thereafter. **Figure E5.26** shows a graph of the friction force on this block as a function of the pull. (a) Identify the regions of the graph where static friction and kinetic friction occur. (b) Find the coefficients of static friction and kinetic friction between the block and the table. (c) Why does the graph slant upward at first but then level out? (d) What would the graph look like if a 135-N brick were placed on the block, and what would the coefficients of friction be?

Figure **E5.26**

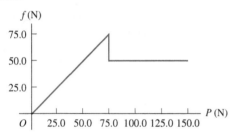

5.27 •• CP A stockroom worker pushes a box with mass 16.8 kg on a horizontal surface with a constant speed of 3.50 m/s. The coefficient of kinetic friction between the box and the surface is 0.20. (a) What horizontal force must the worker apply to maintain the motion? (b) If the force calculated in part (a) is removed, how far does the box slide before coming to rest?

5.28 •• A box of bananas weighing 40.0 N rests on a horizontal surface. The coefficient of static friction between the box and the surface is 0.40, and the coefficient of kinetic friction is 0.20. (a) If no horizontal force is applied to the box and the box is at rest, how large is the friction force exerted on it? (b) What is the magnitude of the friction force if a monkey applies a horizontal force of 6.0 N to the box and the box is initially at rest? (c) What minimum horizontal force must the monkey apply to start the box in motion? (d) What minimum horizontal force must the monkey apply to keep the box moving at constant velocity once it has been started? (e) If the monkey applies a horizontal force of 18.0 N, what is the magnitude of the friction force and what is the box's acceleration?

5.29 •• A 45.0-kg crate of tools rests on a horizontal floor. You exert a gradually increasing horizontal push on it, and the crate just begins to move when your force exceeds 313 N. Then you must reduce your push to 208 N to keep it moving at a steady 25.0 cm/s. (a) What are the coefficients of static and kinetic friction between the crate and the floor? (b) What push must you exert to give it an acceleration of 1.10 m/s²? (c) Suppose you were performing the same experiment on the moon, where the acceleration due to gravity is 1.62 m/s². (i) What magnitude push would cause it to move? (ii) What would its acceleration be if you maintained the push in part (b)?

5.30 •• Some sliding rocks approach the base of a hill with a speed of 12 m/s. The hill rises at 36° above the horizontal and has coefficients of kinetic friction and static friction of 0.45 and 0.65, respectively, with these rocks. (a) Find the acceleration of the rocks as they slide up the hill. (b) Once a rock reaches its highest point, will it stay there or slide down the hill? If it stays, show why. If it slides, find its acceleration on the way down.

5.31 •• A box with mass 10.0 kg moves on a ramp that is inclined at an angle of 55.0° above the horizontal. The coefficient of kinetic friction between the box and the ramp surface is $\mu_k = 0.300$. Calculate the magnitude of the acceleration of the box if you push on the box with a constant force $F = 120.0$ N that is parallel to the ramp surface and (a) directed down the ramp, moving the box down the ramp; (b) directed up the ramp, moving the box up the ramp.

5.32 •• A pickup truck is carrying a toolbox, but the rear gate of the truck is missing. The toolbox will slide out if it is set moving. The coefficients of kinetic friction and static friction between the box and the level bed of the truck are 0.355 and 0.650, respectively. Starting from rest, what is the shortest time this truck could accelerate uniformly to 30.0 m/s without causing the box to slide? Draw a free-body diagram of the toolbox.

5.33 •• You are lowering two boxes, one on top of the other, down a ramp by pulling on a rope parallel to the surface of the ramp (**Fig. E5.33**). Both boxes move together at a constant speed of 15.0 cm/s. The coefficient of kinetic friction between the ramp and the lower box is 0.444, and the coefficient of static friction between the two boxes is 0.800. (a) What force do you need to exert to accomplish this? (b) What are the magnitude and direction of the friction force on the upper box?

Figure **E5.33**

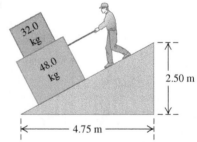

5.34 •• Consider the system shown in **Fig. E5.34**. Block A weighs 45.0 N, and block B weighs 25.0 N. Once block B is set into downward motion, it descends at a constant speed. (a) Calculate the coefficient of kinetic friction between block A and the tabletop. (b) A cat, also of weight 45.0 N, falls asleep on top of block A. If block B is now set into downward motion, what is its acceleration (magnitude and direction)?

Figure **E5.34**

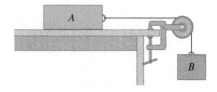

5.35 •• CP **Stopping Distance.**   (a) If the coefficient of kinetic friction between tires and dry pavement is 0.80, what is the shortest distance in which you can stop a car by locking the brakes when the car is traveling at 28.7 m/s (about 65 mi/h)? (b) On wet pavement the coefficient of kinetic friction may be only 0.25. How fast should you drive on wet pavement to be able to stop in the same distance as in part (a)? (*Note:* Locking the brakes is *not* the safest way to stop.)

5.36 •• CP A 25.0-kg box of textbooks rests on a loading ramp that makes an angle α with the horizontal. The coefficient of kinetic friction is 0.25, and the coefficient of static friction is 0.35. (a) As α is increased, find the minimum angle at which the box starts to slip. (b) At this angle, find the acceleration once the box has begun to move. (c) At this angle, how fast will the box be moving after it has slid 5.0 m along the loading ramp?

5.37 • Two crates connected by a rope lie on a horizontal surface (**Fig. E5.37**). Crate A has mass m_A, and crate B has mass m_B. The coefficient of kinetic friction between each crate and the surface is μ_k. The crates are pulled to the right at constant velocity by a horizontal force $\vec{F}$. Draw one or more free-body diagrams to calculate the following in terms of m_A, m_B, and μ_k: (a) the magnitude of $\vec{F}$ and (b) the tension in the rope connecting the blocks.

Figure **E5.37**

5.38 •• A box with mass m is dragged across a level floor with coefficient of kinetic friction μ_k by a rope that is pulled upward at an angle θ above the horizontal with a force of magnitude F. (a) In terms of m, μ_k, θ, and g, obtain an expression for the magnitude of the force required to move the box with constant speed. (b) Knowing that you are studying physics, a CPR instructor asks you how much force it would take to slide a 90-kg patient across a floor at constant speed by pulling on him at an angle of 25° above the horizontal. By dragging weights wrapped in an old pair of pants down the hall with a spring balance, you find that $\mu_k = 0.35$. Use the result of part (a) to answer the instructor's question.

5.39 •• CP As shown in Fig. E5.34, block A (mass 2.25 kg) rests on a tabletop. It is connected by a horizontal cord passing over a light, frictionless pulley to a hanging block B (mass 1.30 kg). The coefficient of kinetic friction between block A and the tabletop is 0.450. The blocks are released then from rest. Draw one or more free-body diagrams to find (a) the speed of each block after they move 3.00 cm and (b) the tension in the cord.

5.40 •• You throw a baseball straight upward. The drag force is proportional to v^2. In terms of g, what is the y-component of the ball's acceleration when the ball's speed is half its terminal speed and (a) it is moving up? (b) It is moving back down?

5.41 •• A large crate with mass m rests on a horizontal floor. The coefficients of friction between the crate and the floor are μ_s and μ_k. A woman pushes downward with a force $\vec{F}$ on the crate at an angle θ below the horizontal. (a) What magnitude of force $\vec{F}$ is required to keep the crate moving at constant velocity? (b) If μ_s is greater than some critical value, the woman cannot start the crate moving no matter how hard she pushes. Calculate this critical value of μ_s.

5.42 • (a) In Example 5.18 (Section 5.3), what value of D is required to make $v_t = 42$ m/s for the skydiver? (b) If the skydiver's daughter, whose mass is 45 kg, is falling through the air and has the same D (0.25 kg/m) as her father, what is the daughter's terminal speed?

Section 5.4 Dynamics of Circular Motion

5.43 • A stone with mass 0.80 kg is attached to one end of a string 0.90 m long. The string will break if its tension exceeds 60.0 N. The stone is whirled in a horizontal circle on a frictionless tabletop; the other end of the string remains fixed. (a) Draw a free-body diagram of the stone. (b) Find the maximum speed the stone can attain without the string breaking.

5.44 • BIO **Force on a Skater's Wrist.**   A 52-kg ice skater spins about a vertical axis through her body with her arms horizontally outstretched; she makes 2.0 turns each second. The distance from one hand to the other is 1.50 m. Biometric measurements indicate that each hand typically makes up about 1.25% of body weight. (a) Draw a free-body diagram of one of the skater's hands. (b) What horizontal force must her wrist exert on her hand? (c) Express the force in part (b) as a multiple of the weight of her hand.

5.45 •• A small remote-controlled car with mass 1.60 kg moves at a constant speed of $v = 12.0$ m/s in a track formed by a vertical circle inside a hollow metal cylinder that has a radius of 5.00 m (**Fig. E5.45**). What is the magnitude of the normal force exerted on the car by the walls of the cylinder at (a) point A (bottom of the track) and (b) point B (top of the track)?

Figure **E5.45**

5.46 •• A small car with mass 0.800 kg travels at constant speed on the inside of a track that is a vertical circle with radius 5.00 m (Fig. E5.45). If the normal force exerted by the track on the car when it is at the top of the track (point B) is 6.00 N, what is the normal force on the car when it is at the bottom of the track (point A)?

5.47 • A small model car with mass m travels at constant speed on the inside of a track that is a vertical circle with radius 5.00 m (Fig. E5.45). If the normal force exerted by the track on the car when it is at the bottom of the track (point A) is equal to $2.50mg$, how much time does it take the car to complete one revolution around the track?

5.48 • A flat (unbanked) curve on a highway has a radius of 170.0 m. A car rounds the curve at a speed of 25.0 m/s. (a) What is the minimum coefficient of static friction that will prevent sliding? (b) Suppose that the highway is icy and the coefficient of static friction between the tires and pavement is only one-third of what you found in part (a). What should be the maximum speed of the car so that it can round the curve safely?

5.49 •• A 1125-kg car and a 2250-kg pickup truck approach a curve on a highway that has a radius of 225 m. (a) At what angle should the highway engineer bank this curve so that vehicles traveling at 65.0 mi/h can safely round it regardless of the condition of their tires? Should the heavy truck go slower than the lighter car? (b) As the car and truck round the curve at 65.0 mi/h, find the normal force on each one due to the highway surface.

5.50 •• The "Giant Swing" at a county fair consists of a vertical central shaft with a number of horizontal arms attached at its upper end. Each arm supports a seat suspended from a cable 5.00 m long, and the upper end of the cable is fastened to the arm at a point 3.00 m from the central shaft (**Fig. E5.50**). (a) Find the time of one revolution of the swing if the cable supporting a seat makes an angle of 30.0° with the vertical. (b) Does the angle depend on the weight of the passenger for a given rate of revolution?

Figure **E5.50**

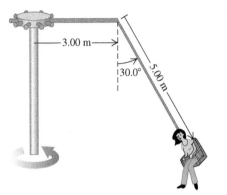

5.51 •• In another version of the "Giant Swing" (see Exercise 5.50), the seat is connected to two cables, one of which is horizontal (**Fig. E5.51**). The seat swings in a horizontal circle at a rate of 28.0 rpm (rev/min). If the seat weighs 255 N and an 825-N person is sitting in it, find the tension in each cable.

Figure **E5.51**

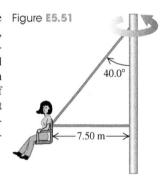

5.52 •• A small button placed on a horizontal rotating platform with diameter 0.520 m will revolve with the platform when it is brought up to a speed of 40.0 rev/min, provided the button is no more than 0.220 m from the axis. (a) What is the coefficient of static friction between the button and the platform? (b) How far from the axis can the button be placed, without slipping, if the platform rotates at 60.0 rev/min?

5.53 •• **Rotating Space Stations.** One problem for humans living in outer space is that they are apparently weightless. One way around this problem is to design a space station that spins about its center at a constant rate. This creates "artificial gravity" at the outside rim of the station. (a) If the diameter of the space station is 800 m, how many revolutions per minute are needed for the "artificial gravity" acceleration to be 9.80 m/s^2? (b) If the space station is a waiting area for travelers going to Mars, it might be desirable to simulate the acceleration due to gravity on the Martian surface (3.70 m/s^2). How many revolutions per minute are needed in this case?

5.54 • The Cosmo Clock 21 Ferris wheel in Yokohama, Japan, has a diameter of 100 m. Its name comes from its 60 arms, each of which can function as a second hand (so that it makes one revolution every 60.0 s). (a) Find the speed of the passengers when the Ferris wheel is rotating at this rate. (b) A passenger weighs 882 N at the weight-guessing booth on the ground. What is his apparent weight at the highest and at the lowest point on the Ferris wheel?

(c) What would be the time for one revolution if the passenger's apparent weight at the highest point were zero? (d) What then would be the passenger's apparent weight at the lowest point?

5.55 •• An airplane flies in a loop (a circular path in a vertical plane) of radius 150 m. The pilot's head always points toward the center of the loop. The speed of the airplane is not constant; the airplane goes slowest at the top of the loop and fastest at the bottom. (a) What is the speed of the airplane at the top of the loop, where the pilot feels weightless? (b) What is the apparent weight of the pilot at the bottom of the loop, where the speed of the airplane is 280 km/h? His true weight is 700 N.

5.56 •• A 50.0-kg stunt pilot who has been diving her airplane vertically pulls out of the dive by changing her course to a circle in a vertical plane. (a) If the plane's speed at the lowest point of the circle is 95.0 m/s, what is the minimum radius of the circle so that the acceleration at this point will not exceed 4.00g? (b) What is the apparent weight of the pilot at the lowest point of the pullout?

5.57 • **Stay Dry!** You tie a cord to a pail of water and swing the pail in a vertical circle of radius 0.600 m. What minimum speed must you give the pail at the highest point of the circle to avoid spilling water?

5.58 •• A bowling ball weighing 71.2 N (16.0 lb) is attached to the ceiling by a 3.80-m rope. The ball is pulled to one side and released; it then swings back and forth as a pendulum. As the rope swings through the vertical, the speed of the bowling ball is 4.20 m/s. At this instant, what are (a) the acceleration of the bowling ball, in magnitude and direction, and (b) the tension in the rope?

5.59 •• BIO **Effect on Blood of Walking.** While a person is walking, his arms swing through approximately a 45° angle in $\frac{1}{2}$ s. As a reasonable approximation, assume that the arm moves with constant speed during each swing. A typical arm is 70.0 cm long, measured from the shoulder joint. (a) What is the acceleration of a 1.0-g drop of blood in the fingertips at the bottom of the swing? (b) Draw a free-body diagram of the drop of blood in part (a). (c) Find the force that the blood vessel must exert on the drop of blood in part (a). Which way does this force point? (d) What force would the blood vessel exert if the arm were not swinging?

PROBLEMS

5.60 •• An adventurous archaeologist crosses between two rock cliffs by slowly going hand over hand along a rope stretched between the cliffs. He stops to rest at the middle of the rope (**Fig. P5.60**). The rope will break if the tension in it exceeds 2.50×10^4 N, and our hero's mass is 90.0 kg. (a) If the angle θ is 10.0°, what is the tension in the rope? (b) What is the smallest value θ can have if the rope is not to break?

Figure **P5.60**

5.61 ••• Two ropes are connected to a steel cable that supports a hanging weight (**Fig. P5.61**). (a) Draw a free-body diagram showing all of the forces acting at the knot that connects the two ropes to the steel cable. Based on your diagram, which of the two ropes will have the greater tension? (b) If the maximum tension either rope can sustain without breaking is 5000 N, determine the maximum value of the hanging weight that these ropes can safely support. Ignore the weight of the ropes and of the steel cable.

Figure **P5.61**

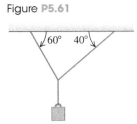

5.62 •• In **Fig. P5.62** a worker lifts a weight w by pulling down on a rope with a force $\vec{F}$. The upper pulley is attached to the ceiling by a chain, and the lower pulley is attached to the weight by another chain. Draw one or more free-body diagrams to find the tension in each chain and the magnitude of $\vec{F}$, in terms of w, if the weight is lifted at constant speed. Assume that the rope, pulleys, and chains have negligible weights.

Figure **P5.62**

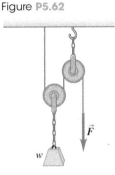

5.63 •• In a repair shop a truck engine that has mass 409 kg is held in place by four light cables (**Fig. P5.63**). Cable A is horizontal, cables B and D are vertical, and cable C makes an angle of $37.1°$ with a vertical wall. If the tension in cable A is 722 N, what are the tensions in cables B and C?

Figure **P5.63**

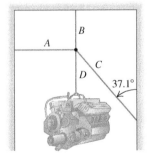

5.64 ••• A horizontal wire holds a solid uniform ball of mass m in place on a tilted ramp that rises $35.0°$ above the horizontal. The surface of this ramp is perfectly smooth, and the wire is directed away from the center of the ball (**Fig. P5.64**). (a) Draw a free-body diagram of the ball. (b) How hard does the surface of the ramp push on the ball? (c) What is the tension in the wire?

Figure **P5.64**

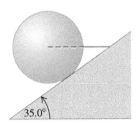

5.65 ••• A solid uniform 45.0-kg ball of diameter 32.0 cm is supported against a vertical, frictionless wall by a thin 30.0-cm wire of negligible mass (**Fig. P5.65**). (a) Draw a free-body diagram for the ball, and use the diagram to find the tension in the wire. (b) How hard does the ball push against the wall?

Figure **P5.65**

5.66 •• CP A box is sliding with a constant speed of 4.00 m/s in the $+x$-direction on a horizontal, frictionless surface. At $x = 0$ the box encounters a rough patch of the surface, and then the surface becomes even rougher. Between $x = 0$ and $x = 2.00$ m, the coefficient of kinetic friction between the box and the surface is 0.200; between $x = 2.00$ m and $x = 4.00$ m, it is 0.400. (a) What is the x-coordinate of the point where the box comes to rest? (b) How much time does it take the box to come to rest after it first encounters the rough patch at $x = 0$?

5.67 •• CP BIO **Forces During Chin-ups.** When you do a chin-up, you raise your chin just over a bar (the chinning bar), supporting yourself with only your arms. Typically, the body below the arms is raised by about 30 cm in a time of 1.0 s, starting from rest. Assume that the entire body of a 680-N person doing chin-ups is raised by 30 cm, and that half the 1.0 s is spent accelerating upward and the other half accelerating downward, uniformly in both cases. Draw a free-body diagram of the person's body, and use it to find the force his arms must exert on him during the accelerating part of the chin-up.

5.68 •• CP CALC A 2.00-kg box is suspended from the end of a light vertical rope. A time-dependent force is applied to the upper end of the rope, and the box moves upward with a velocity magnitude that varies in time according to $v(t) = (2.00 \text{ m/s}^2)t + (0.600 \text{ m/s}^3)t^2$. What is the tension in the rope when the velocity of the box is 9.00 m/s?

5.69 ••• CALC A 3.00-kg box that is several hundred meters above the earth's surface is suspended from the end of a short vertical rope of negligible mass. A time-dependent upward force is applied to the upper end of the rope and results in a tension in the rope of $T(t) = (36.0 \text{ N/s})t$. The box is at rest at $t = 0$. The only forces on the box are the tension in the rope and gravity. (a) What is the velocity of the box at (i) $t = 1.00$ s and (ii) $t = 3.00$ s? (b) What is the maximum distance that the box descends below its initial position? (c) At what value of t does the box return to its initial position?

5.70 •• CP A 5.00-kg box sits at rest at the bottom of a ramp that is 8.00 m long and is inclined at $30.0°$ above the horizontal. The coefficient of kinetic friction is $\mu_k = 0.40$, and the coefficient of static friction is $\mu_s = 0.43$. What constant force F, applied parallel to the surface of the ramp, is required to push the box to the top of the ramp in a time of 6.00 s?

5.71 •• Two boxes connected by a light horizontal rope are on a horizontal surface (Fig. E5.37). The coefficient of kinetic friction between each box and the surface is $\mu_k = 0.30$. Box B has mass 5.00 kg, and box A has mass m. A force F with magnitude 40.0 N and direction $53.1°$ above the horizontal is applied to the 5.00-kg box, and both boxes move to the right with $a = 1.50 \text{ m/s}^2$. (a) What is the tension T in the rope that connects the boxes? (b) What is m?

5.72 ··· A 6.00-kg box sits on a ramp that is inclined at 37.0° above the horizontal. The coefficient of kinetic friction between the box and the ramp is $\mu_k = 0.30$. What *horizontal* force is required to move the box up the incline with a constant acceleration of 3.60 m/s²?

5.73 ·· CP An 8.00-kg box sits on a ramp that is inclined at 33.0° above the horizontal. The coefficient of kinetic friction between the box and the surface of the ramp is $\mu_k = 0.300$. A constant *horizontal* force $F = 26.0$ N is applied to the box (**Fig. P5.73**), and the box moves down the ramp. If the box is initially at rest, what is its speed 2.00 s after the force is applied?

Figure **P5.73**

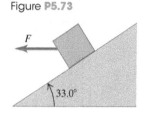

5.74 ·· CP In **Fig. P5.74**, $m_1 = 20.0$ kg and $\alpha = 53.1°$. The coefficient of kinetic friction between the block of mass m_1 and the incline is $\mu_k = 0.40$. What must be the mass m_2 of the hanging block if it is to descend 12.0 m in the first 3.00 s after the system is released from rest?

Figure **P5.74**

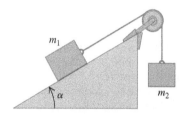

5.75 ·· CP You place a book of mass 5.00 kg against a vertical wall. You apply a constant force $\vec{F}$ to the book, where $F = 96.0$ N and the force is at an angle of 60.0° above the horizontal (**Fig. P5.75**). The coefficient of kinetic friction between the book and the wall is 0.300. If the book is initially at rest, what is its speed after it has traveled 0.400 m up the wall?

Figure **P5.75**

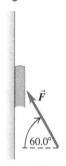

5.76 ·· Block A in **Fig. P5.76** weighs 60.0 N. The coefficient of static friction between the block and the surface on which it rests is 0.25. The weight w is 12.0 N, and the system is in equilibrium. (a) Find the friction force exerted on block A. (b) Find the maximum weight w for which the system will remain in equilibrium.

Figure **P5.76**

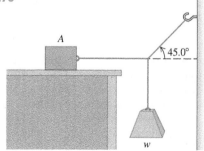

5.77 ·· A block with mass m_1 is placed on an inclined plane with slope angle α and is connected to a hanging block with mass m_2 by a cord passing over a small, frictionless pulley (Fig. P5.74). The coefficient of static friction is μ_s, and the coefficient of kinetic friction is μ_k. (a) Find the value of m_2 for which the block of mass m_1 moves up the plane at constant speed once it is set in motion. (b) Find the value of m_2 for which the block of mass m_1 moves down the plane at constant speed once it is set in motion. (c) For what range of values of m_2 will the blocks remain at rest if they are released from rest?

5.78 ·· BIO **The Flying Leap of a Flea.** High-speed motion pictures (3500 frames/second) of a jumping 210-μg flea yielded the data to plot the flea's acceleration as a function of time, as shown in **Fig. P5.78**. (See "The Flying Leap of the Flea," by M. Rothschild et al., *Scientific American,* November 1973.) This flea was about 2 mm long and jumped at a nearly vertical takeoff angle. Using the graph, (a) find the *initial* net external force on the flea. How does it compare to the flea's weight? (b) Find the *maximum* net external force on this jumping flea. When does this maximum force occur? (c) Use the graph to find the flea's maximum speed.

Figure **P5.78**

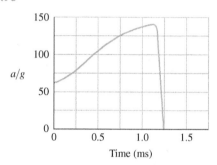

5.79 ·· Block A in **Fig. P5.79** weighs 1.20 N, and block B weighs 3.60 N. The coefficient of kinetic friction between all surfaces is 0.300. Find the magnitude of the horizontal force $\vec{F}$ necessary to drag block B to the left at constant speed (a) if A rests on B and moves with it (Fig. P5.79a), (b) if A is held at rest (Fig. P5.79b).

Figure **P5.79**

(a) 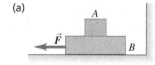   (b)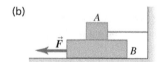

5.80 ··· CP **Elevator Design.** You are designing an elevator for a hospital. The force exerted on a passenger by the floor of the elevator is not to exceed 1.60 times the passenger's weight. The elevator accelerates upward with constant acceleration for a distance of 3.0 m and then starts to slow down. What is the maximum speed of the elevator?

5.81 ··· CP CALC You are standing on a bathroom scale in an elevator in a tall building. Your mass is 64 kg. The elevator starts from rest and travels upward with a speed that varies with time according to $v(t) = (3.0 \text{ m/s}^2)t + (0.20 \text{ m/s}^3)t^2$. When $t = 4.0$ s, what is the reading on the bathroom scale?

5.82 •• A hammer is hanging by a light rope from the ceiling of a bus. The ceiling is parallel to the roadway. The bus is traveling in a straight line on a horizontal street. You observe that the hammer hangs at rest with respect to the bus when the angle between the rope and the ceiling of the bus is 56.0°. What is the acceleration of the bus?

5.83 •• A 40.0-kg packing case is initially at rest on the floor of a 1500-kg pickup truck. The coefficient of static friction between the case and the truck floor is 0.30, and the coefficient of kinetic friction is 0.20. Before each acceleration given below, the truck is traveling due north at constant speed. Find the magnitude and direction of the friction force acting on the case (a) when the truck accelerates at 2.20 m/s² northward and (b) when it accelerates at 3.40 m/s² southward.

5.84 ••• If the coefficient of static friction between a table and a uniform, massive rope is μ_s, what fraction of the rope can hang over the edge of the table without the rope sliding?

5.85 ••• Two identical 15.0-kg balls, each 25.0 cm in diameter, are suspended by two 35.0-cm wires (**Fig. P5.85**). The entire apparatus is supported by a single 18.0-cm wire, and the surfaces of the balls are perfectly smooth. (a) Find the tension in each of the three wires. (b) How hard does each ball push on the other one?

Figure **P5.85**

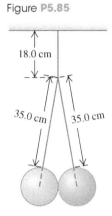

5.86 • CP **Traffic Court.** You are called as an expert witness in a trial for a traffic violation. The facts are these: A driver slammed on his brakes and came to a stop with constant acceleration. Measurements of his tires and the skid marks on the pavement indicate that he locked his car's wheels, the car traveled 192 ft before stopping, and the coefficient of kinetic friction between the road and his tires was 0.750. He was charged with speeding in a 45-mi/h zone but pleads innocent. What is your conclusion: guilty or innocent? How fast was he going when he hit his brakes?

5.87 ••• Block A in **Fig. P5.87** weighs 1.90 N, and block B weighs 4.20 N. The coefficient of kinetic friction between all surfaces is 0.30. Find the magnitude of the horizontal force $\vec{F}$ necessary to drag block B to the left at constant speed if A and B are connected by a light, flexible cord passing around a fixed, frictionless pulley.

Figure **P5.87**

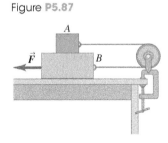

5.88 •• CP **Losing Cargo.** A 12.0-kg box rests on the level bed of a truck. The coefficients of friction between the box and bed are $\mu_s = 0.19$ and $\mu_k = 0.15$. The truck stops at a stop sign and then starts to move with an acceleration of 2.20 m/s². If the box is 1.80 m from the rear of the truck when the truck starts, how much time elapses before the box falls off the truck? How far does the truck travel in this time?

5.89 •• Block A in **Fig. P5.89** has mass 4.00 kg, and block B has mass 12.0 kg. The coefficient of kinetic friction between block B and the horizontal surface is 0.25. (a) What is the mass of block C if block B is moving to the right and speeding up with an acceleration of 2.00 m/s²? (b) What is the tension in each cord when block B has this acceleration?

Figure **P5.89**

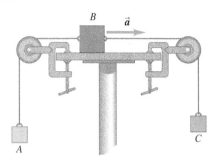

5.90 •• Two blocks connected by a cord passing over a small, frictionless pulley rest on frictionless planes (**Fig. P5.90**). (a) Which way will the system move when the blocks are released from rest? (b) What is the acceleration of the blocks? (c) What is the tension in the cord?

Figure **P5.90**

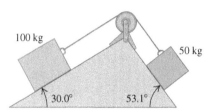

5.91 •• In terms of m_1, m_2, and g, find the acceleration of each block in **Fig. P5.91**. There is no friction anywhere in the system.

Figure **P5.91**

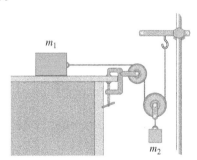

5.92 ••• Block B, with mass 5.00 kg, rests on block A, with mass 8.00 kg, which in turn is on a horizontal tabletop (**Fig. P5.92**). There is no friction between block A and the tabletop, but the coefficient of static friction between blocks A and B is 0.750. A light string attached to block A passes over a frictionless, massless pulley, and block C is suspended from the other end of the string. What is the largest mass that block C can have so that blocks A and B still slide together when the system is released from rest?

Figure **P5.92**

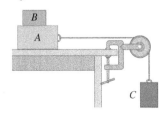

5.93 ••• Two objects, with masses 5.00 kg and 2.00 kg, hang 0.600 m above the floor from the ends of a cord that is 6.00 m long and passes over a frictionless pulley. Both objects start from rest. Find the maximum height reached by the 2.00-kg object.

5.94 •• **Friction in an Elevator.** You are riding in an elevator on the way to the 18th floor of your dormitory. The elevator is accelerating upward with $a = 1.90$ m/s². Beside you is the box containing your new computer; the box and its contents have a total mass of 36.0 kg. While the elevator is accelerating upward, you push horizontally on the box to slide it at constant speed toward the elevator door. If the coefficient of kinetic friction between the box and the elevator floor is $\mu_k = 0.32$, what magnitude of force must you apply?

5.95 • A block is placed against the vertical front of a cart (**Fig. P5.95**). What acceleration must the cart have so that block A does not fall? The coefficient of static friction between the block and the cart is μ_s. How would an observer on the cart describe the behavior of the block?

Figure **P5.95**

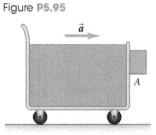

5.96 ••• Two blocks, with masses 4.00 kg and 8.00 kg, are connected by a string and slide down a 30.0° inclined plane (**Fig. P5.96**). The coefficient of kinetic friction between the 4.00-kg block and the plane is 0.25; that between the 8.00-kg block and the plane is 0.35. Calculate (a) the acceleration of each block and (b) the tension in the string. (c) What happens if the positions of the blocks are reversed, so that the 4.00-kg block is uphill from the 8.00-kg block?

Figure **P5.96**

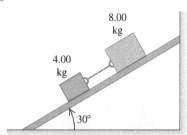

5.97 ••• Block A, with weight $3w$, slides down an inclined plane S of slope angle 36.9° at a constant speed while plank B, with weight w, rests on top of A. The plank is attached by a cord to the wall (**Fig. P5.97**). (a) Draw a diagram of all the forces acting on block A. (b) If the coefficient of kinetic friction is the same between A and B and between S and A, determine its value.

Figure **P5.97**

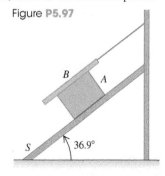

5.98 •• Jack sits in the chair of a Ferris wheel that is rotating at a constant 0.100 rev/s. As Jack passes through the highest point of his circular path, the upward force that the chair exerts on him is equal to one-fourth of his weight. What is the radius of the circle in which Jack travels? Treat him as a point mass.

5.99 ••• **Banked Curve I.** A curve with a 120-m radius on a level road is banked at the correct angle for a speed of 20 m/s. If an automobile rounds this curve at 30 m/s, what is the minimum coefficient of static friction needed between tires and road to prevent skidding?

5.100 •• **Banked Curve II.** Consider a wet roadway banked as in Example 5.22 (Section 5.4), where there is a coefficient of static friction of 0.30 and a coefficient of kinetic friction of 0.25 between the tires and the roadway. The radius of the curve is $R = 50$ m. (a) If the bank angle is $\beta = 25°$, what is the *maximum* speed the automobile can have before sliding *up* the banking? (b) What is the *minimum* speed the automobile can have before sliding *down* the banking?

5.101 ••• Blocks A, B, and C are placed as in **Fig. P5.101** and connected by ropes of negligible mass. Both A and B weigh 25.0 N each, and the coefficient of kinetic friction between each block and the surface is 0.35. Block C descends with constant velocity. (a) Draw separate free-body diagrams showing the forces acting on A and on B. (b) Find the tension in the rope connecting blocks A and B. (c) What is the weight of block C? (d) If the rope connecting A and B were cut, what would be the acceleration of C?

Figure **P5.101**

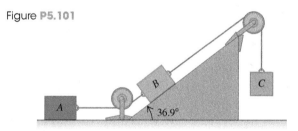

5.102 •• You are riding in a school bus. As the bus rounds a flat curve at constant speed, a lunch box with mass 0.500 kg, suspended from the ceiling of the bus by a string 1.80 m long, is found to hang at rest relative to the bus when the string makes an angle of 30.0° with the vertical. In this position the lunch box is 50.0 m from the curve's center of curvature. What is the speed v of the bus?

5.103 •• CALC You throw a rock downward into water with a speed of $3mg/k$, where k is the coefficient in Eq. (5.5). Assume that the relationship between fluid resistance and speed is as given in Eq. (5.5), and calculate the speed of the rock as a function of time.

5.104 ••• A 4.00-kg block is attached to a vertical rod by means of two strings. When the system rotates about the axis of the rod, the strings are extended as shown in **Fig. P5.104** and the tension in the upper string is 80.0 N. (a) What is the tension in the lower cord? (b) How many revolutions per minute does the system make? (c) Find the number of revolutions per minute at which the lower cord just goes slack. (d) Explain what happens if the number of revolutions per minute is less than that in part (c).

Figure **P5.104**

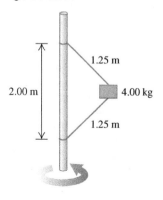

5.105 •• On the ride "Spindletop" at the amusement park Six Flags Over Texas, people stood against the inner wall of a hollow vertical cylinder with radius 2.5 m. The cylinder started to rotate, and when it reached a constant rotation rate of 0.60 rev/s, the floor dropped about 0.5 m. The people remained pinned against the wall without touching the floor. (a) Draw a force diagram for a person on this ride after the floor has dropped. (b) What minimum coefficient of static friction was required for the person not to slide downward to the new position of the floor? (c) Does your answer in part (b) depend on the person's mass? (*Note:* When such a ride is over, the cylinder is slowly brought to rest. As it slows down, people slide down the walls to the floor.)

5.106 •• A 70-kg person rides in a 30-kg cart moving at 12 m/s at the top of a hill that is in the shape of an arc of a circle with a radius of 40 m. (a) What is the apparent weight of the person as the cart passes over the top of the hill? (b) Determine the maximum speed that the cart can travel at the top of the hill without losing contact with the surface. Does your answer depend on the mass of the cart or the mass of the person? Explain.

5.107 •• A small bead can slide without friction on a circular hoop that is in a vertical plane and has a radius of 0.100 m. The hoop rotates at a constant rate of 4.00 rev/s about a vertical diameter (**Fig. P5.107**). (a) Find the angle β at which the bead is in vertical equilibrium. (It has a radial acceleration toward the axis.) (b) Is it possible for the bead to "ride" at the same elevation as the center of the hoop? (c) What will happen if the hoop rotates at 1.00 rev/s?

Figure **P5.107**

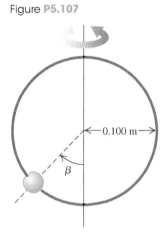

5.108 •• A physics major is working to pay her college tuition by performing in a traveling carnival. She rides a motorcycle inside a hollow, transparent plastic sphere. After gaining sufficient speed, she travels in a vertical circle with radius 13.0 m. She has mass 70.0 kg, and her motorcycle has mass 40.0 kg. (a) What minimum speed must she have at the top of the circle for the motorcycle tires to remain in contact with the sphere? (b) At the bottom of the circle, her speed is twice the value calculated in part (a). What is the magnitude of the normal force exerted on the motorcycle by the sphere at this point?

5.109 •• DATA In your physics lab, a block of mass m is at rest on a horizontal surface. You attach a light cord to the block and apply a horizontal force to the free end of the cord. You find that the block remains at rest until the tension T in the cord exceeds 20.0 N. For $T > 20.0$ N, you measure the acceleration of the block when T is maintained at a constant value, and you plot the results (**Fig. P5.109**). The equation for the straight line that best fits your data is $a = [0.182 \text{ m/(N} \cdot \text{s}^2)]T - 2.842 \text{ m/s}^2$. For this block and surface, what are (a) the coefficient of static friction and (b) the coefficient of kinetic friction? (c) If the experiment were done on the earth's moon, where g is much smaller than on the earth, would the graph of a versus T still be fit well by a straight line? If so, how would the slope and intercept of the line differ from the values in Fig. P5.109? Or, would each of them be the same?

Figure **P5.109**

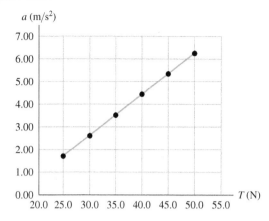

5.110 •• DATA A road heading due east passes over a small hill. You drive a car of mass m at constant speed v over the top of the hill, where the shape of the roadway is well approximated as an arc of a circle with radius R. Sensors have been placed on the road surface there to measure the downward force that cars exert on the surface at various speeds. The table gives values of this force versus speed for your car:

Speed (m/s)	6.00	8.00	10.0	12.0	14.0	16.0
Force (N)	8100	7690	7050	6100	5200	4200

Treat the car as a particle. (a) Plot the values in such a way that they are well fitted by a straight line. You might need to raise the speed, the force, or both to some power. (b) Use your graph from part (a) to calculate m and R. (c) What maximum speed can the car have at the top of the hill and still not lose contact with the road?

5.111 •• DATA You are an engineer working for a manufacturing company. You are designing a mechanism that uses a cable to drag heavy metal blocks a distance of 8.00 m along a ramp that is sloped at 40.0° above the horizontal. The coefficient of kinetic friction between these blocks and the incline is $\mu_k = 0.350$. Each block has a mass of 2170 kg. The block will be placed on the bottom of the ramp, the cable will be attached, and the block will then be given just enough of a momentary push to overcome static friction. The block is then to accelerate at a constant rate to move the 8.00 m in 4.20 s. The cable is made of wire rope and is parallel to the ramp surface. The table gives the breaking strength of the cable as a function of its diameter; the safe load tension, which is 20% of the breaking strength; and the mass per meter of the cable:

Cable Diameter (in.)	Breaking Strength (kN)	Safe Load (kN)	Mass per Meter (kg/m)
$\frac{1}{4}$	24.4	4.89	0.16
$\frac{3}{8}$	54.3	10.9	0.36
$\frac{1}{2}$	95.2	19.0	0.63
$\frac{5}{8}$	149	29.7	0.98
$\frac{3}{4}$	212	42.3	1.41
$\frac{7}{8}$	286	57.4	1.92
1	372	74.3	2.50

Source: www.engineeringtoolbox.com

(a) What is the minimum diameter of the cable that can be used to pull a block up the ramp without exceeding the safe load value of the tension in the cable? Ignore the mass of the cable, and select the diameter from those listed in the table. (b) You need to know safe load values for diameters that aren't in the table, so you hypothesize that the breaking strength and safe load limit are proportional to the cross-sectional area of the cable. Draw a graph that tests this hypothesis, and discuss its accuracy. What is your estimate of the safe load value for a cable with diameter $\frac{9}{16}$ in.? (c) The coefficient of static friction between the crate and the ramp is $\mu_s = 0.620$, which is nearly twice the value of the coefficient of kinetic friction. If the machinery jams and the block stops in the middle of the ramp, what is the tension in the cable? Is it larger or smaller than the value when the block is moving? (d) Is the actual tension in the cable, at its upper end, larger or smaller than the value calculated when you ignore the mass of the cable? If the cable is 9.00 m long, how accurate is it to ignore the cable's mass?

CHALLENGE PROBLEMS

5.112 ··· **Moving Wedge.** A wedge with mass M rests on a frictionless, horizontal tabletop. A block with mass m is placed on the wedge (**Fig. P5.112a**). There is no friction between the block and the wedge. The system is released from rest. (a) Calculate the acceleration of the wedge and the horizontal and vertical components of the acceleration of the block. (b) Do your answers to part (a) reduce to the correct results when M is very large? (c) As seen by a stationary observer, what is the shape of the trajectory of the block?

Figure **P5.112**

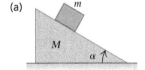

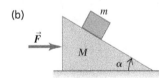

5.113 ··· A wedge with mass M rests on a frictionless, horizontal tabletop. A block with mass m is placed on the wedge, and a horizontal force $\vec{F}$ is applied to the wedge (Fig. P5.112b). What must the magnitude of $\vec{F}$ be if the block is to remain at a constant height above the tabletop?

5.114 ··· **Double Atwood's Machine.** In **Fig. P5.114** masses m_1 and m_2 are connected by a light string A over a light, frictionless pulley B. The axle of pulley B is connected by a light string C over a light, frictionless pulley D to a mass m_3. Pulley D is suspended from the ceiling by an attachment to its axle. The system is released from rest. In terms of m_1, m_2, m_3, and g, what are (a) the acceleration of block m_3; (b) the acceleration of pulley B; (c) the acceleration of block m_1; (d) the acceleration of block m_2; (e) the tension in string A; (f) the tension in string C? (g) What do your expressions give for the special case of $m_1 = m_2$ and $m_3 = m_1 + m_2$? Is this reasonable?

Figure **P5.114**

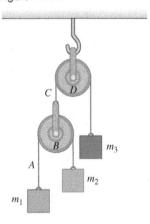

5.115 ··· A ball is held at rest at position A in **Fig. P5.115** by two light strings. The horizontal string is cut, and the ball starts swinging as a pendulum. Position B is the farthest to the right that the ball can go as it swings back and forth. What is the ratio of the tension in the supporting string at B to its value at A before the string was cut?

Figure **P5.115**

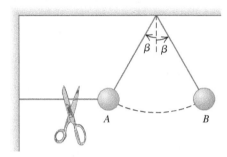

PASSAGE PROBLEMS

FRICTION AND CLIMBING SHOES. Shoes made for the sports of bouldering and rock climbing are designed to provide a great deal of friction between the foot and the surface of the ground. Such shoes on smooth rock might have a coefficient of static friction of 1.2 and a coefficient of kinetic friction of 0.90.

5.116 For a person wearing these shoes, what's the maximum angle (with respect to the horizontal) of a smooth rock that can be walked on without slipping? (a) 42°; (b) 50°; (c) 64°; (d) larger than 90°.

5.117 If the person steps onto a smooth rock surface that's inclined at an angle large enough that these shoes begin to slip, what will happen? (a) She will slide a short distance and stop; (b) she will accelerate down the surface; (c) she will slide down the surface at constant speed; (d) we can't tell what will happen without knowing her mass.

5.118 A person wearing these shoes stands on a smooth, horizontal rock. She pushes against the ground to begin running. What is the maximum horizontal acceleration she can have without slipping? (a) $0.20g$; (b) $0.75g$; (c) $0.90g$; (d) $1.2g$.

Answers

Chapter Opening Question **?**

(iii) The upward force exerted by the air has the same magnitude as the force of gravity. Although the seed and pappus are descending, their vertical velocity is constant, so their vertical acceleration is zero. According to Newton's first law, the net vertical force on the seed and pappus must also be zero. The individual vertical forces must balance.

Test Your Understanding Questions

5.1 (ii) The two cables are arranged symmetrically, so the tension in either cable has the same magnitude T. The vertical component of the tension from each cable is $T\sin 45°$ (or, equivalently, $T\cos 45°$), so Newton's first law applied to the vertical forces tells us that $2T\sin 45° - w = 0$. Hence $T = w/(2\sin 45°) = w/\sqrt{2} = 0.71w$. Each cable supports half of the weight of the traffic light, but the tension is greater than $w/2$ because only the vertical component of the tension counteracts the weight.

5.2 (ii) No matter what the instantaneous velocity of the glider, its acceleration is constant and has the value found in Example 5.12. In the same way, the acceleration of a body in free fall is the same whether it is ascending, descending, or at the high point of its motion (see Section 2.5).

5.3 (a): (i), (iii); (b): (ii), (iv); (c): (v) In situations (i) and (iii) the box is not accelerating (so the net force on it must be zero) and no other force is acting parallel to the horizontal surface; hence no friction force is needed to prevent sliding. In situations (ii) and (iv) the box would start to slide over the surface if no friction were present, so a static friction force must act to prevent this. In situation (v) the box is sliding over a rough surface, so a kinetic friction force acts on it.

5.4 (iii) A satellite of mass m orbiting the earth at speed v in an orbit of radius r has an acceleration of magnitude v^2/r, so the net force acting on it from the earth's gravity has magnitude $F = mv^2/r$. The farther the satellite is from the earth, the greater the value of r, the smaller the value of v, and hence the smaller the values of v^2/r and of F. In other words, the earth's gravitational force decreases with increasing distance.

Bridging Problem

(a) $T_{max} = 2\pi\sqrt{\dfrac{h(\cos\beta + \mu_s\sin\beta)}{g\tan\beta(\sin\beta - \mu_s\cos\beta)}}$

(b) $T_{min} = 2\pi\sqrt{\dfrac{h(\cos\beta - \mu_s\sin\beta)}{g\tan\beta(\sin\beta + \mu_s\cos\beta)}}$

? A baseball pitcher does work with his throwing arm to give the ball a property called kinetic energy, which depends on the ball's mass and speed. Which has the greatest kinetic energy? (i) A ball of mass 0.145 kg moving at 20.0 m/s; (ii) a smaller ball of mass 0.0145 kg moving at 200 m/s; (iii) a larger ball of mass 1.45 kg moving at 2.00 m/s; (iv) all three balls have the same kinetic energy; (v) it depends on the directions in which the balls move.

6 WORK AND KINETIC ENERGY

LEARNING GOALS

Looking forward at …

6.1 What it means for a force to do work on a body, and how to calculate the amount of work done.

6.2 The definition of the kinetic energy (energy of motion) of a body, and how the total work done on a body changes the body's kinetic energy.

6.3 How to use the relationship between total work and change in kinetic energy when the forces are not constant, the body follows a curved path, or both.

6.4 How to solve problems involving power (the rate of doing work).

Looking back at …

1.10 The scalar product (or dot product) of two vectors.

2.4 Straight-line motion with constant acceleration.

4.3 Newton's second law.

4.5 Newton's third law.

5.1, 5.2 Using components to find the net force.

Suppose you try to find the speed of an arrow that has been shot from a bow. You apply Newton's laws and all the problem-solving techniques that we've learned, but you run across a major stumbling block: After the archer releases the arrow, the bow string exerts a *varying* force that depends on the arrow's position. As a result, the simple methods that we've learned aren't enough to calculate the speed. Never fear; we aren't by any means finished with mechanics, and there are other methods for dealing with such problems.

The new method that we're about to introduce uses the ideas of *work* and *energy*. The importance of the energy idea stems from the *principle of conservation of energy*: Energy is a quantity that can be converted from one form to another but cannot be created or destroyed. In an automobile engine, chemical energy stored in the fuel is converted partially to the energy of the automobile's motion and partially to thermal energy. In a microwave oven, electromagnetic energy obtained from your power company is converted to thermal energy of the food being cooked. In these and all other processes, the *total* energy—the sum of all energy present in all different forms—remains the same. No exception has ever been found.

We'll use the energy idea throughout the rest of this book to study a tremendous range of physical phenomena. This idea will help you understand how automotive engines work, how a camera's flash unit can produce a short burst of light, and the meaning of Einstein's famous equation $E = mc^2$.

In this chapter, though, our concentration will be on mechanics. We'll learn about one important form of energy called *kinetic energy*, or energy of motion, and how it relates to the concept of *work*. We'll also consider *power*, which is the time rate of doing work. In Chapter 7 we'll expand these ideas into a deeper understanding of the concepts of energy and the conservation of energy.

6.1 WORK

You'd probably agree that it's hard work to pull a heavy sofa across the room, to lift a stack of encyclopedias from the floor to a high shelf, or to push a stalled car off the road. Indeed, all of these examples agree with the everyday meaning of *work*—any activity that requires muscular or mental effort.

In physics, work has a much more precise definition. By making use of this definition we'll find that in any motion, no matter how complicated, the total work done on a particle by all forces that act on it equals the change in its *kinetic energy*—a quantity that's related to the particle's mass and speed. This relationship holds even when the forces acting on the particle aren't constant, a situation that can be difficult or impossible to handle with the techniques you learned in Chapters 4 and 5. The ideas of work and kinetic energy enable us to solve problems in mechanics that we could not have attempted before.

In this section we'll see how work is defined and how to calculate work in a variety of situations involving *constant* forces. Later in this chapter we'll relate work and kinetic energy, and then apply these ideas to problems in which the forces are *not* constant.

The three examples of work described above—pulling a sofa, lifting encyclopedias, and pushing a car—have something in common. In each case you do work by exerting a *force* on a body while that body *moves* from one place to another—that is, undergoes a *displacement* (**Fig. 6.1**). You do more work if the force is greater (you push harder on the car) or if the displacement is greater (you push the car farther down the road).

The physicist's definition of work is based on these observations. Consider a body that undergoes a displacement of magnitude s along a straight line. (For now, we'll assume that any body we discuss can be treated as a particle so that we can ignore any rotation or changes in shape of the body.) While the body moves, a constant force $\vec{F}$ acts on it in the same direction as the displacement $\vec{s}$ (**Fig. 6.2**). We define the **work** W done by this constant force under these circumstances as the product of the force magnitude F and the displacement magnitude s:

$$W = Fs \qquad \text{(constant force in direction of straight-line displacement)} \qquad (6.1)$$

The work done on the body is greater if either the force F or the displacement s is greater, in agreement with our observations above.

CAUTION **Work = W, weight = w** Don't confuse uppercase W (work) with lowercase w (weight). Though the symbols are similar, work and weight are different quantities. ❙

The SI unit of work is the **joule** (abbreviated J, pronounced "jool," and named in honor of the 19th-century English physicist James Prescott Joule). From Eq. (6.1) we see that in any system of units, the unit of work is the unit of force multiplied by the unit of distance. In SI units the unit of force is the newton and the unit of distance is the meter, so 1 joule is equivalent to 1 *newton-meter* (N·m):

$$1 \text{ joule} = (1 \text{ newton})(1 \text{ meter}) \quad \text{or} \quad 1 \text{ J} = 1 \text{ N·m}$$

If you lift an object with a weight of 1 N (about the weight of a medium-sized apple) a distance of 1 m at a constant speed, you exert a 1-N force on the object in the same direction as its 1-m displacement and so do 1 J of work on it.

As an illustration of Eq. (6.1), think of a person pushing a stalled car. If he pushes the car through a displacement $\vec{s}$ with a constant force $\vec{F}$ in the direction of motion, the amount of work he does on the car is given by Eq. (6.1): $W = Fs$.

6.1 These people are doing work as they push on the car because they exert a force on the car as it moves.

6.2 The work done by a constant force acting in the same direction as the displacement.

If a body moves through a displacement $\vec{s}$ while a constant force $\vec{F}$ acts on it in the same direction ...

... the work done by the force on the body is $W = Fs$.

BIO **Application Work and Muscle Fibers** Our ability to do work with our bodies comes from our skeletal muscles. The fiberlike cells of skeletal muscle, shown in this micrograph, can shorten, causing the muscle as a whole to contract and to exert force on the tendons to which it attaches. Muscle can exert a force of about 0.3 N per square millimeter of cross-sectional area: The greater the cross-sectional area, the more fibers the muscle has and the more force it can exert when it contracts.

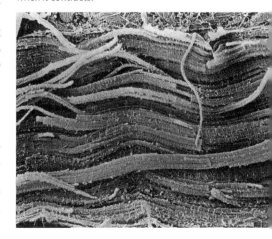

6.3 The work done by a constant force acting at an angle to the displacement.

The car moves through displacement $\vec{s}$ while a constant force $\vec{F}$ acts on it at an angle ϕ to the displacement.

$F_\perp$ does *no* work on the car.
$F_\perp = F\sin\phi$

Only $F_\parallel$ does work on the car:
$W = F_\parallel s = (F\cos\phi)s$
$= Fs\cos\phi$

$F_\parallel = F\cos\phi$

But what if the person pushes at an angle ϕ to the car's displacement (**Fig. 6.3**)? Then $\vec{F}$ has a component $F_\parallel = F\cos\phi$ in the direction of the displacement $\vec{s}$ and a component $F_\perp = F\sin\phi$ that acts perpendicular to $\vec{s}$. (Other forces must act on the car so that it moves along $\vec{s}$, not in the direction of $\vec{F}$. We're interested in only the work that the person does, however, so we'll consider only the force he exerts.) Only the parallel component $F_\parallel$ is effective in moving the car, so we define the work as the product of this force component and the magnitude of the displacement. Hence $W = F_\parallel s = (F\cos\phi)s$, or

Work done on a particle by **constant force** $\vec{F}$ during **straight-line displacement** $\vec{s}$ ⋯ $W = Fs\cos\phi$ ⟵ Magnitude of $\vec{F}$ / Angle between $\vec{F}$ and $\vec{s}$ / Magnitude of $\vec{s}$ ⠀⠀⠀⠀(6.2)

If $\phi = 0$, so that $\vec{F}$ and $\vec{s}$ are in the same direction, then $\cos\phi = 1$ and we are back to Eq. (6.1).

Equation (6.2) has the form of the *scalar product* of two vectors, which we introduced in Section 1.10: $\vec{A} \cdot \vec{B} = AB\cos\phi$. You may want to review that definition. Hence we can write Eq. (6.2) more compactly as

Work done on a particle by **constant force** $\vec{F}$ during **straight-line displacement** $\vec{s}$ ⋯ $W = \vec{F} \cdot \vec{s}$ ⠀⠀⠀⠀(6.3)
Scalar product (dot product) of vectors $\vec{F}$ and $\vec{s}$

CAUTION **Work is a scalar** An essential point: Work is a *scalar* quantity, even though it's calculated from two vector quantities (force and displacement). A 5-N force toward the east acting on a body that moves 6 m to the east does the same amount of work as a 5-N force toward the north acting on a body that moves 6 m to the north. ▌

EXAMPLE 6.1 WORK DONE BY A CONSTANT FORCE

(a) Steve exerts a steady force of magnitude 210 N (about 47 lb) on the stalled car in Fig. 6.3 as he pushes it a distance of 18 m. The car also has a flat tire, so to make the car track straight Steve must push at an angle of 30° to the direction of motion. How much work does Steve do? (b) In a helpful mood, Steve pushes a second stalled car with a steady force $\vec{F} = (160\ \text{N})\hat{\imath} - (40\ \text{N})\hat{\jmath}$. The displacement of the car is $\vec{s} = (14\ \text{m})\hat{\imath} + (11\ \text{m})\hat{\jmath}$. How much work does Steve do in this case?

SOLUTION

IDENTIFY and SET UP: In both parts (a) and (b), the target variable is the work W done by Steve. In each case the force is constant and the displacement is along a straight line, so we can use Eq. (6.2) or (6.3). The angle between $\vec{F}$ and $\vec{s}$ is given in part (a), so we can apply Eq. (6.2) directly. In part (b) both $\vec{F}$ and $\vec{s}$ are given in terms

of components, so it's best to calculate the scalar product by using Eq. (1.19): $\vec{A} \cdot \vec{B} = A_xB_x + A_yB_y + A_zB_z$.

EXECUTE: (a) From Eq. (6.2),

$$W = Fs\cos\phi = (210\ \text{N})(18\ \text{m})\cos 30° = 3.3 \times 10^3\ \text{J}$$

(b) The components of $\vec{F}$ are $F_x = 160\ \text{N}$ and $F_y = -40\ \text{N}$, and the components of $\vec{s}$ are $x = 14\ \text{m}$ and $y = 11\ \text{m}$. (There are no z-components for either vector.) Hence, using Eqs. (1.19) and (6.3), we have

$$W = \vec{F} \cdot \vec{s} = F_xx + F_yy$$
$$= (160\ \text{N})(14\ \text{m}) + (-40\ \text{N})(11\ \text{m})$$
$$= 1.8 \times 10^3\ \text{J}$$

EVALUATE: In each case the work that Steve does is more than 1000 J. This shows that 1 joule is a rather small amount of work.

6.4 A constant force $\vec{F}$ can do positive, negative, or zero work depending on the angle between $\vec{F}$ and the displacement $\vec{s}$.

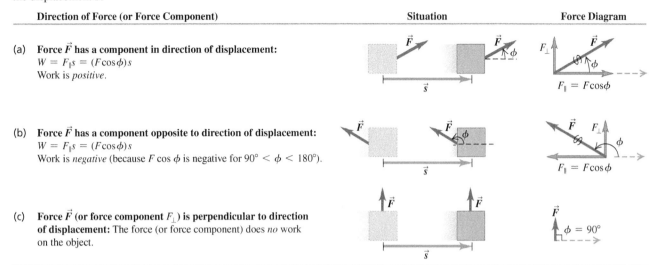

Direction of Force (or Force Component)	Situation	Force Diagram
(a) **Force $\vec{F}$ has a component in direction of displacement:** $W = F_{\parallel}s = (F\cos\phi)s$ Work is *positive*.		$F_{\parallel} = F\cos\phi$
(b) **Force $\vec{F}$ has a component opposite to direction of displacement:** $W = F_{\parallel}s = (F\cos\phi)s$ Work is *negative* (because $F\cos\phi$ is negative for $90° < \phi < 180°$).		$F_{\parallel} = F\cos\phi$
(c) **Force $\vec{F}$ (or force component $F_{\perp}$) is perpendicular to direction of displacement:** The force (or force component) does *no* work on the object.		$\phi = 90°$

Work: Positive, Negative, or Zero

In Example 6.1 the work done in pushing the cars was positive. But it's important to understand that work can also be negative or zero. This is the essential way in which work as defined in physics differs from the "everyday" definition of work. When the force has a component in the *same direction* as the displacement (ϕ between 0° and 90°), $\cos\phi$ in Eq. (6.2) is positive and the work W is *positive* (**Fig. 6.4a**). When the force has a component *opposite* to the displacement (ϕ between 90° and 180°), $\cos\phi$ is negative and the work is *negative* (Fig. 6.4b). When the force is *perpendicular* to the displacement, $\phi = 90°$ and the work done by the force is *zero* (Fig. 6.4c). The cases of zero work and negative work bear closer examination, so let's look at some examples.

There are many situations in which forces act but do zero work. You might think it's "hard work" to hold a barbell motionless in the air for 5 minutes (**Fig. 6.5**). But in fact, you aren't doing any work on the barbell because there is no displacement. (Holding the barbell requires you to keep the muscles of your arms contracted, and this consumes energy stored in carbohydrates and fat within your body. As these energy stores are used up, your muscles feel fatigued even though you do no work on the barbell.) Even when you carry a book while you walk with constant velocity on a level floor, you do no work on the book. It has a displacement, but the (vertical) supporting force that you exert on the book has no component in the direction of the (horizontal) motion. Then $\phi = 90°$ in Eq. (6.2), and $\cos\phi = 0$. When a body slides along a surface, the work done on the body by the normal force is zero; and when a ball on a string moves in uniform circular motion, the work done on the ball by the tension in the string is also zero. In both cases the work is zero because the force has no component in the direction of motion.

What does it mean to do *negative* work? The answer comes from Newton's third law of motion. When a weightlifter lowers a barbell as in **Fig. 6.6a** (next page), his hands and the barbell move together with the same displacement $\vec{s}$. The barbell exerts a force $\vec{F}_{\text{barbell on hands}}$ on his hands in the same direction as the hands' displacement, so the work done by the *barbell* on his *hands* is positive (Fig. 6.6b). But by Newton's third law the weightlifter's hands exert an equal and opposite force $\vec{F}_{\text{hands on barbell}} = -\vec{F}_{\text{barbell on hands}}$ on the barbell (Fig. 6.6c). This force, which keeps the barbell from crashing to the floor, acts opposite to the barbell's displacement. Thus the work done by his *hands* on the *barbell* is negative. Because the weightlifter's hands and the barbell have the same displacement, the

6.5 A weightlifter does no work on a barbell as long as he holds it stationary.

The weightlifter exerts an upward force on the barbell ...

... but because the barbell is stationary (its displacement is zero), he does no work on it.

6.6 This weightlifter's hands do negative work on a barbell as the barbell does positive work on his hands.

(a) A weightlifter lowers a barbell to the floor.

(b) The barbell does *positive* work on the weightlifter's hands.

The force of the barbell on the weightlifter's hands is in the *same* direction as the hands' displacement.

$\vec{F}_{\text{barbell on hands}}$

$\vec{s}$

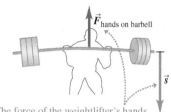

(c) The weightlifter's hands do *negative* work on the barbell.

$\vec{F}_{\text{hands on barbell}}$

The force of the weightlifter's hands on the barbell is *opposite* to the barbell's displacement.

$\vec{s}$

work that his hands do on the barbell is just the negative of the work that the barbell does on his hands. In general, when one body does negative work on a second body, the second body does an equal amount of *positive* work on the first body.

CAUTION **Keep track of who's doing the work** We always speak of work done *on* a particular body *by* a specific force. Always specify exactly what force is doing the work. When you lift a book, you exert an upward force on it and the book's displacement is upward, so the work done by the lifting force on the book is positive. But the work done by the *gravitational* force (weight) on a book being lifted is *negative* because the downward gravitational force is opposite to the upward displacement.

Total Work

How do we calculate work when *several* forces act on a body? One way is to use Eq. (6.2) or (6.3) to compute the work done by each separate force. Then, because work is a scalar quantity, the *total* work W_{tot} done on the body by all the forces is the algebraic sum of the quantities of work done by the individual forces. An alternative way to find the total work W_{tot} is to compute the vector sum of the forces (that is, the net force) and then use this vector sum as $\vec{F}$ in Eq. (6.2) or (6.3). The following example illustrates both of these techniques.

DATA *SPEAKS*

Positive, Negative, and Zero Work

When students were given a problem that required them to find the work done by a constant force during a straight-line displacement, more than 59% gave an incorrect answer. Common errors:

- Forgetting that a force does negative work if it acts opposite to the direction of the object's displacement.
- Forgetting that, even if a force is present, it does zero work if it acts perpendicular to the direction of the displacement.

EXAMPLE 6.2   WORK DONE BY SEVERAL FORCES

SOLUTION

A farmer hitches her tractor to a sled loaded with firewood and pulls it a distance of 20 m along level ground (**Fig. 6.7a**). The total weight of sled and load is 14,700 N. The tractor exerts a constant 5000-N force at an angle of 36.9° above the horizontal. A 3500-N friction force opposes the sled's motion. Find the work done by each force acting on the sled and the total work done by all the forces.

6.7 Calculating the work done on a sled of firewood being pulled by a tractor.

(a)

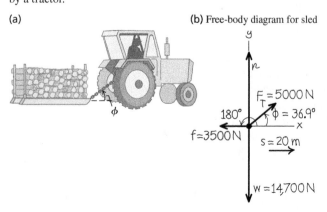

(b) Free-body diagram for sled

IDENTIFY and SET UP: Each force is constant and the sled's displacement is along a straight line, so we can use the ideas of this section to calculate the work. We'll find the total work in two ways: (1) by adding the work done on the sled by each force and (2) by finding the work done by the net force on the sled. We first draw a free-body diagram showing all of the forces acting on the sled, and we choose a coordinate system (Fig. 6.7b). For each force—weight, normal force, force of the tractor, and friction force—we know the angle between the displacement (in the positive x-direction) and the force. Hence we can use Eq. (6.2) to calculate the work each force does.

As in Chapter 5, we'll find the net force by adding the components of the four forces. Newton's second law tells us that because the sled's motion is purely horizontal, the net force can have only a horizontal component.

EXECUTE: (1) The work W_w done by the weight is zero because its direction is perpendicular to the displacement (compare Fig. 6.4c). For the same reason, the work W_n done by the normal force is also zero. (Note that we don't need to calculate the magnitude n to conclude this.) So $W_w = W_n = 0$.

That leaves the work W_T done by the force F_T exerted by the tractor and the work W_f done by the friction force f. From Eq. (6.2),

$$W_T = F_T s \cos 36.9° = (5000 \text{ N})(20 \text{ m})(0.800) = 80,000 \text{ N} \cdot \text{m}$$
$$= 80 \text{ kJ}$$

The friction force $\vec{f}$ is opposite to the displacement, so for this force $\phi = 180°$ and $\cos \phi = -1$. Again from Eq. (6.2),

$$W_f = f s \cos 180° = (3500 \text{ N})(20 \text{ m})(-1) = -70,000 \text{ N} \cdot \text{m}$$
$$= -70 \text{ kJ}$$

The total work W_{tot} done on the sled by all forces is the *algebraic* sum of the work done by the individual forces:

$$W_{\text{tot}} = W_w + W_n + W_T + W_f = 0 + 0 + 80 \text{ kJ} + (-70 \text{ kJ})$$
$$= 10 \text{ kJ}$$

(2) In the second approach, we first find the *vector* sum of all the forces (the net force) and then use it to compute the total work. It's easiest to find the net force by using components. From Fig. 6.7b,

$$\sum F_x = F_T \cos \phi + (-f) = (5000 \text{ N}) \cos 36.9° - 3500 \text{ N}$$
$$= 500 \text{ N}$$

$$\sum F_y = F_T \sin \phi + n + (-w)$$
$$= (5000 \text{ N}) \sin 36.9° + n - 14,700 \text{ N}$$

We don't need the second equation; we know that the y-component of force is perpendicular to the displacement, so it does no work. Besides, there is no y-component of acceleration, so $\sum F_y$ must be zero anyway. The total work is therefore the work done by the total x-component:

$$W_{\text{tot}} = (\sum \vec{F}) \cdot \vec{s} = (\sum F_x)s = (500 \text{ N})(20 \text{ m}) = 10,000 \text{ J}$$
$$= 10 \text{ kJ}$$

EVALUATE: We get the same result for W_{tot} with either method, as we should. Note that the net force in the x-direction is *not* zero, and so the sled must accelerate as it moves. In Section 6.2 we'll return to this example and see how to use the concept of work to explore the sled's changes of speed.

TEST YOUR UNDERSTANDING OF SECTION 6.1 An electron moves in a straight line toward the east with a constant speed of 8×10^7 m/s. It has electric, magnetic, and gravitational forces acting on it. During a 1-m displacement, the total work done on the electron is (i) positive; (ii) negative; (iii) zero; (iv) not enough information is given. ▍

6.2 KINETIC ENERGY AND THE WORK–ENERGY THEOREM

The total work done on a body by external forces is related to the body's displacement—that is, to changes in its position. But the total work is also related to changes in the *speed* of the body. To see this, consider **Fig. 6.8**, which shows a block sliding on a frictionless table. The forces acting on the block are its weight $\vec{w}$, the normal force $\vec{n}$, and the force $\vec{F}$ exerted on it by the hand.

In Fig. 6.8a the net force on the block is in the direction of its motion. From Newton's second law, this means that the block speeds up; from Eq. (6.1), this also means that the total work W_{tot} done on the block is positive. The total work

MP

PhET: The Ramp

6.8 The relationship between the total work done on a body and how the body's speed changes.

(a)

A block slides to the right on a frictionless surface.

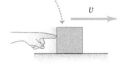

If you push to the right on the block as it moves, the net force on the block is to the right.

• The total work done on the block during a displacement $\vec{s}$ is positive: $W_{\text{tot}} > 0$.
• The block speeds up.

(b)

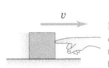

If you push to the left on the block as it moves, the net force on the block is to the left.

• The total work done on the block during a displacement $\vec{s}$ is negative: $W_{\text{tot}} < 0$.
• The block slows down.

(c)

If you push straight down on the block as it moves, the net force on the block is zero.

• The total work done on the block during a displacement $\vec{s}$ is zero: $W_{\text{tot}} = 0$.
• The block's speed stays the same.

is *negative* in Fig. 6.8b because the net force opposes the displacement; in this case the block slows down. The net force is zero in Fig. 6.8c, so the speed of the block stays the same and the total work done on the block is zero. We can conclude that *when a particle undergoes a displacement, it speeds up if* $W_{tot} > 0$, *slows down if* $W_{tot} < 0$, *and maintains the same speed if* $W_{tot} = 0$.

Let's make this more quantitative. In **Fig. 6.9** a particle with mass m moves along the x-axis under the action of a constant net force with magnitude F that points in the positive x-direction. The particle's acceleration is constant and given by Newton's second law (Section 4.3): $F = ma_x$. As the particle moves from point x_1 to x_2, it undergoes a displacement $s = x_2 - x_1$ and its speed changes from v_1 to v_2. Using a constant-acceleration equation from Section 2.4, Eq. (2.13), and replacing v_{0x} by v_1, v_x by v_2, and $(x - x_0)$ by s, we have

$$v_2^2 = v_1^2 + 2a_x s$$

$$a_x = \frac{v_2^2 - v_1^2}{2s}$$

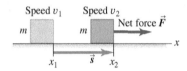

6.9 A constant net force $\vec{F}$ does work on a moving body.

When we multiply this equation by m and equate ma_x to the net force F, we find

$$F = ma_x = m\frac{v_2^2 - v_1^2}{2s} \quad \text{and}$$

$$Fs = \tfrac{1}{2}mv_2^2 - \tfrac{1}{2}mv_1^2 \tag{6.4}$$

In Eq. (6.4) the product Fs is the work done by the net force F and thus is equal to the total work W_{tot} done by all the forces acting on the particle. The quantity $\frac{1}{2}mv^2$ is called the **kinetic energy K** of the particle:

$$\underset{\substack{\text{Kinetic energy}\\\text{of a particle}}}{} K = \tfrac{1}{2}mv^2 \underset{\substack{\text{Mass of particle}\\\text{Speed of particle}}}{} \tag{6.5}$$

6.10 Comparing the kinetic energy $K = \tfrac{1}{2}mv^2$ of different bodies.

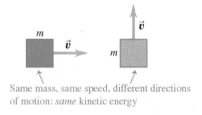

Same mass, same speed, different directions of motion: *same* kinetic energy

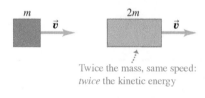

Twice the mass, same speed: *twice* the kinetic energy

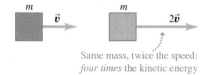

Same mass, twice the speed: *four times* the kinetic energy

Like work, the kinetic energy of a particle is a scalar quantity; it depends on only the particle's mass and speed, not its direction of motion (**Fig. 6.10**). Kinetic energy can never be negative, and it is zero only when the particle is at rest.

We can now interpret Eq. (6.4) in terms of work and kinetic energy. The first term on the right side of Eq. (6.4) is $K_2 = \tfrac{1}{2}mv_2^2$, the final kinetic energy of the particle (that is, after the displacement). The second term is the initial kinetic energy, $K_1 = \tfrac{1}{2}mv_1^2$, and the difference between these terms is the *change* in kinetic energy. So Eq. (6.4) says:

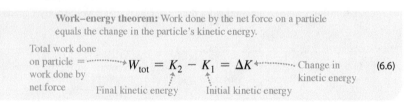

Work–energy theorem: Work done by the net force on a particle equals the change in the particle's kinetic energy.

$$\underset{\substack{\text{Total work done}\\\text{on particle} =\\\text{work done by}\\\text{net force}}}{} W_{tot} = \underset{\text{Final kinetic energy}}{K_2} - \underset{\text{Initial kinetic energy}}{K_1} = \underset{\substack{\text{Change in}\\\text{kinetic energy}}}{\Delta K} \tag{6.6}$$

This **work–energy theorem** agrees with our observations about the block in Fig. 6.8. When W_{tot} is *positive,* the kinetic energy *increases* (the final kinetic energy K_2 is greater than the initial kinetic energy K_1) and the particle is going faster at the end of the displacement than at the beginning. When W_{tot} is *negative,* the kinetic energy *decreases* (K_2 is less than K_1) and the speed is less after the displacement. When $W_{tot} = 0$, the kinetic energy stays the same $(K_1 = K_2)$ and the speed is unchanged. Note that the work–energy theorem by itself tells us only about changes in *speed,* not velocity, since the kinetic energy doesn't depend on the direction of motion.

From Eq. (6.4) or Eq. (6.6), kinetic energy and work must have the same units. Hence the joule is the SI unit of both work and kinetic energy (and, as we will see later, of all kinds of energy). To verify this, note that in SI the quantity $K = \frac{1}{2}mv^2$ has units $kg \cdot (m/s)^2$ or $kg \cdot m^2/s^2$; we recall that $1\ N = 1\ kg \cdot m/s^2$, so

$$1\ J = 1\ N \cdot m = 1\ (kg \cdot m/s^2) \cdot m = 1\ kg \cdot m^2/s^2$$

Because we used Newton's laws in deriving the work–energy theorem, we can use this theorem only in an inertial frame of reference. Note that the work–energy theorem is valid in *any* inertial frame, but the values of W_{tot} and $K_2 - K_1$ may differ from one inertial frame to another (because the displacement and speed of a body may be different in different frames).

We've derived the work–energy theorem for the special case of straight-line motion with constant forces, and in the following examples we'll apply it to this special case only. We'll find in the next section that the theorem is valid even when the forces are not constant and the particle's trajectory is curved.

PROBLEM-SOLVING STRATEGY 6.1 | WORK AND KINETIC ENERGY

IDENTIFY *the relevant concepts:* The work–energy theorem, $W_{tot} = K_2 - K_1$, is extremely useful when you want to relate a body's speed v_1 at one point in its motion to its speed v_2 at a different point. (It's less useful for problems that involve the *time* it takes a body to go from point 1 to point 2 because the work–energy theorem doesn't involve time at all. For such problems it's usually best to use the relationships among time, position, velocity, and acceleration described in Chapters 2 and 3.)

SET UP *the problem* using the following steps:
1. Identify the initial and final positions of the body, and draw a free-body diagram showing all the forces that act on the body.
2. Choose a coordinate system. (If the motion is along a straight line, it's usually easiest to have both the initial and final positions lie along one of the axes.)
3. List the unknown and known quantities, and decide which unknowns are your target variables. The target variable may be the body's initial or final speed, the magnitude of one of the forces acting on the body, or the body's displacement.

EXECUTE *the solution:* Calculate the work W done by each force. If the force is constant and the displacement is a straight line, you can use Eq. (6.2) or Eq. (6.3). (Later in this chapter we'll see how to handle varying forces and curved trajectories.) Be sure

to check signs; W must be positive if the force has a component in the direction of the displacement, negative if the force has a component opposite to the displacement, and zero if the force and displacement are perpendicular.

Add the amounts of work done by each force to find the total work W_{tot}. Sometimes it's easier to calculate the vector sum of the forces (the net force) and then find the work done by the net force; this value is also equal to W_{tot}.

Write expressions for the initial and final kinetic energies, K_1 and K_2. Note that kinetic energy involves *mass,* not *weight;* if you are given the body's weight, use $w = mg$ to find the mass.

Finally, use Eq. (6.6), $W_{tot} = K_2 - K_1$, and Eq. (6.5), $K = \frac{1}{2}mv^2$, to solve for the target variable. Remember that the right-hand side of Eq. (6.6) represents the change of the body's kinetic energy between points 1 and 2; that is, it is the *final* kinetic energy minus the *initial* kinetic energy, never the other way around. (If you can predict the sign of W_{tot}, you can predict whether the body speeds up or slows down.)

EVALUATE *your answer:* Check whether your answer makes sense. Remember that kinetic energy $K = \frac{1}{2}mv^2$ can never be negative. If you come up with a negative value of K, perhaps you interchanged the initial and final kinetic energies in $W_{tot} = K_2 - K_1$ or made a sign error in one of the work calculations.

EXAMPLE 6.3 | USING WORK AND ENERGY TO CALCULATE SPEED

Let's look again at the sled in Fig. 6.7 and our results from Example 6.2. Suppose the sled's initial speed v_1 is 2.0 m/s. What is the speed of the sled after it moves 20 m?

SOLUTION

IDENTIFY and SET UP: We'll use the work–energy theorem, Eq. (6.6), $W_{tot} = K_2 - K_1$, since we are given the initial speed $v_1 = 2.0$ m/s and want to find the final speed v_2. **Figure 6.11** shows our sketch of the situation. The motion is in the positive x-direction. In Example 6.2 we calculated the total work done by all the forces: $W_{tot} = 10$ kJ. Hence the kinetic energy of the sled and its load must increase by 10 kJ, and the speed of the sled must also increase.

6.11 Our sketch for this problem.

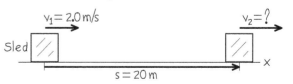

EXECUTE: To write expressions for the initial and final kinetic energies, we need the mass of the sled and load. The combined *weight* is 14,700 N, so the mass is

$$m = \frac{w}{g} = \frac{14{,}700\ N}{9.8\ m/s^2} = 1500\ kg$$

Continued

Then the initial kinetic energy K_1 is

$$K_1 = \tfrac{1}{2}mv_1^2 = \tfrac{1}{2}(1500 \text{ kg})(2.0 \text{ m/s})^2 = 3000 \text{ kg} \cdot \text{m}^2/\text{s}^2$$
$$= 3000 \text{ J}$$

The final kinetic energy K_2 is

$$K_2 = \tfrac{1}{2}mv_2^2 = \tfrac{1}{2}(1500 \text{ kg})v_2^2$$

The work–energy theorem, Eq. (6.6), gives

$$K_2 = K_1 + W_{\text{tot}} = 3000 \text{ J} + 10{,}000 \text{ J} = 13{,}000 \text{ J}$$

Setting these two expressions for K_2 equal, substituting $1 \text{ J} = 1 \text{ kg} \cdot \text{m}^2/\text{s}^2$, and solving for the final speed v_2, we find

$$v_2 = 4.2 \text{ m/s}$$

EVALUATE: The total work is positive, so the kinetic energy increases $(K_2 > K_1)$ and the speed increases $(v_2 > v_1)$.

This problem can also be solved without the work–energy theorem. We can find the acceleration from $\Sigma \vec{F} = m\vec{a}$ and then use the equations of motion for constant acceleration to find v_2. Since the acceleration is along the x-axis,

$$a = a_x = \frac{\Sigma F_x}{m} = \frac{500 \text{ N}}{1500 \text{ kg}} = 0.333 \text{ m/s}^2$$

Then, using Eq. (2.13),

$$v_2^2 = v_1^2 + 2as = (2.0 \text{ m/s})^2 + 2(0.333 \text{ m/s}^2)(20 \text{ m})$$
$$= 17.3 \text{ m}^2/\text{s}^2$$
$$v_2 = 4.2 \text{ m/s}$$

This is the same result we obtained with the work–energy approach, but there we avoided the intermediate step of finding the acceleration. You will find several other examples in this chapter and the next that *can* be done without using energy considerations but that are easier when energy methods are used. When a problem can be done by two methods, doing it by both methods (as we did here) is a good way to check your work.

EXAMPLE 6.4 **FORCES ON A HAMMERHEAD**

The 200-kg steel hammerhead of a pile driver is lifted 3.00 m above the top of a vertical I-beam being driven into the ground (**Fig. 6.12a**). The hammerhead is then dropped, driving the I-beam 7.4 cm deeper into the ground. The vertical guide rails exert a constant 60-N friction force on the hammerhead. Use the work–energy theorem to find (a) the speed of the hammerhead just as it hits the I-beam and (b) the average force the hammerhead exerts on the I-beam. Ignore the effects of the air.

SOLUTION

IDENTIFY: We'll use the work–energy theorem to relate the hammerhead's speed at different locations and the forces acting on it.

There are *three* locations of interest: point 1, where the hammerhead starts from rest; point 2, where it first contacts the I-beam; and point 3, where the hammerhead and I-beam come to a halt (Fig. 6.12a). The two target variables are the hammerhead's speed at point 2 and the average force the hammerhead exerts between points 2 and 3. Hence we'll apply the work–energy theorem twice: once for the motion from 1 to 2, and once for the motion from 2 to 3.

SET UP: Figure 6.12b shows the vertical forces on the hammerhead as it falls from point 1 to point 2. (We can ignore any horizontal forces that may be present because they do no work as the hammerhead moves vertically.) For this part of the motion, our target variable is the hammerhead's final speed v_2.

6.12 (a) A pile driver pounds an I-beam into the ground. (b), (c) Free-body diagrams. Vector lengths are not to scale.

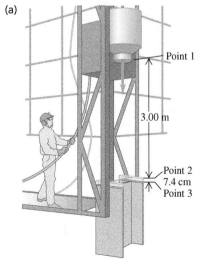

(a)

Point 1

3.00 m

Point 2
7.4 cm
Point 3

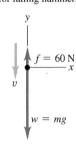

(b) Free-body diagram for falling hammerhead

$f = 60$ N

v

$w = mg$

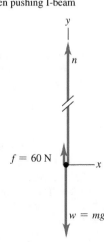

(c) Free-body diagram for hammerhead when pushing I-beam

n

$f = 60$ N

$w = mg$

Figure 6.12c shows the vertical forces on the hammerhead during the motion from point 2 to point 3. In addition to the forces shown in Fig. 6.12b, the I-beam exerts an upward normal force of magnitude n on the hammerhead. This force actually varies as the hammerhead comes to a halt, but for simplicity we'll treat n as a constant. Hence n represents the *average* value of this upward force during the motion. Our target variable for this part of the motion is the force that the *hammerhead* exerts on the I-beam; it is the reaction force to the normal force exerted by the I-beam, so by Newton's third law its magnitude is also n.

EXECUTE: (a) From point 1 to point 2, the vertical forces are the downward weight $w = mg = (200 \text{ kg})(9.8 \text{ m/s}^2) = 1960 \text{ N}$ and the upward friction force $f = 60 \text{ N}$. Thus the net downward force is $w - f = 1900 \text{ N}$. The displacement of the hammerhead from point 1 to point 2 is downward and equal to $s_{12} = 3.00 \text{ m}$. The total work done on the hammerhead between point 1 and point 2 is then

$$W_{\text{tot}} = (w - f)s_{12} = (1900 \text{ N})(3.00 \text{ m}) = 5700 \text{ J}$$

At point 1 the hammerhead is at rest, so its initial kinetic energy K_1 is zero. Hence the kinetic energy K_2 at point 2 equals the total work done on the hammerhead between points 1 and 2:

$$W_{\text{tot}} = K_2 - K_1 = K_2 - 0 = \tfrac{1}{2}mv_2^2 - 0$$

$$v_2 = \sqrt{\frac{2W_{\text{tot}}}{m}} = \sqrt{\frac{2(5700 \text{ J})}{200 \text{ kg}}} = 7.55 \text{ m/s}$$

This is the hammerhead's speed at point 2, just as it hits the I-beam.

(b) As the hammerhead moves downward from point 2 to point 3, its displacement is $s_{23} = 7.4 \text{ cm} = 0.074 \text{ m}$ and the net downward force acting on it is $w - f - n$ (Fig. 6.12c). The total work done on the hammerhead during this displacement is

$$W_{\text{tot}} = (w - f - n)s_{23}$$

The initial kinetic energy for this part of the motion is K_2, which from part (a) equals 5700 J. The final kinetic energy is $K_3 = 0$ (the hammerhead ends at rest). From the work–energy theorem,

$$W_{\text{tot}} = (w - f - n)s_{23} = K_3 - K_2$$

$$n = w - f - \frac{K_3 - K_2}{s_{23}}$$

$$= 1960 \text{ N} - 60 \text{ N} - \frac{0 \text{ J} - 5700 \text{ J}}{0.074 \text{ m}} = 79{,}000 \text{ N}$$

The downward force that the hammerhead exerts on the I-beam has this same magnitude, 79,000 N (about 9 tons)—more than 40 times the weight of the hammerhead.

EVALUATE: The net change in the hammerhead's kinetic energy from point 1 to point 3 is zero; a relatively small net force does positive work over a large distance, and then a much larger net force does negative work over a much smaller distance. The same thing happens if you speed up your car gradually and then drive it into a brick wall. The very large force needed to reduce the kinetic energy to zero over a short distance is what does the damage to your car—and possibly to you.

The Meaning of Kinetic Energy

Example 6.4 gives insight into the physical meaning of kinetic energy. The hammerhead is dropped from rest, and its kinetic energy when it hits the I-beam equals the total work done on it up to that point by the net force. This result is true in general: To accelerate a particle of mass m from rest (zero kinetic energy) up to a speed v, the total work done on it must equal the change in kinetic energy from zero to $K = \tfrac{1}{2}mv^2$:

$$W_{\text{tot}} = K - 0 = K$$

So *the kinetic energy of a particle is equal to the total work that was done to accelerate it from rest to its present speed* (**Fig. 6.13**). The definition $K = \tfrac{1}{2}mv^2$, Eq. (6.5), wasn't chosen at random; it's the *only* definition that agrees with this interpretation of kinetic energy.

In the second part of Example 6.4 the kinetic energy of the hammerhead did work on the I-beam and drove it into the ground. This gives us another interpretation of kinetic energy: *The kinetic energy of a particle is equal to the total work that particle can do in the process of being brought to rest.* This is why you pull your hand and arm backward when you catch a ball. As the ball comes to rest, it does an amount of work (force times distance) on your hand equal to the ball's initial kinetic energy. By pulling your hand back, you maximize the distance over which the force acts and so minimize the force on your hand.

6.13 Imparting kinetic energy to a cue ball.

When a billiards player hits a cue ball at rest, the ball's kinetic energy after being hit is equal to the work that was done on it by the cue.

The greater the force exerted by the cue and the greater the distance the ball moves while in contact with it, the greater the ball's kinetic energy.

CONCEPTUAL EXAMPLE 6.5   COMPARING KINETIC ENERGIES

Two iceboats like the one in Example 5.6 (Section 5.2) hold a race on a frictionless horizontal lake (**Fig. 6.14**). The two iceboats have masses m and $2m$. The iceboats have identical sails, so the wind exerts the same constant force $\vec{F}$ on each iceboat. They start from rest and cross the finish line a distance s away. Which iceboat crosses the finish line with greater kinetic energy?

SOLUTION

If you use the definition of kinetic energy, $K = \frac{1}{2}mv^2$, Eq. (6.5), the answer to this problem isn't obvious. The iceboat of mass $2m$

6.14 A race between iceboats.

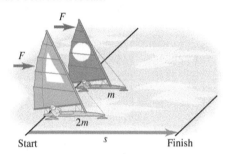

has greater mass, so you might guess that it has greater kinetic energy at the finish line. But the lighter iceboat, of mass m, has greater acceleration and crosses the finish line with a greater speed, so you might guess that *this* iceboat has the greater kinetic energy. How can we decide?

The key is to remember that *the kinetic energy of a particle is equal to the total work done to accelerate it from rest.* Both iceboats travel the same distance s from rest, and only the horizontal force F in the direction of motion does work on either iceboat. Hence the total work done between the starting line and the finish line is the *same* for each iceboat, $W_{tot} = Fs$. At the finish line, each iceboat has a kinetic energy equal to the work W_{tot} done on it, because each iceboat started from rest. So both iceboats have the *same* kinetic energy at the finish line!

You might think this is a "trick" question, but it isn't. If you really understand the meanings of quantities such as kinetic energy, you can solve problems more easily and with better insight.

Notice that we didn't need to know anything about how much time each iceboat took to reach the finish line. This is because the work–energy theorem makes no direct reference to time, only to displacement. In fact the iceboat of mass m has greater acceleration and so takes less time to reach the finish line than does the iceboat of mass $2m$.

Work and Kinetic Energy in Composite Systems

In this section we've been careful to apply the work–energy theorem only to bodies that we can represent as *particles*—that is, as moving point masses. New subtleties appear for more complex systems that have to be represented as many particles with different motions. We can't go into these subtleties in detail in this chapter, but here's an example.

Suppose a boy stands on frictionless roller skates on a level surface, facing a rigid wall (**Fig. 6.15**). He pushes against the wall, which makes him move to the right. The forces acting on him are his weight $\vec{w}$, the upward normal forces $\vec{n}_1$ and $\vec{n}_2$ exerted by the ground on his skates, and the horizontal force $\vec{F}$ exerted on him by the wall. There is no vertical displacement, so $\vec{w}$, $\vec{n}_1$, and $\vec{n}_2$ do no work. Force $\vec{F}$ accelerates him to the right, but the parts of his body where that force is applied (the boy's hands) do not move while the force acts. Thus the force $\vec{F}$ also does no work. Where, then, does the boy's kinetic energy come from?

The explanation is that it's not adequate to represent the boy as a single point mass. Different parts of the boy's body have different motions; his hands remain stationary against the wall while his torso is moving away from the wall. The various parts of his body interact with each other, and one part can exert forces and do work on another part. Therefore the *total* kinetic energy of this *composite* system of body parts can change, even though no work is done by forces applied by bodies (such as the wall) that are outside the system. In Chapter 8 we'll consider further the motion of a collection of particles that interact with each other. We'll discover that just as for the boy in this example, the total kinetic energy of such a system can change even when no work is done on any part of the system by anything outside it.

6.15 The external forces acting on a skater pushing off a wall. The work done by these forces is zero, but the skater's kinetic energy changes nonetheless.

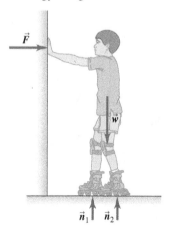

TEST YOUR UNDERSTANDING OF SECTION 6.2   Rank the following bodies in order of their kinetic energy, from least to greatest. (i) A 2.0-kg body moving at 5.0 m/s; (ii) a 1.0-kg body that initially was at rest and then had 30 J of work done on it; (iii) a 1.0-kg body that initially was moving at 4.0 m/s and then had 20 J of work done on it; (iv) a 2.0-kg body that initially was moving at 10 m/s and then did 80 J of work on another body. ∎

6.3 WORK AND ENERGY WITH VARYING FORCES

So far we've considered work done by *constant forces* only. But what happens when you stretch a spring? The more you stretch it, the harder you have to pull, so the force you exert is *not* constant as the spring is stretched. We've also restricted our discussion to *straight-line* motion. There are many situations in which a body moves along a curved path and is acted on by a force that varies in magnitude, direction, or both. We need to be able to compute the work done by the force in these more general cases. Fortunately, the work–energy theorem holds true even when forces are varying and when the body's path is not straight.

Work Done by a Varying Force, Straight-Line Motion

To add only one complication at a time, let's consider straight-line motion along the *x*-axis with a force whose *x*-component F_x may change as the body moves. (A real-life example is driving a car along a straight road with stop signs, so the driver has to alternately step on the gas and apply the brakes.) Suppose a particle moves along the *x*-axis from point x_1 to x_2 (**Fig. 6.16a**). Figure 6.16b is a graph of the *x*-component of force as a function of the particle's coordinate *x*. To find the work done by this force, we divide the total displacement into narrow segments Δx_a, Δx_b, and so on (Fig. 6.16c). We approximate the work done by the force during segment Δx_a as the average *x*-component of force F_{ax} in that segment multiplied by the *x*-displacement Δx_a. We do this for each segment and then add the results for all the segments. The work done by the force in the total displacement from x_1 to x_2 is approximately

$$W = F_{ax}\Delta x_a + F_{bx}\Delta x_b + \cdots$$

In the limit that the number of segments becomes very large and the width of each becomes very small, this sum becomes the *integral* of F_x from x_1 to x_2:

Work done on a particle by a varying *x*-component of force F_x during **straight-line** displacement along *x*-axis
$$W = \int_{x_1}^{x_2} F_x\, dx$$ (6.7)
Upper limit = final position
Integral of *x*-component of force
Lower limit = initial position

Note that $F_{ax}\Delta x_a$ represents the *area* of the first vertical strip in Fig. 6.16c and that the integral in Eq. (6.7) represents the area under the curve of Fig. 6.16b between x_1 and x_2. *On such a graph of force as a function of position, the total work done by the force is represented by the area under the curve between the initial and final positions.* Alternatively, the work *W* equals the average force that acts over the entire displacement, multiplied by the displacement.

In the special case that F_x, the *x*-component of the force, is constant, we can take it outside the integral in Eq. (6.7):

$$W = \int_{x_1}^{x_2} F_x\, dx = F_x \int_{x_1}^{x_2} dx = F_x(x_2 - x_1) \quad \text{(constant force)}$$

But $x_2 - x_1 = s$, the total displacement of the particle. So in the case of a constant force *F*, Eq. (6.7) says that $W = Fs$, in agreement with Eq. (6.1). The interpretation of work as the area under the curve of F_x as a function of *x* also holds for a constant force: $W = Fs$ is the area of a rectangle of height *F* and width *s* (**Fig. 6.17**).

Now let's apply these ideas to the stretched spring. To keep a spring stretched beyond its unstretched length by an amount *x*, we have to apply a force of equal

6.16 Calculating the work done by a varying force F_x in the *x*-direction as a particle moves from x_1 to x_2.

(a) A particle moves from x_1 to x_2 in response to a changing force in the *x*-direction.

(b) The force F_x varies with position *x* ...

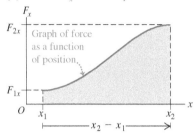

(c) ... but over a short displacement Δx, the force is essentially constant.

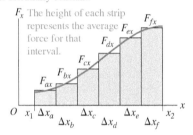

PhET: Molecular Motors
PhET: Stretching DNA

6.17 The work done by a constant force *F* in the *x*-direction as a particle moves from x_1 to x_2.

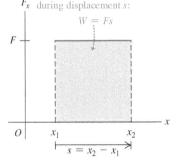

6.18 The force needed to stretch an ideal spring is proportional to the spring's elongation: $F_x = kx$.

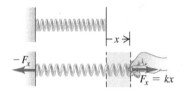

6.19 Calculating the work done to stretch a spring by a length X.

The area under the graph represents the work done on the spring as the spring is stretched from $x = 0$ to a maximum value X:
$$W = \tfrac{1}{2}kX^2$$

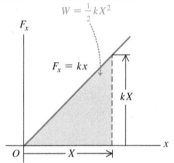

magnitude at each end (**Fig. 6.18**). If the elongation x is not too great, the force we apply to the right-hand end has an x-component directly proportional to x:

$$F_x = kx \quad \text{(force required to stretch a spring)} \quad (6.8)$$

where k is a constant called the **force constant** (or spring constant) of the spring. The units of k are force divided by distance: N/m in SI units. A floppy toy spring such as a Slinky™ has a force constant of about 1 N/m; for the much stiffer springs in an automobile's suspension, k is about 10^5 N/m. The observation that force is directly proportional to elongation for elongations that are not too great was made by Robert Hooke in 1678 and is known as **Hooke's law.** It really shouldn't be called a "law," since it's a statement about a specific device and not a fundamental law of nature. Real springs don't always obey Eq. (6.8) precisely, but it's still a useful idealized model. We'll discuss Hooke's law more fully in Chapter 11.

To stretch a spring, we must do work. We apply equal and opposite forces to the ends of the spring and gradually increase the forces. We hold the left end stationary, so the force we apply at this end does no work. The force at the moving end *does* do work. **Figure 6.19** is a graph of F_x as a function of x, the elongation of the spring. The work done by this force when the elongation goes from zero to a maximum value X is

$$W = \int_0^X F_x \, dx = \int_0^X kx \, dx = \tfrac{1}{2}kX^2 \quad (6.9)$$

We can also obtain this result graphically. The area of the shaded triangle in Fig. 6.19, representing the total work done by the force, is equal to half the product of the base and altitude, or

$$W = \tfrac{1}{2}(X)(kX) = \tfrac{1}{2}kX^2$$

This equation also says that the work is the *average* force $kX/2$ multiplied by the total displacement X. We see that the total work is proportional to the *square* of the final elongation X. To stretch an ideal spring by 2 cm, you must do four times as much work as is needed to stretch it by 1 cm.

Equation (6.9) assumes that the spring was originally unstretched. If initially the spring is already stretched a distance x_1, the work we must do to stretch it to a greater elongation x_2 (**Fig. 6.20a**) is

$$W = \int_{x_1}^{x_2} F_x \, dx = \int_{x_1}^{x_2} kx \, dx = \tfrac{1}{2}kx_2^2 - \tfrac{1}{2}kx_1^2 \quad (6.10)$$

Use your knowledge of geometry to convince yourself that the trapezoidal area under the graph in Fig. 6.20b is given by the expression in Eq. (6.10).

6.20 Calculating the work done to stretch a spring from one elongation to a greater one.

(a) Stretching a spring from elongation x_1 to elongation x_2

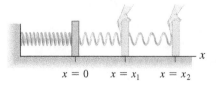

$x = 0$ $x = x_1$ $x = x_2$

(b) Force-versus-distance graph

The trapezoidal area under the graph represents the work done on the spring to stretch it from $x = x_1$ to $x = x_2$: $W = \tfrac{1}{2} kx_2^2 - \tfrac{1}{2} kx_1^2$.

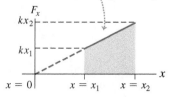

If the spring has spaces between the coils when it is unstretched, then it can also be compressed, and Hooke's law holds for compression as well as stretching. In this case the force and displacement are in the opposite directions from those shown in Fig. 6.18, so both F_x and x in Eq. (6.8) are negative. Since both F_x and x are reversed, the force again is in the same direction as the displacement, and the work done by F_x is again positive. So the total work is still given by Eq. (6.9) or (6.10), even when X is negative or either or both of x_1 and x_2 are negative.

CAUTION **Work done *on* a spring vs. work done *by* a spring** Equation (6.10) gives the work that *you* must do *on* a spring to change its length. If you stretch a spring that's originally relaxed, then $x_1 = 0$, $x_2 > 0$, and $W > 0$: The force you apply to one end of the spring is in the same direction as the displacement, and the work you do is positive. By contrast, the work that the *spring* does on whatever it's attached to is given by the *negative* of Eq. (6.10). Thus, as you pull on the spring, the spring does negative work on you.

EXAMPLE 6.6 WORK DONE ON A SPRING SCALE

A woman weighing 600 N steps on a bathroom scale that contains a stiff spring (**Fig. 6.21**). In equilibrium, the spring is compressed 1.0 cm under her weight. Find the force constant of the spring and the total work done on it during the compression.

SOLUTION

IDENTIFY and SET UP: In equilibrium the upward force exerted by the spring balances the downward force of the woman's weight. We'll use this principle and Eq. (6.8) to determine the force

constant k, and we'll use Eq. (6.10) to calculate the work W that the woman does on the spring to compress it. We take positive values of x to correspond to elongation (upward in Fig. 6.21), so that both the displacement of the end of the spring (x) and the x-component of the force that the woman exerts on it (F_x) are negative. The applied force and the displacement are in the same direction, so the work done on the spring will be positive.

EXECUTE: The top of the spring is displaced by $x = -1.0\text{ cm} = -0.010$ m, and the woman exerts a force $F_x = -600$ N on the spring. From Eq. (6.8) the force constant is then

$$k = \frac{F_x}{x} = \frac{-600\text{ N}}{-0.010\text{ m}} = 6.0 \times 10^4 \text{ N/m}$$

Then, using $x_1 = 0$ and $x_2 = -0.010$ m in Eq. (6.10), we have

$$W = \tfrac{1}{2}kx_2^2 - \tfrac{1}{2}kx_1^2$$
$$= \tfrac{1}{2}(6.0 \times 10^4 \text{ N/m})(-0.010\text{ m})^2 - 0 = 3.0\text{ J}$$

EVALUATE: The work done is positive, as expected. Our arbitrary choice of the positive direction has no effect on the answer for W. You can test this by taking the positive x-direction to be downward, corresponding to compression. Do you get the same values for k and W as we found here?

6.21 Compressing a spring in a bathroom scale.

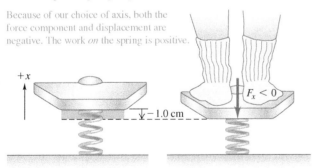

Because of our choice of axis, both the force component and displacement are negative. The work *on* the spring is positive.

$+x$

$F_x < 0$

-1.0 cm

Work–Energy Theorem for Straight-Line Motion, Varying Forces

In Section 6.2 we derived the work–energy theorem, $W_{\text{tot}} = K_2 - K_1$, for the special case of straight-line motion with a constant net force. We can now prove that this theorem is true even when the force varies with position. As in Section 6.2, let's consider a particle that undergoes a displacement x while being acted on by a net force with x-component F_x, which we now allow to vary. Just as in Fig. 6.16, we divide the total displacement x into a large number of small segments Δx. We can apply the work–energy theorem, Eq. (6.6), to each segment because the value

Application Tendons Are Nonideal Springs Muscles exert forces via the tendons that attach them to bones. A tendon consists of long, stiff, elastic collagen fibers. The graph shows how the tendon from the hind leg of a wallaby (a small kangaroo-like marsupial) stretches in response to an applied force. The tendon does not exhibit the simple, straight-line behavior of an ideal spring, so the work it does has to be found by integration [Eq. (6.7)]. The tendon exerts less force while relaxing than while stretching. As a result, the relaxing tendon does only about 93% of the work that was done to stretch it.

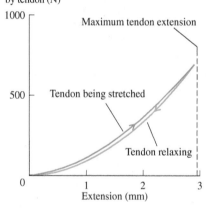

Force exerted by tendon (N)

of F_x in each small segment is approximately constant. The change in kinetic energy in segment Δx_a is equal to the work $F_{ax}\Delta x_a$, and so on. The total change of kinetic energy is the sum of the changes in the individual segments, and thus is equal to the total work done on the particle during the entire displacement. So $W_{\text{tot}} = \Delta K$ holds for varying forces as well as for constant ones.

Here's an alternative derivation of the work–energy theorem for a force that may vary with position. It involves making a change of variable from x to v_x in the work integral. Note first that the acceleration a of the particle can be expressed in various ways, using $a_x = dv_x/dt$, $v_x = dx/dt$, and the chain rule for derivatives:

$$a_x = \frac{dv_x}{dt} = \frac{dv_x}{dx}\frac{dx}{dt} = v_x\frac{dv_x}{dx} \tag{6.11}$$

From this result, Eq. (6.7) tells us that the total work done by the *net* force F_x is

$$W_{\text{tot}} = \int_{x_1}^{x_2} F_x \, dx = \int_{x_1}^{x_2} ma_x \, dx = \int_{x_1}^{x_2} mv_x\frac{dv_x}{dx} \, dx \tag{6.12}$$

Now $(dv_x/dx)dx$ is the change in velocity dv_x during the displacement dx, so we can make that substitution in Eq. (6.12). This changes the integration variable from x to v_x, so we change the limits from x_1 and x_2 to the corresponding x-velocities v_1 and v_2:

$$W_{\text{tot}} = \int_{v_1}^{v_2} mv_x \, dv_x$$

The integral of $v_x \, dv_x$ is just $v_x^2/2$. Substituting the upper and lower limits, we finally find

$$W_{\text{tot}} = \tfrac{1}{2}mv_2^2 - \tfrac{1}{2}mv_1^2 \tag{6.13}$$

This is the same as Eq. (6.6), so the work–energy theorem is valid even without the assumption that the net force is constant.

EXAMPLE 6.7 MOTION WITH A VARYING FORCE

An air-track glider of mass 0.100 kg is attached to the end of a horizontal air track by a spring with force constant 20.0 N/m (**Fig. 6.22a**). Initially the spring is unstretched and the glider is moving at 1.50 m/s to the right. Find the maximum distance d that the glider moves to the right (a) if the air track is turned on, so that there is no friction, and (b) if the air is turned off, so that there is kinetic friction with coefficient $\mu_k = 0.47$.

6.22 (a) A glider attached to an air track by a spring. (b), (c) Our free-body diagrams.

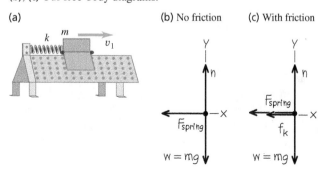

SOLUTION

IDENTIFY and SET UP: The force exerted by the spring is not constant, so we *cannot* use the constant-acceleration formulas of Chapter 2 to solve this problem. Instead, we'll use the work–energy theorem, since the total work done involves the distance moved (our target variable). In Figs. 6.22b and 6.22c we choose the positive x-direction to be to the right (in the direction of the glider's motion). We take $x = 0$ at the glider's initial position (where the spring is unstretched) and $x = d$ (the target variable) at the position where the glider stops. The motion is purely horizontal, so only the horizontal forces do work. Note that Eq. (6.10) gives the work done by the *glider* on the *spring* as it stretches; to use the work–energy theorem we need the work done by the *spring* on the *glider*, which is the negative of Eq. (6.10). We expect the glider to move farther without friction than with friction.

EXECUTE: (a) Equation (6.10) says that as the glider moves from $x_1 = 0$ to $x_2 = d$, it does an amount of work $W = \frac{1}{2}kd^2 - \frac{1}{2}k(0)^2 = \frac{1}{2}kd^2$ on the spring. The amount of work that the *spring* does on the *glider* is the negative of this, $-\frac{1}{2}kd^2$. The spring stretches until the glider comes instantaneously to rest, so the final kinetic energy K_2 is zero. The initial kinetic energy is $\frac{1}{2}mv_1^2$, where $v_1 = 1.50$ m/s is the glider's initial speed. From the work–energy theorem,

$$-\tfrac{1}{2}kd^2 = 0 - \tfrac{1}{2}mv_1^2$$

We solve for the distance d the glider moves:

$$d = v_1\sqrt{\frac{m}{k}} = (1.50 \text{ m/s})\sqrt{\frac{0.100 \text{ kg}}{20.0 \text{ N/m}}}$$

$$= 0.106 \text{ m} = 10.6 \text{ cm}$$

The stretched spring subsequently pulls the glider back to the left, so the glider is at rest only instantaneously.

(b) If the air is turned off, we must include the work done by the kinetic friction force. The normal force n is equal in magnitude to the weight of the glider, since the track is horizontal and there are no other vertical forces. Hence the kinetic friction force has constant magnitude $f_k = \mu_k n = \mu_k mg$. The friction force is directed opposite to the displacement, so the work done by friction is

$$W_{\text{fric}} = f_k d\cos 180° = -f_k d = -\mu_k mgd$$

The total work is the sum of W_{fric} and the work done by the spring, $-\frac{1}{2}kd^2$. The work–energy theorem then says that

$$-\mu_k mgd - \tfrac{1}{2}kd^2 = 0 - \tfrac{1}{2}mv_1^2 \quad \text{or}$$

$$\tfrac{1}{2}kd^2 + \mu_k mgd - \tfrac{1}{2}mv_1^2 = 0$$

This is a quadratic equation for d. The solutions are

$$d = -\frac{\mu_k mg}{k} \pm \sqrt{\left(\frac{\mu_k mg}{k}\right)^2 + \frac{mv_1^2}{k}}$$

We have

$$\frac{\mu_k mg}{k} = \frac{(0.47)(0.100 \text{ kg})(9.80 \text{ m/s}^2)}{20.0 \text{ N/m}} = 0.02303 \text{ m}$$

$$\frac{mv_1^2}{k} = \frac{(0.100 \text{ kg})(1.50 \text{ m/s})^2}{20.0 \text{ N/m}} = 0.01125 \text{ m}^2$$

so

$$d = -(0.02303 \text{ m}) \pm \sqrt{(0.02303 \text{ m})^2 + 0.01125 \text{ m}^2}$$

$$= 0.086 \text{ m} \quad \text{or} \quad -0.132 \text{ m}$$

The quantity d is a positive displacement, so only the positive value of d makes sense. Thus with friction the glider moves a distance $d = 0.086$ m $= 8.6$ cm.

EVALUATE: If we set $\mu_k = 0$, our algebraic solution for d in part (b) reduces to $d = v_1\sqrt{m/k}$, the zero-friction result from part (a). With friction, the glider goes a shorter distance. Again the glider stops instantaneously, and again the spring force pulls it toward the left; whether it moves or not depends on how great the *static* friction force is. How large would the coefficient of static friction μ_s have to be to keep the glider from springing back to the left?

Work–Energy Theorem for Motion Along a Curve

We can generalize our definition of work further to include a force that varies in direction as well as magnitude, and a displacement that lies along a curved path. **Figure 6.23a** shows a particle moving from P_1 to P_2 along a curve. We divide the curve between these points into many infinitesimal vector displacements, and we call a typical one of these $d\vec{l}$. Each $d\vec{l}$ is tangent to the path at its position. Let $\vec{F}$ be the force at a typical point along the path, and let ϕ be the angle between $\vec{F}$ and $d\vec{l}$ at this point. Then the small element of work dW done on the particle during the displacement $d\vec{l}$ may be written as

$$dW = \vec{F} \cdot d\vec{l} = F\cos\phi\,dl = F_\parallel\,dl$$

where $F_\parallel = F\cos\phi$ is the component of $\vec{F}$ in the direction parallel to $d\vec{l}$ (Fig. 6.23b). The work done by $\vec{F}$ on the particle as it moves from P_1 to P_2 is

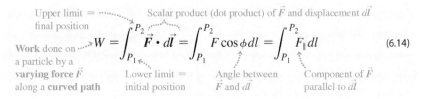

Upper limit = final position

Scalar product (dot product) of $\vec{F}$ and displacement $d\vec{l}$

Work done on a particle by a varying force $\vec{F}$ along a **curved path**

$$W = \int_{P_1}^{P_2} \vec{F} \cdot d\vec{l} = \int_{P_1}^{P_2} F\cos\phi\,dl = \int_{P_1}^{P_2} F_\parallel\,dl \qquad (6.14)$$

Lower limit = initial position

Angle between $\vec{F}$ and $d\vec{l}$

Component of $\vec{F}$ parallel to $d\vec{l}$

The integral in Eq. (6.14) (shown in three versions) is called a *line integral*. We'll see shortly how to evaluate an integral of this kind.

6.23 A particle moves along a curved path from point P_1 to P_2, acted on by a force $\vec{F}$ that varies in magnitude and direction.

(a)

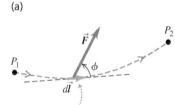

During an infinitesimal displacement $d\vec{l}$, the force $\vec{F}$ does work dW on the particle:

$$dW = \vec{F} \cdot d\vec{l} = F\cos\phi\,dl$$

(b)

Only the component of $\vec{F}$ parallel to the displacement, $F_\parallel = F\cos\phi$, contributes to the work done by $\vec{F}$.

We can now show that the work–energy theorem, Eq. (6.6), holds true even with varying forces and a displacement along a curved path. The force $\vec{F}$ is essentially constant over any given infinitesimal segment $d\vec{l}$ of the path, so we can apply the work–energy theorem for straight-line motion to that segment. Thus the change in the particle's kinetic energy K over that segment equals the work $dW = F_{\parallel}\,dl = \vec{F} \cdot d\vec{l}$ done on the particle. Adding up these infinitesimal quantities of work from all the segments along the whole path gives the total work done, Eq. (6.14), which equals the total change in kinetic energy over the whole path. So $W_{\text{tot}} = \Delta K = K_2 - K_1$ is true *in general,* no matter what the path and no matter what the character of the forces. This can be proved more rigorously by using steps like those in Eqs. (6.11) through (6.13).

Note that only the component of the net force parallel to the path, $F_{\parallel}$, does work on the particle, so only this component can change the speed and kinetic energy of the particle. The component perpendicular to the path, $F_{\perp} = F\sin\phi$, has no effect on the particle's speed; it acts only to change the particle's direction.

To evaluate the line integral in Eq. (6.14) in a specific problem, we need some sort of detailed description of the path and of the way in which $\vec{F}$ varies along the path. We usually express the line integral in terms of some scalar variable, as in the following example.

EXAMPLE 6.8 | **MOTION ON A CURVED PATH**

At a family picnic you are appointed to push your obnoxious cousin Throckmorton in a swing (**Fig. 6.24a**). His weight is w, the length of the chains is R, and you push Throcky until the chains make an angle θ_0 with the vertical. To do this, you exert a varying horizontal force $\vec{F}$ that starts at zero and gradually increases just enough that Throcky and the swing move very slowly and remain very nearly in equilibrium throughout the process. (a) What is the total work done on Throcky by all forces? (b) What is the work done by the tension T in the chains? (c) What is the work you do by exerting force $\vec{F}$? (Ignore the weight of the chains and seat.)

SOLUTION

IDENTIFY and SET UP: The motion is along a curve, so we'll use Eq. (6.14) to calculate the work done by the net force, by the tension force, and by the force $\vec{F}$. Figure 6.24b shows our free-body diagram and coordinate system for some arbitrary point in Throcky's motion. We have replaced the sum of the tensions in the two chains with a single tension T.

6.24 (a) Pushing cousin Throckmorton in a swing. (b) Our free-body diagram.

(a)

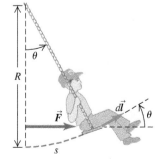

(b) Free-body diagram for Throckmorton (neglecting the weight of the chains and seat)

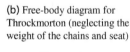

EXECUTE: (a) There are two ways to find the total work done during the motion: (1) by calculating the work done by each force and then adding those quantities, and (2) by calculating the work done by the net force. The second approach is far easier here because Throcky is nearly in equilibrium at every point. Hence the net force on him is zero, the integral of the net force in Eq. (6.14) is zero, and the total work done on him is zero.

(b) It's also easy to find the work done by the chain tension T because this force is perpendicular to the direction of motion at all points along the path. Hence at all points the angle between the chain tension and the displacement vector $d\vec{l}$ is $90°$ and the scalar product in Eq. (6.14) is zero. Thus the chain tension does zero work.

(c) To compute the work done by $\vec{F}$, we need to calculate the line integral in Eq. (6.14). Inside the integral is the quantity $F\cos\phi\,dl$; let's see how to express each term in this quantity.

Figure 6.24a shows that the angle between $\vec{F}$ and $d\vec{l}$ is θ, so we replace ϕ in Eq. (6.14) with θ. The value of θ changes as Throcky moves.

To find the magnitude F of force $\vec{F}$, note that the net force on Throcky is zero (he is nearly in equilibrium at all points), so $\Sigma F_x = 0$ and $\Sigma F_y = 0$. From Fig. 6.24b,

$$\Sigma F_x = F + (-T\sin\theta) = 0 \qquad \Sigma F_y = T\cos\theta + (-w) = 0$$

If you eliminate T from these two equations, you can show that $F = w\tan\theta$. As the angle θ increases, the tangent increases and F increases (you have to push harder).

To find the magnitude dl of the infinitesimal displacement $d\vec{l}$, note that Throcky moves through a circular arc of radius R (Fig. 6.24a). The arc length s equals the radius R multiplied by the length θ (in radians): $s = R\theta$. Therefore the displacement $d\vec{l}$ corresponding to a small change of angle $d\theta$ has a magnitude $dl = ds = R\,d\theta$.

When we put all the pieces together, the integral in Eq. (6.14) becomes

$$W = \int_{P_1}^{P_2} F\cos\phi\,dl = \int_0^{\theta_0} (w\tan\theta)\cos\theta\,(R\,d\theta) = \int_0^{\theta_0} wR\sin\theta\,d\theta$$

(Recall that $\tan\theta = \sin\theta/\cos\theta$, so $\tan\theta\cos\theta = \sin\theta$.) We've converted the *line* integral into an *ordinary* integral in terms of the angle θ. The limits of integration are from the starting position at $\theta = 0$ to the final position at $\theta = \theta_0$. The final result is

$$W = wR\int_0^{\theta_0} \sin\theta\, d\theta = -wR\cos\theta\big|_0^{\theta_0} = -wR(\cos\theta_0 - 1)$$

$$= wR(1 - \cos\theta_0)$$

EVALUATE: If $\theta_0 = 0$, there is no displacement; then $\cos\theta_0 = 1$ and $W = 0$, as we should expect. As θ_0 increases, $\cos\theta_0$ decreases and $W = wR(1 - \cos\theta_0)$ increases. So the farther along the arc you push Throcky, the more work you do. You can confirm that the quantity $R(1 - \cos\theta_0)$ is equal to h, the increase in Throcky's height during the displacement. So the work that you do to raise Throcky is just equal to his weight multiplied by the height that you raise him.

We can check our results by calculating the work done by the force of gravity $\vec{w}$. From part (a) the total work done on Throcky is zero, and from part (b) the work done by tension is zero. So gravity must do a negative amount of work that just balances the positive work done by the force $\vec{F}$ that we calculated in part (c).

For variety, let's calculate the work done by gravity by using the form of Eq. (6.14) that involves the quantity $\vec{F} \cdot d\vec{l}$, and express the force $\vec{w}$ and displacement $d\vec{l}$ in terms of their x- and y-components. The force of gravity has zero x-component and a y-component of $-w$. Figure 6.24a shows that $d\vec{l}$ has a magnitude of ds, an x-component of $ds\cos\theta$, and a y-component of $ds\sin\theta$. So

$$\vec{w} = \hat{\jmath}(-w)$$

$$d\vec{l} = \hat{\imath}(ds\cos\theta) + \hat{\jmath}(ds\sin\theta)$$

Use Eq. (1.19) to calculate the scalar product $\vec{w} \cdot d\vec{l}$:

$$\vec{w} \cdot d\vec{l} = (-w)(ds\sin\theta) = -w\sin\theta\, ds$$

Using $ds = R\, d\theta$, we find the work done by the force of gravity:

$$\int_{P_1}^{P_2} \vec{w} \cdot d\vec{l} = \int_0^{\theta_0} (-w\sin\theta)R\, d\theta = -wR\int_0^{\theta_0}\sin\theta\, d\theta$$

$$= -wR(1 - \cos\theta_0)$$

The work done by gravity is indeed the negative of the work done by force $\vec{F}$ that we calculated in part (c). Gravity does negative work because the force pulls downward while Throcky moves upward.

As we saw earlier, $R(1 - \cos\theta_0)$ is equal to h, the increase in Throcky's height during the displacement. So the work done by gravity along the curved path is $-mgh$, the *same* work that gravity would have done if Throcky had moved *straight upward* a distance h. This is an example of a more general result that we'll prove in Section 7.1.

TEST YOUR UNDERSTANDING OF SECTION 6.3 In Example 5.20 (Section 5.4) we examined a conical pendulum. The speed of the pendulum bob remains constant as it travels around the circle shown in Fig. 5.32a. (a) Over one complete circle, how much work does the tension force F do on the bob? (i) A positive amount; (ii) a negative amount; (iii) zero. (b) Over one complete circle, how much work does the weight do on the bob? (i) A positive amount; (ii) a negative amount; (iii) zero. ∎

6.4 POWER

The definition of work makes no reference to the passage of time. If you lift a barbell weighing 100 N through a vertical distance of 1.0 m at constant velocity, you do $(100\,\text{N})(1.0\,\text{m}) = 100\,\text{J}$ of work whether it takes you 1 second, 1 hour, or 1 year to do it. But often we need to know how quickly work is done. We describe this in terms of *power*. In ordinary conversation the word "power" is often synonymous with "energy" or "force." In physics we use a much more precise definition: **Power** is the time *rate* at which work is done. Like work and energy, power is a scalar quantity.

The average work done per unit time, or **average power** P_{av}, is defined to be

$$P_{av} = \frac{\Delta W}{\Delta t} \qquad (6.15)$$

Average power during time interval Δt ⟶ P_{av} ⟵ Work done during time interval / Duration of time interval

The rate at which work is done might not be constant. We define **instantaneous power** P as the quotient in Eq. (6.15) as Δt approaches zero:

$$P = \lim_{\Delta t \to 0} \frac{\Delta W}{\Delta t} = \frac{dW}{dt} \qquad (6.16)$$

Instantaneous power ⟶ P ⟵ Time rate of doing work / Average power over infinitesimally short time interval

The SI unit of power is the **watt** (W), named for the English inventor James Watt. One watt equals 1 joule per second: $1\,\text{W} = 1\,\text{J/s}$ (**Fig. 6.25**). The kilowatt $(1\,\text{kW} = 10^3\,\text{W})$ and the megawatt $(1\,\text{MW} = 10^6\,\text{W})$ are also commonly used.

6.25 The same amount of work is done in both of these situations, but the power (the rate at which work is done) is different.

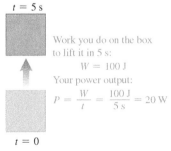

$t = 5\,\text{s}$

Work you do on the box to lift it in 5 s:
$W = 100\,\text{J}$
Your power output:
$P = \dfrac{W}{t} = \dfrac{100\,\text{J}}{5\,\text{s}} = 20\,\text{W}$

$t = 0$

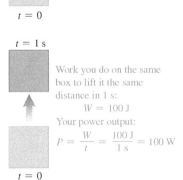

$t = 1\,\text{s}$

Work you do on the same box to lift it the same distance in 1 s:
$W = 100\,\text{J}$
Your power output:
$P = \dfrac{W}{t} = \dfrac{100\,\text{J}}{1\,\text{s}} = 100\,\text{W}$

$t = 0$

6.26 A one-horsepower (746-W) propulsion system.

Anaerobic muscle

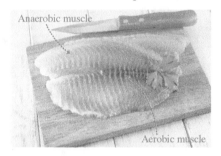

Aerobic muscle

Another common unit of power is the *horsepower* (hp) (**Fig. 6.26**). The value of this unit derives from experiments by James Watt, who measured that in one minute a horse could do an amount of work equivalent to lifting 33,000 pounds (lb) a distance of 1 foot (ft), or 33,000 ft · lb. Thus 1 hp = 33,000 ft · lb/min. Using 1 ft = 0.3048 m, 1 lb = 4.448 N, and 1 min = 60 s, we can show that

$$1 \text{ hp} = 746 \text{ W} = 0.746 \text{ kW}$$

The watt is a familiar unit of *electrical* power; a 100-W light bulb converts 100 J of electrical energy into light and heat each second. But there's nothing inherently electrical about a watt. A light bulb could be rated in horsepower, and an engine can be rated in kilowatts.

The *kilowatt-hour* (kW · h) is the usual commercial unit of electrical energy. One kilowatt-hour is the total work done in 1 hour (3600 s) when the power is 1 kilowatt (10^3 J/s), so

$$1 \text{ kW} \cdot \text{h} = (10^3 \text{ J/s})(3600 \text{ s}) = 3.6 \times 10^6 \text{ J} = 3.6 \text{ MJ}$$

The kilowatt-hour is a unit of *work* or *energy*, not power.

In mechanics we can also express power in terms of force and velocity. Suppose that a force $\vec{F}$ acts on a body while it undergoes a vector displacement $\Delta \vec{s}$. If $F_\parallel$ is the component of $\vec{F}$ tangent to the path (parallel to $\Delta \vec{s}$), then the work done by the force is $\Delta W = F_\parallel \Delta s$. The average power is

$$P_{av} = \frac{F_\parallel \Delta s}{\Delta t} = F_\parallel \frac{\Delta s}{\Delta t} = F_\parallel v_{av} \qquad (6.17)$$

Instantaneous power P is the limit of this expression as $\Delta t \to 0$:

$$P = F_\parallel v \qquad (6.18)$$

where v is the magnitude of the instantaneous velocity. We can also express Eq. (6.18) in terms of the scalar product:

Instantaneous power for a force doing work on a particle $\longrightarrow P = \vec{F} \cdot \vec{v}$ ....Force that acts on particle ....Velocity of particle $\qquad (6.19)$

SOLUTION

EXAMPLE 6.9 FORCE AND POWER

Each of the four jet engines on an Airbus A380 airliner develops a thrust (a forward force on the airliner) of 322,000 N (72,000 lb). When the airplane is flying at 250 m/s (900 km/h, or roughly 560 mi/h), what horsepower does each engine develop?

SOLUTION

IDENTIFY, SET UP, and EXECUTE: Our target variable is the instantaneous power P, which is the rate at which the thrust does work. We use Eq. (6.18). The thrust is in the direction of motion, so $F_\parallel$ is just equal to the thrust. At $v = 250$ m/s, the power developed by each engine is

$$P = F_\parallel v = (3.22 \times 10^5 \text{ N})(250 \text{ m/s}) = 8.05 \times 10^7 \text{ W}$$

$$= (8.05 \times 10^7 \text{ W})\frac{1 \text{ hp}}{746 \text{ W}} = 108,000 \text{ hp}$$

EVALUATE: The speed of modern airliners is directly related to the power of their engines (**Fig. 6.27**). The largest propeller-driven

6.27 (a) Propeller-driven and (b) jet airliners.

(a)  (b)

airliners of the 1950s had engines that each developed about 3400 hp (2.5×10^6 W), giving them maximum speeds of about 600 km/h (370 mi/h). Each engine on an Airbus A380 develops more than 30 times more power, enabling it to fly at about 900 km/h (560 mi/h) and to carry a much heavier load.

If the engines are at maximum thrust while the airliner is at rest on the ground so that $v = 0$, the engines develop *zero* power. Force and power are not the same thing!

EXAMPLE 6.10 A "POWER CLIMB"

A 50.0-kg marathon runner runs up the stairs to the top of Chicago's 443-m-tall Willis Tower, the second tallest building in the United States (**Fig. 6.28**). To lift herself to the top in 15.0 minutes, what must be her average power output? Express your answer in watts, in kilowatts, and in horsepower.

SOLUTION

IDENTIFY and SET UP: We'll treat the runner as a particle of mass m. Her average power output P_{av} must be enough to lift her at constant speed against gravity.

We can find P_{av} in two ways: (1) by determining how much work she must do and dividing that quantity by the elapsed time,

as in Eq. (6.15), or (2) by calculating the average upward force she must exert (in the direction of the climb) and multiplying that quantity by her upward velocity, as in Eq. (6.17).

EXECUTE: (1) As in Example 6.8, lifting a mass m against gravity requires an amount of work equal to the weight mg multiplied by the height h it is lifted. Hence the work the runner must do is

$$W = mgh = (50.0 \text{ kg})(9.80 \text{ m/s}^2)(443 \text{ m})$$
$$= 2.17 \times 10^5 \text{ J}$$

She does this work in a time 15.0 min = 900 s, so from Eq. (6.15) the average power is

$$P_{av} = \frac{2.17 \times 10^5 \text{ J}}{900 \text{ s}} = 241 \text{ W} = 0.241 \text{ kW} = 0.323 \text{ hp}$$

(2) The force exerted is vertical and the average vertical component of velocity is $(443 \text{ m})/(900 \text{ s}) = 0.492 \text{ m/s}$, so from Eq. (6.17) the average power is

$$P_{av} = F_{\parallel}v_{av} = (mg)v_{av}$$
$$= (50.0 \text{ kg})(9.80 \text{ m/s}^2)(0.492 \text{ m/s}) = 241 \text{ W}$$

which is the same result as before.

EVALUATE: The runner's *total* power output will be several times greater than 241 W. The reason is that the runner isn't really a particle but a collection of parts that exert forces on each other and do work, such as the work done to inhale and exhale and to make her arms and legs swing. What we've calculated is only the part of her power output that lifts her to the top of the building.

6.28 How much power is required to run up the stairs of Chicago's Willis Tower in 15 minutes?

TEST YOUR UNDERSTANDING OF SECTION 6.4 The air surrounding an airplane in flight exerts a drag force that acts opposite to the airplane's motion. When the Airbus A380 in Example 6.9 is flying in a straight line at a constant altitude at a constant 250 m/s, what is the rate at which the drag force does work on it? (i) 432,000 hp; (ii) 108,000 hp; (iii) 0; (iv) −108,000 hp; (v) −432,000 hp. ❚

Work done by a force: When a constant force $\vec{F}$ acts on a particle that undergoes a straight-line displacement $\vec{s}$, the work done by the force on the particle is defined to be the scalar product of $\vec{F}$ and $\vec{s}$. The unit of work in SI units is 1 joule = 1 newton-meter (1 J = 1 N·m). Work is a scalar quantity; it can be positive or negative, but it has no direction in space. (See Examples 6.1 and 6.2.)

$$W = \vec{F} \cdot \vec{s} = Fs\cos\phi \qquad (6.2),\ (6.3)$$
$$\phi = \text{angle between } \vec{F} \text{ and } \vec{s}$$

Kinetic energy: The kinetic energy K of a particle equals the amount of work required to accelerate the particle from rest to speed v. It is also equal to the amount of work the particle can do in the process of being brought to rest. Kinetic energy is a scalar that has no direction in space; it is always positive or zero. Its units are the same as the units of work: 1 J = 1 N·m = 1 kg·m²/s².

$$K = \tfrac{1}{2}mv^2 \qquad (6.5)$$

Doubling m doubles K.

Doubling v quadruples K.

The work–energy theorem: When forces act on a particle while it undergoes a displacement, the particle's kinetic energy changes by an amount equal to the total work done on the particle by all the forces. This relationship, called the work–energy theorem, is valid whether the forces are constant or varying and whether the particle moves along a straight or curved path. It is applicable only to bodies that can be treated as particles. (See Examples 6.3–6.5.)

$$W_{\text{tot}} = K_2 - K_1 = \Delta K \qquad (6.6)$$

$W_{\text{tot}} = $ Total work done on particle along path

$$K_1 = \tfrac{1}{2}mv_1^2$$
$$K_2 = \tfrac{1}{2}mv_2^2 = K_1 + W_{\text{tot}}$$

Work done by a varying force or on a curved path: When a force varies during a straight-line displacement, the work done by the force is given by an integral, Eq. (6.7). (See Examples 6.6 and 6.7.) When a particle follows a curved path, the work done on it by a force $\vec{F}$ is given by an integral that involves the angle ϕ between the force and the displacement. This expression is valid even if the force magnitude and the angle ϕ vary during the displacement. (See Example 6.8.)

$$W = \int_{x_1}^{x_2} F_x\, dx \qquad (6.7)$$

$$W = \int_{P_1}^{P_2} \vec{F} \cdot d\vec{l} \qquad (6.14)$$
$$= \int_{P_1}^{P_2} F\cos\phi\, dl = \int_{P_1}^{P_2} F_\parallel\, dl$$

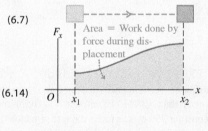

Area = Work done by force during displacement

Power: Power is the time rate of doing work. The average power P_{av} is the amount of work ΔW done in time Δt divided by that time. The instantaneous power is the limit of the average power as Δt goes to zero. When a force $\vec{F}$ acts on a particle moving with velocity $\vec{v}$, the instantaneous power (the rate at which the force does work) is the scalar product of $\vec{F}$ and $\vec{v}$. Like work and kinetic energy, power is a scalar quantity. The SI unit of power is 1 watt = 1 joule/second (1 W = 1 J/s). (See Examples 6.9 and 6.10.)

$$P_{\text{av}} = \frac{\Delta W}{\Delta t} \qquad (6.15)$$

$$P = \lim_{\Delta t \to 0} \frac{\Delta W}{\Delta t} = \frac{dW}{dt} \qquad (6.16)$$

$$P = \vec{F} \cdot \vec{v} \qquad (6.19)$$

$t = 5\ \text{s}$

Work you do on the box to lift it in 5 s:
$$W = 100\ \text{J}$$
Your power output:
$$P = \frac{W}{t} = \frac{100\ \text{J}}{5\ \text{s}} = 20\ \text{W}$$

$t = 0$

BRIDGING PROBLEM   A SPRING THAT DISOBEYS HOOKE'S LAW

Consider a hanging spring of negligible mass that does *not* obey Hooke's law. When the spring is pulled downward by a distance x, the spring exerts an upward force of magnitude αx^2, where α is a positive constant. Initially the hanging spring is relaxed (not extended). We then attach a block of mass m to the spring and release the block. The block stretches the spring as it falls (**Fig. 6.29**). (a) How fast is the block moving when it has fallen a distance x_1? (b) At what rate does the spring do work on the block at this point? (c) Find the maximum distance x_2 that the spring stretches. (d) Will the block *remain* at the point found in part (c)?

SOLUTION GUIDE

IDENTIFY and SET UP

1. The spring force in this problem isn't constant, so you have to use the work–energy theorem. You'll also need Eq. (6.7) to find the work done by the spring over a given displacement.

6.29 The block is attached to a spring that does not obey Hooke's law.

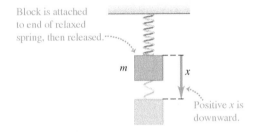

Block is attached to end of relaxed spring, then released.

m

x

Positive x is downward.

2. Draw a free-body diagram for the block, including your choice of coordinate axes. Note that x represents how far the spring is *stretched,* so choose the positive x-direction to be downward, as in Fig. 6.29. On your coordinate axis, label the points $x = x_1$ and $x = x_2$.
3. Make a list of the unknown quantities, and decide which of these are the target variables.

EXECUTE

4. Calculate the work done on the block by the spring as the block falls an arbitrary distance x. (The integral isn't a difficult one. Use Appendix B if you need a reminder.) Is the work done by the spring positive, negative, or zero?
5. Calculate the work done on the block by any other forces as the block falls an arbitrary distance x. Is this work positive, negative, or zero?
6. Use the work–energy theorem to find the target variables. (You'll also need an equation for power.) *Hint:* When the spring is at its maximum stretch, what is the speed of the block?
7. To answer part (d), consider the *net* force that acts on the block when it is at the point found in part (c).

EVALUATE

8. We learned in Section 2.5 that after an object dropped from rest has fallen freely a distance x_1, its speed is $\sqrt{2gx_1}$. Use this to decide whether your answer in part (a) makes sense. In addition, ask yourself whether the algebraic sign of your answer in part (b) makes sense.
9. Find the value of x where the net force on the block would be zero. How does this compare to your result for x_2? Is this consistent with your answer in part (d)?

Problems

For assigned homework and other learning materials, go to MasteringPhysics®. (MP)

•, ••, •••: Difficulty levels. CP: Cumulative problems incorporating material from earlier chapters. CALC: Problems requiring calculus.
DATA: Problems involving real data, scientific evidence, experimental design, and/or statistical reasoning. BIO: Biosciences problems.

DISCUSSION QUESTIONS

Q6.1 The sign of many physical quantities depends on the choice of coordinates. For example, a_y for free-fall motion can be negative or positive, depending on whether we choose upward or downward as positive. Is the same true of work? In other words, can we make positive work negative by a different choice of coordinates? Explain.

Q6.2 An elevator is hoisted by its cables at constant speed. Is the total work done on the elevator positive, negative, or zero? Explain.

Q6.3 A rope tied to a body is pulled, causing the body to accelerate. But according to Newton's third law, the body pulls back on the rope with a force of equal magnitude and opposite direction. Is the total work done then zero? If so, how can the body's kinetic energy change? Explain.

Q6.4 If it takes total work W to give an object a speed v and kinetic energy K, starting from rest, what will be the object's speed (in terms of v) and kinetic energy (in terms of K) if we do twice as much work on it, again starting from rest?

Q6.5 If there is a net nonzero force on a moving object, can the total work done on the object be zero? Explain, using an example.

Q6.6 In Example 5.5 (Section 5.1), how does the work done on the bucket by the tension in the cable compare with the work done on the cart by the tension in the cable?

Q6.7 In the conical pendulum of Example 5.20 (Section 5.4), which of the forces do work on the bob while it is swinging?

Q6.8 For the cases shown in **Fig. Q6.8**, the object is released from rest at the top and feels no friction or air resistance. In which (if any) cases will the mass have (i) the greatest speed at the bottom and (ii) the most work done on it by the time it reaches the bottom?

Figure Q6.8

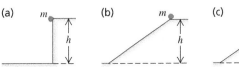

Q6.9 A force $\vec{F}$ is in the *x*-direction and has a magnitude that depends on *x*. Sketch a possible graph of *F* versus *x* such that the force does zero work on an object that moves from x_1 to x_2, even though the force magnitude is not zero at all *x* in this range.

Q6.10 Does a car's kinetic energy change more when the car speeds up from 10 to 15 m/s or from 15 to 20 m/s? Explain.

Q6.11 A falling brick has a mass of 1.5 kg and is moving straight downward with a speed of 5.0 m/s. A 1.5-kg physics book is sliding across the floor with a speed of 5.0 m/s. A 1.5-kg melon is traveling with a horizontal velocity component 3.0 m/s to the right and a vertical component 4.0 m/s upward. Do all of these objects have the same velocity? Do all of them have the same kinetic energy? For both questions, give your reasoning.

Q6.12 Can the *total* work done on an object during a displacement be negative? Explain. If the total work is negative, can its magnitude be larger than the initial kinetic energy of the object? Explain.

Q6.13 A net force acts on an object and accelerates it from rest to a speed v_1. In doing so, the force does an amount of work W_1. By what factor must the work done on the object be increased to produce three times the final speed, with the object again starting from rest?

Q6.14 A truck speeding down the highway has a lot of kinetic energy relative to a stopped state trooper but no kinetic energy relative to the truck driver. In these two frames of reference, is the same amount of work required to stop the truck? Explain.

Q6.15 You are holding a briefcase by the handle, with your arm straight down by your side. Does the force your hand exerts do work on the briefcase when (a) you walk at a constant speed down a horizontal hallway and (b) you ride an escalator from the first to second floor of a building? In both cases justify your answer.

Q6.16 When a book slides along a tabletop, the force of friction does negative work on it. Can friction ever do *positive* work? Explain. (*Hint:* Think of a box in the back of an accelerating truck.)

Q6.17 Time yourself while running up a flight of steps, and compute the average rate at which you do work against the force of gravity. Express your answer in watts and in horsepower.

Q6.18 Fractured Physics. Many terms from physics are badly misused in everyday language. In both cases, explain the errors involved. (a) A *strong* person is called *powerful*. What is wrong with this use of *power*? (b) When a worker carries a bag of concrete along a level construction site, people say he did a lot of *work*. Did he?

Q6.19 An advertisement for a portable electrical generating unit claims that the unit's diesel engine produces 28,000 hp to drive an electrical generator that produces 30 MW of electrical power. Is this possible? Explain.

Q6.20 A car speeds up while the engine delivers constant power. Is the acceleration greater at the beginning of this process or at the end? Explain.

Q6.21 Consider a graph of instantaneous power versus time, with the vertical *P*-axis starting at *P* = 0. What is the physical significance of the area under the *P*-versus-*t* curve between vertical lines at t_1 and t_2? How could you find the average power from the graph? Draw a *P*-versus-*t* curve that consists of two straight-line sections and for which the peak power is equal to twice the average power.

Q6.22 A nonzero net force acts on an object. Is it possible for any of the following quantities to be constant: the object's (a) speed; (b) velocity; (c) kinetic energy?

Q6.23 When a certain force is applied to an ideal spring, the spring stretches a distance *x* from its unstretched length and does work *W*. If instead twice the force is applied, what distance (in terms of *x*) does the spring stretch from its unstretched length, and how much work (in terms of *W*) is required to stretch it this distance?

Q6.24 If work *W* is required to stretch a spring a distance *x* from its unstretched length, what work (in terms of *W*) is required to stretch the spring an *additional* distance *x*?

EXERCISES

Section 6.1 Work

6.1 • You push your physics book 1.50 m along a horizontal tabletop with a horizontal push of 2.40 N while the opposing force of friction is 0.600 N. How much work does each of the following forces do on the book: (a) your 2.40-N push, (b) the friction force, (c) the normal force from the tabletop, and (d) gravity? (e) What is the net work done on the book?

6.2 • Using a cable with a tension of 1350 N, a tow truck pulls a car 5.00 km along a horizontal roadway. (a) How much work does the cable do on the car if it pulls horizontally? If it pulls at 35.0° above the horizontal? (b) How much work does the cable do on the tow truck in both cases of part (a)? (c) How much work does gravity do on the car in part (a)?

6.3 • A factory worker pushes a 30.0-kg crate a distance of 4.5 m along a level floor at constant velocity by pushing horizontally on it. The coefficient of kinetic friction between the crate and the floor is 0.25. (a) What magnitude of force must the worker apply? (b) How much work is done on the crate by this force? (c) How much work is done on the crate by friction? (d) How much work is done on the crate by the normal force? By gravity? (e) What is the total work done on the crate?

6.4 •• Suppose the worker in Exercise 6.3 pushes downward at an angle of 30° below the horizontal. (a) What magnitude of force must the worker apply to move the crate at constant velocity? (b) How much work is done on the crate by this force when the crate is pushed a distance of 4.5 m? (c) How much work is done on the crate by friction during this displacement? (d) How much work is done on the crate by the normal force? By gravity? (e) What is the total work done on the crate?

6.5 •• A 75.0-kg painter climbs a ladder that is 2.75 m long and leans against a vertical wall. The ladder makes a 30.0° angle with the wall. (a) How much work does gravity do on the painter? (b) Does the answer to part (a) depend on whether the painter climbs at constant speed or accelerates up the ladder?

6.6 •• Two tugboats pull a disabled supertanker. Each tug exerts a constant force of 1.80×10^6 N, one 14° west of north and the other 14° east of north, as they pull the tanker 0.75 km toward the north. What is the total work they do on the supertanker?

6.7 • Two blocks are connected by a very light string passing over a massless and frictionless pulley (**Fig. E6.7**). Traveling at constant speed, the 20.0-N block moves 75.0 cm to the right and the 12.0-N block moves 75.0 cm downward. How much work is done

Figure **E6.7**

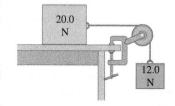

(a) on the 12.0-N block by (i) gravity and (ii) the tension in the string? (b) How much work is done on the 20.0-N block by

(i) gravity, (ii) the tension in the string, (iii) friction, and (iv) the normal force? (c) Find the total work done on each block.

6.8 •• A loaded grocery cart is rolling across a parking lot in a strong wind. You apply a constant force $\vec{F} = (30 \text{ N})\hat{\imath} - (40 \text{ N})\hat{\jmath}$ to the cart as it undergoes a displacement $\vec{s} = (-9.0 \text{ m})\hat{\imath} - (3.0 \text{ m})\hat{\jmath}$. How much work does the force you apply do on the grocery cart?

6.9 • A 0.800-kg ball is tied to the end of a string 1.60 m long and swung in a vertical circle. (a) During one complete circle, starting anywhere, calculate the total work done on the ball by (i) the tension in the string and (ii) gravity. (b) Repeat part (a) for motion along the semicircle from the lowest to the highest point on the path.

6.10 •• A 12.0-kg package in a mail-sorting room slides 2.00 m down a chute that is inclined at 53.0° below the horizontal. The coefficient of kinetic friction between the package and the chute's surface is 0.40. Calculate the work done on the package by (a) friction, (b) gravity, and (c) the normal force. (d) What is the net work done on the package?

6.11 • A 128.0-N carton is pulled up a frictionless baggage ramp inclined at 30.0° above the horizontal by a rope exerting a 72.0-N pull parallel to the ramp's surface. If the carton travels 5.20 m along the surface of the ramp, calculate the work done on it by (a) the rope, (b) gravity, and (c) the normal force of the ramp. (d) What is the net work done on the carton? (e) Suppose that the rope is angled at 50.0° above the horizontal, instead of being parallel to the ramp's surface. How much work does the rope do on the carton in this case?

6.12 •• A boxed 10.0-kg computer monitor is dragged by friction 5.50 m upward along a conveyor belt inclined at an angle of 36.9° above the horizontal. If the monitor's speed is a constant 2.10 cm/s, how much work is done on the monitor by (a) friction, (b) gravity, and (c) the normal force of the conveyor belt?

6.13 •• A large crate sits on the floor of a warehouse. Paul and Bob apply constant horizontal forces to the crate. The force applied by Paul has magnitude 48.0 N and direction 61.0° south of west. How much work does Paul's force do during a displacement of the crate that is 12.0 m in the direction 22.0° east of north?

6.14 •• You apply a constant force $\vec{F} = (-68.0 \text{ N})\hat{\imath} + (36.0 \text{ N})\hat{\jmath}$ to a 380-kg car as the car travels 48.0 m in a direction that is 240.0° counterclockwise from the +x-axis. How much work does the force you apply do on the car?

6.15 •• On a farm, you are pushing on a stubborn pig with a constant horizontal force with magnitude 30.0 N and direction 37.0° counterclockwise from the +x-axis. How much work does this force do during a displacement of the pig that is (a) $\vec{s} = (5.00 \text{ m})\hat{\imath}$; (b) $\vec{s} = -(6.00 \text{ m})\hat{\jmath}$; (c) $\vec{s} = -(2.00 \text{ m})\hat{\imath} + (4.00 \text{ m})\hat{\jmath}$?

Section 6.2 Kinetic Energy and the Work-Energy Theorem

6.16 •• A 1.50-kg book is sliding along a rough horizontal surface. At point A it is moving at 3.21 m/s, and at point B it has slowed to 1.25 m/s. (a) How much work was done on the book between A and B? (b) If −0.750 J of work is done on the book from B to C, how fast is it moving at point C? (c) How fast would it be moving at C if +0.750 J of work was done on it from B to C?

6.17 •• BIO **Animal Energy.** Adult cheetahs, the fastest of the great cats, have a mass of about 70 kg and have been clocked to run at up to 72 mi/h (32 m/s). (a) How many joules of kinetic energy does such a swift cheetah have? (b) By what factor would its kinetic energy change if its speed were doubled?

6.18 • **Some Typical Kinetic Energies.** (a) In the Bohr model of the atom, the ground-state electron in hydrogen has an orbital speed of 2190 km/s. What is its kinetic energy? (Consult Appendix F.) (b) If you drop a 1.0-kg weight (about 2 lb) from a height of 1.0 m, how many joules of kinetic energy will it have when it reaches the ground? (c) Is it reasonable that a 30-kg child could run fast enough to have 100 J of kinetic energy?

6.19 • **Meteor Crater.** About 50,000 years ago, a meteor crashed into the earth near present-day Flagstaff, Arizona. Measurements from 2005 estimate that this meteor had a mass of about 1.4×10^8 kg (around 150,000 tons) and hit the ground at a speed of 12 km/s. (a) How much kinetic energy did this meteor deliver to the ground? (b) How does this energy compare to the energy released by a 1.0-megaton nuclear bomb? (A megaton bomb releases the same amount of energy as a million tons of TNT, and 1.0 ton of TNT releases 4.184×10^9 J of energy.)

6.20 • A 4.80-kg watermelon is dropped from rest from the roof of an 18.0-m-tall building and feels no appreciable air resistance. (a) Calculate the work done by gravity on the watermelon during its displacement from the roof to the ground. (b) Just before it strikes the ground, what is the watermelon's (i) kinetic energy and (ii) speed? (c) Which of the answers in parts (a) and (b) would be *different* if there were appreciable air resistance?

6.21 •• Use the work–energy theorem to solve each of these problems. You can use Newton's laws to check your answers. Neglect air resistance in all cases. (a) A branch falls from the top of a 95.0-m-tall redwood tree, starting from rest. How fast is it moving when it reaches the ground? (b) A volcano ejects a boulder directly upward 525 m into the air. How fast was the boulder moving just as it left the volcano?

6.22 •• Use the work–energy theorem to solve each of these problems. You can use Newton's laws to check your answers. (a) A skier moving at 5.00 m/s encounters a long, rough horizontal patch of snow having a coefficient of kinetic friction of 0.220 with her skis. How far does she travel on this patch before stopping? (b) Suppose the rough patch in part (a) was only 2.90 m long. How fast would the skier be moving when she reached the end of the patch? (c) At the base of a frictionless icy hill that rises at 25.0° above the horizontal, a toboggan has a speed of 12.0 m/s toward the hill. How high vertically above the base will it go before stopping?

6.23 •• You are a member of an Alpine Rescue Team. You must project a box of supplies up an incline of constant slope angle α so that it reaches a stranded skier who is a vertical distance h above the bottom of the incline. The incline is slippery, but there is some friction present, with kinetic friction coefficient μ_k. Use the work–energy theorem to calculate the minimum speed you must give the box at the bottom of the incline so that it will reach the skier. Express your answer in terms of g, h, μ_k, and α.

6.24 •• You throw a 3.00-N rock vertically into the air from ground level. You observe that when it is 15.0 m above the ground, it is traveling at 25.0 m/s upward. Use the work–energy theorem to find (a) the rock's speed just as it left the ground and (b) its maximum height.

6.25 • A sled with mass 12.00 kg moves in a straight line on a frictionless, horizontal surface. At one point in its path, its speed is 4.00 m/s; after it has traveled 2.50 m beyond this point, its speed is 6.00 m/s. Use the work–energy theorem to find the force acting on the sled, assuming that this force is constant and that it acts in the direction of the sled's motion.

6.26 •• A mass m slides down a smooth inclined plane from an initial vertical height h, making an angle α with the horizontal. (a) The work done by a force is the sum of the work done by the components of the force. Consider the components of gravity parallel and perpendicular to the surface of the plane. Calculate the work done on the mass by each of the components, and use these results to show that the work done by gravity is exactly the same as if the mass had fallen straight down through the air from a height h. (b) Use the work–energy theorem to prove that the speed of the mass at the bottom of the incline is the same as if the mass had been dropped from height h, independent of the angle α of the incline. Explain how this speed can be independent of the slope angle. (c) Use the results of part (b) to find the speed of a rock that slides down an icy frictionless hill, starting from rest 15.0 m above the bottom.

6.27 • A 12-pack of Omni-Cola (mass 4.30 kg) is initially at rest on a horizontal floor. It is then pushed in a straight line for 1.20 m by a trained dog that exerts a horizontal force with magnitude 36.0 N. Use the work–energy theorem to find the final speed of the 12-pack if (a) there is no friction between the 12-pack and the floor, and (b) the coefficient of kinetic friction between the 12-pack and the floor is 0.30.

6.28 •• A soccer ball with mass 0.420 kg is initially moving with speed 2.00 m/s. A soccer player kicks the ball, exerting a constant force of magnitude 40.0 N in the same direction as the ball's motion. Over what distance must the player's foot be in contact with the ball to increase the ball's speed to 6.00 m/s?

6.29 • A little red wagon with mass 7.00 kg moves in a straight line on a frictionless horizontal surface. It has an initial speed of 4.00 m/s and then is pushed 3.0 m in the direction of the initial velocity by a force with a magnitude of 10.0 N. (a) Use the work–energy theorem to calculate the wagon's final speed. (b) Calculate the acceleration produced by the force. Use this acceleration in the kinematic relationships of Chapter 2 to calculate the wagon's final speed. Compare this result to that calculated in part (a).

6.30 •• A block of ice with mass 2.00 kg slides 1.35 m down an inclined plane that slopes downward at an angle of 36.9° below the horizontal. If the block of ice starts from rest, what is its final speed? Ignore friction.

6.31 • **Stopping Distance.** A car is traveling on a level road with speed v_0 at the instant when the brakes lock, so that the tires slide rather than roll. (a) Use the work–energy theorem to calculate the minimum stopping distance of the car in terms of v_0, g, and the coefficient of kinetic friction μ_k between the tires and the road. (b) By what factor would the minimum stopping distance change if (i) the coefficient of kinetic friction were doubled, or (ii) the initial speed were doubled, or (iii) both the coefficient of kinetic friction and the initial speed were doubled?

6.32 •• A 30.0-kg crate is initially moving with a velocity that has magnitude 3.90 m/s in a direction 37.0° west of north. How much work must be done on the crate to change its velocity to 5.62 m/s in a direction 63.0° south of east?

Section 6.3 Work and Energy with Varying Forces

6.33 • BIO **Heart Repair.** A surgeon is using material from a donated heart to repair a patient's damaged aorta and needs to know the elastic characteristics of this aortal material. Tests performed on a 16.0-cm strip of the donated aorta reveal that it stretches 3.75 cm when a 1.50-N pull is exerted on it. (a) What is the force constant of this strip of aortal material? (b) If the maximum distance it will be able to stretch when it replaces the aorta in the damaged heart is 1.14 cm, what is the greatest force it will be able to exert there?

6.34 •• To stretch a spring 3.00 cm from its unstretched length, 12.0 J of work must be done. (a) What is the force constant of this spring? (b) What magnitude force is needed to stretch the spring 3.00 cm from its unstretched length? (c) How much work must be done to compress this spring 4.00 cm from its unstretched length, and what force is needed to compress it this distance?

6.35 • Three identical 8.50-kg masses are hung by three identical springs (**Fig. E6.35**). Each spring has a force constant of 7.80 kN/m and was 12.0 cm long before any masses were attached to it. (a) Draw a free-body diagram of each mass. (b) How long is each spring when hanging as shown? (*Hint:* First isolate only the bottom mass. Then treat the bottom two masses as a system. Finally, treat all three masses as a system.)

Figure **E6.35**

6.36 • A child applies a force $\vec{F}$ parallel to the x-axis to a 10.0-kg sled moving on the frozen surface of a small pond. As the child controls the speed of the sled, the x-component of the force she applies varies with the x-coordinate of the sled as shown in **Fig. E6.36**. Calculate the work done by $\vec{F}$ when the sled moves (a) from $x = 0$ to $x = 8.0$ m; (b) from $x = 8.0$ m to $x = 12.0$ m; (c) from $x = 0$ to 12.0 m.

Figure **E6.36**

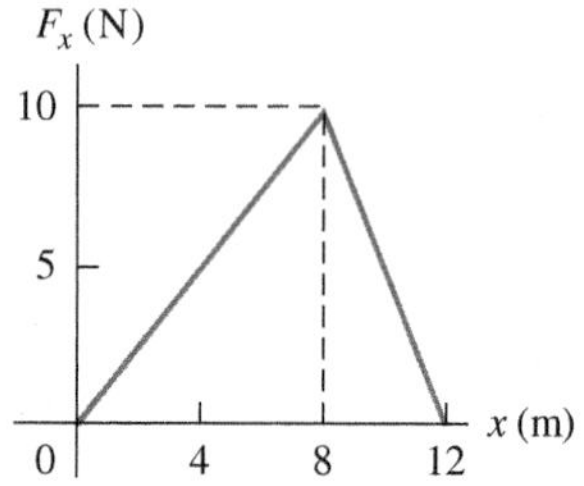

F_x (N)

10

5

0   4   8   12 x (m)

6.37 •• Suppose the sled in Exercise 6.36 is initially at rest at $x = 0$. Use the work–energy theorem to find the speed of the sled at (a) $x = 8.0$ m and (b) $x = 12.0$ m. Ignore friction between the sled and the surface of the pond.

6.38 •• A spring of force constant 300.0 N/m and unstretched length 0.240 m is stretched by two forces, pulling in opposite directions at opposite ends of the spring, that increase to 15.0 N. How long will the spring now be, and how much work was required to stretch it that distance?

6.39 •• A 6.0-kg box moving at 3.0 m/s on a horizontal, frictionless surface runs into a light spring of force constant 75 N/cm. Use the work–energy theorem to find the maximum compression of the spring.

6.40 •• **Leg Presses.** As part of your daily workout, you lie on your back and push with your feet against a platform attached to two stiff springs arranged side by side so that they are parallel to each other. When you push the platform, you compress the springs. You do 80.0 J of work when you compress the springs 0.200 m from their uncompressed length. (a) What magnitude of force must you apply to hold the platform in this position? (b) How much *additional* work must you do to move the platform 0.200 m *farther*, and what maximum force must you apply?

6.41 •• (a) In Example 6.7 (Section 6.3) it was calculated that with the air track turned off, the glider travels 8.6 cm before it stops instantaneously. How large would the coefficient of static friction μ_s have to be to keep the glider from springing back to the left? (b) If the coefficient of static friction between the glider and the track is $\mu_s = 0.60$, what is the maximum initial speed v_1 that the glider can be given and still remain at rest after it stops instantaneously? With the air track turned off, the coefficient of kinetic friction is $\mu_k = 0.47$.

6.42 • A 4.00-kg block of ice is placed against a horizontal spring that has force constant $k = 200$ N/m and is compressed 0.025 m. The spring is released and accelerates the block along a horizontal surface. Ignore friction and the mass of the spring. (a) Calculate the work done on the block by the spring during the motion of the block from its initial position to where the spring has returned to its uncompressed length. (b) What is the speed of the block after it leaves the spring?

6.43 • A force $\vec{F}$ is applied to a 2.0-kg, radio-controlled model car parallel to the x-axis as it moves along a straight track. The x-component of the force varies with the x-coordinate of the car (**Fig. E6.43**). Calculate the work done by the force $\vec{F}$ when the car moves from (a) $x = 0$ to $x = 3.0$ m; (b) $x = 3.0$ m to $x = 4.0$ m; (c) $x = 4.0$ m to $x = 7.0$ m; (d) $x = 0$ to $x = 7.0$ m; (e) $x = 7.0$ m to $x = 2.0$ m.

Figure **E6.43**

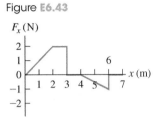

6.44 • Suppose the 2.0-kg model car in Exercise 6.43 is initially at rest at $x = 0$ and $\vec{F}$ is the net force acting on it. Use the work–energy theorem to find the speed of the car at (a) $x = 3.0$ m; (b) $x = 4.0$ m; (c) $x = 7.0$ m.

6.45 •• At a waterpark, sleds with riders are sent along a slippery, horizontal surface by the release of a large compressed spring. The spring, with force constant $k = 40.0$ N/cm and negligible mass, rests on the frictionless horizontal surface. One end is in contact with a stationary wall. A sled and rider with total mass 70.0 kg are pushed against the other end, compressing the spring 0.375 m. The sled is then released with zero initial velocity. What is the sled's speed when the spring (a) returns to its uncompressed length and (b) is still compressed 0.200 m?

6.46 • **Half of a Spring.** (a) Suppose you cut a massless ideal spring in half. If the full spring had a force constant k, what is the force constant of each half, in terms of k? (*Hint:* Think of the original spring as two equal halves, each producing the same force as the entire spring. Do you see why the forces must be equal?) (b) If you cut the spring into three equal segments instead, what is the force constant of each one, in terms of k?

6.47 •• A small glider is placed against a compressed spring at the bottom of an air track that slopes upward at an angle of 40.0° above the horizontal. The glider has mass 0.0900 kg. The spring has $k = 640$ N/m and negligible mass. When the spring is released, the glider travels a maximum distance of 1.80 m along the air track before sliding back down. Before reaching this maximum distance, the glider loses contact with the spring. (a) What distance was the spring originally compressed? (b) When the glider has traveled along the air track 0.80 m from its initial position against the compressed spring, is it still in contact with the spring? What is the kinetic energy of the glider at this point?

6.48 •• An ingenious bricklayer builds a device for shooting bricks up to the top of the wall where he is working. He places a brick on a vertical compressed spring with force constant $k = 450$ N/m and negligible mass. When the spring is released, the brick is propelled upward. If the brick has mass 1.80 kg and is to reach a maximum height of 3.6 m above its initial position on the compressed spring, what distance must the bricklayer compress the spring initially? (The brick loses contact with the spring when the spring returns to its uncompressed length. Why?)

6.49 •• CALC A force in the $+x$-direction with magnitude $F(x) = 18.0$ N $- (0.530$ N/m$)x$ is applied to a 6.00-kg box that is sitting on the horizontal, frictionless surface of a frozen lake. $F(x)$ is the only horizontal force on the box. If the box is initially at rest at $x = 0$, what is its speed after it has traveled 14.0 m?

Section 6.4 Power

6.50 •• A crate on a motorized cart starts from rest and moves with a constant eastward acceleration of $a = 2.80$ m/s². A worker assists the cart by pushing on the crate with a force that is eastward and has magnitude that depends on time according to $F(t) = (5.40$ N/s$)t$. What is the instantaneous power supplied by this force at $t = 5.00$ s?

6.51 • How many joules of energy does a 100-watt light bulb use per hour? How fast would a 70-kg person have to run to have that amount of kinetic energy?

6.52 •• BIO **Should You Walk or Run?** It is 5.0 km from your home to the physics lab. As part of your physical fitness program, you could run that distance at 10 km/h (which uses up energy at the rate of 700 W), or you could walk it leisurely at 3.0 km/h (which uses energy at 290 W). Which choice would burn up more energy, and how much energy (in joules) would it burn? Why does the more intense exercise burn up less energy than the less intense exercise?

6.53 •• **Magnetar.** On December 27, 2004, astronomers observed the greatest flash of light ever recorded from outside the solar system. It came from the highly magnetic neutron star SGR 1806-20 (a *magnetar*). During 0.20 s, this star released as much energy as our sun does in 250,000 years. If P is the average power output of our sun, what was the average power output (in terms of P) of this magnetar?

6.54 •• A 20.0-kg rock is sliding on a rough, horizontal surface at 8.00 m/s and eventually stops due to friction. The coefficient of kinetic friction between the rock and the surface is 0.200. What average power is produced by friction as the rock stops?

6.55 • A tandem (two-person) bicycle team must overcome a force of 165 N to maintain a speed of 9.00 m/s. Find the power required per rider, assuming that each contributes equally. Express your answer in watts and in horsepower.

6.56 •• When its 75-kW (100-hp) engine is generating full power, a small single-engine airplane with mass 700 kg gains altitude at a rate of 2.5 m/s (150 m/min, or 500 ft/min). What fraction of the engine power is being used to make the airplane climb? (The remainder is used to overcome the effects of air resistance and of inefficiencies in the propeller and engine.)

6.57 •• **Working Like a Horse.** Your job is to lift 30-kg crates a vertical distance of 0.90 m from the ground onto the bed of a truck. How many crates would you have to load onto the truck in 1 minute (a) for the average power output you use to lift the crates to equal 0.50 hp; (b) for an average power output of 100 W?

6.58 •• An elevator has mass 600 kg, not including passengers. The elevator is designed to ascend, at constant speed, a vertical distance of 20.0 m (five floors) in 16.0 s, and it is driven by a motor that can provide up to 40 hp to the elevator. What is the maximum number of passengers that can ride in the elevator? Assume that an average passenger has mass 65.0 kg.

6.59 •• A ski tow operates on a 15.0° slope of length 300 m. The rope moves at 12.0 km/h and provides power for 50 riders at one time, with an average mass per rider of 70.0 kg. Estimate the power required to operate the tow.

6.60 • You are applying a constant horizontal force $\vec{F} = (-8.00\ \mathrm{N})\hat{\imath} + (3.00\ \mathrm{N})\hat{\jmath}$ to a crate that is sliding on a factory floor. At the instant that the velocity of the crate is $\vec{v} = (3.20\ \mathrm{m/s})\hat{\imath} + (2.20\ \mathrm{m/s})\hat{\jmath}$, what is the instantaneous power supplied by this force?

6.61 • BIO While hovering, a typical flying insect applies an average force equal to twice its weight during each downward stroke. Take the mass of the insect to be 10 g, and assume the wings move an average downward distance of 1.0 cm during each stroke. Assuming 100 downward strokes per second, estimate the average power output of the insect.

PROBLEMS

6.62 ••• CALC A balky cow is leaving the barn as you try harder and harder to push her back in. In coordinates with the origin at the barn door, the cow walks from $x = 0$ to $x = 6.9$ m as you apply a force with x-component $F_x = -[20.0\ \mathrm{N} + (3.0\ \mathrm{N/m})x]$. How much work does the force you apply do on the cow during this displacement?

6.63 • A luggage handler pulls a 20.0-kg suitcase up a ramp inclined at $32.0°$ above the horizontal by a force $\vec{F}$ of magnitude 160 N that acts parallel to the ramp. The coefficient of kinetic friction between the ramp and the incline is $\mu_k = 0.300$. If the suitcase travels 3.80 m along the ramp, calculate (a) the work done on the suitcase by $\vec{F}$; (b) the work done on the suitcase by the gravitational force; (c) the work done on the suitcase by the normal force; (d) the work done on the suitcase by the friction force; (e) the total work done on the suitcase. (f) If the speed of the suitcase is zero at the bottom of the ramp, what is its speed after it has traveled 3.80 m along the ramp?

6.64 • BIO **Chin-ups.** While doing a chin-up, a man lifts his body 0.40 m. (a) How much work must the man do per kilogram of body mass? (b) The muscles involved in doing a chin-up can generate about 70 J of work per kilogram of muscle mass. If the man can just barely do a 0.40-m chin-up, what percentage of his body's mass do these muscles constitute? (For comparison, the *total* percentage of muscle in a typical 70-kg man with 14% body fat is about 43%.) (c) Repeat part (b) for the man's young son, who has arms half as long as his father's but whose muscles can also generate 70 J of work per kilogram of muscle mass. (d) Adults and children have about the same percentage of muscle in their bodies. Explain why children can commonly do chin-ups more easily than their fathers.

6.65 ••• Consider the blocks in Exercise 6.7 as they move 75.0 cm. Find the total work done on each one (a) if there is no friction between the table and the 20.0-N block, and (b) if $\mu_s = 0.500$ and $\mu_k = 0.325$ between the table and the 20.0-N block.

6.66 •• A 5.00-kg package slides 2.80 m down a long ramp that is inclined at $24.0°$ below the horizontal. The coefficient of kinetic friction between the package and the ramp is $\mu_k = 0.310$. Calculate (a) the work done on the package by friction; (b) the work done on the package by gravity; (c) the work done on the package by the normal force; (d) the total work done on the package. (e) If the package has a speed of 2.20 m/s at the top of the ramp, what is its speed after it has slid 2.80 m down the ramp?

6.67 •• CP BIO **Whiplash Injuries.** When a car is hit from behind, its passengers undergo sudden forward acceleration, which can cause a severe neck injury known as *whiplash*. During normal acceleration, the neck muscles play a large role in accelerating the head so that the bones are not injured. But during a very

sudden acceleration, the muscles do not react immediately because they are flexible; most of the accelerating force is provided by the neck bones. Experiments have shown that these bones will fracture if they absorb more than 8.0 J of energy. (a) If a car waiting at a stoplight is rear-ended in a collision that lasts for 10.0 ms, what is the greatest speed this car and its driver can reach without breaking neck bones if the driver's head has a mass of 5.0 kg (which is about right for a 70-kg person)? Express your answer in m/s and in mi/h. (b) What is the acceleration of the passengers during the collision in part (a), and how large a force is acting to accelerate their heads? Express the acceleration in $\mathrm{m/s^2}$ and in g's.

6.68 •• CALC A net force along the x-axis that has x-component $F_x = -12.0\ \mathrm{N} + (0.300\ \mathrm{N/m^2})x^2$ is applied to a 5.00-kg object that is initially at the origin and moving in the $-x$-direction with a speed of 6.00 m/s. What is the speed of the object when it reaches the point $x = 5.00$ m?

6.69 • CALC **Varying Coefficient of Friction.** A box is sliding with a speed of 4.50 m/s on a horizontal surface when, at point P, it encounters a rough section. The coefficient of friction there is not constant; it starts at 0.100 at P and increases linearly with distance past P, reaching a value of 0.600 at 12.5 m past point P. (a) Use the work–energy theorem to find how far this box slides before stopping. (b) What is the coefficient of friction at the stopping point? (c) How far would the box have slid if the friction coefficient didn't increase but instead had the constant value of 0.100?

6.70 •• CALC Consider a spring that does not obey Hooke's law very faithfully. One end of the spring is fixed. To keep the spring stretched or compressed an amount x, a force along the x-axis with x-component $F_x = kx - bx^2 + cx^3$ must be applied to the free end. Here $k = 100\ \mathrm{N/m}$, $b = 700\ \mathrm{N/m^2}$, and $c = 12{,}000\ \mathrm{N/m^3}$. Note that $x > 0$ when the spring is stretched and $x < 0$ when it is compressed. How much work must be done (a) to stretch this spring by 0.050 m from its unstretched length? (b) To *compress* this spring by 0.050 m from its unstretched length? (c) Is it easier to stretch or compress this spring? Explain why in terms of the dependence of F_x on x. (Many real springs behave qualitatively in the same way.)

6.71 •• CP A small block with a mass of 0.0600 kg is attached to a cord passing through a hole in a frictionless, horizontal surface (**Fig. P6.71**). The block is originally revolving at a distance of 0.40 m from the hole with a speed of 0.70 m/s. The cord is then pulled from below, shortening the radius of the circle in which the block revolves

Figure **P6.71**

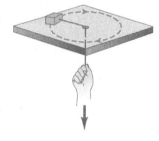

to 0.10 m. At this new distance, the speed of the block is 2.80 m/s. (a) What is the tension in the cord in the original situation, when the block has speed $v = 0.70$ m/s? (b) What is the tension in the cord in the final situation, when the block has speed $v = 2.80$ m/s? (c) How much work was done by the person who pulled on the cord?

6.72 •• CALC **Proton Bombardment.** A proton with mass 1.67×10^{-27} kg is propelled at an initial speed of 3.00×10^5 m/s directly toward a uranium nucleus 5.00 m away. The proton is repelled by the uranium nucleus with a force of magnitude $F = \alpha/x^2$, where x is the separation between the two objects and $\alpha = 2.12 \times 10^{-26}\ \mathrm{N \cdot m^2}$. Assume that the uranium nucleus remains at rest. (a) What is the speed of the proton when it is 8.00×10^{-10} m from the uranium nucleus? (b) As the proton approaches the uranium nucleus, the repulsive force slows down the proton until it comes momentarily to rest, after which the proton moves away from the uranium nucleus. How close to the uranium nucleus does the proton get? (c) What is the speed of the proton when it is again 5.00 m away from the uranium nucleus?

6.73 •• You are asked to design spring bumpers for the walls of a parking garage. A freely rolling 1200-kg car moving at 0.65 m/s is to compress the spring no more than 0.090 m before stopping. What should be the force constant of the spring? Assume that the spring has negligible mass.

6.74 •• You and your bicycle have combined mass 80.0 kg. When you reach the base of a bridge, you are traveling along the road at 5.00 m/s (**Fig. P6.74**). At the top of the bridge, you have climbed a vertical distance of 5.20 m and slowed to 1.50 m/s. Ignore work done by friction and any inefficiency in the bike or your legs. (a) What is the total work done on you and your bicycle when you go from the base to the top of the bridge? (b) How much work have you done with the force you apply to the pedals?

Figure **P6.74**

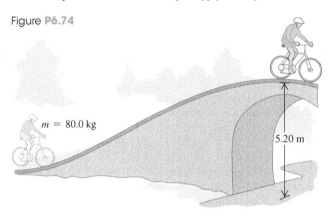

$m = 80.0$ kg

5.20 m

6.75 ••• A 2.50-kg textbook is forced against a horizontal spring of negligible mass and force constant 250 N/m, compressing the spring a distance of 0.250 m. When released, the textbook slides on a horizontal tabletop with coefficient of kinetic friction $\mu_k = 0.30$. Use the work–energy theorem to find how far the textbook moves from its initial position before it comes to rest.

6.76 •• The spring of a spring gun has force constant $k = 400$ N/m and negligible mass. The spring is compressed 6.00 cm, and a ball with mass 0.0300 kg is placed in the horizontal barrel against the compressed spring. The spring is then released, and the ball is propelled out the barrel of the gun. The barrel is 6.00 cm long, so the ball leaves the barrel at the same point that it loses contact with the spring. The gun is held so that the barrel is horizontal. (a) Calculate the speed with which the ball leaves the barrel if you can ignore friction. (b) Calculate the speed of the ball as it leaves the barrel if a constant resisting force of 6.00 N acts on the ball as it moves along the barrel. (c) For the situation in part (b), at what position along the barrel does the ball have the greatest speed, and what is that speed? (In this case, the maximum speed does not occur at the end of the barrel.)

6.77 •• One end of a horizontal spring with force constant 130.0 N/m is attached to a vertical wall. A 4.00-kg block sitting on the floor is placed against the spring. The coefficient of kinetic friction between the block and the floor is $\mu_k = 0.400$. You apply a constant force $\vec{F}$ to the block. $\vec{F}$ has magnitude $F = 82.0$ N and is directed toward the wall. At the instant that the spring is compressed 80.0 cm, what are (a) the speed of the block, and (b) the magnitude and direction of the block's acceleration?

6.78 •• One end of a horizontal spring with force constant 76.0 N/m is attached to a vertical post. A 2.00-kg block of frictionless ice is attached to the other end and rests on the floor. The spring is initially neither stretched nor compressed. A constant horizontal force of 54.0 N is then applied to the block, in the direction away from the post. (a) What is the speed of the block when the spring is stretched 0.400 m? (b) At that instant, what are the magnitude and direction of the acceleration of the block?

6.79 • A 5.00-kg block is moving at $v_0 = 6.00$ m/s along a frictionless, horizontal surface toward a spring with force constant $k = 500$ N/m that is attached to a wall (**Fig. P6.79**). The spring has negligible mass. (a) Find the maximum distance the spring will be compressed. (b) If the spring is to compress by no more than 0.150 m, what should be the maximum value of v_0?

Figure **P6.79**

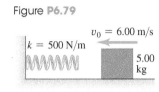

$v_0 = 6.00$ m/s

$k = 500$ N/m

5.00 kg

6.80 ••• A physics professor is pushed up a ramp inclined upward at 30.0° above the horizontal as she sits in her desk chair, which slides on frictionless rollers. The combined mass of the professor and chair is 85.0 kg. She is pushed 2.50 m along the incline by a group of students who together exert a constant horizontal force of 600 N. The professor's speed at the bottom of the ramp is 2.00 m/s. Use the work–energy theorem to find her speed at the top of the ramp.

6.81 •• Consider the system shown in **Fig. P6.81**. The rope and pulley have negligible mass, and the pulley is frictionless. Initially the 6.00-kg block is moving downward and the 8.00-kg block is moving to the right, both with a speed of 0.900 m/s. The blocks come to rest after moving 2.00 m. Use the work–energy theorem to calculate the coefficient of kinetic friction between the 8.00-kg block and the tabletop.

Figure **P6.81**

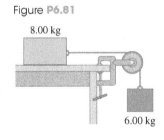

8.00 kg

6.00 kg

6.82 •• Consider the system shown in Fig. P6.81. The rope and pulley have negligible mass, and the pulley is frictionless. The coefficient of kinetic friction between the 8.00-kg block and the tabletop is $\mu_k = 0.250$. The blocks are released from rest. Use energy methods to calculate the speed of the 6.00-kg block after it has descended 1.50 m.

6.83 •• On an essentially frictionless, horizontal ice rink, a skater moving at 3.0 m/s encounters a rough patch that reduces her speed to 1.65 m/s due to a friction force that is 25% of her weight. Use the work–energy theorem to find the length of this rough patch.

6.84 •• BIO All birds, independent of their size, must maintain a power output of 10–25 watts per kilogram of body mass in order to fly by flapping their wings. (a) The Andean giant hummingbird (*Patagona gigas*) has mass 70 g and flaps its wings 10 times per second while hovering. Estimate the amount of work done by such a hummingbird in each wingbeat. (b) A 70-kg athlete can maintain a power output of 1.4 kW for no more than a few seconds; the *steady* power output of a typical athlete is only 500 W or so. Is it possible for a human-powered aircraft to fly for extended periods by flapping its wings? Explain.

6.85 •• A pump is required to lift 800 kg of water (about 210 gallons) per minute from a well 14.0 m deep and eject it with a speed of 18.0 m/s. (a) How much work is done per minute in lifting the water? (b) How much work is done in giving the water the kinetic energy it has when ejected? (c) What must be the power output of the pump?

6.86 ••• The Grand Coulee Dam is 1270 m long and 170 m high. The electrical power output from generators at its base is approximately 2000 MW. How many cubic meters of water must flow from the top of the dam per second to produce this amount of power if 92% of the work done on the water by gravity is converted to electrical energy? (Each cubic meter of water has a mass of 1000 kg.)

6.87 ••• A physics student spends part of her day walking between classes or for recreation, during which time she expends energy at an average rate of 280 W. The remainder of the day she is sitting in class, studying, or resting; during these activities, she expends energy at an average rate of 100 W. If she expends a total of 1.1×10^7 J of energy in a 24-hour day, how much of the day did she spend walking?

6.88 • CALC An object has several forces acting on it. One of these forces is $\vec{F} = \alpha xy\hat{\imath}$, a force in the x-direction whose magnitude depends on the position of the object, with $\alpha = 2.50$ N/m². Calculate the work done on the object by this force for the following displacements of the object: (a) The object starts at the point ($x = 0$, $y = 3.00$ m) and moves parallel to the x-axis to the point ($x = 2.00$ m, $y = 3.00$ m). (b) The object starts at the point ($x = 2.00$ m, $y = 0$) and moves in the y-direction to the point ($x = 2.00$ m, $y = 3.00$ m). (c) The object starts at the origin and moves on the line $y = 1.5x$ to the point ($x = 2.00$ m, $y = 3.00$ m).

6.89 • BIO **Power of the Human Heart.** The human heart is a powerful and extremely reliable pump. Each day it takes in and discharges about 7500 L of blood. Assume that the work done by the heart is equal to the work required to lift this amount of blood a height equal to that of the average American woman (1.63 m). The density (mass per unit volume) of blood is 1.05×10^3 kg/m³. (a) How much work does the heart do in a day? (b) What is the heart's power output in watts?

6.90 •• DATA **Figure P6.90** shows the results of measuring the force F exerted on both ends of a rubber band to stretch it a distance x from its unstretched position. (Source: www.sciencebuddies.org) The data points are well fit by the equation $F = 33.55x^{0.4871}$, where F is in newtons and x is in meters. (a) Does this rubber band obey Hooke's law over the range of x shown in the graph? Explain. (b) The stiffness of a spring that obeys Hooke's law is measured by the value of its force constant k, where $k = F/x$. This can be

written as $k = dF/dx$ to emphasize the quantities that are changing. Define $k_{eff} = dF/dx$ and calculate k_{eff} as a function of x for this rubber band. For a spring that obeys Hooke's law, k_{eff} is constant, independent of x. Does the stiffness of this band, as measured by k_{eff}, increase or decrease as x is increased, within the range of the data? (c) How much work must be done to stretch the rubber band from $x = 0$ to $x = 0.0400$ m? From $x = 0.0400$ m to $x = 0.0800$ m? (d) One end of the rubber band is attached to a stationary vertical rod, and the band is stretched horizontally 0.0800 m from its unstretched length. A 0.300-kg object on a horizontal, frictionless surface is attached to the free end of the rubber band and released from rest. What is the speed of the object after it has traveled 0.0400 m?

6.91 ••• DATA In a physics lab experiment, one end of a horizontal spring that obeys Hooke's law is attached to a wall. The spring is compressed 0.400 m, and a block with mass 0.300 kg is attached to it. The spring is then released, and the block moves along a horizontal surface. Electronic sensors measure the speed v of the block after it has traveled a distance d from its initial position against the compressed spring. The measured values are listed in the table. (a) The data show that the speed v of the block increases

d (m)	v (m/s)
0	0
0.05	0.85
0.10	1.11
0.15	1.24
0.25	1.26
0.30	1.14
0.35	0.90
0.40	0.36

and then decreases as the spring returns to its unstretched length. Explain why this happens, in terms of the work done on the block by the forces that act on it. (b) Use the work–energy theorem to derive an expression for v^2 in terms of d. (c) Use a computer graphing program (for example, Excel or Matlab) to graph the data as v^2 (vertical axis) versus d (horizontal axis). The equation that you derived in part (b) should show that v^2 is a quadratic function of d, so, in your graph, fit the data by a second-order polynomial (quadratic) and have the graphing program display the equation for this trendline. Use that equation to find the block's maximum speed v and the value of d at which this speed occurs. (d) By comparing the equation from the graphing program to the formula you derived in part (b), calculate the force constant k for the spring and the coefficient of kinetic friction for the friction force that the surface exerts on the block.

6.92 •• DATA For a physics lab experiment, four classmates run up the stairs from the basement to the top floor of their physics building—a vertical distance of 16.0 m. The classmates and their masses are: Tatiana, 50.2 kg; Bill, 68.2 kg; Ricardo, 81.8 kg; and Melanie, 59.1 kg. The time it takes each of them is shown in **Fig. P6.92**. (a) Considering only the work done against gravity, which person had the largest average power output? The smallest? (b) Chang is very fit and has mass 62.3 kg. If his average power output is 1.00 hp, how many seconds does it take him to run up the stairs?

Figure P6.90

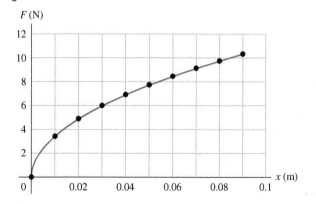

Figure P6.92

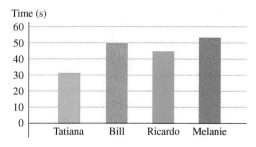

CHALLENGE PROBLEMS

6.93 ••• CALC **A Spring with Mass.** We usually ignore the kinetic energy of the moving coils of a spring, but let's try to get a reasonable approximation to this. Consider a spring of mass M, equilibrium length L_0, and force constant k. The work done to stretch or compress the spring by a distance L is $\frac{1}{2}kX^2$, where $X = L - L_0$. Consider a spring, as described above, that has one end fixed and the other end moving with speed v. Assume that the speed of points along the length of the spring varies linearly with distance l from the fixed end. Assume also that the mass M of the spring is distributed uniformly along the length of the spring. (a) Calculate the kinetic energy of the spring in terms of M and v. (*Hint:* Divide the spring into pieces of length dl; find the speed of each piece in terms of l, v, and L; find the mass of each piece in terms of dl, M, and L; and integrate from 0 to L. The result is *not* $\frac{1}{2}Mv^2$, since not all of the spring moves with the same speed.) In a spring gun, a spring of mass 0.243 kg and force constant 3200 N/m is compressed 2.50 cm from its unstretched length. When the trigger is pulled, the spring pushes horizontally on a 0.053-kg ball. The work done by friction is negligible. Calculate the ball's speed when the spring reaches its uncompressed length (b) ignoring the mass of the spring and (c) including, using the results of part (a), the mass of the spring. (d) In part (c), what is the final kinetic energy of the ball and of the spring?

6.94 ••• CALC An airplane in flight is subject to an air resistance force proportional to the square of its speed v. But there is an additional resistive force because the airplane has wings. Air flowing over the wings is pushed down and slightly forward, so from Newton's third law the air exerts a force on the wings and airplane that is up and slightly backward (**Fig. P6.94**). The upward force is the lift force that keeps the airplane aloft, and the backward force is called *induced drag*. At flying speeds, induced drag is inversely proportional to v^2, so the total air resistance force can be expressed by $F_{\text{air}} = \alpha v^2 + \beta/v^2$, where α and β are positive constants that depend on the shape and size of the airplane and the density of the air. For a Cessna 150, a small single-engine airplane, $\alpha = 0.30 \text{ N} \cdot \text{s}^2/\text{m}^2$ and $\beta = 3.5 \times 10^5 \text{ N} \cdot \text{m}^2/\text{s}^2$. In steady flight, the engine must provide a forward force that exactly balances the air resistance force. (a) Calculate the speed (in km/h) at which this airplane will have the maximum *range* (that is, travel the greatest distance) for a given quantity of fuel. (b) Calculate the speed (in km/h) for which the airplane will have the maximum *endurance* (that is, remain in the air the longest time).

Figure **P6.94**

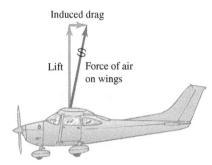

Induced drag

Lift | Force of air on wings

PASSAGE PROBLEMS

BIO **ENERGY OF LOCOMOTION.** On flat ground, a 70-kg person requires about 300 W of metabolic power to walk at a steady pace of 5.0 km/h (1.4 m/s). Using the same metabolic power output, that person can bicycle over the same ground at 15 km/h.

6.95 Based on the given data, how does the energy used in biking 1 km compare with that used in walking 1 km? Biking takes (a) $\frac{1}{3}$ of the energy of walking the same distance; (b) the same energy as walking the same distance; (c) 3 times the energy of walking the same distance; (d) 9 times the energy of walking the same distance.

6.96 A 70-kg person walks at a steady pace of 5.0 km/h on a treadmill at a 5.0% grade. (That is, the vertical distance covered is 5.0% of the horizontal distance covered.) If we assume the metabolic power required is equal to that required for walking on a flat surface plus the rate of doing work for the vertical climb, how much power is required? (a) 300 W; (b) 315 W; (c) 350 W; (d) 370 W.

6.97 How many times greater is the kinetic energy of the person when biking than when walking? Ignore the mass of the bike. (a) 1.7; (b) 3; (c) 6; (d) 9.

Answers

Chapter Opening Question ?

(ii) The expression for kinetic energy is $K = \frac{1}{2}mv^2$. If we calculate K for the three balls, we find (i) $K = \frac{1}{2}(0.145 \text{ kg}) \times (20.0 \text{ m/s})^2 = 29.0 \text{ kg} \cdot \text{m}^2/\text{s}^2 = 29.0 \text{ J}$, (ii) $K = \frac{1}{2}(0.0145 \text{ kg}) \times (200 \text{ m/s})^2 = 290 \text{ J}$, and (iii) $K = \frac{1}{2}(1.45 \text{ kg})(2.00 \text{ m/s})^2 = 2.90 \text{ J}$. The smaller ball has the least mass of all three, but it also has the greatest speed and so the most kinetic energy. Since kinetic energy is a scalar, it does not depend on the direction of motion.

Test Your Understanding Questions

6.1 (iii) The electron has constant velocity, so its acceleration is zero and (by Newton's second law) the net force on the electron is also zero. Therefore the total work done by all the forces (equal to the work done by the net force) must be zero as well. The individual forces may do nonzero work, but that's not what the question asks.

6.2 (iv), (i), (iii), (ii) Body (i) has kinetic energy $K = \frac{1}{2}mv^2 = \frac{1}{2}(2.0 \text{ kg})(5.0 \text{ m/s})^2 = 25 \text{ J}$. Body (ii) had zero kinetic energy initially and then had 30 J of work done on it, so its final kinetic energy is $K_2 = K_1 + W = 0 + 30 \text{ J} = 30 \text{ J}$. Body (iii) had initial kinetic energy $K_1 = \frac{1}{2}mv_1^2 = \frac{1}{2}(1.0 \text{ kg})(4.0 \text{ m/s})^2 = 8.0 \text{ J}$ and then had 20 J of work done on it, so its final kinetic energy is $K_2 = K_1 + W = 8.0 \text{ J} + 20 \text{ J} = 28 \text{ J}$. Body (iv) had initial kinetic energy $K_1 = \frac{1}{2}mv_1^2 = \frac{1}{2}(2.0 \text{ kg})(10 \text{ m/s})^2 = 100 \text{ J}$; when it did 80 J of work on another body, the other body did -80 J of work on body (iv), so the final kinetic energy of body (iv) is $K_2 = K_1 + W = 100 \text{ J} + (-80 \text{ J}) = 20 \text{ J}$.

6.3 (a) (iii), (b) (iii) At any point during the pendulum bob's motion, both the tension force and the weight act perpendicular to the motion—that is, perpendicular to an infinitesimal displacement $d\vec{l}$ of the bob. (In Fig. 5.32b, the displacement $d\vec{l}$ would be directed outward from the plane of the free-body diagram.) Hence for either force the scalar product inside the integral in Eq. (6.14) is $\vec{F} \cdot d\vec{l} = 0$, and the work done along any part of the circular path (including a complete circle) is $W = \int \vec{F} \cdot d\vec{l} = 0$.

6.4 (v) The airliner has a constant horizontal velocity, so the net horizontal force on it must be zero. Hence the backward drag force must have the same magnitude as the forward force due to the combined thrust of the four engines. This means that the drag force must do *negative* work on the airplane at the same rate that the combined thrust force does *positive* work. The combined thrust does work at a rate of $4(108,000 \text{ hp}) = 432,000 \text{ hp}$, so the drag force must do work at a rate of $-432,000 \text{ hp}$.

Bridging Problem

(a) $v_1 = \sqrt{\frac{2}{m}\left(mgx_1 - \frac{1}{3}\alpha x_1^3\right)} = \sqrt{2gx_1 - \frac{2\alpha x_1^3}{3m}}$

(b) $P = -F_{\text{spring}-1}v_1 = -\alpha x_1^2 \sqrt{2gx_1 - \frac{2\alpha x_1^3}{3m}}$

(c) $x_2 = \sqrt{\frac{3mg}{\alpha}}$ **(d)** No

As this sandhill crane (*Grus canadensis*) glides in to a landing, it descends along a straight-line path at a constant speed. During the glide, what happens to the mechanical energy (the sum of kinetic energy and gravitational potential energy)? (i) It stays the same; (ii) it increases due to the effect of gravity; (iii) it increases due to the effect of the air; (iv) it decreases due to the effect of gravity; (v) it decreases due to the effect of the air.

7 POTENTIAL ENERGY AND ENERGY CONSERVATION

LEARNING GOALS

Looking forward at …

7.1 How to use the concept of gravitational potential energy in problems that involve vertical motion.

7.2 How to use the concept of elastic potential energy in problems that involve a moving body attached to a stretched or compressed spring.

7.3 The distinction between conservative and nonconservative forces, and how to solve problems in which both kinds of forces act on a moving body.

7.4 How to calculate the properties of a conservative force if you know the corresponding potential-energy function.

7.5 How to use energy diagrams to understand how an object moves in a straight line under the influence of a conservative force.

Looking back at …

5.3 Kinetic friction and fluid resistance.

5.4 Dynamics of circular motion.

6.1, 6.2 Work and the work–energy theorem.

6.3 Work done by an ideal spring.

When a diver jumps off a high board into a swimming pool, she hits the water moving pretty fast, with a lot of kinetic energy—energy of *motion*. Where does that energy come from? The answer we learned in Chapter 6 was that the gravitational force does work on the diver as she falls, and her kinetic energy increases by an amount equal to the work done.

However, there's a useful alternative way to think about work and kinetic energy. This new approach uses the idea of *potential energy*, which is associated with the *position* of a system rather than with its motion. In this approach, there is *gravitational potential energy* even when the diver is at rest on the high board. As she falls, this potential energy is *transformed* into her kinetic energy.

If the diver bounces on the end of the board before she jumps, the bent board stores a second kind of potential energy called *elastic potential energy*. We'll discuss elastic potential energy of simple systems such as a stretched or compressed spring. (An important third kind of potential energy is associated with the forces between electrically charged objects. We'll return to this in Chapter 23.)

We will prove that in some cases the sum of a system's kinetic and potential energies, called the *total mechanical energy* of the system, is constant during the motion of the system. This will lead us to the general statement of the *law of conservation of energy*, one of the most fundamental principles in all of science.

7.1 GRAVITATIONAL POTENTIAL ENERGY

In many situations it seems as though energy has been stored in a system, to be recovered later. For example, you must do work to lift a heavy stone over your head. It seems reasonable that in hoisting the stone into the air you are storing energy in the system, energy that is later converted into kinetic energy when you let the stone fall.

7.1 The greater the height of a basketball, the greater the associated gravitational potential energy. As the basketball descends, gravitational potential energy is converted to kinetic energy and the basketball's speed increases.

7.2 When a body moves vertically from an initial height y_1 to a final height y_2, the gravitational force $\vec{w}$ does work and the gravitational potential energy changes.

(a) A body moves downward

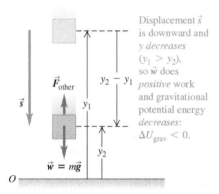

Displacement $\vec{s}$ is downward and y *decreases* $(y_1 > y_2)$, so $\vec{w}$ does *positive* work and gravitational potential energy *decreases:* $\Delta U_{\text{grav}} < 0$.

(b) A body moves upward

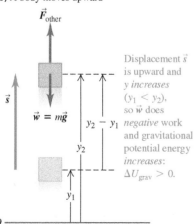

Displacement $\vec{s}$ is upward and y *increases* $(y_1 < y_2)$, so $\vec{w}$ does *negative* work and gravitational potential energy *increases:* $\Delta U_{\text{grav}} > 0$.

This example points to the idea of an energy associated with the *position* of bodies in a system. This kind of energy is a measure of the *potential* or *possibility* for work to be done; if you raise a stone into the air, there is a potential for the gravitational force to do work on it, but only if you allow the stone to fall to the ground. For this reason, energy associated with position is called **potential energy.** The potential energy associated with a body's weight and its height above the ground is called *gravitational potential energy* (**Fig. 7.1**).

We now have *two* ways to describe what happens when a body falls without air resistance. One way, which we learned in Chapter 6, is to say that a falling body's kinetic energy increases because the force of the earth's gravity does work on the body. The other way is to say that the kinetic energy increases as the gravitational potential energy decreases. Later in this section we'll use the work–energy theorem to show that these two descriptions are equivalent.

Let's derive the expression for gravitational potential energy. Suppose a body with mass m moves along the (vertical) y-axis, as in **Fig. 7.2.** The forces acting on it are its weight, with magnitude $w = mg$, and possibly some other forces; we call the vector sum (resultant) of all the other forces $\vec{F}_{\text{other}}$. We'll assume that the body stays close enough to the earth's surface that the weight is constant. (We'll find in Chapter 13 that weight decreases with altitude.) We want to find the work done by the weight when the body moves downward from a height y_1 above the origin to a lower height y_2 (Fig. 7.2a). The weight and displacement are in the same direction, so the work W_{grav} done on the body by its weight is positive:

$$W_{\text{grav}} = Fs = w(y_1 - y_2) = mgy_1 - mgy_2 \qquad (7.1)$$

This expression also gives the correct work when the body moves *upward* and y_2 is greater than y_1 (Fig. 7.2b). In that case the quantity $(y_1 - y_2)$ is negative, and W_{grav} is negative because the weight and displacement are opposite in direction.

Equation (7.1) shows that we can express W_{grav} in terms of the values of the quantity mgy at the beginning and end of the displacement. This quantity is called the **gravitational potential energy,** U_{grav}:

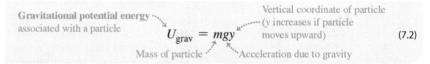

Gravitational potential energy associated with a particle ⋯ Vertical coordinate of particle (y increases if particle moves upward)
$$U_{\text{grav}} = mgy \qquad (7.2)$$
Mass of particle ⋯ Acceleration due to gravity

Its initial value is $U_{\text{grav},1} = mgy_1$ and its final value is $U_{\text{grav},2} = mgy_2$. The change in U_{grav} is the final value minus the initial value, or $\Delta U_{\text{grav}} = U_{\text{grav},2} - U_{\text{grav},1}$. Using Eq. (7.2), we can rewrite Eq. (7.1) for the work done by the gravitational force during the displacement from y_1 to y_2:

$$W_{\text{grav}} = U_{\text{grav},1} - U_{\text{grav},2} = -(U_{\text{grav},2} - U_{\text{grav},1}) = -\Delta U_{\text{grav}}$$

or

Work done by the gravitational force on a particle ⋯ ⋯ equals the **negative of the change in** the gravitational potential energy.
$$W_{\text{grav}} = mgy_1 - mgy_2 = U_{\text{grav},1} - U_{\text{grav},2} = -\Delta U_{\text{grav}} \qquad (7.3)$$
Mass of particle ⋯ Acceleration due to gravity ⋯ Initial and final vertical coordinates of particle

The negative sign in front of ΔU_{grav} is *essential.* When the body moves up, y increases, the work done by the gravitational force is negative, and the gravitational potential energy increases ($\Delta U_{\text{grav}} > 0$). When the body moves down, y decreases, the gravitational force does positive work, and the gravitational potential energy decreases ($\Delta U_{\text{grav}} < 0$). It's like drawing money out of the bank (decreasing U_{grav}) and spending it (doing positive work). The unit of potential energy is the joule (J), the same unit as is used for work.

CAUTION To what body does gravitational potential energy "belong"? It is *not* correct to call $U_{grav} = mgy$ the "gravitational potential energy of the body." The reason is that U_{grav} is a *shared* property of the body and the earth. The value of U_{grav} increases if the earth stays fixed and the body moves upward, away from the earth; it also increases if the body stays fixed and the earth is moved away from it. Notice that the formula $U_{grav} = mgy$ involves characteristics of both the body (its mass m) and the earth (the value of g).

Conservation of Mechanical Energy (Gravitational Forces Only)

To see what gravitational potential energy is good for, suppose a body's weight is the *only* force acting on it, so $\vec{F}_{other} = 0$. The body is then falling freely with no air resistance and can be moving either up or down. Let its speed at point y_1 be v_1 and let its speed at y_2 be v_2. The work–energy theorem, Eq. (6.6), says that the total work done on the body equals the change in the body's kinetic energy: $W_{tot} = \Delta K = K_2 - K_1$. If gravity is the only force that acts, then from Eq. (7.3), $W_{tot} = W_{grav} = -\Delta U_{grav} = U_{grav, 1} - U_{grav, 2}$. Putting these together, we get

$$\Delta K = -\Delta U_{grav} \quad \text{or} \quad K_2 - K_1 = U_{grav, 1} - U_{grav, 2}$$

which we can rewrite as

If only the gravitational force does work, total mechanical energy is conserved:

Initial kinetic energy $\quad$ Initial gravitational potential energy
$K_1 = \frac{1}{2}mv_1^2 \quad\quad\quad U_{grav,1} = mgy_1$

$$K_1 + U_{grav, 1} = K_2 + U_{grav, 2} \tag{7.4}$$

Final kinetic energy $\quad$ Final gravitational potential energy
$K_2 = \frac{1}{2}mv_2^2 \quad\quad\quad U_{grav, 2} = mgy_2$

The sum $K + U_{grav}$ of kinetic and potential energies is called E, the **total mechanical energy of the system.** By "system" we mean the body of mass m and the earth considered together, because gravitational potential energy U is a shared property of both bodies. Then $E_1 = K_1 + U_{grav, 1}$ is the total mechanical energy at y_1 and $E_2 = K_2 + U_{grav, 2}$ is the total mechanical energy at y_2. Equation (7.4) says that when the body's weight is the only force doing work on it, $E_1 = E_2$. That is, E is constant; it has the same value at y_1 and y_2. But since positions y_1 and y_2 are arbitrary points in the motion of the body, the total mechanical energy E has the same value at *all* points during the motion:

$$E = K + U_{grav} = \text{constant} \quad \text{(if only gravity does work)}$$

A quantity that always has the same value is called a *conserved* quantity. *When only the force of gravity does work, the total mechanical energy is constant—that is, it is conserved* (**Fig. 7.3**). This is our first example of the **conservation of mechanical energy.**

DEMO

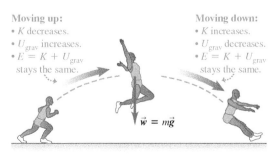

Moving up:
- K decreases.
- U_{grav} increases.
- $E = K + U_{grav}$ stays the same.

Moving down:
- K increases.
- U_{grav} decreases.
- $E = K + U_{grav}$ stays the same.

$\vec{w} = m\vec{g}$

7.3 While this athlete is in midair, only gravity does work on him (if we neglect the minor effects of air resistance). Mechanical energy E—the sum of kinetic and gravitational potential energy—is conserved.

When we throw a ball into the air, its speed decreases on the way up as kinetic energy is converted to potential energy: $\Delta K < 0$ and $\Delta U_{grav} > 0$. On the way back down, potential energy is converted back to kinetic energy and the ball's speed increases: $\Delta K > 0$ and $\Delta U_{grav} < 0$. But the *total* mechanical energy (kinetic plus potential) is the same at every point in the motion, provided that no force other than gravity does work on the ball (that is, air resistance must be negligible). It's still true that the gravitational force does work on the body as it moves up or down, but we no longer have to calculate work directly; keeping track of changes in the value of U_{grav} takes care of this completely.

Equation (7.4) is also valid if forces other than gravity are present but do *not* do work. We'll see a situation of this kind later, in Example 7.4.

CAUTION **Choose "zero height" to be wherever you like** When working with gravitational potential energy, we may choose any height to be $y = 0$. If we shift the origin for y, the values of y_1 and y_2 change, as do the values of $U_{grav,1}$ and $U_{grav,2}$. But this shift has no effect on the *difference* in height $y_2 - y_1$ or on the *difference* in gravitational potential energy $U_{grav,2} - U_{grav,1} = mg(y_2 - y_1)$. As Example 7.1 shows, the physically significant quantity is not the value of U_{grav} at a particular point but the *difference* in U_{grav} between two points. We can define U_{grav} to be zero at whatever point we choose. ▮

EXAMPLE 7.1 HEIGHT OF A BASEBALL FROM ENERGY CONSERVATION

You throw a 0.145-kg baseball straight up, giving it an initial velocity of magnitude 20.0 m/s. Find how high it goes, ignoring air resistance.

SOLUTION

IDENTIFY and SET UP: After the ball leaves your hand, only gravity does work on it. Hence mechanical energy is conserved, and we can use Eq. (7.4). We take point 1 to be where the ball leaves your hand and point 2 to be where it reaches its maximum height. As in Fig. 7.2, we take the positive y-direction to be upward. The ball's speed at point 1 is $v_1 = 20.0$ m/s; at its maximum height it is instantaneously at rest, so $v_2 = 0$. We take the origin at point 1, so $y_1 = 0$ (**Fig. 7.4**). Our target variable, the distance the ball moves vertically between the two points, is the displacement $y_2 - y_1 = y_2 - 0 = y_2$.

7.4 After a baseball leaves your hand, mechanical energy $E = K + U$ is conserved.

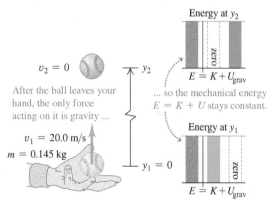

$v_2 = 0$

$v_1 = 20.0$ m/s
$m = 0.145$ kg

$y_1 = 0$

After the ball leaves your hand, the only force acting on it is gravity ...

... so the mechanical energy $E = K + U$ stays constant.

Energy at y_2

$E = K + U_{grav}$

Energy at y_1

$E = K + U_{grav}$

EXECUTE: We have $y_1 = 0$, $U_{grav,1} = mgy_1 = 0$, and $K_2 = \frac{1}{2}mv_2^2 = 0$. Then Eq. (7.4), $K_1 + U_{grav,1} = K_2 + U_{grav,2}$, becomes

$$K_1 = U_{grav,2}$$

As the energy bar graphs in Fig. 7.4 show, this equation says that the kinetic energy of the ball at point 1 is completely converted to gravitational potential energy at point 2. We substitute $K_1 = \frac{1}{2}mv_1^2$ and $U_{grav,2} = mgy_2$ and solve for y_2:

$$\frac{1}{2}mv_1^2 = mgy_2$$

$$y_2 = \frac{v_1^2}{2g} = \frac{(20.0 \text{ m/s})^2}{2(9.80 \text{ m/s}^2)} = 20.4 \text{ m}$$

EVALUATE: As a check, use the given value of v_1 and our result for y_2 to calculate the kinetic energy at point 1 and the gravitational potential energy at point 2. You should find that these are equal: $K_1 = \frac{1}{2}mv_1^2 = 29.0$ J and $U_{grav,2} = mgy_2 = 29.0$ J. Note that we could have found the result $y_2 = v_1^2/2g$ by using Eq. (2.13) in the form $v_{2y}^2 = v_{1y}^2 - 2g(y_2 - y_1)$.

What if we put the origin somewhere else—for example, 5.0 m below point 1, so that $y_1 = 5.0$ m? Then the total mechanical energy at point 1 is part kinetic and part potential; at point 2 it's still purely potential because $v_2 = 0$. You'll find that this choice of origin yields $y_2 = 25.4$ m, but again $y_2 - y_1 = 20.4$ m. In problems like this, you are free to choose the height at which $U_{grav} = 0$. The physics doesn't depend on your choice.

When Forces Other Than Gravity Do Work

If other forces act on the body in addition to its weight, then $\vec{F}_{other}$ in Fig. 7.2 is *not* zero. For the pile driver described in Example 6.4 (Section 6.2), the force applied by the hoisting cable and the friction with the vertical guide rails are examples of forces that might be included in $\vec{F}_{other}$. The gravitational work W_{grav} is still given by Eq. (7.3), but the total work W_{tot} is then the sum of W_{grav} and the work done by $\vec{F}_{other}$. We will call this additional work W_{other}, so the total work done by all forces is $W_{tot} = W_{grav} + W_{other}$. Equating this to the change in kinetic energy, we have

$$W_{other} + W_{grav} = K_2 - K_1 \qquad (7.5)$$

Also, from Eq. (7.3), $W_{grav} = U_{grav,1} - U_{grav,2}$, so Eq. (7.5) becomes

$$W_{other} + U_{grav,1} - U_{grav,2} = K_2 - K_1$$

which we can rearrange in the form

$$K_1 + U_{grav,1} + W_{other} = K_2 + U_{grav,2} \qquad \begin{array}{l}\text{(if forces other than}\\ \text{gravity do work)}\end{array} \qquad (7.6)$$

We can use the expressions for the various energy terms to rewrite Eq. (7.6):

$$\tfrac{1}{2}mv_1^2 + mgy_1 + W_{other} = \tfrac{1}{2}mv_2^2 + mgy_2 \qquad \begin{array}{l}\text{(if forces other than}\\ \text{gravity do work)}\end{array} \qquad (7.7)$$

The meaning of Eqs. (7.6) and (7.7) is this: *The work done by all forces other than the gravitational force equals the change in the total mechanical energy $E = K + U_{grav}$ of the system, where U_{grav} is the gravitational potential energy.* When W_{other} is positive, E increases and $K_2 + U_{grav,2}$ is greater than $K_1 + U_{grav,1}$. When W_{other} is negative, E decreases (**Fig. 7.5**). In the special case in which no forces other than the body's weight do work, $W_{other} = 0$. The total mechanical energy is then constant, and we are back to Eq. (7.4).

7.5 As this parachutist moves downward, the upward force of air resistance does negative work W_{other} on him. Hence the total mechanical energy $E = K + U$ decreases.

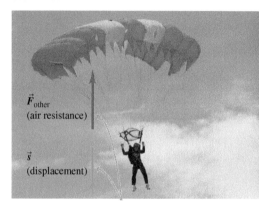

$\vec{F}_{other}$
(air resistance)

$\vec{s}$
(displacement)

- $\vec{F}_{other}$ and $\vec{s}$ are opposite, so $W_{other} < 0$.
- Hence $E = K + U_{grav}$ must decrease.
- The parachutist's speed remains constant, so K is constant.
- The parachutist descends, so U_{grav} decreases.

| PROBLEM-SOLVING STRATEGY 7.1 | **PROBLEMS USING MECHANICAL ENERGY I** |

IDENTIFY *the relevant concepts:* Decide whether the problem should be solved by energy methods, by using $\Sigma \vec{F} = m\vec{a}$ directly, or by a combination of these. The energy approach is best when the problem involves varying forces or motion along a curved path (discussed later in this section). If the problem involves elapsed time, the energy approach is usually *not* the best choice because it doesn't involve time directly.

SET UP *the problem* using the following steps:

1. When using the energy approach, first identify the initial and final states (the positions and velocities) of the bodies in question. Use the subscript 1 for the initial state and the subscript 2 for the final state. Draw sketches showing these states.
2. Define a coordinate system, and choose the level at which $y = 0$. Choose the positive y-direction to be upward. (The equations in this section require this.)
3. Identify any forces that do work on each body and that *cannot* be described in terms of potential energy. (So far, this means

any forces other than gravity. In Section 7.2 we'll see that the work done by an ideal spring can also be expressed as a change in potential energy.) Sketch a free-body diagram for each body.

4. List the unknown and known quantities, including the coordinates and velocities at each point. Identify the target variables.

EXECUTE *the solution:* Write expressions for the initial and final kinetic and potential energies K_1, K_2, $U_{grav,1}$, and $U_{grav,2}$. If no other forces do work, use Eq. (7.4). If there are other forces that do work, use Eq. (7.6). Draw bar graphs showing the initial and final values of K, $U_{grav,1}$, and $E = K + U_{grav}$. Then solve to find your target variables.

EVALUATE *your answer:* Check whether your answer makes physical sense. Remember that the gravitational work is included in ΔU_{grav}, so do not include it in W_{other}.

EXAMPLE 7.2 **WORK AND ENERGY IN THROWING A BASEBALL**

In Example 7.1 suppose your hand moves upward by 0.50 m while you are throwing the ball. The ball leaves your hand with an upward velocity of 20.0 m/s. (a) Find the magnitude of the force (assumed constant) that your hand exerts on the ball. (b) Find the speed of the ball at a point 15.0 m above the point where it leaves your hand. Ignore air resistance.

SOLUTION

IDENTIFY and SET UP: In Example 7.1 only gravity did work. Here we must include the nongravitational, "other" work done by your hand. **Figure 7.6** shows a diagram of the situation, including a free-body diagram for the ball while it is being thrown. We let point 1 be where your hand begins to move, point 2 be where the ball leaves your hand, and point 3 be where the ball is 15.0 m above point 2. The nongravitational force $\vec{F}$ of your hand acts only between points 1 and 2. Using the same coordinate system as in Example 7.1, we have $y_1 = -0.50$ m, $y_2 = 0$, and $y_3 = 15.0$ m. The ball starts at rest at point 1, so $v_1 = 0$, and the ball's speed as it leaves your hand is $v_2 = 20.0$ m/s. Our target variables are (a) the magnitude F of the force of your hand and (b) the magnitude of the ball's velocity v_{3y} at point 3.

EXECUTE: (a) To determine F, we'll first use Eq. (7.6) to calculate the work W_{other} done by this force. We have

$$K_1 = 0$$

$$U_{\text{grav},1} = mgy_1 = (0.145 \text{ kg})(9.80 \text{ m/s}^2)(-0.50 \text{ m}) = -0.71 \text{ J}$$

$$K_2 = \tfrac{1}{2}mv_2^2 = \tfrac{1}{2}(0.145 \text{ kg})(20.0 \text{ m/s})^2 = 29.0 \text{ J}$$

$$U_{\text{grav},2} = mgy_2 = (0.145 \text{ kg})(9.80 \text{ m/s}^2)(0) = 0$$

(Don't worry that $U_{\text{grav},1}$ is less than zero; all that matters is the *difference* in potential energy from one point to another.) From Eq. (7.6),

$$K_1 + U_{\text{grav},1} + W_{\text{other}} = K_2 + U_{\text{grav},2}$$

$$W_{\text{other}} = (K_2 - K_1) + (U_{\text{grav},2} - U_{\text{grav},1})$$

$$= (29.0 \text{ J} - 0) + [0 - (-0.71 \text{ J})] = 29.7 \text{ J}$$

But since $\vec{F}$ is constant and upward, the work done by $\vec{F}$ equals the force magnitude times the displacement: $W_{\text{other}} = F(y_2 - y_1)$. So

$$F = \frac{W_{\text{other}}}{y_2 - y_1} = \frac{29.7 \text{ J}}{0.50 \text{ m}} = 59 \text{ N}$$

This is more than 40 times the weight of the ball (1.42 N).

(b) To find v_{3y}, note that between points 2 and 3 only gravity acts on the ball. So between these points mechanical energy is

7.6 (a) Applying energy ideas to a ball thrown vertically upward. (b) Free-body diagram for the ball as you throw it.

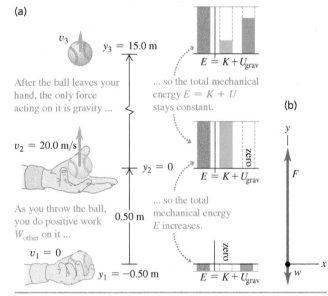

(a)

v_3

$y_3 = 15.0$ m

$E = K + U_{\text{grav}}$

After the ball leaves your hand, the only force acting on it is gravity ...

... so the total mechanical energy $E = K + U$ stays constant.

(b)

$v_2 = 20.0$ m/s

$y_2 = 0$

$E = K + U_{\text{grav}}$

As you throw the ball, you do positive work W_{other} on it ...

... so the total mechanical energy E increases.

0.50 m

$v_1 = 0$

$y_1 = -0.50$ m

$E = K + U_{\text{grav}}$

y

F

x

w

conserved and $W_{\text{other}} = 0$. From Eq. (7.4), we can solve for K_3 and from that solve for v_{3y}:

$$K_2 + U_{\text{grav},2} = K_3 + U_{\text{grav},3}$$

$$U_{\text{grav},3} = mgy_3 = (0.145 \text{ kg})(9.80 \text{ m/s}^2)(15.0 \text{ m}) = 21.3 \text{ J}$$

$$K_3 = (K_2 + U_{\text{grav},2}) - U_{\text{grav},3}$$

$$= (29.0 \text{ J} + 0 \text{ J}) - 21.3 \text{ J} = 7.7 \text{ J}$$

Since $K_3 = \tfrac{1}{2}mv_{3y}^2$, we find

$$v_{3y} = \pm\sqrt{\frac{2K_3}{m}} = \pm\sqrt{\frac{2(7.7 \text{ J})}{0.145 \text{ kg}}} = \pm 10 \text{ m/s}$$

The plus-or-minus sign reminds us that the ball passes point 3 on the way up and again on the way down. The ball's kinetic energy $K_3 = 7.7$ J at point 3, and hence its speed at that point, doesn't depend on the direction the ball is moving. The velocity v_{3y} is positive ($+10$ m/s) when the ball is moving up and negative (-10 m/s) when it is moving down; the speed v_3 is 10 m/s in either case.

EVALUATE: In Example 7.1 we found that the ball reaches a maximum height $y = 20.4$ m. At that point all of the kinetic energy it had when it left your hand at $y = 0$ has been converted to gravitational potential energy. At $y = 15.0$ m, the ball is about three-fourths of the way to its maximum height, so about three-fourths of its mechanical energy should be in the form of potential energy. Can you verify this from our results for K_3 and $U_{\text{grav},3}$?

Gravitational Potential Energy for Motion Along a Curved Path

In our first two examples the body moved along a straight vertical line. What happens when the path is slanted or curved (**Fig. 7.7a**)? The body is acted on by the gravitational force $\vec{w} = m\vec{g}$ and possibly by other forces whose resultant we call $\vec{F}_{\text{other}}$. To find the work W_{grav} done by the gravitational force during this displacement, we divide the path into small segments $\Delta\vec{s}$; Fig. 7.7b shows a typical segment. The work done by the gravitational force over this segment is the scalar product of the force and the displacement. In terms of unit vectors, the force is $\vec{w} = m\vec{g} = -mg\hat{j}$ and the displacement is $\Delta\vec{s} = \Delta x\hat{i} + \Delta y\hat{j}$, so

$$W_{\text{grav}} = \vec{w} \cdot \Delta\vec{s} = -mg\hat{j} \cdot (\Delta x\hat{i} + \Delta y\hat{j}) = -mg\Delta y$$

The work done by gravity is the same as though the body had been displaced vertically a distance Δy, with no horizontal displacement. This is true for every segment, so the *total* work done by the gravitational force is $-mg$ multiplied by the *total* vertical displacement $(y_2 - y_1)$:

$$W_{\text{grav}} = -mg(y_2 - y_1) = mgy_1 - mgy_2 = U_{\text{grav},1} - U_{\text{grav},2}$$

This is the same as Eq. (7.1) or (7.3), in which we assumed a purely vertical path. So even if the path a body follows between two points is curved, the total work done by the gravitational force depends on only the difference in height between the two points of the path. This work is unaffected by any horizontal motion that may occur. So *we can use the same expression for gravitational potential energy whether the body's path is curved or straight.*

7.7 Calculating the change in gravitational potential energy for a displacement along a curved path.

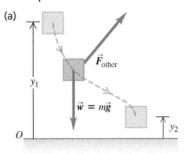
(a)

(b)

The work done by the gravitational force depends only on the vertical component of displacement Δy.
In this case Δy is negative.

CONCEPTUAL EXAMPLE 7.3   **ENERGY IN PROJECTILE MOTION**

A batter hits two identical baseballs with the same initial speed and from the same initial height but at different initial angles. Prove that both balls have the same speed at any height h if air resistance can be ignored.

SOLUTION

The only force acting on each ball after it is hit is its weight. Hence the total mechanical energy for each ball is constant. **Figure 7.8** shows the trajectories of two balls batted at the same height with the same initial speed, and thus the same total mechanical energy, but with different initial angles. At all points at the same height the potential energy is the same. Thus the kinetic energy at this height must be the same for both balls, and the speeds are the same.

7.8 For the same initial speed and initial height, the speed of a projectile at a given elevation h is always the same, if we ignore air resistance.

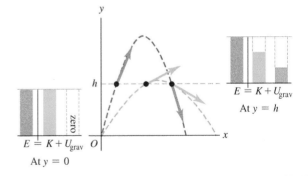

EXAMPLE 7.4   **SPEED AT THE BOTTOM OF A VERTICAL CIRCLE**

Your cousin Throckmorton skateboards from rest down a curved, frictionless ramp. If we treat Throcky and his skateboard as a particle, he moves through a quarter-circle with radius $R = 3.00$ m (**Fig. 7.9**, next page). Throcky and his skateboard have a total mass of 25.0 kg. (a) Find his speed at the bottom of the ramp. (b) Find the normal force that acts on him at the bottom of the curve.

SOLUTION

IDENTIFY: We can't use the constant-acceleration equations of Chapter 2 because Throcky's acceleration isn't constant; the slope decreases as he descends. Instead, we'll use the energy approach. Throcky moves along a circular arc, so we'll also use what we learned about circular motion in Section 5.4.

SET UP: The only forces on Throcky are his weight and the normal force $\vec{n}$ exerted by the ramp (Fig. 7.9b). Although $\vec{n}$ acts all along the path, it does zero work because $\vec{n}$ is perpendicular to Throcky's displacement at every point. Hence $W_{\text{other}} = 0$ and mechanical energy is conserved. We treat Throcky as a particle located at the center of his body, take point 1 at the particle's starting point, and take point 2 (which we let be $y = 0$) at the particle's low point. We take the positive y-direction upward; then $y_1 = R$ and $y_2 = 0$. Throcky starts at rest at the top, so $v_1 = 0$. In part (a) our target variable is his speed v_2 at the bottom; in part (b) the target variable is the magnitude n of the normal force at point 2. To find n, we'll use Newton's second law and the relation $a = v^2/R$.

Continued

7.9 (a) Throcky skateboarding down a frictionless circular ramp. The total mechanical energy is constant.
(b) Free-body diagrams for Throcky and his skateboard at various points on the ramp.

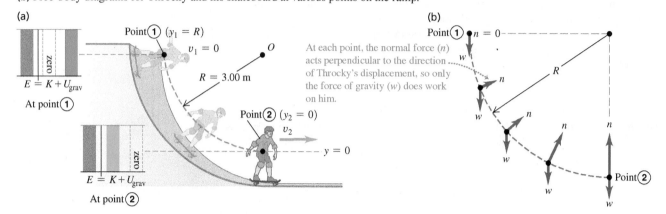

EXECUTE: (a) The various energy quantities are

$$K_1 = 0 \qquad U_{\text{grav},1} = mgR$$

$$K_2 = \tfrac{1}{2}mv_2^2 \qquad U_{\text{grav},2} = 0$$

From conservation of mechanical energy, Eq. (7.4),

$$K_1 + U_{\text{grav},1} = K_2 + U_{\text{grav},2}$$

$$0 + mgR = \tfrac{1}{2}mv_2^2 + 0$$

$$v_2 = \sqrt{2gR} = \sqrt{2(9.80 \text{ m/s}^2)(3.00 \text{ m})} = 7.67 \text{ m/s}$$

This answer doesn't depend on the ramp being circular; Throcky would have the same speed $v_2 = \sqrt{2gR}$ at the bottom of any ramp of height R, no matter what its shape.

(b) To use Newton's second law to find n at point 2, we need the free-body diagram at that point (Fig. 7.9b). At point 2, Throcky is moving at speed $v_2 = \sqrt{2gR}$ in a circle of radius R; his acceleration is toward the center of the circle and has magnitude

$$a_{\text{rad}} = \frac{v_2^2}{R} = \frac{2gR}{R} = 2g$$

The y-component of Newton's second law is

$$\Sigma F_y = n + (-w) = ma_{\text{rad}} = 2mg$$

$$n = w + 2mg = 3mg$$

$$= 3(25.0 \text{ kg})(9.80 \text{ m/s}^2) = 735 \text{ N}$$

At point 2 the normal force is three times Throcky's weight. This result doesn't depend on the radius R of the ramp. We saw in Examples 5.9 and 5.23 that the magnitude of n is the *apparent weight*, so at the bottom of the *curved part* of the ramp Throcky feels as though he weighs three times his true weight mg. But when he reaches the *horizontal* part of the ramp, immediately to the right of point 2, the normal force decreases to $w = mg$ and thereafter Throcky feels his true weight again. Can you see why?

EVALUATE: This example shows a general rule about the role of forces in problems in which we use energy techniques: What matters is not simply whether a force *acts*, but whether that force *does work*. If the force does no work, like the normal force $\vec{n}$ here, then it does not appear in Eqs. (7.4) and (7.6).

EXAMPLE 7.5   **A VERTICAL CIRCLE WITH FRICTION**

Suppose that the ramp of Example 7.4 is not frictionless and that Throcky's speed at the bottom is only 6.00 m/s, not the 7.67 m/s we found there. What work was done on him by the friction force?

SOLUTION

IDENTIFY and SET UP: The setup is the same as in Example 7.4. **Figure 7.10** shows that again the normal force does no work, but now there is a friction force $\vec{f}$ that *does* do work W_f. Hence the nongravitational work W_{other} done on Throcky between points 1 and 2 is equal to W_f and is not zero. Our target variable is $W_f = W_{\text{other}}$, which we'll find by using Eq. (7.6). Since $\vec{f}$ points opposite to Throcky's motion, W_f is negative.

EXECUTE: The energy quantities are

$$K_1 = 0$$

$$U_{\text{grav},1} = mgR = (25.0 \text{ kg})(9.80 \text{ m/s}^2)(3.00 \text{ m}) = 735 \text{ J}$$

$$K_2 = \tfrac{1}{2}mv_2^2 = \tfrac{1}{2}(25.0 \text{ kg})(6.00 \text{ m/s})^2 = 450 \text{ J}$$

$$U_{\text{grav},2} = 0$$

7.10 Energy bar graphs and free-body diagrams for Throcky skateboarding down a ramp with friction.

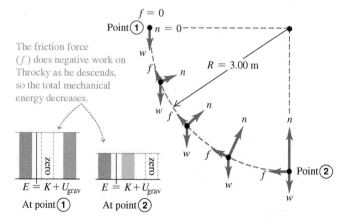

From Eq. (7.6),

$$W_f = W_{\text{other}}$$
$$= K_2 + U_{\text{grav},2} - K_1 - U_{\text{grav},1}$$
$$= 450\ \text{J} + 0 - 0 - 735\ \text{J}$$
$$= -285\ \text{J}$$

The work done by the friction force is -285 J, and the total mechanical energy *decreases* by 285 J.

EVALUATE: Our result for W_f is negative. Can you see from the free-body diagrams in Fig. 7.10 why this must be so?

It would be very difficult to apply Newton's second law, $\sum \vec{F} = m\vec{a}$, directly to this problem because the normal and friction forces and the acceleration are continuously changing in both magnitude and direction as Throcky descends. The energy approach, by contrast, relates the motions at the top and bottom of the ramp without involving the details of the motion in between.

EXAMPLE 7.6   AN INCLINED PLANE WITH FRICTION

We want to slide a 12-kg crate up a 2.5-m-long ramp inclined at 30°. A worker, ignoring friction, calculates that he can do this by giving it an initial speed of 5.0 m/s at the bottom and letting it go. But friction is *not* negligible; the crate slides only 1.6 m up the ramp, stops, and slides back down (**Fig. 7.11a**). (a) Find the magnitude of the friction force acting on the crate, assuming that it is constant. (b) How fast is the crate moving when it reaches the bottom of the ramp?

SOLUTION

IDENTIFY and SET UP: The friction force does work on the crate as it slides from point 1, at the bottom of the ramp, to point 2, where the crate stops instantaneously ($v_2 = 0$). Friction also does work as the crate returns to the bottom of the ramp, which we'll call point 3 (Fig. 7.11a). We take the positive y-direction upward. We take $y = 0$ (and hence $U_{\text{grav}} = 0$) to be at ground level (point 1), so $y_1 = 0$, $y_2 = (1.6\ \text{m})\sin 30° = 0.80\ \text{m}$, and $y_3 = 0$. We are given $v_1 = 5.0$ m/s. In part (a) our target variable is f, the magnitude of the friction force as the crate slides up; we'll find this by using the energy approach. In part (b) our target variable is v_3, the crate's speed at the bottom of the ramp. We'll calculate the work

done by friction as the crate slides back down, then use the energy approach to find v_3.

EXECUTE: (a) The energy quantities are

$$K_1 = \tfrac{1}{2}(12\ \text{kg})(5.0\ \text{m/s})^2 = 150\ \text{J}$$
$$U_{\text{grav},1} = 0$$
$$K_2 = 0$$
$$U_{\text{grav},2} = (12\ \text{kg})(9.8\ \text{m/s}^2)(0.80\ \text{m}) = 94\ \text{J}$$
$$W_{\text{other}} = -fs$$

Here $s = 1.6$ m. Using Eq. (7.6), we find

$$K_1 + U_{\text{grav},1} + W_{\text{other}} = K_2 + U_{\text{grav},2}$$
$$W_{\text{other}} = -fs = (K_2 + U_{\text{grav},2}) - (K_1 + U_{\text{grav},1})$$
$$= (0 + 94\ \text{J}) - (150\ \text{J} + 0) = -56\ \text{J} = -fs$$
$$f = \frac{W_{\text{other}}}{s} = \frac{56\ \text{J}}{1.6\ \text{m}} = 35\ \text{N}$$

The friction force of 35 N, acting over 1.6 m, causes the mechanical energy of the crate to decrease from 150 J to 94 J (Fig. 7.11b).

(b) As the crate moves from point 2 to point 3, the work done by friction has the same negative value as from point 1 to point 2. (Both the friction force and the displacement reverse direction, but their magnitudes don't change.) The total work done by friction between points 1 and 3 is therefore

$$W_{\text{other}} = W_{\text{fric}} = -2fs = -2(56\ \text{J}) = -112\ \text{J}$$

From part (a), $K_1 = 150$ J and $U_{\text{grav},1} = 0$; in addition, $U_{\text{grav},3} = 0$ since $y_3 = 0$. Equation (7.6) then gives

$$K_1 + U_{\text{grav},1} + W_{\text{other}} = K_3 + U_{\text{grav},3}$$
$$K_3 = K_1 + U_{\text{grav},1} - U_{\text{grav},3} + W_{\text{other}}$$
$$= 150\ \text{J} + 0 - 0 + (-112\ \text{J}) = 38\ \text{J}$$

The crate returns to the bottom of the ramp with only 38 J of the original 150 J of mechanical energy (Fig. 7.11b). Since $K_3 = \tfrac{1}{2}mv_3^2$,

$$v_3 = \sqrt{\frac{2K_3}{m}} = \sqrt{\frac{2(38\ \text{J})}{12\ \text{kg}}} = 2.5\ \text{m/s}$$

EVALUATE: Energy is lost due to friction, so the crate's speed $v_3 = 2.5$ m/s when it returns to the bottom of the ramp is less than the speed $v_1 = 5.0$ m/s at which it left that point. In part (b) we applied Eq. (7.6) to points 1 and 3, considering the round trip as a whole. Alternatively, we could have considered the second part of the motion by itself and applied Eq. (7.6) to points 2 and 3. Try it; do you get the same result for v_3?

7.11 (a) A crate slides partway up the ramp, stops, and slides back down. (b) Energy bar graphs for points 1, 2, and 3.

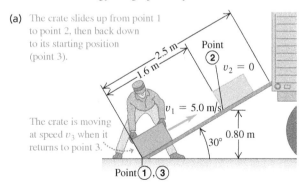

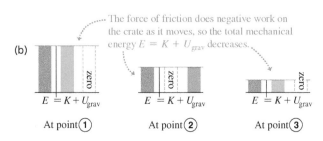

TEST YOUR UNDERSTANDING OF SECTION 7.1   The figure shows two friction-less ramps. The heights y_1 and y_2 are the same for both ramps. If a block of mass m is released from rest at the left-hand end of each ramp, which block arrives at the right-hand end with the greater speed? (i) Block I; (ii) block II; (iii) the speed is the same for both blocks.

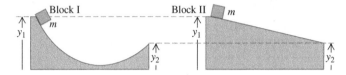

7.2 ELASTIC POTENTIAL ENERGY

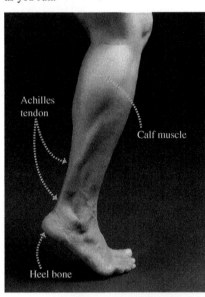

7.12 The Achilles tendon, which runs along the back of the ankle to the heel bone, acts like a natural spring. When it stretches and then relaxes, this tendon stores and then releases elastic potential energy. This spring action reduces the amount of work your leg muscles must do as you run.

In many situations we encounter potential energy that is not gravitational in nature. One example is a rubber-band slingshot. Work is done on the rubber band by the force that stretches it, and that work is stored in the rubber band until you let it go. Then the rubber band gives kinetic energy to the projectile.

This is the same pattern we saw with the baseball in Example 7.2: Do work on the system to store energy, which can later be converted to kinetic energy. We'll describe the process of storing energy in a deformable body such as a spring or rubber band in terms of *elastic potential energy* (**Fig. 7.12**). A body is called *elastic* if it returns to its original shape and size after being deformed.

To be specific, we'll consider storing energy in an ideal spring, like the ones we discussed in Section 6.3. To keep such an ideal spring stretched by a distance x, we must exert a force $F = kx$, where k is the force constant of the spring. Many elastic bodies show this same direct proportionality between force $\vec{F}$ and displacement x, provided that x is sufficiently small.

Let's proceed just as we did for gravitational potential energy. We begin with the work done by the elastic (spring) force and then combine this with the work–energy theorem. The difference is that gravitational potential energy is a shared property of a body and the earth, but elastic potential energy is stored in just the spring (or other deformable body).

Figure 7.13 shows the ideal spring from Fig. 6.18 but with its left end held stationary and its right end attached to a block with mass m that can move along the x-axis. In Fig. 7.13a the block is at $x = 0$ when the spring is neither stretched nor compressed. We move the block to one side, thereby stretching or compressing the spring, then let it go. As the block moves from a different position x_1 to a different position x_2, how much work does the elastic (spring) force do on the block?

We found in Section 6.3 that the work we must do *on* the spring to move one end from an elongation x_1 to a different elongation x_2 is

$$W = \tfrac{1}{2}kx_2^2 - \tfrac{1}{2}kx_1^2 \qquad \text{(work done } on \text{ a spring)} \qquad (7.8)$$

where k is the force constant of the spring. If we stretch the spring farther, we do positive work on the spring; if we let the spring relax while holding one end, we do negative work on it. This expression for work is also correct when the spring is compressed such that x_1, x_2, or both are negative. Now, from Newton's third law the work done *by* the spring is just the negative of the work done *on* the spring. So by changing the signs in Eq. (7.8), we find that in a displacement from x_1 to x_2 the spring does an amount of work W_{el} given by

$$W_{\text{el}} = \tfrac{1}{2}kx_1^2 - \tfrac{1}{2}kx_2^2 \qquad \text{(work done } by \text{ a spring)} \qquad (7.9)$$

The subscript "el" stands for *elastic*. When both x_1 and x_2 are positive and $x_2 > x_1$ (Fig. 7.13b), the spring does negative work on the block, which moves in the $+x$-direction while the spring pulls on it in the $-x$-direction. The spring stretches farther, and the block slows down. When both x_1 and x_2 are positive and $x_2 < x_1$ (Fig. 7.13c), the spring does positive work as it relaxes and the block speeds up. If the spring can be compressed as well as stretched, x_1, x_2, or both may be negative, but the expression for W_{el} is still valid. In Fig. 7.13d, both x_1 and x_2 are negative, but x_2 is less negative than x_1; the compressed spring does positive work as it relaxes, speeding the block up.

Just as for gravitational work, we can express Eq. (7.9) for the work done by the spring in terms of a quantity at the beginning and end of the displacement. This quantity is $\frac{1}{2}kx^2$, and we define it to be the **elastic potential energy:**

$$\underset{\substack{\text{Elastic potential energy} \\ \text{stored in a spring}}}{\longrightarrow} U_{el} = \tfrac{1}{2}kx^2 \quad \underset{\substack{(x > 0 \text{ if stretched,} \\ x < 0 \text{ if compressed})}}{\overset{\substack{\text{Force constant of spring} \\ \text{Elongation of spring}}}{}} \tag{7.10}$$

Figure 7.14 is a graph of Eq. (7.10). As for all other energy and work quantities, the unit of U_{el} is the joule (J); to see this from Eq. (7.10), recall that the units of k are N/m and that $1 \text{ N} \cdot \text{m} = 1 \text{ J}$. We can now use Eq. (7.10) to rewrite Eq. (7.9) for the work W_{el} done by the spring:

$$\underset{\substack{\text{Force constant of spring} \qquad \text{Initial and final elongations of spring}}}{\overset{\substack{\text{Work done by the elastic force} \dots \qquad \dots \text{ equals the \textbf{negative of the}} \\ \textbf{change in elastic potential energy.}}}{W_{el} = \tfrac{1}{2}kx_1^2 - \tfrac{1}{2}kx_2^2 = U_{el,1} - U_{el,2} = -\Delta U_{el}}} \tag{7.11}$$

When a stretched spring is stretched farther, as in Fig. 7.13b, W_{el} is negative and U_{el} increases; more elastic potential energy is stored in the spring. When a stretched spring relaxes, as in Fig. 7.13c, x decreases, W_{el} is positive, and U_{el} decreases; the spring loses elastic potential energy. Figure 7.14 shows that U_{el} is positive for both positive and negative x values; Eqs. (7.10) and (7.11) are valid for both cases. The more a spring is compressed or stretched, the greater its elastic potential energy.

CAUTION **Gravitational potential energy vs. elastic potential energy** An important difference between gravitational potential energy $U_{grav} = mgy$ and elastic potential energy $U_{el} = \frac{1}{2}kx^2$ is that we *cannot* choose $x = 0$ to be wherever we wish. In Eq. (7.10), $x = 0$ *must* be the position at which the spring is neither stretched nor compressed. At that position, both its elastic potential energy and the force that it exerts are zero. ▮

The work–energy theorem says that $W_{tot} = K_2 - K_1$, no matter what kind of forces are acting on a body. If the elastic force is the *only* force that does work on the body, then

$$W_{tot} = W_{el} = U_{el,1} - U_{el,2}$$

and so

$$\underset{\substack{\text{Final kinetic energy} \\ K_2 = \frac{1}{2}mv_2^2}}{\overset{\substack{\textbf{If only the elastic force does work, total mechanical energy is conserved:}} \\ \substack{\text{Initial kinetic energy} \qquad \text{Initial elastic potential energy} \\ K_1 = \frac{1}{2}mv_1^2 \qquad \qquad U_{el,1} = \frac{1}{2}kx_1^2} }{K_1 + U_{el,1} = K_2 + U_{el,2}}} \tag{7.12}$$

In this case the total mechanical energy $E = K + U_{el}$—the sum of kinetic and *elastic* potential energies—is *conserved*. An example of this is the motion of the block in Fig. 7.13, provided the horizontal surface is frictionless so no force does work other than that exerted by the spring.

For Eq. (7.12) to be strictly correct, the ideal spring that we've been discussing must also be *massless*. If the spring has mass, it also has kinetic energy as the

7.13 Calculating the work done by a spring attached to a block on a horizontal surface. The quantity x is the extension or compression of the spring.

(a)

Here the spring is neither stretched nor compressed.

$x = 0$

(b)

As the spring stretches, it does negative work on the block.

$\vec{s}$

x_2

x_1

$\vec{F}_{spring}$

(c)

As the spring relaxes, it does positive work on the block.

$\vec{s}$

x_1

x_2

$\vec{F}_{spring}$

(d)

$\vec{s}$

x_1

x_2

A compressed spring also does positive work on the block as it relaxes.

$\vec{F}_{spring}$

7.14 The graph of elastic potential energy for an ideal spring is a parabola: $U_{el} = \frac{1}{2}kx^2$, where x is the extension or compression of the spring. Elastic potential energy U_{el} is never negative.

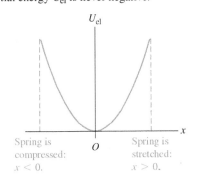

U_{el}

Spring is compressed: $x < 0$.

O

Spring is stretched: $x > 0$.

BIO Application Elastic Potential Energy of a Cheetah When a cheetah (*Acinonyx jubatus*) gallops, its back flexes and extends dramatically. Flexion of the back stretches tendons and muscles along the top of the spine and also compresses the spine, storing elastic potential energy. When the cheetah launches into its next bound, this energy is released, enabling the cheetah to run more efficiently.

Difference in nose-to-tail length

7.15 Trampoline jumping involves an interplay among kinetic energy, gravitational potential energy, and elastic potential energy. Due to air resistance and friction forces within the trampoline, mechanical energy is not conserved. That's why the bouncing eventually stops unless the jumper does work with his or her legs to compensate for the lost energy.

Gravitational potential energy increases as jumper ascends.

Kinetic energy increases as jumper moves faster.

Elastic potential energy increases when trampoline is stretched.

coils of the spring move back and forth. We can ignore the kinetic energy of the spring if its mass is much less than the mass m of the body attached to the spring. For instance, a typical automobile has a mass of 1200 kg or more. The springs in its suspension have masses of only a few kilograms, so their mass can be ignored if we want to study how a car bounces on its suspension.

Situations with Both Gravitational and Elastic Potential Energy

Equation (7.12) is valid when the only potential energy in the system is elastic potential energy. What happens when we have *both* gravitational and elastic forces, such as a block attached to the lower end of a vertically hanging spring? And what if work is also done by other forces that *cannot* be described in terms of potential energy, such as the force of air resistance on a moving block? Then the total work is the sum of the work done by the gravitational force (W_{grav}), the work done by the elastic force (W_{el}), and the work done by other forces (W_{other}): $W_{tot} = W_{grav} + W_{el} + W_{other}$. The work–energy theorem then gives

$$W_{grav} + W_{el} + W_{other} = K_2 - K_1$$

The work done by the gravitational force is $W_{grav} = U_{grav,1} - U_{grav,2}$ and the work done by the spring is $W_{el} = U_{el,1} - U_{el,2}$. Hence we can rewrite the work–energy theorem for this most general case as

$$K_1 + U_{grav,1} + U_{el,1} + W_{other} = K_2 + U_{grav,2} + U_{el,2} \quad \text{(valid in general)} \quad (7.13)$$

or, equivalently,

General relationship for kinetic energy and potential energy:

Initial kinetic energy ⋯ Final kinetic energy

$$K_1 + U_1 + W_{other} = K_2 + U_2 \quad (7.14)$$

Initial potential energy of all kinds ⋯ Work done by other forces (not associated with potential energy) ⋯ Final potential energy of all kinds

where $U = U_{grav} + U_{el} = mgy + \frac{1}{2}kx^2$ is the *sum* of gravitational potential energy and elastic potential energy. We call U simply "the potential energy."

Equation (7.14) is *the most general statement* of the relationship among kinetic energy, potential energy, and work done by other forces. It says:

> **The work done by all forces other than the gravitational force or elastic force equals the change in the total mechanical energy $E = K + U$ of the system.**

The "system" is made up of the body of mass m, the earth with which it interacts through the gravitational force, and the spring of force constant k.

If W_{other} is positive, $E = K + U$ increases; if W_{other} is negative, E decreases. If the gravitational and elastic forces are the *only* forces that do work on the body, then $W_{other} = 0$ and the total mechanical energy $E = K + U$ is conserved. [Compare Eq. (7.14) to Eqs. (7.6) and (7.7), which include gravitational potential energy but not elastic potential energy.]

Trampoline jumping (**Fig. 7.15**) involves transformations among kinetic energy, elastic potential energy, and gravitational potential energy. As the jumper descends through the air from the high point of the bounce, gravitational potential energy U_{grav} decreases and kinetic energy K increases. Once the jumper touches the trampoline, some of the mechanical energy goes into elastic potential energy U_{el} stored in the trampoline's springs. At the lowest point of the trajectory (U_{grav} is minimum), the jumper comes to a momentary halt ($K = 0$) and the springs are maximally stretched (U_{el} is maximum). The springs then convert their energy back into K and U_{grav}, propelling the jumper upward.

PROBLEMS USING MECHANICAL ENERGY II

Problem-Solving Strategy 7.1 (Section 7.1) is useful in solving problems that involve elastic forces as well as gravitational forces. The only new wrinkle is that the potential energy U now includes the elastic potential energy $U_{el} = \frac{1}{2}kx^2$, where x is the displacement of the spring *from its unstretched length.* The work done by the gravitational and elastic forces is accounted for by their potential energies; the work done by other forces, W_{other}, must still be included separately.

EXAMPLE 7.7 **MOTION WITH ELASTIC POTENTIAL ENERGY**

A glider with mass $m = 0.200$ kg sits on a frictionless, horizontal air track, connected to a spring with force constant $k = 5.00$ N/m. You pull on the glider, stretching the spring 0.100 m, and release it from rest. The glider moves back toward its equilibrium position ($x = 0$). What is its x-velocity when $x = 0.080$ m?

SOLUTION

IDENTIFY and SET UP: As the glider starts to move, elastic potential energy is converted to kinetic energy. The glider remains at the same height throughout the motion, so gravitational potential energy is not a factor and $U = U_{el} = \frac{1}{2}kx^2$. **Figure 7.16** shows our sketches. Only the spring force does work on the glider, so

7.16 Our sketches and energy bar graphs for this problem.

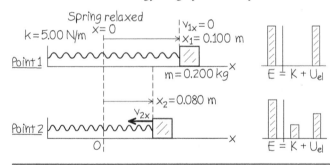

$W_{other} = 0$ in Eq. (7.14). We designate the point where the glider is released as point 1 (that is, $x_1 = 0.100$ m) and $x_2 = 0.080$ m as point 2. We are given $v_{1x} = 0$; our target variable is v_{2x}.

EXECUTE: The energy quantities are

$$K_1 = \tfrac{1}{2}mv_{1x}^2 = \tfrac{1}{2}(0.200 \text{ kg})(0)^2 = 0$$
$$U_1 = \tfrac{1}{2}kx_1^2 = \tfrac{1}{2}(5.00 \text{ N/m})(0.100 \text{ m})^2 = 0.0250 \text{ J}$$
$$K_2 = \tfrac{1}{2}mv_{2x}^2$$
$$U_2 = \tfrac{1}{2}kx_2^2 = \tfrac{1}{2}(5.00 \text{ N/m})(0.080 \text{ m})^2 = 0.0160 \text{ J}$$

We use Eq. (7.14) with $W_{other} = 0$ to solve for K_2 and then find v_{2x}:

$$K_2 = K_1 + U_1 - U_2 = 0 + 0.0250 \text{ J} - 0.0160 \text{ J} = 0.0090 \text{ J}$$

$$v_{2x} = \pm\sqrt{\frac{2K_2}{m}} = \pm\sqrt{\frac{2(0.0090 \text{ J})}{0.200 \text{ kg}}} = \pm 0.30 \text{ m/s}$$

We choose the negative root because the glider is moving in the $-x$-direction. Our answer is $v_{2x} = -0.30$ m/s.

EVALUATE: Eventually the spring will reverse the glider's motion, pushing it back in the $+x$-direction (see Fig. 7.13d). The solution $v_{2x} = +0.30$ m/s tells us that when the glider passes through $x = 0.080$ m on this return trip, its speed will be 0.30 m/s, just as when it passed through this point while moving to the left.

EXAMPLE 7.8 **MOTION WITH ELASTIC POTENTIAL ENERGY AND WORK DONE BY OTHER FORCES**

Suppose the glider in Example 7.7 is initially at rest at $x = 0$, with the spring unstretched. You then push on the glider with a constant force $\vec{F}$ (magnitude 0.610 N) in the $+x$-direction. What is the glider's velocity when it has moved to $x = 0.100$ m?

SOLUTION

IDENTIFY and SET UP: Although the force $\vec{F}$ you apply is constant, the spring force isn't, so the acceleration of the glider won't be constant. Total mechanical energy is not conserved because of the work done by force $\vec{F}$, so W_{other} in Eq. (7.14) is not zero. As in Example 7.7, we ignore gravitational potential energy because the glider's height doesn't change. Hence we again have $U = U_{el} = \frac{1}{2}kx^2$. This time, we let point 1 be at $x_1 = 0$, where the velocity is $v_{1x} = 0$, and let point 2 be at $x = 0.100$ m. The glider's

displacement is then $\Delta x = x_2 - x_1 = 0.100$ m. Our target variable is v_{2x}, the velocity at point 2.

EXECUTE: Force $\vec{F}$ is constant and in the same direction as the displacement, so the work done by this force is $F\Delta x$. Then the energy quantities are

$$K_1 = 0$$
$$U_1 = \tfrac{1}{2}kx_1^2 = 0$$
$$K_2 = \tfrac{1}{2}mv_{2x}^2$$
$$U_2 = \tfrac{1}{2}kx_2^2 = \tfrac{1}{2}(5.00 \text{ N/m})(0.100 \text{ m})^2 = 0.0250 \text{ J}$$
$$W_{other} = F\Delta x = (0.610 \text{ N})(0.100 \text{ m}) = 0.0610 \text{ J}$$

Continued

The initial total mechanical energy is zero; the work done by $\vec{F}$ increases the total mechanical energy to 0.0610 J, of which $U_2 = 0.0250$ J is elastic potential energy. The remainder is kinetic energy. From Eq. (7.14),

$$K_1 + U_1 + W_{\text{other}} = K_2 + U_2$$
$$K_2 = K_1 + U_1 + W_{\text{other}} - U_2$$
$$= 0 + 0 + 0.0610 \text{ J} - 0.0250 \text{ J} = 0.0360 \text{ J}$$
$$v_{2x} = \sqrt{\frac{2K_2}{m}} = \sqrt{\frac{2(0.0360 \text{ J})}{0.200 \text{ kg}}} = 0.60 \text{ m/s}$$

We choose the positive square root because the glider is moving in the +x-direction.

EVALUATE: What would be different if we disconnected the glider from the spring? Then only $\vec{F}$ would do work, there would be zero elastic potential energy at all times, and Eq. (7.14) would give us

$$K_2 = K_1 + W_{\text{other}} = 0 + 0.0610 \text{ J}$$
$$v_{2x} = \sqrt{\frac{2K_2}{m}} = \sqrt{\frac{2(0.0610 \text{ J})}{0.200 \text{ kg}}} = 0.78 \text{ m/s}$$

Our answer $v_{2x} = 0.60$ m/s is less than 0.78 m/s because the spring does negative work on the glider as it stretches (see Fig. 7.13b).

If you stop pushing on the glider when it reaches $x = 0.100$ m, only the spring force does work on it thereafter. Hence for $x > 0.100$ m, the total mechanical energy $E = K + U = 0.0610$ J is constant. As the spring continues to stretch, the glider slows down and the kinetic energy K decreases as the potential energy increases. The glider comes to rest at some point $x = x_3$, at which the kinetic energy is zero and the potential energy $U = U_{\text{el}} = \frac{1}{2}kx_3^2$ equals the total mechanical energy 0.0610 J. Can you show that $x_3 = 0.156$ m? (It moves an additional 0.056 m after you stop pushing.) If there is no friction, will the glider remain at rest?

EXAMPLE 7.9 MOTION WITH GRAVITATIONAL, ELASTIC, AND FRICTION FORCES

A 2000-kg (19,600-N) elevator with broken cables in a test rig is falling at 4.00 m/s when it contacts a cushioning spring at the bottom of the shaft. The spring is intended to stop the elevator, compressing 2.00 m as it does so (**Fig. 7.17**). During the motion a safety clamp applies a constant 17,000-N friction force to the elevator. What is the necessary force constant k for the spring?

SOLUTION

IDENTIFY and SET UP: We'll use the energy approach and Eq. (7.14) to determine k, which appears in the expression for elastic potential energy. This problem involves *both* gravitational and elastic potential energies. Total mechanical energy is not conserved because the friction force does negative work W_{other} on the elevator. We take point 1 as the position of the bottom of the elevator when it contacts the spring, and point 2 as its position when it stops. We choose the origin to be at point 1, so $y_1 = 0$

7.17 The fall of an elevator is stopped by a spring and by a constant friction force.

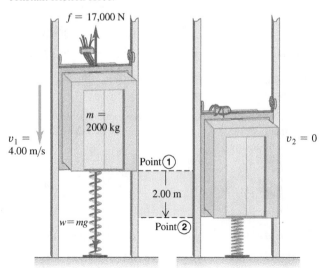

and $y_2 = -2.00$ m. With this choice the coordinate of the upper end of the spring after contact is the same as the coordinate of the elevator, so the elastic potential energy at any point between points 1 and 2 is $U_{\text{el}} = \frac{1}{2}ky^2$. The gravitational potential energy is $U_{\text{grav}} = mgy$ as usual. We know the initial and final speeds of the elevator and the magnitude of the friction force, so the only unknown is the force constant k (our target variable).

EXECUTE: The elevator's initial speed is $v_1 = 4.00$ m/s, so its initial kinetic energy is

$$K_1 = \frac{1}{2}mv_1^2 = \frac{1}{2}(2000 \text{ kg})(4.00 \text{ m/s})^2 = 16,000 \text{ J}$$

The elevator stops at point 2, so $K_2 = 0$. At point 1 the potential energy $U_1 = U_{\text{grav}} + U_{\text{el}}$ is zero; U_{grav} is zero because $y_1 = 0$, and $U_{\text{el}} = 0$ because the spring is uncompressed. At point 2 there are both gravitational and elastic potential energies, so

$$U_2 = mgy_2 + \frac{1}{2}ky_2^2$$

The gravitational potential energy at point 2 is

$$mgy_2 = (2000 \text{ kg})(9.80 \text{ m/s}^2)(-2.00 \text{ m}) = -39,200 \text{ J}$$

The "other" force is the constant 17,000-N friction force. It acts opposite to the 2.00-m displacement, so

$$W_{\text{other}} = -(17,000 \text{ N})(2.00 \text{ m}) = -34,000 \text{ J}$$

We put these terms into Eq. (7.14), $K_1 + U_1 + W_{\text{other}} = K_2 + U_2$:

$$K_1 + 0 + W_{\text{other}} = 0 + (mgy_2 + \frac{1}{2}ky_2^2)$$
$$k = \frac{2(K_1 + W_{\text{other}} - mgy_2)}{y_2^2}$$
$$= \frac{2[16,000 \text{ J} + (-34,000 \text{ J}) - (-39,200 \text{ J})]}{(-2.00 \text{ m})^2}$$
$$= 1.06 \times 10^4 \text{ N/m}$$

This is about one-tenth the force constant of a spring in an automobile suspension.

EVALUATE: There might seem to be a paradox here. The elastic potential energy at point 2 is

$$\tfrac{1}{2}ky_2^2 = \tfrac{1}{2}(1.06 \times 10^4 \text{ N/m})(-2.00 \text{ m})^2 = 21{,}200 \text{ J}$$

This is *more* than the total mechanical energy at point 1:

$$E_1 = K_1 + U_1 = 16{,}000 \text{ J} + 0 = 16{,}000 \text{ J}$$

But the friction force *decreased* the mechanical energy of the system by 34,000 J between points 1 and 2. Did energy appear from nowhere? No. At point 2, which is below the origin, there is also *negative* gravitational potential energy $mgy_2 = -39{,}200$ J. The total mechanical energy at point 2 is therefore not 21,200 J but

$$E_2 = K_2 + U_2 = 0 + \tfrac{1}{2}ky_2^2 + mgy_2$$

$$= 0 + 21{,}200 \text{ J} + (-39{,}200 \text{ J}) = -18{,}000 \text{ J}$$

This is just the initial mechanical energy of 16,000 J minus 34,000 J lost to friction.

Will the elevator stay at the bottom of the shaft? At point 2 the compressed spring exerts an upward force of magnitude $F_{\text{spring}} = (1.06 \times 10^4 \text{ N/m})(2.00 \text{ m}) = 21{,}200 \text{ N}$, while the downward force of gravity is only $w = mg = (2000 \text{ kg})(9.80 \text{ m/s}^2) = 19{,}600 \text{ N}$. If there were no friction, there would be a net upward force of $21{,}200 \text{ N} - 19{,}600 \text{ N} = 1600 \text{ N}$, and the elevator would rebound. But the safety clamp can exert a kinetic friction force of 17,000 N, and it can presumably exert a maximum static friction force greater than that. Hence the clamp will keep the elevator from rebounding.

TEST YOUR UNDERSTANDING OF SECTION 7.2 Consider the situation in Example 7.9 at the instant when the elevator is still moving downward and the spring is compressed by 1.00 m. Which of the energy bar graphs in the figure most accurately shows the kinetic energy K, gravitational potential energy U_{grav}, and elastic potential energy U_{el} at this instant?

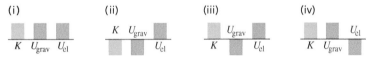

(i)   (ii)   (iii)   (iv)

7.3 CONSERVATIVE AND NONCONSERVATIVE FORCES

In our discussions of potential energy we have talked about "storing" kinetic energy by converting it to potential energy, with the idea that we can retrieve it again as kinetic energy. For example, when you throw a ball up in the air, it slows down as kinetic energy is converted to gravitational potential energy. But on the way down the ball speeds up as potential energy is converted back to kinetic energy. If there is no air resistance, the ball is moving just as fast when you catch it as when you threw it.

Another example is a glider moving on a frictionless horizontal air track that runs into a spring bumper. The glider compresses the spring and then bounces back. If there is no friction, the glider ends up with the same speed and kinetic energy it had before the collision. Again, there is a two-way conversion from kinetic to potential energy and back. In both cases the total mechanical energy, kinetic plus potential, is constant or *conserved* during the motion.

Conservative Forces

A force that offers this opportunity of two-way conversion between kinetic and potential energies is called a **conservative force.** We have seen two examples of conservative forces: the gravitational force and the spring force. (Later in this book we'll study another conservative force, the electric force between charged objects.) An essential feature of conservative forces is that their work is always *reversible.* Anything that we deposit in the energy "bank" can later be withdrawn without loss. Another important aspect of conservative forces is that if a body follows different paths from point 1 to point 2, the work done by a conservative force is the same for all of these paths (**Fig. 7.18**). For example, if a body stays close to the surface of the earth, the gravitational force $m\vec{g}$ is independent of

DATA *SPEAKS*

Conservation of Energy

When students were given a problem about conservation of mechanical energy for motion along a curved path, more than 32% gave an incorrect answer. Common errors:

- Forgetting that the change in gravitational potential energy along a curved path depends on only the difference between the final and initial heights, not the shape of the path.

- Forgetting that if gravity is the only force that does work, mechanical energy is conserved. Then the change in kinetic energy along the path is determined by solely the change in gravitational potential energy. The shape of the path doesn't matter.

7.18 The work done by a conservative force such as gravity depends on only the endpoints of a path, not the specific path taken between those points.

Because the gravitational force is conservative, the work it does is the same for all three paths.

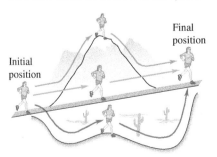

Initial position

Final position

PhET: The Ramp

height, and the work done by this force depends on only the change in height. If the body moves around a closed path, ending at the same height where it started, the *total* work done by the gravitational force is always zero.

In summary, the work done by a conservative force has four properties:

1. It can be expressed as the difference between the initial and final values of a *potential-energy* function.

2. It is reversible.

3. It is independent of the path of the body and depends on only the starting and ending points.

4. When the starting and ending points are the same, the total work is zero.

When the *only* forces that do work are conservative forces, the total mechanical energy $E = K + U$ is constant.

Nonconservative Forces

Not all forces are conservative. Consider the friction force acting on the crate sliding on a ramp in Example 7.6 (Section 7.1). When the body slides up and then back down to the starting point, the total work done on it by the friction force is *not* zero. When the direction of motion reverses, so does the friction force, and friction does *negative* work in *both* directions. Friction also acts when a car with its brakes locked skids with decreasing speed (and decreasing kinetic energy). The lost kinetic energy can't be recovered by reversing the motion or in any other way, and mechanical energy is *not* conserved. So there is *no* potential-energy function for the friction force.

In the same way, the force of fluid resistance (see Section 5.3) is not conservative. If you throw a ball up in the air, air resistance does negative work on the ball while it's rising *and* while it's descending. The ball returns to your hand with less speed and less kinetic energy than when it left, and there is no way to get back the lost mechanical energy.

A force that is not conservative is called a **nonconservative force.** The work done by a nonconservative force *cannot* be represented by a potential-energy function. Some nonconservative forces, like kinetic friction or fluid resistance, cause mechanical energy to be lost or dissipated; a force of this kind is called a **dissipative force.** There are also nonconservative forces that *increase* mechanical energy. The fragments of an exploding firecracker fly off with very large kinetic energy, thanks to a chemical reaction of gunpowder with oxygen. The forces unleashed by this reaction are nonconservative because the process is not reversible. (The fragments never spontaneously reassemble themselves into a complete firecracker!)

EXAMPLE 7.10 FRICTIONAL WORK DEPENDS ON THE PATH

You are rearranging your furniture and wish to move a 40.0-kg futon 2.50 m across the room. A heavy coffee table, which you don't want to move, blocks this straight-line path. Instead, you slide the futon along a dogleg path; the doglegs are 2.00 m and 1.50 m long. How much more work must you do to push the futon along the dogleg path than along the straight-line path? The coefficient of kinetic friction is $\mu_k = 0.200$.

SOLUTION

IDENTIFY and SET UP: Here both you and friction do work on the futon, so we must use the energy relationship that includes "other" forces. We'll use this relationship to find a connection between the work that *you* do and the work that *friction* does. **Figure 7.19**

shows our sketch. The futon is at rest at both point 1 and point 2, so $K_1 = K_2 = 0$. There is no elastic potential energy (there are no springs), and the gravitational potential energy does not

---

7.19 Our sketch for this problem.

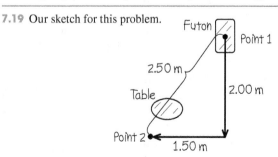

change because the futon moves only horizontally, so $U_1 = U_2$. From Eq. (7.14) it follows that $W_{\text{other}} = 0$. That "other" work done on the futon is the sum of the positive work you do, W_{you}, and the negative work done by friction, W_{fric}. Since the sum of these is zero, we have

$$W_{\text{you}} = -W_{\text{fric}}$$

So we can calculate the work done by friction to determine W_{you}.

EXECUTE: The floor is horizontal, so the normal force on the futon equals its weight mg and the magnitude of the friction force is $f_k = \mu_k n = \mu_k mg$. The work you do over each path is then

$$W_{\text{you}} = -W_{\text{fric}} = -(-f_k s) = +\mu_k mgs$$
$$= (0.200)(40.0 \text{ kg})(9.80 \text{ m/s}^2)(2.50 \text{ m})$$
$$= 196 \text{ J} \quad \text{(straight-line path)}$$

$$W_{\text{you}} = -W_{\text{fric}} = +\mu_k mgs$$
$$= (0.200)(40.0 \text{ kg})(9.80 \text{ m/s}^2)(2.00 \text{ m} + 1.50 \text{ m})$$
$$= 274 \text{ J} \quad \text{(dogleg path)}$$

The extra work you must do is $274 \text{ J} - 196 \text{ J} = 78 \text{ J}$.

EVALUATE: Friction does different amounts of work on the futon, -196 J and -274 J, on these different paths between points 1 and 2. Hence friction is a *nonconservative* force.

EXAMPLE 7.11 CONSERVATIVE OR NONCONSERVATIVE?

In a region of space the force on an electron is $\vec{F} = Cx\hat{\jmath}$, where C is a positive constant. The electron moves around a square loop in the xy-plane (**Fig. 7.20**). Calculate the work done on the electron by force $\vec{F}$ during a counterclockwise trip around the square. Is this force conservative or nonconservative?

SOLUTION

IDENTIFY and SET UP: Force $\vec{F}$ is not constant and in general is not in the same direction as the displacement. To calculate the work done by $\vec{F}$, we'll use the general expression Eq. (6.14):

$$W = \int_{P_1}^{P_2} \vec{F} \cdot d\vec{l}$$

where $d\vec{l}$ is an infinitesimal displacement. We'll calculate the work done on each leg of the square separately, and add the results to find the work done on the round trip. If this round-trip work is zero, force $\vec{F}$ is conservative and can be represented by a potential-energy function.

EXECUTE: On the first leg, from $(0, 0)$ to $(L, 0)$, the force is everywhere perpendicular to the displacement. So $\vec{F} \cdot d\vec{l} = 0$,

7.20 An electron moving around a square loop while being acted on by the force $\vec{F} = Cx\hat{\jmath}$.

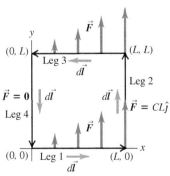

and the work done on the first leg is $W_1 = 0$. The force has the same value $\vec{F} = CL\hat{\jmath}$ everywhere on the second leg, from $(L, 0)$ to (L, L). The displacement on this leg is in the $+y$-direction, so $d\vec{l} = dy\hat{\jmath}$ and

$$\vec{F} \cdot d\vec{l} = CL\hat{\jmath} \cdot dy\hat{\jmath} = CL \, dy$$

The work done on the second leg is then

$$W_2 = \int_{(L,0)}^{(L,L)} \vec{F} \cdot d\vec{l} = \int_{y=0}^{y=L} CL \, dy = CL \int_0^L dy = CL^2$$

On the third leg, from (L, L) to $(0, L)$, $\vec{F}$ is again perpendicular to the displacement and so $W_3 = 0$. The force is zero on the final leg, from $(0, L)$ to $(0, 0)$, so $W_4 = 0$. The work done by $\vec{F}$ on the round trip is therefore

$$W = W_1 + W_2 + W_3 + W_4 = 0 + CL^2 + 0 + 0 = CL^2$$

The starting and ending points are the same, but the total work done by $\vec{F}$ is not zero. This is a *nonconservative* force; it *cannot* be represented by a potential-energy function.

EVALUATE: Because $W > 0$, the mechanical energy *increases* as the electron goes around the loop. This is actually what happens in an electric generating plant: A loop of wire is moved through a magnetic field, which gives rise to a nonconservative force similar to the one here. Electrons in the wire gain energy as they move around the loop, and this energy is carried via transmission lines to the consumer. (We'll discuss this in Chapter 29.)

If the electron went *clockwise* around the loop, $\vec{F}$ would be unaffected but the direction of each infinitesimal displacement $d\vec{l}$ would be reversed. Thus the sign of work would also reverse, and the work for a clockwise round trip would be $W = -CL^2$. This is a different behavior than the nonconservative friction force. The work done by friction on a body that slides in any direction over a stationary surface is always negative (see Example 7.6 in Section 7.1).

Application Nonconservative Forces and Internal Energy in a Tire An automobile tire deforms and flexes like a spring as it rolls, but it is not an ideal spring: Nonconservative internal friction forces act within the rubber. As a result, mechanical energy is lost and converted to internal energy of the tire. Thus the temperature of a tire increases as it rolls, which causes the pressure of the air inside the tire to increase as well. That's why tire pressures are best checked before the car is driven, when the tire is cold.

7.21 The battery pack in this radio-controlled helicopter contains 2.4×10^4 J of electric energy. When this energy is used up, the internal energy of the battery pack decreases by this amount, so $\Delta U_{int} = -2.4 \times 10^4$ J. This energy can be converted to kinetic energy to make the rotor blades and helicopter go faster, or to gravitational potential energy to make the helicopter climb.

The Law of Conservation of Energy

Nonconservative forces cannot be represented in terms of potential energy. But we can describe the effects of these forces in terms of kinds of energy other than kinetic or potential energy. When a car with locked brakes skids to a stop, both the tires and the road surface become hotter. The energy associated with this change in the state of the materials is called **internal energy.** Raising the temperature of a body increases its internal energy; lowering the body's temperature decreases its internal energy.

To see the significance of internal energy, let's consider a block sliding on a rough surface. Friction does *negative* work on the block as it slides, and the change in internal energy of the block and surface (both of which get hotter) is *positive*. Careful experiments show that the increase in the internal energy is *exactly* equal to the absolute value of the work done by friction. In other words,

$$\Delta U_{int} = -W_{other}$$

where ΔU_{int} is the change in internal energy. We substitute this into Eq. (7.14):

$$K_1 + U_1 - \Delta U_{int} = K_2 + U_2$$

Writing $\Delta K = K_2 - K_1$ and $\Delta U = U_2 - U_1$, we can finally express this as

Law of conservation of energy:

$$\Delta K + \Delta U + \Delta U_{int} = 0 \qquad (7.15)$$

Change in kinetic energy   Change in potential energy   Change in internal energy

This remarkable statement is the general form of the **law of conservation of energy.** In a given process, the kinetic energy, potential energy, and internal energy of a system may all change. But the *sum* of those changes is always zero. If there is a decrease in one form of energy, it is made up for by an increase in the other forms (**Fig. 7.21**). When we expand our definition of energy to include internal energy, Eq. (7.15) says: *Energy is never created or destroyed; it only changes form.* No exception to this rule has ever been found.

The concept of work has been banished from Eq. (7.15); instead, it suggests that we think purely in terms of the conversion of energy from one form to another. For example, when you throw a baseball straight up, you convert a portion of the internal energy of your molecules to kinetic energy of the baseball. This is converted to gravitational potential energy as the ball climbs and back to kinetic energy as the ball falls. If there is air resistance, part of the energy is used to heat up the air and the ball and increase their internal energy. Energy is converted back to the kinetic form as the ball falls. If you catch the ball in your hand, whatever energy was not lost to the air once again becomes internal energy; the ball and your hand are now warmer than they were at the beginning.

In Chapters 19 and 20, we will study the relationship of internal energy to temperature changes, heat, and work. This is the heart of the area of physics called *thermodynamics*.

CONCEPTUAL EXAMPLE 7.12   **WORK DONE BY FRICTION**

Let's return to Example 7.5 (Section 7.1), in which Throcky skateboards down a curved ramp. He starts with zero kinetic energy and 735 J of potential energy, and at the bottom he has 450 J of kinetic energy and zero potential energy; hence $\Delta K = +450$ J and $\Delta U = -735$ J. The work $W_{other} = W_{fric}$ done by the friction forces is -285 J, so the change in internal energy is $\Delta U_{int} = -W_{other} = +285$ J. The skateboard wheels and bearings and the ramp all get a little warmer. In accordance with Eq. (7.15), the sum of the energy changes equals zero:

$$\Delta K + \Delta U + \Delta U_{int} = +450 \text{ J} + (-735 \text{ J}) + 285 \text{ J} = 0$$

The total energy of the system (including internal, nonmechanical forms of energy) is conserved.

In a hydroelectric generating station, falling water is used to drive turbines ("water wheels"), which in turn run electric generators. Compared to the amount of gravitational potential energy released by the falling water, how much electrical energy is produced? (i) The same; (ii) more; (iii) less. ∎

7.4 FORCE AND POTENTIAL ENERGY

For the two kinds of conservative forces (gravitational and elastic) we have studied, we started with a description of the behavior of the *force* and derived from that an expression for the *potential energy*. For example, for a body with mass m in a uniform gravitational field, the gravitational force is $F_y = -mg$. We found that the corresponding potential energy is $U(y) = mgy$. The force that an ideal spring exerts on a body is $F_x = -kx$, and the corresponding potential-energy function is $U(x) = \frac{1}{2}kx^2$.

In studying physics, however, you'll encounter situations in which you are given an expression for the *potential energy* as a function of position and have to find the corresponding *force*. We'll see several examples of this kind when we study electric forces later in this book: It's often far easier to calculate the electric potential energy first and then determine the corresponding electric force afterward.

Here's how we find the force that corresponds to a given potential-energy expression. First let's consider motion along a straight line, with coordinate x. We denote the x-component of force, a function of x, by $F_x(x)$ and the potential energy as $U(x)$. This notation reminds us that both F_x and U are *functions* of x. Now we recall that in any displacement, the work W done by a conservative force equals the negative of the change ΔU in potential energy:

$$W = -\Delta U$$

Let's apply this to a small displacement Δx. The work done by the force $F_x(x)$ during this displacement is approximately equal to $F_x(x)\,\Delta x$. We have to say "approximately" because $F_x(x)$ may vary a little over the interval Δx. So

$$F_x(x)\,\Delta x = -\Delta U \qquad \text{and} \qquad F_x(x) = -\frac{\Delta U}{\Delta x}$$

You can probably see what's coming. We take the limit as $\Delta x \to 0$; in this limit, the variation of F_x becomes negligible, and we have the exact relationship

Force from potential energy:
In **one-dimensional motion,**
the value of a conservative
force at point x ...
$$F_x(x) = -\frac{dU(x)}{dx}$$
... is the negative
of the derivative at x
of the associated
potential-energy function.
(7.16)

This result makes sense; in regions where $U(x)$ changes most rapidly with x (that is, where $dU(x)/dx$ is large), the greatest amount of work is done during a given displacement, and this corresponds to a large force magnitude. Also, when $F_x(x)$ is in the positive x-direction, $U(x)$ *decreases* with increasing x. So $F_x(x)$ and $dU(x)/dx$ should indeed have opposite signs. The physical meaning of Eq. (7.16) is that *a conservative force always acts to push the system toward lower potential energy.*

As a check, let's consider the function for elastic potential energy, $U(x) = \frac{1}{2}kx^2$. Substituting this into Eq. (7.16) yields

$$F_x(x) = -\frac{d}{dx}\left(\tfrac{1}{2}kx^2\right) = -kx$$

which is the correct expression for the force exerted by an ideal spring (**Fig. 7.22a**, next page). Similarly, for gravitational potential energy we have $U(y) = mgy$; taking care to change x to y for the choice of axis, we get $F_y = -dU/dy = -d(mgy)/dy = -mg$, which is the correct expression for gravitational force (Fig. 7.22b).

7.22 A conservative force is the negative derivative of the corresponding potential energy.

(a) Elastic potential energy and force as functions of x

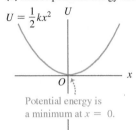

$U = \frac{1}{2}kx^2$

Potential energy is a minimum at $x = 0$.

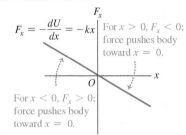

$F_x = -\dfrac{dU}{dx} = -kx$

For $x > 0$, $F_x < 0$; force pushes body toward $x = 0$.

For $x < 0$, $F_x > 0$; force pushes body toward $x = 0$.

(b) Gravitational potential energy and force as functions of y

Potential energy decreases as y decreases.

$U = mgy$

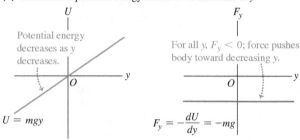

For all y, $F_y < 0$; force pushes body toward decreasing y.

$F_y = -\dfrac{dU}{dy} = -mg$

SOLUTION

EXAMPLE 7.13 **AN ELECTRIC FORCE AND ITS POTENTIAL ENERGY**

An electrically charged particle is held at rest at the point $x = 0$; a second particle with equal charge is free to move along the positive x-axis. The potential energy of the system is $U(x) = C/x$, where C is a positive constant that depends on the magnitude of the charges. Derive an expression for the x-component of force acting on the movable particle as a function of its position.

SOLUTION

IDENTIFY and SET UP: We are given the potential-energy function $U(x)$. We'll find the corresponding force function by using Eq. (7.16), $F_x(x) = -dU(x)/dx$.

EXECUTE: The derivative of $1/x$ with respect to x is $-1/x^2$. So for $x > 0$ the force on the movable charged particle is

$$F_x(x) = -\frac{dU(x)}{dx} = -C\left(-\frac{1}{x^2}\right) = \frac{C}{x^2}$$

EVALUATE: The x-component of force is positive, corresponding to a repulsion between like electric charges. Both the potential energy and the force are very large when the particles are close together (small x), and both get smaller as the particles move farther apart (large x). The force pushes the movable particle toward large positive values of x, where the potential energy is lower. (We'll study electric forces in detail in Chapter 21.)

Force and Potential Energy in Three Dimensions

We can extend this analysis to three dimensions, for a particle that may move in the x-, y-, or z-direction, or all at once, under the action of a conservative force that has components F_x, F_y, and F_z. Each component of force may be a function of the coordinates x, y, and z. The potential-energy function U is also a function of all three space coordinates. The potential-energy change ΔU when the particle moves a small distance Δx in the x-direction is again given by $-F_x \Delta x$; it doesn't depend on F_y and F_z, which represent force components that are perpendicular to the displacement and do no work. So we again have the approximate relationship

$$F_x = -\frac{\Delta U}{\Delta x}$$

We determine the y- and z-components in exactly the same way:

$$F_y = -\frac{\Delta U}{\Delta y} \qquad F_z = -\frac{\Delta U}{\Delta z}$$

To make these relationships exact, we take the limits $\Delta x \to 0$, $\Delta y \to 0$, and $\Delta z \to 0$ so that these ratios become derivatives. Because U may be a function of all three coordinates, we need to remember that when we calculate each of these derivatives, only one coordinate changes at a time. We compute the derivative of U with respect to x by assuming that y and z are constant and only x varies, and so on. Such a derivative is called a *partial derivative*. The usual notation for a partial derivative is $\partial U/\partial x$ and so on; the symbol ∂ is a modified d. So we write

Force from potential energy: In **three-dimensional motion,** the value at a given point of each component of a conservative force ...

$$F_x = -\frac{\partial U}{\partial x} \qquad F_y = -\frac{\partial U}{\partial y} \qquad F_z = -\frac{\partial U}{\partial z} \tag{7.17}$$

... is the negative of the partial derivative at that point of the associated potential-energy function.

We can use unit vectors to write a single compact vector expression for the force $\vec{F}$:

Force from potential energy: The vector value of a conservative force at a given point ...

$$\vec{F} = -\left(\frac{\partial U}{\partial x}\hat{\imath} + \frac{\partial U}{\partial y}\hat{\jmath} + \frac{\partial U}{\partial z}\hat{k}\right) = -\vec{\nabla}U \tag{7.18}$$

... is the negative of the gradient at that point of the associated potential-energy function.

In Eq. (7.18) we take the partial derivative of U with respect to each coordinate, multiply by the corresponding unit vector, and then take the vector sum. This operation is called the **gradient** of U and is often abbreviated as $\vec{\nabla}U$.

As a check, let's substitute into Eq. (7.18) the function $U = mgy$ for gravitational potential energy:

$$\vec{F} = -\vec{\nabla}(mgy) = -\left(\frac{\partial(mgy)}{\partial x}\hat{\imath} + \frac{\partial(mgy)}{\partial y}\hat{\jmath} + \frac{\partial(mgy)}{\partial z}\hat{k}\right) = (-mg)\hat{\jmath}$$

This is just the familiar expression for the gravitational force.

Application Topography and Potential Energy Gradient The greater the elevation of a hiker in Canada's Banff National Park, the greater the gravitational potential energy U_{grav}. Think of an x-axis that runs horizontally from west to east and a y-axis that runs horizontally from south to north. Then the function $U_{grav}(x, y)$ tells us the elevation as a function of position in the park. Where the mountains have steep slopes, $\vec{F} = -\vec{\nabla}U_{grav}$ has a large magnitude and there's a strong force pushing you along the mountain's surface toward a region of lower elevation (and hence lower U_{grav}). There's zero force along the surface of the lake, which is all at the same elevation. Hence U_{grav} is constant at all points on the lake surface, and $\vec{F} = -\vec{\nabla}U_{grav} = \mathbf{0}.$

EXAMPLE 7.14 FORCE AND POTENTIAL ENERGY IN TWO DIMENSIONS

A puck with coordinates x and y slides on a level, frictionless air-hockey table. It is acted on by a conservative force described by the potential-energy function

$$U(x, y) = \tfrac{1}{2}k(x^2 + y^2)$$

Note that $r = \sqrt{x^2 + y^2}$ is the distance on the table surface from the puck to the origin. Find a vector expression for the force acting on the puck, and find an expression for the magnitude of the force.

SOLUTION

IDENTIFY and SET UP: Starting with the function $U(x, y)$, we need to find the vector components and magnitude of the corresponding force $\vec{F}$. We'll use Eq. (7.18) to find the components. The function U doesn't depend on z, so the partial derivative of U with respect to z is $\partial U/\partial z = 0$ and the force has no z-component. We'll determine the magnitude F of the force by using $F = \sqrt{F_x^2 + F_y^2}$.

EXECUTE: The x- and y-components of $\vec{F}$ are

$$F_x = -\frac{\partial U}{\partial x} = -kx \qquad F_y = -\frac{\partial U}{\partial y} = -ky$$

From Eq. (7.18), the vector expression for the force is

$$\vec{F} = (-kx)\hat{\imath} + (-ky)\hat{\jmath} = -k(x\hat{\imath} + y\hat{\jmath})$$

The magnitude of the force is

$$F = \sqrt{(-kx)^2 + (-ky)^2} = k\sqrt{x^2 + y^2} = kr$$

EVALUATE: Because $x\hat{\imath} + y\hat{\jmath}$ is just the position vector $\vec{r}$ of the particle, we can rewrite our result as $\vec{F} = -k\vec{r}$. This represents a force that is opposite in direction to the particle's position vector—that is, a force directed toward the origin, $r = 0$. This is the force that would be exerted on the puck if it were attached to one end of a spring that obeys Hooke's law and has a negligibly small unstretched length compared to the other distances in the problem. (The other end is attached to the air-hockey table at $r = 0$.)

To check our result, note that $U = \tfrac{1}{2}kr^2$. We can find the force from this expression using Eq. (7.16) with x replaced by r:

$$F_r = -\frac{dU}{dr} = -\frac{d}{dr}\left(\tfrac{1}{2}kr^2\right) = -kr$$

As we found above, the force has magnitude kr; the minus sign indicates that the force is toward the origin (at $r = 0$).

7.23 (a) A glider on an air track. The spring exerts a force $F_x = -kx$. (b) The potential-energy function.

(a)

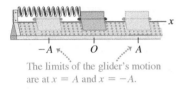

The limits of the glider's motion are at $x = A$ and $x = -A$.

(b)

On the graph, the limits of motion are the points where the U curve intersects the horizontal line representing total mechanical energy E.

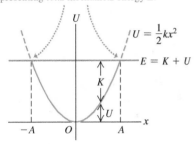

Application Acrobats in Equilibrium
Each of these acrobats is in *unstable* equilibrium. The gravitational potential energy is lower no matter which way an acrobat tips, so if she begins to fall she will keep on falling. Staying balanced requires the acrobats' constant attention.

TEST YOUR UNDERSTANDING OF SECTION 7.4   A particle moving along the x-axis is acted on by a conservative force F_x. At a certain point, the force is zero. (a) Which of the following statements about the value of the potential-energy function $U(x)$ at that point is correct? (i) $U(x) = 0$; (ii) $U(x) > 0$; (iii) $U(x) < 0$; (iv) not enough information is given to decide. (b) Which of the following statements about the value of the derivative of $U(x)$ at that point is correct? (i) $dU(x)/dx = 0$; (ii) $dU(x)/dx > 0$; (iii) $dU(x)/dx < 0$; (iv) not enough information is given to decide. ∎

7.5 ENERGY DIAGRAMS

When a particle moves along a straight line under the action of a conservative force, we can get a lot of insight into its possible motions by looking at the graph of the potential-energy function $U(x)$. **Figure 7.23a** shows a glider with mass m that moves along the x-axis on an air track. The spring exerts on the glider a force with x-component $F_x = -kx$. Figure 7.23b is a graph of the corresponding potential-energy function $U(x) = \frac{1}{2}kx^2$. If the elastic force of the spring is the *only* horizontal force acting on the glider, the total mechanical energy $E = K + U$ is constant, independent of x. A graph of E as a function of x is thus a straight horizontal line. We use the term **energy diagram** for a graph like this, which shows both the potential-energy function $U(x)$ and the energy of the particle subjected to the force that corresponds to $U(x)$.

The vertical distance between the U and E graphs at each point represents the difference $E - U$, equal to the kinetic energy K at that point. We see that K is greatest at $x = 0$. It is zero at the values of x where the two graphs cross, labeled A and $-A$ in Fig. 7.23b. Thus the speed v is greatest at $x = 0$, and it is zero at $x = \pm A$, the points of *maximum* possible displacement from $x = 0$ for a given value of the total energy E. The potential energy U can never be greater than the total energy E; if it were, K would be negative, and that's impossible. The motion is a back-and-forth oscillation between the points $x = A$ and $x = -A$.

From Eq. (7.16), at each point the force F_x on the glider is equal to the negative of the slope of the $U(x)$ curve: $F_x = -dU/dx$ (see Fig. 7.22a). When the particle is at $x = 0$, the slope and the force are zero, so this is an *equilibrium* position. When x is positive, the slope of the $U(x)$ curve is positive and the force F_x is negative, directed toward the origin. When x is negative, the slope is negative and F_x is positive, again directed toward the origin. Such a force is called a *restoring force;* when the glider is displaced to either side of $x = 0$, the force tends to "restore" it back to $x = 0$. An analogous situation is a marble rolling around in a round-bottomed bowl. We say that $x = 0$ is a point of **stable equilibrium.** More generally, *any minimum in a potential-energy curve is a stable equilibrium position.*

Figure 7.24a shows a hypothetical but more general potential-energy function $U(x)$. Figure 7.24b shows the corresponding force $F_x = -dU/dx$. Points x_1 and x_3 are stable equilibrium points. At both points, F_x is zero because the slope of the $U(x)$ curve is zero. When the particle is displaced to either side, the force pushes back toward the equilibrium point. The slope of the $U(x)$ curve is also zero at points x_2 and x_4, and these are also equilibrium points. But when the particle is displaced a little to the right of either point, the slope of the $U(x)$ curve becomes negative, corresponding to a positive F_x that tends to push the particle still farther from the point. When the particle is displaced a little to the left, F_x is negative, again pushing away from equilibrium. This is analogous to a marble rolling on the top of a bowling ball. Points x_2 and x_4 are called **unstable equilibrium** points; *any maximum in a potential-energy curve is an unstable equilibrium position.*

7.24 The maxima and minima of a potential-energy function $U(x)$ correspond to points where $F_x = 0$.

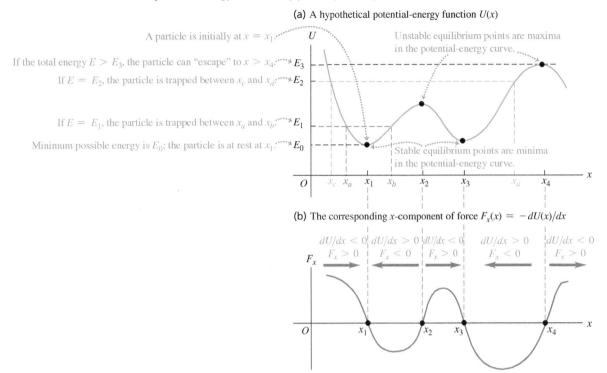

(a) A hypothetical potential-energy function $U(x)$

A particle is initially at $x = x_1$.

If the total energy $E > E_3$, the particle can "escape" to $x > x_4$.

If $E = E_2$, the particle is trapped between x_c and x_d.

If $E = E_1$, the particle is trapped between x_a and x_b.

Minimum possible energy is E_0; the particle is at rest at x_1.

Unstable equilibrium points are maxima in the potential-energy curve.

Stable equilibrium points are minima in the potential-energy curve.

(b) The corresponding x-component of force $F_x(x) = -dU(x)/dx$

$dU/dx < 0$ $dU/dx > 0$ $dU/dx < 0$ $dU/dx > 0$ $dU/dx < 0$
$F_x > 0$ $F_x < 0$ $F_x > 0$ $F_x < 0$ $F_x > 0$

CAUTION   **Potential energy and the direction of a conservative force**   The direction of the force on a body is *not* determined by the sign of the potential energy U. Rather, it's the sign of $F_x = -dU/dx$ that matters. The physically significant quantity is the *difference* in the values of U between two points (Section 7.1), which is what the derivative $F_x = -dU/dx$ measures. You can always add a constant to the potential-energy function without changing the physics. ▮

PhET: Energy Skate Park

If the total energy is E_1 and the particle is initially near x_1, it can move only in the region between x_a and x_b determined by the intersection of the E_1 and U graphs (Fig. 7.24a). Again, U cannot be greater than E_1 because K can't be negative. We speak of the particle as moving in a *potential well,* and x_a and x_b are the *turning points* of the particle's motion (since at these points, the particle stops and reverses direction). If we increase the total energy to the level E_2, the particle can move over a wider range, from x_c to x_d. If the total energy is greater than E_3, the particle can "escape" and move to indefinitely large values of x. At the other extreme, E_0 represents the minimum total energy the system can have.

TEST YOUR UNDERSTANDING OF SECTION 7.5   The curve in Fig. 7.24b has a maximum at a point between x_2 and x_3. Which statement correctly describes what happens to the particle when it is at this point? (i) The particle's acceleration is zero. (ii) The particle accelerates in the positive x-direction; the magnitude of the acceleration is less than at any other point between x_2 and x_3. (iii) The particle accelerates in the positive x-direction; the magnitude of the acceleration is greater than at any other point between x_2 and x_3. (iv) The particle accelerates in the negative x-direction; the magnitude of the acceleration is less than at any other point between x_2 and x_3. (v) The particle accelerates in the negative x-direction; the magnitude of the acceleration is greater than at any other point between x_2 and x_3. ▮

Gravitational potential energy and elastic potential energy: The work done on a particle by a constant gravitational force can be represented as a change in the gravitational potential energy, $U_{grav} = mgy$. This energy is a shared property of the particle and the earth. A potential energy is also associated with the elastic force $F_x = -kx$ exerted by an ideal spring, where x is the amount of stretch or compression. The work done by this force can be represented as a change in the elastic potential energy of the spring, $U_{el} = \frac{1}{2}kx^2$.

$$W_{grav} = mgy_1 - mgy_2$$
$$= U_{grav,1} - U_{grav,2}$$
$$= -\Delta U_{grav} \qquad (7.2), (7.3)$$

$$W_{el} = \frac{1}{2}kx_1^2 - \frac{1}{2}kx_2^2 \qquad (7.10), (7.11)$$
$$= U_{el,1} - U_{el,2} = -\Delta U_{el}$$

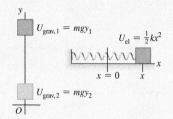

When total mechanical energy is conserved: The total potential energy U is the sum of the gravitational and elastic potential energies: $U = U_{grav} + U_{el}$. If no forces other than the gravitational and elastic forces do work on a particle, the sum of kinetic and potential energies is conserved. This sum $E = K + U$ is called the total mechanical energy. (See Examples 7.1, 7.3, 7.4, and 7.7.)

$$K_1 + U_1 = K_2 + U_2 \qquad (7.4), (7.12)$$

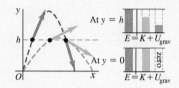

When total mechanical energy is not conserved: When forces other than the gravitational and elastic forces do work on a particle, the work W_{other} done by these other forces equals the change in total mechanical energy (kinetic energy plus total potential energy). (See Examples 7.2, 7.5, 7.6, 7.8, and 7.9.)

$$K_1 + U_1 + W_{other} = K_2 + U_2 \qquad (7.14)$$

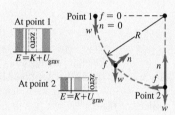

Conservative forces, nonconservative forces, and the law of conservation of energy: All forces are either conservative or nonconservative. A conservative force is one for which the work–kinetic energy relationship is completely reversible. The work of a conservative force can always be represented by a potential-energy function, but the work of a nonconservative force cannot. The work done by nonconservative forces manifests itself as changes in the internal energy of bodies. The sum of kinetic, potential, and internal energies is always conserved. (See Examples 7.10–7.12.)

$$\Delta K + \Delta U + \Delta U_{int} = 0 \qquad (7.15)$$

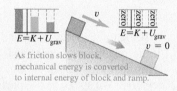

As friction slows block, mechanical energy is converted to internal energy of block and ramp.

Determining force from potential energy: For motion along a straight line, a conservative force $F_x(x)$ is the negative derivative of its associated potential-energy function U. In three dimensions, the components of a conservative force are negative partial derivatives of U. (See Examples 7.13 and 7.14.)

$$F_x(x) = -\frac{dU(x)}{dx} \qquad (7.16)$$

$$F_x = -\frac{\partial U}{\partial x} \qquad F_y = -\frac{\partial U}{\partial y}$$
$$F_z = -\frac{\partial U}{\partial z} \qquad (7.17)$$

$$\vec{F} = -\left(\frac{\partial U}{\partial x}\hat{i} + \frac{\partial U}{\partial y}\hat{j} + \frac{\partial U}{\partial z}\hat{k}\right) \qquad (7.18)$$
$$= -\vec{\nabla}U$$

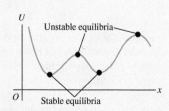

BRIDGING PROBLEM — A SPRING AND FRICTION ON AN INCLINE

A 2.00-kg package is released on a 53.1° incline, 4.00 m from a long spring with force constant 1.20×10^2 N/m that is attached at the bottom of the incline (**Fig. 7.25**). The coefficients of friction between the package and incline are $\mu_s = 0.400$ and $\mu_k = 0.200$. The mass of the spring is negligible. (a) What is the maximum compression of the spring? (b) The package rebounds up the incline. How close does it get to its original position? (c) What is the change in the internal energy of the package and incline from the point at which the package is released until it rebounds to its maximum height?

7.25 The initial situation.

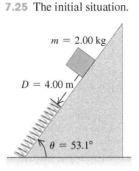

$m = 2.00$ kg

$D = 4.00$ m

$\theta = 53.1°$

SOLUTION GUIDE

IDENTIFY and SET UP

1. This problem involves the gravitational force, a spring force, and the friction force, as well as the normal force that acts on the package. Since the spring force isn't constant, you'll have to use energy methods. Is mechanical energy conserved during any part of the motion? Why or why not?
2. Draw free-body diagrams for the package as it is sliding down the incline and sliding back up the incline. Include your choice of coordinate axes (see below). (*Hint:* If you choose $x = 0$ to be at the end of the uncompressed spring, you'll be able to use $U_{el} = \frac{1}{2}kx^2$ for the elastic potential energy of the spring.)

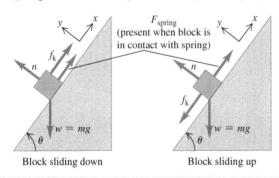

F_{spring}
(present when block is in contact with spring)

Block sliding down

Block sliding up

3. Label the three critical points in the package's motion: its starting position, its position when it comes to rest with the spring maximally compressed, and its position when it has rebounded as far as possible up the incline. (*Hint:* You can assume that the package is no longer in contact with the spring at the last of these positions. If this turns out to be incorrect, you'll calculate a value of x that tells you the spring is still partially compressed at this point.)
4. List the unknown quantities and decide which of these are the target variables.

EXECUTE

5. Find the magnitude of the friction force that acts on the package. Does the magnitude of this force depend on whether the package is moving up or down the incline, or on whether the package is in contact with the spring? Does the *direction* of the friction force depend on any of these?
6. Write the general energy equation for the motion of the package between the first two points you labeled in step 3. Use this equation to solve for the distance that the spring is compressed when the package is at its lowest point. (*Hint:* You'll have to solve a quadratic equation. To decide which of the two solutions of this equation is the correct one, remember that the distance the spring is compressed is positive.)
7. Write the general energy equation for the motion of the package between the second and third points you labeled in step 3. Use this equation to solve for how far the package rebounds.
8. Calculate the change in internal energy for the package's trip down and back up the incline. Remember that the amount the internal energy *increases* is equal to the amount the total mechanical energy *decreases*.

EVALUATE

9. Was it correct to assume in part (b) that the package is no longer in contact with the spring when it reaches its maximum rebound height?
10. Check your result for part (c) by finding the total work done by the force of friction over the entire trip. Is this in accordance with your result from step 8?

Problems

For assigned homework and other learning materials, go to MasteringPhysics®. **MP**

•, ••, •••: Difficulty levels. CP: Cumulative problems incorporating material from earlier chapters. CALC: Problems requiring calculus. DATA: Problems involving real data, scientific evidence, experimental design, and/or statistical reasoning. BIO: Biosciences problems.

DISCUSSION QUESTIONS

Q7.1 A baseball is thrown straight up with initial speed v_0. If air resistance cannot be ignored, when the ball returns to its initial height its speed is less than v_0. Explain why, using energy concepts.

Q7.2 A projectile has the same initial kinetic energy no matter what the angle of projection. Why doesn't it rise to the same maximum height in each case?

Q7.3 An object is released from rest at the top of a ramp. If the ramp is frictionless, does the object's speed at the bottom of the ramp depend on the shape of the ramp or just on its height? Explain. What if the ramp is *not* frictionless?

Q7.4 An egg is released from rest from the roof of a building and falls to the ground. Its fall is observed by a student on the roof of the building, who uses coordinates with origin at the roof, and by a student on the ground, who uses coordinates with origin at the ground. Do the values the two students assign to the following quantities match each other: initial gravitational potential energy, final gravitational potential energy, change in gravitational potential energy, and kinetic energy of the egg just before it strikes the ground? Explain.

Q7.5 A physics teacher had a bowling ball suspended from a very long rope attached to the high ceiling of a large lecture hall.

To illustrate his faith in conservation of energy, he would back up to one side of the stage, pull the ball far to one side until the taut rope brought it just to the end of his nose, and then release it. The massive ball would swing in a mighty arc across the stage and then return to stop momentarily just in front of the nose of the stationary, unflinching teacher. However, one day after the demonstration he looked up just in time to see a student at the other side of the stage *push* the ball away from his nose as he tried to duplicate the demonstration. Tell the rest of the story, and explain the reason for the potentially tragic outcome.

Q7.6 Is it possible for a friction force to *increase* the mechanical energy of a system? If so, give examples.

Q7.7 A woman bounces on a trampoline, going a little higher with each bounce. Explain how she increases the total mechanical energy.

Q7.8 Fractured Physics. People often call their electric bill a *power* bill, yet the quantity on which the bill is based is expressed in *kilowatt-hours*. What are people really being billed for?

Q7.9 (a) A book is lifted upward a vertical distance of 0.800 m. During this displacement, does the gravitational force acting on the book do positive work or negative work? Does the gravitational potential energy of the book increase or decrease? (b) A can of beans is released from rest and falls downward a vertical distance of 2.00 m. During this displacement, does the gravitational force acting on the can do positive work or negative work? Does the gravitational potential energy of the can increase or decrease?

Q7.10 (a) A block of wood is pushed against a spring, which is compressed 0.080 m. Does the force on the block exerted by the spring do positive or negative work? Does the potential energy stored in the spring increase or decrease? (b) A block of wood is placed against a vertical spring that is compressed 6.00 cm. The spring is released and pushes the block upward. From the point where the spring is compressed 6.00 cm to where it is compressed 2.00 cm from its equilibrium length and the block has moved 4.00 cm upward, does the spring force do positive or negative work on the block? During this motion, does the potential energy stored in the spring increase or decrease?

Q7.11 A 1.0-kg stone and a 10.0-kg stone are released from rest at the same height above the ground. Ignore air resistance. Which of these statements about the stones are true? Justify each answer. (a) Both have the same initial gravitational potential energy. (b) Both will have the same acceleration as they fall. (c) Both will have the same speed when they reach the ground. (d) Both will have the same kinetic energy when they reach the ground.

Q7.12 Two objects with different masses are launched vertically into the air by placing them on identical compressed springs and then releasing the springs. The two springs are compressed by the same amount before launching. Ignore air resistance and the masses of the springs. Which of these statements about the masses are true? Justify each answer. (a) Both reach the same maximum height. (b) At their maximum height, both have the same gravitational potential energy, if the initial gravitational potential of each mass is taken to be zero.

Q7.13 When people are cold, they often rub their hands together to warm up. How does doing this produce heat? Where does the heat come from?

Q7.14 A box slides down a ramp and work is done on the box by the forces of gravity and friction. Can the work of each of these forces be expressed in terms of the change in a potential-energy function? For each force explain why or why not.

Q7.15 In physical terms, explain why friction is a nonconservative force. Does it store energy for future use?

Q7.16 Since only changes in potential energy are important in any problem, a student decides to let the elastic potential energy of a spring be zero when the spring is stretched a distance x_1. The student decides, therefore, to let $U = \frac{1}{2}k(x - x_1)^2$. Is this correct? Explain.

Q7.17 Figure 7.22a shows the potential-energy function for the force $F_x = -kx$. Sketch the potential-energy function for the force $F_x = +kx$. For this force, is $x = 0$ a point of equilibrium? Is this equilibrium stable or unstable? Explain.

Q7.18 Figure 7.22b shows the potential-energy function associated with the gravitational force between an object and the earth. Use this graph to explain why objects always fall toward the earth when they are released.

Q7.19 For a system of two particles we often let the potential energy for the force between the particles approach zero as the separation of the particles approaches infinity. If this choice is made, explain why the potential energy at noninfinite separation is positive if the particles repel one another and negative if they attract.

Q7.20 Explain why the points $x = A$ and $x = -A$ in Fig. 7.23b are called *turning points*. How are the values of E and U related at a turning point?

Q7.21 A particle is in *neutral equilibrium* if the net force on it is zero and remains zero if the particle is displaced slightly in any direction. Sketch the potential-energy function near a point of neutral equilibrium for the case of one-dimensional motion. Give an example of an object in neutral equilibrium.

Q7.22 The net force on a particle of mass m has the potential-energy function graphed in Fig. 7.24a. If the total energy is E_1, graph the speed v of the particle versus its position x. At what value of x is the speed greatest? Sketch v versus x if the total energy is E_2.

Q7.23 The potential-energy function for a force $\vec{F}$ is $U = \alpha x^3$, where α is a positive constant. What is the direction of $\vec{F}$?

EXERCISES

Section 7.1 Gravitational Potential Energy

7.1 • In one day, a 75-kg mountain climber ascends from the 1500-m level on a vertical cliff to the top at 2400 m. The next day, she descends from the top to the base of the cliff, which is at an elevation of 1350 m. What is her change in gravitational potential energy (a) on the first day and (b) on the second day?

7.2 • BIO **How High Can We Jump?** The maximum height a typical human can jump from a crouched start is about 60 cm. By how much does the gravitational potential energy increase for a 72-kg person in such a jump? Where does this energy come from?

7.3 •• CP A 90.0-kg mail bag hangs by a vertical rope 3.5 m long. A postal worker then displaces the bag to a position 2.0 m sideways from its original position, always keeping the rope taut. (a) What horizontal force is necessary to hold the bag in the new position? (b) As the bag is moved to this position, how much work is done (i) by the rope and (ii) by the worker?

7.4 •• BIO **Food Calories.** The *food calorie,* equal to 4186 J, is a measure of how much energy is released when the body metabolizes food. A certain fruit-and-cereal bar contains 140 food calories. (a) If a 65-kg hiker eats one bar, how high a mountain must he climb to "work off" the calories, assuming that all the food energy goes into increasing gravitational potential energy? (b) If, as is typical, only 20% of the food calories go into mechanical energy, what would be the answer to part (a)? (*Note:* In this and all other problems, we are assuming that 100% of the food calories that are eaten are absorbed and used by the body. This is not true. A person's "metabolic efficiency" is the percentage of calories eaten that are actually used; the body eliminates the rest. Metabolic efficiency varies considerably from person to person.)

7.5 • A baseball is thrown from the roof of a 22.0-m-tall building with an initial velocity of magnitude 12.0 m/s and directed at an angle of 53.1° above the horizontal. (a) What is the speed of the ball just before it strikes the ground? Use energy methods and ignore air resistance. (b) What is the answer for part (a) if the initial velocity is at an angle of 53.1° *below* the horizontal? (c) If the effects of air resistance are included, will part (a) or (b) give the higher speed?

7.6 •• A crate of mass M starts from rest at the top of a frictionless ramp inclined at an angle α above the horizontal. Find its speed at the bottom of the ramp, a distance d from where it started. Do this in two ways: Take the level at which the potential energy is zero to be (a) at the bottom of the ramp with y positive upward, and (b) at the top of the ramp with y positive upward. (c) Why didn't the normal force enter into your solution?

7.7 •• BIO **Human Energy vs. Insect Energy.** For its size, the common flea is one of the most accomplished jumpers in the animal world. A 2.0-mm-long, 0.50-mg flea can reach a height of 20 cm in a single leap. (a) Ignoring air drag, what is the takeoff speed of such a flea? (b) Calculate the kinetic energy of this flea at takeoff and its kinetic energy per kilogram of mass. (c) If a 65-kg, 2.0-m-tall human could jump to the same height compared with his length as the flea jumps compared with its length, how high could the human jump, and what takeoff speed would the man need? (d) Most humans can jump no more than 60 cm from a crouched start. What is the kinetic energy per kilogram of mass at takeoff for such a 65-kg person? (e) Where does the flea store the energy that allows it to make sudden leaps?

7.8 •• BIO **Bone Fractures.** The maximum energy that a bone can absorb without breaking depends on characteristics such as its cross-sectional area and elasticity. For healthy human leg bones of approximately 6.0 cm^2 cross-sectional area, this energy has been experimentally measured to be about 200 J. (a) From approximately what maximum height could a 60-kg person jump and land rigidly upright on both feet without breaking his legs? (b) You are probably surprised at how small the answer to part (a) is. People obviously jump from much greater heights without breaking their legs. How can that be? What else absorbs the energy when they jump from greater heights? (*Hint:* How did the person in part (a) land? How do people normally land when they jump from greater heights?) (c) Why might older people be much more prone than younger ones to bone fractures from simple falls (such as a fall in the shower)?

7.9 •• CP A small rock with mass 0.20 kg is released from rest at point A, which is at the top edge of a large, hemispherical bowl with radius $R = 0.50$ m (**Fig. E7.9**). Assume that the size of the rock is small compared to R, so that the rock can be treated as a particle, and assume that the rock slides rather than rolls. The work done by friction on the rock when it moves from point A to point B at the bottom of the bowl has magnitude 0.22 J. (a) Between points A and B, how much work is done on the rock by (i) the normal force and (ii) gravity? (b) What is the speed of the rock as it reaches point B? (c) Of the three forces acting on the rock as it slides down the bowl, which (if any) are constant and which are not? Explain. (d) Just as the rock reaches point B, what is the normal force on it due to the bottom of the bowl?

Figure **E7.9**

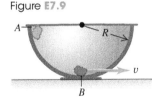

7.10 •• A 25.0-kg child plays on a swing having support ropes that are 2.20 m long. Her brother pulls her back until the ropes are 42.0° from the vertical and releases her from rest. (a) What is her potential energy just as she is released, compared with the potential energy at the bottom of the swing's motion? (b) How fast will she be moving at the bottom? (c) How much work does the tension in the ropes do as she swings from the initial position to the bottom of the motion?

7.11 •• You are testing a new amusement park roller coaster with an empty car of mass 120 kg. One part of the track is a vertical loop with radius 12.0 m. At the bottom of the loop (point A) the car has speed 25.0 m/s, and at the top of the loop (point B) it has speed 8.0 m/s. As the car rolls from point A to point B, how much work is done by friction?

7.12 • **Tarzan and Jane.** Tarzan, in one tree, sights Jane in another tree. He grabs the end of a vine with length 20 m that makes an angle of 45° with the vertical, steps off his tree limb, and swings down and then up to Jane's open arms. When he arrives, his vine makes an angle of 30° with the vertical. Determine whether he gives her a tender embrace or knocks her off her limb by calculating Tarzan's speed just before he reaches Jane. Ignore air resistance and the mass of the vine.

7.13 •• CP A 10.0-kg microwave oven is pushed 6.00 m up the sloping surface of a loading ramp inclined at an angle of 36.9° above the horizontal, by a constant force $\vec{F}$ with a magnitude 110 N and acting parallel to the ramp. The coefficient of kinetic friction between the oven and the ramp is 0.250. (a) What is the work done on the oven by the force $\vec{F}$? (b) What is the work done on the oven by the friction force? (c) Compute the increase in potential energy for the oven. (d) Use your answers to parts (a), (b), and (c) to calculate the increase in the oven's kinetic energy. (e) Use $\sum \vec{F} = m\vec{a}$ to calculate the oven's acceleration. Assuming that the oven is initially at rest, use the acceleration to calculate the oven's speed after the oven has traveled 6.00 m. From this, compute the increase in the oven's kinetic energy, and compare it to your answer for part (d).

Section 7.2 Elastic Potential Energy

7.14 •• An ideal spring of negligible mass is 12.00 cm long when nothing is attached to it. When you hang a 3.15-kg weight from it, you measure its length to be 13.40 cm. If you wanted to store 10.0 J of potential energy in this spring, what would be its *total* length? Assume that it continues to obey Hooke's law.

7.15 •• A force of 520 N keeps a certain spring stretched a distance of 0.200 m. (a) What is the potential energy of the spring when it is stretched 0.200 m? (b) What is its potential energy when it is compressed 5.00 cm?

7.16 • BIO **Tendons.** Tendons are strong elastic fibers that attach muscles to bones. To a reasonable approximation, they obey Hooke's law. In laboratory tests on a particular tendon, it was found that, when a 250-g object was hung from it, the tendon stretched 1.23 cm. (a) Find the force constant of this tendon in N/m. (b) Because of its thickness, the maximum tension this tendon can support without rupturing is 138 N. By how much can the tendon stretch without rupturing, and how much energy is stored in it at that point?

7.17 • A spring stores potential energy U_0 when it is compressed a distance x_0 from its uncompressed length. (a) In terms of U_0, how much energy does the spring store when it is compressed (i) twice as much and (ii) half as much? (b) In terms of x_0, how much must the spring be compressed from its uncompressed length to store (i) twice as much energy and (ii) half as much energy?

7.18 • A slingshot will shoot a 10-g pebble 22.0 m straight up. (a) How much potential energy is stored in the slingshot's rubber band? (b) With the same potential energy stored in the rubber band, how high can the slingshot shoot a 25-g pebble? (c) What physical effects did you ignore in solving this problem?

7.19 •• A spring of negligible mass has force constant $k = 800$ N/m. (a) How far must the spring be compressed for 1.20 J of potential energy to be stored in it? (b) You place the spring vertically with one end on the floor. You then lay a 1.60-kg book on top of the spring and release the book from rest. Find the maximum distance the spring will be compressed.

7.20 • A 1.20-kg piece of cheese is placed on a vertical spring of negligible mass and force constant $k = 1800$ N/m that is compressed 15.0 cm. When the spring is released, how high does the cheese rise from this initial position? (The cheese and the spring are *not* attached.)

7.21 •• A spring of negligible mass has force constant $k = 1600$ N/m. (a) How far must the spring be compressed for 3.20 J of potential energy to be stored in it? (b) You place the spring vertically with one end on the floor. You then drop a 1.20-kg book onto it from a height of 0.800 m above the top of the spring. Find the maximum distance the spring will be compressed.

7.22 •• (a) For the elevator of Example 7.9 (Section 7.2), what is the speed of the elevator after it has moved downward 1.00 m from point 1 in Fig. 7.17? (b) When the elevator is 1.00 m below point 1 in Fig. 7.17, what is its acceleration?

7.23 •• A 2.50-kg mass is pushed against a horizontal spring of force constant 25.0 N/cm on a frictionless air table. The spring is attached to the tabletop, and the mass is not attached to the spring in any way. When the spring has been compressed enough to store 11.5 J of potential energy in it, the mass is suddenly released from rest. (a) Find the greatest speed the mass reaches. When does this occur? (b) What is the greatest acceleration of the mass, and when does it occur?

7.24 •• A 2.50-kg block on a horizontal floor is attached to a horizontal spring that is initially compressed 0.0300 m. The spring has force constant 840 N/m. The coefficient of kinetic friction between the floor and the block is $\mu_k = 0.40$. The block and spring are released from rest, and the block slides along the floor. What is the speed of the block when it has moved a distance of 0.0200 m from its initial position? (At this point the spring is compressed 0.0100 m.)

7.25 •• You are asked to design a spring that will give a 1160-kg satellite a speed of 2.50 m/s relative to an orbiting space shuttle. Your spring is to give the satellite a maximum acceleration of 5.00g. The spring's mass, the recoil kinetic energy of the shuttle, and changes in gravitational potential energy will all be negligible. (a) What must the force constant of the spring be? (b) What distance must the spring be compressed?

Section 7.3 Conservative and Nonconservative Forces

7.26 • A 75-kg roofer climbs a vertical 7.0-m ladder to the flat roof of a house. He then walks 12 m on the roof, climbs down another vertical 7.0-m ladder, and finally walks on the ground back to his starting point. How much work is done on him by gravity (a) as he climbs up; (b) as he climbs down; (c) as he walks on the roof and on the ground? (d) What is the total work done on him by gravity during this round trip? (e) On the basis of your answer to part (d), would you say that gravity is a conservative or nonconservative force? Explain.

7.27 • A 0.60-kg book slides on a horizontal table. The kinetic friction force on the book has magnitude 1.8 N. (a) How much work is done on the book by friction during a displacement of 3.0 m to the left? (b) The book now slides 3.0 m to the right, returning to its starting point. During this second 3.0-m displacement, how much work is done on the book by friction? (c) What is the total work done on the book by friction during the complete round trip? (d) On the basis of your answer to part (c), would you say that the friction force is conservative or nonconservative? Explain.

7.28 •• CALC In an experiment, one of the forces exerted on a proton is $\vec{F} = -\alpha x^2 \hat{i}$, where $\alpha = 12$ N/m². (a) How much work does $\vec{F}$ do when the proton moves along the straight-line path from the point $(0.10 \text{ m}, 0)$ to the point $(0.10 \text{ m}, 0.40 \text{ m})$? (b) Along the straight-line path from the point $(0.10 \text{ m}, 0)$ to the point $(0.30 \text{ m}, 0)$? (c) Along the straight-line path from the point $(0.30 \text{ m}, 0)$ to the point $(0.10 \text{ m}, 0)$? (d) Is the force $\vec{F}$ conservative? Explain. If $\vec{F}$ is conservative, what is the potential-energy function for it? Let $U = 0$ when $x = 0$.

7.29 •• A 62.0-kg skier is moving at 6.50 m/s on a frictionless, horizontal, snow-covered plateau when she encounters a rough patch 4.20 m long. The coefficient of kinetic friction between this patch and her skis is 0.300. After crossing the rough patch and returning to friction-free snow, she skis down an icy, frictionless hill 2.50 m high. (a) How fast is the skier moving when she gets to the bottom of the hill? (b) How much internal energy was generated in crossing the rough patch?

7.30 • While a roofer is working on a roof that slants at 36° above the horizontal, he accidentally nudges his 85.0-N toolbox, causing it to start sliding downward from rest. If it starts 4.25 m from the lower edge of the roof, how fast will the toolbox be moving just as it reaches the edge of the roof if the kinetic friction force on it is 22.0 N?

Section 7.4 Force and Potential Energy

7.31 •• CALC A force parallel to the x-axis acts on a particle moving along the x-axis. This force produces potential energy $U(x)$ given by $U(x) = \alpha x^4$, where $\alpha = 0.630$ J/m⁴. What is the force (magnitude and direction) when the particle is at $x = -0.800$ m?

7.32 •• CALC The potential energy of a pair of hydrogen atoms separated by a large distance x is given by $U(x) = -C_6/x^6$, where C_6 is a positive constant. What is the force that one atom exerts on the other? Is this force attractive or repulsive?

7.33 •• CALC A small block with mass 0.0400 kg is moving in the xy-plane. The net force on the block is described by the potential-energy function $U(x, y) = (5.80 \text{ J/m}^2)x^2 - (3.60 \text{ J/m}^3)y^3$. What are the magnitude and direction of the acceleration of the block when it is at the point $(x = 0.300 \text{ m}, y = 0.600 \text{ m})$?

7.34 •• CALC An object moving in the xy-plane is acted on by a conservative force described by the potential-energy function $U(x, y) = \alpha[(1/x^2) + (1/y^2)]$, where α is a positive constant. Derive an expression for the force expressed in terms of the unit vectors $\hat{i}$ and $\hat{j}$.

Section 7.5 Energy Diagrams

7.35 • CALC The potential energy of two atoms in a diatomic molecule is approximated by $U(r) = (a/r^{12}) - (b/r^6)$, where r is the spacing between atoms and a and b are positive constants. (a) Find the force $F(r)$ on one atom as a function of r. Draw two graphs: one of $U(r)$ versus r and one of $F(r)$ versus r. (b) Find the equilibrium distance between the two atoms. Is this equilibrium stable? (c) Suppose the distance between the two atoms is equal to the equilibrium distance found in part (b). What minimum energy must be added to the molecule to *dissociate* it—that is, to separate the two atoms to an infinite distance apart? This is called the *dissociation energy* of the molecule. (d) For the molecule CO, the equilibrium distance between the carbon and oxygen atoms is 1.13×10^{-10} m and the dissociation energy is 1.54×10^{-18} J per molecule. Find the values of the constants a and b.

7.36 • A marble moves along the *x*-axis. The potential-energy function is shown in **Fig. E7.36.** (a) At which of the labeled *x*-coordinates is the force on the marble zero? (b) Which of the labeled *x*-coordinates is a position of stable equilibrium? (c) Which of the labeled *x*-coordinates is a position of unstable equilibrium?

Figure E7.36

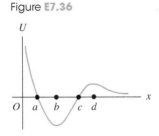

PROBLEMS

7.37 ••• At a construction site, a 65.0-kg bucket of concrete hangs from a light (but strong) cable that passes over a light, friction-free pulley and is connected to an 80.0-kg box on a horizontal roof (**Fig. P7.37**). The cable pulls horizontally on the box, and a 50.0-kg bag of gravel rests on top of the box. The coefficients of friction between the box and roof are shown. (a) Find the friction force on the bag of gravel and on the box. (b) Suddenly a worker picks up the bag of gravel. Use energy conservation to find the speed of the bucket after it has descended 2.00 m from rest. (Use Newton's laws to check your answer.)

Figure P7.37

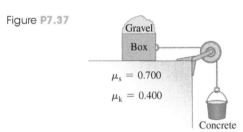

7.38 •• Two blocks with different masses are attached to either end of a light rope that passes over a light, frictionless pulley suspended from the ceiling. The masses are released from rest, and the more massive one starts to descend. After this block has descended 1.20 m, its speed is 3.00 m/s. If the total mass of the two blocks is 22.0 kg, what is the mass of each block?

7.39 • A block with mass 0.50 kg is forced against a horizontal spring of negligible mass, compressing the spring a distance of 0.20 m (**Fig. P7.39**). When released, the block moves on a horizontal tabletop for 1.00 m before coming to rest. The force constant k is 100 N/m. What is the coefficient of kinetic friction μ_k between the block and the tabletop?

Figure P7.39

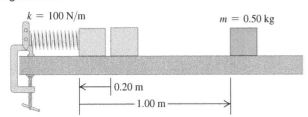

7.40 • A 2.00-kg block is pushed against a spring with negligible mass and force constant $k = 400$ N/m, compressing it 0.220 m. When the block is released, it moves along a frictionless, horizontal surface and then up a frictionless incline with slope 37.0° (**Fig. P7.40**). (a) What is the speed of the block as it slides along the horizontal surface after having left the spring? (b) How far does the block travel up the incline before starting to slide back down?

Figure P7.40

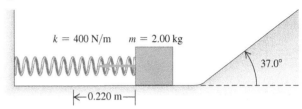

7.41 •• A 350-kg roller coaster car starts from rest at point A and slides down a frictionless loop-the-loop (**Fig. P7.41**). (a) How fast is this roller coaster car moving at point B? (b) How hard does it press against the track at point B?

Figure P7.41

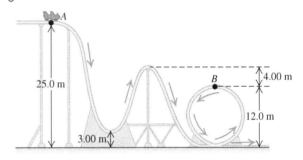

7.42 •• CP **Riding a Loop-the-Loop.** A car in an amusement park ride rolls without friction around a track (**Fig. P7.42**). The car starts from rest at point A at a height h above the bottom of the loop. Treat the car as a particle. (a) What is the minimum value of h (in terms of R) such that the car moves around the loop without falling off at the top (point B)? (b) If $h = 3.50R$ and $R = 14.0$ m, compute the speed, radial acceleration, and tangential acceleration of the passengers when the car is at point C, which is at the end of a horizontal diameter. Show these acceleration components in a diagram, approximately to scale.

Figure P7.42

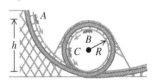

7.43 •• A 2.0-kg piece of wood slides on a curved surface (**Fig. P7.43**). The sides of the surface are perfectly smooth, but the rough horizontal bottom is 30 m long and has a kinetic friction coefficient of 0.20 with the wood. The piece of wood starts from rest 4.0 m above the rough bottom. (a) Where will this wood eventually come to rest? (b) For the motion from the initial release until the piece of wood comes to rest, what is the total amount of work done by friction?

Figure P7.43

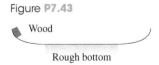

Wood

Rough bottom

7.44 •• **Up and Down the Hill.** A 28-kg rock approaches the foot of a hill with a speed of 15 m/s. This hill slopes upward at a constant angle of 40.0° above the horizontal. The coefficients of static and kinetic friction between the hill and the rock are 0.75 and 0.20, respectively. (a) Use energy conservation to find the maximum height above the foot of the hill reached by the rock. (b) Will the rock remain at rest at its highest point, or will it slide back down the hill? (c) If the rock does slide back down, find its speed when it returns to the bottom of the hill.

7.45 •• A 15.0-kg stone slides down a snow-covered hill (**Fig. P7.45**), leaving point A at a speed of 10.0 m/s. There is no friction on the hill between points A and B, but there is friction on the level ground at the bottom of the hill, between B and the wall.

Figure **P7.45**

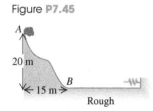

After entering the rough horizontal region, the stone travels 100 m and then runs into a very long, light spring with force constant 2.00 N/m. The coefficients of kinetic and static friction between the stone and the horizontal ground are 0.20 and 0.80, respectively. (a) What is the speed of the stone when it reaches point B? (b) How far will the stone compress the spring? (c) Will the stone move again after it has been stopped by the spring?

7.46 •• CP A 2.8-kg block slides over the smooth, icy hill shown in **Fig. P7.46**. The top of the hill is horizontal and 70 m higher than its base. What minimum speed must the block have at the base of the 70-m hill to pass over the pit at the far (right-hand) side of that hill?

Figure **P7.46**

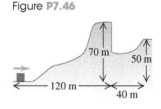

7.47 ••• **Bungee Jump.** A bungee cord is 30.0 m long and, when stretched a distance x, it exerts a restoring force of magnitude kx. Your father-in-law (mass 95.0 kg) stands on a platform 45.0 m above the ground, and one end of the cord is tied securely to his ankle and the other end to the platform. You have promised him that when he steps off the platform he will fall a maximum distance of only 41.0 m before the cord stops him. You had several bungee cords to select from, and you tested them by stretching them out, tying one end to a tree, and pulling on the other end with a force of 380.0 N. When you do this, what distance will the bungee cord that you should select have stretched?

7.48 ••• You are designing a delivery ramp for crates containing exercise equipment. The 1470-N crates will move at 1.8 m/s at the top of a ramp that slopes downward at 22.0°. The ramp exerts a 515-N kinetic friction force on each crate, and the maximum static friction force also has this value. Each crate will compress a spring at the bottom of the ramp and will come to rest after traveling a total distance of 5.0 m along the ramp. Once stopped, a crate must not rebound back up the ramp. Calculate the largest force constant of the spring that will be needed to meet the design criteria.

7.49 ••• The Great Sandini is a 60-kg circus performer who is shot from a cannon (actually a spring gun). You don't find many men of his caliber, so you help him design a new gun. This new gun has a very large spring with a very small mass and a force constant of 1100 N/m that he will compress with a force of 4400 N. The inside of the gun barrel is coated with Teflon, so the average friction force will be only 40 N during the 4.0 m he moves in the barrel. At what speed will he emerge from the end of the barrel, 2.5 m above his initial rest position?

7.50 •• A 1500-kg rocket is to be launched with an initial upward speed of 50.0 m/s. In order to assist its engines, the engineers will start it from rest on a ramp that rises 53° above the horizontal (**Fig. P7.50**). At the bottom, the ramp turns upward and launches the rocket vertically. The engines provide a constant forward thrust of 2000 N, and friction with the

Figure **P7.50**

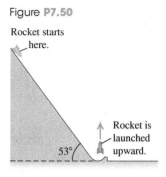

ramp surface is a constant 500 N. How far from the base of the ramp should the rocket start, as measured along the surface of the ramp?

7.51 •• A system of two paint buckets connected by a light-weight rope is released from rest with the 12.0-kg bucket 2.00 m above the floor (**Fig. P7.51**). Use the principle of conservation of energy to find the speed with which this bucket strikes the floor. Ignore friction and the mass of the pulley.

Figure **P7.51**

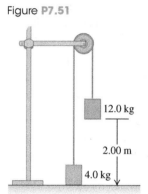

7.52 •• These results are from a computer simulation for a batted baseball with mass 0.145 kg, including air resistance:

t	x	y	v_x	v_y
0	0	0	30.0 m/s	40.0 m/s
3.05 s	70.2 m	53.6 m	18.6 m/s	0
6.59 s	124.4 m	0	11.9 m/s	−28.7 m/s

How much work did the air do on the baseball (a) as the ball moved from its initial position to its maximum height, and (b) as the ball moved from its maximum height back to the starting elevation? (c) Explain why the magnitude of the answer in part (b) is smaller than the magnitude of the answer in part (a).

7.53 •• CP A 0.300-kg potato is tied to a string with length 2.50 m, and the other end of the string is tied to a rigid support. The potato is held straight out horizontally from the point of support, with the string pulled taut, and is then released. (a) What is the speed of the potato at the lowest point of its motion? (b) What is the tension in the string at this point?

7.54 •• A 60.0-kg skier starts from rest at the top of a ski slope 65.0 m high. (a) If friction forces do −10.5 kJ of work on her as she descends, how fast is she going at the bottom of the slope? (b) Now moving horizontally, the skier crosses a patch of soft snow where $\mu_k = 0.20$. If the patch is 82.0 m wide and the average force of air resistance on the skier is 160 N, how fast is she going after crossing the patch? (c) The skier hits a snowdrift and penetrates 2.5 m into it before coming to a stop. What is the average force exerted on her by the snowdrift as it stops her?

7.55 • CP A skier starts at the top of a very large, frictionless snowball, with a very small initial speed, and skis straight down the side (**Fig. P7.55**). At what point does she lose contact with the snowball and fly off at a tangent? That is, at the instant she loses contact with the snowball, what angle α does a radial line from the center of the snowball to the skier make with the vertical?

Figure **P7.55**

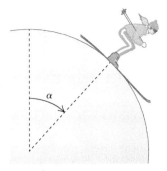

7.56 ·· A ball is thrown upward with an initial velocity of 15 m/s at an angle of 60.0° above the horizontal. Use energy conservation to find the ball's greatest height above the ground.

7.57 ·· In a truck-loading station at a post office, a small 0.200-kg package is released from rest at point *A* on a track that is one-quarter of a circle with radius 1.60 m (**Fig. P7.57**). The size of the package is much less than 1.60 m, so the package can be treated as a particle. It slides down the track and reaches point *B* with a speed of 4.80 m/s. From point *B*, it slides on a level surface a distance of 3.00 m to point *C*, where it comes to rest. (a) What is the coefficient of kinetic friction on the horizontal surface? (b) How much work is done on the package by friction as it slides down the circular arc from *A* to *B*?

Figure **P7.57**

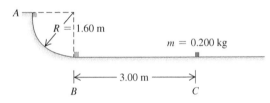

7.58 ··· A truck with mass *m* has a brake failure while going down an icy mountain road of constant downward slope angle α (**Fig. P7.58**). Initially the truck is moving downhill at speed v_0. After careening downhill a distance *L* with negligible friction, the truck driver steers the runaway vehicle onto a runaway truck ramp of constant upward slope angle β. The truck ramp has a soft sand surface for which the coefficient of rolling friction is μ_r. What is the distance that the truck moves up the ramp before coming to a halt? Solve by energy methods.

Figure **P7.58**

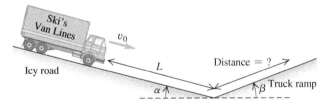

7.59 ·· CALC A certain spring found *not* to obey Hooke's law exerts a restoring force $F_x(x) = -\alpha x - \beta x^2$ if it is stretched or compressed, where α = 60.0 N/m and β = 18.0 N/m². The mass of the spring is negligible. (a) Calculate the potential-energy function $U(x)$ for this spring. Let $U = 0$ when $x = 0$. (b) An object with mass 0.900 kg on a frictionless, horizontal surface is attached to this spring, pulled a distance 1.00 m to the right (the +*x*-direction) to stretch the spring, and released. What is the speed of the object when it is 0.50 m to the right of the $x = 0$ equilibrium position?

7.60 ·· CP A sled with rider having a combined mass of 125 kg travels over a perfectly smooth icy hill (**Fig. P7.60**). How far does the sled land from the foot of the cliff?

Figure **P7.60**

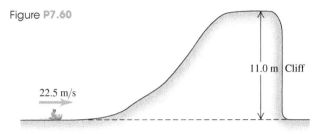

7.61 ·· CALC A conservative force $\vec{F}$ is in the +*x*-direction and has magnitude $F(x) = \alpha/(x + x_0)^2$, where α = 0.800 N·m² and $x_0 = 0.200$ m. (a) What is the potential-energy function $U(x)$ for this force? Let $U(x) \to 0$ as $x \to \infty$. (b) An object with mass $m = 0.500$ kg is released from rest at $x = 0$ and moves in the +*x*-direction. If $\vec{F}$ is the only force acting on the object, what is the object's speed when it reaches $x = 0.400$ m?

7.62 ·· A 3.00-kg block is connected to two ideal horizontal springs having force constants $k_1 = 25.0$ N/cm and $k_2 = 20.0$ N/cm (**Fig. P7.62**).

Figure **P7.62**

The system is initially in equilibrium on a horizontal, frictionless surface. The block is now pushed 15.0 cm to the right and released from rest. (a) What is the maximum speed of the block? Where in the motion does the maximum speed occur? (b) What is the maximum compression of spring 1?

7.63 ·· A 0.150-kg block of ice is placed against a horizontal, compressed spring mounted on a horizontal tabletop that is 1.20 m above the floor. The spring has force constant 1900 N/m and is initially compressed 0.045 m. The mass of the spring is negligible. The spring is released, and the block slides along the table, goes off the edge, and travels to the floor. If there is negligible friction between the block of ice and the tabletop, what is the speed of the block of ice when it reaches the floor?

7.64 ·· If a fish is attached to a vertical spring and slowly lowered to its equilibrium position, it is found to stretch the spring by an amount *d*. If the same fish is attached to the end of the unstretched spring and then allowed to fall from rest, through what maximum distance does it stretch the spring? (*Hint:* Calculate the force constant of the spring in terms of the distance *d* and the mass *m* of the fish.)

7.65 ··· CALC You are an industrial engineer with a shipping company. As part of the package-handling system, a small box with mass 1.60 kg is placed against a light spring that is compressed 0.280 m. The spring has force constant $k = 45.0$ N/m. The spring and box are released from rest, and the box travels along a horizontal surface for which the coefficient of kinetic friction with the box is $\mu_k = 0.300$. When the box has traveled 0.280 m and the spring has reached its equilibrium length, the box loses contact with the spring. (a) What is the speed of the box at the instant when it leaves the spring? (b) What is the maximum speed of the box during its motion?

7.66 ·· A basket of negligible weight hangs from a vertical spring scale of force constant 1500 N/m. (a) If you suddenly put a 3.0-kg adobe brick in the basket, find the maximum distance that the spring will stretch. (b) If, instead, you release the brick from 1.0 m above the basket, by how much will the spring stretch at its maximum elongation?

7.67 ••• CALC A 3.00-kg fish is attached to the lower end of a vertical spring that has negligible mass and force constant 900 N/m. The spring initially is neither stretched nor compressed. The fish is released from rest. (a) What is its speed after it has descended 0.0500 m from its initial position? (b) What is the maximum speed of the fish as it descends?

7.68 •• You are designing an amusement park ride. A cart with two riders moves horizontally with speed $v = 6.00$ m/s. You assume that the total mass of cart plus riders is 300 kg. The cart hits a light spring that is attached to a wall, momentarily comes to rest as the spring is compressed, and then regains speed as it moves back in the opposite direction. For the ride to be thrilling but safe, the maximum acceleration of the cart during this motion should be 3.00g. Ignore friction. What is (a) the required force constant of the spring, (b) the maximum distance the spring will be compressed?

7.69 • A 0.500-kg block, attached to a spring with length 0.60 m and force constant 40.0 N/m, is at rest with the back of the block at point A on a frictionless, horizontal air table (**Fig. P7.69**). The mass of the spring is negligible. You move the block to the right along the surface by pulling with a constant 20.0-N horizontal force. (a) What is the block's speed when the back of the block reaches point B, which is 0.25 m to the right of point A? (b) When the back of the block reaches point B, you let go of the block. In the subsequent motion, how close does the block get to the wall where the left end of the spring is attached?

Figure **P7.69**

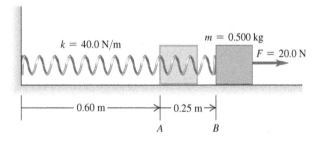

$k = 40.0$ N/m $m = 0.500$ kg

$F = 20.0$ N

0.60 m   0.25 m

A   B

7.70 ••• CP A small block with mass 0.0400 kg slides in a vertical circle of radius $R = 0.500$ m on the inside of a circular track. During one of the revolutions of the block, when the block is at the bottom of its path, point A, the normal force exerted on the block by the track has magnitude 3.95 N. In this same revolution, when the block reaches the top of its path, point B, the normal force exerted on the block has magnitude 0.680 N. How much work is done on the block by friction during the motion of the block from point A to point B?

7.71 ••• CP A small block with mass 0.0500 kg slides in a vertical circle of radius $R = 0.800$ m on the inside of a circular track. There is no friction between the track and the block. At the bottom of the block's path, the normal force the track exerts on the block has magnitude 3.40 N. What is the magnitude of the normal force that the track exerts on the block when it is at the top of its path?

7.72 •• CP **Pendulum.** A small rock with mass 0.12 kg is fastened to a massless string with length 0.80 m to form a pendulum. The pendulum is swinging so as to make a maximum angle of 45° with the vertical. Air resistance is negligible. (a) What is the speed of the rock when the string passes through the vertical position? What is the tension in the string (b) when it makes an angle of 45° with the vertical, (c) as it passes through the vertical?

7.73 ••• A wooden block with mass 1.50 kg is placed against a compressed spring at the bottom of an incline of slope 30.0° (point A). When the spring is released, it projects the block up the incline. At point B, a distance of 6.00 m up the incline from A, the block is moving up the incline at 7.00 m/s and is no longer in contact with the spring. The coefficient of kinetic friction between the block and the incline is $\mu_k = 0.50$. The mass of the spring is negligible. Calculate the amount of potential energy that was initially stored in the spring.

7.74 •• CALC A small object with mass $m = 0.0900$ kg moves along the $+x$-axis. The only force on the object is a conservative force that has the potential-energy function $U(x) = -\alpha x^2 + \beta x^3$, where $\alpha = 2.00$ J/m^2 and $\beta = 0.300$ J/m^3. The object is released from rest at small x. When the object is at $x = 4.00$ m, what are its (a) speed and (b) acceleration (magnitude and direction)? (c) What is the maximum value of x reached by the object during its motion?

7.75 ••• CALC A cutting tool under microprocessor control has several forces acting on it. One force is $\vec{F} = -\alpha xy^2\hat{j}$, a force in the negative y-direction whose magnitude depends on the position of the tool. For $\alpha = 2.50$ N/m^3, consider the displacement of the tool from the origin to the point ($x = 3.00$ m, $y = 3.00$ m). (a) Calculate the work done on the tool by $\vec{F}$ if this displacement is along the straight line $y = x$ that connects these two points. (b) Calculate the work done on the tool by $\vec{F}$ if the tool is first moved out along the x-axis to the point ($x = 3.00$ m, $y = 0$) and then moved parallel to the y-axis to the point ($x = 3.00$ m, $y = 3.00$ m). (c) Compare the work done by $\vec{F}$ along these two paths. Is $\vec{F}$ conservative or nonconservative? Explain.

7.76 • A particle moves along the x-axis while acted on by a single conservative force parallel to the x-axis. The force corresponds to the potential-energy function graphed in **Fig. P7.76**. The particle is released from rest at point A. (a) What is the direction of the force on the particle when it is at point A? (b) At point B? (c) At what value of x is the kinetic energy of the particle a maximum? (d) What is the force on the particle when it is at point C? (e) What is the largest value of x reached by the particle during its motion? (f) What value or values of x correspond to points of stable equilibrium? (g) Of unstable equilibrium?

Figure **P7.76**

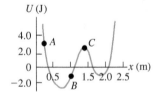

U (J)

4.0

2.0

0

−2.0

A

C

B

0.5   1.5 2.0 2.5

x (m)

7.77 •• DATA You are designing a pendulum for a science museum. The pendulum is made by attaching a brass sphere with mass m to the lower end of a long, light metal wire of (unknown) length L. A device near the top of the wire measures the tension in the wire and transmits that information to your laptop computer. When the wire is vertical and the sphere is at rest, the sphere's center is 0.800 m above the floor and the tension in the wire is 265 N. Keeping the wire taut, you then pull the sphere to one side (using a ladder if necessary) and gently release it. You record the height h of the center of the sphere above the floor at the point where the sphere is released and the tension T in the wire as the sphere swings through its lowest point. You collect your results:

h (m)	0.800	2.00	4.00	6.00	8.00	10.0	12.0
T (N)	265	274	298	313	330	348	371

Assume that the sphere can be treated as a point mass, ignore the mass of the wire, and assume that mechanical energy is conserved through each measurement. (a) Plot T versus h, and use this graph to calculate L. (b) If the breaking strength of the wire is 822 N, from what maximum height h can the sphere be released if the tension in the wire is not to exceed half the breaking strength? (c) The pendulum is swinging when you leave at the end of the day. You lock the museum doors, and no one enters the building until you return the next morning. You find that the sphere is hanging at rest. Using energy considerations, how can you explain this behavior?

7.78 •• DATA A long ramp made of cast iron is sloped at a constant angle $\theta = 52.0°$ above the horizontal. Small blocks, each with mass 0.42 kg but made of different materials, are released from rest at a vertical height h above the bottom of the ramp. In each case the coefficient of static friction is small enough that the blocks start to slide down the ramp as soon as they are released. You are asked to find h so that each block will have a speed of 4.00 m/s when it reaches the bottom of the ramp. You are given these coefficients of sliding (kinetic) friction for different pairs of materials:

Material 1	Material 2	Coefficient of Sliding Friction
Cast iron	Cast iron	0.15
Cast iron	Copper	0.29
Cast iron	Lead	0.43
Cast iron	Zinc	0.85

Source: www.engineershandbook.com

(a) Use work and energy considerations to find the required value of h if the block is made from (i) cast iron; (ii) copper; (iii) zinc. (b) What is the required value of h for the copper block if its mass is doubled to 0.84 kg? (c) For a given block, if θ is increased while h is kept the same, does the speed v of the block at the bottom of the ramp increase, decrease, or stay the same?

7.79 •• DATA A single conservative force $F(x)$ acts on a small sphere of mass m while the sphere moves along the x-axis. You release the sphere from rest at $x = -1.50$ m. As the sphere moves, you measure its velocity as a function of position. You use the velocity data to calculate the kinetic energy K; **Fig. P7.79** shows your data. (a) Let $U(x)$ be the potential-energy function for $F(x)$. Is $U(x)$ symmetric about $x = 0$? [If so, then $U(x) = U(-x)$.] (b) If you set $U = 0$ at $x = 0$, what is the value of U at $x = -1.50$ m? (c) Sketch $U(x)$. (d) At what values of x (if any) is $F = 0$? (e) For

Figure **P7.79**

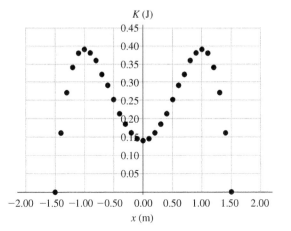

K (J)

x (m)

what range of values of x between $x = -1.50$ m and $x = +1.50$ m is F positive? Negative? (f) If you release the sphere from rest at $x = -1.30$ m, what is the largest value of x that it reaches during its motion? The largest value of kinetic energy that it has during its motion?

CHALLENGE PROBLEM

7.80 ••• CALC A proton with mass m moves in one dimension. The potential-energy function is $U(x) = (\alpha/x^2) - (\beta/x)$, where α and β are positive constants. The proton is released from rest at $x_0 = \alpha/\beta$. (a) Show that $U(x)$ can be written as

$$U(x) = \frac{\alpha}{x_0^2}\left[\left(\frac{x_0}{x}\right)^2 - \frac{x_0}{x}\right]$$

Graph $U(x)$. Calculate $U(x_0)$ and thereby locate the point x_0 on the graph. (b) Calculate $v(x)$, the speed of the proton as a function of position. Graph $v(x)$ and give a qualitative description of the motion. (c) For what value of x is the speed of the proton a maximum? What is the value of that maximum speed? (d) What is the force on the proton at the point in part (c)? (e) Let the proton be released instead at $x_1 = 3\alpha/\beta$. Locate the point x_1 on the graph of $U(x)$. Calculate $v(x)$ and give a qualitative description of the motion. (f) For each release point ($x = x_0$ and $x = x_1$), what are the maximum and minimum values of x reached during the motion?

PASSAGE PROBLEMS

BIO **THE DNA SPRING.** A DNA molecule, with its double-helix structure, can in some situations behave like a spring. Measuring the force required to stretch single DNA molecules under various conditions can provide information about the biophysical properties of DNA. A technique for measuring the stretching force makes use of a very small cantilever, which consists of a beam that is supported at one end and is free to move at the other end, like a tiny diving board. The cantilever is constructed so that it obeys Hooke's law—that is, the displacement of its free end is proportional to the force applied to it. Because different cantilevers have different force constants, the cantilever's response must first be calibrated by applying a known force and determining the resulting deflection of the cantilever. Then one end of a DNA molecule is attached to the free end of the cantilever, and the other end of the DNA molecule is attached to a small stage that can be moved away from the cantilever, stretching the DNA. The stretched DNA pulls on the cantilever, deflecting the end of the cantilever very slightly. The measured deflection is then used to determine the force on the DNA molecule.

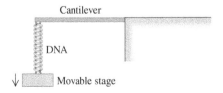

Cantilever

DNA

Movable stage

7.81 During the calibration process, the cantilever is observed to deflect by 0.10 nm when a force of 3.0 pN is applied to it. What deflection of the cantilever would correspond to a force of 6.0 pN? (a) 0.07 nm; (b) 0.14 nm; (c) 0.20 nm; (d) 0.40 nm.

7.82 A segment of DNA is put in place and stretched. **Figure P7.82** shows a graph of the force exerted on the DNA as a function of the displacement of the stage. Based on this graph, which statement is the best interpretation of the DNA's behavior over this range of displacements? The DNA (a) does not follow Hooke's law, because its force constant increases as the force on it increases; (b) follows Hooke's law and has a force constant of about 0.1 pN/nm; (c) follows Hooke's law and has a force constant of about 10 pN/nm; (d) does not follow Hooke's law, because its force constant decreases as the force on it increases.

Figure **P7.82**

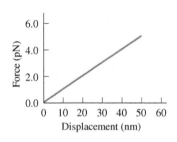

7.83 Based on Fig. P7.82, how much elastic potential energy is stored in the DNA when it is stretched 50 nm? (a) 2.5×10^{-19} J; (b) 1.2×10^{-19} J; (c) 5.0×10^{-12} J; (d) 2.5×10^{-12} J.

7.84 The stage moves at a constant speed while stretching the DNA. Which of the graphs in **Fig. P7.84** best represents the power supplied to the stage versus time?

Figure **P7.84**

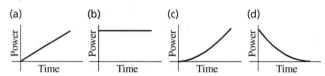

Answers

Chapter Opening Question ?

(v) As the crane descends, air resistance directed opposite to the bird's motion prevents its speed from increasing. Because the crane's speed stays the same, its kinetic energy K remains constant, but the gravitational potential energy U_{grav} decreases as the crane descends. Hence the total mechanical energy $E = K + U_{grav}$ decreases. The lost mechanical energy goes into warming the crane's skin (that is, an increase in the crane's internal energy) and stirring up the air through which the crane passes (an increase in the internal energy of the air). See Section 7.3.

Test Your Understanding Questions

7.1 (iii) The initial kinetic energy $K_1 = 0$, the initial potential energy $U_1 = mgy_1$, and the final potential energy $U_2 = mgy_2$ are the same for both blocks. Mechanical energy is conserved in both cases, so the final kinetic energy $K_2 = \frac{1}{2}mv_2^2$ is also the same for both blocks. Hence the speed at the right-hand end is the *same* in both cases!

7.2 (iii) The elevator is still moving downward, so the kinetic energy K is positive (remember that K can never be negative); the elevator is below point 1, so $y < 0$ and $U_{grav} < 0$; and the spring is compressed, so $U_{el} > 0$.

7.3 (iii) Because of friction in the turbines and between the water and turbines, some of the potential energy goes into raising the temperatures of the water and the mechanism.

7.4 (a) (iv), (b) (i) If $F_x = 0$ at a point, then the derivative of $U(x)$ must be zero at that point because $F_x = -dU(x)/dx$. However, this tells us absolutely nothing about the *value* of $U(x)$ at that point.

7.5 (iii) Figure 7.24b shows the x-component of force, F_x. Where this is maximum (most positive), the x-component of force and the x-acceleration have more positive values than at adjacent values of x.

Bridging Problem

(a) 1.06 m **(b)** 1.32 m **(c)** 20.7 J

? Which of the following three bullets (all of the same length and diameter) can do greater damage to this carrot? (i) A .22-caliber bullet moving at 220 m/s, as shown here; (ii) a bullet with half the mass moving at twice the speed; (iii) a bullet with double the mass moving at half the speed; (iv) all do the same amount of damage.

8 MOMENTUM, IMPULSE, AND COLLISIONS

Many questions involving forces can't be answered by directly applying Newton's second law, $\sum \vec{F} = m\vec{a}$. For example, when a truck collides head-on with a compact car, what determines which way the wreckage moves after the collision? In playing pool, how do you decide how to aim the cue ball in order to knock the eight ball into the pocket? And when a meteorite collides with the earth, how much of the meteorite's kinetic energy is released in the impact?

All of these questions involve forces about which we know very little: the forces between the car and the truck, between the two pool balls, or between the meteorite and the earth. Remarkably, we will find in this chapter that we don't have to know *anything* about these forces to answer questions of this kind!

Our approach uses two new concepts, *momentum* and *impulse,* and a new conservation law, *conservation of momentum.* This conservation law is every bit as important as the law of conservation of energy. The law of conservation of momentum is valid even in situations in which Newton's laws are inadequate, such as bodies moving at very high speeds (near the speed of light) or objects on a very small scale (such as the constituents of atoms). Within the domain of Newtonian mechanics, conservation of momentum enables us to analyze many situations that would be very difficult if we tried to use Newton's laws directly. Among these are *collision* problems, in which two bodies collide and can exert very large forces on each other for a short time. We'll also use momentum ideas to solve problems in which an object's mass changes as it moves, including the important special case of a rocket (which loses mass as it expends fuel).

8.1 MOMENTUM AND IMPULSE

In Section 6.2 we re-expressed Newton's second law for a particle, $\sum \vec{F} = m\vec{a}$, in terms of the work–energy theorem. This theorem helped us tackle a great number of problems and led us to the law of conservation of energy. Let's return to $\sum \vec{F} = m\vec{a}$ and see yet another useful way to restate this fundamental law.

Newton's Second Law in Terms of Momentum

Consider a particle of constant mass m. Because $\vec{a} = d\vec{v}/dt$, we can write Newton's second law for this particle as

$$\sum \vec{F} = m\frac{d\vec{v}}{dt} = \frac{d}{dt}(m\vec{v}) \tag{8.1}$$

We can move the mass m inside the derivative because it is constant. Thus Newton's second law says that the net force $\sum \vec{F}$ acting on a particle equals the time rate of change of the product of the particle's mass and velocity. We'll call this product the **momentum,** or **linear momentum,** of the particle:

Momentum of a particle $\cdots\!\!\rightarrow$ $\vec{p} = m\vec{v}$ $\qquad$ Particle mass
(a vector quantity) $\qquad\qquad\qquad\qquad\qquad\qquad$ Particle velocity $\tag{8.2}$

The greater the mass m and speed v of a particle, the greater is its magnitude of momentum mv. Keep in mind that momentum is a *vector* quantity with the same direction as the particle's velocity (**Fig. 8.1**). A car driving north at $20\ \text{m/s}$ and an identical car driving east at $20\ \text{m/s}$ have the same *magnitude* of momentum (mv) but different momentum *vectors* $(m\vec{v})$ because their directions are different.

We often express the momentum of a particle in terms of its components. If the particle has velocity components v_x, v_y, and v_z, then its momentum components p_x, p_y, and p_z (which we also call the *x-momentum, y-momentum,* and *z-momentum*) are

$$p_x = mv_x \qquad p_y = mv_y \qquad p_z = mv_z \tag{8.3}$$

These three component equations are equivalent to Eq. (8.2).

The units of the magnitude of momentum are units of mass times speed; the SI units of momentum are $\text{kg} \cdot \text{m/s}$. The plural of momentum is "momenta."

Let's now substitute the definition of momentum, Eq. (8.2), into Eq. (8.1):

Newton's second law
in terms of momentum:
The net force acting on $\cdots\!\!\rightarrow$ $\sum \vec{F} = \dfrac{d\vec{p}}{dt}$ $\leftarrow\cdots$ ... equals the rate of change
a particle ... $\qquad\qquad\qquad\qquad\qquad\qquad$ of the particle's momentum. $\tag{8.4}$

The net force (vector sum of all forces) acting on a particle equals the time rate of change of momentum of the particle. This, not $\sum \vec{F} = m\vec{a}$, is the form in which Newton originally stated his second law (although he called momentum the "quantity of motion"). This law is valid only in inertial frames of reference (see Section 4.2). As Eq. 8.4 shows, a rapid change in momentum requires a large net force, while a gradual change in momentum requires a smaller net force (**Fig. 8.2**).

The Impulse–Momentum Theorem

Both a particle's momentum $\vec{p} = m\vec{v}$ and its kinetic energy $K = \frac{1}{2}mv^2$ depend on the mass and velocity of the particle. What is the fundamental difference between these two quantities? A purely mathematical answer is that momentum

8.1 The velocity and momentum vectors of a particle.

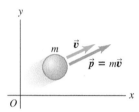

Momentum $\vec{p}$ is a vector quantity; a particle's momentum has the same direction as its velocity $\vec{v}$.

8.2 When you land after jumping upward, your momentum changes from a downward value to zero. It's best to land with your knees bent so that your legs can flex: You then take a relatively long time to stop, and the force that the ground exerts on your legs is small. If you land with your legs extended, you stop in a short time, the force on your legs is larger, and the possibility of injury is greater.

is a vector whose magnitude is proportional to speed, while kinetic energy is a scalar proportional to the speed squared. But to see the *physical* difference between momentum and kinetic energy, we must first define a quantity closely related to momentum called *impulse*.

Let's first consider a particle acted on by a *constant* net force $\Sigma \vec{F}$ during a time interval Δt from t_1 to t_2. The **impulse** of the net force, denoted by $\vec{J}$, is defined to be the product of the net force and the time interval:

Impulse of a
constant net force $\cdots\to$ $\vec{J} = \Sigma\vec{F}(t_2 - t_1) = \Sigma\vec{F}\Delta t$ $\cdots$ Constant net force
   Time interval over
   $\cdots\cdots$ which net force acts   (8.5)

Impulse is a vector quantity; its direction is the same as the net force $\Sigma\vec{F}$. The SI unit of impulse is the newton-second (N·s). Because $1 \text{ N} = 1 \text{ kg}\cdot\text{m/s}^2$, an alternative set of units for impulse is kg·m/s, the same as for momentum.

To see what impulse is good for, let's go back to Newton's second law as restated in terms of momentum, Eq. (8.4). If the net force $\Sigma\vec{F}$ is constant, then $d\vec{p}/dt$ is also constant. In that case, $d\vec{p}/dt$ is equal to the *total* change in momentum $\vec{p}_2 - \vec{p}_1$ during the time interval $t_2 - t_1$, divided by the interval:

$$\Sigma\vec{F} = \frac{\vec{p}_2 - \vec{p}_1}{t_2 - t_1}$$

Multiplying this equation by $(t_2 - t_1)$, we have

$$\Sigma\vec{F}(t_2 - t_1) = \vec{p}_2 - \vec{p}_1$$

Comparing with Eq. (8.5), we end up with

Impulse–momentum theorem: The impulse of the net force
on a particle during a time interval equals the change in
momentum of that particle during that interval:
Impulse of net force over $\cdots$ $\vec{J} = \vec{p}_2 - \vec{p}_1 = \Delta\vec{p}$ $\cdots$ Change in
a time interval   momentum   (8.6)
   Final momentum $\cdots$ $\cdots$ Initial momentum

The impulse–momentum theorem also holds when forces are not constant. To see this, we integrate both sides of Newton's second law $\Sigma\vec{F} = d\vec{p}/dt$ over time between the limits t_1 and t_2:

$$\int_{t_1}^{t_2} \Sigma\vec{F}\, dt = \int_{t_1}^{t_2} \frac{d\vec{p}}{dt} dt = \int_{\vec{p}_1}^{\vec{p}_2} d\vec{p} = \vec{p}_2 - \vec{p}_1$$

We see from Eq. (8.6) that the integral on the left is the impulse of the net force:

Impulse of a
general net force $\cdots$ $\vec{J} = \int_{t_1}^{t_2} \Sigma\vec{F}\, dt$ $\cdots$ Upper limit = final time
(either constant $\cdots$ Time integral of
or varying)   net force   (8.7)
   $\cdots$ Lower limit = initial time

If the net force $\Sigma\vec{F}$ is constant, the integral in Eq. (8.7) reduces to Eq. (8.5). We can define an *average* net force $\vec{F}_{av}$ such that even when $\Sigma\vec{F}$ is not constant, the impulse $\vec{J}$ is given by

$$\vec{J} = \vec{F}_{av}(t_2 - t_1) \tag{8.8}$$

When $\Sigma\vec{F}$ is constant, $\Sigma\vec{F} = \vec{F}_{av}$ and Eq. (8.8) reduces to Eq. (8.5).

Figure 8.3a shows the x-component of net force ΣF_x as a function of time during a collision. This might represent the force on a soccer ball that is in contact with a player's foot from time t_1 to t_2. The x-component of impulse during this interval is represented by the red area under the curve between t_1 and t_2. This area is equal to the green rectangular area bounded by t_1, t_2, and $(F_{av})_x$,

Application Woodpecker Impulse The pileated woodpecker (*Dryocopus pileatus*) has been known to strike its beak against a tree up to 20 times a second and up to 12,000 times a day. The impact force can be as much as 1200 times the weight of the bird's head. Because the impact lasts such a short time, the impulse—the product of the net force during the impact multiplied by the duration of the impact—is relatively small. (The woodpecker has a thick skull of spongy bone as well as shock-absorbing cartilage at the base of the lower jaw, and so avoids injury.)

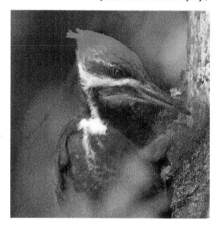

8.3 The meaning of the area under a graph of ΣF_x versus t.

(a)

The area under the curve of net force versus time equals the impulse of the net force:

$$\text{Area} = J_x = \int_{t_1}^{t_2} \Sigma F_x\, dt$$

We can also calculate the impulse by replacing the varying net force with an average net force:

$$\text{Area} = J_x = (F_{av})_x(t_2 - t_1)$$

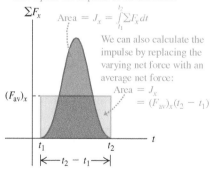

(b)

Large force that acts for a short time

The area under both curves is the same, so both forces deliver the same impulse.

Smaller force that acts for a longer time

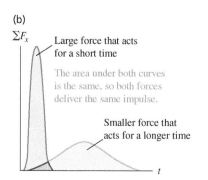

8.4 The impulse–momentum theorem explains how air bags reduce the chance of injury by minimizing the force on an occupant of an automobile.

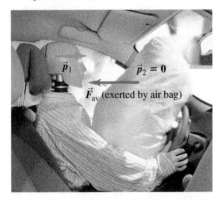

- Impulse–momentum theorem:
$$\vec{J} = \vec{p}_2 - \vec{p}_1 = \vec{F}_{av}\Delta t$$
- Impulse is the same no matter how the driver is brought to rest (so $\vec{p}_2 = \mathbf{0}$).
- Compared to striking the steering wheel, striking the air bag brings the driver to rest over a longer time interval Δt.
- Hence with an air bag, average force $\vec{F}_{av}$ on the driver is less.

so $(F_{av})_x(t_2 - t_1)$ is equal to the impulse of the actual time-varying force during the same interval. Note that a large force acting for a short time can have the same impulse as a smaller force acting for a longer time if the areas under the force–time curves are the same (Fig. 8.3b). We used this idea in Fig. 8.2: A small force acting for a relatively long time (as when you land with your legs bent) has the same effect as a larger force acting for a short time (as when you land stiff-legged). Automotive air bags use the same principle (**Fig. 8.4**).

Both impulse and momentum are vector quantities, and Eqs. (8.5)–(8.8) are vector equations. It's often easiest to use them in component form:

$$J_x = \int_{t_1}^{t_2} \Sigma F_x \, dt = (F_{av})_x(t_2 - t_1) = p_{2x} - p_{1x} = mv_{2x} - mv_{1x}$$

(8.9)

$$J_y = \int_{t_1}^{t_2} \Sigma F_y \, dt = (F_{av})_y(t_2 - t_1) = p_{2y} - p_{1y} = mv_{2y} - mv_{1y}$$

and similarly for the z-component.

Momentum and Kinetic Energy Compared

We can now see the fundamental difference between momentum and kinetic energy. The impulse–momentum theorem, $\vec{J} = \vec{p}_2 - \vec{p}_1$, says that changes in a particle's momentum are due to impulse, which depends on the *time* over which the net force acts. By contrast, the work–energy theorem, $W_{tot} = K_2 - K_1$, tells us that kinetic energy changes when work is done on a particle; the total work depends on the *distance* over which the net force acts.

Let's consider a particle that starts from rest at t_1 so that $\vec{v}_1 = \mathbf{0}$. Its initial momentum is $\vec{p}_1 = m\vec{v}_1 = \mathbf{0}$, and its initial kinetic energy is $K_1 = \frac{1}{2}mv_1^2 = 0$. Now let a constant net force equal to $\vec{F}$ act on that particle from time t_1 until time t_2. During this interval, the particle moves a distance s in the direction of the force. From Eq. (8.6), the particle's momentum at time t_2 is

$$\vec{p}_2 = \vec{p}_1 + \vec{J} = \vec{J}$$

8.5 The *kinetic energy* of a pitched baseball is equal to the work the pitcher does on it (force multiplied by the distance the ball moves during the throw). The *momentum* of the ball is equal to the impulse the pitcher imparts to it (force multiplied by the time it took to bring the ball up to speed).

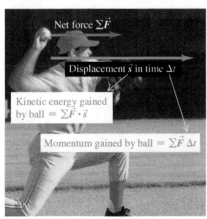

where $\vec{J} = \vec{F}(t_2 - t_1)$ is the impulse that acts on the particle. So *the momentum of a particle equals the impulse that accelerated it from rest to its present speed;* impulse is the product of the net force that accelerated the particle and the *time* required for the acceleration. By comparison, the kinetic energy of the particle at t_2 is $K_2 = W_{tot} = Fs$, the total *work* done on the particle to accelerate it from rest. The total work is the product of the net force and the *distance* required to accelerate the particle (**Fig. 8.5**).

Here's an application of the distinction between momentum and kinetic energy. Which is easier to catch: a 0.50-kg ball moving at 4.0 m/s or a 0.10-kg ball moving at 20 m/s? Both balls have the same magnitude of momentum, $p = mv = (0.50\text{ kg})(4.0\text{ m/s}) = (0.10\text{ kg})(20\text{ m/s}) = 2.0\text{ kg}\cdot\text{m/s}$. However, the two balls have different values of kinetic energy $K = \frac{1}{2}mv^2$: The large, slow-moving ball has $K = 4.0$ J, while the small, fast-moving ball has $K = 20$ J. Since the momentum is the same for both balls, both require the same *impulse* to be brought to rest. But stopping the 0.10-kg ball with your hand requires five times more *work* than stopping the 0.50-kg ball because the smaller ball has five times more kinetic energy. For a given force that you exert with your hand, it takes the same amount of time (the duration of the catch) to stop either ball, but your hand and arm will be pushed back five times farther if you choose to catch the small, fast-moving ball. To minimize arm strain, you should choose to catch the 0.50-kg ball with its lower kinetic energy.

Both the impulse–momentum and work–energy theorems rest on the foundation of Newton's laws. They are *integral* principles, relating the motion at two different times separated by a finite interval. By contrast, Newton's second law itself (in either of the forms $\sum \vec{F} = m\vec{a}$ or $\sum \vec{F} = d\vec{p}/dt$) is a *differential* principle that concerns the rate of change of velocity or momentum at each instant.

CONCEPTUAL EXAMPLE 8.1 MOMENTUM VERSUS KINETIC ENERGY

Consider again the race described in Conceptual Example 6.5 (Section 6.2) between two iceboats on a frictionless frozen lake. The boats have masses m and $2m$, and the wind exerts the same constant horizontal force $\vec{F}$ on each boat (see Fig. 6.14). The boats start from rest and cross the finish line a distance s away. Which boat crosses the finish line with greater momentum?

SOLUTION

In Conceptual Example 6.5 we asked how the *kinetic energies* of the boats compare when they cross the finish line. We answered this by remembering that *a body's kinetic energy equals the total work done to accelerate it from rest.* Both boats started from rest, and the total work done was the same for both boats (because the net force and the displacement were the same for both). Hence both boats had the same kinetic energy at the finish line.

Similarly, to compare the *momenta* of the boats we use the idea that *the momentum of each boat equals the impulse that*

accelerated it from rest. As in Conceptual Example 6.5, the net force on each boat equals the constant horizontal wind force $\vec{F}$. Let Δt be the time a boat takes to reach the finish line, so that the impulse on the boat during that time is $\vec{J} = \vec{F}\Delta t$. Since the boat starts from rest, this equals the boat's momentum $\vec{p}$ at the finish line:

$$\vec{p} = \vec{F}\Delta t$$

Both boats are subjected to the same force $\vec{F}$, but they take different times Δt to reach the finish line. The boat of mass $2m$ accelerates more slowly and takes a longer time to travel the distance s; thus there is a greater impulse on this boat between the starting and finish lines. So the boat of mass $2m$ crosses the finish line with a greater magnitude of momentum than the boat of mass m (but with the same kinetic energy). Can you show that the boat of mass $2m$ has $\sqrt{2}$ times as much momentum at the finish line as the boat of mass m?

EXAMPLE 8.2 A BALL HITS A WALL

You throw a ball with a mass of 0.40 kg against a brick wall. It is moving horizontally to the left at 30 m/s when it hits the wall; it rebounds horizontally to the right at 20 m/s. (a) Find the impulse of the net force on the ball during its collision with the wall. (b) If the ball is in contact with the wall for 0.010 s, find the average horizontal force that the wall exerts on the ball during the impact.

SOLUTION

IDENTIFY and SET UP: We're given enough information to determine the initial and final values of the ball's momentum, so we can use the impulse–momentum theorem to find the impulse. We'll then use the definition of impulse to determine the average force. **Figure 8.6** shows our sketch. We need only a single axis because the motion is purely horizontal. We'll take the positive x-direction to be to the right. In part (a) our target variable is the x-component of impulse, J_x, which we'll find by using Eqs. (8.9). In part (b), our target variable is the average x-component of force $(F_{av})_x$; once we know J_x, we can also find this force by using Eqs. (8.9).

8.6 Our sketch for this problem.

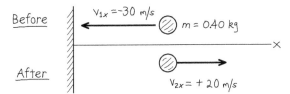

EXECUTE: (a) With our choice of x-axis, the initial and final x-components of momentum of the ball are

$$p_{1x} = mv_{1x} = (0.40 \text{ kg})(-30 \text{ m/s}) = -12 \text{ kg} \cdot \text{m/s}$$
$$p_{2x} = mv_{2x} = (0.40 \text{ kg})(+20 \text{ m/s}) = +8.0 \text{ kg} \cdot \text{m/s}$$

From the x-equation in Eqs. (8.9), the x-component of impulse equals the *change* in the x-momentum:

$$J_x = p_{2x} - p_{1x}$$
$$= 8.0 \text{ kg} \cdot \text{m/s} - (-12 \text{ kg} \cdot \text{m/s}) = 20 \text{ kg} \cdot \text{m/s} = 20 \text{ N} \cdot \text{s}$$

(b) The collision time is $t_2 - t_1 = \Delta t = 0.010$ s. From the x-equation in Eqs. (8.9), $J_x = (F_{av})_x(t_2 - t_1) = (F_{av})_x\Delta t$, so

$$(F_{av})_x = \frac{J_x}{\Delta t} = \frac{20 \text{ N} \cdot \text{s}}{0.010 \text{ s}} = 2000 \text{ N}$$

EVALUATE: The x-component of impulse J_x is positive—that is, to the right in Fig. 8.6. The impulse represents the "kick" that the wall imparts to the ball, and this "kick" is certainly to the right.

CAUTION Momentum is a vector Because momentum is a vector, we had to include the negative sign in writing $p_{1x} = -12 \text{ kg} \cdot \text{m/s}$. Had we omitted it, we would have calculated the impulse to be $8.0 \text{ kg} \cdot \text{m/s} - (12 \text{ kg} \cdot \text{m/s}) = -4 \text{ kg} \cdot \text{m/s}$. This would say that the wall had somehow given the ball a kick to the *left*! Remember the *direction* of momentum in your calculations.

Continued

The force that the wall exerts on the ball must have such a large magnitude (2000 N, equal to the weight of a 200-kg object) to change the ball's momentum in such a short time. Other forces that act on the ball during the collision are comparatively weak; for instance, the gravitational force is only 3.9 N. Thus, during the short time that the collision lasts, we can ignore all other forces on the ball. **Figure 8.7** shows the impact of a tennis ball and racket.

Note that the 2000-N value we calculated is the *average* horizontal force that the wall exerts on the ball during the impact. It corresponds to the horizontal line $(F_{av})_x$ in Fig. 8.3a. The horizontal force is zero before impact, rises to a maximum, and then decreases to zero when the ball loses contact with the wall. If the ball is relatively rigid, like a baseball or golf ball, the collision lasts a short time and the maximum force is large, as in the blue curve in Fig. 8.3b. If the ball is softer, like a tennis ball, the collision time is longer and the maximum force is less, as in the orange curve in Fig. 8.3b.

8.7 Typically, a tennis ball is in contact with the racket for approximately 0.01 s. The ball flattens noticeably due to the tremendous force exerted by the racket.

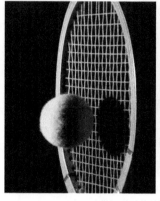
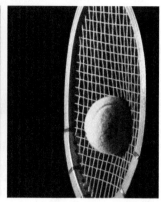

EXAMPLE 8.3 KICKING A SOCCER BALL

A soccer ball has a mass of 0.40 kg. Initially it is moving to the left at 20 m/s, but then it is kicked. After the kick it is moving at 45° upward and to the right with speed 30 m/s (**Fig. 8.8a**). Find the impulse of the net force and the average net force, assuming a collision time $\Delta t = 0.010$ s.

8.8 (a) Kicking a soccer ball. (b) Finding the average force on the ball from its components.

(a) Before-and-after diagram

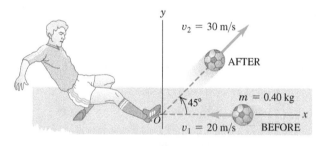

(b) Average force on the ball

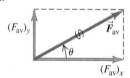

SOLUTION

IDENTIFY and SET UP: The ball moves in two dimensions, so we must treat momentum and impulse as vector quantities. We take the x-axis to be horizontally to the right and the y-axis to be vertically upward. Our target variables are the components of the net

impulse on the ball, J_x and J_y, and the components of the average net force on the ball, $(F_{av})_x$ and $(F_{av})_y$. We'll find them by using the impulse–momentum theorem in its component form, Eqs. (8.9).

EXECUTE: Using $\cos 45° = \sin 45° = 0.707$, we find the ball's velocity components before and after the kick:

$$v_{1x} = -20 \text{ m/s} \qquad v_{1y} = 0$$
$$v_{2x} = v_{2y} = (30 \text{ m/s})(0.707) = 21.2 \text{ m/s}$$

From Eqs. (8.9), the impulse components are

$$J_x = p_{2x} - p_{1x} = m(v_{2x} - v_{1x})$$
$$= (0.40 \text{ kg})[21.2 \text{ m/s} - (-20 \text{ m/s})] = 16.5 \text{ kg} \cdot \text{m/s}$$

$$J_y = p_{2y} - p_{1y} = m(v_{2y} - v_{1y})$$
$$= (0.40 \text{ kg})(21.2 \text{ m/s} - 0) = 8.5 \text{ kg} \cdot \text{m/s}$$

From Eq. (8.8), the average net force components are

$$(F_{av})_x = \frac{J_x}{\Delta t} = 1650 \text{ N} \qquad (F_{av})_y = \frac{J_y}{\Delta t} = 850 \text{ N}$$

The magnitude and direction of the $\vec{F}_{av}$ vector (Fig. 8.8b) are

$$F_{av} = \sqrt{(1650 \text{ N})^2 + (850 \text{ N})^2} = 1.9 \times 10^3 \text{ N}$$

$$\theta = \arctan \frac{850 \text{ N}}{1650 \text{ N}} = 27°$$

The ball was not initially at rest, so its final velocity does *not* have the same direction as the average force that acted on it.

EVALUATE: $\vec{F}_{av}$ includes the force of gravity, which is very small; the weight of the ball is only 3.9 N. As in Example 8.2, the average force acting during the collision is exerted almost entirely by the object that the ball hit (in this case, the soccer player's foot).

TEST YOUR UNDERSTANDING OF SECTION 8.1 Rank the following situations according to the magnitude of the impulse of the net force, from largest value to smallest value. In each situation a 1000-kg automobile is moving along a straight east–west road. The automobile is initially (i) moving east at 25 m/s and comes to a stop in 10 s; (ii) moving east at 25 m/s and comes to a stop in 5 s; (iii) at rest, and a 2000-N net force toward the east is applied to it for 10 s; (iv) moving east at 25 m/s, and a 2000-N net force toward the west is applied to it for 10 s; (v) moving east at 25 m/s; over a 30-s period, the automobile reverses direction and ends up moving west at 25 m/s. ∎

8.2 CONSERVATION OF MOMENTUM

The concept of momentum is particularly important in situations in which we have two or more bodies that *interact*. To see why, let's consider first an idealized system of two bodies that interact with each other but not with anything else— for example, two astronauts who touch each other as they float freely in the zero-gravity environment of outer space (**Fig. 8.9**). Think of the astronauts as particles. Each particle exerts a force on the other; according to Newton's third law, the two forces are always equal in magnitude and opposite in direction. Hence, the *impulses* that act on the two particles are equal in magnitude and opposite in direction, as are the changes in momentum of the two particles.

Let's go over that again with some new terminology. For any system, the forces that the particles of the system exert on each other are called **internal forces**. Forces exerted on any part of the system by some object outside it are called **external forces**. For the system shown in Fig. 8.9, the internal forces are $\vec{F}_{B \text{ on } A}$, exerted by particle B on particle A, and $\vec{F}_{A \text{ on } B}$, exerted by particle A on particle B. There are *no* external forces; when this is the case, we have an **isolated system**.

The net force on particle A is $\vec{F}_{B \text{ on } A}$ and the net force on particle B is $\vec{F}_{A \text{ on } B}$, so from Eq. (8.4) the rates of change of the momenta of the two particles are

$$\vec{F}_{B \text{ on } A} = \frac{d\vec{p}_A}{dt} \qquad \vec{F}_{A \text{ on } B} = \frac{d\vec{p}_B}{dt} \tag{8.10}$$

The momentum of each particle changes, but these changes are related to each other by Newton's third law: Forces $\vec{F}_{B \text{ on } A}$ and $\vec{F}_{A \text{ on } B}$ are always equal in magnitude and opposite in direction. That is, $\vec{F}_{B \text{ on } A} = -\vec{F}_{A \text{ on } B}$, so $\vec{F}_{B \text{ on } A} + \vec{F}_{A \text{ on } B} = \mathbf{0}$. Adding together the two equations in Eq. (8.10), we have

$$\vec{F}_{B \text{ on } A} + \vec{F}_{A \text{ on } B} = \frac{d\vec{p}_A}{dt} + \frac{d\vec{p}_B}{dt} = \frac{d(\vec{p}_A + \vec{p}_B)}{dt} = \mathbf{0} \tag{8.11}$$

The rates of change of the two momenta are equal and opposite, so the rate of change of the vector sum $\vec{p}_A + \vec{p}_B$ is zero. We define the **total momentum** $\vec{P}$ of the system of two particles as the vector sum of the momenta of the individual particles; that is,

$$\vec{P} = \vec{p}_A + \vec{p}_B \tag{8.12}$$

Then Eq. (8.11) becomes

$$\vec{F}_{B \text{ on } A} + \vec{F}_{A \text{ on } B} = \frac{d\vec{P}}{dt} = \mathbf{0} \tag{8.13}$$

The time rate of change of the *total* momentum $\vec{P}$ is zero. Hence the total momentum of the system is constant, even though the individual momenta of the particles that make up the system can change.

If external forces are also present, they must be included on the left side of Eq. (8.13) along with the internal forces. Then the total momentum is, in general, not constant. But if the vector sum of the external forces is zero, as in **Fig. 8.10**, these forces have no effect on the left side of Eq. (8.13), and $d\vec{P}/dt$ is again zero. Thus we have the following general result:

> **If the vector sum of the external forces on a system is zero, the total momentum of the system is constant.**

This is the simplest form of the **principle of conservation of momentum**. This principle is a direct consequence of Newton's third law. What makes this principle useful is that it doesn't depend on the detailed nature of the internal forces

8.9 Two astronauts push each other as they float freely in the zero-gravity environment of space.

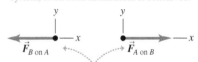

No external forces act on the two-astronaut system, so its total momentum is conserved.

The forces the astronauts exert on each other form an action–reaction pair.

8.10 Two ice skaters push each other as they skate on a frictionless, horizontal surface. (Compare to Fig. 8.9.)

The forces the skaters exert on each other form an action–reaction pair.

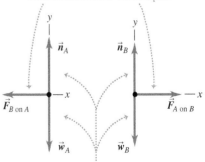

Although the normal and gravitational forces are external, their vector sum is zero, so the total momentum is conserved.

that act between members of the system. This means that we can apply conservation of momentum even if (as is often the case) we know very little about the internal forces. We have used Newton's second law to derive this principle, so we have to be careful to use it only in inertial frames of reference.

We can generalize this principle for a system that contains any number of particles A, B, C, ... interacting only with one another, with total momentum

Total momentum of a system of particles A, B, C, ...

$$\vec{P} = \vec{p}_A + \vec{p}_B + \cdots = m_A\vec{v}_A + m_B\vec{v}_B + \cdots \qquad (8.14)$$

... equals vector sum of momenta of all particles in the system.

We make the same argument as before: The total rate of change of momentum of the system due to each action–reaction pair of internal forces is zero. Thus the total rate of change of momentum of the entire system is zero whenever the vector sum of the external forces acting on it is zero. The internal forces can change the momenta of individual particles but not the *total* momentum of the system.

8.11 When applying conservation of momentum, remember that momentum is a vector quantity!

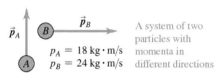

$\vec{p}_A$ $\vec{p}_B$ A system of two particles with momenta in different directions

$p_A = 18 \text{ kg} \cdot \text{m/s}$
$p_B = 24 \text{ kg} \cdot \text{m/s}$

You CANNOT find the magnitude of the total momentum by adding the magnitudes of the individual momenta!

$P = p_A + p_B = 42 \text{ kg} \cdot \text{m/s}$ ◀ **WRONG**

Instead, use vector addition:

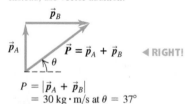

$\vec{p}_B$

$\vec{p}_A$ $\vec{P} = \vec{p}_A + \vec{p}_B$ ◀ **RIGHT!**

θ

$P = |\vec{p}_A + \vec{p}_B|$
$= 30 \text{ kg} \cdot \text{m/s at } \theta = 37°$

CAUTION **Conservation of momentum means conservation of its components** When you apply the conservation of momentum to a system, remember that momentum is a *vector* quantity. Hence you must use vector addition to compute the total momentum of a system (**Fig. 8.11**). Using components is usually the simplest method. If p_{Ax}, p_{Ay}, and p_{Az} are the components of momentum of particle A, and similarly for the other particles, then Eq. (8.14) is equivalent to the component equations

$$P_x = p_{Ax} + p_{Bx} + \cdots, \quad P_y = p_{Ay} + p_{By} + \cdots, \quad P_z = p_{Az} + p_{Bz} + \cdots \qquad (8.15)$$

If the vector sum of the external forces on the system is zero, then P_x, P_y, and P_z are all constant.

In some ways the principle of conservation of momentum is more general than the principle of conservation of mechanical energy. For example, mechanical energy is conserved only when the internal forces are *conservative*—that is, when the forces allow two-way conversion between kinetic and potential energies. But conservation of momentum is valid even when the internal forces are *not* conservative. In this chapter we will analyze situations in which both momentum and mechanical energy are conserved, and others in which only momentum is conserved. These two principles play a fundamental role in all areas of physics, and we will encounter them throughout our study of physics.

PROBLEM-SOLVING STRATEGY 8.1 | **CONSERVATION OF MOMENTUM**

IDENTIFY *the relevant concepts:* Confirm that the vector sum of the external forces acting on the system of particles is zero. If it isn't zero, you can't use conservation of momentum.

SET UP *the problem* using the following steps:
1. Treat each body as a particle. Draw "before" and "after" sketches, including velocity vectors. Assign algebraic symbols to each magnitude, angle, and component. Use letters to label each particle and subscripts 1 and 2 for "before" and "after" quantities. Include any given values.
2. Define a coordinate system and show it in your sketches; define the positive direction for each axis.
3. Identify the target variables.

EXECUTE *the solution:*
4. Write an equation in symbols equating the total initial and final x-components of momentum, using $p_x = mv_x$ for each particle. Write a corresponding equation for the y-components. Components can be positive or negative, so be careful with signs!
5. In some problems, energy considerations (discussed in Section 8.4) give additional equations relating the velocities.
6. Solve your equations to find the target variables.

EVALUATE *your answer:* Does your answer make physical sense? If your target variable is a certain body's momentum, check that the direction of the momentum is reasonable.

EXAMPLE 8.4   RECOIL OF A RIFLE

A marksman holds a rifle of mass $m_R = 3.00$ kg loosely, so it can recoil freely. He fires a bullet of mass $m_B = 5.00$ g horizontally with a velocity relative to the ground of $v_{Bx} = 300$ m/s. What is the recoil velocity v_{Rx} of the rifle? What are the final momentum and kinetic energy of the bullet and rifle?

SOLUTION

IDENTIFY and SET UP: If the marksman exerts negligible horizontal forces on the rifle, then there is no net horizontal force on the system (the bullet and rifle) during the firing, and the total horizontal momentum of the system is conserved. **Figure 8.12** shows our sketch. We take the positive x-axis in the direction of aim. The rifle and the bullet are initially at rest, so the initial x-component of total momentum is zero. After the shot is fired, the bullet's x-momentum is $p_{Bx} = m_B v_{Bx}$ and the rifle's x-momentum is $p_{Rx} = m_R v_{Rx}$. Our target variables are v_{Rx}, p_{Bx}, p_{Rx}, and the final kinetic energies $K_B = \frac{1}{2}m_B v_{Bx}^2$ and $K_R = \frac{1}{2}m_R v_{Rx}^2$.

8.12 Our sketch for this problem.

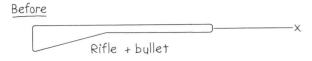

Before

Rifle + bullet

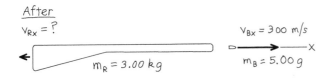

After
$v_{Rx} = ?$

$m_R = 3.00$ kg

$v_{Bx} = 300$ m/s

$m_B = 5.00$ g

EXECUTE: Conservation of the x-component of total momentum gives

$$P_x = 0 = m_B v_{Bx} + m_R v_{Rx}$$

$$v_{Rx} = -\frac{m_B}{m_R}v_{Bx} = -\left(\frac{0.00500 \text{ kg}}{3.00 \text{ kg}}\right)(300 \text{ m/s}) = -0.500 \text{ m/s}$$

The negative sign means that the recoil is in the direction opposite to that of the bullet.

The final momenta and kinetic energies are

$$p_{Bx} = m_B v_{Bx} = (0.00500 \text{ kg})(300 \text{ m/s}) = 1.50 \text{ kg} \cdot \text{m/s}$$
$$K_B = \tfrac{1}{2}m_B v_{Bx}^2 = \tfrac{1}{2}(0.00500 \text{ kg})(300 \text{ m/s})^2 = 225 \text{ J}$$
$$p_{Rx} = m_R v_{Rx} = (3.00 \text{ kg})(-0.500 \text{ m/s}) = -1.50 \text{ kg} \cdot \text{m/s}$$
$$K_R = \tfrac{1}{2}m_R v_{Rx}^2 = \tfrac{1}{2}(3.00 \text{ kg})(-0.500 \text{ m/s})^2 = 0.375 \text{ J}$$

EVALUATE: The bullet and rifle have equal and opposite final *momenta* thanks to Newton's third law: They experience equal and opposite interaction forces that act for the same *time*, so the impulses are equal and opposite. But the bullet travels a much greater *distance* than the rifle during the interaction. Hence the force on the bullet does more work than the force on the rifle, giving the bullet much greater *kinetic energy* than the rifle. The 600:1 ratio of the two kinetic energies is the inverse of the ratio of the masses; in fact, you can show that this always happens in recoil situations (see Exercise 8.26).

EXAMPLE 8.5   COLLISION ALONG A STRAIGHT LINE

Two gliders with different masses move toward each other on a frictionless air track (**Fig. 8.13a**). After they collide (Fig. 8.13b), glider B has a final velocity of $+2.0$ m/s (Fig. 8.13c). What is the final velocity of glider A? How do the changes in momentum and in velocity compare?

SOLUTION

IDENTIFY and SET UP: As for the skaters in Fig. 8.10, the total vertical force on each glider is zero, and the net force on each individual glider is the horizontal force exerted on it by the other glider. The net external force on the *system* of two gliders is zero, so their total momentum is conserved. We take the positive x-axis to be to the right. We are given the masses and initial velocities of both gliders and the final velocity of glider B. Our target variables are v_{A2x} (the final x-component of velocity of glider A), and the changes in momentum and in velocity of the two gliders (the value *after* the collision minus the value *before* the collision).

8.13 Two gliders colliding on an air track.

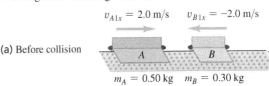

(a) Before collision

$v_{A1x} = 2.0$ m/s $v_{B1x} = -2.0$ m/s

$m_A = 0.50$ kg $m_B = 0.30$ kg

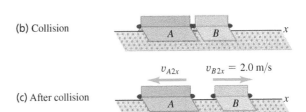

(b) Collision

(c) After collision

v_{A2x} $v_{B2x} = 2.0$ m/s

Continued

EXECUTE: The x-component of total momentum before the collision is

$$P_x = m_A v_{A1x} + m_B v_{B1x}$$
$$= (0.50 \text{ kg})(2.0 \text{ m/s}) + (0.30 \text{ kg})(-2.0 \text{ m/s})$$
$$= 0.40 \text{ kg} \cdot \text{m/s}$$

This is positive (to the right in Fig. 8.13) because A has a greater magnitude of momentum than B. The x-component of total momentum has the same value after the collision, so

$$P_x = m_A v_{A2x} + m_B v_{B2x}$$

We solve for v_{A2x}:

$$v_{A2x} = \frac{P_x - m_B v_{B2x}}{m_A} = \frac{0.40 \text{ kg} \cdot \text{m/s} - (0.30 \text{ kg})(2.0 \text{ m/s})}{0.50 \text{ kg}}$$
$$= -0.40 \text{ m/s}$$

The changes in the x-momenta are

$$m_A v_{A2x} - m_A v_{A1x} = (0.50 \text{ kg})(-0.40 \text{ m/s})$$
$$- (0.50 \text{ kg})(2.0 \text{ m/s})$$
$$= -1.2 \text{ kg} \cdot \text{m/s}$$

$$m_B v_{B2x} - m_B v_{B1x} = (0.30 \text{ kg})(2.0 \text{ m/s})$$
$$- (0.30 \text{ kg})(-2.0 \text{ m/s})$$
$$= +1.2 \text{ kg} \cdot \text{m/s}$$

The changes in x-velocities are

$$v_{A2x} - v_{A1x} = (-0.40 \text{ m/s}) - 2.0 \text{ m/s} = -2.4 \text{ m/s}$$
$$v_{B2x} - v_{B1x} = 2.0 \text{ m/s} - (-2.0 \text{ m/s}) = +4.0 \text{ m/s}$$

EVALUATE: The gliders were subjected to equal and opposite interaction forces for the same time during their collision. By the impulse–momentum theorem, they experienced equal and opposite impulses and therefore equal and opposite changes in momentum. But by Newton's second law, the less massive glider (B) had a greater magnitude of acceleration and hence a greater velocity change.

EXAMPLE 8.6   COLLISION IN A HORIZONTAL PLANE

Figure 8.14a shows two battling robots on a frictionless surface. Robot A, with mass 20 kg, initially moves at 2.0 m/s parallel to the x-axis. It collides with robot B, which has mass 12 kg and is initially at rest. After the collision, robot A moves at 1.0 m/s in a direction that makes an angle $\alpha = 30°$ with its initial direction (Fig. 8.14b). What is the final velocity of robot B?

SOLUTION

IDENTIFY and SET UP: There are no horizontal external forces, so the x- and y-components of the total momentum of the system are conserved. Hence the sum of the x-components of momentum

8.14 Views from above of the robot velocities.

(a) Before collision

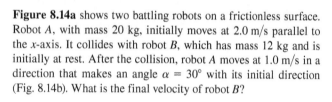

(b) After collision

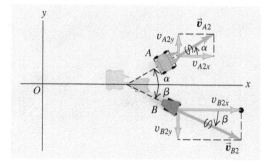

before the collision (subscript 1) must equal the sum *after* the collision (subscript 2), and similarly for the sums of the y-components. Our target variable is $\vec{v}_{B2}$, the final velocity of robot B.

EXECUTE: The momentum-conservation equations and their solutions for v_{B2x} and v_{B2y} are

$$m_A v_{A1x} + m_B v_{B1x} = m_A v_{A2x} + m_B v_{B2x}$$

$$v_{B2x} = \frac{m_A v_{A1x} + m_B v_{B1x} - m_A v_{A2x}}{m_B}$$

$$= \frac{\left[\begin{array}{l}(20 \text{ kg})(2.0 \text{ m/s}) + (12 \text{ kg})(0) \\ - (20 \text{ kg})(1.0 \text{ m/s})(\cos 30°)\end{array}\right]}{12 \text{ kg}}$$

$$= 1.89 \text{ m/s}$$

$$m_A v_{A1y} + m_B v_{B1y} = m_A v_{A2y} + m_B v_{B2y}$$

$$v_{B2y} = \frac{m_A v_{A1y} + m_B v_{B1y} - m_A v_{A2y}}{m_B}$$

$$= \frac{\left[\begin{array}{l}(20 \text{ kg})(0) + (12 \text{ kg})(0) \\ - (20 \text{ kg})(1.0 \text{ m/s})(\sin 30°)\end{array}\right]}{12 \text{ kg}}$$

$$= -0.83 \text{ m/s}$$

Figure 8.14b shows the motion of robot B after the collision. The magnitude of $\vec{v}_{B2}$ is

$$v_{B2} = \sqrt{(1.89 \text{ m/s})^2 + (-0.83 \text{ m/s})^2} = 2.1 \text{ m/s}$$

and the angle of its direction from the positive x-axis is

$$\beta = \arctan \frac{-0.83 \text{ m/s}}{1.89 \text{ m/s}} = -24°$$

EVALUATE: Let's confirm that the components of total momentum before and after the collision are equal. Initially robot A has x-momentum $m_A v_{A1x} = (20 \text{ kg})(2.0 \text{ m/s}) = 40 \text{ kg} \cdot \text{m/s}$ and zero y-momentum; robot B has zero momentum. Afterward, the momentum components are $m_A v_{A2x} = (20 \text{ kg})(1.0 \text{ m/s})(\cos 30°) =$ 17 kg·m/s and $m_B v_{B2x} = (12 \text{ kg})(1.89 \text{ m/s}) = 23 \text{ kg} \cdot \text{m/s}$; the total x-momentum is 40 kg·m/s, the same as before the collision. The final y-components are $m_A v_{A2y} = (20 \text{ kg})(1.0 \text{ m/s})(\sin 30°) = 10 \text{ kg} \cdot \text{m/s}$ and $m_B v_{B2y} = (12 \text{ kg})(-0.83 \text{ m/s}) = -10 \text{ kg} \cdot \text{m/s}$; the total y-component of momentum is zero, as before the collision.

TEST YOUR UNDERSTANDING OF SECTION 8.2 A spring-loaded toy sits at rest on a horizontal, frictionless surface. When the spring releases, the toy breaks into equal-mass pieces A, B, and C, which slide along the surface. Piece A moves off in the negative x-direction, while piece B moves off in the negative y-direction. (a) What are the signs of the velocity components of piece C? (b) Which of the three pieces is moving the fastest? ∎

8.3 MOMENTUM CONSERVATION AND COLLISIONS

To most people the term *collision* is likely to mean some sort of automotive disaster. We'll broaden the meaning to include any strong interaction between bodies that lasts a relatively short time. So we include not only car accidents but also balls colliding on a billiard table, neutrons hitting atomic nuclei in a nuclear reactor, and a close encounter of a spacecraft with the planet Saturn.

If the forces between the colliding bodies are much larger than any external forces, as is the case in most collisions, we can ignore the external forces and treat the bodies as an *isolated* system. Then momentum is conserved and the total momentum of the system has the same value before and after the collision. Two cars colliding at an icy intersection provide a good example. Even two cars colliding on dry pavement can be treated as an isolated system during the collision if the forces between the cars are much larger than the friction forces of pavement against tires.

Elastic and Inelastic Collisions

If the forces between the bodies are also *conservative,* so no mechanical energy is lost or gained in the collision, the total *kinetic* energy of the system is the same after the collision as before. Such a collision is called an **elastic collision.** A collision between two marbles or two billiard balls is almost completely elastic. **Figure 8.15** shows a model for an elastic collision. When the gliders collide, their springs are momentarily compressed and some of the original kinetic energy is momentarily converted to elastic potential energy. Then the gliders bounce apart, the springs expand, and this potential energy is converted back to kinetic energy.

A collision in which the total kinetic energy after the collision is *less* than before the collision is called an **inelastic collision.** A meatball landing on a plate of spaghetti and a bullet embedding itself in a block of wood are examples of inelastic collisions. An inelastic collision in which the colliding bodies stick together and move as one body after the collision is called a **completely inelastic collision. Figure 8.16** shows an example; we have replaced the spring bumpers in Fig. 8.15 with Velcro®, which sticks the two bodies together.

8.15 Two gliders undergoing an elastic collision on a frictionless surface. Each glider has a steel spring bumper that exerts a conservative force on the other glider.

(a) Before collision

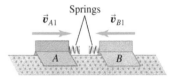

(b) Elastic collision

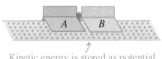

Kinetic energy is stored as potential energy in compressed springs.

(c) After collision

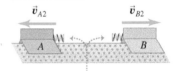

The system of the two gliders has the same kinetic energy after the collision as before it.

DEMO

8.16 Two gliders undergoing a completely inelastic collision. The spring bumpers on the gliders are replaced by Velcro®, so the gliders stick together after collision.

(a) Before collision

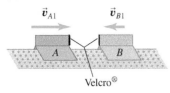

Velcro®

(b) Completely inelastic collision

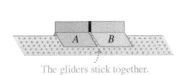

The gliders stick together.

(c) After collision

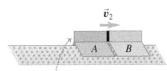

The system of the two gliders has less kinetic energy after the collision than before it.

CAUTION An inelastic collision doesn't have to be *completely* inelastic Inelastic collisions include many situations in which the bodies do *not* stick. If two cars bounce off each other in a "fender bender," the work done to deform the fenders cannot be recovered as kinetic energy of the cars, so the collision is inelastic (**Fig. 8.17**). ▌

8.17 Cars are designed so that collisions are inelastic—the structure of the car absorbs as much of the energy of the collision as possible. This absorbed energy cannot be recovered, since it goes into a permanent deformation of the car.

Remember this rule: **In any collision in which external forces can be ignored, momentum is conserved and the total momentum before equals the total momentum after; in elastic collisions *only,* the total kinetic energy before equals the total kinetic energy after.**

Completely Inelastic Collisions

Let's look at what happens to momentum and kinetic energy in a *completely* inelastic collision of two bodies (A and B), as in Fig. 8.16. Because the two bodies stick together after the collision, they have the same final velocity $\vec{v}_2$:

$$\vec{v}_{A2} = \vec{v}_{B2} = \vec{v}_2$$

Conservation of momentum gives the relationship

$$m_A\vec{v}_{A1} + m_B\vec{v}_{B1} = (m_A + m_B)\vec{v}_2 \quad \text{(completely inelastic collision)} \quad (8.16)$$

If we know the masses and initial velocities, we can compute the common final velocity $\vec{v}_2$.

Suppose, for example, that a body with mass m_A and initial x-component of velocity v_{A1x} collides inelastically with a body with mass m_B that is initially at rest ($v_{B1x} = 0$). From Eq. (8.16) the common x-component of velocity v_{2x} of both bodies after the collision is

$$v_{2x} = \frac{m_A}{m_A + m_B}v_{A1x} \quad \begin{array}{l}\text{(completely inelastic collision,}\\ B \text{ initially at rest)}\end{array} \quad (8.17)$$

Let's verify that the total kinetic energy after this completely inelastic collision is less than before the collision. The motion is purely along the x-axis, so the kinetic energies K_1 and K_2 before and after the collision, respectively, are

$$K_1 = \tfrac{1}{2}m_A v_{A1x}^2$$

$$K_2 = \tfrac{1}{2}(m_A + m_B)v_{2x}^2 = \tfrac{1}{2}(m_A + m_B)\left(\frac{m_A}{m_A + m_B}\right)^2 v_{A1x}^2$$

The ratio of final to initial kinetic energy is

$$\frac{K_2}{K_1} = \frac{m_A}{m_A + m_B} \quad \begin{array}{l}\text{(completely inelastic collision,}\\ B \text{ initially at rest)}\end{array} \quad (8.18)$$

The right side is always less than unity because the denominator is always greater than the numerator. Even when the initial velocity of m_B is not zero, the kinetic energy after a completely inelastic collision is always less than before.

Please note: Don't memorize Eq. (8.17) or (8.18)! We derived them only to prove that kinetic energy is always lost in a completely inelastic collision.

EXAMPLE 8.7   **A COMPLETELY INELASTIC COLLISION**

We repeat the collision described in Example 8.5 (Section 8.2), but this time equip the gliders so that they stick together when they collide. Find the common final x-velocity, and compare the initial and final kinetic energies of the system.

8.18 Our sketch for this problem.

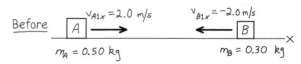

SOLUTION

IDENTIFY and SET UP: There are no external forces in the x-direction, so the x-component of momentum is conserved. **Figure 8.18** shows our sketch. Our target variables are the final x-velocity, v_{2x}, and the initial and final kinetic energies, K_1 and K_2.

EXECUTE: From conservation of momentum,

$$m_A v_{A1x} + m_B v_{B1x} = (m_A + m_B)v_{2x}$$

$$v_{2x} = \frac{m_A v_{A1x} + m_B v_{B1x}}{m_A + m_B}$$

$$= \frac{(0.50 \text{ kg})(2.0 \text{ m/s}) + (0.30 \text{ kg})(-2.0 \text{ m/s})}{0.50 \text{ kg} + 0.30 \text{ kg}}$$

$$= 0.50 \text{ m/s}$$

Because v_{2x} is positive, the gliders move together to the right after the collision. Before the collision, the kinetic energies are

$$K_A = \tfrac{1}{2}m_A v_{A1x}^2 = \tfrac{1}{2}(0.50 \text{ kg})(2.0 \text{ m/s})^2 = 1.0 \text{ J}$$

$$K_B = \tfrac{1}{2}m_B v_{B1x}^2 = \tfrac{1}{2}(0.30 \text{ kg})(-2.0 \text{ m/s})^2 = 0.60 \text{ J}$$

The total kinetic energy before the collision is $K_1 = K_A + K_B = 1.6$ J. The kinetic energy after the collision is

$$K_2 = \tfrac{1}{2}(m_A + m_B)v_{2x}^2 = \tfrac{1}{2}(0.50 \text{ kg} + 0.30 \text{ kg})(0.50 \text{ m/s})^2$$

$$= 0.10 \text{ J}$$

EVALUATE: The final kinetic energy is only $\tfrac{1}{16}$ of the original; $\tfrac{15}{16}$ is converted from mechanical energy to other forms. If there is a wad of chewing gum between the gliders, it squashes and becomes warmer. If there is a spring between the gliders that is compressed as they lock together, the energy is stored as potential energy of the spring. In both cases the *total* energy of the system is conserved, although *kinetic* energy is not. In an isolated system, however, momentum is *always* conserved whether the collision is elastic or not.

EXAMPLE 8.8 THE BALLISTIC PENDULUM

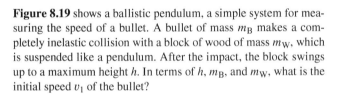

Figure 8.19 shows a ballistic pendulum, a simple system for measuring the speed of a bullet. A bullet of mass m_B makes a completely inelastic collision with a block of wood of mass m_W, which is suspended like a pendulum. After the impact, the block swings up to a maximum height h. In terms of h, m_B, and m_W, what is the initial speed v_1 of the bullet?

SOLUTION

IDENTIFY: We'll analyze this event in two stages: (1) the bullet embeds itself in the block, and (2) the block swings upward. The first stage happens so quickly that the block does not move appreciably. The supporting strings remain nearly vertical, so negligible external horizontal force acts on the bullet–block system, and the horizontal component of momentum is conserved. Mechanical energy is *not* conserved during this stage, however, because a nonconservative force does work (the force of friction between bullet and block).

In the second stage, the block and bullet move together. The only forces acting on this system are gravity (a conservative force) and the string tensions (which do no work). Thus, as the block swings,

mechanical energy is conserved. Momentum is *not* conserved during this stage, however, because there is a net external force (the forces of gravity and string tension don't cancel when the strings are inclined).

SET UP: We take the positive x-axis to the right and the positive y-axis upward. Our target variable is v_1. Another unknown quantity is the speed v_2 of the system just after the collision. We'll use momentum conservation in the first stage to relate v_1 to v_2, and we'll use energy conservation in the second stage to relate v_2 to h.

EXECUTE: In the first stage, all velocities are in the $+x$-direction. Momentum conservation gives

$$m_B v_1 = (m_B + m_W)v_2$$

$$v_1 = \frac{m_B + m_W}{m_B}v_2$$

At the beginning of the second stage, the system has kinetic energy $K = \tfrac{1}{2}(m_B + m_W)v_2^2$. The system swings up and comes to rest for an instant at a height h, where its kinetic energy is zero and the potential energy is $(m_B + m_W)gh$; it then swings back down. Energy conservation gives

$$\tfrac{1}{2}(m_B + m_W)v_2^2 = (m_B + m_W)gh$$

$$v_2 = \sqrt{2gh}$$

We substitute this expression for v_2 into the momentum equation:

$$v_1 = \frac{m_B + m_W}{m_B}\sqrt{2gh}$$

EVALUATE: Let's plug in the realistic numbers $m_B = 5.00 \text{ g} = 0.00500 \text{ kg}$, $m_W = 2.00 \text{ kg}$, and $h = 3.00 \text{ cm} = 0.0300 \text{ m}$:

$$v_1 = \frac{0.00500 \text{ kg} + 2.00 \text{ kg}}{0.00500 \text{ kg}}\sqrt{2(9.80 \text{ m/s}^2)(0.0300 \text{ m})}$$

$$= 307 \text{ m/s}$$

$$v_2 = \sqrt{2gh} = \sqrt{2(9.80 \text{ m/s}^2)(0.0300 \text{ m})} = 0.767 \text{ m/s}$$

The speed v_2 of the block after impact is *much* lower than the initial speed v_1 of the bullet. The kinetic energy of the bullet before impact is $\tfrac{1}{2}(0.00500 \text{ kg})(307 \text{ m/s})^2 = 236 \text{ J}$. Just after impact the kinetic energy of the system is $\tfrac{1}{2}(2.005 \text{ kg})(0.767 \text{ m/s})^2 = 0.590 \text{ J}$. Nearly all the kinetic energy disappears as the wood splinters and the bullet and block become warmer.

8.19 A ballistic pendulum.

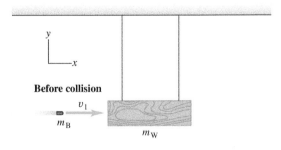

Before collision

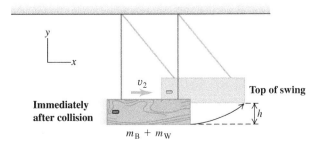

Immediately after collision

Top of swing

EXAMPLE 8.9 AN AUTOMOBILE COLLISION

A 1000-kg car traveling north at 15 m/s collides with a 2000-kg truck traveling east at 10 m/s. The occupants, wearing seat belts, are uninjured, but the two vehicles move away from the impact point as one. The insurance adjustor asks you to find the velocity of the wreckage just after impact. What is your answer?

_____

SOLUTION

IDENTIFY and SET UP: Any horizontal external forces (such as friction) on the vehicles during the collision are very small compared with the forces that the colliding vehicles exert on each other. (We'll verify this below.) So we can treat the cars as an isolated system, and the momentum of the system is conserved. **Figure 8.20** shows our sketch and the *x*- and *y*-axes. We can use Eqs. (8.15) to find the total momentum $\vec{P}$ before the collision. The momentum has the same value just after the collision; hence we can find the velocity $\vec{V}$ just after the collision (our target variable) by using $\vec{P} = M\vec{V}$, where $M = m_C + m_T = 3000$ kg is the mass of the wreckage.

EXECUTE: From Eqs. (8.15), the components of $\vec{P}$ are

$$P_x = p_{Cx} + p_{Tx} = m_C v_{Cx} + m_T v_{Tx}$$
$$= (1000 \text{ kg})(0) + (2000 \text{ kg})(10 \text{ m/s})$$
$$= 2.0 \times 10^4 \text{ kg} \cdot \text{m/s}$$

$$P_y = p_{Cy} + p_{Ty} = m_C v_{Cy} + m_T v_{Ty}$$
$$= (1000 \text{ kg})(15 \text{ m/s}) + (2000 \text{ kg})(0)$$
$$= 1.5 \times 10^4 \text{ kg} \cdot \text{m/s}$$

The magnitude of $\vec{P}$ is

$$P = \sqrt{(2.0 \times 10^4 \text{ kg} \cdot \text{m/s})^2 + (1.5 \times 10^4 \text{ kg} \cdot \text{m/s})^2}$$
$$= 2.5 \times 10^4 \text{ kg} \cdot \text{m/s}$$

and its direction is given by the angle θ shown in Fig. 8.20:

$$\tan \theta = \frac{P_y}{P_x} = \frac{1.5 \times 10^4 \text{ kg} \cdot \text{m/s}}{2.0 \times 10^4 \text{ kg} \cdot \text{m/s}} = 0.75 \quad \theta = 37°$$

8.20 Our sketch for this problem.

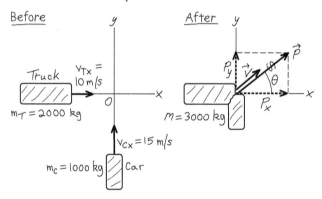

From $\vec{P} = M\vec{V}$, the direction of the velocity $\vec{V}$ just after the collision is also $\theta = 37°$. The velocity magnitude is

$$V = \frac{P}{M} = \frac{2.5 \times 10^4 \text{ kg} \cdot \text{m/s}}{3000 \text{ kg}} = 8.3 \text{ m/s}$$

EVALUATE: As you can show, the initial kinetic energy is 2.1×10^5 J and the final value is 1.0×10^5 J. In this inelastic collision, the total kinetic energy is less after the collision than before.

We can now justify our neglect of the external forces on the vehicles during the collision. The car's weight is about 10,000 N; if the coefficient of kinetic friction is 0.5, the friction force on the car during the impact is about 5000 N. The car's initial kinetic energy is $\frac{1}{2}(1000 \text{ kg})(15 \text{ m/s})^2 = 1.1 \times 10^5$ J, so -1.1×10^5 J of work must be done to stop it. If the car crumples by 0.20 m in stopping, a force of magnitude $(1.1 \times 10^5 \text{ J})/(0.20 \text{ m}) = 5.5 \times 10^5$ N would be needed; that's 110 times the friction force. So it's reasonable to treat the external force of friction as negligible compared with the internal forces the vehicles exert on each other.

Classifying Collisions

It's important to remember that we can classify collisions according to energy considerations (**Fig. 8.21**). A collision in which kinetic energy is conserved is called *elastic*. (We'll explore this type in more depth in the next section.) A collision in which the total kinetic energy decreases is called *inelastic*. When the two bodies have a common final velocity, we say that the collision is *completely inelastic*. There are also cases in which the final kinetic energy is *greater* than the initial value. Rifle recoil, discussed in Example 8.4 (Section 8.2), is an example.

8.21 Collisions are classified according to energy considerations.

Elastic:
Kinetic energy conserved.

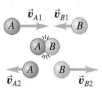

Inelastic:
Some kinetic energy lost.

Completely inelastic:
Bodies have same final velocity.

Finally, we emphasize again that we can sometimes use momentum conservation even when external forces are acting on the system, if the net external force acting on the colliding bodies is small in comparison with the internal forces during the collision (as in Example 8.9).

TEST YOUR UNDERSTANDING OF SECTION 8.3 For each situation, state whether the collision is elastic or inelastic. If it is inelastic, state whether it is completely inelastic. (a) You drop a ball from your hand. It collides with the floor and bounces back up so that it just reaches your hand. (b) You drop a different ball from your hand and let it collide with the ground. This ball bounces back up to half the height from which it was dropped. (c) You drop a ball of clay from your hand. When it collides with the ground, it stops. ▮

8.4 ELASTIC COLLISIONS

We saw in Section 8.3 that an *elastic collision* in an isolated system is one in which kinetic energy (as well as momentum) is conserved. Elastic collisions occur when the forces between the colliding bodies are *conservative*. When two billiard balls collide, they squash a little near the surface of contact, but then they spring back. Some of the kinetic energy is stored temporarily as elastic potential energy, but at the end it is reconverted to kinetic energy (**Fig. 8.22**).

Let's look at a *one-dimensional* elastic collision between two bodies A and B, in which all the velocities lie along the same line. We call this line the x-axis, so each momentum and velocity has only an x-component. We call the x-velocities before the collision v_{A1x} and v_{B1x}, and those after the collision v_{A2x} and v_{B2x}. From conservation of kinetic energy we have

$$\tfrac{1}{2}m_A v_{A1x}^2 + \tfrac{1}{2}m_B v_{B1x}^2 = \tfrac{1}{2}m_A v_{A2x}^2 + \tfrac{1}{2}m_B v_{B2x}^2$$

and conservation of momentum gives

$$m_A v_{A1x} + m_B v_{B1x} = m_A v_{A2x} + m_B v_{B2x}$$

If the masses m_A and m_B and the initial velocities v_{A1x} and v_{B1x} are known, we can solve these two equations to find the two final velocities v_{A2x} and v_{B2x}.

Elastic Collisions, One Body Initially at Rest

The general solution to the above equations is a little complicated, so we will concentrate on the particular case in which body B is at rest before the collision (so $v_{B1x} = 0$). Think of body B as a target for body A to hit. Then the kinetic energy and momentum conservation equations are, respectively,

$$\tfrac{1}{2}m_A v_{A1x}^2 = \tfrac{1}{2}m_A v_{A2x}^2 + \tfrac{1}{2}m_B v_{B2x}^2 \tag{8.19}$$

$$m_A v_{A1x} = m_A v_{A2x} + m_B v_{B2x} \tag{8.20}$$

We can solve for v_{A2x} and v_{B2x} in terms of the masses and the initial velocity v_{A1x}. This involves some fairly strenuous algebra, but it's worth it. No pain, no gain! The simplest approach is somewhat indirect, but along the way it uncovers an additional interesting feature of elastic collisions.

First we rearrange Eqs. (8.19) and (8.20) as follows:

$$m_B v_{B2x}^2 = m_A(v_{A1x}^2 - v_{A2x}^2) = m_A(v_{A1x} - v_{A2x})(v_{A1x} + v_{A2x}) \tag{8.21}$$

$$m_B v_{B2x} = m_A(v_{A1x} - v_{A2x}) \tag{8.22}$$

Now we divide Eq. (8.21) by Eq. (8.22) to obtain

$$v_{B2x} = v_{A1x} + v_{A2x} \tag{8.23}$$

8.22 Billiard balls deform very little when they collide, and they quickly spring back from any deformation they do undergo. Hence the force of interaction between the balls is almost perfectly conservative, and the collision is almost perfectly elastic.

DATA *SPEAKS*

Conservation of Momentum

When students were given a problem about conservation of momentum, more than 29% gave an incorrect response. Common errors:

- Forgetting that momentum $\vec{p}$ is a vector. Its components can be positive or negative depending on the direction of $\vec{p}$.

- Adding momenta incorrectly. If two momentum vectors point in different directions, you cannot find the total momentum by simply adding the magnitudes of the two momenta.

8.23 One-dimensional elastic collisions between bodies with different masses.

(a) Moving Ping-Pong ball strikes initially stationary bowling ball.

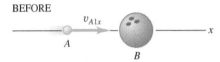

BEFORE

AFTER

(b) Moving bowling ball strikes initially stationary Ping-Pong ball.

BEFORE

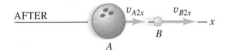

AFTER

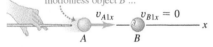

8.24 A one-dimensional elastic collision between bodies of equal mass.

When a moving object A has a 1-D elastic collision with an equal-mass, motionless object B ...

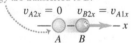

... all of A's momentum and kinetic energy are transferred to B.

We substitute this expression back into Eq. (8.22) to eliminate v_{B2x} and then solve for v_{A2x}:

$$m_B(v_{A1x} + v_{A2x}) = m_A(v_{A1x} - v_{A2x})$$

$$v_{A2x} = \frac{m_A - m_B}{m_A + m_B}v_{A1x} \qquad (8.24)$$

Finally, we substitute this result back into Eq. (8.23) to obtain

$$v_{B2x} = \frac{2m_A}{m_A + m_B}v_{A1x} \qquad (8.25)$$

Now we can interpret the results. Suppose A is a Ping-Pong ball and B is a bowling ball. Then we expect A to bounce off after the collision with a velocity nearly equal to its original value but in the opposite direction (**Fig. 8.23a**), and we expect B's velocity to be much less. That's just what the equations predict. When m_A is much smaller than m_B, the fraction in Eq. (8.24) is approximately equal to (-1), so v_{A2x} is approximately equal to $-v_{A1x}$. The fraction in Eq. (8.25) is much smaller than unity, so v_{B2x} is much less than v_{A1x}. Figure 8.23b shows the opposite case, in which A is the bowling ball and B the Ping-Pong ball and m_A is much larger than m_B. What do you expect to happen then? Check your predictions against Eqs. (8.24) and (8.25).

Another interesting case occurs when the masses are equal (**Fig. 8.24**). If $m_A = m_B$, then Eqs. (8.24) and (8.25) give $v_{A2x} = 0$ and $v_{B2x} = v_{A1x}$. That is, the body that was moving stops dead; it gives all its momentum and kinetic energy to the body that was at rest. This behavior is familiar to all pool players.

Elastic Collisions and Relative Velocity

Let's return to the more general case in which A and B have different masses. Equation (8.23) can be rewritten as

$$v_{A1x} = v_{B2x} - v_{A2x} \qquad (8.26)$$

Here $v_{B2x} - v_{A2x}$ is the velocity of B relative to A *after* the collision; from Eq. (8.26), this equals v_{A1x}, which is the *negative* of the velocity of B relative to A *before* the collision. (We discussed relative velocity in Section 3.5.) The relative velocity has the same magnitude, but opposite sign, before and after the collision. The sign changes because A and B are approaching each other before the collision but moving apart after the collision. If we view this collision from a second coordinate system moving with constant velocity relative to the first, the velocities of the bodies are different but the *relative* velocities are the same. Hence our statement about relative velocities holds for *any* straight-line elastic collision, even when neither body is at rest initially. *In a straight-line elastic collision of two bodies, the relative velocities before and after the collision have the same magnitude but opposite sign.* This means that if B is moving before the collision, Eq. (8.26) becomes

$$v_{B2x} - v_{A2x} = -(v_{B1x} - v_{A1x}) \qquad (8.27)$$

It turns out that a *vector* relationship similar to Eq. (8.27) is a general property of *all* elastic collisions, even when both bodies are moving initially and the velocities do not all lie along the same line. This result provides an alternative and equivalent definition of an elastic collision: *In an elastic collision, the relative velocity of the two bodies has the same magnitude before and after the collision.* Whenever this condition is satisfied, the total kinetic energy is also conserved.

When an elastic two-body collision isn't head-on, the velocities don't all lie along a single line. If they all lie in a plane, then each final velocity has two unknown components, and there are four unknowns in all. Conservation of energy and conservation of the x- and y-components of momentum give only three equations. To determine the final velocities uniquely, we need additional information, such as the direction or magnitude of one of the final velocities.

EXAMPLE 8.10   AN ELASTIC STRAIGHT-LINE COLLISION

We repeat the air-track collision of Example 8.5 (Section 8.2), but now we add ideal spring bumpers to the gliders so that the collision is elastic. What are the final velocities of the gliders?

SOLUTION

IDENTIFY and SET UP: The net external force on the system is zero, so the momentum of the system is conserved. **Figure 8.25** shows our sketch. We'll find our target variables, v_{A2x} and v_{B2x}, by using Eq. (8.27), the relative-velocity relationship for an elastic collision, and the momentum-conservation equation.

EXECUTE: From Eq. (8.27),

$$v_{B2x} - v_{A2x} = -(v_{B1x} - v_{A1x})$$
$$= -(-2.0 \text{ m/s} - 2.0 \text{ m/s}) = 4.0 \text{ m/s}$$

From conservation of momentum,

$$m_A v_{A1x} + m_B v_{B1x} = m_A v_{A2x} + m_B v_{B2x}$$
$$(0.50 \text{ kg})(2.0 \text{ m/s}) + (0.30 \text{ kg})(-2.0 \text{ m/s})$$
$$= (0.50 \text{ kg})v_{A2x} + (0.30 \text{ kg})v_{B2x}$$
$$0.50 v_{A2x} + 0.30 v_{B2x} = 0.40 \text{ m/s}$$

(To get the last equation we divided both sides of the equation just above it by 1 kg. This makes the units the same as in the first equation.) Solving these equations simultaneously, we find

$$v_{A2x} = -1.0 \text{ m/s} \qquad v_{B2x} = 3.0 \text{ m/s}$$

8.25 Our sketch for this problem.

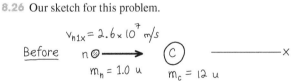

EVALUATE: Both bodies reverse their direction of motion; A moves to the left at 1.0 m/s and B moves to the right at 3.0 m/s. This is unlike the result of Example 8.5 because that collision was *not* elastic. The more massive glider A slows down in the collision and so loses kinetic energy. The less massive glider B speeds up and gains kinetic energy. The total kinetic energy before the collision (which we calculated in Example 8.7) is 1.6 J. The total kinetic energy after the collision is

$$\tfrac{1}{2}(0.50 \text{ kg})(-1.0 \text{ m/s})^2 + \tfrac{1}{2}(0.30 \text{ kg})(3.0 \text{ m/s})^2 = 1.6 \text{ J}$$

The kinetic energies before and after this elastic collision are equal. Kinetic energy is transferred from A to B, but none of it is lost.

CAUTION **Be careful with the elastic collision equations** You could *not* have solved this problem by using Eqs. (8.24) and (8.25), which apply only if body B is initially *at rest*. Always be sure that you use equations that are applicable! ▮

EXAMPLE 8.11   MODERATING FISSION NEUTRONS IN A NUCLEAR REACTOR

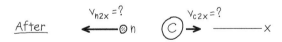

The fission of uranium nuclei in a nuclear reactor produces high-speed neutrons. Before such neutrons can efficiently cause additional fissions, they must be slowed down by collisions with nuclei in the *moderator* of the reactor. The first nuclear reactor (built in 1942 at the University of Chicago) used carbon (graphite) as the moderator. Suppose a neutron (mass 1.0 u) traveling at 2.6×10^7 m/s undergoes a head-on elastic collision with a carbon nucleus (mass 12 u) initially at rest. Neglecting external forces during the collision, find the velocities after the collision. (1 u is the *atomic mass unit,* equal to 1.66×10^{-27} kg.)

SOLUTION

IDENTIFY and SET UP: We ignore external forces, so momentum is conserved in the collision. The collision is elastic, so kinetic energy is also conserved. **Figure 8.26** shows our sketch. We take the x-axis to be in the direction in which the neutron is moving initially. The collision is head-on, so both particles move along this same axis after the collision. The carbon nucleus is initially at rest, so we can use Eqs. (8.24) and (8.25); we replace A by n (for the neutron) and B by C (for the carbon nucleus). We have $m_n = 1.0$ u, $m_C = 12$ u, and $v_{n1x} = 2.6 \times 10^7$ m/s. The target variables are the final velocities v_{n2x} and v_{C2x}.

8.26 Our sketch for this problem.

EXECUTE: You can do the arithmetic. (*Hint:* There's no reason to convert atomic mass units to kilograms.) The results are

$$v_{n2x} = -2.2 \times 10^7 \text{ m/s} \qquad v_{C2x} = 0.4 \times 10^7 \text{ m/s}$$

EVALUATE: The neutron ends up with $|(m_n - m_C)/(m_n + m_C)| = \tfrac{11}{13}$ of its initial speed, and the speed of the recoiling carbon nucleus is $|2m_n/(m_n + m_C)| = \tfrac{2}{13}$ of the neutron's initial speed. Kinetic energy is proportional to speed squared, so the neutron's final kinetic energy is $\left(\tfrac{11}{13}\right)^2 \approx 0.72$ of its original value. After a second head-on collision, its kinetic energy is $(0.72)^2$, or about half its original value, and so on. After a few dozen collisions (few of which are head-on), the neutron speed will be low enough that it can efficiently cause a fission reaction in a uranium nucleus.

EXAMPLE 8.12 A TWO-DIMENSIONAL ELASTIC COLLISION

Figure 8.27 shows an elastic collision of two pucks (masses $m_A = 0.500$ kg and $m_B = 0.300$ kg) on a frictionless air-hockey table. Puck A has an initial velocity of 4.00 m/s in the positive x-direction and a final velocity of 2.00 m/s in an unknown direction α. Puck B is initially at rest. Find the final speed v_{B2} of puck B and the angles α and β.

8.27 An elastic collision that isn't head-on.

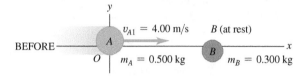

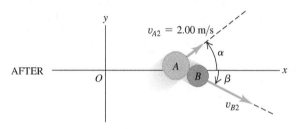

SOLUTION

IDENTIFY and SET UP: We'll use the equations for conservation of energy and conservation of x- and y-momentum. These three equations should be enough to solve for the three target variables.

EXECUTE: The collision is elastic, so the initial and final kinetic energies of the system are equal:

$$\tfrac{1}{2}m_A v_{A1}^2 = \tfrac{1}{2}m_A v_{A2}^2 + \tfrac{1}{2}m_B v_{B2}^2$$

$$v_{B2}^2 = \frac{m_A v_{A1}^2 - m_A v_{A2}^2}{m_B}$$

$$= \frac{(0.500 \text{ kg})(4.00 \text{ m/s})^2 - (0.500 \text{ kg})(2.00 \text{ m/s})^2}{0.300 \text{ kg}}$$

$$v_{B2} = 4.47 \text{ m/s}$$

Conservation of the x- and y-components of total momentum gives

$$m_A v_{A1x} = m_A v_{A2x} + m_B v_{B2x}$$

$$(0.500 \text{ kg})(4.00 \text{ m/s}) = (0.500 \text{ kg})(2.00 \text{ m/s})(\cos\alpha)$$
$$+ (0.300 \text{ kg})(4.47 \text{ m/s})(\cos\beta)$$

$$0 = m_A v_{A2y} + m_B v_{B2y}$$

$$0 = (0.500 \text{ kg})(2.00 \text{ m/s})(\sin\alpha)$$
$$- (0.300 \text{ kg})(4.47 \text{ m/s})(\sin\beta)$$

These are two simultaneous equations for α and β. You can supply the details of the solution. (*Hint:* Solve the first equation for $\cos\beta$ and the second for $\sin\beta$; square each equation and add. Since $\sin^2\beta + \cos^2\beta = 1$, this eliminates β and leaves an equation that you can solve for $\cos\alpha$ and hence for α. Substitute this value into either of the two equations and solve for β.) The results are

$$\alpha = 36.9° \qquad \beta = 26.6°$$

EVALUATE: To check the answers we confirm that the y-momentum, which was zero before the collision, is in fact zero after the collision. The y-momenta are

$$p_{A2y} = (0.500 \text{ kg})(2.00 \text{ m/s})(\sin 36.9°) = +0.600 \text{ kg} \cdot \text{m/s}$$
$$p_{B2y} = -(0.300 \text{ kg})(4.47 \text{ m/s})(\sin 26.6°) = -0.600 \text{ kg} \cdot \text{m/s}$$

and their sum is indeed zero.

TEST YOUR UNDERSTANDING OF SECTION 8.4 Most present-day nuclear reactors use water as a moderator (see Example 8.11). Are water molecules (mass $m_w = 18.0$ u) a better or worse moderator than carbon atoms? (One advantage of water is that it also acts as a coolant for the reactor's radioactive core.) ∎

8.5 CENTER OF MASS

We can restate the principle of conservation of momentum in a useful way by using the concept of **center of mass**. Suppose we have several particles with masses m_1, m_2, and so on. Let the coordinates of m_1 be (x_1, y_1), those of m_2 be (x_2, y_2), and so on. We define the center of mass of the system as the point that has coordinates (x_{cm}, y_{cm}) given by

$$x_{cm} = \frac{m_1 x_1 + m_2 x_2 + m_3 x_3 + \cdots}{m_1 + m_2 + m_3 + \cdots} = \frac{\sum_i m_i x_i}{\sum_i m_i}$$

$$y_{cm} = \frac{m_1 y_1 + m_2 y_2 + m_3 y_3 + \cdots}{m_1 + m_2 + m_3 + \cdots} = \frac{\sum_i m_i y_i}{\sum_i m_i}$$

(center of mass) (8.28)

We can express the position of the center of mass as a vector $\vec{r}_{cm}$:

Position vectors of individual particles

Position vector of **center of mass** of a system of particles $\vec{r}_{cm} = \dfrac{m_1\vec{r}_1 + m_2\vec{r}_2 + m_3\vec{r}_3 + \cdots}{m_1 + m_2 + m_3 + \cdots} = \dfrac{\sum\limits_i m_i\vec{r}_i}{\sum\limits_i m_i}$ (8.29)

Masses of individual particles

We say that the center of mass is a *mass-weighted average* position of the particles.

EXAMPLE 8.13   CENTER OF MASS OF A WATER MOLECULE

Figure 8.28 shows a simple model of a water molecule. The oxygen–hydrogen separation is $d = 9.57 \times 10^{-11}$ m. Each hydrogen atom has mass 1.0 u, and the oxygen atom has mass 16.0 u. Find the position of the center of mass.

SOLUTION

IDENTIFY and SET UP: Nearly all the mass of each atom is concentrated in its nucleus, whose radius is only about 10^{-5} times the overall radius of the atom. Hence we can safely represent each atom as a point particle. Figure 8.28 shows our coordinate system, with the x-axis chosen to lie along the molecule's symmetry axis. We'll use Eqs. (8.28) to find x_{cm} and y_{cm}.

8.28 Where is the center of mass of a water molecule?

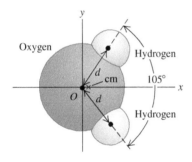

EXECUTE: The oxygen atom is at $x = 0$, $y = 0$. The x-coordinate of each hydrogen atom is $d\cos(105°/2)$; the y-coordinates are $\pm d\sin(105°/2)$. From Eqs. (8.28),

$$x_{cm} = \dfrac{\left[\begin{array}{c}(1.0\text{ u})(d\cos 52.5°) + (1.0\text{ u})(d\cos 52.5°) \\ + (16.0\text{ u})(0)\end{array}\right]}{1.0\text{ u} + 1.0\text{ u} + 16.0\text{ u}} = 0.068d$$

$$y_{cm} = \dfrac{\left[\begin{array}{c}(1.0\text{ u})(d\sin 52.5°) + (1.0\text{ u})(-d\sin 52.5°) \\ + (16.0\text{ u})(0)\end{array}\right]}{1.0\text{ u} + 1.0\text{ u} + 16.0\text{ u}} = 0$$

Substituting $d = 9.57 \times 10^{-11}$ m, we find

$$x_{cm} = (0.068)(9.57 \times 10^{-11}\text{ m}) = 6.5 \times 10^{-12}\text{ m}$$

EVALUATE: The center of mass is much closer to the oxygen atom (located at the origin) than to either hydrogen atom because the oxygen atom is much more massive. The center of mass lies along the molecule's *axis of symmetry*. If the molecule is rotated 180° around this axis, it looks exactly the same as before. The position of the center of mass can't be affected by this rotation, so it *must* lie on the axis of symmetry.

For solid bodies, in which we have (at least on a macroscopic level) a continuous distribution of matter, the sums in Eqs. (8.28) have to be replaced by integrals. The calculations can get quite involved, but we can say three general things about such problems (**Fig. 8.29**). First, whenever a homogeneous body has a geometric center, such as a billiard ball, a sugar cube, or a can of frozen orange juice, the center of mass is at the geometric center. Second, whenever a body has an axis of symmetry, such as a wheel or a pulley, the center of mass always lies on that axis. Third, there is no law that says the center of mass has to be within the body. For example, the center of mass of a donut is in the middle of the hole.

8.29 Locating the center of mass of a symmetric object.

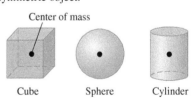

If a homogeneous object has a geometric center, that is where the center of mass is located.

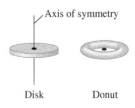

If an object has an axis of symmetry, the center of mass lies along it. As in the case of the donut, the center of mass may not be within the object.

Motion of the Center of Mass

To see the significance of the center of mass of a collection of particles, we must ask what happens to the center of mass when the particles move. The x- and y-components of velocity of the center of mass, $v_{cm\text{-}x}$ and $v_{cm\text{-}y}$, are the time derivatives of x_{cm} and y_{cm}. Also, dx_1/dt is the x-component of velocity of particle 1, so $dx_1/dt = v_{1x}$, and so on. Taking time derivatives of Eqs. (8.28), we get

$$v_{cm\text{-}x} = \dfrac{m_1v_{1x} + m_2v_{2x} + m_3v_{3x} + \cdots}{m_1 + m_2 + m_3 + \cdots}$$

$$v_{cm\text{-}y} = \dfrac{m_1v_{1y} + m_2v_{2y} + m_3v_{3y} + \cdots}{m_1 + m_2 + m_3 + \cdots}$$ (8.30)

8.30 The net external force on this wrench is almost zero as it spins on a smooth, horizontal surface (seen from above). Hence the center of mass moves in a straight line with nearly constant velocity.

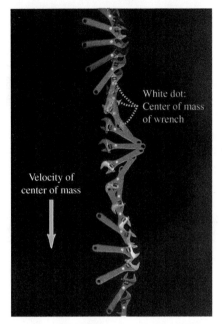

White dot: Center of mass of wrench

Velocity of center of mass

These equations are equivalent to the single vector equation obtained by taking the time derivative of Eq. (8.29):

$$\vec{v}_{cm} = \frac{m_1\vec{v}_1 + m_2\vec{v}_2 + m_3\vec{v}_3 + \cdots}{m_1 + m_2 + m_3 + \cdots} \tag{8.31}$$

We denote the *total* mass $m_1 + m_2 + \cdots$ by M. We can then rewrite Eq. (8.31) as

Total mass of a system of particles

Momenta of individual particles

Velocity of center of mass

$$M\vec{v}_{cm} = m_1\vec{v}_1 + m_2\vec{v}_2 + m_3\vec{v}_3 + \cdots = \vec{P} \tag{8.32}$$

Total momentum of system

So *the total momentum $\vec{P}$ of a system equals the total mass times the velocity of the center of mass.* When you catch a baseball, you are really catching a collection of a very large number of molecules of masses $m_1, m_2, m_3, \ldots$. The impulse you feel is due to the total momentum of this entire collection. But this impulse is the same as if you were catching a single particle of mass $M = m_1 + m_2 + m_3 + \cdots$ moving with $\vec{v}_{cm}$, the velocity of the collection's center of mass. So Eq. (8.32) helps us justify representing an extended body as a particle.

For a system of particles on which the net external force is zero, so that the total momentum $\vec{P}$ is constant, the velocity of the center of mass $\vec{v}_{cm} = \vec{P}/M$ is also constant. **Figure 8.30** shows an example. The overall motion of the wrench appears complicated, but the center of mass follows a straight line, as though all the mass were concentrated at that point.

SOLUTION

EXAMPLE 8.14   **A TUG-OF-WAR ON THE ICE**

James (mass 90.0 kg) and Ramon (mass 60.0 kg) are 20.0 m apart on a frozen pond. Midway between them is a mug of their favorite beverage. They pull on the ends of a light rope stretched between them. When James has moved 6.0 m toward the mug, how far and in what direction has Ramon moved?

SOLUTION

IDENTIFY and SET UP: The surface is horizontal and (we assume) frictionless, so the net external force on the system of James, Ramon, and the rope is zero; their total momentum is conserved. Initially there is no motion, so the total momentum is zero. The velocity of the center of mass is therefore zero, and it remains at rest. Let's take the origin at the position of the mug and let the $+x$-axis extend from the mug toward Ramon. **Figure 8.31** shows our sketch. We use the first of Eqs. (8.28) to calculate the position of the center of mass; we ignore the mass of the light rope.

8.31 Our sketch for this problem.

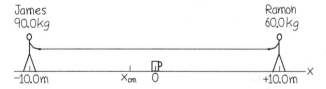

EXECUTE: The initial x-coordinates of James and Ramon are -10.0 m and $+10.0$ m, respectively, so the x-coordinate of the center of mass is

$$x_{cm} = \frac{(90.0\ \text{kg})(-10.0\ \text{m}) + (60.0\ \text{kg})(10.0\ \text{m})}{90.0\ \text{kg} + 60.0\ \text{kg}} = -2.0\ \text{m}$$

When James moves 6.0 m toward the mug, his new x-coordinate is -4.0 m; we'll call Ramon's new x-coordinate x_2. The center of mass doesn't move, so

$$x_{cm} = \frac{(90.0\ \text{kg})(-4.0\ \text{m}) + (60.0\ \text{kg})x_2}{90.0\ \text{kg} + 60.0\ \text{kg}} = -2.0\ \text{m}$$

$$x_2 = 1.0\ \text{m}$$

James has moved 6.0 m and is still 4.0 m from the mug, but Ramon has moved 9.0 m and is only 1.0 m from it.

EVALUATE: The ratio of the distances moved, $(6.0\ \text{m})/(9.0\ \text{m}) = \frac{2}{3}$, is the *inverse* ratio of the masses. Can you see why? Because the surface is frictionless, the two men will keep moving and collide at the center of mass; Ramon will reach the mug first. This is independent of how hard either person pulls; pulling harder just makes them move faster.

External Forces and Center-of-Mass Motion

If the net external force on a system of particles is not zero, then total momentum is not conserved and the velocity of the center of mass changes. Let's look at this situation in more detail.

Equations (8.31) and (8.32) give the *velocity* of the center of mass in terms of the velocities of the individual particles. We take the time derivatives of these equations to show that the *accelerations* are related in the same way. Let $\vec{a}_{cm} = d\vec{v}_{cm}/dt$ be the acceleration of the center of mass; then

$$M\vec{a}_{cm} = m_1\vec{a}_1 + m_2\vec{a}_2 + m_3\vec{a}_3 + \cdots \tag{8.33}$$

Now $m_1\vec{a}_1$ is equal to the vector sum of forces on the first particle, and so on, so the right side of Eq. (8.33) is equal to the vector sum $\Sigma\vec{F}$ of *all* the forces on *all* the particles. Just as we did in Section 8.2, we can classify each force as *external* or *internal*. The sum of all forces on all the particles is then

$$\Sigma\vec{F} = \Sigma\vec{F}_{ext} + \Sigma\vec{F}_{int} = M\vec{a}_{cm}$$

Because of Newton's third law, all of the internal forces cancel in pairs, and $\Sigma\vec{F}_{int} = 0$. What survives on the left side is the sum of only the *external* forces:

Net external force on a body or a collection of particles $\qquad \Sigma\vec{F}_{ext} = M\vec{a}_{cm} \qquad$ Total mass of body or collection of particles $\qquad$ (8.34)

Acceleration of center of mass

When a body or a collection of particles is acted on by external forces, the center of mass moves as though all the mass were concentrated at that point and it were acted on by a net force equal to the sum of the external forces on the system.

This result is central to the whole subject of mechanics. In fact, we've been using this result all along; without it, we would not be able to represent an extended body as a point particle when we apply Newton's laws. It explains why only *external* forces can affect the motion of an extended body. If you pull upward on your belt, your belt exerts an equal downward force on your hands; these are *internal* forces that cancel and have no effect on the overall motion of your body.

As an example, suppose that a cannon shell traveling in a parabolic trajectory (ignoring air resistance) explodes in flight, splitting into two fragments with equal mass (**Fig. 8.32**). The fragments follow new parabolic paths, but the center of mass continues on the original parabolic trajectory, as though all the mass were still concentrated at that point.

This property of the center of mass is important when we analyze the motion of rigid bodies. In Chapter 10 we'll describe the motion of an extended body as a combination of translational motion of the center of mass and rotational motion about an axis through the center of mass. This property also plays an important role in the motion of astronomical objects. It's not correct to say that the moon orbits the earth; rather, both the earth and the moon move in orbits around their common center of mass.

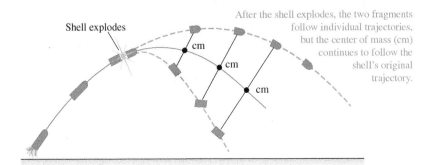

8.32 A shell explodes into two fragments in flight. If air resistance is ignored, the center of mass continues on the same trajectory as the shell's path before the explosion.

Shell explodes

After the shell explodes, the two fragments follow individual trajectories, but the center of mass (cm) continues to follow the shell's original trajectory.

cm

cm

cm

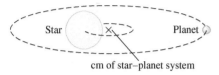

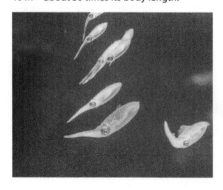

There's one more useful way to describe the motion of a system of particles. Using $\vec{a}_{\text{cm}} = d\vec{v}_{\text{cm}}/dt$, we can rewrite Eq. (8.33) as

$$M\vec{a}_{\text{cm}} = M\frac{d\vec{v}_{\text{cm}}}{dt} = \frac{d(M\vec{v}_{\text{cm}})}{dt} = \frac{d\vec{P}}{dt} \tag{8.35}$$

The total system mass M is constant, so we're allowed to move it inside the derivative. Substituting Eq. (8.35) into Eq. (8.34), we find

$$\sum\vec{F}_{\text{ext}} = \frac{d\vec{P}}{dt} \quad \text{(extended body or system of particles)} \tag{8.36}$$

This equation looks like Eq. (8.4). The difference is that Eq. (8.36) describes a *system* of particles, such as an extended body, while Eq. (8.4) describes a single particle. The interactions between the particles that make up the system can change the individual momenta of the particles, but the *total* momentum $\vec{P}$ of the system can be changed only by external forces acting from outside the system.

If the net external force is zero, Eqs. (8.34) and (8.36) show that the center-of-mass acceleration $\vec{a}_{\text{cm}}$ is zero (so the center-of-mass velocity $\vec{v}_{\text{cm}}$ is constant) and the total momentum $\vec{P}$ is constant. This is just our statement from Section 8.3: If the net external force on a system is zero, momentum is conserved.

TEST YOUR UNDERSTANDING OF SECTION 8.5 Will the center of mass in Fig. 8.32 continue on the same parabolic trajectory even after one of the fragments hits the ground? Why or why not? ▮

8.6 ROCKET PROPULSION

Momentum considerations are particularly useful for analyzing a system in which the masses of parts of the system change with time. In such cases we can't use Newton's second law $\sum\vec{F} = m\vec{a}$ directly because m changes. Rocket propulsion is an important example of this situation. A rocket is propelled forward by rearward ejection of burned fuel that initially was in the rocket (which is why rocket fuel is also called *propellant*). The forward force on the rocket is the reaction to the backward force on the ejected material. The total mass of the system is constant, but the mass of the rocket itself decreases as material is ejected.

For simplicity, let's consider a rocket in outer space, where there is no gravitational force and no air resistance. Let m denote the mass of the rocket, which will change as it expends fuel. We choose our x-axis to be along the rocket's direction of motion. **Figure 8.33a** shows the rocket at a time t, when its mass is m and its x-velocity relative to our coordinate system is v. (To simplify, we will drop the subscript x in this discussion.) The x-component of total momentum at this instant is $P_1 = mv$. In a short time interval dt, the mass of the rocket changes by an amount dm. This is an inherently negative quantity because the rocket's mass m *decreases* with time. During dt, a *positive* mass $-dm$ of burned fuel is ejected from the rocket. Let v_{ex} be the exhaust *speed* of this material *relative*

8.33 A rocket moving in gravity-free outer space at (a) time t and (b) time $t + dt$.

(a)   (b)

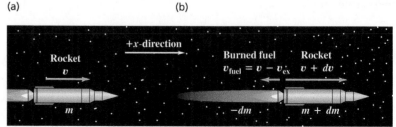

At time t, the rocket has mass m and x-component of velocity v.

At time $t + dt$, the rocket has mass $m + dm$ (where dm is inherently *negative*) and x-component of velocity $v + dv$. The burned fuel has x-component of velocity $v_{\text{fuel}} = v - v_{\text{ex}}$ and mass $-dm$. (The minus sign is needed to make $-dm$ *positive* because dm is negative.)

DEMO

to the rocket; the burned fuel is ejected opposite the direction of motion, so its x-component of *velocity* relative to the rocket is $-v_{\text{ex}}$. The x-velocity v_{fuel} of the burned fuel relative to our coordinate system is then

$$v_{\text{fuel}} = v + (-v_{\text{ex}}) = v - v_{\text{ex}}$$

and the x-component of momentum of the ejected mass $(-dm)$ is

$$(-dm)v_{\text{fuel}} = (-dm)(v - v_{\text{ex}})$$

Figure 8.33b shows that at the end of the time interval dt, the x-velocity of the rocket and unburned fuel has increased to $v + dv$, and its mass has decreased to $m + dm$ (remember that dm is negative). The rocket's momentum at this time is

$$(m + dm)(v + dv)$$

Thus the *total x*-component of momentum P_2 of the rocket plus ejected fuel at time $t + dt$ is

$$P_2 = (m + dm)(v + dv) + (-dm)(v - v_{\text{ex}})$$

According to our initial assumption, the rocket and fuel are an isolated system. Thus momentum is conserved, and the total x-component of momentum of the system must be the same at time t and at time $t + dt$: $P_1 = P_2$. Hence

$$mv = (m + dm)(v + dv) + (-dm)(v - v_{\text{ex}})$$

This can be simplified to

$$m\,dv = -dm\,v_{\text{ex}} - dm\,dv$$

We can ignore the term $(-dm\,dv)$ because it is a product of two small quantities and thus is much smaller than the other terms. Dropping this term, dividing by dt, and rearranging, we find

$$m\frac{dv}{dt} = -v_{\text{ex}}\frac{dm}{dt} \qquad (8.37)$$

Now dv/dt is the acceleration of the rocket, so the left side of Eq. (8.37) (mass times acceleration) equals the net force F, or *thrust,* on the rocket:

$$F = -v_{\text{ex}}\frac{dm}{dt} \qquad (8.38)$$

The thrust is proportional both to the relative speed v_{ex} of the ejected fuel and to the mass of fuel ejected per unit time, $-dm/dt$. (Remember that dm/dt is negative because it is the rate of change of the rocket's mass, so F is positive.)

The x-component of acceleration of the rocket is

$$a = \frac{dv}{dt} = -\frac{v_{\text{ex}}}{m}\frac{dm}{dt} \qquad (8.39)$$

This is positive because v_{ex} is positive (remember, it's the exhaust *speed*) and dm/dt is negative. The rocket's mass m decreases continuously while the fuel is being consumed. If v_{ex} and dm/dt are constant, the acceleration increases until all the fuel is gone.

Equation (8.38) tells us that an effective rocket burns fuel at a rapid rate (large $-dm/dt$) and ejects the burned fuel at a high relative speed (large v_{ex}), as in **Fig. 8.34**. In the early days of rocket propulsion, people who didn't understand conservation of momentum thought that a rocket couldn't function in outer space because "it doesn't have anything to push against." In fact, rockets work *best* in outer space, where there is no air resistance! The launch vehicle in Fig. 8.34 is *not* "pushing against the ground" to ascend.

If the exhaust speed v_{ex} is constant, we can integrate Eq. (8.39) to relate the velocity v at any time to the remaining mass m. At time $t = 0$, let the mass be m_0 and the velocity be v_0. Then we rewrite Eq. (8.39) as

$$dv = -v_{\text{ex}}\frac{dm}{m}$$

8.34 To provide enough thrust to lift its payload into space, this *Atlas V* launch vehicle ejects more than 1000 kg of burned fuel per second at speeds of nearly 4000 m/s.

We change the integration variables to v' and m', so we can use v and m as the upper limits (the final speed and mass). Then we integrate both sides, using limits v_0 to v and m_0 to m, and take the constant v_{ex} outside the integral:

$$\int_{v_0}^{v} dv' = -\int_{m_0}^{m} v_{ex}\frac{dm'}{m'} = -v_{ex}\int_{m_0}^{m}\frac{dm'}{m'}$$

$$v - v_0 = -v_{ex}\ln\frac{m}{m_0} = v_{ex}\ln\frac{m_0}{m} \tag{8.40}$$

The ratio m_0/m is the original mass divided by the mass after the fuel has been exhausted. In practical spacecraft this ratio is made as large as possible to maximize the speed gain, which means that the initial mass of the rocket is almost all fuel. The final velocity of the rocket will be greater in magnitude (and is often *much* greater) than the relative speed v_{ex} if $\ln(m_0/m) > 1$—that is, if $m_0/m > e = 2.71828\ldots$.

We've assumed throughout this analysis that the rocket is in gravity-free outer space. However, gravity must be taken into account when a rocket is launched from the surface of a planet, as in Fig. 8.34.

EXAMPLE 8.15 ACCELERATION OF A ROCKET

The engine of a rocket in outer space, far from any planet, is turned on. The rocket ejects burned fuel at a constant rate; in the first second of firing, it ejects $\frac{1}{120}$ of its initial mass m_0 at a relative speed of 2400 m/s. What is the rocket's initial acceleration?

SOLUTION

IDENTIFY and SET UP: We are given the rocket's exhaust speed v_{ex} and the fraction of the initial mass lost during the first second of firing, from which we can find dm/dt. We'll use Eq. (8.39) to find the acceleration of the rocket.

EXECUTE: The initial rate of change of mass is

$$\frac{dm}{dt} = -\frac{m_0/120}{1\text{ s}} = -\frac{m_0}{120\text{ s}}$$

From Eq. (8.39),

$$a = -\frac{v_{ex}}{m_0}\frac{dm}{dt} = -\frac{2400\text{ m/s}}{m_0}\left(-\frac{m_0}{120\text{ s}}\right) = 20\text{ m/s}^2$$

EVALUATE: The answer doesn't depend on m_0. If v_{ex} is the same, the initial acceleration is the same for a 120,000-kg spacecraft that ejects 1000 kg/s as for a 60-kg astronaut equipped with a small rocket that ejects 0.5 kg/s.

EXAMPLE 8.16 SPEED OF A ROCKET

Suppose that $\frac{3}{4}$ of the initial mass of the rocket in Example 8.15 is fuel, so the fuel is completely consumed at a constant rate in 90 s. The final mass of the rocket is $m = m_0/4$. If the rocket starts from rest in our coordinate system, find its speed at the end of this time.

SOLUTION

IDENTIFY, SET UP, and EXECUTE: We are given the initial velocity $v_0 = 0$, the exhaust speed $v_{ex} = 2400$ m/s, and the final mass m as a fraction of the initial mass m_0. We'll use Eq. (8.40) to find the final speed v:

$$v = v_0 + v_{ex}\ln\frac{m_0}{m} = 0 + (2400\text{ m/s})(\ln 4) = 3327\text{ m/s}$$

EVALUATE: Let's examine what happens as the rocket gains speed. (To illustrate our point, we use more figures than are significant.) At the start of the flight, when the velocity of the rocket is zero, the ejected fuel is moving backward at 2400 m/s relative to our frame of reference. As the rocket moves forward and speeds up, the fuel's speed relative to our system decreases; when the rocket speed reaches 2400 m/s, this relative speed is *zero*. [Knowing the rate of fuel consumption, you can solve Eq. (8.40) to show that this occurs at about $t = 75.6$ s.] After this time the ejected burned fuel moves *forward*, not backward, in our system. Relative to our frame of reference, the last bit of ejected fuel has a forward velocity of 3327 m/s $-$ 2400 m/s = 927 m/s.

TEST YOUR UNDERSTANDING OF SECTION 8.6 (a) If a rocket in gravity-free outer space has the same thrust at all times, is its acceleration constant, increasing, or decreasing? (b) If the rocket has the same acceleration at all times, is the thrust constant, increasing, or decreasing? ∎

Momentum of a particle: The momentum $\vec{p}$ of a particle is a vector quantity equal to the product of the particle's mass m and velocity $\vec{v}$. Newton's second law says that the net force on a particle is equal to the rate of change of the particle's momentum.

$$\vec{p} = m\vec{v} \tag{8.2}$$

$$\sum \vec{F} = \frac{d\vec{p}}{dt} \tag{8.4}$$

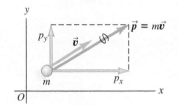

Impulse and momentum: If a constant net force $\sum \vec{F}$ acts on a particle for a time interval Δt from t_1 to t_2, the impulse $\vec{J}$ of the net force is the product of the net force and the time interval. If $\sum \vec{F}$ varies with time, $\vec{J}$ is the integral of the net force over the time interval. In any case, the change in a particle's momentum during a time interval equals the impulse of the net force that acted on the particle during that interval. The momentum of a particle equals the impulse that accelerated it from rest to its present speed. (See Examples 8.1–8.3.)

$$\vec{J} = \sum \vec{F}(t_2 - t_1) = \sum \vec{F} \, \Delta t \tag{8.5}$$

$$\vec{J} = \int_{t_1}^{t_2} \sum \vec{F} \, dt \tag{8.7}$$

$$\vec{J} = \vec{p}_2 - \vec{p}_1 \tag{8.6}$$

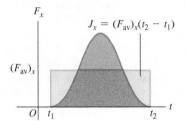

Conservation of momentum: An internal force is a force exerted by one part of a system on another. An external force is a force exerted on any part of a system by something outside the system. If the net external force on a system is zero, the total momentum of the system $\vec{P}$ (the vector sum of the momenta of the individual particles that make up the system) is constant, or conserved. Each component of total momentum is separately conserved. (See Examples 8.4–8.6.)

$$\vec{P} = \vec{p}_A + \vec{p}_B + \cdots$$
$$= m_A \vec{v}_A + m_B \vec{v}_B + \cdots \tag{8.14}$$

If $\sum \vec{F} = 0$, then $\vec{P} = \text{constant}$.

Collisions: In collisions of all kinds, the initial and final total momenta are equal. In an elastic collision between two bodies, the initial and final total kinetic energies are also equal, and the initial and final relative velocities have the same magnitude. In an inelastic two-body collision, the total kinetic energy is less after the collision than before. If the two bodies have the same final velocity, the collision is completely inelastic. (See Examples 8.7–8.12.)

Center of mass: The position vector of the center of mass of a system of particles, $\vec{r}_{cm}$, is a weighted average of the positions $\vec{r}_1, \vec{r}_2, \ldots$ of the individual particles. The total momentum $\vec{P}$ of a system equals the system's total mass M multiplied by the velocity of its center of mass, $\vec{v}_{cm}$. The center of mass moves as though all the mass M were concentrated at that point. If the net external force on the system is zero, the center-of-mass velocity $\vec{v}_{cm}$ is constant. If the net external force is not zero, the center of mass accelerates as though it were a particle of mass M being acted on by the same net external force. (See Examples 8.13 and 8.14.)

$$\vec{r}_{cm} = \frac{m_1 \vec{r}_1 + m_2 \vec{r}_2 + m_3 \vec{r}_3 + \cdots}{m_1 + m_2 + m_3 + \cdots}$$

$$= \frac{\sum_i m_i \vec{r}_i}{\sum_i m_i} \tag{8.29}$$

$$\vec{P} = m_1 \vec{v}_1 + m_2 \vec{v}_2 + m_3 \vec{v}_3 + \cdots$$
$$= M \vec{v}_{cm} \tag{8.32}$$

$$\sum \vec{F}_{ext} = M \vec{a}_{cm} \tag{8.34}$$

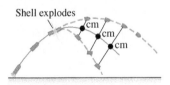

Rocket propulsion: In rocket propulsion, the mass of a rocket changes as the fuel is used up and ejected from the rocket. Analysis of the motion of the rocket must include the momentum carried away by the spent fuel as well as the momentum of the rocket itself. (See Examples 8.15 and 8.16.)

BRIDGING PROBLEM ONE COLLISION AFTER ANOTHER

Sphere A, of mass 0.600 kg, is initially moving to the right at 4.00 m/s. Sphere B, of mass 1.80 kg, is initially to the right of sphere A and moving to the right at 2.00 m/s. After the two spheres collide, sphere B is moving at 3.00 m/s in the same direction as before. (a) What is the velocity (magnitude and direction) of sphere A after this collision? (b) Is this collision elastic or inelastic? (c) Sphere B then has an off-center collision with sphere C, which has mass 1.20 kg and is initially at rest. After this collision, sphere B is moving at 19.0° to its initial direction at 2.00 m/s. What is the velocity (magnitude and direction) of sphere C after this collision? (d) What is the impulse (magnitude and direction) imparted to sphere B by sphere C when they collide? (e) Is this second collision elastic or inelastic? (f) What is the velocity (magnitude and direction) of the center of mass of the system of three spheres (A, B, and C) after the second collision? No external forces act on any of the spheres in this problem.

SOLUTION GUIDE

IDENTIFY and SET UP

1. Momentum is conserved in these collisions. Can you explain why?
2. Choose the x- and y-axes, and use your choice of axes to draw three figures that show the spheres (i) before the first collision, (ii) after the first collision but before the second collision, and (iii) after the second collision. Assign subscripts to values in each of situations (i), (ii), and (iii).
3. Make a list of the target variables, and choose the equations that you'll use to solve for these.

EXECUTE

4. Solve for the velocity of sphere A after the first collision. Does A slow down or speed up in the collision? Does this make sense?
5. Now that you know the velocities of both A and B after the first collision, decide whether or not this collision is elastic. (How will you do this?)
6. The second collision is two-dimensional, so you'll have to demand that *both* components of momentum are conserved. Use this to find the speed and direction of sphere C after the second collision. (*Hint:* After the first collision, sphere B maintains the same velocity until it hits sphere C.)
7. Use the definition of impulse to find the impulse imparted to sphere B by sphere C. Remember that impulse is a vector.
8. Use the same technique that you employed in step 5 to decide whether the second collision is elastic.
9. Find the velocity of the center of mass after the second collision.

EVALUATE

10. Compare the directions of the vectors you found in steps 6 and 7. Is this a coincidence? Why or why not?
11. Find the velocity of the center of mass before and after the first collision. Compare to your result from step 9. Again, is this a coincidence? Why or why not?

Problems

•, ••, •••: Difficulty levels. **CP**: Cumulative problems incorporating material from earlier chapters. **CALC**: Problems requiring calculus. **DATA**: Problems involving real data, scientific evidence, experimental design, and/or statistical reasoning. **BIO**: Biosciences problems.

DISCUSSION QUESTIONS

Q8.1 In splitting logs with a hammer and wedge, is a heavy hammer more effective than a lighter hammer? Why?

Q8.2 Suppose you catch a baseball and then someone invites you to catch a bowling ball with either the same momentum or the same kinetic energy as the baseball. Which would you choose? Explain.

Q8.3 When rain falls from the sky, what happens to its momentum as it hits the ground? Is your answer also valid for Newton's famous apple?

Q8.4 A car has the same kinetic energy when it is traveling south at 30 m/s as when it is traveling northwest at 30 m/s. Is the momentum of the car the same in both cases? Explain.

Q8.5 A truck is accelerating as it speeds down the highway. One inertial frame of reference is attached to the ground with its origin at a fence post. A second frame of reference is attached to a police car that is traveling down the highway at constant velocity. Is the momentum of the truck the same in these two reference frames? Explain. Is the rate of change of the truck's momentum the same in these two frames? Explain.

Q8.6 (a) If the momentum of a *single* point object is equal to zero, must the object's kinetic energy also be zero? (b) If the momentum of a *pair* of point objects is equal to zero, must the kinetic energy of those objects also be zero? (c) If the kinetic energy of a pair of point objects is equal to zero, must the momentum of those objects also be zero? Explain your reasoning in each case.

Q8.7 A woman holding a large rock stands on a frictionless, horizontal sheet of ice. She throws the rock with speed v_0 at an angle α above the horizontal. Consider the system consisting of the woman plus the rock. Is the momentum of the system conserved? Why or why not? Is any component of the momentum of the system conserved? Again, why or why not?

Q8.8 In Example 8.7 (Section 8.3), where the two gliders of Fig. 8.18 stick together after the collision, the collision is inelastic because $K_2 < K_1$. In Example 8.5 (Section 8.2), is the collision inelastic? Explain.

Q8.9 In a completely inelastic collision between two objects, where the objects stick together after the collision, is it possible for the final kinetic energy of the system to be zero? If so, give an example in which this would occur. If the final kinetic energy is zero, what must the initial momentum of the system be? Is the initial kinetic energy of the system zero? Explain.

Q8.10 Since for a particle the kinetic energy is given by $K = \frac{1}{2}mv^2$ and the momentum by $\vec{P} = m\vec{v}$, it is easy to show that $K = p^2/2m$. How, then, is it possible to have an event during which the total momentum of the system is constant but the total kinetic energy changes?

Q8.11 In each of Examples 8.10, 8.11, and 8.12 (Section 8.4), verify that the relative velocity vector of the two bodies has the same magnitude before and after the collision. In each case, what happens to the *direction* of the relative velocity vector?

Q8.12 A glass dropped on the floor is more likely to break if the floor is concrete than if it is wood. Why? (Refer to Fig. 8.3b.)

Q8.13 In Fig. 8.23b, the kinetic energy of the Ping-Pong ball is larger after its interaction with the bowling ball than before. From where does the extra energy come? Describe the event in terms of conservation of energy.

Q8.14 A machine gun is fired at a steel plate. Is the average force on the plate from the bullet impact greater if the bullets bounce off or if they are squashed and stick to the plate? Explain.

Q8.15 A net force of 4 N acts on an object initially at rest for 0.25 s and gives it a final speed of 5 m/s. How could a net force of 2 N produce the same final speed?

Q8.16 A net force with x-component ΣF_x acts on an object from time t_1 to time t_2. The x-component of the momentum of the object is the same at t_1 as it is at t_2, but ΣF_x is not zero at all times between t_1 and t_2. What can you say about the graph of ΣF_x versus t?

Q8.17 A tennis player hits a tennis ball with a racket. Consider the system made up of the ball and the racket. Is the total momentum of the system the same just before and just after the hit? Is the total momentum just after the hit the same as 2 s later, when the ball is in midair at the high point of its trajectory? Explain any differences between the two cases.

Q8.18 In Example 8.4 (Section 8.2), consider the system consisting of the rifle plus the bullet. What is the speed of the system's center of mass after the rifle is fired? Explain.

Q8.19 An egg is released from rest from the roof of a building and falls to the ground. As the egg falls, what happens to the momentum of the system of the egg plus the earth?

Q8.20 A woman stands in the middle of a perfectly smooth, frictionless, frozen lake. She can set herself in motion by throwing things, but suppose she has nothing to throw. Can she propel herself to shore *without* throwing anything?

Q8.21 At the highest point in its parabolic trajectory, a shell explodes into two fragments. Is it possible for *both* fragments to fall straight down after the explosion? Why or why not?

Q8.22 When an object breaks into two pieces (explosion, radioactive decay, recoil, etc.), the lighter fragment gets more kinetic energy than the heavier one. This is a consequence of momentum conservation, but can you also explain it by using Newton's laws of motion?

Q8.23 An apple falls from a tree and feels no air resistance. As it is falling, which of these statements about it are true? (a) Only its momentum is conserved; (b) only its mechanical energy is conserved; (c) both its momentum and its mechanical energy are conserved; (d) its kinetic energy is conserved.

Q8.24 Two pieces of clay collide and stick together. During the collision, which of these statements are true? (a) Only the momentum of the clay is conserved; (b) only the mechanical energy of the clay is conserved; (c) both the momentum and the

mechanical energy of the clay are conserved; (d) the kinetic energy of the clay is conserved.

Q8.25 Two objects of mass M and $5M$ are at rest on a horizontal, frictionless table with a compressed spring of negligible mass between them. When the spring is released, which of the following statements are true? (a) The two objects receive equal magnitudes of momentum. (b) The two objects receive equal amounts of kinetic energy from the spring. (c) The heavier object gains more kinetic energy than the lighter object. (d) The lighter object gains more kinetic energy than the heavier object. Explain your reasoning in each case.

Q8.26 A very heavy SUV collides head-on with a very light compact car. Which of these statements about the collision are correct? (a) The amount of kinetic energy lost by the SUV is equal to the amount of kinetic energy gained by the compact; (b) the amount of momentum lost by the SUV is equal to the amount of momentum gained by the compact; (c) the compact feels a considerably greater force during the collision than the SUV does; (d) both cars lose the same amount of kinetic energy.

EXERCISES

Section 8.1 Momentum and Impulse

8.1 • (a) What is the magnitude of the momentum of a 10,000-kg truck whose speed is 12.0 m/s? (b) What speed would a 2000-kg SUV have to attain in order to have (i) the same momentum? (ii) the same kinetic energy?

8.2 • In a certain track and field event, the shotput has a mass of 7.30 kg and is released with a speed of 15.0 m/s at 40.0° above the horizontal over a competitor's straight left leg. What are the initial horizontal and vertical components of the momentum of this shotput?

8.3 • Objects A, B, and C are moving as shown in **Fig. E8.3**. Find the x- and y-components of the net momentum of the particles if we define the system to consist of (a) A and C, (b) B and C, (c) all three objects.

Figure **E8.3**

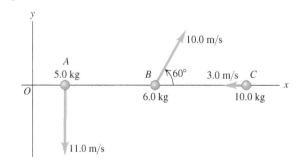

8.4 • Two vehicles are approaching an intersection. One is a 2500-kg pickup traveling at 14.0 m/s from east to west (the $-x$-direction), and the other is a 1500-kg sedan going from south to north (the $+y$-direction) at 23.0 m/s. (a) Find the x- and y-components of the net momentum of this system. (b) What are the magnitude and direction of the net momentum?

8.5 • One 110-kg football lineman is running to the right at 2.75 m/s while another 125-kg lineman is running directly toward him at 2.60 m/s. What are (a) the magnitude and direction of the net momentum of these two athletes, and (b) their total kinetic energy?

8.6 •• BIO **Biomechanics.** The mass of a regulation tennis ball is 57 g (although it can vary slightly), and tests have shown that the ball is in contact with the tennis racket for 30 ms. (This number can also vary, depending on the racket and swing.) We shall assume a 30.0-ms contact time. The fastest-known served tennis ball was served by "Big Bill" Tilden in 1931, and its speed was measured to be 73 m/s. (a) What impulse and what force did Big Bill exert on the tennis ball in his record serve? (b) If Big Bill's opponent returned his serve with a speed of 55 m/s, what force and what impulse did he exert on the ball, assuming only horizontal motion?

8.7 • **Force of a Golf Swing.** A 0.0450-kg golf ball initially at rest is given a speed of 25.0 m/s when a club strikes it. If the club and ball are in contact for 2.00 ms, what average force acts on the ball? Is the effect of the ball's weight during the time of contact significant? Why or why not?

8.8 • **Force of a Baseball Swing.** A baseball has mass 0.145 kg. (a) If the velocity of a pitched ball has a magnitude of 45.0 m/s and the batted ball's velocity is 55.0 m/s in the opposite direction, find the magnitude of the change in momentum of the ball and of the impulse applied to it by the bat. (b) If the ball remains in contact with the bat for 2.00 ms, find the magnitude of the average force applied by the bat.

8.9 • A 0.160-kg hockey puck is moving on an icy, frictionless, horizontal surface. At $t = 0$, the puck is moving to the right at 3.00 m/s. (a) Calculate the velocity of the puck (magnitude and direction) after a force of 25.0 N directed to the right has been applied for 0.050 s. (b) If, instead, a force of 12.0 N directed to the left is applied from $t = 0$ to $t = 0.050$ s, what is the final velocity of the puck?

8.10 •• A bat strikes a 0.145-kg baseball. Just before impact, the ball is traveling horizontally to the right at 40.0 m/s; when it leaves the bat, the ball is traveling to the left at an angle of 30° above horizontal with a speed of 52.0 m/s. If the ball and bat are in contact for 1.75 ms, find the horizontal and vertical components of the average force on the ball.

8.11 • CALC At time $t = 0$ a 2150-kg rocket in outer space fires an engine that exerts an increasing force on it in the $+x$-direction. This force obeys the equation $F_x = At^2$, where t is time, and has a magnitude of 781.25 N when $t = 1.25$ s. (a) Find the SI value of the constant A, including its units. (b) What impulse does the engine exert on the rocket during the 1.50-s interval starting 2.00 s after the engine is fired? (c) By how much does the rocket's velocity change during this interval? Assume constant mass.

8.12 •• BIO **Bone Fracture.** Experimental tests have shown that bone will rupture if it is subjected to a force density of 1.03×10^8 N/m². Suppose a 70.0-kg person carelessly roller-skates into an overhead metal beam that hits his forehead and completely stops his forward motion. If the area of contact with the person's forehead is 1.5 cm², what is the greatest speed with which he can hit the wall without breaking any bone if his head is in contact with the beam for 10.0 ms?

8.13 • A 2.00-kg stone is sliding to the right on a frictionless, horizontal surface at 5.00 m/s when it is suddenly struck by an object that exerts a large horizontal force on it for a short period of time. The graph in **Fig. E8.13** shows the magnitude of this force as a function of time. (a) What impulse does this

Figure **E8.13**

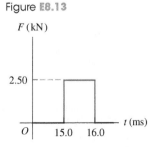

force exert on the stone? (b) Just after the force stops acting, find the magnitude and direction of the stone's velocity if the force acts (i) to the right or (ii) to the left.

8.14 •• CALC Starting at $t = 0$, a horizontal net force $\vec{F} = (0.280 \text{ N/s})t\hat{i} + (-0.450 \text{ N/s}^2)t^2\hat{j}$ is applied to a box that has an initial momentum $\vec{p} = (-3.00 \text{ kg} \cdot \text{m/s})\hat{i} + (4.00 \text{ kg} \cdot \text{m/s})\hat{j}$. What is the momentum of the box at $t = 2.00$ s?

8.15 •• To warm up for a match, a tennis player hits the 57.0-g ball vertically with her racket. If the ball is stationary just before it is hit and goes 5.50 m high, what impulse did she impart to it?

Section 8.2 Conservation of Momentum

8.16 • A 68.5-kg astronaut is doing a repair in space on the orbiting space station. She throws a 2.25-kg tool away from her at 3.20 m/s relative to the space station. With what speed and in what direction will she begin to move?

8.17 •• The expanding gases that leave the muzzle of a rifle also contribute to the recoil. A .30-caliber bullet has mass 0.00720 kg and a speed of 601 m/s relative to the muzzle when fired from a rifle that has mass 2.80 kg. The loosely held rifle recoils at a speed of 1.85 m/s relative to the earth. Find the momentum of the propellant gases in a coordinate system attached to the earth as they leave the muzzle of the rifle.

8.18 • Two figure skaters, one weighing 625 N and the other 725 N, push off against each other on frictionless ice. (a) If the heavier skater travels at 1.50 m/s, how fast will the lighter one travel? (b) How much kinetic energy is "created" during the skaters' maneuver, and where does this energy come from?

8.19 • BIO **Animal Propulsion.** Squids and octopuses propel themselves by expelling water. They do this by keeping water in a cavity and then suddenly contracting the cavity to force out the water through an opening. A 6.50-kg squid (including the water in the cavity) at rest suddenly sees a dangerous predator. (a) If the squid has 1.75 kg of water in its cavity, at what speed must it expel this water suddenly to achieve a speed of 2.50 m/s to escape the predator? Ignore any drag effects of the surrounding water. (b) How much kinetic energy does the squid create by this maneuver?

8.20 •• You are standing on a sheet of ice that covers the football stadium parking lot in Buffalo; there is negligible friction between your feet and the ice. A friend throws you a 0.600-kg ball that is traveling horizontally at 10.0 m/s. Your mass is 70.0 kg. (a) If you catch the ball, with what speed do you and the ball move afterward? (b) If the ball hits you and bounces off your chest, so afterward it is moving horizontally at 8.0 m/s in the opposite direction, what is your speed after the collision?

8.21 •• On a frictionless, horizontal air table, puck A (with mass 0.250 kg) is moving toward puck B (with mass 0.350 kg), which is initially at rest. After the collision, puck A has a velocity of 0.120 m/s to the left, and puck B has a velocity of 0.650 m/s to the right. (a) What was the speed of puck A before the collision? (b) Calculate the change in the total kinetic energy of the system that occurs during the collision.

8.22 •• When cars are equipped with flexible bumpers, they will bounce off each other during low-speed collisions, thus causing less damage. In one such accident, a 1750-kg car traveling to the right at 1.50 m/s collides with a 1450-kg car going to the left at 1.10 m/s. Measurements show that the heavier car's speed just after the collision was 0.250 m/s in its original direction. Ignore any road friction during the collision. (a) What was the speed of the lighter car just after the collision? (b) Calculate the change in the combined kinetic energy of the two-car system during this collision.

8.23 ·· Two identical 0.900-kg masses are pressed against opposite ends of a light spring of force constant 1.75 N/cm, compressing the spring by 20.0 cm from its normal length. Find the speed of each mass when it has moved free of the spring on a frictionless, horizontal table.

8.24 · Block A in **Fig. E8.24** has mass 1.00 kg, and block B has mass 3.00 kg. The blocks are forced together, compressing a spring S between them; then the system is released from rest on a level, frictionless surface. The spring, which has negligible mass, is not fastened to either block and drops to the surface after it has expanded. Block B acquires a speed of 1.20 m/s. (a) What is the final speed of block A? (b) How much potential energy was stored in the compressed spring?

Figure **E8.24** $m_A = 1.00 \text{ kg}$ $m_B = 3.00 \text{ kg}$

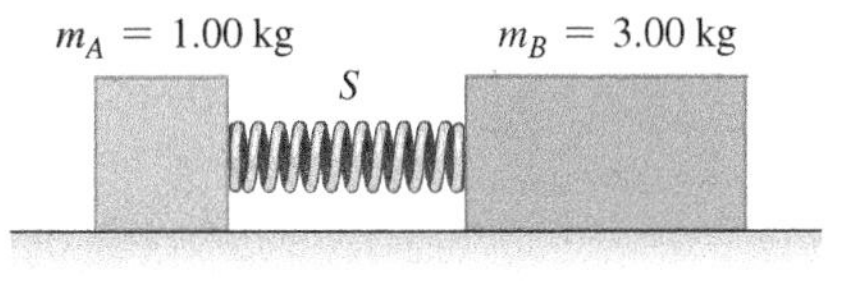

8.25 ·· A hunter on a frozen, essentially frictionless pond uses a rifle that shoots 4.20-g bullets at 965 m/s. The mass of the hunter (including his gun) is 72.5 kg, and the hunter holds tight to the gun after firing it. Find the recoil velocity of the hunter if he fires the rifle (a) horizontally and (b) at 56.0° above the horizontal.

8.26 · An atomic nucleus suddenly bursts apart (fissions) into two pieces. Piece A, of mass m_A, travels off to the left with speed v_A. Piece B, of mass m_B, travels off to the right with speed v_B. (a) Use conservation of momentum to solve for v_B in terms of m_A, m_B, and v_A. (b) Use the results of part (a) to show that $K_A/K_B = m_B/m_A$, where K_A and K_B are the kinetic energies of the two pieces.

8.27 ·· Two ice skaters, Daniel (mass 65.0 kg) and Rebecca (mass 45.0 kg), are practicing. Daniel stops to tie his shoelace and, while at rest, is struck by Rebecca, who is moving at 13.0 m/s before she collides with him. After the collision, Rebecca has a velocity of magnitude 8.00 m/s at an angle of 53.1° from her initial direction. Both skaters move on the frictionless, horizontal surface of the rink. (a) What are the magnitude and direction of Daniel's velocity after the collision? (b) What is the change in total kinetic energy of the two skaters as a result of the collision?

8.28 ·· You are standing on a large sheet of frictionless ice and holding a large rock. In order to get off the ice, you throw the rock so it has velocity 12.0 m/s relative to the earth at an angle of 35.0° above the horizontal. If your mass is 70.0 kg and the rock's mass is 3.00 kg, what is your speed after you throw the rock? (See Discussion Question Q8.7.)

8.29 ·· You (mass 55 kg) are riding a frictionless skateboard (mass 5.0 kg) in a straight line at a speed of 4.5 m/s. A friend standing on a balcony above you drops a 2.5-kg sack of flour straight down into your arms. (a) What is your new speed while you hold the sack? (b) Since the sack was dropped vertically, how can it affect your *horizontal* motion? Explain. (c) Now you try to rid yourself of the extra weight by throwing the sack straight up. What will be your speed while the sack is in the air? Explain.

8.30 · An astronaut in space cannot use a conventional means, such as a scale or balance, to determine the mass of an object. But she does have devices to measure distance and time accurately. She knows her own mass is 78.4 kg, but she is unsure of the mass of a large gas canister in the airless rocket. When this canister is approaching her at 3.50 m/s, she pushes against it, which slows it down to 1.20 m/s (but does not reverse it) and gives her a speed of 2.40 m/s. What is the mass of this canister?

8.31 ·· **Asteroid Collision.** Two asteroids of equal mass in the asteroid belt between Mars and Jupiter collide with a glancing blow. Asteroid A, which was initially traveling at 40.0 m/s, is deflected 30.0° from its original direction, while asteroid B, which was initially at rest, travels at 45.0° to the original direction of A (**Fig. E8.31**). (a) Find the speed of each asteroid after the collision. (b) What fraction of the original kinetic energy of asteroid A dissipates during this collision?

Figure **E8.31**

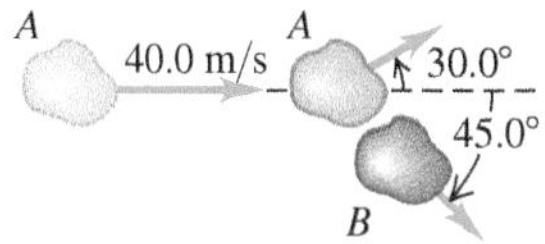

A → 40.0 m/s   *A* ↗ 30.0°   45.0°   *B*

Section 8.3 Momentum Conservation and Collisions

8.32 · Two skaters collide and grab on to each other on frictionless ice. One of them, of mass 70.0 kg, is moving to the right at 4.00 m/s, while the other, of mass 65.0 kg, is moving to the left at 2.50 m/s. What are the magnitude and direction of the velocity of these skaters just after they collide?

8.33 ·· A 15.0-kg fish swimming at 1.10 m/s suddenly gobbles up a 4.50-kg fish that is initially stationary. Ignore any drag effects of the water. (a) Find the speed of the large fish just after it eats the small one. (b) How much mechanical energy was dissipated during this meal?

8.34 · Two fun-loving otters are sliding toward each other on a muddy (and hence frictionless) horizontal surface. One of them, of mass 7.50 kg, is sliding to the left at 5.00 m/s, while the other, of mass 5.75 kg, is slipping to the right at 6.00 m/s. They hold fast to each other after they collide. (a) Find the magnitude and direction of the velocity of these free-spirited otters right after they collide. (b) How much mechanical energy dissipates during this play?

8.35 · **Deep Impact Mission.** In July 2005, NASA's "Deep Impact" mission crashed a 372-kg probe directly onto the surface of the comet Tempel 1, hitting the surface at 37,000 km/h. The original speed of the comet at that time was about 40,000 km/h, and its mass was estimated to be in the range $(0.10 - 2.5) \times 10^{14}$ kg. Use the smallest value of the estimated mass. (a) What change in the comet's velocity did this collision produce? Would this change be noticeable? (b) Suppose this comet were to hit the earth and fuse with it. By how much would it change our planet's velocity? Would this change be noticeable? (The mass of the earth is 5.97×10^{24} kg.)

8.36 · A 1050-kg sports car is moving westbound at 15.0 m/s on a level road when it collides with a 6320-kg truck driving east on the same road at 10.0 m/s. The two vehicles remain locked together after the collision. (a) What is the velocity (magnitude and direction) of the two vehicles just after the collision? (b) At what speed should the truck have been moving so that both it and the car are stopped in the collision? (c) Find the change in kinetic energy of the system of two vehicles for the situations of part (a) and part (b). For which situation is the change in kinetic energy greater in magnitude?

8.37 ·· On a very muddy football field, a 110-kg linebacker tackles an 85-kg halfback. Immediately before the collision, the linebacker is slipping with a velocity of 8.8 m/s north and the halfback is sliding with a velocity of 7.2 m/s east. What is the velocity (magnitude and direction) at which the two players move together immediately after the collision?

8.38 •• **Accident Analysis.** Two cars collide at an intersection. Car A, with a mass of 2000 kg, is going from west to east, while car B, of mass 1500 kg, is going from north to south at 15 m/s. As a result, the two cars become enmeshed and move as one. As an expert witness, you inspect the scene and determine that, after the collision, the enmeshed cars moved at an angle of 65° south of east from the point of impact. (a) How fast were the enmeshed cars moving just after the collision? (b) How fast was car A going just before the collision?

8.39 •• Jack (mass 55.0 kg) is sliding due east with speed 8.00 m/s on the surface of a frozen pond. He collides with Jill (mass 48.0 kg), who is initially at rest. After the collision, Jack is traveling at 5.00 m/s in a direction 34.0° north of east. What is Jill's velocity (magnitude and direction) after the collision? Ignore friction.

8.40 •• BIO **Bird Defense.** To protect their young in the nest, peregrine falcons will fly into birds of prey (such as ravens) at high speed. In one such episode, a 600-g falcon flying at 20.0 m/s hit a 1.50-kg raven flying at 9.0 m/s. The falcon hit the raven at right angles to its original path and bounced back at 5.0 m/s. (These figures were estimated by the author as he watched this attack occur in northern New Mexico.) (a) By what angle did the falcon change the raven's direction of motion? (b) What was the raven's speed right after the collision?

8.41 • At the intersection of Texas Avenue and University Drive, a yellow subcompact car with mass 950 kg traveling east on University collides with a red pickup truck with mass 1900 kg that is traveling north on Texas and has run a red light (**Fig. E8.41**). The two vehicles stick together as a result of the collision, and the wreckage slides at 16.0 m/s in the direction 24.0° east of north. Calculate the speed of each vehicle before the collision. The collision occurs during a heavy rainstorm; ignore friction forces between the vehicles and the wet road.

Figure E8.41

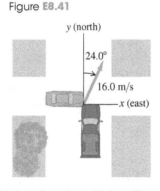

8.42 •• A 5.00-g bullet is fired horizontally into a 1.20-kg wooden block resting on a horizontal surface. The coefficient of kinetic friction between block and surface is 0.20. The bullet remains embedded in the block, which is observed to slide 0.310 m along the surface before stopping. What was the initial speed of the bullet?

8.43 •• **A Ballistic Pendulum.** A 12.0-g rifle bullet is fired with a speed of 380 m/s into a ballistic pendulum with mass 6.00 kg, suspended from a cord 70.0 cm long (see Example 8.8 in Section 8.3). Compute (a) the vertical height through which the pendulum rises, (b) the initial kinetic energy of the bullet, and (c) the kinetic energy of the bullet and pendulum immediately after the bullet becomes embedded in the wood.

8.44 •• **Combining Conservation Laws.** A 15.0-kg block is attached to a very light horizontal spring of force constant 500.0 N/m and is resting on a frictionless horizontal table (**Fig. E8.44**).

Figure E8.44

3.00 kg 8.00 m/s 15.0 kg

Suddenly it is struck by a 3.00-kg stone traveling horizontally at 8.00 m/s to the right, whereupon the stone rebounds at 2.00 m/s horizontally to the left. Find the maximum distance that the block will compress the spring after the collision.

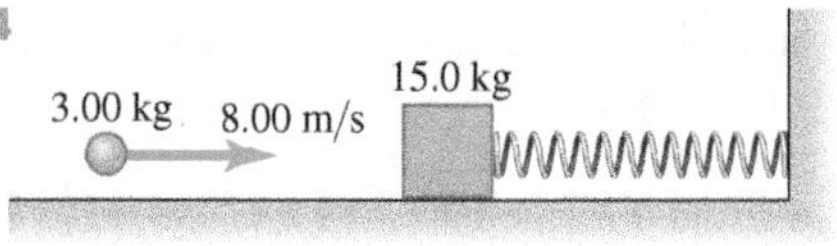

8.45 •• CP A 0.800-kg ornament is hanging by a 1.50-m wire when the ornament is suddenly hit by a 0.200-kg missile traveling horizontally at 12.0 m/s. The missile embeds itself in the ornament during the collision. What is the tension in the wire immediately after the collision?

Section 8.4 Elastic Collisions

8.46 •• A 0.150-kg glider is moving to the right with a speed of 0.80 m/s on a frictionless, horizontal air track. The glider has a head-on collision with a 0.300-kg glider that is moving to the left with a speed of 2.20 m/s. Find the final velocity (magnitude and direction) of each glider if the collision is elastic.

8.47 •• Blocks A (mass 2.00 kg) and B (mass 6.00 kg) move on a frictionless, horizontal surface. Initially, block B is at rest and block A is moving toward it at 2.00 m/s. The blocks are equipped with ideal spring bumpers, as in Example 8.10 (Section 8.4). The collision is head-on, so all motion before and after the collision is along a straight line. (a) Find the maximum energy stored in the spring bumpers and the velocity of each block at that time. (b) Find the velocity of each block after they have moved apart.

8.48 • A 10.0-g marble slides to the left at a speed of 0.400 m/s on the frictionless, horizontal surface of an icy New York sidewalk and has a head-on, elastic collision with a larger 30.0-g marble sliding to the right at a speed of 0.200 m/s (**Fig. E8.48**).

Figure E8.48

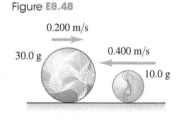

(a) Find the velocity of each marble (magnitude and direction) after the collision. (Since the collision is head-on, all motion is along a line.) (b) Calculate the *change in momentum* (the momentum after the collision minus the momentum before the collision) for each marble. Compare your values for each marble. (c) Calculate the *change in kinetic energy* (the kinetic energy after the collision minus the kinetic energy before the collision) for each marble. Compare your values for each marble.

8.49 •• **Moderators.** Canadian nuclear reactors use *heavy water* moderators in which elastic collisions occur between the neutrons and deuterons of mass 2.0 u (see Example 8.11 in Section 8.4). (a) What is the speed of a neutron, expressed as a fraction of its original speed, after a head-on, elastic collision with a deuteron that is initially at rest? (b) What is its kinetic energy, expressed as a fraction of its original kinetic energy? (c) How many such successive collisions will reduce the speed of a neutron to 1/59,000 of its original value?

8.50 •• You are at the controls of a particle accelerator, sending a beam of 1.50×10^7 m/s protons (mass m) at a gas target of an unknown element. Your detector tells you that some protons bounce straight back after a collision with one of the nuclei of the unknown element. All such protons rebound with a speed of 1.20×10^7 m/s. Assume that the initial speed of the target nucleus is negligible and the collision is elastic. (a) Find the mass of one nucleus of the unknown element. Express your answer in terms of the proton mass m. (b) What is the speed of the unknown nucleus immediately after such a collision?

Section 8.5 Center of Mass

8.51 • Three odd-shaped blocks of chocolate have the following masses and center-of-mass coordinates: (1) 0.300 kg, (0.200 m, 0.300 m); (2) 0.400 kg, (0.100 m, −0.400 m); (3) 0.200 kg, (−0.300 m, 0.600 m). Find the coordinates of the center of mass of the system of three chocolate blocks.

8.52 • Find the position of the center of mass of the system of the sun and Jupiter. (Since Jupiter is more massive than the rest of the solar planets combined, this is essentially the position of the center of mass of the solar system.) Does the center of mass lie inside or outside the sun? Use the data in Appendix F.

8.53 •• **Pluto and Charon.** Pluto's diameter is approximately 2370 km, and the diameter of its satellite Charon is 1250 km. Although the distance varies, they are often about 19,700 km apart, center to center. Assuming that both Pluto and Charon have the same composition and hence the same average density, find the location of the center of mass of this system relative to the center of Pluto.

8.54 • A 1200-kg SUV is moving along a straight highway at 12.0 m/s. Another car, with mass 1800 kg and speed 20.0 m/s, has its center of mass 40.0 m ahead of the center of mass of the SUV (**Fig. E8.54**). Find (a) the position of the center of mass of the system consisting of the two cars; (b) the magnitude of the system's total momentum, by using the given data; (c) the speed of the system's center of mass; (d) the system's total momentum, by using the speed of the center of mass. Compare your result with that of part (b).

Figure **E8.54**

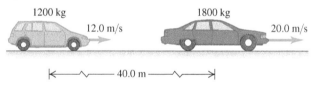

8.55 • A machine part consists of a thin, uniform 4.00-kg bar that is 1.50 m long, hinged perpendicular to a similar vertical bar of mass 3.00 kg and length 1.80 m. The longer bar has a small but dense 2.00-kg ball at one end (**Fig. E8.55**). By what distance will the center of mass of this part move horizontally and vertically if the vertical bar is pivoted counterclockwise through 90° to make the entire part horizontal?

Figure **E8.55**

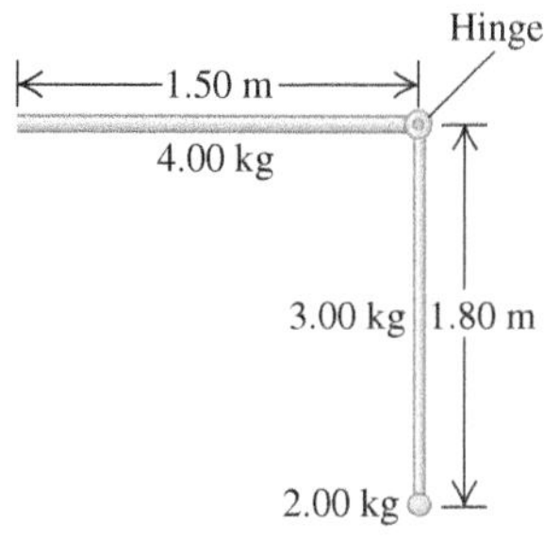

8.56 • At one instant, the center of mass of a system of two particles is located on the x-axis at $x = 2.0$ m and has a velocity of $(5.0 \text{ m/s})\hat{\imath}$. One of the particles is at the origin. The other particle has a mass of 0.10 kg and is at rest on the x-axis at $x = 8.0$ m. (a) What is the mass of the particle at the origin? (b) Calculate the total momentum of this system. (c) What is the velocity of the particle at the origin?

8.57 •• In Example 8.14 (Section 8.5), Ramon pulls on the rope to give himself a speed of 1.10 m/s. What is James's speed?

8.58 • CALC A system consists of two particles. At $t = 0$ one particle is at the origin; the other, which has a mass of 0.50 kg,

is on the y-axis at $y = 6.0$ m. At $t = 0$ the center of mass of the system is on the y-axis at $y = 2.4$ m. The velocity of the center of mass is given by $(0.75 \text{ m/s}^3)t^2\hat{\imath}$. (a) Find the total mass of the system. (b) Find the acceleration of the center of mass at any time t. (c) Find the net external force acting on the system at $t = 3.0$ s.

8.59 • CALC A radio-controlled model airplane has a momentum given by $[(-0.75 \text{ kg·m/s}^3)t^2 + (3.0 \text{ kg·m/s})]\hat{\imath} + (0.25 \text{ kg·m/s}^2)t\hat{\jmath}$. What are the x-, y-, and z-components of the net force on the airplane?

8.60 •• BIO **Changing Your Center of Mass.** To keep the calculations fairly simple but still reasonable, we model a human leg that is 92.0 cm long (measured from the hip joint) by assuming that the upper leg and the lower leg (which includes the foot) have equal lengths and are uniform. For a 70.0-kg person, the mass of the upper leg is 8.60 kg, while that of the lower leg (including foot) is 5.25 kg. Find the location of the center of mass of this leg, relative to the hip joint, if it is (a) stretched out horizontally and (b) bent at the knee to form a right angle with the upper leg remaining horizontal.

Section 8.6 Rocket Propulsion

8.61 •• A 70-kg astronaut floating in space in a 110-kg MMU (manned maneuvering unit) experiences an acceleration of 0.029 m/s² when he fires one of the MMU's thrusters. (a) If the speed of the escaping N_2 gas relative to the astronaut is 490 m/s, how much gas is used by the thruster in 5.0 s? (b) What is the thrust of the thruster?

8.62 • A small rocket burns 0.0500 kg of fuel per second, ejecting it as a gas with a velocity relative to the rocket of magnitude 1600 m/s. (a) What is the thrust of the rocket? (b) Would the rocket operate in outer space where there is no atmosphere? If so, how would you steer it? Could you brake it?

8.63 •• Obviously, we can make rockets to go very fast, but what is a reasonable top speed? Assume that a rocket is fired from rest at a space station in deep space, where gravity is negligible. (a) If the rocket ejects gas at a relative speed of 2000 m/s and you want the rocket's speed eventually to be $1.00 \times 10^{-3}c$, where c is the speed of light in vacuum, what fraction of the initial mass of the rocket and fuel is *not* fuel? (b) What is this fraction if the final speed is to be 3000 m/s?

PROBLEMS

8.64 •• A steel ball with mass 40.0 g is dropped from a height of 2.00 m onto a horizontal steel slab. The ball rebounds to a height of 1.60 m. (a) Calculate the impulse delivered to the ball during impact. (b) If the ball is in contact with the slab for 2.00 ms, find the average force on the ball during impact.

8.65 •• Just before it is struck by a racket, a tennis ball weighing 0.560 N has a velocity of $(20.0 \text{ m/s})\hat{\imath} - (4.0 \text{ m/s})\hat{\jmath}$. During the 3.00 ms that the racket and ball are in contact, the net force on the ball is constant and equal to $-(380 \text{ N})\hat{\imath} + (110 \text{ N})\hat{\jmath}$. What are the x- and y-components (a) of the impulse of the net force applied to the ball; (b) of the final velocity of the ball?

8.66 • Three identical pucks on a horizontal air table have repelling magnets. They are held together and then released simultaneously. Each has the same speed at any instant. One puck moves due west. What is the direction of the velocity of each of the other two pucks?

8.67 •• Blocks *A* (mass 2.00 kg) and *B* (mass 10.00 kg, to the right of *A*) move on a frictionless, horizontal surface. Initially, block *B* is moving to the left at 0.500 m/s and block *A* is moving to the right at 2.00 m/s. The blocks are equipped with ideal spring bumpers, as in Example 8.10 (Section 8.4). The collision is head-on, so all motion before and after it is along a straight line. Find (a) the maximum energy stored in the spring bumpers and the velocity of each block at that time; (b) the velocity of each block after they have moved apart.

8.68 •• A railroad handcar is moving along straight, frictionless tracks with negligible air resistance. In the following cases, the car initially has a total mass (car and contents) of 200 kg and is traveling east with a velocity of magnitude 5.00 m/s. Find the *final velocity* of the car in each case, assuming that the handcar does not leave the tracks. (a) A 25.0-kg mass is thrown sideways out of the car with a velocity of magnitude 2.00 m/s relative to the car's initial velocity. (b) A 25.0-kg mass is thrown backward out of the car with a velocity of 5.00 m/s relative to the initial motion of the car. (c) A 25.0-kg mass is thrown into the car with a velocity of 6.00 m/s relative to the ground and opposite in direction to the initial velocity of the car.

8.69 • Spheres *A* (mass 0.020 kg), *B* (mass 0.030 kg), and *C* (mass 0.050 kg) are approaching the origin as they slide on a frictionless air table. The initial velocities of *A* and *B* are given in **Fig. P8.69**. All three spheres arrive at the origin at the same time and stick together. (a) What must the *x*- and *y*-components of the initial velocity of *C* be if all three objects are to end up moving at 0.50 m/s in the +*x*-direction after the collision? (b) If *C* has the velocity found in part (a), what is the change in the kinetic energy of the system of three spheres as a result of the collision?

Figure **P8.69**

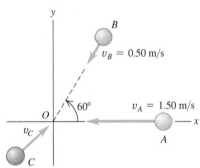

8.70 ••• You and your friends are doing physics experiments on a frozen pond that serves as a frictionless, horizontal surface. Sam, with mass 80.0 kg, is given a push and slides eastward. Abigail, with mass 50.0 kg, is sent sliding northward. They collide, and after the collision Sam is moving at 37.0° north of east with a speed of 6.00 m/s and Abigail is moving at 23.0° south of east with a speed of 9.00 m/s. (a) What was the speed of each person before the collision? (b) By how much did the total kinetic energy of the two people decrease during the collision?

8.71 •• CP An 8.00-kg block of wood sits at the edge of a frictionless table, 2.20 m above the floor. A 0.500-kg blob of clay slides along the length of the table with a speed of 24.0 m/s, strikes the block of wood, and sticks to it. The combined object leaves the edge of the table and travels to the floor. What horizontal distance has the combined object traveled when it reaches the floor?

8.72 ••• CP A small wooden block with mass 0.800 kg is suspended from the lower end of a light cord that is 1.60 m long. The

block is initially at rest. A bullet with mass 12.0 g is fired at the block with a horizontal velocity v_0. The bullet strikes the block and becomes embedded in it. After the collision the combined object swings on the end of the cord. When the block has risen a vertical height of 0.800 m, the tension in the cord is 4.80 N. What was the initial speed v_0 of the bullet?

8.73 •• **Combining Conservation Laws.** A 5.00-kg chunk of ice is sliding at 12.0 m/s on the floor of an ice-covered valley when it collides with and sticks to another 5.00-kg chunk of ice that is initially at rest (**Fig. P8.73**). Since the valley is icy, there is no friction. After the collision, how high above the valley floor will the combined chunks go?

Figure **P8.73**

8.74 •• CP Block *B* (mass 4.00 kg) is at rest at the edge of a smooth platform, 2.60 m above the floor. Block *A* (mass 2.00 kg) is sliding with a speed of 8.00 m/s along the platform toward block *B*. *A* strikes *B* and rebounds with a speed of 2.00 m/s. The collision projects *B* horizontally off the platform. What is the speed of *B* just before it strikes the floor?

8.75 •• Two blocks have a spring compressed between them, as in Exercise 8.24. The spring has force constant 720 N/m and is initially compressed 0.225 m from its original length. For each block, what is (a) the acceleration just after the blocks are released; (b) the final speed after the blocks leave the spring?

8.76 •• **Automobile Accident Analysis.** You are called as an expert witness to analyze the following auto accident: Car *B*, of mass 1900 kg, was stopped at a red light when it was hit from behind by car *A*, of mass 1500 kg. The cars locked bumpers during the collision and slid to a stop with brakes locked on all wheels. Measurements of the skid marks left by the tires showed them to be 7.15 m long. The coefficient of kinetic friction between the tires and the road was 0.65. (a) What was the speed of car *A* just before the collision? (b) If the speed limit was 35 mph, was car *A* speeding, and if so, by how many miles per hour was it *exceeding* the speed limit?

8.77 •• **Accident Analysis.** A 1500-kg sedan goes through a wide intersection traveling from north to south when it is hit by a 2200-kg SUV traveling from east to west. The two cars become enmeshed due to the impact and slide as one thereafter. On-the-scene measurements show that the coefficient of kinetic friction between the tires of these cars and the pavement is 0.75, and the cars slide to a halt at a point 5.39 m west and 6.43 m south of the impact point. How fast was each car traveling just before the collision?

8.78 ••• CP A 0.150-kg frame, when suspended from a coil spring, stretches the spring 0.0400 m. A 0.200-kg lump of putty is dropped from rest onto the frame from a height of 30.0 cm (**Fig. P8.78**). Find the maximum distance the frame moves downward from its initial equilibrium position.

Figure **P8.78**

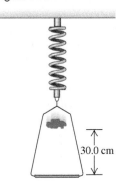

8.79 · A rifle bullet with mass 8.00 g strikes and embeds itself in a block with mass 0.992 kg that rests on a frictionless, horizontal surface and is attached to a coil spring (**Fig. P8.79**). The impact compresses the spring 15.0 cm. Calibration of the spring shows that a force of 0.750 N is required to compress the spring 0.250 cm. (a) Find the magnitude of the block's velocity just after impact. (b) What was the initial speed of the bullet?

Figure **P8.79**

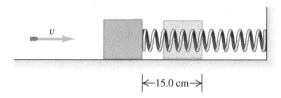

|←15.0 cm→|

8.80 ·· **A Ricocheting Bullet.** A 0.100-kg stone rests on a frictionless, horizontal surface. A bullet of mass 6.00 g, traveling horizontally at 350 m/s, strikes the stone and rebounds horizontally at right angles to its original direction with a speed of 250 m/s. (a) Compute the magnitude and direction of the velocity of the stone after it is struck. (b) Is the collision perfectly elastic?

8.81 ·· A movie stuntman (mass 80.0 kg) stands on a window ledge 5.0 m above the floor (**Fig. P8.81**). Grabbing a rope attached to a chandelier, he swings down to grapple with the movie's villain (mass 70.0 kg), who is standing directly under the chandelier. (Assume that the stuntman's center of mass moves downward 5.0 m. He releases the rope just as he reaches the villain.) (a) With what speed do the entwined foes start to slide across the floor? (b) If the coefficient of kinetic friction of their bodies with the floor is $\mu_k = 0.250$, how far do they slide?

Figure **P8.81**

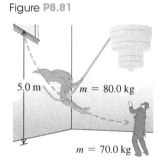

5.0 m $m = 80.0$ kg

$m = 70.0$ kg

8.82 ·· CP Two identical masses are released from rest in a smooth hemispherical bowl of radius R from the positions shown in **Fig. P8.82**. Ignore friction between the masses and the surface of the bowl. If the masses stick together when they collide, how high above the bottom of the bowl will they go after colliding?

Figure **P8.82**

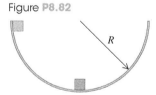

R

8.83 ·· A ball with mass M, moving horizontally at 4.00 m/s, collides elastically with a block with mass $3M$ that is initially hanging at rest from the ceiling on the end of a 50.0-cm wire. Find the maximum angle through which the block swings after it is hit.

8.84 ··· CP A 20.00-kg lead sphere is hanging from a hook by a thin wire 2.80 m long and is free to swing in a complete circle. Suddenly it is struck horizontally by a 5.00-kg steel dart that embeds itself in the lead sphere. What must be the minimum initial speed of the dart so that the combination makes a complete circular loop after the collision?

8.85 ·· A 4.00-g bullet, traveling horizontally with a velocity of magnitude 400 m/s, is fired into a wooden block with mass 0.800 kg, initially at rest on a level surface. The bullet passes through the block and emerges with its speed reduced to 190 m/s. The block slides a distance of 72.0 cm along the surface from its initial position. (a) What is the coefficient of kinetic friction between block and surface? (b) What is the decrease in kinetic energy of the bullet? (c) What is the kinetic energy of the block at the instant after the bullet passes through it?

8.86 ·· A 5.00-g bullet is shot *through* a 1.00-kg wood block suspended on a string 2.00 m long. The center of mass of the block rises a distance of 0.38 cm. Find the speed of the bullet as it emerges from the block if its initial speed is 450 m/s.

8.87 ·· CP In a shipping company distribution center, an open cart of mass 50.0 kg is rolling to the left at a speed of 5.00 m/s (**Fig. P8.87**). Ignore friction between the cart and the floor. A 15.0-kg package slides down a chute that is inclined at 37° from the horizontal and leaves the end of the chute with a speed of 3.00 m/s. The package lands in the cart and they roll together. If the lower end of the chute is a vertical distance of 4.00 m above the bottom of the cart, what are (a) the speed of the package just before it lands in the cart and (b) the final speed of the cart?

Figure **P8.87**

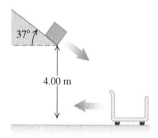

37°

4.00 m

8.88 ··· **Neutron Decay.** A neutron at rest decays (breaks up) to a proton and an electron. Energy is released in the decay and appears as kinetic energy of the proton and electron. The mass of a proton is 1836 times the mass of an electron. What fraction of the total energy released goes into the kinetic energy of the proton?

8.89 · **Antineutrino.** In beta decay, a nucleus emits an electron. A ^{210}Bi (bismuth) nucleus at rest undergoes beta decay to ^{210}Po (polonium). Suppose the emitted electron moves to the right with a momentum of 5.60×10^{-22} kg · m/s. The ^{210}Po nucleus, with mass 3.50×10^{-25} kg, recoils to the left at a speed of 1.14×10^3 m/s. Momentum conservation requires that a second particle, called an antineutrino, must also be emitted. Calculate the magnitude and direction of the momentum of the antineutrino that is emitted in this decay.

8.90 ·· Jonathan and Jane are sitting in a sleigh that is at rest on frictionless ice. Jonathan's weight is 800 N, Jane's weight is 600 N, and that of the sleigh is 1000 N. They see a poisonous spider on the floor of the sleigh and immediately jump off. Jonathan jumps to the left with a velocity of 5.00 m/s at 30.0° above the horizontal (relative to the ice), and Jane jumps to the right at 7.00 m/s at 36.9° above the horizontal (relative to the ice). Calculate the sleigh's horizontal velocity (magnitude and direction) after they jump out.

8.91 ·· Friends Burt and Ernie stand at opposite ends of a uniform log that is floating in a lake. The log is 3.0 m long and has mass 20.0 kg. Burt has mass 30.0 kg; Ernie has mass 40.0 kg. Initially, the log and the two friends are at rest relative to the shore. Burt then offers Ernie a cookie, and Ernie walks to Burt's end of the log to get it. Relative to the shore, what distance has the log moved by the time Ernie reaches Burt? Ignore any horizontal force that the water exerts on the log, and assume that neither friend falls off the log.

8.92 •• A 45.0-kg woman stands up in a 60.0-kg canoe 5.00 m long. She walks from a point 1.00 m from one end to a point 1.00 m from the other end (**Fig. P8.92**). If you ignore resistance to motion of the canoe in the water, how far does the canoe move during this process?

Figure **P8.92**

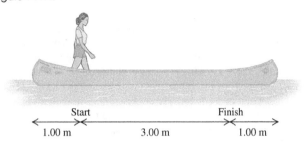

Start   Finish

1.00 m   3.00 m   1.00 m

8.93 •• You are standing on a concrete slab that in turn is resting on a frozen lake. Assume there is no friction between the slab and the ice. The slab has a weight five times your weight. If you begin walking forward at 2.00 m/s relative to the ice, with what speed, relative to the ice, does the slab move?

8.94 •• CP In a fireworks display, a rocket is launched from the ground with a speed of 18.0 m/s and a direction of 51.0° above the horizontal. During the flight, the rocket explodes into two pieces of equal mass (see Fig. 8.32). (a) What horizontal distance from the launch point will the center of mass of the two pieces be after both have landed on the ground? (b) If one piece lands a horizontal distance of 26.0 m from the launch point, where does the other piece land?

8.95 •• A 7.0-kg shell at rest explodes into two fragments, one with a mass of 2.0 kg and the other with a mass of 5.0 kg. If the heavier fragment gains 100 J of kinetic energy from the explosion, how much kinetic energy does the lighter one gain?

8.96 •• CP A 20.0-kg projectile is fired at an angle of 60.0° above the horizontal with a speed of 80.0 m/s. At the highest point of its trajectory, the projectile explodes into two fragments with equal mass, one of which falls vertically with zero initial speed. Ignore air resistance. (a) How far from the point of firing does the other fragment strike if the terrain is level? (b) How much energy is released during the explosion?

8.97 ••• CP A fireworks rocket is fired vertically upward. At its maximum height of 80.0 m, it explodes and breaks into two pieces: one with mass 1.40 kg and the other with mass 0.28 kg. In the explosion, 860 J of chemical energy is converted to kinetic energy of the two fragments. (a) What is the speed of each fragment just after the explosion? (b) It is observed that the two fragments hit the ground at the same time. What is the distance between the points on the ground where they land? Assume that the ground is level and air resistance can be ignored.

8.98 ••• A 12.0-kg shell is launched at an angle of 55.0° above the horizontal with an initial speed of 150 m/s. At its highest point, the shell explodes into two fragments, one three times heavier than the other. The two fragments reach the ground at the same time. Ignore air resistance. If the heavier fragment lands back at the point from which the shell was launched, where will the lighter fragment land, and how much energy was released in the explosion?

8.99 • CP An outlaw cuts loose a wagon with two boxes of gold, of total mass 300 kg, when the wagon is at rest 50 m up a 6.0° slope. The outlaw plans to have the wagon roll down the slope and across the level ground, and then fall into a canyon where his accomplices wait. But in a tree 40 m from the canyon's cliff wait the

Lone Ranger (mass 75.0 kg) and Tonto (mass 60.0 kg). They drop vertically into the wagon as it passes beneath them (**Fig. P8.99**). (a) If they require 5.0 s to grab the gold and jump out, will they make it before the wagon goes over the cliff? The wagon rolls with negligible friction. (b) When the two heroes drop into the wagon, is the kinetic energy of the system of heroes plus wagon conserved? If not, does it increase or decrease, and by how much?

Figure **P8.99**

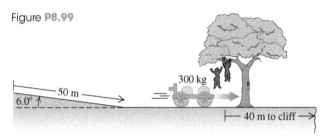

50 m

6.0°

300 kg

40 m to cliff →

8.100 •• DATA A 2004 Prius with a 150-lb driver and no passengers weighs 3071 lb. The car is initially at rest. Starting at $t = 0$, a net horizontal force $F_x(t)$ in the +x-direction is applied to the car. The force as a function of time is given in **Fig. P8.100**. (a) For the time interval $t = 0$ to $t = 4.50$ s, what is the impulse applied to the car? (b) What is the speed of the car at $t = 4.50$ s? (c) At $t = 4.50$ s, the 3500-N net force is replaced by a constant net braking force $B_x = -5200$ N. Once the braking force is first applied, how long does it take the car to stop? (d) How much work must be done on the car by the braking force to stop the car? (e) What distance does the car travel from the time the braking force is first applied until the car stops?

Figure **P8.100**

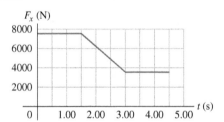

F_x (N)

8000

6000

4000

2000

0   1.00   2.00   3.00   4.00   5.00 t (s)

8.101 •• DATA In your job in a police lab, you must design an apparatus to measure the muzzle velocities of bullets fired from handguns. Your solution is to attach a 2.00-kg wood block that rests on a horizontal surface to a light horizontal spring. The other end of the spring is attached to a wall. Initially the spring is at its equilibrium length. A bullet is fired horizontally into the block and remains embedded in it. After the bullet strikes the block, the block compresses the spring a maximum distance d. You have measured that the coefficient of kinetic friction between the block and the horizontal surface is 0.38. The table lists some firearms that you will test:

Bullet ID	Type	Bullet Mass (grains)	Muzzle Velocity (ft/s)
A	.38Spec Glaser Blue	80	1667
B	.38Spec Federal	125	945
C	.44Spec Remington	240	851
D	.44Spec Winchester	200	819
E	0.45ACP Glaser Blue	140	1355

Source: www.chuckhawks.com

A grain is a unit of mass equal to 64.80 mg. (a) Of bullets A through E, which will produce the maximum compression of the spring? The minimum? (b) You want the maximum compression of the spring to be 0.25 m. What must be the force constant of the spring? (c) For the bullet that produces the minimum spring compression, what is the compression d if the spring has the force constant calculated in part (b)?

8.102 •• DATA For the Texas Department of Public Safety, you are investigating an accident that occurred early on a foggy morning in a remote section of the Texas Panhandle. A 2012 Prius traveling due north collided in a highway intersection with a 2013 Dodge Durango that was traveling due east. After the collision, the wreckage of the two vehicles was locked together and skidded across the level ground until it struck a tree. You measure that the tree is 35 ft from the point of impact. The line from the point of impact to the tree is in a direction 39° north of east. From experience, you estimate that the coefficient of kinetic friction between the ground and the wreckage is 0.45. Shortly before the collision, a highway patrolman with a radar gun measured the speed of the Prius to be 50 mph and, according to a witness, the Prius driver made no attempt to slow down. Four people with a total weight of 460 lb were in the Durango. The only person in the Prius was the 150-lb driver. The Durango with its passengers had a weight of 6500 lb, and the Prius with its driver had a weight of 3042 lb. (a) What was the Durango's speed just before the collision? (b) How fast was the wreckage traveling just before it struck the tree?

CHALLENGE PROBLEMS

8.103 • CALC **A Variable-Mass Raindrop.** In a rocket-propulsion problem the mass is variable. Another such problem is a raindrop falling through a cloud of small water droplets. Some of these small droplets adhere to the raindrop, thereby *increasing* its mass as it falls. The force on the raindrop is

$$F_{ext} = \frac{dp}{dt} = m\frac{dv}{dt} + v\frac{dm}{dt}$$

Suppose the mass of the raindrop depends on the distance x that it has fallen. Then $m = kx$, where k is a constant, and $dm/dt = kv$. This gives, since $F_{ext} = mg$,

$$mg = m\frac{dv}{dt} + v(kv)$$

Or, dividing by k,

$$xg = x\frac{dv}{dt} + v^2$$

This is a differential equation that has a solution of the form $v = at$, where a is the acceleration and is constant. Take the initial velocity of the raindrop to be zero. (a) Using the proposed solution for v, find the acceleration a. (b) Find the distance the raindrop has fallen in $t = 3.00$ s. (c) Given that $k = 2.00$ g/m, find the mass of the raindrop at $t = 3.00$ s. (For many more intriguing aspects of this problem, see K. S. Krane, *American Journal of Physics,* Vol. 49 (1981), pp. 113–117.)

8.104 •• CALC In Section 8.5 we calculated the center of mass by considering objects composed of a *finite* number of point masses or objects that, by symmetry, could be represented by a finite number of point masses. For a solid object whose mass distribution does not allow for a simple determination of the center of mass by symmetry, the sums of Eqs. (8.28) must be generalized to integrals

$$x_{cm} = \frac{1}{M}\int x\,dm \qquad y_{cm} = \frac{1}{M}\int y\,dm$$

where x and y are the coordinates of the small piece of the object that has mass dm. The integration is over the whole of the object. Consider a thin rod of length L, mass M, and cross-sectional area A. Let the origin of the coordinates be at the left end of the rod and the positive x-axis lie along the rod. (a) If the density $\rho = M/V$ of the object is uniform, perform the integration described above to show that the x-coordinate of the center of mass of the rod is at its geometrical center. (b) If the density of the object varies linearly with x—that is, $\rho = \alpha x$, where α is a positive constant—calculate the x-coordinate of the rod's center of mass.

8.105 •• CALC Use the methods of Challenge Problem 8.104 to calculate the x- and y-coordinates of the center of mass of a semicircular metal plate with uniform density ρ and thickness t. Let the radius of the plate be a. The mass of the plate is thus $M = \frac{1}{2}\rho\pi a^2 t$. Use the coordinate system indicated in **Fig. P8.105**.

Figure **P8.105**

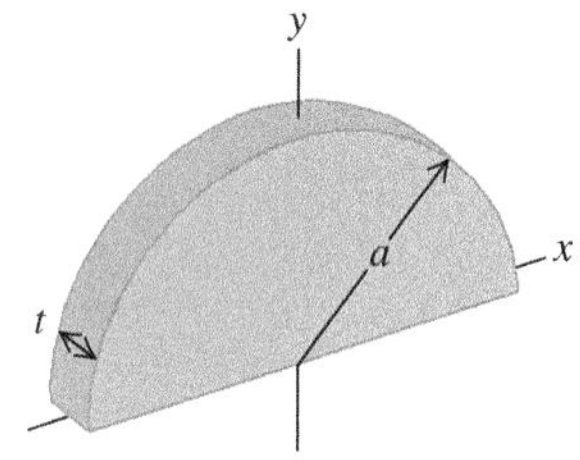

PASSAGE PROBLEMS

BIO **MOMENTUM AND THE ARCHERFISH.** Archerfish are tropical fish that hunt by shooting drops of water from their mouths at insects above the water's surface to knock them into the water, where the fish can eat them. A 65-g fish at rest just at the surface of the water can expel a 0.30-g drop of water in a short burst of 5.0 ms. High-speed measurements show that the water has a speed of 2.5 m/s just after the archerfish expels it.

8.106 What is the momentum of one drop of water immediately after it leaves the fish's mouth? (a) 7.5×10^{-4} kg·m/s; (b) 1.5×10^{-4} kg·m/s; (c) 7.5×10^{-3} kg·m/s; (d) 1.5×10^{-3} kg·m/s.

8.107 What is the speed of the archerfish immediately after it expels the drop of water? (a) 0.0025 m/s; (b) 0.012 m/s; (c) 0.75 m/s; (d) 2.5 m/s.

8.108 What is the average force the fish exerts on the drop of water? (a) 0.00015 N; (b) 0.00075 N; (c) 0.075 N; (d) 0.15 N.

8.109 The fish shoots the drop of water at an insect that hovers on the water's surface, so just before colliding with the insect, the drop is still moving at the speed it had when it left the fish's mouth. In the collision, the drop sticks to the insect, and the speed of the insect and water just after the collision is measured to be 2.0 m/s. What is the insect's mass? (a) 0.038 g; (b) 0.075 g; (c) 0.24 g; (d) 0.38 g.

Answers

Chapter Opening Question ?

(ii) All three bullets have the same magnitude of momentum $p = mv$ (the product of mass and speed), but the fast, lightweight bullet has twice the kinetic energy $K = \frac{1}{2}mv^2$ of the .22-caliber bullet and four times the kinetic energy of the heavyweight bullet. Hence, the lightweight bullet can do the most work on the carrot (and do the most damage) in the process of coming to a halt (see Section 8.1).

Test Your Understanding Questions

8.1 **(v), (i) and (ii) (tied for second place), (iii) and (iv) (tied for third place)** We use two interpretations of the impulse of the net force: (1) the net force multiplied by the time that the net force acts, and (2) the change in momentum of the particle on which the net force acts. Which interpretation we use depends on what information we are given. We take the positive x-direction to be to the east. (i) The force is not given, so we use interpretation 2: $J_x = mv_{2x} - mv_{1x} = (1000 \text{ kg})(0) - (1000 \text{ kg})(25 \text{ m/s}) = -25{,}000 \text{ kg} \cdot \text{m/s}$, so the magnitude of the impulse is $25{,}000 \text{ kg} \cdot \text{m/s} = 25{,}000 \text{ N} \cdot \text{s}$. (ii) For the same reason and values as in (i), we use interpretation 2, and the magnitude of the impulse is again $25{,}000 \text{ N} \cdot \text{s}$. (iii) The final velocity is not given, so we use interpretation 1: $J_x = (\Sigma F_x)_{av}(t_2 - t_1) = (2000 \text{ N})(10 \text{ s}) = 20{,}000 \text{ N} \cdot \text{s}$, so the magnitude of the impulse is $20{,}000 \text{ N} \cdot \text{s}$. (iv) For the same reason as in (iii), we use interpretation 1: $J_x = (\Sigma F_x)_{av}(t_2 - t_1) = (-2000 \text{ N})(10 \text{ s}) = -20{,}000 \text{ N} \cdot \text{s}$, so the magnitude of the impulse is $20{,}000 \text{ N} \cdot \text{s}$. (v) The force is not given, so we use interpretation 2: $J_x = mv_{2x} - mv_{1x} = (1000 \text{ kg})(-25 \text{ m/s}) - (1000 \text{ kg})(25 \text{ m/s}) = -50{,}000 \text{ kg} \cdot \text{m/s}$, so the magnitude of the impulse is $50{,}000 \text{ kg} \cdot \text{m/s} = 50{,}000 \text{ N} \cdot \text{s}$.

8.2 **(a)** $v_{C2x} > 0, v_{C2y} > 0$, **(b) piece C** There are no external horizontal forces, so the x- and y-components of the total momentum of the system are conserved. Both components of the total momentum are zero before the spring releases, so they must be zero after the spring releases. Hence,

$$P_x = 0 = m_A v_{A2x} + m_B v_{B2x} + m_C v_{C2x}$$
$$P_y = 0 = m_A v_{A2y} + m_B v_{B2y} + m_C v_{C2y}$$

We are given that $m_A = m_B = m_C$, $v_{A2x} < 0$, $v_{A2y} = 0$, $v_{B2x} = 0$, and $v_{B2y} < 0$. You can solve the above equations to show that $v_{C2x} = -v_{A2x} > 0$ and $v_{C2y} = -v_{B2y} > 0$, so both velocity components of piece C are positive. Piece C has speed $\sqrt{v_{C2x}^2 + v_{C2y}^2} = \sqrt{v_{A2x}^2 + v_{B2y}^2}$, which is greater than the speed of either piece A or piece B.

8.3 **(a) elastic, (b) inelastic, (c) completely inelastic** In each case gravitational potential energy is converted to kinetic energy as the ball falls, and the collision is between the ball and the ground. In (a) all of the initial energy is converted back to gravitational potential energy, so no kinetic energy is lost in the bounce and the collision is elastic. In (b) there is less gravitational potential energy at the end than at the beginning, so some kinetic energy is lost in the bounce. Hence the collision is inelastic. In (c) the ball loses all of its kinetic energy, the ball and the ground stick together, and the collision is completely inelastic.

8.4 **worse** After colliding with a water molecule initially at rest, the neutron has speed $|(m_n - m_w)/(m_n + m_w)| = |(1.0 \text{ u} - 18 \text{ u})/(1.0 \text{ u} + 18 \text{ u})| = \frac{17}{19}$ of its initial speed, and its kinetic energy is $\left(\frac{17}{19}\right)^2 = 0.80$ of the initial value. Hence a water molecule is a worse moderator than a carbon atom, for which the corresponding numbers are $\frac{11}{13}$ and $\left(\frac{11}{13}\right)^2 = 0.72$.

8.5 **no** If gravity is the only force acting on the system of two fragments, the center of mass will follow the parabolic trajectory of a freely falling object. Once a fragment lands, however, the ground exerts a normal force on that fragment. Hence the net force on the system has changed, and the trajectory of the center of mass changes in response.

8.6 **(a) increasing, (b) decreasing** From Eqs. (8.37) and (8.38), the thrust F is equal to $m(dv/dt)$, where m is the rocket's mass and dv/dt is its acceleration. Because m decreases with time, if the thrust F is constant, then the acceleration must increase with time (the same force acts on a smaller mass); if the acceleration dv/dt is constant, then the thrust must decrease with time (a smaller force is all that's needed to accelerate a smaller mass).

Bridging Problem

(a) 1.00 m/s to the right **(b)** Elastic
(c) 1.93 m/s at $-30.4°$
(d) 2.31 kg $\cdot$ m/s at $149.6°$ **(e)** Inelastic
(f) 1.67 m/s in the positive x-direction

9 ROTATION OF RIGID BODIES

What do the motions of an airplane propeller, a Blu-ray disc, a Ferris wheel, and a circular saw blade have in common? None of these can be represented adequately as a moving *point;* each involves a body that *rotates* about an axis that is stationary in some inertial frame of reference.

Rotation occurs at all scales, from the motions of electrons in atoms to the motions of entire galaxies. We need to develop some general methods for analyzing the motion of a rotating body. In this chapter and the next we consider bodies that have definite size and definite shape, and that in general can have rotational as well as translational motion.

Real-world bodies can be very complicated; the forces that act on them can deform them—stretching, twisting, and squeezing them. We'll ignore these deformations for now and assume that the body has a perfectly definite and unchanging shape and size. We call this idealized model a **rigid body.** This chapter and the next are mostly about rotational motion of a rigid body.

We begin with kinematic language for *describing* rotational motion. Next we look at the kinetic energy of rotation, the key to using energy methods for rotational motion. Then in Chapter 10 we'll develop dynamic principles that relate the forces on a body to its rotational motion.

9.1 ANGULAR VELOCITY AND ACCELERATION

In analyzing rotational motion, let's think first about a rigid body that rotates about a *fixed axis*—an axis that is at rest in some inertial frame of reference and does not change direction relative to that frame. The rotating rigid body might be a motor shaft, a chunk of beef on a barbecue skewer, or a merry-go-round.

Figure 9.1 (next page) shows a rigid body rotating about a fixed axis. The axis passes through point *O* and is perpendicular to the plane of the diagram, which we'll call the *xy*-plane. One way to describe the rotation of this body would be to choose a particular point *P* on the body and to keep track of the *x*- and

9.1 A speedometer needle (an example of a rigid body) rotating counterclockwise about a fixed axis.

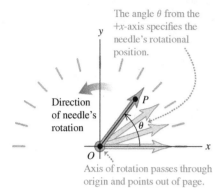

The angle θ from the +x-axis specifies the needle's rotational position.

Direction of needle's rotation

Axis of rotation passes through origin and points out of page.

9.2 Measuring angles in radians.

(a)

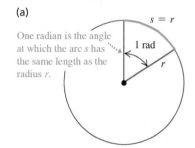

One radian is the angle at which the arc s has the same length as the radius r.

$s = r$

1 rad

r

(b)

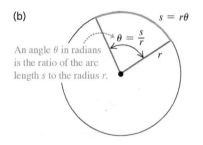

An angle θ in radians is the ratio of the arc length s to the radius r.

$s = r\theta$

$\theta = \dfrac{s}{r}$

r

y-coordinates of P. This isn't very convenient, since it takes two numbers (the two coordinates x and y) to specify the rotational position of the body. Instead, we notice that the line OP is fixed in the body and rotates with it. The angle θ that OP makes with the +x-axis is a single **angular cooordinate** that completely describes the body's rotational position.

The angular coordinate θ of a rigid body rotating around a fixed axis can be positive or negative. If we choose positive angles to be measured counterclockwise from the positive x-axis, then the angle θ in Fig. 9.1 is positive. If we instead choose the positive rotation direction to be clockwise, then θ in Fig. 9.1 is negative. When we considered the motion of a particle along a straight line, it was essential to specify the direction of positive displacement along that line; when we discuss rotation around a fixed axis, it's just as essential to specify the direction of positive rotation.

The most natural way to measure the angle θ is not in degrees but in **radians.** As **Fig. 9.2a** shows, one radian (1 rad) is the angle subtended at the center of a circle by an arc with a length equal to the radius of the circle. In Fig. 9.2b an angle θ is subtended by an arc of length s on a circle of radius r. The value of θ (in radians) is equal to s divided by r:

$$\theta = \frac{s}{r} \quad \text{or} \quad s = r\theta \quad (\theta \text{ in radians}) \quad (9.1)$$

An angle in radians is the ratio of two lengths, so it is a pure number, without dimensions. If $s = 3.0$ m and $r = 2.0$ m, then $\theta = 1.5$, but we will often write this as 1.5 rad to distinguish it from an angle measured in degrees or revolutions.

The circumference of a circle (that is, the arc length all the way around the circle) is 2π times the radius, so there are 2π (about 6.283) radians in one complete revolution (360°). Therefore

$$1 \text{ rad} = \frac{360°}{2\pi} = 57.3°$$

Similarly, $180° = \pi$ rad, $90° = \pi/2$ rad, and so on. If we had measured angle θ in degrees, we would have needed an extra factor of $(2\pi/360)$ on the right-hand side of $s = r\theta$ in Eq. (9.1). By measuring angles in radians, we keep the relationship between angle and distance along an arc as simple as possible.

Angular Velocity

The coordinate θ shown in Fig. 9.1 specifies the rotational position of a rigid body at a given instant. We can describe the rotational *motion* of such a rigid body in terms of the rate of change of θ. We'll do this in an analogous way to our description of straight-line motion in Chapter 2. In **Fig. 9.3a**, a reference line OP in a rotating body makes an angle θ_1 with the +x-axis at time t_1. At a later time t_2 the angle has changed to θ_2. We define the **average angular velocity** $\omega_{\text{av-}z}$ (the

9.3 (a) Angular displacement $\Delta\theta$ of a rotating body. (b) Every part of a rotating rigid body has the same average angular velocity $\Delta\theta/\Delta t$.

(a)

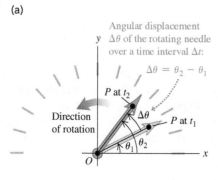

Angular displacement $\Delta\theta$ of the rotating needle over a time interval Δt:

$\Delta\theta = \theta_2 - \theta_1$

P at t_2

Direction of rotation

$\Delta\theta$

P at t_1

θ_1 θ_2

(b)

Greek letter omega) of the body in the time interval $\Delta t = t_2 - t_1$ as the ratio of the **angular displacement** $\Delta\theta = \theta_2 - \theta_1$ to Δt:

$$\omega_{\text{av-}z} = \frac{\theta_2 - \theta_1}{t_2 - t_1} = \frac{\Delta\theta}{\Delta t} \qquad (9.2)$$

The subscript z indicates that the body in Fig. 9.3a is rotating about the z-axis, which is perpendicular to the plane of the diagram. The **instantaneous angular velocity** ω_z is the limit of $\omega_{\text{av-}z}$ as Δt approaches zero:

The **instantaneous angular velocity** of a rigid body rotating around the z-axis ...

$$\omega_z = \lim_{\Delta t \to 0} \frac{\Delta\theta}{\Delta t} = \frac{d\theta}{dt} \qquad (9.3)$$

... equals the limit of the body's average angular velocity as the time interval approaches zero ...

... and equals the instantaneous rate of change of the body's angular coordinate.

When we refer simply to "angular velocity," we mean the instantaneous angular velocity, not the average angular velocity.

The angular velocity ω_z can be positive or negative, depending on the direction in which the rigid body is rotating (**Fig. 9.4**). The angular *speed* ω, which we'll use in Sections 9.3 and 9.4, is the magnitude of angular velocity. Like linear speed v, the angular speed is never negative.

CAUTION **Angular velocity vs. linear velocity** Keep in mind the distinction between angular velocity ω_z and *linear velocity* v_x (see Section 2.2). If an object has a linear velocity v_x, the object as a whole is *moving* along the x-axis. By contrast, if an object has an angular velocity ω_z, then it is *rotating* around the z-axis. We do *not* mean that the object is moving along the z-axis. ∎

Different points on a rotating rigid body move different distances in a given time interval, depending on how far each point lies from the rotation axis. But because the body is rigid, *all* points rotate through the same angle in the same time (Fig. 9.3b). Hence *at any instant, every part of a rotating rigid body has the same angular velocity.*

If angle θ is in radians, the unit of angular velocity is the radian per second (rad/s). Other units, such as the revolution per minute (rev/min or rpm), are often used. Since 1 rev = 2π rad, two useful conversions are

$$1 \text{ rev/s} = 2\pi \text{ rad/s} \quad \text{and} \quad 1 \text{ rev/min} = 1 \text{ rpm} = \frac{2\pi}{60} \text{rad/s}$$

That is, 1 rad/s is about 10 rpm.

9.4 A rigid body's average angular velocity (shown here) and instantaneous angular velocity can be positive or negative.

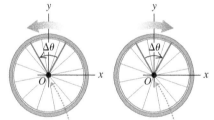

We choose the angle θ to increase in the counterclockwise rotation.

Counterclockwise rotation:	Clockwise rotation:
θ increases, so angular velocity is positive. $\Delta\theta > 0$, so $\omega_{\text{av-}z} = \Delta\theta/\Delta t > 0$	θ decreases, so angular velocity is negative. $\Delta\theta < 0$, so $\omega_{\text{av-}z} = \Delta\theta/\Delta t < 0$

Axis of rotation (z-axis) passes through origin and points out of page.

EXAMPLE 9.1   CALCULATING ANGULAR VELOCITY

The angular position θ of a 0.36-m-diameter flywheel is given by

$$\theta = (2.0 \text{ rad/s}^3)t^3$$

(a) Find θ, in radians and in degrees, at $t_1 = 2.0$ s and $t_2 = 5.0$ s. (b) Find the distance that a particle on the flywheel rim moves from $t_1 = 2.0$ s to $t_2 = 5.0$ s. (c) Find the average angular velocity, in rad/s and in rev/min, over that interval. (d) Find the instantaneous angular velocities at $t_1 = 2.0$ s and $t_2 = 5.0$ s.

SOLUTION

IDENTIFY and SET UP: Our target variables are θ_1 and θ_2 (the angular positions at times t_1 and t_2) and the angular displacement $\Delta\theta = \theta_2 - \theta_1$. We'll find these from the given expression for θ as a function of time. Knowing $\Delta\theta$, we'll find the distance traveled

and the average angular velocity between t_1 and t_2 by using Eqs. (9.1) and (9.2), respectively. To find the instantaneous angular velocities ω_{1z} (at time t_1) and ω_{2z} (at time t_2), we'll take the derivative of the given equation for θ with respect to time, as in Eq. (9.3).

EXECUTE: (a) We substitute the values of t into the equation for θ:

$$\theta_1 = (2.0 \text{ rad/s}^3)(2.0 \text{ s})^3 = 16 \text{ rad}$$

$$= (16 \text{ rad})\frac{360°}{2\pi \text{ rad}} = 920°$$

$$\theta_2 = (2.0 \text{ rad/s}^3)(5.0 \text{ s})^3 = 250 \text{ rad}$$

$$= (250 \text{ rad})\frac{360°}{2\pi \text{ rad}} = 14{,}000°$$

Continued

(b) During the interval from t_1 to t_2 the flywheel's angular displacement is $\Delta\theta = \theta_2 - \theta_1 = 250 \text{ rad} - 16 \text{ rad} = 234 \text{ rad}$. The radius r is half the diameter, or 0.18 m. To use Eq. (9.1), the angles *must* be expressed in radians:

$$s = r\theta_2 - r\theta_1 = r\Delta\theta = (0.18 \text{ m})(234 \text{ rad}) = 42 \text{ m}$$

We can drop "radians" from the unit for s because θ is a dimensionless number; like r, s is measured in meters.

(c) From Eq. (9.2),

$$\omega_{\text{av-}z} = \frac{\theta_2 - \theta_1}{t_2 - t_1} = \frac{250 \text{ rad} - 16 \text{ rad}}{5.0 \text{ s} - 2.0 \text{ s}} = 78 \text{ rad/s}$$

$$= \left(78 \frac{\text{rad}}{\text{s}}\right)\left(\frac{1 \text{ rev}}{2\pi \text{ rad}}\right)\left(\frac{60 \text{ s}}{1 \text{ min}}\right) = 740 \text{ rev/min}$$

(d) From Eq. (9.3),

$$\omega_z = \frac{d\theta}{dt} = \frac{d}{dt}\left[(2.0 \text{ rad/s}^3)t^3\right] = (2.0 \text{ rad/s}^3)(3t^2)$$

$$= (6.0 \text{ rad/s}^3)t^2$$

At times $t_1 = 2.0$ s and $t_2 = 5.0$ s we have

$$\omega_{1z} = (6.0 \text{ rad/s}^3)(2.0 \text{ s})^2 = 24 \text{ rad/s}$$

$$\omega_{2z} = (6.0 \text{ rad/s}^3)(5.0 \text{ s})^2 = 150 \text{ rad/s}$$

EVALUATE: The angular velocity $\omega_z = (6.0 \text{ rad/s}^3)t^2$ increases with time. Our results are consistent with this; the instantaneous angular velocity at the end of the interval ($\omega_{2z} = 150 \text{ rad/s}$) is greater than at the beginning ($\omega_{1z} = 24 \text{ rad/s}$), and the average angular velocity $\omega_{\text{av-}z} = 78 \text{ rad/s}$ over the interval is intermediate between these two values.

Angular Velocity As a Vector

As we have seen, our notation for the angular velocity ω_z about the z-axis is reminiscent of the notation v_x for the ordinary velocity along the x-axis (see Section 2.2). Just as v_x is the x-component of the velocity vector $\vec{v}$, ω_z is the z-component of an angular velocity *vector* $\vec{\omega}$ directed along the axis of rotation. As **Fig. 9.5a** shows, the direction of $\vec{\omega}$ is given by the right-hand rule that we used to define the vector product in Section 1.10. If the rotation is about the z-axis, then $\vec{\omega}$ has only a z-component. This component is positive if $\vec{\omega}$ is along the positive z-axis and negative if $\vec{\omega}$ is along the negative z-axis (Fig. 9.5b).

The vector formulation is especially useful when the direction of the rotation axis *changes*. We'll examine such situations briefly at the end of Chapter 10. In this chapter, however, we'll consider only situations in which the rotation axis is fixed. Hence throughout this chapter we'll use "angular velocity" to refer to ω_z, the component of $\vec{\omega}$ along the axis.

> CAUTION **The angular velocity vector is perpendicular to the plane of rotation, not in it** It's a common error to think that an object's angular velocity vector $\vec{\omega}$ points in the direction in which some particular part of the object is moving. Another error is to think that $\vec{\omega}$ is a "curved vector" that points around the rotation axis in the direction of rotation (like the curved arrows in Figs. 9.1, 9.3, and 9.4). Neither of these is true! Angular velocity is an attribute of the *entire* rotating rigid body, not any one part, and there's no such thing as a curved vector. We choose the direction of $\vec{\omega}$ to be along the rotation axis—*perpendicular* to the plane of rotation—because that axis is common to every part of a rotating rigid body. ▌

9.5 (a) The right-hand rule for the direction of the angular velocity vector $\vec{\omega}$. Reversing the direction of rotation reverses the direction of $\vec{\omega}$. (b) The sign of ω_z for rotation along the z-axis.

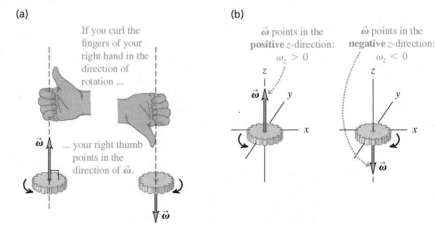

(a)

If you curl the fingers of your right hand in the direction of rotation ...

... your right thumb points in the direction of $\vec{\omega}$.

$\vec{\omega}$

(b)

$\vec{\omega}$ points in the **positive** z-direction: $\omega_z > 0$

$\vec{\omega}$ points in the **negative** z-direction: $\omega_z < 0$

Angular Acceleration

A rigid body whose angular velocity changes has an *angular acceleration*. When you pedal your bicycle harder to make the wheels turn faster or apply the brakes to bring the wheels to a stop, you're giving the wheels an angular acceleration.

If ω_{1z} and ω_{2z} are the instantaneous angular velocities at times t_1 and t_2, we define the **average angular acceleration** $\alpha_{\text{av-}z}$ over the interval $\Delta t = t_2 - t_1$ as the change in angular velocity divided by Δt (**Fig. 9.6**):

$$\alpha_{\text{av-}z} = \frac{\omega_{2z} - \omega_{1z}}{t_2 - t_1} = \frac{\Delta\omega_z}{\Delta t} \qquad (9.4)$$

The **instantaneous angular acceleration** α_z is the limit of $\alpha_{\text{av-}z}$ as $\Delta t \to 0$:

The **instantaneous angular acceleration** of a rigid body rotating around the z-axis ...

$$\alpha_z = \lim_{\Delta t \to 0} \frac{\Delta\omega_z}{\Delta t} = \frac{d\omega_z}{dt} \qquad (9.5)$$

... equals the limit of the body's average angular acceleration as the time interval approaches zero ...

... and equals the instantaneous rate of change of the body's angular velocity.

The usual unit of angular acceleration is the radian per second per second, or rad/s². From now on we will use the term "angular acceleration" to mean the instantaneous angular acceleration rather than the average angular acceleration.

Because $\omega_z = d\theta/dt$, we can also express angular acceleration as the second derivative of the angular coordinate:

$$\alpha_z = \frac{d}{dt}\frac{d\theta}{dt} = \frac{d^2\theta}{dt^2} \qquad (9.6)$$

You've probably noticed that we use Greek letters for angular kinematic quantities: θ for angular position, ω_z for angular velocity, and α_z for angular acceleration. These are analogous to x for position, v_x for velocity, and a_x for acceleration in straight-line motion. In each case, velocity is the rate of change of position with respect to time and acceleration is the rate of change of velocity with respect to time. We sometimes use the terms "*linear* velocity" for v_x and "*linear* acceleration" for a_x to distinguish clearly between these and the *angular* quantities introduced in this chapter.

If the angular acceleration α_z is positive, then the angular velocity ω_z is increasing; if α_z is negative, then ω_z is decreasing. The rotation is speeding up if α_z and ω_z have the same sign and slowing down if α_z and ω_z have opposite signs. (These are exactly the same relationships as those between *linear* acceleration a_x and *linear* velocity v_x for straight-line motion; see Section 2.3.)

9.6 Calculating the average angular acceleration of a rotating rigid body.

The average angular acceleration is the change in angular velocity divided by the time interval:

$$\alpha_{\text{av-}z} = \frac{\omega_{2z} - \omega_{1z}}{t_2 - t_1} = \frac{\Delta\omega_z}{\Delta t}$$

ω_{1z}

ω_{2z}

At t_1 At t_2

EXAMPLE 9.2   CALCULATING ANGULAR ACCELERATION

For the flywheel of Example 9.1, (a) find the average angular acceleration between $t_1 = 2.0$ s and $t_2 = 5.0$ s. (b) Find the instantaneous angular accelerations at $t_1 = 2.0$ s and $t_2 = 5.0$ s.

SOLUTION

IDENTIFY and SET UP: We use Eqs. (9.4) and (9.5) for the average and instantaneous angular accelerations.

EXECUTE: (a) From Example 9.1, the values of ω_z at the two times are

$$\omega_{1z} = 24 \text{ rad/s} \qquad \omega_{2z} = 150 \text{ rad/s}$$

From Eq. (9.4), the average angular acceleration is

$$\alpha_{\text{av-}z} = \frac{150 \text{ rad/s} - 24 \text{ rad/s}}{5.0 \text{ s} - 2.0 \text{ s}} = 42 \text{ rad/s}^2$$

(b) We found in Example 9.1 that $\omega_z = (6.0 \text{ rad/s}^3)t^2$ for the flywheel. From Eq. (9.5), the value of α_z at any time t is

$$\alpha_z = \frac{d\omega_z}{dt} = \frac{d}{dt}[(6.0 \text{ rad/s}^3)(t^2)] = (6.0 \text{ rad/s}^3)(2t)$$

$$= (12 \text{ rad/s}^3)t$$

Hence

$$\alpha_{1z} = (12 \text{ rad/s}^3)(2.0 \text{ s}) = 24 \text{ rad/s}^2$$

$$\alpha_{2z} = (12 \text{ rad/s}^3)(5.0 \text{ s}) = 60 \text{ rad/s}^2$$

EVALUATE: The angular acceleration is *not* constant in this situation. The angular velocity ω_z is always increasing because α_z is always positive. Furthermore, the rate at which angular velocity increases is itself increasing, since α_z increases with time.

9.7 When the rotation axis is fixed, both the angular acceleration and angular velocity vectors lie along that axis.

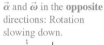

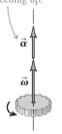

$\vec{\alpha}$ and $\vec{\omega}$ in the **same** direction: Rotation speeding up.

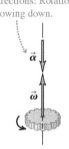

$\vec{\alpha}$ and $\vec{\omega}$ in the **opposite** directions: Rotation slowing down.

Angular Acceleration As a Vector

Just as we did for angular velocity, it's useful to define an angular acceleration *vector* $\vec{\alpha}$. Mathematically, $\vec{\alpha}$ is the time derivative of the angular velocity vector $\vec{\omega}$. If the object rotates around the fixed z-axis, then $\vec{\alpha}$ has only a z-component α_z. In this case, $\vec{\alpha}$ is in the same direction as $\vec{\omega}$ if the rotation is speeding up and opposite to $\vec{\omega}$ if the rotation is slowing down (**Fig. 9.7**).

The vector $\vec{\alpha}$ will be particularly useful in Chapter 10 when we discuss what happens when the rotation axis changes direction. In this chapter, however, the rotation axis will always be fixed and we need only the z-component α_z.

TEST YOUR UNDERSTANDING OF SECTION 9.1
The figure shows a graph of ω_z and α_z versus time for a particular rotating body. (a) During which time intervals is the rotation speeding up? (i) $0 < t < 2$ s; (ii) 2 s $< t < 4$ s; (iii) 4 s $< t < 6$ s. (b) During which time intervals is the rotation slowing down? (i) $0 < t < 2$ s; (ii) 2 s $< t < 4$ s; (iii) 4 s $< t < 6$ s.

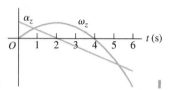

9.2 ROTATION WITH CONSTANT ANGULAR ACCELERATION

In Chapter 2 we found that straight-line motion is particularly simple when the acceleration is constant. This is also true of rotational motion about a fixed axis. When the angular acceleration is constant, we can derive equations for angular velocity and angular position by using the same procedure that we used for straight-line motion in Section 2.4. In fact, the equations we are about to derive are identical to Eqs. (2.8), (2.12), (2.13), and (2.14) if we replace x with θ, v_x with ω_z, and a_x with α_z. We suggest that you review Section 2.4 before continuing.

Let ω_{0z} be the angular velocity of a rigid body at time $t = 0$ and ω_z be its angular velocity at a later time t. The angular acceleration α_z is constant and equal to the average value for any interval. From Eq. (9.4) with the interval from 0 to t,

$$\alpha_z = \frac{\omega_z - \omega_{0z}}{t - 0} \qquad \text{or}$$

Angular velocity at time t of a rigid body with **constant angular acceleration** ⋯⋯ Angular velocity of body at time 0

$$\omega_z = \omega_{0z} + \alpha_z t \qquad \text{(9.7)}$$

⋯⋯ Time

Constant angular acceleration of body

The product $\alpha_z t$ is the total change in ω_z between $t = 0$ and the later time t; angular velocity ω_z at time t is the sum of the initial value ω_{0z} and this total change.

With constant angular acceleration, the angular velocity changes at a uniform rate, so its average value between 0 and t is the average of the initial and final values:

$$\omega_{\text{av-}z} = \frac{\omega_{0z} + \omega_z}{2} \qquad \text{(9.8)}$$

We also know that $\omega_{\text{av-}z}$ is the total angular displacement $(\theta - \theta_0)$ divided by the time interval $(t - 0)$:

$$\omega_{\text{av-}z} = \frac{\theta - \theta_0}{t - 0} \qquad \text{(9.9)}$$

When we equate Eqs. (9.8) and (9.9) and multiply the result by t, we get

Angular position at time t of a rigid body with **constant angular acceleration** ⋯⋯ Angular position of body at time 0

$$\theta - \theta_0 = \tfrac{1}{2}(\omega_{0z} + \omega_z)t \qquad \text{(9.10)}$$

⋯⋯ Time

Angular velocity of body at time 0   Angular velocity of body at time t

Flagella

To obtain a relationship between θ and t that doesn't contain ω_z, we substitute Eq. (9.7) into Eq. (9.10):

$$\theta - \theta_0 = \tfrac{1}{2}\left[\omega_{0z} + (\omega_{0z} + \alpha_z t)\right]t \quad \cdot \quad \text{or}$$

Angular position at time t of a rigid body with **constant angular acceleration**

Angular position of body at time 0 ⋯⋯ Time

$$\theta = \theta_0 + \omega_{0z}t + \tfrac{1}{2}\alpha_z t^2 \qquad (9.11)$$

Angular velocity of body at time 0   Constant angular acceleration of body

That is, if at the initial time $t = 0$ the body is at angular position θ_0 and has angular velocity ω_{0z}, then its angular position θ at any later time t is θ_0, plus the rotation $\omega_{0z}t$ it would have if the angular velocity were constant, plus an additional rotation $\tfrac{1}{2}\alpha_z t^2$ caused by the changing angular velocity.

Following the same procedure as for straight-line motion in Section 2.4, we can combine Eqs. (9.7) and (9.11) to obtain a relationship between θ and ω_z that does not contain t. We invite you to work out the details, following the same procedure we used to get Eq. (2.13). (See Exercise 9.12.) We get

Angular velocity at time t of a rigid body with **constant angular acceleration**

Angular velocity of body at time 0

$$\omega_z^2 = \omega_{0z}^2 + 2\alpha_z(\theta - \theta_0) \qquad (9.12)$$

Constant angular acceleration of body ⋯ Angular position of body at time t ⋯ Angular position of body at time 0

CAUTION Constant angular acceleration Keep in mind that all of these results are valid *only* when the angular acceleration α_z is *constant;* do not try to apply them to problems in which α_z is *not* constant. **Table 9.1** shows the analogy between Eqs. (9.7), (9.10), (9.11), and (9.12) for fixed-axis rotation with constant angular acceleration and the corresponding equations for straight-line motion with constant linear acceleration. ▮

Comparison of Linear and Angular Motions
TABLE 9.1 with Constant Acceleration

Straight-Line Motion with Constant Linear Acceleration		Fixed-Axis Rotation with Constant Angular Acceleration	
$a_x = \text{constant}$		$\alpha_z = \text{constant}$	
$v_x = v_{0x} + a_x t$	(2.8)	$\omega_z = \omega_{0z} + \alpha_z t$	(9.7)
$x = x_0 + v_{0x}t + \tfrac{1}{2}a_x t^2$	(2.12)	$\theta = \theta_0 + \omega_{0z}t + \tfrac{1}{2}\alpha_z t^2$	(9.11)
$v_x^2 = v_{0x}^2 + 2a_x(x - x_0)$	(2.13)	$\omega_z^2 = \omega_{0z}^2 + 2\alpha_z(\theta - \theta_0)$	(9.12)
$x - x_0 = \tfrac{1}{2}(v_{0x} + v_x)t$	(2.14)	$\theta - \theta_0 = \tfrac{1}{2}(\omega_{0z} + \omega_z)t$	(9.10)

SOLUTION

EXAMPLE 9.3   **ROTATION WITH CONSTANT ANGULAR ACCELERATION**

You have finished watching a movie on Blu-ray and the disc is slowing to a stop. The disc's angular velocity at $t = 0$ is 27.5 rad/s, and its angular acceleration is a constant -10.0 rad/s². A line PQ on the disc's surface lies along the $+x$-axis at $t = 0$ (**Fig. 9.8**). (a) What is the disc's angular velocity at $t = 0.300$ s? (b) What angle does the line PQ make with the $+x$-axis at this time?

9.8 A line PQ on a rotating Blu-ray disc at $t = 0$.

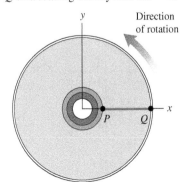

SOLUTION

IDENTIFY and SET UP: The angular acceleration of the disc is constant, so we can use any of the equations derived in this section (Table 9.1). Our target variables are the angular velocity ω_z and the angular displacement θ at $t = 0.300$ s. Given $\omega_{0z} = 27.5$ rad/s, $\theta_0 = 0$, and $\alpha_z = -10.0$ rad/s², it's easiest to use Eqs. (9.7) and (9.11) to find the target variables.

Continued

EXECUTE: (a) From Eq. (9.7), at $t = 0.300$ s we have

$$\omega_z = \omega_{0z} + \alpha_z t = 27.5 \text{ rad/s} + (-10.0 \text{ rad/s}^2)(0.300 \text{ s})$$
$$= 24.5 \text{ rad/s}$$

(b) From Eq. (9.11),

$$\theta = \theta_0 + \omega_{0z} t + \tfrac{1}{2}\alpha_z t^2$$
$$= 0 + (27.5 \text{ rad/s})(0.300 \text{ s}) + \tfrac{1}{2}(-10.0 \text{ rad/s}^2)(0.300 \text{ s})^2$$
$$= 7.80 \text{ rad} = 7.80 \text{ rad}\left(\frac{1 \text{ rev}}{2\pi \text{ rad}}\right) = 1.24 \text{ rev}$$

The disc has made one complete revolution plus an additional 0.24 revolution—that is, 360° plus $(0.24 \text{ rev})(360°/\text{rev}) = 87°$. Hence the line PQ makes an angle of 87° with the $+x$-axis.

EVALUATE: Our answer to part (a) tells us that the disc's angular velocity has decreased, as it should since $\alpha_z < 0$. We can use our result for ω_z from part (a) with Eq. (9.12) to check our result for θ from part (b). To do so, we solve Eq. (9.12) for θ:

$$\omega_z^2 = \omega_{0z}^2 + 2\alpha_z(\theta - \theta_0)$$
$$\theta = \theta_0 + \left(\frac{\omega_z^2 - \omega_{0z}^2}{2\alpha_z}\right)$$
$$= 0 + \frac{(24.5 \text{ rad/s})^2 - (27.5 \text{ rad/s})^2}{2(-10.0 \text{ rad/s}^2)} = 7.80 \text{ rad}$$

This agrees with our previous result from part (b).

TEST YOUR UNDERSTANDING OF SECTION 9.2 Suppose the disc in Example 9.3 was initially spinning at twice the rate (55.0 rad/s rather than 27.5 rad/s) and slowed down at twice the rate (-20.0 rad/s² rather than -10.0 rad/s²). (a) Compared to the situation in Example 9.3, how long would it take the disc to come to a stop? (i) The same amount of time; (ii) twice as much time; (iii) 4 times as much time; (iv) $\tfrac{1}{2}$ as much time; (v) $\tfrac{1}{4}$ as much time. (b) Compared to the situation in Example 9.3, through how many revolutions would the disc rotate before coming to a stop? (i) The same number of revolutions; (ii) twice as many revolutions; (iii) 4 times as many revolutions; (iv) $\tfrac{1}{2}$ as many revolutions; (v) $\tfrac{1}{4}$ as many revolutions. ▌

9.3 RELATING LINEAR AND ANGULAR KINEMATICS

How do we find the linear speed and acceleration of a particular point in a rotating rigid body? We need to answer this question to proceed with our study of rotation. For example, to find the kinetic energy of a rotating body, we have to start from $K = \tfrac{1}{2}mv^2$ for a particle, and this requires that we know the speed v for each particle in the body. So it's worthwhile to develop general relationships between the *angular* speed and acceleration of a rigid body rotating about a fixed axis and the *linear* speed and acceleration of a specific point or particle in the body.

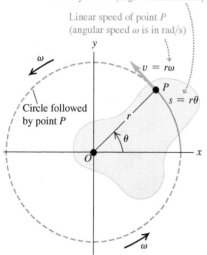

9.9 A rigid body rotating about a fixed axis through point O.

Distance through which point P on the body moves (angle θ is in radians)

Linear speed of point P (angular speed ω is in rad/s)

$v = r\omega$

$s = r\theta$

Circle followed by point P

Linear Speed in Rigid-Body Rotation

When a rigid body rotates about a fixed axis, every particle in the body moves in a circular path that lies in a plane perpendicular to the axis and is centered on the axis. A particle's speed is directly proportional to the body's angular velocity; the faster the rotation, the greater the speed of each particle. In **Fig. 9.9**, point P is a constant distance r from the axis, so it moves in a circle of radius r. At any time, Eq. (9.1) relates the angle θ (in radians) and the arc length s:

$$s = r\theta$$

We take the time derivative of this, noting that r is constant for any specific particle, and take the absolute value of both sides:

$$\left|\frac{ds}{dt}\right| = r\left|\frac{d\theta}{dt}\right|$$

Now $|ds/dt|$ is the absolute value of the rate of change of arc length, which is equal to the instantaneous *linear* speed v of the particle. The absolute value of the rate of change of the angle, $|d\theta/dt|$, is the instantaneous **angular speed** ω— that is, the magnitude of the instantaneous angular velocity in rad/s. Thus

$$\underset{\substack{\text{Linear speed of a point} \\ \text{on a rotating rigid body}}}{\cdots} v = r\omega \underset{\substack{\text{Angular speed of the} \\ \text{rotating rigid body}}}{\cdots} \tag{9.13}$$

Distance of that point from rotation axis

The farther a point is from the axis, the greater its linear speed. The *direction* of the linear velocity *vector* is tangent to its circular path at each point (Fig. 9.9).

> CAUTION Speed vs. velocity Keep in mind the distinction between the linear and angular *speeds* v and ω, which appear in Eq. (9.13), and the linear and angular *velocities* v_x and ω_z. The quantities without subscripts, v and ω, are never negative; they are the magnitudes of the vectors $\vec{v}$ and $\vec{\omega}$, respectively, and their values tell you only how fast a particle is moving (v) or how fast a body is rotating (ω). The quantities with subscripts, v_x and ω_z, can be either positive or negative; their signs tell you the direction of the motion.

Linear Acceleration in Rigid-Body Rotation

We can represent the acceleration $\vec{a}$ of a particle moving in a circle in terms of its centripetal and tangential components, a_{rad} and a_{tan} (**Fig. 9.10**), as we did in Section 3.4. (You should review that section now.) We found that the **tangential component of acceleration** a_{tan}, the component parallel to the instantaneous velocity, acts to change the *magnitude* of the particle's velocity (i.e., the speed) and is equal to the rate of change of speed. Taking the derivative of Eq. (9.13), we find

$$\underset{\substack{\text{Tangential} \\ \text{acceleration of a} \\ \text{point on a rotating} \\ \text{rigid body}}}{\cdots} a_{tan} = \frac{dv}{dt} = r\frac{d\omega}{dt} = r\alpha \underset{\substack{\text{Distance of that point from rotation axis}}}{} \tag{9.14}$$

Rate of change of linear speed of that point   Rate of change of angular speed of body

This component of $\vec{a}$ is always tangent to the circular path of point P (Fig. 9.10).

The quantity $\alpha = d\omega/dt$ in Eq. (9.14) is the rate of change of the angular *speed*. It is not quite the same as $\alpha_z = d\omega_z/dt$, which is the rate of change of the angular *velocity*. For example, consider a body rotating so that its angular velocity vector points in the $-z$-direction (see Fig. 9.5b). If the body is gaining angular speed at a rate of 10 rad/s per second, then $\alpha = 10$ rad/s^2. But ω_z is negative and becoming more negative as the rotation gains speed, so $\alpha_z = -10$ rad/s^2. The rule for rotation about a fixed axis is that α is equal to α_z if ω_z is positive but equal to $-\alpha_z$ if ω_z is negative.

The component of $\vec{a}$ in Fig. 9.10 directed toward the rotation axis, the **centripetal component of acceleration** a_{rad}, is associated with the change of *direction* of the velocity of point P. In Section 3.4 we worked out the relationship $a_{rad} = v^2/r$. We can express this in terms of ω by using Eq. (9.13):

$$\underset{\substack{\text{Centripetal} \\ \text{acceleration of a} \\ \text{point on a rotating} \\ \text{rigid body}}}{\cdots} a_{rad} = \frac{v^2}{r} = \omega^2 r \underset{\substack{\text{Angular speed of body}}}{} \tag{9.15}$$

Linear speed of that point   Distance of that point from rotation axis

This is true at each instant, *even when ω and v are not constant*. The centripetal component always points toward the axis of rotation.

> CAUTION Use angles in radians Remember that Eq. (9.1), $s = r\theta$, is valid *only* when θ is measured in radians. The same is true of any equation derived from this, including Eqs. (9.13), (9.14), and (9.15). When you use these equations, you *must* express the angular quantities in radians, not revolutions or degrees (**Fig. 9.11**).

PhET: Ladybug Revolution

9.10 A rigid body whose rotation is speeding up. The acceleration of point P has a component a_{rad} toward the rotation axis (perpendicular to $\vec{v}$) and a component a_{tan} along the circle that point P follows (parallel to $\vec{v}$).

Radial and tangential acceleration components:
• $a_{rad} = \omega^2 r$ is point P's centripetal acceleration.
• $a_{tan} = r\alpha$ means that P's rotation is speeding up (the body has angular acceleration).

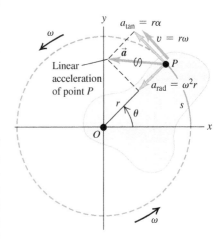

9.11 Always use radians when relating linear and angular quantities.

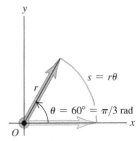

In any equation that relates linear quantities to angular quantities, the angles MUST be expressed in radians ...

RIGHT! ▶ $s = (\pi/3)r$

... never in degrees or revolutions.

WRONG ▶ $s = \cancel{60}r$

Equations (9.1), (9.13), and (9.14) also apply to any particle that has the same tangential velocity as a point in a rotating rigid body. For example, when a rope wound around a circular cylinder unwraps without stretching or slipping, its speed and acceleration at any instant are equal to the speed and tangential acceleration of the point at which it is tangent to the cylinder. The same principle holds for situations such as bicycle chains and sprockets, belts and pulleys that turn without slipping, and so on. We will have several opportunities to use these relationships later in this chapter and in Chapter 10. Note that Eq. (9.15) for the centripetal component a_{rad} is applicable to the rope or chain *only* at points that are in contact with the cylinder or sprocket. Other points do not have the same acceleration toward the center of the circle that points on the cylinder or sprocket have.

EXAMPLE 9.4 THROWING A DISCUS

An athlete whirls a discus in a circle of radius 80.0 cm. At a certain instant, the athlete is rotating at 10.0 rad/s and the angular speed is increasing at 50.0 rad/s². For this instant, find the tangential and centripetal components of the acceleration of the discus and the magnitude of the acceleration.

SOLUTION

IDENTIFY and SET UP: We treat the discus as a particle traveling in a circular path (**Fig. 9.12a**), so we can use the ideas developed in this section. We are given $r = 0.800$ m, $\omega = 10.0$ rad/s, and $\alpha = 50.0$ rad/s² (Fig. 9.12b). We'll use Eqs. (9.14) and (9.15) to find the acceleration components a_{tan} and a_{rad}, respectively; we'll then find the magnitude a by using the Pythagorean theorem.

EXECUTE: From Eqs. (9.14) and (9.15),

$$a_{\text{tan}} = r\alpha = (0.800 \text{ m})(50.0 \text{ rad/s}^2) = 40.0 \text{ m/s}^2$$
$$a_{\text{rad}} = \omega^2 r = (10.0 \text{ rad/s})^2(0.800 \text{ m}) = 80.0 \text{ m/s}^2$$

Then

$$a = \sqrt{a_{\text{tan}}^2 + a_{\text{rad}}^2} = 89.4 \text{ m/s}^2$$

EVALUATE: Note that we dropped the unit "radian" from our results for a_{tan}, a_{rad}, and a. We can do this because "radian" is a dimensionless quantity. Can you show that if the angular speed doubles to 20.0 rad/s while α remains the same, the acceleration magnitude a increases to 322 m/s²?

9.12 (a) Whirling a discus in a circle. (b) Our sketch showing the acceleration components for the discus.

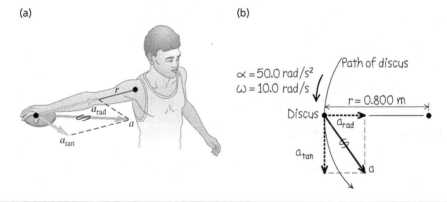

EXAMPLE 9.5 DESIGNING A PROPELLER

You are designing an airplane propeller that is to turn at 2400 rpm (**Fig. 9.13a**). The forward airspeed of the plane is to be 75.0 m/s, and the speed of the propeller tips through the air must not exceed 270 m/s. (This is about 80% of the speed of sound in air. If the propeller tips moved faster, they would produce a lot of noise.) (a) What is the maximum possible propeller radius? (b) With this radius, what is the acceleration of the propeller tip?

SOLUTION

IDENTIFY and SET UP: We consider a particle at the tip of the propeller; our target variables are the particle's distance from the axis and its acceleration. The speed of this particle through the air, which cannot exceed 270 m/s, is due to both the propeller's rotation and the forward motion of the airplane. Figure 9.13b shows

9.13 (a) A propeller-driven airplane in flight. (b) Our sketch showing the velocity components for the propeller tip.

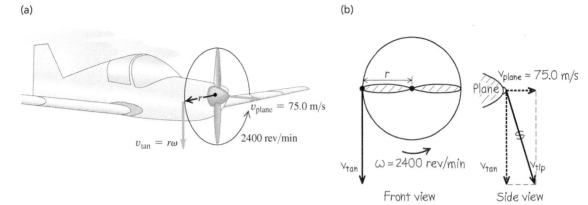

(a)

$v_{plane} = 75.0$ m/s

$v_{tan} = r\omega$

2400 rev/min

(b)

$v_{plane} \approx 75.0$ m/s

Plane

$\omega = 2400$ rev/min

Front view   Side view

that the particle's velocity $\vec{v}_{tip}$ is the vector sum of its tangential velocity due to the propeller's rotation of magnitude $v_{tan} = \omega r$, given by Eq. (9.13), and the forward velocity of the airplane of magnitude $v_{plane} = 75.0$ m/s. The propeller rotates in a plane perpendicular to the direction of flight, so $\vec{v}_{tan}$ and $\vec{v}_{plane}$ are perpendicular to each other, and we can use the Pythagorean theorem to obtain an expression for v_{tip} from v_{tan} and v_{plane}. We will then set $v_{tip} = 270$ m/s and solve for the radius r. The angular speed of the propeller is constant, so the acceleration of the propeller tip has only a radial component; we'll find it by using Eq. (9.15).

EXECUTE: We first convert ω to rad/s (see Fig. 9.11):

$$\omega = 2400 \text{ rpm} = \left(2400\frac{\text{rev}}{\text{min}}\right)\left(\frac{2\pi \text{ rad}}{1 \text{ rev}}\right)\left(\frac{1 \text{ min}}{60 \text{ s}}\right) = 251 \text{ rad/s}$$

(a) From Fig. 9.13b and Eq. (9.13),

$$v_{tip}^2 = v_{plane}^2 + v_{tan}^2 = v_{plane}^2 + r^2\omega^2 \quad \text{so}$$

$$r^2 = \frac{v_{tip}^2 - v_{plane}^2}{\omega^2} \quad \text{and} \quad r = \frac{\sqrt{v_{tip}^2 - v_{plane}^2}}{\omega}$$

If $v_{tip} = 270$ m/s, the maximum propeller radius is

$$r = \frac{\sqrt{(270 \text{ m/s})^2 - (75.0 \text{ m/s})^2}}{251 \text{ rad/s}} = 1.03 \text{ m}$$

(b) The centripetal acceleration of the particle is, from Eq. (9.15),

$$a_{rad} = \omega^2 r = (251 \text{ rad/s})^2(1.03 \text{ m})$$

$$= 6.5 \times 10^4 \text{ m/s}^2 = 6600g$$

The tangential acceleration a_{tan} is zero because ω is constant.

EVALUATE: From $\Sigma\vec{F} = m\vec{a}$, the propeller must exert a force of 6.5×10^4 N on each kilogram of material at its tip! This is why propellers are made out of tough material, usually aluminum alloy.

TEST YOUR UNDERSTANDING OF SECTION 9.3 Information is stored on a Blu-ray disc (see Fig. 9.8) in a coded pattern of tiny pits. The pits are arranged in a track that spirals outward toward the rim of the disc. As the disc spins inside a player, the track is scanned at a constant *linear* speed. How must the rotation speed ω of the disc change as the player's scanning head moves outward over the track? (i) ω must increase; (ii) ω must decrease; (iii) ω must stay the same. ∎

9.4 ENERGY IN ROTATIONAL MOTION

A rotating rigid body consists of mass in motion, so it has kinetic energy. As we will see, we can express this kinetic energy in terms of the body's angular speed and a new quantity, called *moment of inertia,* that depends on the body's mass and how the mass is distributed.

To begin, we think of a body as being made up of a large number of particles, with masses $m_1, m_2, \ldots$ at distances $r_1, r_2, \ldots$ from the axis of rotation. We label the particles with the index i: The mass of the ith particle is m_i and r_i is the *perpendicular* distance from the axis to the ith particle. (The particles need not all lie in the same plane.)

When a rigid body rotates about a fixed axis, the speed v_i of the ith particle is given by Eq. (9.13), $v_i = r_i\omega$, where ω is the body's angular speed. Different

DATA SPEAKS

Relating Linear and Angular Quantities

When students were given a problem about the motion of points on a rotating rigid body, more than 21% gave an incorrect response. Common errors:

• Confusing centripetal and tangential acceleration. Points on a rigid body have a centripetal (radial) acceleration a_{rad} whenever the body is rotating but have a tangential acceleration a_{tan} only if the angular speed is changing.

• Forgetting that the values of a_{rad} and a_{tan} at a point depend on the point's distance from the rotation axis.

particles have different values of r_i, but ω is the same for all (otherwise, the body wouldn't be rigid). The kinetic energy of the ith particle can be expressed as

$$\tfrac{1}{2}m_i v_i^2 = \tfrac{1}{2}m_i r_i^2 \omega^2$$

The body's *total* kinetic energy is the sum of the kinetic energies of all its particles:

$$K = \tfrac{1}{2}m_1 r_1^2 \omega^2 + \tfrac{1}{2}m_2 r_2^2 \omega^2 + \cdots = \sum_i \tfrac{1}{2}m_i r_i^2 \omega^2$$

Taking the common factor $\omega^2/2$ out of this expression, we get

$$K = \tfrac{1}{2}(m_1 r_1^2 + m_2 r_2^2 + \cdots)\omega^2 = \tfrac{1}{2}\left(\sum_i m_i r_i^2\right)\omega^2$$

DEMO

The quantity in parentheses, obtained by multiplying the mass of each particle by the square of its distance from the axis of rotation and adding these products, is called the **moment of inertia** I of the body for this rotation axis:

Masses of the particles that make up the body

Moment of inertia of a body for a given rotation axis $\longrightarrow I = m_1 r_1^2 + m_2 r_2^2 + \cdots = \sum_i m_i r_i^2$ (9.16)

Perpendicular distances of the particles from rotation axis

"Moment" means that I depends on how the body's mass is distributed in space; it has nothing to do with a "moment" of time. For a body with a given rotation axis and a given total mass, the greater the distances from the axis to the particles that make up the body, the greater the moment of inertia I. In a rigid body, all distances r_i are constant and I is independent of how the body rotates around the given axis. The SI unit of I is the kilogram-meter^2 (kg $\cdot$ m^2).

Using Eq. (9.16), we see that the **rotational kinetic energy** K of a rigid body is

Rotational kinetic energy of a rigid body rotating around an axis $\longrightarrow K = \tfrac{1}{2}I\omega^2$ Moment of inertia of body for given rotation axis   (9.17)

Angular speed of body

The kinetic energy given by Eq. (9.17) is *not* a new form of energy; it's simply the sum of the kinetic energies of the individual particles that make up the rotating rigid body. To use Eq. (9.17), ω *must* be measured in radians per second, not revolutions or degrees per second, to give K in joules. That's because we used $v_i = r_i\omega$ in our derivation.

Equation (9.17) gives a simple physical interpretation of moment of inertia: *The greater the moment of inertia, the greater the kinetic energy of a rigid body rotating with a given angular speed ω.* We learned in Chapter 6 that the kinetic energy of a body equals the amount of work done to accelerate that body from rest. So the greater a body's moment of inertia, the harder it is to start the body rotating if it's at rest and the harder it is to stop its rotation if it's already rotating (**Fig. 9.14**). For this reason, I is also called the *rotational inertia*.

9.14 An apparatus free to rotate around a vertical axis. To vary the moment of inertia, the two equal-mass cylinders can be locked into different positions on the horizontal shaft.

• Mass close to axis
• Small moment of inertia
• Easy to start apparatus rotating

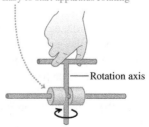

• Mass farther from axis
• Greater moment of inertia
• Harder to start apparatus rotating

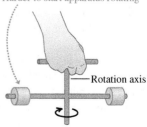

SOLUTION

EXAMPLE 9.6 **MOMENTS OF INERTIA FOR DIFFERENT ROTATION AXES**

A machine part (**Fig. 9.15**) consists of three disks linked by light-weight struts. (a) What is this body's moment of inertia about axis 1 through the center of disk A, perpendicular to the plane of the diagram? (b) What is its moment of inertia about axis 2 through the centers of disks B and C? (c) What is the body's kinetic energy if it rotates about axis 1 with angular speed $\omega = 4.0$ rad/s?

SOLUTION

IDENTIFY and SET UP: We'll consider the disks as massive particles located at the centers of the disks, and consider the struts as massless. In parts (a) and (b), we'll use Eq. (9.16) to find the moments of inertia. Given the moment of inertia about axis 1, we'll use Eq. (9.17) in part (c) to find the rotational kinetic energy.

EXECUTE: (a) The particle at point A lies *on* axis 1 through A, so its distance r from the axis is zero and it contributes nothing to the moment of inertia. Hence only B and C contribute in Eq. (9.16):

$$I_1 = \sum m_i r_i^2 = (0.10 \text{ kg})(0.50 \text{ m})^2 + (0.20 \text{ kg})(0.40 \text{ m})^2$$
$$= 0.057 \text{ kg} \cdot \text{m}^2$$

(b) The particles at B and C both lie on axis 2, so neither particle contributes to the moment of inertia. Hence only A contributes:

$$I_2 = \sum m_i r_i^2 = (0.30 \text{ kg})(0.40 \text{ m})^2 = 0.048 \text{ kg} \cdot \text{m}^2$$

(c) From Eq. (9.17),

$$K_1 = \tfrac{1}{2} I_1 \omega^2 = \tfrac{1}{2}(0.057 \text{ kg} \cdot \text{m}^2)(4.0 \text{ rad/s})^2 = 0.46 \text{ J}$$

EVALUATE: The moment of inertia about axis 2 is smaller than that about axis 1. Hence, of the two axes, it's easier to make the machine part rotate about axis 2.

9.15 An oddly shaped machine part.

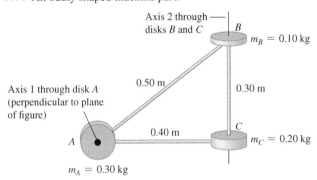

CAUTION **Moment of inertia depends on the choice of axis** Example 9.6 shows that the moment of inertia of a body depends on the location and orientation of the axis. It's not enough to say, "The moment of inertia is 0.048 kg·m²." We have to be specific and say, "The moment of inertia *about the axis through B and C* is 0.048 kg·m²." ▮

In Example 9.6 we represented the body as several point masses, and we evaluated the sum in Eq. (9.16) directly. When the body is a *continuous* distribution of matter, such as a solid cylinder or plate, the sum becomes an integral, and we need to use calculus to calculate the moment of inertia. We will give several examples of such calculations in Section 9.6; meanwhile, **Table 9.2** (next page) gives moments of inertia for several familiar shapes in terms of their masses and dimensions. Each body shown in Table 9.2 is *uniform;* that is, the density has the same value at all points within the solid parts of the body.

CAUTION **Computing moments of inertia** You may be tempted to try to compute the moment of inertia of a body by assuming that all the mass is concentrated at the center of mass and multiplying the total mass by the square of the distance from the center of mass to the axis. That doesn't work! For example, when a uniform thin rod of length L and mass M is pivoted about an axis through one end, perpendicular to the rod, the moment of inertia is $I = ML^2/3$ [case (b) in Table 9.2]. If we took the mass as concentrated at the center, a distance $L/2$ from the axis, we would obtain the *incorrect* result $I = M(L/2)^2 = ML^2/4$. ▮

Now that we know how to calculate the kinetic energy of a rotating rigid body, we can apply the energy principles of Chapter 7 to rotational motion. The Problem-Solving Strategy on the next page, along with the examples that follow, show how this is done.

BIO **Application Moment of Inertia of a Bird's Wing** When a bird flaps its wings, it rotates the wings up and down around the shoulder. A hummingbird has small wings with a small moment of inertia, so the bird can move its wings rapidly (up to 70 beats per second). By contrast, the Andean condor (*Vultur gryphus*) has immense wings that are hard to move due to their large moment of inertia. Condors flap their wings at about one beat per second on takeoff, but at most times prefer to soar while holding their wings steady.

| TABLE 9.2 | Moments of Inertia of Various Bodies

(a) Slender rod, axis through center

$$I = \frac{1}{12}ML^2$$

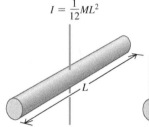

(b) Slender rod, axis through one end

$$I = \frac{1}{3}ML^2$$

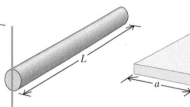

(c) Rectangular plate, axis through center

$$I = \frac{1}{12}M(a^2 + b^2)$$

(d) Thin rectangular plate, axis along edge

$$I = \frac{1}{3}Ma^2$$

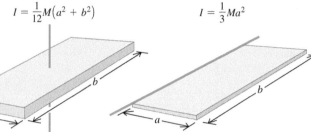

(e) Hollow cylinder

$$I = \frac{1}{2}M(R_1^2 + R_2^2)$$

(f) Solid cylinder

$$I = \frac{1}{2}MR^2$$

(g) Thin-walled hollow cylinder

$$I = MR^2$$

(h) Solid sphere

$$I = \frac{2}{5}MR^2$$

(i) Thin-walled hollow sphere

$$I = \frac{2}{3}MR^2$$

| PROBLEM-SOLVING STRATEGY 9.1 | **ROTATIONAL ENERGY**

IDENTIFY *the relevant concepts:* You can use work–energy relationships and conservation of energy to find relationships involving the position and motion of a rigid body rotating around a fixed axis. The energy method is usually not helpful for problems that involve elapsed time. In Chapter 10 we'll see how to approach rotational problems of this kind.

SET UP *the problem* using Problem-Solving Strategy 7.1 (Section 7.1), with the following additional steps:

5. You can use Eqs. (9.13) and (9.14) in problems involving a rope (or the like) wrapped around a rotating rigid body, if the rope doesn't slip. These equations relate the linear speed and tangential acceleration of a point on the body to the body's angular velocity and angular acceleration. (See Examples 9.7 and 9.8.)

6. Use Table 9.2 to find moments of inertia. Use the parallel-axis theorem, Eq. (9.19) (to be derived in Section 9.5), to find

moments of inertia for rotation about axes parallel to those shown in the table.

EXECUTE *the solution:* Write expressions for the initial and final kinetic and potential energies K_1, K_2, U_1, and U_2 and for the nonconservative work W_{other} (if any), where K_1 and K_2 must now include any rotational kinetic energy $K = \frac{1}{2}I\omega^2$. Substitute these expressions into Eq. (7.14), $K_1 + U_1 + W_{other} = K_2 + U_2$ (if nonconservative work is done), or Eq. (7.12), $K_1 + U_1 = K_2 + U_2$ (if only conservative work is done), and solve for the target variables. It's helpful to draw bar graphs showing the initial and final values of K, U, and $E = K + U$.

EVALUATE *your answer:* Check whether your answer makes physical sense.

EXAMPLE 9.7   AN UNWINDING CABLE I

We wrap a light, nonstretching cable around a solid cylinder, of mass 50 kg and diameter 0.120 m, that rotates in frictionless bearings about a stationary horizontal axis (**Fig. 9.16**). We pull the free end of the cable with a constant 9.0-N force for a distance of 2.0 m; it turns the cylinder as it unwinds without slipping. The cylinder is initially at rest. Find its final angular speed and the final speed of the cable.

SOLUTION

IDENTIFY: We'll solve this problem by using energy methods. We'll assume that the cable is massless, so only the cylinder has kinetic energy. There are no changes in gravitational potential energy. There is friction between the cable and the cylinder, but because the cable doesn't slip, there is no motion of the cable relative to

9.16 A cable unwinds from a cylinder (side view).

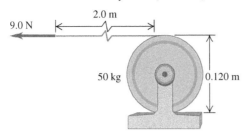

the cylinder and no mechanical energy is lost in frictional work. Because the cable is massless, the force that the cable exerts on the cylinder rim is equal to the applied force F.

SET UP: Point 1 is when the cable begins to move. The cylinder starts at rest, so $K_1 = 0$. Point 2 is when the cable has moved a distance $s = 2.0$ m and the cylinder has kinetic energy $K_2 = \frac{1}{2}I\omega^2$. One of our target variables is ω; the other is the speed of the cable at point 2, which is equal to the tangential speed v of the cylinder at that point. We'll use Eq. (9.13) to find v from ω.

EXECUTE: The work done on the cylinder is $W_{other} = Fs = (9.0 \text{ N})(2.0 \text{ m}) = 18$ J. From Table 9.2 the moment of inertia is

$$I = \tfrac{1}{2}mR^2 = \tfrac{1}{2}(50 \text{ kg})(0.060 \text{ m})^2 = 0.090 \text{ kg} \cdot \text{m}^2$$

(The radius R is half the diameter.) From Eq. (7.14), $K_1 + U_1 + W_{other} = K_2 + U_2$, so

$$0 + 0 + W_{other} = \tfrac{1}{2}I\omega^2 + 0$$

$$\omega = \sqrt{\frac{2W_{other}}{I}} = \sqrt{\frac{2(18 \text{ J})}{0.090 \text{ kg} \cdot \text{m}^2}} = 20 \text{ rad/s}$$

From Eq. (9.13), the final tangential speed of the cylinder, and hence the final speed of the cable, is

$$v = R\omega = (0.060 \text{ m})(20 \text{ rad/s}) = 1.2 \text{ m/s}$$

EVALUATE: If the cable mass is not negligible, some of the 18 J of work would go into the kinetic energy of the cable. Then the cylinder would have less kinetic energy and a lower angular speed than we calculated here.

EXAMPLE 9.8   **AN UNWINDING CABLE II**

We wrap a light, nonstretching cable around a solid cylinder with mass M and radius R. The cylinder rotates with negligible friction about a stationary horizontal axis. We tie the free end of the cable to a block of mass m and release the block from rest at a distance h above the floor. As the block falls, the cable unwinds without stretching or slipping. Find the speed of the falling block and the angular speed of the cylinder as the block strikes the floor.

SOLUTION

IDENTIFY: As in Example 9.7, the cable doesn't slip and so friction does no work. We assume that the cable is massless, so that the forces it exerts on the cylinder and the block have equal magnitudes. At its upper end the force and displacement are in the same direction, and at its lower end they are in opposite directions, so the cable does no *net* work and $W_{other} = 0$. Only gravity does work, and mechanical energy is conserved.

SET UP: Figure 9.17a shows the situation before the block begins to fall (point 1). The initial kinetic energy is $K_1 = 0$. We take the gravitational potential energy to be zero when the block is at floor level (point 2), so $U_1 = mgh$ and $U_2 = 0$. (We ignore the gravitational potential energy for the rotating cylinder, since its height doesn't change.) Just before the block hits the floor (Fig. 9.17b), both the block and the cylinder have kinetic energy, so

$$K_2 = \tfrac{1}{2}mv^2 + \tfrac{1}{2}I\omega^2$$

The moment of inertia of the cylinder is $I = \frac{1}{2}MR^2$. Also, $v = R\omega$ since the speed of the falling block must be equal to the tangential speed at the outer surface of the cylinder.

9.17 Our sketches for this problem.

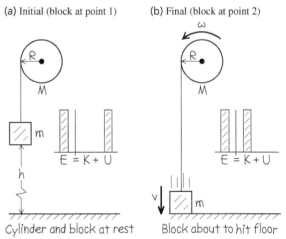

(a) Initial (block at point 1)   (b) Final (block at point 2)

EXECUTE: We use our expressions for K_1, U_1, K_2, and U_2 and the relationship $\omega = v/R$ in Eq. (7.4), $K_1 + U_1 = K_2 + U_2$, and solve for v:

$$0 + mgh = \tfrac{1}{2}mv^2 + \tfrac{1}{2}\left(\tfrac{1}{2}MR^2\right)\left(\frac{v}{R}\right)^2 + 0 = \tfrac{1}{2}\left(m + \tfrac{1}{2}M\right)v^2$$

$$v = \sqrt{\frac{2gh}{1 + M/2m}}$$

The final angular speed of the cylinder is $\omega = v/R$.

EVALUATE: When M is much larger than m, v is very small; when M is much smaller than m, v is nearly equal to $\sqrt{2gh}$, the speed of a body that falls freely from height h. Both of these results are as we would expect.

9.18 In a technique called the "Fosbury flop" after its innovator, this athlete arches her body as she passes over the bar in the high jump. As a result, her center of mass actually passes *under* the bar. This technique requires a smaller increase in gravitational potential energy [Eq. (9.18)] than the older method of straddling the bar.

Gravitational Potential Energy for an Extended Body

In Example 9.8 the cable was of negligible mass, so we could ignore its kinetic energy as well as the gravitational potential energy associated with it. If the mass is *not* negligible, we need to know how to calculate the *gravitational potential energy* associated with such an extended body. If the acceleration of gravity g is the same at all points on the body, the gravitational potential energy is the same as though all the mass were concentrated at the center of mass of the body. Suppose we take the y-axis vertically upward. Then for a body with total mass M, the gravitational potential energy U is simply

$$U = Mgy_{cm} \quad \text{(gravitational potential energy for an extended body)} \quad (9.18)$$

where y_{cm} is the y-coordinate of the center of mass. This expression applies to any extended body, whether it is rigid or not (**Fig. 9.18**).

To prove Eq. (9.18), we again represent the body as a collection of mass elements m_i. The potential energy for element m_i is $m_i gy_i$, so the total potential energy is

$$U = m_1 gy_1 + m_2 gy_2 + \cdots = (m_1 y_1 + m_2 y_2 + \cdots)g$$

But from Eq. (8.28), which defines the coordinates of the center of mass,

$$m_1 y_1 + m_2 y_2 + \cdots = (m_1 + m_2 + \cdots)y_{cm} = My_{cm}$$

where $M = m_1 + m_2 + \cdots$ is the total mass. Combining this with the above expression for U, we find $U = Mgy_{cm}$ in agreement with Eq. (9.18).

We leave the application of Eq. (9.18) to the problems. In Chapter 10 we'll use this equation to help us analyze rigid-body problems in which the axis of rotation moves.

TEST YOUR UNDERSTANDING OF SECTION 9.4   Suppose the cylinder and block in Example 9.8 have the same mass, so $m = M$. Just before the block strikes the floor, which statement is correct about the relationship between the kinetic energy of the falling block and the rotational kinetic energy of the cylinder? (i) The block has more kinetic energy than the cylinder. (ii) The block has less kinetic energy than the cylinder. (iii) The block and the cylinder have equal amounts of kinetic energy. ∎

9.5 PARALLEL-AXIS THEOREM

9.19 The parallel-axis theorem.

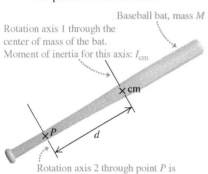

Baseball bat, mass M

Rotation axis 1 through the center of mass of the bat. Moment of inertia for this axis: I_{cm}

× cm

× P d

Rotation axis 2 through point P is parallel to, and a distance d from, axis 1. Moment of inertia for this axis: I_P

Parallel-axis theorem: $I_P = I_{cm} + Md^2$

We pointed out in Section 9.4 that a body doesn't have just one moment of inertia. In fact, it has infinitely many, because there are infinitely many axes about which it might rotate. But there is a simple relationship, called the **parallel-axis theorem,** between the moment of inertia of a body about an axis through its center of mass and the moment of inertia about any other axis parallel to the original axis (**Fig. 9.19**):

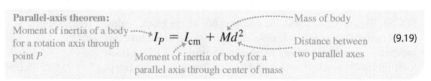

Parallel-axis theorem:
Moment of inertia of a body ⋯⋯→ $I_P = I_{cm} + Md^2$ ⋯⋯ Mass of body
for a rotation axis through
point P Moment of inertia of body for a   Distance between   (9.19)
                    parallel axis through center of mass   two parallel axes

To prove this theorem, we consider two axes, both parallel to the z-axis: one through the center of mass and the other through a point P (**Fig. 9.20**). First we take a very thin slice of the body, parallel to the xy-plane and perpendicular to the z-axis. We take the origin of our coordinate system to be at the center of mass of the body; the coordinates of the center of mass are then $x_{cm} = y_{cm} = z_{cm} = 0$. The axis through the center of mass passes through this thin slice at point O, and the parallel axis passes through point P, whose x- and y-coordinates are (a, b). The distance of this axis from the axis through the center of mass is d, where $d^2 = a^2 + b^2$.

We can write an expression for the moment of inertia I_P about the axis through point P. Let m_i be a mass element in our slice, with coordinates (x_i, y_i, z_i). Then the moment of inertia I_{cm} of the slice about the axis through the center of mass (at O) is

$$I_{cm} = \sum_i m_i(x_i^2 + y_i^2)$$

The moment of inertia of the slice about the axis through P is

$$I_P = \sum_i m_i[(x_i - a)^2 + (y_i - b)^2]$$

These expressions don't involve the coordinates z_i measured perpendicular to the slices, so we can extend the sums to include *all* particles in *all* slices. Then I_P becomes the moment of inertia of the *entire* body for an axis through P. We then expand the squared terms and regroup, and obtain

$$I_P = \sum_i m_i(x_i^2 + y_i^2) - 2a\sum_i m_i x_i - 2b\sum_i m_i y_i + (a^2 + b^2)\sum_i m_i$$

The first sum is I_{cm}. From Eq. (8.28), the definition of the center of mass, the second and third sums are proportional to x_{cm} and y_{cm}; these are zero because we have taken our origin to be the center of mass. The final term is d^2 multiplied by the total mass, or Md^2. This completes our proof that $I_P = I_{cm} + Md^2$.

As Eq. (9.19) shows, a rigid body has a lower moment of inertia about an axis through its center of mass than about any other parallel axis. Thus it's easier to start a body rotating if the rotation axis passes through the center of mass. This suggests that it's somehow most natural for a rotating body to rotate about an axis through its center of mass; we'll make this idea more quantitative in Chapter 10.

9.20 The mass element m_i has coordinates (x_i, y_i) with respect to an axis of rotation through the center of mass (cm) and coordinates $(x_i - a, y_i - b)$ with respect to the parallel axis through point P.

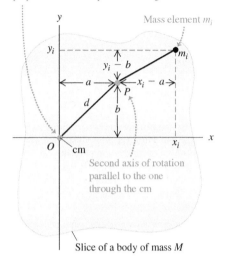

EXAMPLE 9.9   **USING THE PARALLEL-AXIS THEOREM**

A part of a mechanical linkage (**Fig. 9.21**) has a mass of 3.6 kg. Its moment of inertia I_P about an axis 0.15 m from its center of mass is $I_P = 0.132$ kg·m^2. What is the moment of inertia I_{cm} about a parallel axis through the center of mass?

9.21 Calculating I_{cm} from a measurement of I_P.

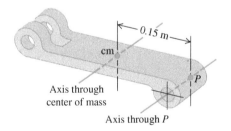

SOLUTION

IDENTIFY, SET UP, and EXECUTE: We'll determine the target variable I_{cm} by using the parallel-axis theorem, Eq. (9.19). Rearranging the equation, we obtain

$$I_{cm} = I_P - Md^2 = 0.132 \text{ kg·m}^2 - (3.6 \text{ kg})(0.15 \text{ m})^2$$
$$= 0.051 \text{ kg·m}^2$$

EVALUATE: As we expect, I_{cm} is less than I_P; the moment of inertia for an axis through the center of mass has a lower value than for any other parallel axis.

TEST YOUR UNDERSTANDING OF SECTION 9.5   A pool cue is a wooden rod of uniform composition and is tapered with a larger diameter at one end than at the other end. Use the parallel-axis theorem to decide whether a pool cue has a larger moment of inertia (i) for an axis through the thicker end and perpendicular to the length of the rod, or (ii) for an axis through the thinner end and perpendicular to the length of the rod. ▮

9.6 MOMENT-OF-INERTIA CALCULATIONS

If a rigid body is a continuous distribution of mass—like a solid cylinder or a solid sphere—it cannot be represented by a few point masses. In this case the *sum* of masses and distances that defines the moment of inertia [Eq. (9.16)] becomes an *integral*. Imagine dividing the body into elements of mass dm that are very small, so that all points in a particular element are at essentially the same perpendicular distance from the axis of rotation. We call this distance r, as before. Then the moment of inertia is

$$I = \int r^2 \, dm \qquad (9.20)$$

To evaluate the integral, we have to represent r and dm in terms of the same integration variable. When the object is effectively one-dimensional, such as the slender rods (a) and (b) in Table 9.2, we can use a coordinate x along the length and relate dm to an increment dx. For a three-dimensional object it is usually easiest to express dm in terms of an element of volume dV and the *density* ρ of the body. Density is mass per unit volume, $\rho = dm/dV$, so we may write Eq. (9.20) as

$$I = \int r^2 \rho \, dV$$

This expression tells us that a body's moment of inertia depends on how its density varies within its volume (**Fig. 9.22**). If the body is uniform in density, then we may take ρ outside the integral:

$$I = \rho \int r^2 \, dV \qquad (9.21)$$

To use this equation, we have to express the volume element dV in terms of the differentials of the integration variables, such as $dV = dx \, dy \, dz$. The element dV must always be chosen so that all points within it are at very nearly the same distance from the axis of rotation. The limits on the integral are determined by the shape and dimensions of the body. For regularly shaped bodies, this integration is often easy to do.

9.22 By measuring small variations in the orbits of satellites, geophysicists can measure the earth's moment of inertia. This tells us how our planet's mass is distributed within its interior. The data show that the earth is far denser at the core than in its outer layers.

EXAMPLE 9.10 HOLLOW OR SOLID CYLINDER, ROTATING ABOUT AXIS OF SYMMETRY

Figure 9.23 shows a hollow cylinder of uniform mass density ρ with length L, inner radius R_1, and outer radius R_2. (It might be a steel cylinder in a printing press.) Using integration, find its moment of inertia about its axis of symmetry.

9.23 Finding the moment of inertia of a hollow cylinder about its symmetry axis.

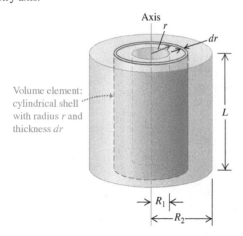

Axis

r

dr

L

Volume element: cylindrical shell with radius r and thickness dr

R_1

R_2

SOLUTION

IDENTIFY and SET UP: We choose as a volume element a thin cylindrical shell of radius r, thickness dr, and length L. All parts of this shell are at very nearly the same distance r from the axis. The volume of the shell is very nearly that of a flat sheet with thickness dr, length L, and width $2\pi r$ (the circumference of the shell). The mass of the shell is

$$dm = \rho \, dV = \rho(2\pi rL \, dr)$$

We'll use this expression in Eq. (9.20), integrating from $r = R_1$ to $r = R_2$.

EXECUTE: From Eq. (9.20), the moment of inertia is

$$I = \int r^2 \, dm = \int_{R_1}^{R_2} r^2 \rho(2\pi rL \, dr)$$

$$= 2\pi\rho L \int_{R_1}^{R_2} r^3 \, dr = \frac{2\pi\rho L}{4}(R_2^4 - R_1^4)$$

$$= \frac{\pi\rho L}{2}(R_2^2 - R_1^2)(R_2^2 + R_1^2)$$

(In the last step we used the identity $a^2 - b^2 = (a - b)(a + b)$.) Let's express this result in terms of the total mass M of the body, which is its density ρ multiplied by the total volume V. The cylinder's volume is

$$V = \pi L(R_2^2 - R_1^2)$$

so its total mass M is

$$M = \rho V = \pi L\rho(R_2^2 - R_1^2)$$

Comparing with the above expression for I, we see that

$$I = \tfrac{1}{2}M(R_1^2 + R_2^2)$$

EVALUATE: Our result agrees with Table 9.2, case (e). If the cylinder is solid, with outer radius $R_2 = R$ and inner radius $R_1 = 0$, its moment of inertia is

$$I = \tfrac{1}{2}MR^2$$

in agreement with case (f). If the cylinder wall is very thin, we have $R_1 \approx R_2 = R$ and the moment of inertia is

$$I = MR^2$$

in agreement with case (g). We could have predicted this last result without calculation; in a thin-walled cylinder, all the mass is at the same distance $r = R$ from the axis, so $I = \int r^2\,dm = R^2 \int dm = MR^2$.

EXAMPLE 9.11   UNIFORM SPHERE WITH RADIUS R, AXIS THROUGH CENTER

Find the moment of inertia of a solid sphere of uniform mass density ρ (like a billiard ball) about an axis through its center.

SOLUTION

IDENTIFY and SET UP: We divide the sphere into thin, solid disks of thickness dx (**Fig. 9.24**), whose moment of inertia we know from Table 9.2, case (f). We'll integrate over these to find the total moment of inertia.

EXECUTE: The radius and hence the volume and mass of a disk depend on its distance x from the center of the sphere. The radius r of the disk shown in Fig. 9.24 is

$$r = \sqrt{R^2 - x^2}$$

Its volume is

$$dV = \pi r^2\,dx = \pi(R^2 - x^2)\,dx$$

and so its mass is

$$dm = \rho\,dV = \pi\rho(R^2 - x^2)\,dx$$

From Table 9.2, case (f), the moment of inertia of a disk of radius r and mass dm is

$$dI = \tfrac{1}{2}r^2\,dm = \tfrac{1}{2}(R^2 - x^2)[\pi\rho(R^2 - x^2)dx]$$
$$= \frac{\pi\rho}{2}(R^2 - x^2)^2\,dx$$

Integrating this expression from $x = 0$ to $x = R$ gives the moment of inertia of the right hemisphere. The total I for the entire sphere, including both hemispheres, is just twice this:

$$I = (2)\frac{\pi\rho}{2}\int_0^R (R^2 - x^2)^2\,dx$$

Carrying out the integration, we find

$$I = \frac{8\pi\rho R^5}{15}$$

The volume of the sphere is $V = 4\pi R^3/3$, so in terms of its mass M its density is

$$\rho = \frac{M}{V} = \frac{3M}{4\pi R^3}$$

Hence our expression for I becomes

$$I = \left(\frac{8\pi R^5}{15}\right)\left(\frac{3M}{4\pi R^3}\right) = \tfrac{2}{5}MR^2$$

EVALUATE: This is just as in Table 9.2, case (h). Note that the moment of inertia $I = \tfrac{2}{5}MR^2$ of a solid sphere of mass M and radius R is less than the moment of inertia $I = \tfrac{1}{2}MR^2$ of a solid *cylinder* of the same mass and radius, because more of the sphere's mass is located close to the axis.

9.24 Finding the moment of inertia of a sphere about an axis through its center.

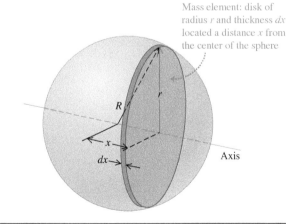

Mass element: disk of radius r and thickness dx located a distance x from the center of the sphere

TEST YOUR UNDERSTANDING OF SECTION 9.6 Two hollow cylinders have the same inner and outer radii and the same mass, but they have different lengths. One is made of low-density wood and the other of high-density lead. Which cylinder has the greater moment of inertia around its axis of symmetry? (i) The wood cylinder; (ii) the lead cylinder; (iii) the two moments of inertia are equal. ▌

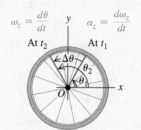

Rotational kinematics: When a rigid body rotates about a stationary axis (usually called the *z*-axis), the body's position is described by an angular coordinate θ. The angular velocity ω_z is the time derivative of θ, and the angular acceleration α_z is the time derivative of ω_z or the second derivative of θ. (See Examples 9.1 and 9.2.) If the angular acceleration is constant, then θ, ω_z, and α_z are related by simple kinematic equations analogous to those for straight-line motion with constant linear acceleration. (See Example 9.3.)

$$\omega_z = \lim_{\Delta t \to 0} \frac{\Delta\theta}{\Delta t} = \frac{d\theta}{dt} \quad (9.3)$$

$$\alpha_z = \lim_{\Delta t \to 0} \frac{\Delta\omega_z}{\Delta t} = \frac{d\omega_z}{dt} \quad (9.5)$$

Constant α_z only:

$$\theta = \theta_0 + \omega_{0z}t + \tfrac{1}{2}\alpha_z t^2 \quad (9.11)$$

$$\theta - \theta_0 = \tfrac{1}{2}(\omega_{0z} + \omega_z)t \quad (9.10)$$

$$\omega_z = \omega_{0z} + \alpha_z t \quad (9.7)$$

$$\omega_z^2 = \omega_{0z}^2 + 2\alpha_z(\theta - \theta_0) \quad (9.12)$$

Relating linear and angular kinematics: The angular speed ω of a rigid body is the magnitude of the body's angular velocity. The rate of change of ω is $\alpha = d\omega/dt$. For a particle in the body a distance r from the rotation axis, the speed v and the components of the acceleration $\vec{a}$ are related to ω and α. (See Examples 9.4 and 9.5.)

$$v = r\omega \quad (9.13)$$

$$a_{\text{tan}} = \frac{dv}{dt} = r\frac{d\omega}{dt} = r\alpha \quad (9.14)$$

$$a_{\text{rad}} = \frac{v^2}{r} = \omega^2 r \quad (9.15)$$

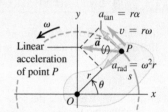

Moment of inertia and rotational kinetic energy: The moment of inertia I of a body about a given axis is a measure of its rotational inertia: The greater the value of I, the more difficult it is to change the state of the body's rotation. The moment of inertia can be expressed as a sum over the particles m_i that make up the body, each of which is at its own perpendicular distance r_i from the axis. The rotational kinetic energy of a rigid body rotating about a fixed axis depends on the angular speed ω and the moment of inertia I for that rotation axis. (See Examples 9.6–9.8.)

$$I = m_1 r_1^2 + m_2 r_2^2 + \cdots$$

$$= \sum_i m_i r_i^2 \quad (9.16)$$

$$K = \tfrac{1}{2}I\omega^2 \quad (9.17)$$

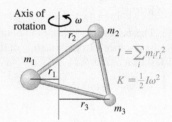

Calculating the moment of inertia: The parallel-axis theorem relates the moments of inertia of a rigid body of mass M about two parallel axes: an axis through the center of mass (moment of inertia I_{cm}) and a parallel axis a distance d from the first axis (moment of inertia I_P). (See Example 9.9.) If the body has a continuous mass distribution, the moment of inertia can be calculated by integration. (See Examples 9.10 and 9.11.)

$$I_P = I_{\text{cm}} + Md^2 \quad (9.19)$$

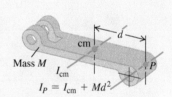

Figure 9.25 shows a slender uniform rod with mass M and length L. It might be a baton held by a twirler in a marching band (without the rubber end caps). (a) Use integration to compute its moment of inertia about an axis through O, at an arbitrary distance h from one end. (b) Initially the rod is at rest. It is given a constant angular acceleration of magnitude α around the axis through O. Find how much work is done on the rod in a time t. (c) At time t, what is the *linear* acceleration of the point on the rod farthest from the axis?

SOLUTION GUIDE

IDENTIFY and SET UP

1. Make a list of the target variables for this problem.
2. To calculate the moment of inertia of the rod, you'll have to divide the rod into infinitesimal elements of mass. If an element

has length dx, what is the mass of the element? What are the limits of integration?

3. What is the angular speed of the rod at time t? How does the work required to accelerate the rod from rest to this angular speed compare to the rod's kinetic energy at time t?
4. At time t, does the point on the rod farthest from the axis have a centripetal acceleration? A tangential acceleration? Why or why not?

EXECUTE

5. Do the integration required to find the moment of inertia.
6. Use your result from step 5 to calculate the work done in time t to accelerate the rod from rest.
7. Find the linear acceleration components for the point in question at time t. Use these to find the magnitude of the acceleration.

EVALUATE

8. Check your results for the special cases $h = 0$ (the axis passes through one end of the rod) and $h = L/2$ (the axis passes through the middle of the rod). Are these limits consistent with Table 9.2? With the parallel-axis theorem?
9. Is the acceleration magnitude from step 7 constant? Would you expect it to be?

9.25 A thin rod with an axis through O.

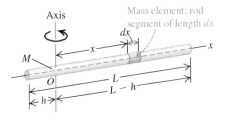

Problems

For assigned homework and other learning materials, go to MasteringPhysics®. (MP)

•, ••, •••: Difficulty levels. CP: Cumulative problems incorporating material from earlier chapters. CALC: Problems requiring calculus.
DATA: Problems involving real data, scientific evidence, experimental design, and/or statistical reasoning. BIO: Biosciences problems.

DISCUSSION QUESTIONS

Q9.1 Which of the following formulas is valid if the angular acceleration of an object is *not* constant? Explain your reasoning in each case. (a) $v = r\omega$; (b) $a_{tan} = r\alpha$; (c) $\omega = \omega_0 + \alpha t$; (d) $a_{tan} = r\omega^2$; (e) $K = \frac{1}{2}I\omega^2$.

Q9.2 A diatomic molecule can be modeled as two point masses, m_1 and m_2, slightly separated (**Fig. Q9.2**). If the molecule is oriented along the y-axis, it has kinetic energy K when it spins about the x-axis. What will its kinetic energy (in terms of K) be if it spins at the same angular speed about (a) the z-axis and (b) the y-axis?

Figure Q9.2

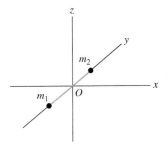

Q9.3 What is the difference between tangential and radial acceleration for a point on a rotating body?

Q9.4 In **Fig. Q9.4**, all points on the chain have the same linear speed. Is the magnitude of the linear acceleration also the same for all points on the chain? How are the angular accelerations of the two sprockets related? Explain.

Figure Q9.4

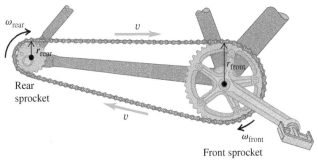

Q9.5 In Fig. Q9.4, how are the radial accelerations of points at the teeth of the two sprockets related? Explain.

Q9.6 A flywheel rotates with constant angular velocity. Does a point on its rim have a tangential acceleration? A radial acceleration?

Are these accelerations constant in magnitude? In direction? In each case give your reasoning.

Q9.7 What is the purpose of the spin cycle of a washing machine? Explain in terms of acceleration components.

Q9.8 You are designing a flywheel to store kinetic energy. If all of the following uniform objects have the same mass and same angular velocity, which one will store the greatest amount of kinetic energy? Which will store the least? Explain. (a) A solid sphere of diameter D rotating about a diameter; (b) a solid cylinder of diameter D rotating about an axis perpendicular to each face through its center; (c) a thin-walled hollow cylinder of diameter D rotating about an axis perpendicular to the plane of the circular face at its center; (d) a solid, thin bar of length D rotating about an axis perpendicular to it at its center.

Q9.9 Can you think of a body that has the same moment of inertia for all possible axes? If so, give an example, and if not, explain why this is not possible. Can you think of a body that has the same moment of inertia for all axes passing through a certain point? If so, give an example and indicate where the point is located.

Q9.10 To maximize the moment of inertia of a flywheel while minimizing its weight, what shape and distribution of mass should it have? Explain.

Q9.11 How might you determine experimentally the moment of inertia of an irregularly shaped body about a given axis?

Q9.12 A cylindrical body has mass M and radius R. Can the mass be distributed within the body in such a way that its moment of inertia about its axis of symmetry is greater than MR^2? Explain.

Q9.13 Describe how you could use part (b) of Table 9.2 to derive the result in part (d).

Q9.14 A hollow spherical shell of radius R that is rotating about an axis through its center has rotational kinetic energy K. If you want to modify this sphere so that it has three times as much kinetic energy at the same angular speed while keeping the same mass, what should be its radius in terms of R?

Q9.15 For the equations for I given in parts (a) and (b) of Table 9.2 to be valid, must the rod have a circular cross section? Is there any restriction on the size of the cross section for these equations to apply? Explain.

Q9.16 In part (d) of Table 9.2, the thickness of the plate must be much less than a for the expression given for I to apply. But in part (c), the expression given for I applies no matter how thick the plate is. Explain.

Q9.17 Two identical balls, A and B, are each attached to very light string, and each string is wrapped around the rim of a frictionless pulley of mass M. The only difference is that the pulley for ball A is a solid disk, while the one for ball B is a hollow disk, like part (e) in Table 9.2. If both balls are released from rest and fall the same distance, which one will have more kinetic energy, or will they have the same kinetic energy? Explain your reasoning.

Q9.18 An elaborate pulley consists of four identical balls at the ends of spokes extending out from a rotating drum (**Fig. Q9.18**). A box is connected to a light, thin rope wound around the rim of the drum. When it is released from rest, the box acquires a speed V after having fallen a distance d. Now the four balls are moved inward closer to the drum, and the box is again released from rest. After it has fallen a distance d,

Figure **Q9.18**

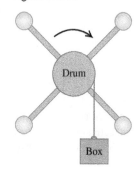

Drum

Box

will its speed be equal to V, greater than V, or less than V? Show or explain why.

Q9.19 You can use any angular measure—radians, degrees, or revolutions—in some of the equations in Chapter 9, but you can use only radian measure in others. Identify those for which using radians is necessary and those for which it is not, and in each case give your reasoning.

Q9.20 When calculating the moment of inertia of an object, can we treat all its mass as if it were concentrated at the center of mass of the object? Justify your answer.

Q9.21 A wheel is rotating about an axis perpendicular to the plane of the wheel and passing through the center of the wheel. The angular speed of the wheel is increasing at a constant rate. Point A is on the rim of the wheel and point B is midway between the rim and center of the wheel. For each of the following quantities, is its magnitude larger at point A or at point B, or is it the same at both points? (a) angular speed; (b) tangential speed; (c) angular acceleration; (d) tangential acceleration; (e) radial acceleration. Justify each answer.

Q9.22 Estimate your own moment of inertia about a vertical axis through the center of the top of your head when you are standing up straight with your arms outstretched. Make reasonable approximations and measure or estimate necessary quantities.

EXERCISES

Section 9.1 Angular Velocity and Acceleration

9.1 • (a) What angle in radians is subtended by an arc 1.50 m long on the circumference of a circle of radius 2.50 m? What is this angle in degrees? (b) An arc 14.0 cm long on the circumference of a circle subtends an angle of $128°$. What is the radius of the circle? (c) The angle between two radii of a circle with radius 1.50 m is 0.700 rad. What length of arc is intercepted on the circumference of the circle by the two radii?

9.2 • An airplane propeller is rotating at 1900 rpm (rev/min). (a) Compute the propeller's angular velocity in rad/s. (b) How many seconds does it take for the propeller to turn through $35°$?

9.3 • CP CALC The angular velocity of a flywheel obeys the equation $\omega_z(t) = A + Bt^2$, where t is in seconds and A and B are constants having numerical values 2.75 (for A) and 1.50 (for B). (a) What are the units of A and B if ω_z is in rad/s? (b) What is the angular acceleration of the wheel at (i) $t = 0$ and (ii) $t = 5.00$ s? (c) Through what angle does the flywheel turn during the first 2.00 s? (*Hint:* See Section 2.6.)

9.4 •• CALC A fan blade rotates with angular velocity given by $\omega_z(t) = \gamma - \beta t^2$, where $\gamma = 5.00$ rad/s and $\beta = 0.800$ rad/s^3. (a) Calculate the angular acceleration as a function of time. (b) Calculate the instantaneous angular acceleration α_z at $t = 3.00$ s and the average angular acceleration $\alpha_{av\text{-}z}$ for the time interval $t = 0$ to $t = 3.00$ s. How do these two quantities compare? If they are different, why?

9.5 •• CALC A child is pushing a merry-go-round. The angle through which the merry-go-round has turned varies with time according to $\theta(t) = \gamma t + \beta t^3$, where $\gamma = 0.400$ rad/s and $\beta = 0.0120$ rad/s^3. (a) Calculate the angular velocity of the merry-go-round as a function of time. (b) What is the initial value of the angular velocity? (c) Calculate the instantaneous value of the angular velocity ω_z at $t = 5.00$ s and the average angular velocity $\omega_{av\text{-}z}$ for the time interval $t = 0$ to $t = 5.00$ s. Show that $\omega_{av\text{-}z}$ is *not* equal to the average of the instantaneous angular velocities at $t = 0$ and $t = 5.00$ s, and explain.

9.6 • CALC At $t = 0$ the current to a dc electric motor is reversed, resulting in an angular displacement of the motor shaft given by $\theta(t) = (250 \text{ rad/s})t - (20.0 \text{ rad/s}^2)t^2 - (1.50 \text{ rad/s}^3)t^3$. (a) At what time is the angular velocity of the motor shaft zero? (b) Calculate the angular acceleration at the instant that the motor shaft has zero angular velocity. (c) How many revolutions does the motor shaft turn through between the time when the current is reversed and the instant when the angular velocity is zero? (d) How fast was the motor shaft rotating at $t = 0$, when the current was reversed? (e) Calculate the average angular velocity for the time period from $t = 0$ to the time calculated in part (a).

9.7 • CALC The angle θ through which a disk drive turns is given by $\theta(t) = a + bt - ct^3$, where a, b, and c are constants, t is in seconds, and θ is in radians. When $t = 0$, $\theta = \pi/4$ rad and the angular velocity is 2.00 rad/s. When $t = 1.50$ s, the angular acceleration is 1.25 rad/s². (a) Find a, b, and c, including their units. (b) What is the angular acceleration when $\theta = \pi/4$ rad? (c) What are θ and the angular velocity when the angular acceleration is 3.50 rad/s²?

9.8 • A wheel is rotating about an axis that is in the z-direction. The angular velocity ω_z is -6.00 rad/s at $t = 0$, increases linearly with time, and is $+4.00$ rad/s at $t = 7.00$ s. We have taken counterclockwise rotation to be positive. (a) Is the angular acceleration during this time interval positive or negative? (b) During what time interval is the speed of the wheel increasing? Decreasing? (c) What is the angular displacement of the wheel at $t = 7.00$ s?

Section 9.2 Rotation with Constant Angular Acceleration

9.9 • A bicycle wheel has an initial angular velocity of 1.50 rad/s. (a) If its angular acceleration is constant and equal to 0.200 rad/s², what is its angular velocity at $t = 2.50$ s? (b) Through what angle has the wheel turned between $t = 0$ and $t = 2.50$ s?

9.10 •• An electric fan is turned off, and its angular velocity decreases uniformly from 500 rev/min to 200 rev/min in 4.00 s. (a) Find the angular acceleration in rev/s² and the number of revolutions made by the motor in the 4.00-s interval. (b) How many more seconds are required for the fan to come to rest if the angular acceleration remains constant at the value calculated in part (a)?

9.11 •• The rotating blade of a blender turns with constant angular acceleration 1.50 rad/s². (a) How much time does it take to reach an angular velocity of 36.0 rad/s, starting from rest? (b) Through how many revolutions does the blade turn in this time interval?

9.12 • (a) Derive Eq. (9.12) by combining Eqs. (9.7) and (9.11) to eliminate t. (b) The angular velocity of an airplane propeller increases from 12.0 rad/s to 16.0 rad/s while turning through 7.00 rad. What is the angular acceleration in rad/s²?

9.13 •• A turntable rotates with a constant 2.25 rad/s² angular acceleration. After 4.00 s it has rotated through an angle of 30.0 rad. What was the angular velocity of the wheel at the beginning of the 4.00-s interval?

9.14 • A circular saw blade 0.200 m in diameter starts from rest. In 6.00 s it accelerates with constant angular acceleration to an angular velocity of 140 rad/s. Find the angular acceleration and the angle through which the blade has turned.

9.15 •• A high-speed flywheel in a motor is spinning at 500 rpm when a power failure suddenly occurs. The flywheel has mass 40.0 kg and diameter 75.0 cm. The power is off for 30.0 s, and during this time the flywheel slows due to friction in its axle bearings. During the time the power is off, the flywheel makes 200 complete revolutions. (a) At what rate is the flywheel spinning when the power comes back on? (b) How long after the beginning of the power failure would it have taken the flywheel to stop if the power had not come back on, and how many revolutions would the wheel have made during this time?

9.16 •• At $t = 0$ a grinding wheel has an angular velocity of 24.0 rad/s. It has a constant angular acceleration of 30.0 rad/s² until a circuit breaker trips at $t = 2.00$ s. From then on, it turns through 432 rad as it coasts to a stop at constant angular acceleration. (a) Through what total angle did the wheel turn between $t = 0$ and the time it stopped? (b) At what time did it stop? (c) What was its acceleration as it slowed down?

9.17 •• A safety device brings the blade of a power mower from an initial angular speed of ω_1 to rest in 1.00 revolution. At the same constant acceleration, how many revolutions would it take the blade to come to rest from an initial angular speed ω_3 that was three times as great, $\omega_3 = 3\omega_1$?

Section 9.3 Relating Linear and Angular Kinematics

9.18 • In a charming 19th-century hotel, an old-style elevator is connected to a counterweight by a cable that passes over a rotating disk 2.50 m in diameter (**Fig. E9.18**). The elevator is raised and lowered by turning the disk, and the cable does not slip on the rim of the disk but turns with it. (a) At how many rpm must the disk turn to raise the elevator at 25.0 cm/s? (b) To start the elevator moving, it must be accelerated at $\frac{1}{8}g$. What must be the angular acceleration of the disk, in rad/s²? (c) Through what angle (in radians and degrees) has the disk turned when it has raised the elevator 3.25 m between floors?

Figure **E9.18**

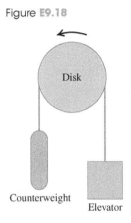

Disk

Counterweight

Elevator

9.19 • Using Appendix F, along with the fact that the earth spins on its axis once per day, calculate (a) the earth's orbital angular speed (in rad/s) due to its motion around the sun, (b) its angular speed (in rad/s) due to its axial spin, (c) the tangential speed of the earth around the sun (assuming a circular orbit), (d) the tangential speed of a point on the earth's equator due to the planet's axial spin, and (e) the radial and tangential acceleration components of the point in part (d).

9.20 • **Compact Disc.** A compact disc (CD) stores music in a coded pattern of tiny pits 10^{-7} m deep. The pits are arranged in a track that spirals outward toward the rim of the disc; the inner and outer radii of this spiral are 25.0 mm and 58.0 mm, respectively. As the disc spins inside a CD player, the track is scanned at a constant *linear* speed of 1.25 m/s. (a) What is the angular speed of the CD when the innermost part of the track is scanned? The outermost part of the track? (b) The maximum playing time of a CD is 74.0 min. What would be the length of the track on such a maximum-duration CD if it were stretched out in a straight line? (c) What is the average angular acceleration of a maximum-duration CD during its 74.0-min playing time? Take the direction of rotation of the disc to be positive.

9.21 •• A wheel of diameter 40.0 cm starts from rest and rotates with a constant angular acceleration of 3.00 rad/s². Compute the radial acceleration of a point on the rim for the instant the wheel completes its second revolution from the relationship (a) $a_{rad} = \omega^2 r$ and (b) $a_{rad} = v^2/r$.

9.22 ·· You are to design a rotating cylindrical axle to lift 800-N buckets of cement from the ground to a rooftop 78.0 m above the ground. The buckets will be attached to a hook on the free end of a cable that wraps around the rim of the axle; as the axle turns, the buckets will rise. (a) What should the diameter of the axle be in order to raise the buckets at a steady 2.00 cm/s when it is turning at 7.5 rpm? (b) If instead the axle must give the buckets an upward acceleration of 0.400 m/s², what should the angular acceleration of the axle be?

9.23 · A flywheel with a radius of 0.300 m starts from rest and accelerates with a constant angular acceleration of 0.600 rad/s². Compute the magnitude of the tangential acceleration, the radial acceleration, and the resultant acceleration of a point on its rim (a) at the start; (b) after it has turned through 60.0°; (c) after it has turned through 120.0°.

9.24 ·· An electric turntable 0.750 m in diameter is rotating about a fixed axis with an initial angular velocity of 0.250 rev/s and a constant angular acceleration of 0.900 rev/s². (a) Compute the angular velocity of the turntable after 0.200 s. (b) Through how many revolutions has the turntable spun in this time interval? (c) What is the tangential speed of a point on the rim of the turntable at $t = 0.200$ s? (d) What is the magnitude of the *resultant* acceleration of a point on the rim at $t = 0.200$ s?

9.25 ·· **Centrifuge.** An advertisement claims that a centrifuge takes up only 0.127 m of bench space but can produce a radial acceleration of 3000g at 5000 rev/min. Calculate the required radius of the centrifuge. Is the claim realistic?

9.26 · At $t = 3.00$ s a point on the rim of a 0.200-m-radius wheel has a tangential speed of 50.0 m/s as the wheel slows down with a tangential acceleration of constant magnitude 10.0 m/s². (a) Calculate the wheel's constant angular acceleration. (b) Calculate the angular velocities at $t = 3.00$ s and $t = 0$. (c) Through what angle did the wheel turn between $t = 0$ and $t = 3.00$ s? (d) At what time will the radial acceleration equal g?

9.27 · **Electric Drill.** According to the shop manual, when drilling a 12.7-mm-diameter hole in wood, plastic, or aluminum, a drill should have a speed of 1250 rev/min. For a 12.7-mm-diameter drill bit turning at a constant 1250 rev/min, find (a) the maximum linear speed of any part of the bit and (b) the maximum radial acceleration of any part of the bit.

Section 9.4 Energy in Rotational Motion

9.28 · Four small spheres, each of which you can regard as a point of mass 0.200 kg, are arranged in a square 0.400 m on a side and connected by extremely light rods (**Fig. E9.28**). Find the moment of inertia of the system about an axis (a) through the center of the square, perpendicular to its plane (an axis through point O in the figure); (b) bisecting two opposite sides of the square (an axis along the line AB in the figure); (c) that passes through the centers of the upper left and lower right spheres and through point O.

Figure E9.28

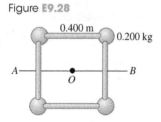

9.29 · Calculate the moment of inertia of each of the following uniform objects about the axes indicated. Consult Table 9.2 as needed. (a) A thin 2.50-kg rod of length 75.0 cm, about an axis perpendicular to it and passing through (i) one end and (ii) its center, and (iii) about an axis parallel to the rod and passing through it. (b) A 3.00-kg sphere 38.0 cm in diameter, about an axis through its center, if the sphere is (i) solid and (ii) a thin-walled hollow shell. (c) An 8.00-kg cylinder, of length 19.5 cm and diameter 12.0 cm, about the central axis of the cylinder, if the cylinder is (i) thin-walled and hollow, and (ii) solid.

9.30 ·· Small blocks, each with mass m, are clamped at the ends and at the center of a rod of length L and negligible mass. Compute the moment of inertia of the system about an axis perpendicular to the rod and passing through (a) the center of the rod and (b) a point one-fourth of the length from one end.

9.31 · A uniform bar has two small balls glued to its ends. The bar is 2.00 m long and has mass 4.00 kg, while the balls each have mass 0.300 kg and can be treated as point masses. Find the moment of inertia of this combination about an axis (a) perpendicular to the bar through its center; (b) perpendicular to the bar through one of the balls; (c) parallel to the bar through both balls; and (d) parallel to the bar and 0.500 m from it.

9.32 ·· You are a project manager for a manufacturing company. One of the machine parts on the assembly line is a thin, uniform rod that is 60.0 cm long and has mass 0.400 kg. (a) What is the moment of inertia of this rod for an axis at its center, perpendicular to the rod? (b) One of your engineers has proposed to reduce the moment of inertia by bending the rod at its center into a V-shape, with a 60.0° angle at its vertex. What would be the moment of inertia of this bent rod about an axis perpendicular to the plane of the V at its vertex?

9.33 ·· A wagon wheel is constructed as shown in **Fig. E9.33**. The radius of the wheel is 0.300 m, and the rim has mass 1.40 kg. Each of the eight spokes that lie along a diameter and are 0.300 m long has mass 0.280 kg. What is the moment of inertia of the wheel about an axis through its center and perpendicular to the plane of the wheel? (Use Table 9.2.)

Figure **E9.33**

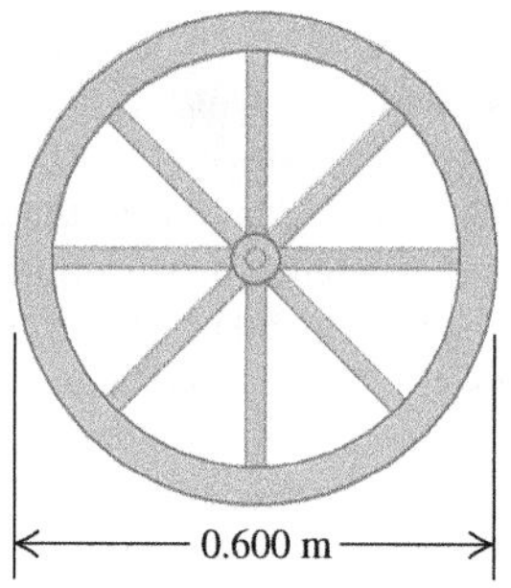

![wagon wheel with eight spokes, overall diameter labeled 0.600 m]

0.600 m

9.34 ·· An airplane propeller is 2.08 m in length (from tip to tip) with mass 117 kg and is rotating at 2400 rpm (rev/min) about an axis through its center. You can model the propeller as a slender rod. (a) What is its rotational kinetic energy? (b) Suppose that, due to weight constraints, you had to reduce the propeller's mass to 75.0% of its original mass, but you still needed to keep the same size and kinetic energy. What would its angular speed have to be, in rpm?

9.35 ·· A compound disk of outside diameter 140.0 cm is made up of a uniform solid disk of radius 50.0 cm and area density 3.00 g/cm² surrounded by a concentric ring of inner radius 50.0 cm, outer radius 70.0 cm, and area density 2.00 g/cm². Find the moment of inertia of this object about an axis perpendicular to the plane of the object and passing through its center.

9.36 · A wheel is turning about an axis through its center with constant angular acceleration. Starting from rest, at $t = 0$, the wheel turns through 8.20 revolutions in 12.0 s. At $t = 12.0$ s the kinetic energy of the wheel is 36.0 J. For an axis through its center, what is the moment of inertia of the wheel?

9.37 · A uniform sphere with mass 28.0 kg and radius 0.380 m is rotating at constant angular velocity about a stationary axis that lies along a diameter of the sphere. If the kinetic energy of the sphere is 236 J, what is the tangential velocity of a point on the rim of the sphere?

9.38 •• A hollow spherical shell has mass 8.20 kg and radius 0.220 m. It is initially at rest and then rotates about a stationary axis that lies along a diameter with a constant acceleration of 0.890 rad/s^2. What is the kinetic energy of the shell after it has turned through 6.00 rev?

9.39 •• The flywheel of a gasoline engine is required to give up 500 J of kinetic energy while its angular velocity decreases from 650 rev/min to 520 rev/min. What moment of inertia is required?

9.40 •• You need to design an industrial turntable that is 60.0 cm in diameter and has a kinetic energy of 0.250 J when turning at 45.0 rpm (rev/min). (a) What must be the moment of inertia of the turntable about the rotation axis? (b) If your workshop makes this turntable in the shape of a uniform solid disk, what must be its mass?

9.41 •• Energy is to be stored in a 70.0-kg flywheel in the shape of a uniform solid disk with radius $R = 1.20$ m. To prevent structural failure of the flywheel, the maximum allowed radial acceleration of a point on its rim is 3500 m/s^2. What is the maximum kinetic energy that can be stored in the flywheel?

9.42 • A light, flexible rope is wrapped several times around a *hollow* cylinder, with a weight of 40.0 N and a radius of 0.25 m, that rotates without friction about a fixed horizontal axis. The cylinder is attached to the axle by spokes of a negligible moment of inertia. The cylinder is initially at rest. The free end of the rope is pulled with a constant force P for a distance of 5.00 m, at which point the end of the rope is moving at 6.00 m/s. If the rope does not slip on the cylinder, what is P?

9.43 •• A frictionless pulley has the shape of a uniform solid disk of mass 2.50 kg and radius 20.0 cm. A 1.50-kg stone is attached to a very light wire that is wrapped around the rim of the pulley (**Fig. E9.43**), and the system is released from rest. (a) How far must the stone fall so that the pulley has 4.50 J of kinetic energy? (b) What percent of the total kinetic energy does the pulley have?

Figure **E9.43**

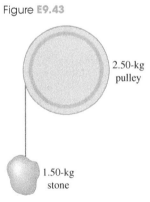

2.50-kg pulley

1.50-kg stone

9.44 •• A bucket of mass m is tied to a massless cable that is wrapped around the outer rim of a frictionless uniform pulley of radius R, similar to the system shown in Fig. E9.43. In terms of the stated variables, what must be the moment of inertia of the pulley so that it always has half as much kinetic energy as the bucket?

9.45 •• CP A thin, light wire is wrapped around the rim of a wheel (**Fig. E9.45**). The wheel rotates without friction about a stationary horizontal axis that passes through the center of the wheel. The wheel is a uniform disk with radius $R = 0.280$ m. An object of mass $m = 4.20$ kg is suspended from the free end of the wire. The system is released from rest and the suspended object descends with constant acceleration. If the suspended object moves downward a distance of 3.00 m in 2.00 s, what is the mass of the wheel?

Figure **E9.45**

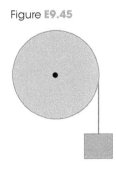

9.46 •• A uniform 2.00-m ladder of mass 9.00 kg is leaning against a vertical wall while making an angle of 53.0° with the floor. A worker pushes the ladder up against the wall until it is vertical. What is the increase in the gravitational potential energy of the ladder?

9.47 •• **How *I* Scales.** If we multiply all the design dimensions of an object by a scaling factor f, its volume and mass will be multiplied by f^3. (a) By what factor will its moment of inertia be multiplied? (b) If a $\frac{1}{48}$-scale model has a rotational kinetic energy of 2.5 J, what will be the kinetic energy for the full-scale object of the same material rotating at the same angular velocity?

Section 9.5 Parallel-Axis Theorem

9.48 •• Find the moment of inertia of a hoop (a thin-walled, hollow ring) with mass M and radius R about an axis perpendicular to the hoop's plane at an edge.

9.49 •• About what axis will a uniform, balsa-wood sphere have the same moment of inertia as does a thin-walled, hollow, lead sphere of the same mass and radius, with the axis along a diameter?

9.50 • (a) For the thin rectangular plate shown in part (d) of Table 9.2, find the moment of inertia about an axis that lies in the plane of the plate, passes through the center of the plate, and is parallel to the axis shown. (b) Find the moment of inertia of the plate for an axis that lies in the plane of the plate, passes through the center of the plate, and is perpendicular to the axis in part (a).

9.51 •• A thin, rectangular sheet of metal has mass M and sides of length a and b. Use the parallel-axis theorem to calculate the moment of inertia of the sheet for an axis that is perpendicular to the plane of the sheet and that passes through one corner of the sheet.

9.52 •• A thin uniform rod of mass M and length L is bent at its center so that the two segments are now perpendicular to each other. Find its moment of inertia about an axis perpendicular to its plane and passing through (a) the point where the two segments meet and (b) the midpoint of the line connecting its two ends.

Section 9.6 Moment-of-Inertia Calculations

9.53 •• CALC Use Eq. (9.20) to calculate the moment of inertia of a uniform, solid disk with mass M and radius R for an axis perpendicular to the plane of the disk and passing through its center.

9.54 • CALC Use Eq. (9.20) to calculate the moment of inertia of a slender, uniform rod with mass M and length L about an axis at one end, perpendicular to the rod.

9.55 •• CALC A slender rod with length L has a mass per unit length that varies with distance from the left end, where $x = 0$, according to $dm/dx = \gamma x$, where γ has units of kg/m^2. (a) Calculate the total mass of the rod in terms of γ and L. (b) Use Eq. (9.20) to calculate the moment of inertia of the rod for an axis at the left end, perpendicular to the rod. Use the expression you derived in part (a) to express I in terms of M and L. How does your result compare to that for a uniform rod? Explain. (c) Repeat part (b) for an axis at the right end of the rod. How do the results for parts (b) and (c) compare? Explain.

PROBLEMS

9.56 •• CALC A uniform disk with radius $R = 0.400$ m and mass 30.0 kg rotates in a horizontal plane on a frictionless vertical axle that passes through the center of the disk. The angle through which the disk has turned varies with time according to $\theta(t) = (1.10 \text{ rad/s})t + (6.30 \text{ rad/s}^2)t^2$. What is the resultant linear acceleration of a point on the rim of the disk at the instant when the disk has turned through 0.100 rev?

9.57 •• **CP** A circular saw blade with radius 0.120 m starts from rest and turns in a vertical plane with a constant angular acceleration of 2.00 rev/s². After the blade has turned through 155 rev, a small piece of the blade breaks loose from the top of the blade. After the piece breaks loose, it travels with a velocity that is initially horizontal and equal to the tangential velocity of the rim of the blade. The piece travels a vertical distance of 0.820 m to the floor. How far does the piece travel horizontally, from where it broke off the blade until it strikes the floor?

9.58 • **CALC** A roller in a printing press turns through an angle $\theta(t)$ given by $\theta(t) = \gamma t^2 - \beta t^3$, where $\gamma = 3.20 \text{ rad/s}^2$ and $\beta = 0.500 \text{ rad/s}^3$. (a) Calculate the angular velocity of the roller as a function of time. (b) Calculate the angular acceleration of the roller as a function of time. (c) What is the maximum positive angular velocity, and at what value of t does it occur?

9.59 •• **CP CALC** A disk of radius 25.0 cm is free to turn about an axle perpendicular to it through its center. It has very thin but strong string wrapped around its rim, and the string is attached to a ball that is pulled tangentially away from the rim of the disk (**Fig. P9.59**). The pull increases in magnitude and produces an acceleration of the ball that obeys the equation $a(t) = At$, where t is in seconds and A is a constant. The cylinder starts from rest, and at the end of the third second, the ball's acceleration is 1.80 m/s². (a) Find A. (b) Express the angular acceleration of the disk as a function of time. (c) How much time after the disk has begun to turn does it reach an angular speed of 15.0 rad/s? (d) Through what angle has the disk turned just as it reaches 15.0 rad/s? (*Hint:* See Section 2.6.)

Figure **P9.59**

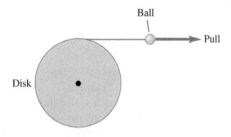

9.60 •• You are designing a rotating metal flywheel that will be used to store energy. The flywheel is to be a uniform disk with radius 25.0 cm. Starting from rest at $t = 0$, the flywheel rotates with constant angular acceleration 3.00 rad/s² about an axis perpendicular to the flywheel at its center. If the flywheel has a density (mass per unit volume) of 8600 kg/m³, what thickness must it have to store 800 J of kinetic energy at $t = 8.00$ s?

9.61 •• You must design a device for shooting a small marble vertically upward. The marble is in a small cup that is attached to the rim of a wheel of radius 0.260 m; the cup is covered by a lid. The wheel starts from rest and rotates about a horizontal axis that is perpendicular to the wheel at its center. After the wheel has turned through 20.0 rev, the cup is the same height as the center of the wheel. At this point in the motion, the lid opens and the marble travels vertically upward to a maximum height h above the center of the wheel. If the wheel rotates with a constant angular acceleration α, what value of α is required for the marble to reach a height of $h = 12.0$ m?

9.62 •• Engineers are designing a system by which a falling mass m imparts kinetic energy to a rotating uniform drum to which it is attached by thin, very light wire wrapped around the rim of the drum (**Fig. P9.62**). There is no appreciable friction in the axle of the drum, and everything starts from rest. This system is being tested on earth, but it is to be used on Mars, where the acceleration due to gravity is 3.71 m/s². In the earth tests, when m is set to 15.0 kg and allowed to fall through 5.00 m, it gives 250.0 J of kinetic energy to the drum. (a) If the system is operated on Mars, through what distance would the 15.0-kg mass have to fall to give the same amount of kinetic energy to the drum? (b) How fast would the 15.0-kg mass be moving on Mars just as the drum gained 250.0 J of kinetic energy?

Figure **P9.62**

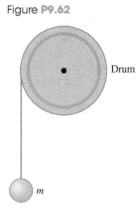

Drum

m

9.63 • A vacuum cleaner belt is looped over a shaft of radius 0.45 cm and a wheel of radius 1.80 cm. The arrangement of the belt, shaft, and wheel is similar to that of the chain and sprockets in Fig. Q9.4. The motor turns the shaft at 60.0 rev/s and the moving belt turns the wheel, which in turn is connected by another shaft to the roller that beats the dirt out of the rug being vacuumed. Assume that the belt doesn't slip on either the shaft or the wheel. (a) What is the speed of a point on the belt? (b) What is the angular velocity of the wheel, in rad/s?

9.64 •• The motor of a table saw is rotating at 3450 rev/min. A pulley attached to the motor shaft drives a second pulley of half the diameter by means of a V-belt. A circular saw blade of diameter 0.208 m is mounted on the same rotating shaft as the second pulley. (a) The operator is careless and the blade catches and throws back a small piece of wood. This piece of wood moves with linear speed equal to the tangential speed of the rim of the blade. What is this speed? (b) Calculate the radial acceleration of points on the outer edge of the blade to see why sawdust doesn't stick to its teeth.

9.65 ••• While riding a multispeed bicycle, the rider can select the radius of the rear sprocket that is fixed to the rear axle. The front sprocket of a bicycle has radius 12.0 cm. If the angular speed of the front sprocket is 0.600 rev/s, what is the radius of the rear sprocket for which the tangential speed of a point on the rim of the rear wheel will be 5.00 m/s? The rear wheel has radius 0.330 m.

9.66 ••• A computer disk drive is turned on starting from rest and has constant angular acceleration. If it took 0.0865 s for the drive to make its *second* complete revolution, (a) how long did it take to make the first complete revolution, and (b) what is its angular acceleration, in rad/s²?

9.67 ••• It has been argued that power plants should make use of off-peak hours (such as late at night) to generate mechanical energy and store it until it is needed during peak load times, such as the middle of the day. One suggestion has been to store the energy in large flywheels spinning on nearly frictionless ball bearings. Consider a flywheel made of iron (density 7800 kg/m³) in the shape of a 10.0-cm-thick uniform disk. (a) What would the diameter of such a disk need to be if it is to store 10.0 megajoules of kinetic energy when spinning at 90.0 rpm about an axis perpendicular to the disk at its center? (b) What would be the centripetal acceleration of a point on its rim when spinning at this rate?

9.68 •• A uniform disk has radius R_0 and mass M_0. Its moment of inertia for an axis perpendicular to the plane of the disk at the disk's center is $\frac{1}{2}M_0R_0^2$. You have been asked to halve the disk's moment of inertia by cutting out a circular piece at the center of the disk. In terms of R_0, what should be the radius of the circular piece that you remove?

9.69 •• **Measuring *I*.** As an intern at an engineering firm, you are asked to measure the moment of inertia of a large wheel for rotation about an axis perpendicular to the wheel at its center. You measure the diameter of the wheel to be 0.640 m. Then you mount the wheel on frictionless bearings on a horizontal frictionless axle at the center of the wheel. You wrap a light rope around the wheel and hang an 8.20-kg block of wood from the free end of the rope, as in Fig. E9.45. You release the system from rest and find that the block descends 12.0 m in 4.00 s. What is the moment of inertia of the wheel for this axis?

9.70 ••• A uniform, solid disk with mass *m* and radius *R* is pivoted about a horizontal axis through its center. A small object of the same mass *m* is glued to the rim of the disk. If the disk is released from rest with the small object at the end of a horizontal radius, find the angular speed when the small object is directly below the axis.

9.71 •• **CP** A meter stick with a mass of 0.180 kg is pivoted about one end so it can rotate without friction about a horizontal axis. The meter stick is held in a horizontal position and released. As it swings through the vertical, calculate (a) the change in gravitational potential energy that has occurred; (b) the angular speed of the stick; (c) the linear speed of the end of the stick opposite the axis. (d) Compare the answer in part (c) to the speed of a particle that has fallen 1.00 m, starting from rest.

9.72 •• A physics student of mass 43.0 kg is standing at the edge of the flat roof of a building, 12.0 m above the sidewalk. An unfriendly dog is running across the roof toward her. Next to her is a large wheel mounted on a horizontal axle at its center. The wheel, used to lift objects from the ground to the roof, has a light crank attached to it and a light rope wrapped around it; the free end of the rope hangs over the edge of the roof. The student grabs the end of the rope and steps off the roof. If the wheel has radius 0.300 m and a moment of inertia of 9.60 kg·m² for rotation about the axle, how long does it take her to reach the sidewalk, and how fast will she be moving just before she lands? Ignore friction.

9.73 ••• A slender rod is 80.0 cm long and has mass 0.120 kg. A small 0.0200-kg sphere is welded to one end of the rod, and a small 0.0500-kg sphere is welded to the other end. The rod, pivoting about a stationary, frictionless axis at its center, is held horizontal and released from rest. What is the linear speed of the 0.0500-kg sphere as it passes through its lowest point?

9.74 •• Exactly one turn of a flexible rope with mass *m* is wrapped around a uniform cylinder with mass *M* and radius *R*. The cylinder rotates without friction about a horizontal axle along the cylinder axis. One end of the rope is attached to the cylinder. The cylinder starts with angular speed ω_0. After one revolution of the cylinder the rope has unwrapped and, at this instant, hangs vertically down, tangent to the cylinder. Find the angular speed of the cylinder and the linear speed of the lower end of the rope at this time. Ignore the thickness of the rope. [*Hint:* Use Eq. (9.18).]

9.75 • The pulley in **Fig. P9.75** has radius *R* and a moment of inertia *I*. The rope does not slip over the pulley, and the pulley spins on a frictionless axle. The coefficient of kinetic friction between block *A* and the tabletop is μ_k. The system is released from rest, and block *B* descends. Block *A* has mass m_A and block *B* has mass m_B. Use energy methods to calculate the speed of block *B* as a function of the distance *d* that it has descended.

Figure **P9.75**

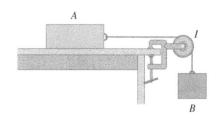

9.76 •• The pulley in **Fig. P9.76** has radius 0.160 m and moment of inertia 0.380 kg·m². The rope does not slip on the pulley rim. Use energy methods to calculate the speed of the 4.00-kg block just before it strikes the floor.

Figure **P9.76**

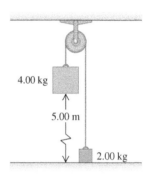

4.00 kg

5.00 m

2.00 kg

9.77 •• Two metal disks, one with radius $R_1 = 2.50$ cm and mass $M_1 = 0.80$ kg and the other with radius $R_2 = 5.00$ cm and mass $M_2 = 1.60$ kg, are welded together and mounted on a frictionless axis through their common center (**Fig. P9.77**). (a) What is the total moment of inertia of the two disks? (b) A light string is wrapped around the edge of the smaller disk, and a 1.50-kg block is suspended from the free end of the string. If the block is released from rest at a distance of 2.00 m above the floor, what is its speed just before it strikes the floor? (c) Repeat part (b), this time with the string wrapped around the edge of the larger disk. In which case is the final speed of the block greater? Explain.

Figure **P9.77**

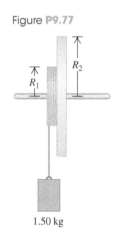

R_2

R_1

1.50 kg

9.78 •• A thin, light wire is wrapped around the rim of a wheel as shown in Fig. E9.45. The wheel rotates about a stationary horizontal axle that passes through the center of the wheel. The wheel has radius 0.180 m and moment of inertia for rotation about the axle of $I = 0.480$ kg·m². A small block with mass 0.340 kg is suspended from the free end of the wire. When the system is released from rest, the block descends with constant acceleration. The bearings in the wheel at the axle are rusty, so friction there does −9.00 J of work as the block descends 3.00 m. What is the magnitude of the angular velocity of the wheel after the block has descended 3.00 m?

9.79 ••• In the system shown in Fig. 9.17, a 12.0-kg mass is released from rest and falls, causing the uniform 10.0-kg cylinder of diameter 30.0 cm to turn about a frictionless axle through its center. How far will the mass have to descend to give the cylinder 480 J of kinetic energy?

9.80 • In **Fig. P9.80**, the cylinder and pulley turn without friction about stationary horizontal axles that pass through their centers. A light rope is wrapped around the cylinder, passes over the pulley, and has a 3.00-kg box suspended from its free end. There is no slipping between the rope and the pulley surface. The uniform cylinder has mass 5.00 kg and radius 40.0 cm. The pulley is a uniform disk with mass 2.00 kg and radius 20.0 cm. The box is released from rest and descends as the rope unwraps from the cylinder. Find the speed of the box when it has fallen 2.50 m.

Figure **P9.80**

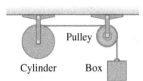
Pulley
Cylinder   Box

9.81 •• BIO **The Kinetic Energy of Walking.** If a person of mass M simply moved forward with speed V, his kinetic energy would be $\frac{1}{2}MV^2$. However, in addition to possessing a forward motion, various parts of his body (such as the arms and legs) undergo rotation. Therefore, his total kinetic energy is the sum of the energy from his forward motion plus the rotational kinetic energy of his arms and legs. The purpose of this problem is to see how much this rotational motion contributes to the person's kinetic energy. Biomedical measurements show that the arms and hands together typically make up 13% of a person's mass, while the legs and feet together account for 37%. For a rough (but reasonable) calculation, we can model the arms and legs as thin uniform bars pivoting about the shoulder and hip, respectively. In a brisk walk, the arms and legs each move through an angle of about $\pm 30°$ (a total of 60°) from the vertical in approximately 1 second. Assume that they are held straight, rather than being bent, which is not quite true. Consider a 75-kg person walking at 5.0 km/h, having arms 70 cm long and legs 90 cm long. (a) What is the average angular velocity of his arms and legs? (b) Using the average angular velocity from part (a), calculate the amount of rotational kinetic energy in this person's arms and legs as he walks. (c) What is the total kinetic energy due to both his forward motion and his rotation? (d) What percentage of his kinetic energy is due to the rotation of his legs and arms?

9.82 •• BIO **The Kinetic Energy of Running.** Using Problem 9.81 as a guide, apply it to a person running at 12 km/h, with his arms and legs each swinging through $\pm 30°$ in $\frac{1}{2}$ s. As before, assume that the arms and legs are kept straight.

9.83 •• BIO **Human Rotational Energy.** A dancer is spinning at 72 rpm about an axis through her center with her arms outstretched (**Fig. P9.83**). From biomedical measurements, the typical distribution of mass in a human body is as follows:

Figure **P9.83**

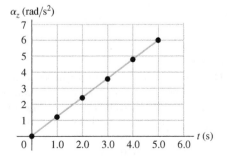

Head: 7.0%
Arms: 13% (for both)
Trunk and legs: 80.0%

Suppose you are this dancer. Using this information plus length measurements on your own body, calculate (a) your moment of inertia about your spin axis and (b) your rotational kinetic energy. Use Table 9.2 to model reasonable approximations for the pertinent parts of your body.

9.84 ••• A thin, uniform rod is bent into a square of side length a. If the total mass is M, find the moment of inertia about an axis through the center and perpendicular to the plane of the square. (*Hint:* Use the parallel-axis theorem.)

9.85 •• CALC A sphere with radius $R = 0.200$ m has density ρ that decreases with distance r from the center of the sphere according to $\rho = 3.00 \times 10^3 \text{ kg/m}^3 - (9.00 \times 10^3 \text{ kg/m}^4)r$. (a) Calculate the total mass of the sphere. (b) Calculate the moment of inertia of the sphere for an axis along a diameter.

9.86 •• CALC **Neutron Stars and Supernova Remnants.** The Crab Nebula is a cloud of glowing gas about 10 light-years across, located about 6500 light-years from the earth (**Fig. P9.86**). It is the remnant of a star that underwent a *supernova explosion,* seen on earth in 1054 A.D. Energy is released by the Crab Nebula at a rate of about 5×10^{31} W, about 10^5 times the rate at which the sun radiates energy. The Crab Nebula obtains its energy from the rotational kinetic energy of a rapidly spinning *neutron star* at its center. This object rotates once every 0.0331 s, and this period is increasing by 4.22×10^{-13} s for each second of time that elapses. (a) If the rate at which energy is lost by the neutron star is equal to the rate at which energy is released by the nebula, find the moment of inertia of the neutron star. (b) Theories of supernovae predict that the neutron star in the Crab Nebula has a mass about 1.4 times that of the sun. Modeling the neutron star as a solid uniform sphere, calculate its radius in kilometers. (c) What is the linear speed of a point on the equator of the neutron star? Compare to the speed of light. (d) Assume that the neutron star is uniform and calculate its density. Compare to the density of ordinary rock (3000 kg/m^3) and to the density of an atomic nucleus (about 10^{17} kg/m^3). Justify the statement that a neutron star is essentially a large atomic nucleus.

Figure **P9.86**

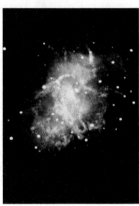

9.87 •• DATA A technician is testing a computer-controlled, variable-speed motor. She attaches a thin disk to the motor shaft, with the shaft at the center of the disk. The disk starts from rest, and sensors attached to the motor shaft measure the angular acceleration α_z of the shaft as a function of time. The results from one test run are shown in **Fig. P9.87**: (a) Through how many revolutions has the disk turned in the first 5.0 s? Can you use Eq. (9.11)? Explain. What is the angular velocity, in rad/s, of the disk (b) at $t = 5.0$ s; (c) when it has turned through 2.00 rev?

Figure **P9.87**

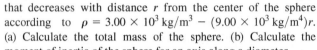

9.88 •• DATA You are analyzing the motion of a large flywheel that has radius 0.800 m. In one test run, the wheel starts from rest and turns with constant angular acceleration. An accelerometer on the rim of the flywheel measures the magnitude of the resultant acceleration a of a point on the rim of the flywheel as a function of the angle $\theta - \theta_0$ through which the wheel has turned. You collect these results:

$\theta - \theta_0$ (rad)	0.50	1.00	1.50	2.00	2.50	3.00	3.50	4.00
a (m/s²)	0.678	1.07	1.52	1.98	2.45	2.92	3.39	3.87

Construct a graph of a^2 (in m²/s⁴) versus $(\theta - \theta_0)^2$ in (rad²). (a) What are the slope and y-intercept of the straight line that gives the best fit to the data? (b) Use the slope from part (a) to find the angular acceleration of the flywheel. (c) What is the linear speed of a point on the rim of the flywheel when the wheel has turned through an angle of 135°? (d) When the flywheel has turned through an angle of 90.0°, what is the angle between the linear velocity of a point on its rim and the resultant acceleration of that point?

9.89 •• DATA You are rebuilding a 1965 Chevrolet. To decide whether to replace the flywheel with a newer, lighter-weight one, you want to determine the moment of inertia of the original, 35.6-cm-diameter flywheel. It is not a uniform disk, so you can't use $I = \frac{1}{2}MR^2$ to calculate the moment of inertia. You remove the flywheel from the car and use low-friction bearings to mount it on a horizontal, stationary rod that passes through the center of the flywheel, which can then rotate freely (about 2 m above the ground). After gluing one end of a long piece of flexible fishing line to the rim of the flywheel, you wrap the line a number of turns around the rim and suspend a 5.60-kg metal block from the free end of the line. When you release the block from rest, it descends as the flywheel rotates. With high-speed photography you measure the distance d the block has moved downward as a function of the time since it was released. The equation for the graph shown in **Fig. P9.89** that gives a good fit to the data points is $d = (165 \text{ cm/s}^2)t^2$. (a) Based on the graph, does the block fall with constant acceleration? Explain. (b) Use the graph to calculate the speed of the block when it has descended 1.50 m. (c) Apply conservation of mechanical energy to the system of flywheel and block to calculate the moment of inertia of the flywheel. (d) You are relieved that the fishing line doesn't break. Apply Newton's second law to the block to find the tension in the line as the block descended.

Figure **P9.89**

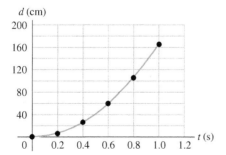

CHALLENGE PROBLEMS

9.90 ••• CALC Calculate the moment of inertia of a uniform solid cone about an axis through its center (**Fig. P9.90**). The cone has mass M and altitude h. The radius of its circular base is R.

Figure **P9.90**

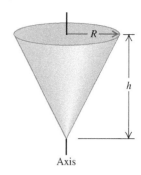

Axis

9.91 ••• CALC On a compact disc (CD), music is coded in a pattern of tiny pits arranged in a track that spirals outward toward the rim of the disc. As the disc spins inside a CD player, the track is scanned at a constant *linear* speed of $v = 1.25$ m/s. Because the radius of the track varies as it spirals outward, the *angular* speed of the disc must change as the CD is played. (See Exercise 9.20.) Let's see what angular acceleration is required to keep v constant. The equation of a spiral is $r(\theta) = r_0 + \beta\theta$, where r_0 is the radius of the spiral at $\theta = 0$ and β is a constant. On a CD, r_0 is the inner radius of the spiral track. If we take the rotation direction of the CD to be positive, β must be positive so that r increases as the disc turns and θ increases. (a) When the disc rotates through a small angle $d\theta$, the distance scanned along the track is $ds = r\,d\theta$. Using the above expression for $r(\theta)$, integrate ds to find the total distance s scanned along the track as a function of the total angle θ through which the disc has rotated. (b) Since the track is scanned at a constant linear speed v, the distance s found in part (a) is equal to vt. Use this to find θ as a function of time. There will be two solutions for θ; choose the positive one, and explain why this is the solution to choose. (c) Use your expression for $\theta(t)$ to find the angular velocity ω_z and the angular acceleration α_z as functions of time. Is α_z constant? (d) On a CD, the inner radius of the track is 25.0 mm, the track radius increases by 1.55 μm per revolution, and the playing time is 74.0 min. Find r_0, β, and the total number of revolutions made during the playing time. (e) Using your results from parts (c) and (d), make graphs of ω_z (in rad/s) versus t and α_z (in rad/s²) versus t between $t = 0$ and $t = 74.0$ min.

PASSAGE PROBLEMS

BIO **THE SPINNING EEL.** American eels (*Anguilla rostrata*) are freshwater fish with long, slender bodies that we can treat as uniform cylinders 1.0 m long and 10 cm in diameter. An eel compensates for its small jaw and teeth by holding onto prey with its mouth and then rapidly spinning its body around its long axis to tear off a piece of flesh. Eels have been recorded to spin at up to 14 revolutions per second when feeding in this way. Although this feeding method is costly in terms of energy, it allows the eel to feed on larger prey than it otherwise could.

9.92 A field researcher uses the slow-motion feature on her phone's camera to shoot a video of an eel spinning at its maximum rate. The camera records at 120 frames per second. Through what angle does the eel rotate from one frame to the next? (a) 1°; (b) 10°; (c) 22°; (d) 42°.

9.93 The eel is observed to spin at 14 spins per second clockwise, and 10 seconds later it is observed to spin at 8 spins per second counterclockwise. What is the magnitude of the eel's average angular acceleration during this time? (a) 6/10 rad/s²; (b) 6π/10 rad/s²; (c) 12π/10 rad/s²; (d) 44π/10 rad/s².

9.94 The eel has a certain amount of rotational kinetic energy when spinning at 14 spins per second. If it swam in a straight line instead, about how fast would the eel have to swim to have the same amount of kinetic energy as when it is spinning? (a) 0.5 m/s; (b) 0.7 m/s; (c) 3 m/s; (d) 5 m/s.

9.95 A new species of eel is found to have the same mass but one-quarter the length and twice the diameter of the American eel.

How does its moment of inertia for spinning around its long axis compare to that of the American eel? The new species has (a) half the moment of inertia as the American eel; (b) the same moment of inertia as the American eel; (c) twice the moment of inertia as the American eel; (d) four times the moment of inertia as the American eel.

Answers

Chapter Opening Question ?

(ii) The rotational kinetic energy of a rigid body rotating around an axis is $K = \frac{1}{2}I\omega^2$, where I is the body's moment of inertia for that axis and ω is the rotational speed. Table 9.2 shows that the moment of inertia for a slender rod of mass M and length L with an axis through one end (like a wind turbine blade) is $I = \frac{1}{3}ML^2$. If we double L while M and ω stay the same, both the moment of inertia I and the kinetic energy K increase by a factor of $2^2 = 4$.

Test Your Understanding Questions

9.1 (a) (i) and (iii), (b) (ii) The rotation is speeding up when the angular velocity and angular acceleration have the same sign, and slowing down when they have opposite signs. Hence it is speeding up for $0 < t < 2$ s (both ω_z and α_z are positive) and for 4 s $< t < 6$ s (both ω_z and α_z are negative) but is slowing down for 2 s $< t < 4$ s (ω_z is positive and α_z is negative). Note that the body is rotating in one direction for $t < 4$ s (ω_z is positive) and in the opposite direction for $t > 4$ s (ω_z is negative).

9.2 (a) (i), (b) (ii) When the disc comes to rest, $\omega_z = 0$. From Eq. (9.7), the *time* when this occurs is $t = (\omega_z - \omega_{0z})/\alpha_z = -\omega_{0z}/\alpha_z$ (this is a positive time because α_z is negative). If we double the initial angular velocity ω_{0z} and also double the angular acceleration α_z, their ratio is unchanged and the rotation stops in the same amount of time. The *angle* through which the disc rotates is given by Eq. (9.10): $\theta - \theta_0 = \frac{1}{2}(\omega_{0z} + \omega_z)t = \frac{1}{2}\omega_{0z}t$ (since the final angular velocity is $\omega_z = 0$). The initial angular velocity ω_{0z} has been doubled but the time t is the same, so the

angular displacement $\theta - \theta_0$ (and hence the number of revolutions) has doubled. You can also come to the same conclusion by using Eq. (9.12).

9.3 (ii) From Eq. (9.13), $v = r\omega$. To maintain a constant linear speed v, the angular speed ω must decrease as the scanning head moves outward (greater r).

9.4 (i) The kinetic energy in the falling block is $\frac{1}{2}mv^2$, and the kinetic energy in the rotating cylinder is $\frac{1}{2}I\omega^2 = \frac{1}{2}(\frac{1}{2}mR^2)(v/R)^2 = \frac{1}{4}mv^2$. Hence the total kinetic energy of the system is $\frac{3}{4}mv^2$, of which two-thirds is in the block and one-third is in the cylinder.

9.5 (ii) More of the mass of the pool cue is concentrated at the thicker end, so the center of mass is closer to that end. The moment of inertia through a point P at either end is $I_P = I_{cm} + Md^2$; the thinner end is farther from the center of mass, so the distance d and the moment of inertia I_P are greater for the thinner end.

9.6 (iii) Our result from Example 9.10 does *not* depend on the cylinder length L. The moment of inertia depends on only the *radial* distribution of mass, not on its distribution along the axis.

Bridging Problem

(a) $I = \left[\frac{M}{L}\left(\frac{x^3}{3}\right)\right]_{-h}^{L-h} = \frac{1}{3}M(L^2 - 3Lh + 3h^2)$

(b) $W = \frac{1}{6}M(L^2 - 3Lh + 3h^2)\alpha^2t^2$

(c) $a = (L - h)\alpha\sqrt{1 + \alpha^2t^4}$

10 DYNAMICS OF ROTATIONAL MOTION

We learned in Chapters 4 and 5 that a net force applied to a body gives that body an acceleration. But what does it take to give a body an *angular* acceleration? That is, what does it take to start a stationary body rotating or to bring a spinning body to a halt? A force is required, but it must be applied in a way that gives a twisting or turning action.

In this chapter we'll define a new physical quantity, *torque*, that describes the twisting or turning effort of a force. We'll find that the net torque acting on a rigid body determines its angular acceleration, in the same way that the net force on a body determines its linear acceleration. We'll also look at work and power in rotational motion so as to understand, for example, how energy is transferred by an electric motor. Next we'll develop a new conservation principle, *conservation of angular momentum*, that is tremendously useful for understanding the rotational motion of both rigid and nonrigid bodies. We'll finish this chapter by studying *gyroscopes*, rotating devices that don't fall over when you might think they should— but that actually behave in accordance with the dynamics of rotational motion.

10.1 TORQUE

We know that forces acting on a body can affect its **translational motion**—that is, the motion of the body as a whole through space. Now we want to learn which aspects of a force determine how effective it is in causing or changing *rotational* motion. The magnitude and direction of the force are important, but so is the point on the body where the force is applied. In **Fig. 10.1** (next page) a wrench is being used to loosen a tight bolt. Force $\vec{F}_b$, applied near the end of the handle, is more effective than an equal force $\vec{F}_a$ applied near the bolt. Force $\vec{F}_c$ does no good; it's applied at the same point and has the same magnitude as $\vec{F}_b$, but it's directed along the length of the handle. The quantitative measure of the tendency of a force to cause or change a body's rotational motion is called *torque;* we say that $\vec{F}_a$

10.1 Which of these three equal-magnitude forces is most likely to loosen the tight bolt?

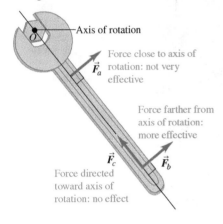

10.2 The torque of a force about a point is the product of the force magnitude and the lever arm of the force.

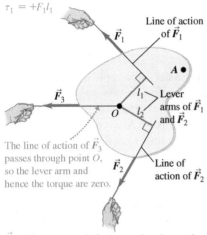

$\vec{F}_1$ tends to cause *counterclockwise* rotation about point O, so its torque is *positive*: $\tau_1 = +F_1 l_1$

The line of action of $\vec{F}_3$ passes through point O, so the lever arm and hence the torque are zero.

$\vec{F}_2$ tends to cause *clockwise* rotation about point O, so its torque is *negative*: $\tau_2 = -F_2 l_2$

10.3 Three ways to calculate the torque of force $\vec{F}$ about point O. In this figure, $\vec{r}$ and $\vec{F}$ are in the plane of the page and the torque vector $\vec{\tau}$ points out of the page toward you.

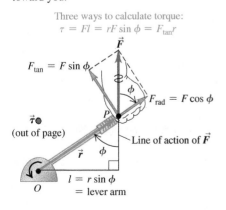

Three ways to calculate torque:
$\tau = Fl = rF\sin\phi = F_{\text{tan}}r$

$F_{\text{tan}} = F\sin\phi$

$F_{\text{rad}} = F\cos\phi$

$\vec{\tau}$ (out of page)

Line of action of $\vec{F}$

$l = r\sin\phi$ = lever arm

applies a torque about point O to the wrench in Fig. 10.1, $\vec{F}_b$ applies a greater torque about O, and $\vec{F}_c$ applies zero torque about O.

Figure 10.2 shows three examples of how to calculate torque. The body can rotate about an axis that is perpendicular to the plane of the figure and passes through point O. Three forces act on the body in the plane of the figure. The tendency of the first of these forces, $\vec{F}_1$, to cause a rotation about O depends on its magnitude F_1. It also depends on the *perpendicular* distance l_1 between point O and the **line of action** of the force (that is, the line along which the force vector lies). We call the distance l_1 the **lever arm** (or **moment arm**) of force $\vec{F}_1$ about O. The twisting effort is directly proportional to both F_1 and l_1, so we define the **torque** (or *moment*) of the force $\vec{F}_1$ with respect to O as the product $F_1 l_1$. We use the Greek letter τ (tau) for torque. If a force of magnitude F has a line of action that is a perpendicular distance l from O, the torque is

$$\tau = Fl \qquad (10.1)$$

Physicists usually use the term "torque," while engineers usually use "moment" (unless they are talking about a rotating shaft).

The lever arm of $\vec{F}_1$ in Fig. 10.2 is the perpendicular distance l_1, and the lever arm of $\vec{F}_2$ is the perpendicular distance l_2. The line of action of $\vec{F}_3$ passes through point O, so the lever arm for $\vec{F}_3$ is zero and its torque with respect to O is zero. In the same way, force $\vec{F}_c$ in Fig. 10.1 has zero torque with respect to point O; $\vec{F}_b$ has a greater torque than $\vec{F}_a$ because its lever arm is greater.

CAUTION Torque is always measured about a point Torque is *always* defined with reference to a specific point. If we shift the position of this point, the torque of each force may change. For example, the torque of force $\vec{F}_3$ in Fig. 10.2 is zero with respect to point O but *not* with respect to point A. It's not enough to refer to "the torque of $\vec{F}$"; you must say "the torque of $\vec{F}$ with respect to point X" or "the torque of $\vec{F}$ about point X." ▮

Force $\vec{F}_1$ in Fig. 10.2 tends to cause *counterclockwise* rotation about O, while $\vec{F}_2$ tends to cause *clockwise* rotation. To distinguish between these two possibilities, we need to choose a positive sense of rotation. With the choice that *counterclockwise torques are positive and clockwise torques are negative*, the torques of $\vec{F}_1$ and $\vec{F}_2$ about O are

$$\tau_1 = +F_1 l_1 \qquad \tau_2 = -F_2 l_2$$

Figure 10.2 shows this choice for the sign of torque. We will often use the symbol ↺ to indicate our choice of the positive sense of rotation.

The SI unit of torque is the newton-meter. In our discussion of work and energy we called this combination the joule. But torque is *not* work or energy, and torque should be expressed in newton-meters, *not* joules.

Figure 10.3 shows a force $\vec{F}$ applied at point P, located at position $\vec{r}$ with respect to point O. There are three ways to calculate the torque of $\vec{F}$:

1. Find the lever arm l and use $\tau = Fl$.
2. Determine the angle ϕ between the vectors $\vec{r}$ and $\vec{F}$; the lever arm is $r\sin\phi$, so $\tau = rF\sin\phi$.
3. Represent $\vec{F}$ in terms of a radial component F_{rad} along the direction of $\vec{r}$ and a tangential component F_{tan} at right angles, perpendicular to $\vec{r}$. (We call this component *tangential* because if the body rotates, the point where the force acts moves in a circle, and this component is tangent to that circle.) Then $F_{\text{tan}} = F\sin\phi$ and $\tau = r(F\sin\phi) = F_{\text{tan}}r$. The component F_{rad} produces *no* torque with respect to O because its lever arm with respect to that point is zero (compare to forces $\vec{F}_c$ in Fig. 10.1 and $\vec{F}_3$ in Fig. 10.2).

Summarizing these three expressions for torque, we have

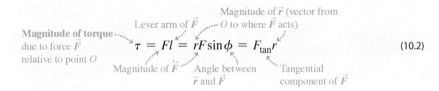

$$\tau = Fl = rF\sin\phi = F_{\text{tan}}r \qquad (10.2)$$

Magnitude of torque due to force $\vec{F}$ relative to point O ···· Lever arm of $\vec{F}$ ···· Magnitude of $\vec{r}$ (vector from O to where $\vec{F}$ acts) ···· Magnitude of $\vec{F}$ ···· Angle between $\vec{r}$ and $\vec{F}$ ···· Tangential component of $\vec{F}$

Torque As a Vector

We saw in Section 9.1 that angular velocity and angular acceleration can be represented as vectors; the same is true for torque. To see how to do this, note that the quantity $rF\sin\phi$ in Eq. (10.2) is the magnitude of the *vector product* $\vec{r} \times \vec{F}$ that we defined in Section 1.10. (Go back and review that definition.) We generalize the definition of torque as follows: When a force $\vec{F}$ acts at a point having a position vector $\vec{r}$ with respect to an origin O, as in Fig. 10.3, the torque $\vec{\tau}$ of the force with respect to O is the *vector* quantity

$$\vec{\tau} = \vec{r} \times \vec{F} \qquad (10.3)$$

Torque vector due to force $\vec{F}$ relative to point O ···· Vector from O to where $\vec{F}$ acts ···· Force $\vec{F}$

The torque as defined in Eq. (10.2) is the magnitude of the torque vector $\vec{r} \times \vec{F}$. The direction of $\vec{\tau}$ is perpendicular to both $\vec{r}$ and $\vec{F}$. In particular, if both $\vec{r}$ and $\vec{F}$ lie in a plane perpendicular to the axis of rotation, as in Fig. 10.3, then the torque vector $\vec{\tau} = \vec{r} \times \vec{F}$ is directed along the axis of rotation, with a sense given by the right-hand rule (see Fig. 1.30 and **Fig. 10.4**).

Because $\vec{\tau} = \vec{r} \times \vec{F}$ is perpendicular to the plane of the vectors $\vec{r}$ and $\vec{F}$, it's common to have diagrams like Fig. 10.4, in which one of the vectors is perpendicular to the page. We use a dot ($\bullet$) to represent a vector that points out of the page and a cross ($\times$) to represent a vector that points into the page (see Figs. 10.3 and 10.4).

In the following sections we will usually be concerned with rotation of a body about an axis oriented in a specified constant direction. In that case, only the component of torque along that axis will matter. We often call that component the torque with respect to the specified *axis*.

10.4 The torque vector $\vec{\tau} = \vec{r} \times \vec{F}$ is directed along the axis of the bolt, perpendicular to both $\vec{r}$ and $\vec{F}$. The fingers of the right hand curl in the direction of the rotation that the torque tends to cause.

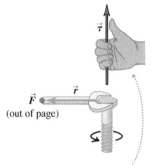

$\vec{F}$ (out of page)

If you point the fingers of your right hand in the direction of $\vec{r}$ and then curl them in the direction of $\vec{F}$, your outstretched thumb points in the direction of $\vec{\tau}$.

$\vec{F}$ (out of page)

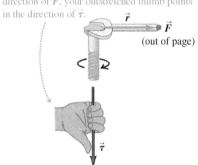

EXAMPLE 10.1 APPLYING A TORQUE

To loosen a pipe fitting, a plumber slips a piece of scrap pipe (a "cheater") over his wrench handle. He stands on the end of the cheater, applying his 900-N weight at a point 0.80 m from the center of the fitting (**Fig. 10.5a**). The wrench handle and cheater make an angle of 19° with the horizontal. Find the magnitude and direction of the torque he applies about the center of the fitting.

10.5 (a) Loosening a pipe fitting by standing on a "cheater." (b) Our vector diagram to find the torque about O.

(a) Diagram of situation

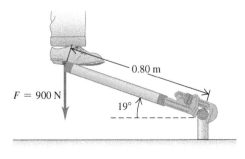

$F = 900\text{ N}$
0.80 m
$19°$

(b) Free-body diagram

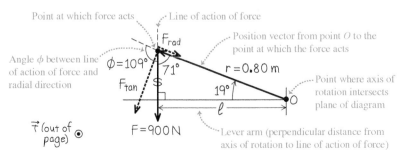

Point at which force acts ···· Line of action of force ···· Position vector from point O to the point at which the force acts ···· Angle ϕ between line of action of force and radial direction ···· F_{rad} ···· $\phi = 109°$ ···· $71°$ ···· $r = 0.80\text{ m}$ ···· F_{tan} ···· $19°$ ···· Point where axis of rotation intersects plane of diagram ···· $\vec{\tau}$ (out of page) ···· ℓ ···· $F = 900\text{ N}$ ···· Lever arm (perpendicular distance from axis of rotation to line of action of force)

Continued

SOLUTION

IDENTIFY and SET UP: Figure 10.5b shows the vectors $\vec{r}$ and $\vec{F}$ and the angle between them ($\phi = 109°$). Equation (10.1) or (10.2) will tell us the magnitude of the torque. The right-hand rule with Eq. (10.3), $\vec{\tau} = \vec{r} \times \vec{F}$, will tell us the direction of the torque.

EXECUTE: To use Eq. (10.1), we first calculate the lever arm l. As Fig. 10.5b shows,

$$l = r\sin\phi = (0.80 \text{ m})\sin 109° = 0.76 \text{ m}$$

Then Eq. (10.1) tells us that the magnitude of the torque is

$$\tau = Fl = (900 \text{ N})(0.76 \text{ m}) = 680 \text{ N} \cdot \text{m}$$

We get the same result from Eq. (10.2):

$$\tau = rF\sin\phi = (0.80 \text{ m})(900 \text{ N})(\sin 109°) = 680 \text{ N} \cdot \text{m}$$

Alternatively, we can find F_{tan}, the tangential component of $\vec{F}$ that acts perpendicular to $\vec{r}$. Figure 10.5b shows that this component is at an angle of $109° - 90° = 19°$ from $\vec{F}$, so $F_{\text{tan}} = F(\cos 19°) = (900 \text{ N})(\cos 19°) = 851 \text{ N}$. Then, from Eq. 10.2,

$$\tau = F_{\text{tan}}r = (851 \text{ N})(0.80 \text{ m}) = 680 \text{ N} \cdot \text{m}$$

Curl the fingers of your right hand from the direction of $\vec{r}$ (in the plane of Fig. 10.5b, to the left and up) into the direction of $\vec{F}$ (straight down). Then your right thumb points out of the plane of the figure: This is the direction of $\vec{\tau}$.

EVALUATE: To check the direction of $\vec{\tau}$, note that the force in Fig. 10.5 tends to produce a counterclockwise rotation about O. If you curl the fingers of your right hand in a counterclockwise direction, the thumb points out of the plane of Fig. 10.5, which is indeed the direction of the torque.

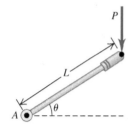

TEST YOUR UNDERSTANDING OF SECTION 10.1 The accompanying figure shows a force P being applied to one end of a lever of length L. What is the magnitude of the torque of this force about point A? (i) $PL\sin\theta$; (ii) $PL\cos\theta$; (iii) $PL\tan\theta$; (iv) $PL/\sin\theta$; (v) PL. ▮

10.2 TORQUE AND ANGULAR ACCELERATION FOR A RIGID BODY

We're now ready to develop the fundamental relationship for the rotational dynamics of a rigid body. We'll show that the angular acceleration of a rotating rigid body is directly proportional to the sum of the torque components along the axis of rotation. The proportionality factor is the moment of inertia.

To develop this relationship, let's begin as we did in Section 9.4 by envisioning the rigid body as being made up of a large number of particles. We choose the axis of rotation to be the z-axis; the first particle has mass m_1 and distance r_1 from this axis (**Fig. 10.6**). The *net force* $\vec{F}_1$ acting on this particle has a component $F_{1,\text{rad}}$ along the radial direction, a component $F_{1,\text{tan}}$ that is tangent to the circle of radius r_1 in which the particle moves as the body rotates, and a component F_{1z} along the axis of rotation. Newton's second law for the tangential component is

$$F_{1,\text{tan}} = m_1 a_{1,\text{tan}} \tag{10.4}$$

We can express the tangential acceleration of the first particle in terms of the angular acceleration α_z of the body by using Eq. (9.14): $a_{1,\text{tan}} = r_1\alpha_z$. Using this relationship and multiplying both sides of Eq. (10.4) by r_1, we obtain

$$F_{1,\text{tan}}r_1 = m_1 r_1^2 \alpha_z \tag{10.5}$$

From Eq. (10.2), $F_{1,\text{tan}}r_1$ is the *torque* of the net force with respect to the rotation axis, equal to the component τ_{1z} of the torque vector along the rotation axis. The subscript z is a reminder that the torque affects rotation around the z-axis, in the same way that the subscript on F_{1z} is a reminder that this force affects the motion of particle 1 along the z-axis.

Neither of the components $F_{1,\text{rad}}$ or F_{1z} contributes to the torque about the z-axis, since neither tends to change the particle's rotation about that axis. So $\tau_{1z} = F_{1,\text{tan}}r_1$ is the total torque acting on the particle with respect to the rotation axis. Also, $m_1 r_1^2$ is I_1, the moment of inertia of the particle about the rotation axis. Hence we can rewrite Eq. (10.5) as

$$\tau_{1z} = I_1\alpha_z = m_1 r_1^2 \alpha_z$$

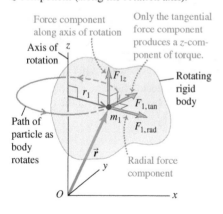

10.6 As a rigid body rotates around the z-axis, a net force $\vec{F}_1$ acts on one particle of the body. Only the force component $F_{1,\text{tan}}$ can affect the rotation, because only $F_{1,\text{tan}}$ exerts a torque about O with a z-component (along the rotation axis).

We write such an equation for every particle in the body, then add all these equations:

$$\tau_{1z} + \tau_{2z} + \cdots = I_1\alpha_z + I_2\alpha_z + \cdots$$
$$= m_1 r_1^2 \alpha_z + m_2 r_2^2 \alpha_z + \cdots$$

or

$$\sum \tau_{iz} = \left(\sum m_i r_i^2 \right) \alpha_z \qquad (10.6)$$

The left side of Eq. (10.6) is the sum of all the torques about the rotation axis that act on all the particles. The right side is $I = \sum m_i r_i^2$, the total moment of inertia about the rotation axis, multiplied by the angular acceleration α_z. Note that α_z is the same for every particle because this is a *rigid* body. Thus Eq. (10.6) says that for the rigid body as a whole,

DATA *SPEAKS*

Torque and Angular Acceleration

When students were given a problem about torque and rotational motion, more than 22% gave an incorrect response. Common errors:

- Forgetting that the torque due to a force depends on the force magnitude, where the force is applied, and the direction of the force.

- Confusion about the sign of torque and angular acceleration: Counterclockwise is positive; clockwise is negative.

Rotational analog of Newton's second law for a rigid body:

Net torque on a rigid body about z-axis ⟶ $$\sum \tau_z = I \alpha_z \qquad (10.7)$$ ⟵ Moment of inertia of rigid body about z-axis; Angular acceleration of rigid body about z-axis

Just as Newton's second law says that a net *force* on a particle causes an *acceleration* in the direction of the net force, Eq. (10.7) says that a net *torque* on a rigid body about an axis causes an *angular acceleration* about that axis (**Fig. 10.7**).

Our derivation assumed that the angular acceleration α_z is the same for all particles in the body. So Eq. (10.7) is valid *only* for *rigid* bodies. Hence this equation doesn't apply to a rotating tank of water or a swirling tornado of air, different parts of which have different angular accelerations. Note that since our derivation used Eq. (9.14), $a_{\text{tan}} = r\alpha_z$, α_z must be measured in rad/s².

The torque on each particle is due to the net force on that particle, which is the vector sum of external and internal forces (see Section 8.2). According to Newton's third law, the *internal* forces that any pair of particles in the rigid body exert on each other are equal in magnitude and opposite in direction (**Fig. 10.8**). If these forces act along the line joining the two particles, their lever arms with respect to any axis are also equal. So the torques for each such pair are equal and opposite, and add to zero. Hence *all* the internal torques add to zero, so the sum $\sum \tau_z$ in Eq. (10.7) includes only the torques of the *external* forces.

Often, an important external force acting on a body is its *weight*. This force is not concentrated at a single point; it acts on every particle in the entire body. Nevertheless, if $\vec{g}$ has the same value at all points, we always get the correct torque (about any specified axis) if we assume that all the weight is concentrated at the *center of mass* of the body. We'll prove this statement in Chapter 11, but meanwhile we'll use it for some of the problems in this chapter.

10.7 Loosening or tightening a screw requires giving it an angular acceleration and hence applying a torque. This is made easier by using a screwdriver with a large-radius handle, which provides a large lever arm for the force you apply with your hand.

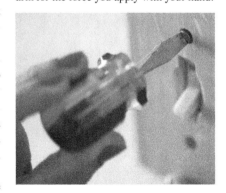

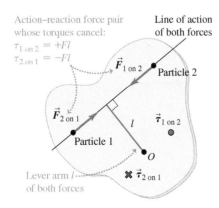

10.8 Why only *external* torques affect a rigid body's rotation: Any two particles in the body exert equal and opposite forces on each other. If the forces act along the line joining the particles, the lever arms of the forces with respect to an axis through O are the same and the torques due to the two forces are equal and opposite.

PROBLEM-SOLVING STRATEGY 10.1 ⟩ ROTATIONAL DYNAMICS FOR RIGID BODIES

Our strategy for solving problems in rotational dynamics is very similar to Problem-Solving Strategy 5.2 for solving problems involving Newton's second law.

IDENTIFY *the relevant concepts:* Equation (10.7), $\sum \tau_z = I\alpha_z$, is useful whenever torques act on a rigid body. Sometimes you can use an energy approach instead, as we did in Section 9.4. However, if the target variable is a force, a torque, an acceleration, an angular acceleration, or an elapsed time, using $\sum \tau_z = I\alpha_z$ is almost always best.

SET UP *the problem* using the following steps:
1. Sketch the situation and identify the body or bodies to be analyzed. Indicate the rotation axis.
2. For each body, draw a free-body diagram that shows the body's *shape,* including all dimensions and angles. Label pertinent quantities with algebraic symbols.
3. Choose coordinate axes for each body and indicate a positive sense of rotation (clockwise or counterclockwise) for each rotating body. If you know the sense of α_z, pick that as the positive sense of rotation.

EXECUTE *the solution:*
1. For each body, decide whether it undergoes translational motion, rotational motion, or both. Then apply $\sum \vec{F} = m\vec{a}$ (as in Section 5.2), $\sum \tau_z = I\alpha_z$, or both to the body.
2. Express in algebraic form any *geometrical* relationships between the motions of two or more bodies. An example is a string that unwinds, without slipping, from a pulley or a wheel that rolls without slipping (discussed in Section 10.3). These relationships usually appear as relationships between linear and/or angular accelerations.
3. Ensure that you have as many independent equations as there are unknowns. Solve the equations to find the target variables.

EVALUATE *your answer:* Check that the algebraic signs of your results make sense. As an example, if you are unrolling thread from a spool, your answers should not tell you that the spool is turning in the direction that rolls the thread back onto the spool! Check that any algebraic results are correct for special cases or for extreme values of quantities.

EXAMPLE 10.2 **AN UNWINDING CABLE I**

Figure 10.9a shows the situation that we analyzed in Example 9.7 using energy methods. What is the cable's acceleration?

SOLUTION

IDENTIFY and SET UP: We can't use the energy method of Section 9.4, which doesn't involve acceleration. Instead we'll apply rotational dynamics to find the angular acceleration of the cylinder (Fig. 10.9b). We'll then find a relationship between the motion of the cable and the motion of the cylinder rim, and use this to find the acceleration of the cable. The cylinder rotates counterclockwise when the cable is pulled, so we take counterclockwise rotation to be positive. The net force on the cylinder must be zero because its center of mass remains at rest. The force F exerted by the cable produces a torque about the rotation axis. The weight (magnitude Mg) and the normal force (magnitude n) exerted by the cylinder's bearings produce *no* torque about the rotation axis because both act along lines through that axis.

EXECUTE: The lever arm of F is equal to the radius $R = 0.060$ m of the cylinder, so the torque is $\tau_z = FR$. (This torque is positive,

as it tends to cause a counterclockwise rotation.) From Table 9.2, case (f), the moment of inertia of the cylinder about the rotation axis is $I = \frac{1}{2}MR^2$. Then Eq. (10.7) tells us that

$$\alpha_z = \frac{\tau_z}{I} = \frac{FR}{MR^2/2} = \frac{2F}{MR} = \frac{2(9.0\ \text{N})}{(50\ \text{kg})(0.060\ \text{m})} = 6.0\ \text{rad/s}^2$$

(We can add "rad" to our result because radians are dimensionless.)

To get the linear acceleration of the cable, recall from Section 9.3 that the acceleration of a cable unwinding from a cylinder is the same as the tangential acceleration of a point on the surface of the cylinder where the cable is tangent to it. This tangential acceleration is given by Eq. (9.14):

$$a_{\text{tan}} = R\alpha_z = (0.060\ \text{m})(6.0\ \text{rad/s}^2) = 0.36\ \text{m/s}^2$$

EVALUATE: Can you use this result, together with an equation from Chapter 2, to determine the speed of the cable after it has been pulled 2.0 m? Does your result agree with that of Example 9.7?

10.9 (a) Cylinder and cable. (b) Our free-body diagram for the cylinder.

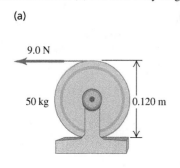

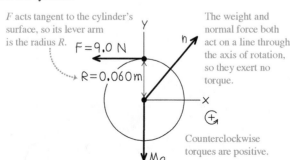

EXAMPLE 10.3   **AN UNWINDING CABLE II**

In Example 9.8 (Section 9.4), what are the acceleration of the falling block and the tension in the cable?

___

SOLUTION

IDENTIFY and SET UP: We'll apply translational dynamics to the block and rotational dynamics to the cylinder. As in Example 10.2, we'll relate the linear acceleration of the block (our target variable) to the angular acceleration of the cylinder. **Figure 10.10** shows our sketch of the situation and a free-body diagram for each body. We take the positive sense of rotation for the cylinder to be counterclockwise and the positive direction of the y-coordinate for the block to be downward.

10.10 (a) Our diagram of the situation. (b) Our free-body diagrams for the cylinder and the block. We assume the cable has negligible mass.

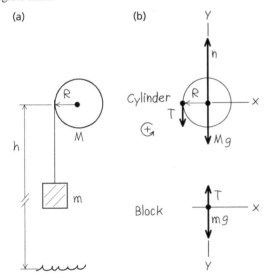

EXECUTE: For the block, Newton's second law gives

$$\sum F_y = mg + (-T) = ma_y$$

For the cylinder, the only torque about its axis is that due to the cable tension T. Hence Eq. (10.7) gives

$$\sum \tau_z = RT = I\alpha_z = \tfrac{1}{2}MR^2\alpha_z$$

As in Example 10.2, the acceleration of the cable is the same as the tangential acceleration of a point on the cylinder rim. From Eq. (9.14), this acceleration is $a_y = a_{\text{tan}} = R\alpha_z$. We use this to replace $R\alpha_z$ with a_y in the cylinder equation above, and divide by R. The result is $T = \tfrac{1}{2}Ma_y$. Now we substitute this expression for T into Newton's second law for the block and solve for the acceleration a_y:

$$mg - \tfrac{1}{2}Ma_y = ma_y$$

$$a_y = \frac{g}{1 + M/2m}$$

To find the cable tension T, we substitute our expression for a_y into the block equation:

$$T = mg - ma_y = mg - m\left(\frac{g}{1 + M/2m}\right) = \frac{mg}{1 + 2m/M}$$

EVALUATE: The acceleration is positive (in the downward direction) and less than g, as it should be, since the cable is holding back the block. The cable tension is *not* equal to the block's weight mg; if it were, the block could not accelerate.

Let's check some particular cases. When M is much larger than m, the tension is nearly equal to mg and the acceleration is correspondingly much less than g. When M is zero, $T = 0$ and $a_y = g$; the object falls freely. If the object starts from rest ($v_{0y} = 0$) a height h above the floor, its y-velocity when it strikes the floor is given by $v_y^2 = v_{0y}^2 + 2a_yh = 2a_yh$, so

$$v_y = \sqrt{2a_yh} = \sqrt{\frac{2gh}{1 + M/2m}}$$

We found this result from energy considerations in Example 9.8.

TEST YOUR UNDERSTANDING OF SECTION 10.2   The figure shows a glider of mass m_1 that can slide without friction on a horizontal air track. It is attached to an object of mass m_2 by a massless string. The pulley has radius R and moment of inertia I about its axis of rotation. When released, the hanging object accelerates downward, the glider accelerates to the right, and the string turns the pulley without slipping or stretching. Rank the magnitudes of the following forces that act during the motion, in order from largest to smallest magnitude. (i) The tension force (magnitude T_1) in the horizontal part of the string; (ii) the tension force (magnitude T_2) in the vertical part of the string; (iii) the weight m_2g of the hanging object. ❙

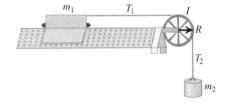

10.3 RIGID-BODY ROTATION ABOUT A MOVING AXIS

We can extend our analysis of the dynamics of rotational motion to some cases in which the axis of rotation moves. When that happens, the motion of the body is **combined translation and rotation.** The key to understanding such situations is this: Every possible motion of a rigid body can be represented as a

10.11 The motion of a rigid body is a combination of translational motion of the center of mass and rotation around the center of mass.

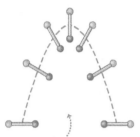

The motion of this tossed baton can be represented as a combination of ...

... **translation** of the center of mass ... ... plus **rotation** about the center of mass.

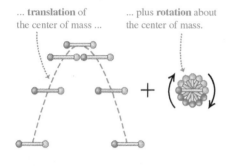

combination of *translational motion of the center of mass* and *rotation about an axis through the center of mass.* This is true even when the center of mass accelerates, so it is not at rest in any inertial frame. **Figure 10.11** illustrates this for the motion of a tossed baton: The center of mass of the baton follows a parabolic curve, as though the baton were a particle located at the center of mass. A rolling ball is another example of combined translational and rotational motions.

Combined Translation and Rotation: Energy Relationships

It's beyond our scope to prove that rigid-body motion can always be divided into translation of the center of mass and rotation about the center of mass. But we *can* prove this for the kinetic energy K of a rigid body that has both translational and rotational motions. For such a body, K is the sum of two parts:

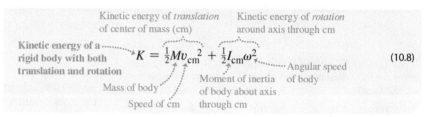

Kinetic energy of *translation* of center of mass (cm)   Kinetic energy of *rotation* around axis through cm

Kinetic energy of a rigid body with both translation and rotation
$$K = \tfrac{1}{2}Mv_{cm}^2 + \tfrac{1}{2}I_{cm}\omega^2 \qquad (10.8)$$
Mass of body   Speed of cm   Moment of inertia of body about axis through cm   Angular speed of body

To prove this relationship, we again imagine the rigid body to be made up of particles. For a typical particle with mass m_i (**Fig. 10.12**), the velocity $\vec{v}_i$ of this particle relative to an inertial frame is the vector sum of the velocity $\vec{v}_{cm}$ of the center of mass and the velocity $\vec{v}_i{}'$ of the particle *relative to* the center of mass:

$$\vec{v}_i = \vec{v}_{cm} + \vec{v}_i{}' \qquad (10.9)$$

The kinetic energy K_i of this particle in the inertial frame is $\tfrac{1}{2}m_i v_i^2$, which we can also express as $\tfrac{1}{2}m_i(\vec{v}_i \cdot \vec{v}_i)$. Substituting Eq. (10.9) into this, we get

$$K_i = \tfrac{1}{2}m_i(\vec{v}_{cm} + \vec{v}_i{}') \cdot (\vec{v}_{cm} + \vec{v}_i{}')$$
$$= \tfrac{1}{2}m_i(\vec{v}_{cm} \cdot \vec{v}_{cm} + 2\vec{v}_{cm} \cdot \vec{v}_i{}' + \vec{v}_i{}' \cdot \vec{v}_i{}')$$
$$= \tfrac{1}{2}m_i(v_{cm}^2 + 2\vec{v}_{cm} \cdot \vec{v}_i{}' + v_i{}'^2)$$

The total kinetic energy is the sum $\sum K_i$ for all the particles making up the body. Expressing the three terms in this equation as separate sums, we get

$$K = \sum K_i = \sum\left(\tfrac{1}{2}m_i v_{cm}^2\right) + \sum(m_i \vec{v}_{cm} \cdot \vec{v}_i{}') + \sum\left(\tfrac{1}{2}m_i v_i{}'^2\right)$$

The first and second terms have common factors that we take outside the sum:

$$K = \tfrac{1}{2}\left(\sum m_i\right)v_{cm}^2 + \vec{v}_{cm} \cdot \left(\sum m_i \vec{v}_i{}'\right) + \sum\left(\tfrac{1}{2}m_i v_i{}'^2\right) \qquad (10.10)$$

Now comes the reward for our effort. In the first term, $\sum m_i$ is the total mass M. The second term is zero because $\sum m_i \vec{v}_i{}'$ is M times the velocity of the center of mass *relative to the center of mass,* and this is zero by definition. The last term is the sum of the kinetic energies of the particles computed by using their speeds with respect to the center of mass; this is just the kinetic energy of rotation around the center of mass. Using the same steps that led to Eq. (9.17) for the rotational kinetic energy of a rigid body, we can write this last term as $\tfrac{1}{2}I_{cm}\omega^2$, where I_{cm} is the moment of inertia with respect to the axis through the center of mass and ω is the angular speed. So Eq. (10.10) becomes Eq. (10.8):

$$K = \tfrac{1}{2}Mv_{cm}^2 + \tfrac{1}{2}I_{cm}\omega^2$$

10.12 A rigid body with both translational and rotational motions.

Axis of rotation

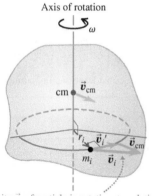

Velocity $\vec{v}_i$ of particle in rotating, translating rigid body = (velocity $\vec{v}_{cm}$ of center of mass) + (particle's velocity $\vec{v}_i{}'$ relative to center of mass)

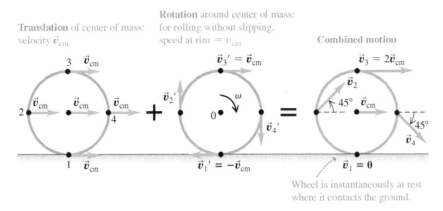

10.13 The motion of a rolling wheel is the sum of the translational motion of the center of mass plus the rotational motion of the wheel around the center of mass.

Rolling Without Slipping

An important case of combined translation and rotation is **rolling without slipping.** The rolling wheel in **Fig. 10.13** is symmetrical, so its center of mass is at its geometric center. We view the motion in an inertial frame of reference in which the surface on which the wheel rolls is at rest. In this frame, the point on the wheel that contacts the surface must be instantaneously *at rest* so that it does not slip. Hence the velocity $\vec{v}_1{}'$ of the point of contact relative to the center of mass must have the same magnitude but opposite direction as the center-of-mass velocity $\vec{v}_{cm}$. If the wheel's radius is R and its angular speed about the center of mass is ω, then the magnitude of $\vec{v}_1{}'$ is $R\omega$; hence

Condition for rolling without slipping:

$$\underset{\text{of rolling wheel}}{\overset{\text{Speed of center of mass}}{v_{cm}}} = R\omega \quad \overset{\text{Radius of wheel}}{\underset{\text{Angular speed of wheel}}{}} \quad (10.11)$$

As Fig. 10.13 shows, the velocity of a point on the wheel is the vector sum of the velocity of the center of mass and the velocity of the point relative to the center of mass. Thus while point 1, the point of contact, is instantaneously at rest, point 3 at the top of the wheel is moving forward *twice as fast* as the center of mass, and points 2 and 4 at the sides have velocities at $45°$ to the horizontal.

At any instant we can think of the wheel as rotating about an "instantaneous axis" of rotation that passes through the point of contact with the ground. The angular velocity ω is the same for this axis as for an axis through the center of mass; an observer at the center of mass sees the rim make the same number of revolutions per second as does an observer at the rim watching the center of mass spin around him. If we think of the motion of the rolling wheel in Fig. 10.13 in this way, the kinetic energy of the wheel is $K = \frac{1}{2}I_1\omega^2$, where I_1 is the moment of inertia of the wheel about an axis through point 1. But by the parallel-axis theorem, Eq. (9.19), $I_1 = I_{cm} + MR^2$, where M is the total mass of the wheel and I_{cm} is the moment of inertia with respect to an axis through the center of mass. Using Eq. (10.11), we find that the wheel's kinetic energy is as given by Eq. (10.8):

$$K = \tfrac{1}{2}I_1\omega^2 = \tfrac{1}{2}I_{cm}\omega^2 + \tfrac{1}{2}MR^2\omega^2 = \tfrac{1}{2}I_{cm}\omega^2 + \tfrac{1}{2}Mv_{cm}^2$$

CAUTION **Rolling without slipping** The relationship $v_{cm} = R\omega$ holds *only* if there is rolling without slipping. When a drag racer first starts to move, the rear tires are spinning very fast even though the racer is hardly moving, so $R\omega$ is greater than v_{cm} (**Fig. 10.14**). If a driver applies the brakes too heavily so that the car skids, the tires will spin hardly at all and $R\omega$ is less than v_{cm}.

If a rigid body changes height as it moves, we must also consider gravitational potential energy. We saw in Section 9.4 that for any extended body of mass M, rigid or not, the gravitational potential energy U is the same as if we replaced the body by a particle of mass M located at the body's center of mass, so

$$U = Mgy_{cm}$$

BIO **Application Combined Translation and Rotation** A maple seed consists of a pod attached to a much lighter, flattened wing. Airflow around the wing slows the falling seed to about 1 m/s and causes the seed to rotate about its center of mass. The seed's slow fall means that a breeze can carry the seed some distance from the parent tree. In the absence of wind, the seed's center of mass falls straight down.

Maple seed

Maple seed falling

10.14 The smoke rising from this drag racer's rear tires shows that the tires are slipping on the road, so v_{cm} is *not* equal to $R\omega$.

EXAMPLE 10.4 SPEED OF A PRIMITIVE YO-YO

A primitive yo-yo has a massless string wrapped around a solid cylinder with mass M and radius R (**Fig. 10.15**). You hold the free end of the string stationary and release the cylinder from rest. The string unwinds but does not slip or stretch as the cylinder descends and rotates. Using energy considerations, find the speed v_{cm} of the cylinder's center of mass after it has descended a distance h.

SOLUTION

IDENTIFY and SET UP: Since you hold the upper end of the string fixed, your hand does no work on the string–cylinder system. There is friction between the string and the cylinder, but the string doesn't slip so no mechanical energy is lost. Hence we can use

10.15 Calculating the speed of a primitive yo-yo.

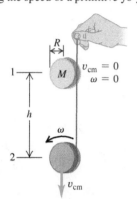

conservation of mechanical energy. The initial kinetic energy of the cylinder is $K_1 = 0$, and its final kinetic energy K_2 is given by Eq. (10.8); the massless string has no kinetic energy. The moment of inertia is $I_{cm} = \frac{1}{2}MR^2$, and by Eq. (9.13) $\omega = v_{cm}/R$ because the string doesn't slip. The potential energies are $U_1 = Mgh$ and $U_2 = 0$.

EXECUTE: From Eq. (10.8), the kinetic energy at point 2 is

$$K_2 = \tfrac{1}{2}Mv_{cm}^2 + \tfrac{1}{2}\left(\tfrac{1}{2}MR^2\right)\left(\frac{v_{cm}}{R}\right)^2 = \tfrac{3}{4}Mv_{cm}^2$$

The kinetic energy is $1\frac{1}{2}$ times what it would be if the yo-yo were falling at speed v_{cm} without rotating. Two-thirds of the total kinetic energy $\left(\tfrac{1}{2}Mv_{cm}^2\right)$ is translational and one-third $\left(\tfrac{1}{4}Mv_{cm}^2\right)$ is rotational. Using conservation of energy,

$$K_1 + U_1 = K_2 + U_2$$

$$0 + Mgh = \tfrac{3}{4}Mv_{cm}^2 + 0$$

$$v_{cm} = \sqrt{\tfrac{4}{3}gh}$$

EVALUATE: No mechanical energy was lost or gained, so from the energy standpoint the string is merely a way to convert some of the gravitational potential energy (which is released as the cylinder falls) into rotational kinetic energy rather than translational kinetic energy. Because not all of the released energy goes into translation, v_{cm} is less than the speed $\sqrt{2gh}$ of an object dropped from height h with no strings attached.

EXAMPLE 10.5 RACE OF THE ROLLING BODIES

In a physics demonstration, an instructor "races" various bodies that roll without slipping from rest down an inclined plane (**Fig. 10.16**). What shape should a body have to reach the bottom of the incline first?

SOLUTION

IDENTIFY and SET UP: Kinetic friction does no work if the bodies roll without slipping. We can also ignore the effects of *rolling friction,* introduced in Section 5.3, if the bodies and the surface of the incline are rigid. (Later in this section we'll explain why this is so.) We can therefore use conservation of energy. Each body starts from rest at the top of an incline with height h, so $K_1 = 0$, $U_1 = Mgh$, and $U_2 = 0$. Equation (10.8) gives the kinetic energy at the bottom of the incline; since the bodies roll without slipping, $\omega = v_{cm}/R$. We can express the moments of inertia of the four round bodies in

10.16 Which body rolls down the incline fastest, and why?

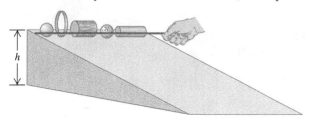

Table 9.2, cases (f)–(i), as $I_{cm} = cMR^2$, where c is a number less than or equal to 1 that depends on the shape of the body. Our goal is to find the value of c that gives the body the greatest speed v_{cm} after its center of mass has descended a vertical distance h.

EXECUTE: From conservation of energy,

$$K_1 + U_1 = K_2 + U_2$$

$$0 + Mgh = \tfrac{1}{2}Mv_{cm}^2 + \tfrac{1}{2}cMR^2\left(\frac{v_{cm}}{R}\right)^2 + 0$$

$$Mgh = \tfrac{1}{2}(1 + c)Mv_{cm}^2$$

$$v_{cm} = \sqrt{\frac{2gh}{1 + c}}$$

EVALUATE: For a given value of c, the speed v_{cm} after descending a distance h is *independent* of the body's mass M and radius R. Hence *all* uniform solid cylinders $\left(c = \tfrac{1}{2}\right)$ have the same speed at the bottom, regardless of their mass and radii. The values of c tell us that the order of finish for uniform bodies will be as follows: (1) any solid sphere $\left(c = \tfrac{2}{5}\right)$, (2) any solid cylinder $\left(c = \tfrac{1}{2}\right)$, (3) any thin-walled, hollow sphere $\left(c = \tfrac{2}{3}\right)$, and (4) any thin-walled, hollow cylinder ($c = 1$). Small-c bodies always beat large-c bodies because less of their kinetic energy is tied up in rotation, so more is available for translation.

Combined Translation and Rotation: Dynamics

We can also analyze the combined translational and rotational motions of a rigid body from the standpoint of dynamics. We showed in Section 8.5 that for an extended body, the acceleration of the center of mass is the same as that of a particle of the same mass acted on by all the external forces on the actual body:

Net external ········· Total mass of body
force on a body $\sum \vec{F}_{\text{ext}} = M\vec{a}_{\text{cm}}$ ········· Acceleration of   (10.12)
center of mass

The rotational motion about the center of mass is described by the rotational analog of Newton's second law, Eq. (10.7):

Net torque on a rigid ········· Moment of inertia of
body about z-axis ········· rigid body about z-axis
through center of mass $\sum \tau_z = I_{\text{cm}}\alpha_z$ ········· Angular acceleration of   (10.13)
rigid body about z-axis

It's not immediately obvious that Eq. (10.13) should apply to the motion of a translating rigid body; after all, our derivation of $\sum \tau_z = I\alpha_z$ in Section 10.2 assumed that the axis of rotation was stationary. But Eq. (10.13) is valid *even when the axis of rotation moves*, provided the following two conditions are met:

1. The axis through the center of mass must be an axis of symmetry.

2. The axis must not change direction.

These conditions are satisfied for many types of rotation (**Fig. 10.17**). Note that in general this moving axis of rotation is *not* at rest in an inertial frame of reference.

We can now solve dynamics problems involving a rigid body that undergoes translational and rotational motions at the same time, provided that the rotation axis satisfies the two conditions just mentioned. Problem-Solving Strategy 10.1 (Section 10.2) is equally useful here, and you should review it now. Keep in mind that when a body undergoes translational and rotational motions at the same time, we need two separate equations of motion *for the same body:* Eq. (10.12) for the translation of the center of mass and Eq. (10.13) for rotation about an axis through the center of mass.

10.17 The axle of a bicycle wheel passes through the wheel's center of mass and is an axis of symmetry. Hence the rotation of the wheel is described by Eq. (10.13), provided the bicycle doesn't turn or tilt to one side (which would change the orientation of the axle).

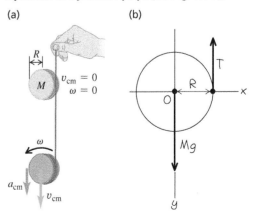

EXAMPLE 10.6   ACCELERATION OF A PRIMITIVE YO-YO

For the primitive yo-yo in Example 10.4 (**Fig. 10.18a**), find the downward acceleration of the cylinder and the tension in the string.

SOLUTION

IDENTIFY and SET UP: Figure 10.18b shows our free-body diagram for the yo-yo, including our choice of positive coordinate directions. Our target variables are $a_{\text{cm-}y}$ and T. We'll use Eq. (10.12) for the translational motion of the center of mass and Eq. (10.13) for the rotational motion around the center of mass. We'll also use Eq. (10.11), which says that the string unwinds without slipping. As in Example 10.4, the moment of inertia of the yo-yo for an axis through its center of mass is $I_{\text{cm}} = \frac{1}{2}MR^2$.

EXECUTE: From Eq. (10.12),

$$\sum F_y = Mg + (-T) = Ma_{\text{cm-}y} \qquad (10.14)$$

10.18 Dynamics of a primitive yo-yo (see Fig. 10.15).

Continued

From Eq. (10.13),

$$\sum \tau_z = TR = I_{cm}\alpha_z = \tfrac{1}{2}MR^2\alpha_z \qquad (10.15)$$

From Eq. (10.11), $v_{cm\text{-}z} = R\omega_z$; the derivative of this expression with respect to time gives us

$$a_{cm\text{-}y} = R\alpha_z \qquad (10.16)$$

We now use Eq. (10.16) to eliminate α_z from Eq. (10.15) and then solve Eqs. (10.14) and (10.15) simultaneously for T and $a_{cm\text{-}y}$:

$$a_{cm\text{-}y} = \tfrac{2}{3}g \qquad T = \tfrac{1}{3}Mg$$

EVALUATE: The string slows the fall of the yo-yo, but not enough to stop it completely. Hence $a_{cm\text{-}y}$ is less than the free-fall value g and T is less than the yo-yo weight Mg.

EXAMPLE 10.7 ACCELERATION OF A ROLLING SPHERE

A bowling ball rolls without slipping down a ramp that is inclined at an angle β to the horizontal (**Fig. 10.19a**). What are the ball's acceleration and the magnitude of the friction force on the ball? Treat the ball as a uniform solid sphere, ignoring the finger holes.

SOLUTION

IDENTIFY and SET UP: The free-body diagram (Fig. 10.19b) shows that only the friction force exerts a torque about the center of mass. Our target variables are the acceleration $a_{cm\text{-}x}$ of the ball's center of mass and the magnitude f of the friction force. (Because the ball does not slip at the instantaneous point of contact with the ramp, this is a *static* friction force; it prevents slipping and gives the ball its angular acceleration.) We use Eqs. (10.12) and (10.13) as in Example 10.6.

10.19 A bowling ball rolling down a ramp.

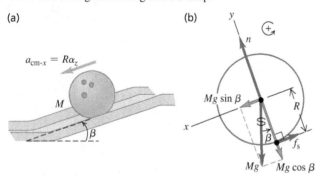

EXECUTE: The ball's moment of inertia is $I_{cm} = \tfrac{2}{5}MR^2$. The equations of motion are

$$\sum F_x = Mg\sin\beta + (-f) = Ma_{cm\text{-}x} \qquad (10.17)$$

$$\sum \tau_z = fR = I_{cm}\alpha_z = \left(\tfrac{2}{5}MR^2\right)\alpha_z \qquad (10.18)$$

The ball rolls without slipping, so as in Example 10.6 we use $a_{cm\text{-}x} = R\alpha_z$ to eliminate α_z from Eq. (10.18):

$$fR = \tfrac{2}{5}MRa_{cm\text{-}x}$$

This equation and Eq. (10.17) are two equations for the unknowns $a_{cm\text{-}x}$ and f. We solve Eq. (10.17) for f, substitute that expression into the above equation to eliminate f, and solve for $a_{cm\text{-}x}$:

$$a_{cm\text{-}x} = \tfrac{5}{7}g\sin\beta$$

Finally, we substitute this acceleration into Eq. (10.17) and solve for f:

$$f = \tfrac{2}{7}Mg\sin\beta$$

EVALUATE: The ball's acceleration is just $\tfrac{5}{7}$ as large as that of an object *sliding* down the slope without friction. If the ball descends a vertical distance h as it rolls down the ramp, its displacement along the ramp is $h/\sin\beta$. You can show that the speed of the ball at the bottom of the ramp is $v_{cm} = \sqrt{\tfrac{10}{7}gh}$, the same as our result from Example 10.5 with $c = \tfrac{2}{5}$.

If the ball were rolling *uphill* without slipping, the force of friction would still be directed uphill as in Fig. 10.19b. Can you see why?

Rolling Friction

In Example 10.5 we said that we can ignore rolling friction if both the rolling body and the surface over which it rolls are perfectly rigid. In **Fig. 10.20a** a perfectly rigid sphere is rolling down a perfectly rigid incline. The line of action of the normal force passes through the center of the sphere, so its torque is zero; there is no sliding at the point of contact, so the friction force does no work. Figure 10.20b shows a more realistic situation, in which the surface "piles up" in front of the sphere and the sphere rides in a shallow trench. Because of these deformations, the contact forces on the sphere no longer act along a single point but over an area; the forces are concentrated on the front of the sphere as shown. As a result, the normal force now exerts a torque that opposes the rotation. In addition, there is some sliding of the sphere over the surface due to the deformation, causing mechanical energy to be lost. The combination of these two effects is the phenomenon of *rolling friction*. Rolling friction also occurs

(a) Perfectly rigid sphere rolling on a perfectly rigid surface

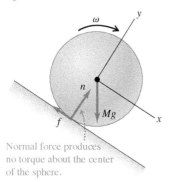

Normal force produces no torque about the center of the sphere.

(b) Rigid sphere rolling on a deformable surface

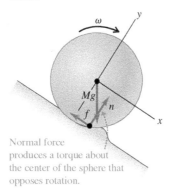

Normal force produces a torque about the center of the sphere that opposes rotation.

10.20 Rolling down (a) a perfectly rigid surface and (b) a deformable surface. In (b) the deformation is greatly exaggerated, and the force n is the component of the contact force that points normal to the plane of the surface before it is deformed.

if the rolling body is deformable, such as an automobile tire. Often the rolling body and the surface are rigid enough that rolling friction can be ignored, as we have assumed in all the examples in this section.

TEST YOUR UNDERSTANDING OF SECTION 10.3 Suppose the solid cylinder used as a yo-yo in Example 10.6 is replaced by a hollow cylinder of the same mass and radius. (a) Will the acceleration of the yo-yo (i) increase, (ii) decrease, or (iii) remain the same? (b) Will the string tension (i) increase, (ii) decrease, or (iii) remain the same? ❚

10.4 WORK AND POWER IN ROTATIONAL MOTION

When you pedal a bicycle, you apply forces to a rotating body and do work on it. Similar things happen in many other real-life situations, such as a rotating motor shaft driving a power tool or a car engine propelling the vehicle. Let's see how to apply our ideas about work from Chapter 6 to rotational motion.

Suppose a tangential force $\vec{F}_{tan}$ acts at the rim of a pivoted disk—for example, a child running while pushing on a playground merry-go-round (**Fig. 10.21a**). The disk rotates through an infinitesimal angle $d\theta$ about a fixed axis during an infinitesimal time interval dt (Fig. 10.21b). The work dW done by the force $\vec{F}_{tan}$ while a point on the rim moves a distance ds is $dW = F_{tan}\,ds$. If $d\theta$ is measured in radians, then $ds = R\,d\theta$ and

$$dW = F_{tan}R\,d\theta$$

Now $F_{tan}R$ is the *torque* τ_z due to the force $\vec{F}_{tan}$, so

$$dW = \tau_z\,d\theta \qquad (10.19)$$

As the disk rotates from θ_1 to θ_2, the total work done by the torque is

Work done by a torque τ_z · · · → Upper limit = final angular position

$$W = \int_{\theta_1}^{\theta_2} \tau_z\,d\theta \qquad (10.20)$$

Integral of the torque with respect to angle

Lower limit = initial angular position

If the torque remains *constant* while the angle changes, then the work is the product of torque and angular displacement:

Work done by a constant torque τ_z · · · → Torque · · · ·

$$W = \tau_z(\theta_2 - \theta_1) = \tau_z\Delta\theta \qquad (10.21)$$

Final minus initial angular position = angular displacement

10.21 A tangential force applied to a rotating body does work.

(a)

Child applies tangential force.

$\vec{F}_{tan}$

(b) Overhead view of merry-go-round

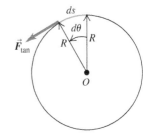

If torque is expressed in newton-meters ($N \cdot m$) and angular displacement in radians, the work is in joules. Equation (10.21) is the rotational analog of Eq. (6.1), $W = Fs$, and Eq. (10.20) is the analog of Eq. (6.7), $W = \int F_x \, dx$, for the work done by a force in a straight-line displacement.

If the force in Fig. 10.21 had an axial component (parallel to the rotation axis) or a radial component (directed toward or away from the axis), that component would do no work because the displacement of the point of application has only a tangential component. An axial or radial component of force would also make no contribution to the torque about the axis of rotation. So Eqs. (10.20) and (10.21) are correct for *any* force, no matter what its components.

When a torque does work on a rotating rigid body, the kinetic energy changes by an amount equal to the work done. We can prove this by using exactly the same procedure that we used in Eqs. (6.11) through (6.13) for the translational kinetic energy of a particle. Let τ_z represent the *net* torque on the body so that $\tau_z = I\alpha_z$ from Eq. (10.7), and assume that the body is rigid so that the moment of inertia I is constant. We then transform the integrand in Eq. (10.20) into an integrand with respect to ω_z as follows:

$$\tau_z \, d\theta = (I\alpha_z) \, d\theta = I\frac{d\omega_z}{dt}d\theta = I\frac{d\theta}{dt}d\omega_z = I\omega_z \, d\omega_z$$

Since τ_z is the net torque, the integral in Eq. (10.20) is the *total* work done on the rotating rigid body. This equation then becomes

Total work done on a rotating rigid body = work done by the net external torque

Final rotational kinetic energy

$$W_{\text{tot}} = \int_{\omega_1}^{\omega_2} I\omega_z \, d\omega_z = \tfrac{1}{2}I\omega_2^2 - \tfrac{1}{2}I\omega_1^2 \qquad (10.22)$$

Initial rotational kinetic energy

The change in the rotational kinetic energy of a *rigid* body equals the work done by forces exerted from outside the body (**Fig. 10.22**). This equation is analogous to Eq. (6.13), the work–energy theorem for a particle.

How does *power* relate to torque? When we divide both sides of Eq. (10.19) by the time interval dt during which the angular displacement occurs, we find

$$\frac{dW}{dt} = \tau_z \frac{d\theta}{dt}$$

But dW/dt is the rate of doing work, or *power P*, and $d\theta/dt$ is angular velocity ω_z:

Torque with respect to body's rotation axis

Power due to a torque acting on a rigid body
$$P = \tau_z \omega_z \qquad (10.23)$$
Angular velocity of body about axis

This is the analog of the relationship $P = \vec{F} \cdot \vec{v}$ that we developed in Section 6.4 for particle motion.

10.22 The rotational kinetic energy of a helicopter's main rotor is equal to the total work done to set it spinning. When it is spinning at a constant rate, positive work is done on the rotor by the engine and negative work is done on it by air resistance. Hence the net work being done is zero and the kinetic energy remains constant.

EXAMPLE 10.8 CALCULATING POWER FROM TORQUE

An electric motor exerts a constant 10-$N \cdot m$ torque on a grindstone, which has a moment of inertia of $2.0 \text{ kg} \cdot \text{m}^2$ about its shaft. The system starts from rest. Find the work W done by the motor in 8.0 s and the grindstone's kinetic energy K at this time. What average power P_{av} is delivered by the motor?

SOLUTION

IDENTIFY and SET UP: The only torque acting is that due to the motor. Since this torque is constant, the grindstone's angular acceleration α_z is constant. We'll use Eq. (10.7) to find α_z, and then

use this in the kinematics equations from Section 9.2 to calculate the angle $\Delta\theta$ through which the grindstone rotates in 8.0 s and its final angular velocity ω_z. From these we'll calculate W, K, and P_{av}.

EXECUTE: We have $\Sigma\tau_z = 10 \text{ N} \cdot \text{m}$ and $I = 2.0 \text{ kg} \cdot \text{m}^2$, so $\Sigma\tau_z = I\alpha_z$ yields $\alpha_z = 5.0 \text{ rad/s}^2$. From Eqs. (9.11) and (10.21),

$$\Delta\theta = \tfrac{1}{2}\alpha_z t^2 = \tfrac{1}{2}(5.0 \text{ rad/s}^2)(8.0 \text{ s})^2 = 160 \text{ rad}$$

$$W = \tau_z \Delta\theta = (10 \text{ N} \cdot \text{m})(160 \text{ rad}) = 1600 \text{ J}$$

From Eqs. (9.7) and (9.17),

$$\omega_z = \alpha_z t = (5.0 \text{ rad/s}^2)(8.0 \text{ s}) = 40 \text{ rad/s}$$

$$K = \tfrac{1}{2} I \omega_z^2 = \tfrac{1}{2}(2.0 \text{ kg} \cdot \text{m}^2)(40 \text{ rad/s})^2 = 1600 \text{ J}$$

The average power is the work done divided by the time interval:

$$P_{av} = \frac{1600 \text{ J}}{8.0 \text{ s}} = 200 \text{ J/s} = 200 \text{ W}$$

EVALUATE: The initial kinetic energy was zero, so the work done W must equal the final kinetic energy K [Eq. (10.22)]. This is just as we calculated. We can check our result $P_{av} = 200$ W by considering the *instantaneous* power $P = \tau_z \omega_z$. Because ω_z increases continuously, P increases continuously as well; its value increases from zero at $t = 0$ to $(10 \text{ N} \cdot \text{m})(40 \text{ rad/s}) = 400$ W at $t = 8.0$ s. Both ω_z and P increase *uniformly* with time, so the *average* power is just half this maximum value, or 200 W.

TEST YOUR UNDERSTANDING OF SECTION 10.4 You apply equal torques to two different cylinders. Cylinder 1 has a moment of inertia twice as large as cylinder 2. Each cylinder is initially at rest. After one complete rotation, which cylinder has the greater kinetic energy? (i) Cylinder 1; (ii) cylinder 2; (iii) both cylinders have the same kinetic energy. ∎

10.5 ANGULAR MOMENTUM

Every rotational quantity that we have encountered in Chapters 9 and 10 is the analog of some quantity in the translational motion of a particle. The analog of *momentum* of a particle is **angular momentum,** a vector quantity denoted as $\vec{L}$. Its relationship to momentum $\vec{p}$ (which we will often call *linear momentum* for clarity) is exactly the same as the relationship of torque to force, $\vec{\tau} = \vec{r} \times \vec{F}$. For a particle with constant mass m and velocity $\vec{v}$, the angular momentum is

Angular momentum of ⋯ a particle relative to origin O of an inertial frame of reference

Position vector of particle relative to O

$$\vec{L} = \vec{r} \times \vec{p} = \vec{r} \times m\vec{v} \qquad (10.24)$$

Linear momentum of particle = mass times velocity

The value of $\vec{L}$ depends on the choice of origin O, since it involves the particle's position vector $\vec{r}$ relative to O. The units of angular momentum are $\text{kg} \cdot \text{m}^2/\text{s}$.

In **Fig. 10.23** a particle moves in the xy-plane; its position vector $\vec{r}$ and momentum $\vec{p} = m\vec{v}$ are shown. The angular momentum vector $\vec{L}$ is perpendicular to the xy-plane. The right-hand rule for vector products shows that its direction is along the $+z$-axis, and its magnitude is

$$L = mvr \sin\phi = mvl \qquad (10.25)$$

where l is the perpendicular distance from the line of $\vec{v}$ to O. This distance plays the role of "lever arm" for the momentum vector.

When a net force $\vec{F}$ acts on a particle, its velocity and momentum change, so its angular momentum may also change. We can show that the *rate of change* of angular momentum is equal to the torque of the net force. We take the time derivative of Eq. (10.24), using the rule for the derivative of a product:

$$\frac{d\vec{L}}{dt} = \left(\frac{d\vec{r}}{dt} \times m\vec{v}\right) + \left(\vec{r} \times m\frac{d\vec{v}}{dt}\right) = (\vec{v} \times m\vec{v}) + (\vec{r} \times m\vec{a})$$

The first term is zero because it contains the vector product of the vector $\vec{v} = d\vec{r}/dt$ with itself. In the second term we replace $m\vec{a}$ with the net force $\vec{F}$:

$$\frac{d\vec{L}}{dt} = \vec{r} \times \vec{F} = \vec{\tau} \qquad \text{(for a particle acted on by net force } \vec{F}\text{)} \qquad (10.26)$$

The rate of change of angular momentum of a particle equals the torque of the net force acting on it. Compare this result to Eq. (8.4): The rate of change $d\vec{p}/dt$ of the *linear* momentum of a particle equals the net force that acts on it.

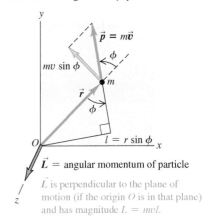

10.23 Calculating the angular momentum $\vec{L} = \vec{r} \times m\vec{v} = \vec{r} \times \vec{p}$ of a particle with mass m moving in the xy-plane.

$\vec{L}$ = angular momentum of particle

$\vec{L}$ is perpendicular to the plane of motion (if the origin O is in that plane) and has magnitude $L = mvl$.

10.24 Calculating the angular momentum of a particle of mass m_i in a rigid body rotating at angular speed ω. (Compare Fig. 10.23.)

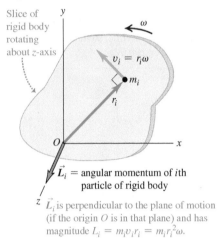

Slice of rigid body rotating about z-axis

$v_i = r_i\omega$

m_i

r_i

$\vec{L}_i$ = angular momentum of *i*th particle of rigid body

$\vec{L}_i$ is perpendicular to the plane of motion (if the origin O is in that plane) and has magnitude $L_i = m_i v_i r_i = m_i r_i^2 \omega$.

10.25 Two particles of the same mass located symmetrically on either side of the rotation axis of a rigid body. The angular momentum vectors $\vec{L}_1$ and $\vec{L}_2$ of the two particles do not lie along the rotation axis, but their vector sum $\vec{L}_1 + \vec{L}_2$ does.

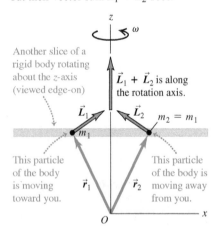

Another slice of a rigid body rotating about the z-axis (viewed edge-on)

$\vec{L}_1 + \vec{L}_2$ is along the rotation axis.

$\vec{L}_1$ $\vec{L}_2$ $m_2 = m_1$

m_1

This particle of the body is moving toward you.

This particle of the body is moving away from you.

$\vec{r}_1$ $\vec{r}_2$

O

Angular Momentum of a Rigid Body

We can use Eq. (10.25) to find the total angular momentum of a *rigid body* rotating about the z-axis with angular speed ω. First consider a thin slice of the body lying in the *xy*-plane (**Fig. 10.24**). Each particle in the slice moves in a circle centered at the origin, and at each instant its velocity $\vec{v}_i$ is perpendicular to its position vector $\vec{r}_i$, as shown. Hence in Eq. (10.25), $\phi = 90°$ for every particle. A particle with mass m_i at a distance r_i from O has a speed v_i equal to $r_i\omega$. From Eq. (10.25) the magnitude L_i of its angular momentum is

$$L_i = m_i(r_i\omega)\,r_i = m_i r_i^2 \omega \qquad (10.27)$$

The direction of each particle's angular momentum, as given by the right-hand rule for the vector product, is along the $+z$-axis.

The *total* angular momentum of the slice of the body lying in the *xy*-plane is the sum $\sum L_i$ of the angular momenta L_i of the particles. Summing Eq. (10.27), we have

$$L = \sum L_i = \left(\sum m_i r_i^2\right)\omega = I\omega$$

where I is the moment of inertia of the slice about the z-axis.

We can do this same calculation for the other slices of the body, all parallel to the *xy*-plane. For points that do not lie in the *xy*-plane, a complication arises because the $\vec{r}$ vectors have components in the z-direction as well as in the *x*- and *y*-directions; this gives the angular momentum of each particle a component perpendicular to the z-axis. But *if the z-axis is an axis of symmetry,* the perpendicular components for particles on opposite sides of this axis add up to zero (**Fig. 10.25**). So when a body rotates about an axis of symmetry, its angular momentum vector $\vec{L}$ lies along the symmetry axis, and its magnitude is $L = I\omega$.

The angular velocity vector $\vec{\omega}$ also lies along the rotation axis, as we saw in Section 9.1. Hence for a rigid body rotating around an axis of symmetry, $\vec{L}$ and $\vec{\omega}$ are in the same direction (**Fig. 10.26**). So we have the *vector* relationship

Angular momentum of a rigid body rotating around a symmetry axis $\quad \vec{L} = I\vec{\omega} \quad$ Moment of inertia of body about symmetry axis $\qquad (10.28)$

Angular velocity vector of body

From Eq. (10.26) the rate of change of angular momentum of a particle equals the torque of the net force acting on the particle. For any system of particles (including both rigid and nonrigid bodies), the rate of change of the *total* angular momentum equals the sum of the torques of all forces acting on all the particles. The torques of the *internal* forces add to zero if these forces act along the line from one particle to another, as in Fig. 10.8, and so the sum of the torques includes only the torques of the *external* forces. (We saw a similar

10.26 For rotation about an axis of symmetry, $\vec{\omega}$ and $\vec{L}$ are parallel and along the axis. The directions of both vectors are given by the right-hand rule (compare Fig. 9.5).

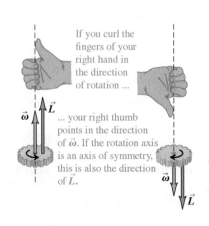

If you curl the fingers of your right hand in the direction of rotation ...

$\vec{\omega}$ $\vec{L}$

... your right thumb points in the direction of $\vec{\omega}$. If the rotation axis is an axis of symmetry, this is also the direction of $\vec{L}$.

$\vec{\omega}$

$\vec{L}$

cancellation in our discussion of center-of-mass motion in Section 8.5.) So we conclude that

For a system of particles:
Sum of external torques ·········→ $\sum \vec{\tau} = \dfrac{d\vec{L}}{dt}$ ←······· Rate of change of total angular momentum $\vec{L}$ of system   (10.29)

Finally, if the system of particles is a rigid body rotating about a symmetry axis (the z-axis), then $L_z = I\omega_z$ and I is constant. If this axis has a fixed direction in space, then vectors $\vec{L}$ and $\vec{\omega}$ change only in magnitude, not in direction. In that case, $dL_z/dt = I\, d\omega_z/dt = I\alpha_z$, or

$$\sum \tau_z = I\alpha_z$$

which is again our basic relationship for the dynamics of rigid-body rotation. If the body is *not* rigid, I may change; in that case, L changes even when ω is constant. For a nonrigid body, Eq. (10.29) is still valid, even though Eq. (10.7) is not.

When the axis of rotation is *not* a symmetry axis, the angular momentum is in general *not* parallel to the axis (**Fig. 10.27**). As the body turns, the angular momentum vector $\vec{L}$ traces out a cone around the rotation axis. Because $\vec{L}$ changes, there must be a net external torque acting on the body even though the angular velocity magnitude ω may be constant. If the body is an unbalanced wheel on a car, this torque is provided by friction in the bearings, which causes the bearings to wear out. "Balancing" a wheel means distributing the mass so that the rotation axis is an axis of symmetry; then $\vec{L}$ points along the rotation axis, and no net torque is required to keep the wheel turning.

In fixed-axis rotation we often use the term "angular momentum of the body" to refer to only the *component* of $\vec{L}$ along the rotation axis of the body (the z-axis in Fig. 10.27), with a positive or negative sign to indicate the sense of rotation just as with angular velocity.

10.27 If the rotation axis of a rigid body is not a symmetry axis, $\vec{L}$ does not in general lie along the rotation axis. Even if $\vec{\omega}$ is constant, the direction of $\vec{L}$ changes and a net torque is required to maintain rotation.

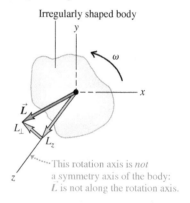

This rotation axis is *not* a symmetry axis of the body: L is not along the rotation axis.

EXAMPLE 10.9   ANGULAR MOMENTUM AND TORQUE

A turbine fan in a jet engine has a moment of inertia of $2.5\ \text{kg}\cdot\text{m}^2$ about its axis of rotation. As the turbine starts up, its angular velocity is given by $\omega_z = (40\ \text{rad/s}^3)t^2$. (a) Find the fan's angular momentum as a function of time, and find its value at $t = 3.0$ s. (b) Find the net torque on the fan as a function of time, and find its value at $t = 3.0$ s.

SOLUTION

IDENTIFY and SET UP: The fan rotates about its axis of symmetry (the z-axis). Hence the angular momentum vector has only a z-component L_z, which we can determine from the angular velocity ω_z. Since the direction of angular momentum is constant, the net torque likewise has only a component τ_z along the rotation axis. We'll use Eq. (10.28) to find L_z from ω_z and then Eq. (10.29) to find τ_z.

EXECUTE: (a) From Eq. (10.28),

$$L_z = I\omega_z = (2.5\ \text{kg}\cdot\text{m}^2)(40\ \text{rad/s}^3)t^2 = (100\ \text{kg}\cdot\text{m}^2/\text{s}^3)t^2$$

(We dropped the dimensionless quantity "rad" from the final expression.) At $t = 3.0$ s, $L_z = 900\ \text{kg}\cdot\text{m}^2/\text{s}$.

(b) From Eq. (10.29),

$$\tau_z = \frac{dL_z}{dt} = (100\ \text{kg}\cdot\text{m}^2/\text{s}^3)(2t) = (200\ \text{kg}\cdot\text{m}^2/\text{s}^3)t$$

At $t = 3.0$ s,

$$\tau_z = (200\ \text{kg}\cdot\text{m}^2/\text{s}^3)(3.0\ \text{s}) = 600\ \text{kg}\cdot\text{m}^2/\text{s}^2 = 600\ \text{N}\cdot\text{m}$$

EVALUATE: As a check on our expression for τ_z, note that the angular acceleration of the turbine is $\alpha_z = d\omega_z/dt = (40\ \text{rad/s}^3)(2t) = (80\ \text{rad/s}^3)t$. Hence from Eq. (10.7), the torque on the fan is $\tau_z = I\alpha_z = (2.5\ \text{kg}\cdot\text{m}^2)(80\ \text{rad/s}^3)t = (200\ \text{kg}\cdot\text{m}^2/\text{s}^3)t$, just as we calculated.

TEST YOUR UNDERSTANDING OF SECTION 10.5   A ball is attached to one end of a piece of string. You hold the other end of the string and whirl the ball in a circle around your hand. (a) If the ball moves at a constant speed, is its linear momentum $\vec{p}$ constant? Why or why not? (b) Is its angular momentum $\vec{L}$ constant? Why or why not? ∎

DEMO   DEMO

(MP)

PhET: Torque

10.28 A falling cat twists different parts of its body in different directions so that it lands feet first. At all times during this process the angular momentum of the cat as a whole remains zero.

10.6 CONSERVATION OF ANGULAR MOMENTUM

We have just seen that angular momentum can be used for an alternative statement of the basic dynamic principle for rotational motion. It also forms the basis for the **principle of conservation of angular momentum.** Like conservation of energy and of linear momentum, this principle is a universal conservation law, valid at all scales from atomic and nuclear systems to the motions of galaxies. This principle follows directly from Eq. (10.29): $\sum \vec{\tau} = d\vec{L}/dt$. If $\sum \vec{\tau} = 0$, then $d\vec{L}/dt = 0$, and $\vec{L}$ is constant.

> **When the net external torque acting on a system is zero, the total angular momentum of the system is constant (conserved).**

A circus acrobat, a diver, and an ice skater pirouetting on one skate all take advantage of this principle. Suppose an acrobat has just left a swing; she has her arms and legs extended and is rotating counterclockwise about her center of mass. When she pulls her arms and legs in, her moment of inertia I_{cm} with respect to her center of mass changes from a large value I_1 to a much smaller value I_2. The only external force acting on her is her weight, which has no torque with respect to an axis through her center of mass. So her angular momentum $L_z = I_{cm}\omega_z$ remains constant, and her angular velocity ω_z increases as I_{cm} decreases. That is,

$$I_1\omega_{1z} = I_2\omega_{2z} \quad \text{(zero net external torque)} \quad (10.30)$$

When a skater or ballerina spins with arms outstretched and then pulls her arms in, her angular velocity increases as her moment of inertia decreases. In each case there is conservation of angular momentum in a system in which the net external torque is zero.

When a system has several parts, the internal forces that the parts exert on one another cause changes in the angular momenta of the parts, but the *total* angular momentum doesn't change. Here's an example. Consider two bodies A and B that interact with each other but not with anything else, such as the astronauts we discussed in Section 8.2 (see Fig. 8.9). Suppose body A exerts a force $\vec{F}_{A \text{ on } B}$ on body B; the corresponding torque (with respect to whatever point we choose) is $\vec{\tau}_{A \text{ on } B}$. According to Eq. (10.29), this torque is equal to the rate of change of angular momentum of B:

$$\vec{\tau}_{A \text{ on } B} = \frac{d\vec{L}_B}{dt}$$

At the same time, body B exerts a force $\vec{F}_{B \text{ on } A}$ on body A, with a corresponding torque $\vec{\tau}_{B \text{ on } A}$, and

$$\vec{\tau}_{B \text{ on } A} = \frac{d\vec{L}_A}{dt}$$

From Newton's third law, $\vec{F}_{B \text{ on } A} = -\vec{F}_{A \text{ on } B}$. Furthermore, if the forces act along the same line, as in Fig. 10.8, their lever arms with respect to the chosen axis are equal. Thus the *torques* of these two forces are equal and opposite, and $\vec{\tau}_{B \text{ on } A} = -\vec{\tau}_{A \text{ on } B}$. So if we add the two preceding equations, we find

$$\frac{d\vec{L}_A}{dt} + \frac{d\vec{L}_B}{dt} = 0$$

or, because $\vec{L}_A + \vec{L}_B$ is the *total* angular momentum $\vec{L}$ of the system,

$$\frac{d\vec{L}}{dt} = 0 \quad \text{(zero net external torque)} \quad (10.31)$$

That is, the total angular momentum of the system is constant. The torques of the internal forces can transfer angular momentum from one body to the other, but they can't change the *total* angular momentum of the system (**Fig. 10.28**).

EXAMPLE 10.10 **ANYONE CAN BE A BALLERINA**

A physics professor stands at the center of a frictionless turntable with arms outstretched and a 5.0-kg dumbbell in each hand (**Fig. 10.29**). He is set rotating about the vertical axis, making one revolution in 2.0 s. Find his final angular velocity if he pulls the dumbbells inward to his stomach. His moment of inertia (without the dumbbells) is 3.0 kg·m² with arms outstretched and 2.2 kg·m² with his hands at his stomach. The dumbbells are 1.0 m from the axis initially and 0.20 m at the end.

SOLUTION

IDENTIFY, SET UP, and EXECUTE: No external torques act about the z-axis, so L_z is constant. We'll use Eq. (10.30) to find the final

10.29 Fun with conservation of angular momentum.

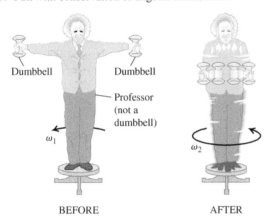

Dumbbell   Dumbbell

Professor (not a dumbbell)

ω_1

ω_2

BEFORE   AFTER

angular velocity ω_{2z}. The moment of inertia of the system is $I = I_{prof} + I_{dumbbells}$. We treat each dumbbell as a particle of mass m that contributes mr^2 to $I_{dumbbells}$, where r is the perpendicular distance from the axis to the dumbbell. Initially we have

$$I_1 = 3.0\ \text{kg}\cdot\text{m}^2 + 2(5.0\ \text{kg})(1.0\ \text{m})^2 = 13\ \text{kg}\cdot\text{m}^2$$

$$\omega_{1z} = \frac{1\ \text{rev}}{2.0\ \text{s}} = 0.50\ \text{rev/s}$$

The final moment of inertia is

$$I_2 = 2.2\ \text{kg}\cdot\text{m}^2 + 2(5.0\ \text{kg})(0.20\ \text{m})^2 = 2.6\ \text{kg}\cdot\text{m}^2$$

From Eq. (10.30), the final angular velocity is

$$\omega_{2z} = \frac{I_1}{I_2}\omega_{1z} = \frac{13\ \text{kg}\cdot\text{m}^2}{2.6\ \text{kg}\cdot\text{m}^2}(0.50\ \text{rev/s}) = 2.5\ \text{rev/s} = 5\omega_{1z}$$

Can you see why we didn't have to change "revolutions" to "radians" in this calculation?

EVALUATE: The angular momentum remained constant, but the angular velocity increased by a factor of 5, from $\omega_{1z} = (0.50\ \text{rev/s}) \times (2\pi\ \text{rad/rev}) = 3.14\ \text{rad/s}$ to $\omega_{2z} = (2.5\ \text{rev/s})(2\pi\ \text{rad/rev}) = 15.7\ \text{rad/s}$. The initial and final kinetic energies are then

$$K_1 = \tfrac{1}{2}I_1\omega_{1z}^2 = \tfrac{1}{2}(13\ \text{kg}\cdot\text{m}^2)(3.14\ \text{rad/s})^2 = 64\ \text{J}$$

$$K_2 = \tfrac{1}{2}I_2\omega_{2z}^2 = \tfrac{1}{2}(2.6\ \text{kg}\cdot\text{m}^2)(15.7\ \text{rad/s})^2 = 320\ \text{J}$$

The fivefold increase in kinetic energy came from the work that the professor did in pulling his arms and the dumbbells inward.

EXAMPLE 10.11 **A ROTATIONAL "COLLISION"**

Figure 10.30 shows two disks: an engine flywheel (A) and a clutch plate (B) attached to a transmission shaft. Their moments of inertia are I_A and I_B; initially, they are rotating with constant angular speeds ω_A and ω_B, respectively. We push the disks together with forces acting along the axis, so as not to apply any torque on either disk. The disks rub against each other and eventually reach a common angular speed ω. Derive an expression for ω.

SOLUTION

IDENTIFY, SET UP, and EXECUTE: There are no external torques, so the only torque acting on either disk is the torque applied by the other disk. Hence the total angular momentum of the system of two disks is conserved. At the end they rotate together as one body with total moment of inertia $I = I_A + I_B$ and angular speed ω. Figure 10.30 shows that all angular velocities are in the same direction, so we can regard ω_A, ω_B, and ω as components of angular velocity along the rotation axis. Conservation of angular momentum gives

$$I_A\omega_A + I_B\omega_B = (I_A + I_B)\omega$$

$$\omega = \frac{I_A\omega_A + I_B\omega_B}{I_A + I_B}$$

10.30 When the net external torque is zero, angular momentum is conserved.

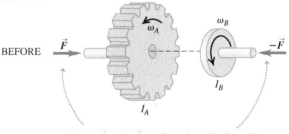

BEFORE

$\vec{F}$ ω_A ω_B $-\vec{F}$

I_B

I_A

Forces $\vec{F}$ and $-\vec{F}$ are along the axis of rotation, and thus exert no torque about this axis on either disk.

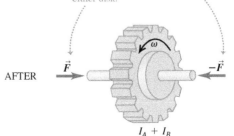

AFTER

$\vec{F}$ ω $-\vec{F}$

$I_A + I_B$

Continued

EVALUATE: This "collision" is analogous to a completely inelastic collision (see Section 8.3). When two objects in translational motion along the same axis collide and stick, the linear momentum of the system is conserved. Here two objects in *rotational* motion around the same axis "collide" and stick, and the *angular* momentum of the system is conserved.

The kinetic energy of a system decreases in a completely inelastic collision. Here kinetic energy is lost because nonconservative (friction) internal forces act while the two disks rub together. Suppose flywheel *A* has a mass of 2.0 kg, a radius of 0.20 m, and an initial angular speed of 50 rad/s (about 500 rpm), and clutch plate *B* has a mass of 4.0 kg, a radius of 0.10 m, and an initial angular speed of 200 rad/s. Can you show that the final kinetic energy is only two-thirds of the initial kinetic energy?

EXAMPLE 10.12 **ANGULAR MOMENTUM IN A CRIME BUST**

A door 1.00 m wide, of mass 15 kg, can rotate freely about a vertical axis through its hinges. A bullet with a mass of 10 g and a speed of 400 m/s strikes the center of the door, in a direction perpendicular to the plane of the door, and embeds itself there. Find the door's angular speed. Is kinetic energy conserved?

SOLUTION

IDENTIFY and SET UP: We consider the door and bullet as a system. There is no external torque about the hinge axis, so angular momentum about this axis is conserved. **Figure 10.31** shows our sketch. The initial angular momentum is that of the bullet, as given by Eq. (10.25). The final angular momentum is that of a rigid body composed of the door and the embedded bullet. We'll equate these quantities and solve for the resulting angular speed ω of the door and bullet.

EXECUTE: From Eq. (10.25), the initial angular momentum of the bullet is

$$L = mvl = (0.010 \text{ kg})(400 \text{ m/s})(0.50 \text{ m}) = 2.0 \text{ kg} \cdot \text{m}^2/\text{s}$$

The final angular momentum is $I\omega$, where $I = I_{\text{door}} + I_{\text{bullet}}$. From Table 9.2, case (d), for a door of width $d = 1.00$ m,

$$I_{\text{door}} = \frac{Md^2}{3} = \frac{(15 \text{ kg})(1.00 \text{ m})^2}{3} = 5.0 \text{ kg} \cdot \text{m}^2$$

The moment of inertia of the bullet (with respect to the axis along the hinges) is

$$I_{\text{bullet}} = ml^2 = (0.010 \text{ kg})(0.50 \text{ m})^2 = 0.0025 \text{ kg} \cdot \text{m}^2$$

Conservation of angular momentum requires that $mvl = I\omega$, or

$$\omega = \frac{mvl}{I} = \frac{2.0 \text{ kg} \cdot \text{m}^2/\text{s}}{5.0 \text{ kg} \cdot \text{m}^2 + 0.0025 \text{ kg} \cdot \text{m}^2} = 0.40 \text{ rad/s}$$

The initial and final kinetic energies are

$$K_1 = \tfrac{1}{2}mv^2 = \tfrac{1}{2}(0.010 \text{ kg})(400 \text{ m/s})^2 = 800 \text{ J}$$

$$K_2 = \tfrac{1}{2}I\omega^2 = \tfrac{1}{2}(5.0025 \text{ kg} \cdot \text{m}^2)(0.40 \text{ rad/s})^2 = 0.40 \text{ J}$$

EVALUATE: The final kinetic energy is only $\frac{1}{2000}$ of the initial value! We did not expect kinetic energy to be conserved: The collision is inelastic because nonconservative friction forces act during the impact. The door's final angular speed is quite slow: At 0.40 rad/s, it takes 3.9 s to swing through 90° ($\pi/2$ radians).

10.31 The swinging door seen from above.

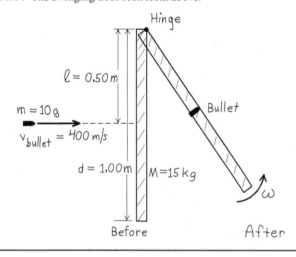

TEST YOUR UNDERSTANDING OF SECTION 10.6 If the polar ice caps were to melt completely due to global warming, the melted ice would redistribute itself over the earth. This change would cause the length of the day (the time needed for the earth to rotate once on its axis) to (i) increase; (ii) decrease; (iii) remain the same. (*Hint:* Use angular momentum ideas. Assume that the sun, moon, and planets exert negligibly small torques on the earth.) ▮

10.7 GYROSCOPES AND PRECESSION

In all the situations we've looked at so far in this chapter, the axis of rotation either has stayed fixed or has moved and kept the same direction (such as rolling without slipping). But a variety of new physical phenomena, some quite unexpected, can occur when the axis of rotation changes direction. For example, consider a toy gyroscope that's supported at one end (**Fig. 10.32**). If we hold it with the flywheel axis horizontal and let go, the free end of the axis simply drops owing to gravity—*if* the flywheel isn't spinning. But if the flywheel *is* spinning, what happens is quite different. One possible motion is a steady circular motion of the axis in a horizontal plane, combined with the spin motion of the flywheel about the axis. This surprising, nonintuitive motion of the axis is called **precession.** Precession is found in nature as well as in rotating machines such as gyroscopes. As you read these words, the earth itself is precessing; its spin axis (through the north and south poles) slowly changes direction, going through a complete cycle of precession every 26,000 years.

To study this strange phenomenon of precession, we must remember that angular velocity, angular momentum, and torque are all *vector* quantities. In particular, we need the general relationship between the net torque $\sum \vec{\tau}$ that acts on a body and the rate of change of the body's angular momentum $\vec{L}$, given by Eq. (10.29), $\sum \vec{\tau} = d\vec{L}/dt$. Let's first apply this equation to the case in which the flywheel is *not* spinning (**Fig. 10.33a**). We take the origin O at the pivot and assume that the flywheel is symmetrical, with mass M and moment of inertia I about the flywheel axis. The flywheel axis is initially along the x-axis. The only external forces on the gyroscope are the normal force $\vec{n}$ acting at the pivot (assumed to be frictionless) and the weight $\vec{w}$ of the flywheel that acts at its center of mass, a distance r from the pivot. The normal force has zero torque with respect to the pivot, and the weight has a torque $\vec{\tau}$ in the y-direction, as shown in Fig. 10.33a. Initially, there is no rotation, and the initial angular momentum $\vec{L}_i$ is zero. From Eq. (10.29) the *change* $d\vec{L}$ in angular momentum in a short time interval dt following this is

$$d\vec{L} = \vec{\tau}\, dt \qquad (10.32)$$

This change is in the y-direction because $\vec{\tau}$ is. As each additional time interval dt elapses, the angular momentum changes by additional increments $d\vec{L}$ in the y-direction because the direction of the torque is constant (Fig. 10.33b). The steadily increasing horizontal angular momentum means that the gyroscope rotates downward faster and faster around the y-axis until it hits either the stand or the table on which it sits.

Now let's see what happens if the flywheel *is* spinning initially, so the initial angular momentum $\vec{L}_i$ is not zero (**Fig. 10.34a**). Since the flywheel rotates around its symmetry axis, $\vec{L}_i$ lies along this axis. But each change in angular momentum $d\vec{L}$ is perpendicular to the flywheel axis because the torque $\vec{\tau} = \vec{r} \times \vec{w}$ is perpendicular to that axis (Fig. 10.34b). This causes the *direction* of $\vec{L}$ to change, but not its magnitude. The changes $d\vec{L}$ are always in the horizontal xy-plane, so the angular momentum vector and the flywheel axis with which it moves are always horizontal. That is, the axis doesn't fall—it precesses.

10.34 (a) The flywheel is spinning initially with angular momentum $\vec{L}_i$. The forces (not shown) are the same as those in Fig. 10.33a. (b) Because the initial angular momentum is not zero, each change $d\vec{L} = \vec{\tau}\, dt$ in angular momentum is perpendicular to $\vec{L}$. As a result, the magnitude of $\vec{L}$ remains the same but its direction changes continuously.

(a) Rotating flywheel

When the flywheel is rotating, the system starts with an angular momentum $\vec{L}_i$ parallel to the flywheel's axis of rotation.

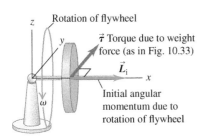

(b) View from above

Now the effect of the torque is to cause the angular momentum to precess around the pivot. The gyroscope circles around its pivot without falling.

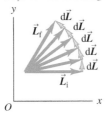

10.32 A gyroscope supported at one end. The horizontal circular motion of the flywheel and axis is called precession. The angular speed of precession is Ω.

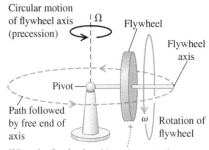

When the flywheel and its axis are stationary, they will fall to the table surface. When the flywheel spins, it and its axis "float" in the air while moving in a circle about the pivot.

10.33 (a) If the flywheel in Fig. 10.32 is initially not spinning, its initial angular momentum is zero. (b) In each successive time interval dt, the torque produces a change $d\vec{L} = \vec{\tau}\, dt$ in the angular momentum. The flywheel acquires an angular momentum $\vec{L}$ in the same direction as $\vec{\tau}$, and the flywheel axis falls.

(a) Nonrotating flywheel falls

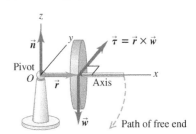

When the flywheel is not rotating, its weight creates a torque around the pivot, causing it to fall along a circular path until its axis rests on the table surface.

(b) View from above as flywheel falls

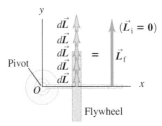

In falling, the flywheel rotates about the pivot and thus acquires an angular momentum $\vec{L}$. The *direction* of $\vec{L}$ stays constant.

If this still seems mystifying to you, think about a ball attached to a string. If the ball is initially at rest and you pull the string toward you, the ball moves toward you also. But if the ball is initially moving and you continuously pull the string in a direction perpendicular to the ball's motion, the ball moves in a circle around your hand; it does not approach your hand at all. In the first case the ball has zero linear momentum $\vec{p}$ to start with; when you apply a force $\vec{F}$ toward you for a time dt, the ball acquires a momentum $d\vec{p} = \vec{F}\,dt$, which is also toward you. But if the ball already has linear momentum $\vec{p}$, a change in momentum $d\vec{p}$ that's perpendicular to $\vec{p}$ changes the direction of motion, not the speed. Replace $\vec{p}$ with $\vec{L}$ and $\vec{F}$ with $\vec{\tau}$ in this argument, and you'll see that precession is simply the rotational analog of uniform circular motion.

At the instant shown in Fig. 10.34a, the gyroscope has angular momentum $\vec{L}$. A short time interval dt later, the angular momentum is $\vec{L} + d\vec{L}$; the infinitesimal change in angular momentum is $d\vec{L} = \vec{\tau}\,dt$, which is perpendicular to $\vec{L}$. As the vector diagram in **Fig. 10.35** shows, this means that the flywheel axis of the gyroscope has turned through a small angle $d\phi$ given by $d\phi = |d\vec{L}|/|\vec{L}|$. The rate at which the axis moves, $d\phi/dt$, is called the **precession angular speed;** denoting this quantity by Ω, we find

$$\Omega = \frac{d\phi}{dt} = \frac{|d\vec{L}|/|\vec{L}|}{dt} = \frac{\tau_z}{L_z} = \frac{wr}{I\omega} \qquad (10.33)$$

Thus the precession angular speed is *inversely* proportional to the angular speed of spin about the axis. A rapidly spinning gyroscope precesses slowly; if friction in its bearings causes the flywheel to slow down, the precession angular speed *increases*! The precession angular speed of the earth is very slow (1 rev/26,000 yr) because its spin angular momentum L_z is large and the torque τ_z, due to the gravitational influences of the moon and sun, is relatively small.

As a gyroscope precesses, its center of mass moves in a circle with radius r in a horizontal plane. Its vertical component of acceleration is zero, so the upward normal force $\vec{n}$ exerted by the pivot must be just equal in magnitude to the weight. The circular motion of the center of mass with angular speed Ω requires a force $\vec{F}$ directed toward the center of the circle, with magnitude $F = M\Omega^2 r$. This force must also be supplied by the pivot.

One key assumption that we made in our analysis of the gyroscope was that the angular momentum vector $\vec{L}$ is associated with only the spin of the flywheel and is purely horizontal. But there will also be a vertical component of angular momentum associated with the precessional motion of the gyroscope. By ignoring this, we've tacitly assumed that the precession is *slow*—that is, that the precession angular speed Ω is very much less than the spin angular speed ω. As Eq. (10.33) shows, a large value of ω automatically gives a small value of Ω, so this approximation is reasonable. When the precession is not slow, additional effects show up, including an up-and-down wobble or *nutation* of the flywheel axis that's superimposed on the precessional motion. You can see nutation occurring in a gyroscope as its spin slows down, so that Ω increases and the vertical component of $\vec{L}$ can no longer be ignored.

10.35 Detailed view of part of Fig. 10.34b.

In a time dt, the angular momentum vector and the flywheel axis (to which it is parallel) precess together through an angle $d\phi$.

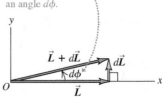

EXAMPLE 10.13   A PRECESSING GYROSCOPE

Figure 10.36a shows a top view of a spinning, cylindrical gyroscope wheel. The pivot is at O, and the mass of the axle is negligible. (a) As seen from above, is the precession clockwise or counterclockwise? (b) If the gyroscope takes 4.0 s for one revolution of precession, what is the angular speed of the wheel?

___

SOLUTION

IDENTIFY and SET UP: We'll determine the direction of precession by using the right-hand rule as in Fig. 10.34, which shows the same kind of gyroscope as Fig. 10.36. We'll use the relationship between precession angular speed Ω and spin angular speed ω, Eq. (10.33), to find ω.

EXECUTE: (a) The right-hand rule shows that $\vec{\omega}$ and $\vec{L}$ are to the left in Fig. 10.36b. The weight $\vec{w}$ points into the page in this top view and acts at the center of mass (denoted by $\times$ in the figure). The torque $\vec{\tau} = \vec{r} \times \vec{w}$ is toward the top of the page, so $d\vec{L}/dt$ is also toward the top of the page. Adding a small $d\vec{L}$ to the initial vector $\vec{L}$ changes the direction of $\vec{L}$ as shown, so the precession is clockwise as seen from above.

(b) Be careful not to confuse ω and Ω! The precession angular speed is $\Omega = (1\ \text{rev})/(4.0\ \text{s}) = (2\pi\ \text{rad})/(4.0\ \text{s}) = 1.57\ \text{rad/s}$. The weight is mg, and if the wheel is a solid, uniform cylinder, its moment of inertia about its symmetry axis is $I = \frac{1}{2}mR^2$. From Eq. (10.33),

10.36 In which direction and at what speed does this gyroscope process?

(a) Top view

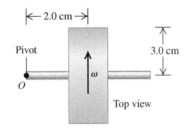

(b) Vector diagram

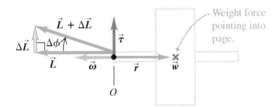

$$\omega = \frac{wr}{I\Omega} = \frac{mgr}{(mR^2/2)\Omega} = \frac{2gr}{R^2\Omega}$$

$$= \frac{2(9.8\ \text{m/s}^2)(2.0 \times 10^{-2}\ \text{m})}{(3.0 \times 10^{-2}\ \text{m})^2(1.57\ \text{rad/s})}$$

$$= 280\ \text{rad/s} = 2600\ \text{rev/min}$$

EVALUATE: The precession angular speed Ω is only about 0.6% of the spin angular speed ω, so this is an example of slow precession.

___

TEST YOUR UNDERSTANDING OF SECTION 10.7 Suppose the mass of the flywheel in Fig. 10.34 is doubled but all other dimensions and the spin angular speed remain the same. What effect would this change have on the precession angular speed Ω? (i) Ω would increase by a factor of 4; (ii) Ω would double; (iii) Ω would be unaffected; (iv) Ω would be one-half as much; (v) Ω would be one-quarter as much. ∎

Torque: When a force $\vec{F}$ acts on a body, the torque of that force with respect to a point O has a magnitude given by the product of the force magnitude F and the lever arm l. More generally, torque is a vector $\vec{\tau}$ equal to the vector product of $\vec{r}$ (the position vector of the point at which the force acts) and $\vec{F}$. (See Example 10.1.)

$$\tau = Fl = rF\sin\phi = F_{\tan}r \quad (10.2)$$

$$\vec{\tau} = \vec{r} \times \vec{F} \quad (10.3)$$

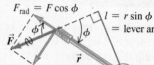

Rotational dynamics: The rotational analog of Newton's second law says that the net torque acting on a body equals the product of the body's moment of inertia and its angular acceleration. (See Examples 10.2 and 10.3.)

$$\sum \tau_z = I\alpha_z \quad (10.7)$$

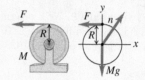

Combined translation and rotation: If a rigid body is both moving through space and rotating, its motion can be regarded as translational motion of the center of mass plus rotational motion about an axis through the center of mass. Thus the kinetic energy is a sum of translational and rotational kinetic energies. For dynamics, Newton's second law describes the motion of the center of mass, and the rotational equivalent of Newton's second law describes rotation about the center of mass. In the case of rolling without slipping, there is a special relationship between the motion of the center of mass and the rotational motion. (See Examples 10.4–10.7.)

$$K = \tfrac{1}{2}Mv_{cm}^2 + \tfrac{1}{2}I_{cm}\omega^2 \quad (10.8)$$

$$\sum \vec{F}_{ext} = M\vec{a}_{cm} \quad (10.12)$$

$$\sum \tau_z = I_{cm}\alpha_z \quad (10.13)$$

$$v_{cm} = R\omega \quad (10.11)$$
(rolling without slipping)

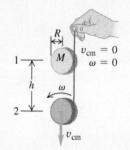

Work done by a torque: A torque that acts on a rigid body as it rotates does work on that body. The work can be expressed as an integral of the torque. The work–energy theorem says that the total rotational work done on a rigid body is equal to the change in rotational kinetic energy. The power, or rate at which the torque does work, is the product of the torque and the angular velocity (See Example 10.8.)

$$W = \int_{\theta_1}^{\theta_2} \tau_z \, d\theta \quad (10.20)$$

$$W = \tau_z(\theta_2 - \theta_1) = \tau_z \Delta\theta \quad (10.21)$$
(constant torque only)

$$W_{tot} = \tfrac{1}{2}I\omega_2^2 - \tfrac{1}{2}I\omega_1^2 \quad (10.22)$$

$$P = \tau_z\omega_z \quad (10.23)$$

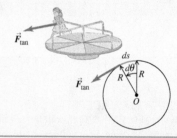

Angular momentum: The angular momentum of a particle with respect to point O is the vector product of the particle's position vector $\vec{r}$ relative to O and its momentum $\vec{p} = m\vec{v}$. When a symmetrical body rotates about a stationary axis of symmetry, its angular momentum is the product of its moment of inertia and its angular velocity vector $\vec{\omega}$. If the body is not symmetrical or the rotation (z) axis is not an axis of symmetry, the component of angular momentum along the rotation axis is $I\omega_z$. (See Example 10.9.)

$$\vec{L} = \vec{r} \times \vec{p} = \vec{r} \times m\vec{v} \quad (10.24)$$
(particle)

$$\vec{L} = I\vec{\omega} \quad (10.28)$$
(rigid body rotating about axis of symmetry)

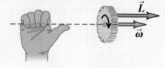

Rotational dynamics and angular momentum: The net external torque on a system is equal to the rate of change of its angular momentum. If the net external torque on a system is zero, the total angular momentum of the system is constant (conserved). (See Examples 10.10–10.13.)

$$\sum \vec{\tau} = \frac{d\vec{L}}{dt} \quad (10.29)$$

BRIDGING PROBLEM BILLIARD PHYSICS

A cue ball (a uniform solid sphere of mass m and radius R) is at rest on a level pool table. Using a pool cue, you give the ball a sharp, horizontal hit of magnitude F at a height h above the center of the ball (**Fig. 10.37**). The force of the hit is much greater than the friction force f that the table surface exerts on the ball. The hit lasts for a short time Δt. (a) For what value of h will the ball roll without slipping? (b) If you hit the ball dead center ($h = 0$), the ball will slide across the table for a while, but eventually it will roll without slipping. What will the speed of its center of mass be then?

10.37

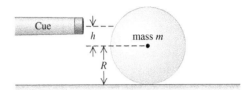

Then use the rotational version of the impulse–momentum theorem to find the angular speed immediately after the hit. (*Hint:* To write the rotational version of the impulse–momentum theorem, remember that the relationship between torque and angular momentum is the same as that between force and linear momentum.)

_____

SOLUTION GUIDE

IDENTIFY and SET UP

1. Draw a free-body diagram for the ball for the situation in part (a), including your choice of coordinate axes. Note that the cue exerts both an impulsive force on the ball and an impulsive torque around the center of mass.
2. The cue force applied for a time Δt gives the ball's center of mass a speed v_{cm}, and the cue torque applied for that same time gives the ball an angular speed ω. How must v_{cm} and ω be related for the ball to roll without slipping?
3. Draw two free-body diagrams for the ball in part (b): one showing the forces during the hit and the other showing the forces after the hit but before the ball is rolling without slipping.
4. What is the angular speed of the ball in part (b) just after the hit? While the ball is sliding, does v_{cm} increase or decrease? Does ω increase or decrease? What is the relationship between v_{cm} and ω when the ball is finally rolling without slipping?

EXECUTE

5. In part (a), use the impulse–momentum theorem to find the speed of the ball's center of mass immediately after the hit.

6. Use your results from step 5 to find the value of h that will cause the ball to roll without slipping immediately after the hit.
7. In part (b), again find the ball's center-of-mass speed and angular speed immediately after the hit. Then write Newton's second law for the translational motion and rotational motion of the ball as it slides. Use these equations to write expressions for v_{cm} and ω as functions of the elapsed time t since the hit.
8. Using your results from step 7, find the time t when v_{cm} and ω have the correct relationship for rolling without slipping. Then find the value of v_{cm} at this time.

EVALUATE

9. If you have access to a pool table, test the results of parts (a) and (b) for yourself!
10. Can you show that if you used a hollow cylinder rather than a solid ball, you would have to hit the top of the cylinder to cause rolling without slipping as in part (a)?

_____

Problems

For assigned homework and other learning materials, go to MasteringPhysics®.

•, ••, •••: Difficulty levels. CP: Cumulative problems incorporating material from earlier chapters. CALC: Problems requiring calculus.
DATA: Problems involving real data, scientific evidence, experimental design, and/or statistical reasoning. BIO: Biosciences problems.

DISCUSSION QUESTIONS

Q10.1 Can a single force applied to a body change both its translational and rotational motions? Explain.

Q10.2 Suppose you could use wheels of any type in the design of a soapbox-derby racer (an unpowered, four-wheel vehicle that coasts from rest down a hill). To conform to the rules on the total weight of the vehicle and rider, should you design with large massive wheels or small light wheels? Should you use solid wheels or wheels with most of the mass at the rim? Explain.

Q10.3 Serious bicyclists say that if you reduce the weight of a bike, it is more effective if you do so in the wheels rather than in the frame. Why would reducing weight in the wheels make it easier on the bicyclist than reducing the same amount in the frame?

Q10.4 The harder you hit the brakes while driving forward, the more the front end of your car will move down (and the rear end move up). Why? What happens when cars accelerate forward? Why do drag racers not use front-wheel drive only?

Q10.5 When an acrobat walks on a tightrope, she extends her arms straight out from her sides. She does this to make it easier for her to catch herself if she should tip to one side or the other. Explain how this works. [*Hint:* Think about Eq. (10.7).]

Q10.6 When you turn on an electric motor, it takes longer to come up to final speed if a grinding wheel is attached to the shaft. Why?

Q10.7 The work done by a force is the product of force and distance. The torque due to a force is the product of force and distance. Does this mean that torque and work are equivalent? Explain.

Q10.8 A valued client brings a treasured ball to your engineering firm, wanting to know whether the ball is solid or hollow. He has tried tapping on it, but that has given insufficient information. Design a simple, inexpensive experiment that you could perform quickly, without injuring the precious ball, to find out whether it is solid or hollow.

Q10.9 You make two versions of the same object out of the same material having uniform density. For one version, all the dimensions are exactly twice as great as for the other one. If the same torque acts on both versions, giving the smaller version angular acceleration α, what will be the angular acceleration of the larger version in terms of α?

Q10.10 Two identical masses are attached to frictionless pulleys by very light strings wrapped around the rim of the pulley and are released from rest. Both pulleys have the same mass and same diameter, but one is solid and the other is a hoop. As the masses fall, in which case is the tension in the string greater, or is it the same in both cases? Justify your answer.

Q10.11 The force of gravity acts on the baton in Fig. 10.11, and forces produce torques that cause a body's angular velocity to change. Why, then, is the angular velocity of the baton in the figure constant?

Q10.12 A certain solid uniform ball reaches a maximum height h_0 when it rolls up a hill without slipping. What maximum height (in terms of h_0) will it reach if you (a) double its diameter, (b) double its mass, (c) double both its diameter and mass, (d) double its angular speed at the bottom of the hill?

Q10.13 A wheel is rolling without slipping on a horizontal surface. In an inertial frame of reference in which the surface is at rest, is there any point on the wheel that has a velocity that is purely vertical? Is there any point that has a horizontal velocity component opposite to the velocity of the center of mass? Explain. Do your answers change if the wheel is slipping as it rolls? Why or why not?

Q10.14 A hoop, a uniform solid cylinder, a spherical shell, and a uniform solid sphere are released from rest at the top of an incline. What is the order in which they arrive at the bottom of the incline? Does it matter whether or not the masses and radii of the objects are all the same? Explain.

Q10.15 A ball is rolling along at speed v without slipping on a horizontal surface when it comes to a hill that rises at a constant angle above the horizontal. In which case will it go higher up the hill: if the hill has enough friction to prevent slipping or if the hill is perfectly smooth? Justify your answers in both cases in terms of energy conservation and in terms of Newton's second law.

Q10.16 You are standing at the center of a large horizontal turntable in a carnival funhouse. The turntable is set rotating on frictionless bearings, and it rotates freely (that is, there is no motor driving the turntable). As you walk toward the edge of the turntable, what happens to the combined angular momentum of you and the turntable? What happens to the rotation speed of the turntable? Explain.

Q10.17 Global Warming. If the earth's climate continues to warm, ice near the poles will melt, and the water will be added to the oceans. What effect will this have on the length of the day? Justify your answer. (*Hint:* Consult a map to see where the oceans lie.)

Q10.18 If two spinning objects have the same angular momentum, do they necessarily have the same rotational kinetic energy? If they have the same rotational kinetic energy, do they necessarily have the same angular momentum? Explain.

Q10.19 A student is sitting on a frictionless rotating stool with her arms outstretched as she holds equal heavy weights in each hand. If she suddenly lets go of the weights, will her angular speed increase, stay the same, or decrease? Explain.

Q10.20 A point particle travels in a straight line at constant speed, and the closest distance it comes to the origin of coordinates is a distance l. With respect to this origin, does the particle have nonzero angular momentum? As the particle moves along its straight-line path, does its angular momentum with respect to the origin change?

Q10.21 In Example 10.10 (Section 10.6) the angular speed ω changes, and this must mean that there is nonzero angular acceleration. But there is no torque about the rotation axis if the forces the professor applies to the weights are directly, radially inward. Then, by Eq. (10.7), α_z must be zero. Explain what is wrong with this reasoning that leads to this apparent contradiction.

Q10.22 In Example 10.10 (Section 10.6) the rotational kinetic energy of the professor and dumbbells increases. But since there are no external torques, no work is being done to change the rotational kinetic energy. Then, by Eq. (10.22), the kinetic energy must remain the same! Explain what is wrong with this reasoning, which leads to an apparent contradiction. Where *does* the extra kinetic energy come from?

Q10.23 As discussed in Section 10.6, the angular momentum of a circus acrobat is conserved as she tumbles through the air. Is her *linear* momentum conserved? Why or why not?

Q10.24 If you stop a spinning raw egg for the shortest possible instant and then release it, the egg will start spinning again. If you do the same to a hard-boiled egg, it will remain stopped. Try it. Explain it.

Q10.25 A helicopter has a large main rotor that rotates in a horizontal plane and provides lift. There is also a small rotor on the tail that rotates in a vertical plane. What is the purpose of the tail rotor? (*Hint:* If there were no tail rotor, what would happen when the pilot changed the angular speed of the main rotor?) Some helicopters have no tail rotor, but instead have two large main rotors that rotate in a horizontal plane. Why is it important that the two main rotors rotate in opposite directions?

Q10.26 In a common design for a gyroscope, the flywheel and flywheel axis are enclosed in a light, spherical frame with the flywheel at the center of the frame. The gyroscope is then balanced on top of a pivot so that the flywheel is directly above the pivot. Does the gyroscope precess if it is released while the flywheel is spinning? Explain.

Q10.27 A gyroscope is precessing about a vertical axis. What happens to the precession angular speed if the following changes are made, with all other variables remaining the same? (a) The angular speed of the spinning flywheel is doubled; (b) the total weight is doubled; (c) the moment of inertia about the axis of the spinning flywheel is doubled; (d) the distance from the pivot to the center of gravity is doubled. (e) What happens if all of the variables in parts (a) through (d) are doubled? In each case justify your answer.

Q10.28 A gyroscope takes 3.8 s to precess 1.0 revolution about a vertical axis. Two minutes later, it takes only 1.9 s to precess 1.0 revolution. No one has touched the gyroscope. Explain.

Q10.29 A gyroscope is precessing as in Fig. 10.32. What happens if you gently add some weight to the end of the flywheel axis farthest from the pivot?

Q10.30 A bullet spins on its axis as it emerges from a rifle. Explain how this prevents the bullet from tumbling and keeps the streamlined end pointed forward.

EXERCISES

Section 10.1 Torque

10.1 · Calculate the torque (magnitude and direction) about point O due to the force $\vec{F}$ in each of the cases sketched in **Fig. E10.1**. In each case, both the force $\vec{F}$ and the rod lie in the plane of the page, the rod has length 4.00 m, and the force has magnitude $F = 10.0$ N.

Figure **E10.1**

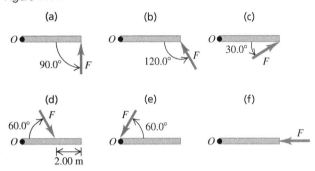

10.2 · Calculate the net torque about point O for the two forces applied as in **Fig. E10.2**. The rod and both forces are in the plane of the page.

Figure **E10.2**

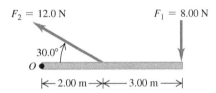

10.3 ·· A square metal plate 0.180 m on each side is pivoted about an axis through point O at its center and perpendicular to the plate (**Fig. E10.3**). Calculate the net torque about this axis due to the three forces shown in the figure if the magnitudes of the forces are $F_1 = 18.0$ N, $F_2 = 26.0$ N, and $F_3 = 14.0$ N. The plate and all forces are in the plane of the page.

Figure **E10.3**

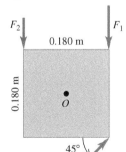

10.4 · Three forces are applied to a wheel of radius 0.350 m, as shown in **Fig. E10.4**. One force is perpendicular to the rim, one is tangent to it, and the other one makes a 40.0° angle with the radius. What is the net torque on the wheel due to these three forces for an axis perpendicular to the wheel and passing through its center?

Figure **E10.4**

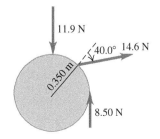

10.5 · One force acting on a machine part is $\vec{F} = (-5.00 \text{ N})\hat{i} + (4.00 \text{ N})\hat{j}$. The vector from the origin to the point where the force is applied is $\vec{r} = (-0.450 \text{ m})\hat{i} + (0.150 \text{ m})\hat{j}$. (a) In a sketch, show $\vec{r}$, $\vec{F}$, and the origin. (b) Use the right-hand rule to determine the direction of the torque. (c) Calculate the vector torque for an axis at the origin produced by this force. Verify that the direction of the torque is the same as you obtained in part (b).

10.6 · A metal bar is in the xy-plane with one end of the bar at the origin. A force $\vec{F} = (7.00 \text{ N})\hat{i} + (-3.00 \text{ N})\hat{j}$ is applied to the bar at the point $x = 3.00$ m, $y = 4.00$ m. (a) In terms of unit vectors $\hat{i}$ and $\hat{j}$, what is the position vector $\vec{r}$ for the point where the force is applied? (b) What are the magnitude and direction of the torque with respect to the origin produced by $\vec{F}$?

10.7 · A machinist is using a wrench to loosen a nut. The wrench is 25.0 cm long, and he exerts a 17.0-N force at the end of the handle at 37° with the handle (**Fig. E10.7**). (a) What torque does the machinist exert about the center of the nut? (b) What is the maximum torque he could exert with this force, and how should the force be oriented?

Figure **E10.7**

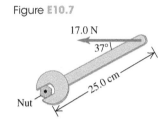

Section 10.2 Torque and Angular Acceleration for a Rigid Body

10.8 ·· A uniform disk with mass 40.0 kg and radius 0.200 m is pivoted at its center about a horizontal, frictionless axle that is stationary. The disk is initially at rest, and then a constant force $F = 30.0$ N is applied tangent to the rim of the disk. (a) What is the magnitude v of the tangential velocity of a point on the rim of the disk after the disk has turned through 0.200 revolution? (b) What is the magnitude a of the resultant acceleration of a point on the rim of the disk after the disk has turned through 0.200 revolution?

10.9 ·· The flywheel of an engine has moment of inertia 1.60 kg·m² about its rotation axis. What constant torque is required to bring it up to an angular speed of 400 rev/min in 8.00 s, starting from rest?

10.10 · A cord is wrapped around the rim of a solid uniform wheel 0.250 m in radius and of mass 9.20 kg. A steady horizontal pull of 40.0 N to the right is exerted on the cord, pulling it off tangentially from the wheel. The wheel is mounted on frictionless bearings on a horizontal axle through its center. (a) Compute the angular acceleration of the wheel and the acceleration of the part of the cord that has already been pulled off the wheel. (b) Find the magnitude and direction of the force that the axle exerts on the wheel. (c) Which of the answers in parts (a) and (b) would change if the pull were upward instead of horizontal?

10.11 ·· A machine part has the shape of a solid uniform sphere of mass 225 g and diameter 3.00 cm. It is spinning about a frictionless axle through its center, but at one point on its equator it is scraping against metal, resulting in a friction force of 0.0200 N at that point. (a) Find its angular acceleration. (b) How long will it take to decrease its rotational speed by 22.5 rad/s?

10.12 ·· CP A stone is suspended from the free end of a wire that is wrapped around the outer rim of a pulley, similar to what is shown in Fig. 10.10. The pulley is a uniform disk with mass 10.0 kg and radius 30.0 cm and turns on frictionless bearings. You measure that the stone travels 12.6 m in the first 3.00 s starting from rest. Find (a) the mass of the stone and (b) the tension in the wire.

10.13 •• CP A 2.00-kg textbook rests on a frictionless, horizontal surface. A cord attached to the book passes over a pulley whose diameter is 0.150 m, to a hanging book with mass 3.00 kg. The system is released from rest, and the books are observed to move 1.20 m in 0.800 s. (a) What is the tension in each part of the cord? (b) What is the moment of inertia of the pulley about its rotation axis?

10.14 •• CP A 15.0-kg bucket of water is suspended by a very light rope wrapped around a solid uniform cylinder 0.300 m in diameter with mass 12.0 kg. The cylinder pivots on a frictionless axle through its center. The bucket is released from rest at the top of a well and falls 10.0 m to the water. (a) What is the tension in the rope while the bucket is falling? (b) With what speed does the bucket strike the water? (c) What is the time of fall? (d) While the bucket is falling, what is the force exerted on the cylinder by the axle?

10.15 • A wheel rotates without friction about a stationary horizontal axis at the center of the wheel. A constant tangential force equal to 80.0 N is applied to the rim of the wheel. The wheel has radius 0.120 m. Starting from rest, the wheel has an angular speed of 12.0 rev/s after 2.00 s. What is the moment of inertia of the wheel?

10.16 •• A 12.0-kg box resting on a horizontal, frictionless surface is attached to a 5.00-kg weight by a thin, light wire that passes over a frictionless pulley (**Fig. E10.16**). The pulley has the shape of a uniform solid disk of mass 2.00 kg and diameter 0.500 m. After the system is released, find (a) the tension in the wire on both sides of the pulley, (b) the acceleration of the box, and (c) the horizontal and vertical components of the force that the axle exerts on the pulley.

Figure **E10.16**

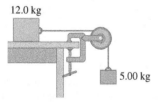

12.0 kg

5.00 kg

Section 10.3 Rigid-Body Rotation About a Moving Axis

10.17 • A 2.20-kg hoop 1.20 m in diameter is rolling to the right without slipping on a horizontal floor at a steady 2.60 rad/s. (a) How fast is its center moving? (b) What is the total kinetic energy of the hoop? (c) Find the velocity vector of each of the following points, as viewed by a person at rest on the ground: (i) the highest point on the hoop; (ii) the lowest point on the hoop; (iii) a point on the right side of the hoop, midway between the top and the bottom. (d) Find the velocity vector for each of the points in part (c), but this time as viewed by someone moving along with the same velocity as the hoop.

10.18 • BIO **Gymnastics.** We can roughly model a gymnastic tumbler as a uniform solid cylinder of mass 75 kg and diameter 1.0 m. If this tumbler rolls forward at 0.50 rev/s, (a) how much total kinetic energy does he have, and (b) what percent of his total kinetic energy is rotational?

10.19 • What fraction of the total kinetic energy is rotational for the following objects rolling without slipping on a horizontal surface? (a) A uniform solid cylinder; (b) a uniform sphere; (c) a thin-walled, hollow sphere; (d) a hollow cylinder with outer radius R and inner radius $R/2$.

10.20 •• A string is wrapped several times around the rim of a small hoop with radius 8.00 cm and mass 0.180 kg. The free end of the string is held in place and the hoop is released from rest (**Fig. E10.20**). After the hoop has descended 75.0 cm, calculate (a) the angular speed of the rotating hoop and (b) the speed of its center.

Figure **E10.20**

0.0800 m

10.21 •• A solid ball is released from rest and slides down a hillside that slopes downward at 65.0° from the horizontal. (a) What minimum value must the coefficient of static friction between the hill and ball surfaces have for no slipping to occur? (b) Would the coefficient of friction calculated in part (a) be sufficient to prevent a hollow ball (such as a soccer ball) from slipping? Justify your answer. (c) In part (a), why did we use the coefficient of static friction and not the coefficient of kinetic friction?

10.22 •• A hollow, spherical shell with mass 2.00 kg rolls without slipping down a 38.0° slope. (a) Find the acceleration, the friction force, and the minimum coefficient of friction needed to prevent slipping. (b) How would your answers to part (a) change if the mass were doubled to 4.00 kg?

10.23 •• A 392-N wheel comes off a moving truck and rolls without slipping along a highway. At the bottom of a hill it is rotating at 25.0 rad/s. The radius of the wheel is 0.600 m, and its moment of inertia about its rotation axis is $0.800MR^2$. Friction does work on the wheel as it rolls up the hill to a stop, a height h above the bottom of the hill; this work has absolute value 2600 J. Calculate h.

10.24 •• A uniform marble rolls down a symmetrical bowl, starting from rest at the top of the left side. The top of each side is a distance h above the bottom of the bowl. The left half of the bowl is rough enough to cause the marble to roll without slipping, but the right half has no friction because it is coated with oil. (a) How far up the smooth side will the marble go, measured vertically from the bottom? (b) How high would the marble go if both sides were as rough as the left side? (c) How do you account for the fact that the marble goes *higher* with friction on the right side than without friction?

10.25 •• A thin, light string is wrapped around the outer rim of a uniform hollow cylinder of mass 4.75 kg having inner and outer radii as shown in **Fig. E10.25**. The cylinder is then released from rest. (a) How far must the cylinder fall before its center is moving at 6.66 m/s? (b) If you just dropped this cylinder without any string, how fast would its center be moving when it had fallen the distance in part (a)? (c) Why do you get two different answers when the cylinder falls the same distance in both cases?

Figure **E10.25**

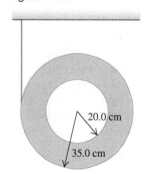

20.0 cm

35.0 cm

10.26 •• **A Ball Rolling Uphill.** A bowling ball rolls without slipping up a ramp that slopes upward at an angle β to the horizontal (see Example 10.7 in Section 10.3). Treat the ball as a uniform solid sphere, ignoring the finger holes. (a) Draw the free-body diagram for the ball. Explain why the friction force must be directed *uphill*. (b) What is the acceleration of the center of mass of the ball? (c) What minimum coefficient of static friction is needed to prevent slipping?

10.27 •• A size-5 soccer ball of diameter 22.6 cm and mass 426 g rolls up a hill without slipping, reaching a maximum height of 5.00 m above the base of the hill. We can model this ball as a thin-walled hollow sphere. (a) At what rate was it rotating at the base of the hill? (b) How much rotational kinetic energy did it have then?

10.28 •• A bicycle racer is going downhill at 11.0 m/s when, to his horror, one of his 2.25-kg wheels comes off as he is 75.0 m above the foot of the hill. We can model the wheel as a thin-walled cylinder 85.0 cm in diameter and ignore the small mass of the spokes. (a) How fast is the wheel moving when it reaches the foot of the hill if it rolled without slipping all the way down? (b) How much total kinetic energy does the wheel have when it reaches the bottom of the hill?

Section 10.4 Work and Power in Rotational Motion

10.29 • A playground merry-go-round has radius 2.40 m and moment of inertia 2100 kg · m² about a vertical axle through its center, and it turns with negligible friction. (a) A child applies an 18.0-N force tangentially to the edge of the merry-go-round for 15.0 s. If the merry-go-round is initially at rest, what is its angular speed after this 15.0-s interval? (b) How much work did the child do on the merry-go-round? (c) What is the average power supplied by the child?

10.30 • An engine delivers 175 hp to an aircraft propeller at 2400 rev/min. (a) How much torque does the aircraft engine provide? (b) How much work does the engine do in one revolution of the propeller?

10.31 • A 2.80-kg grinding wheel is in the form of a solid cylinder of radius 0.100 m. (a) What constant torque will bring it from rest to an angular speed of 1200 rev/min in 2.5 s? (b) Through what angle has it turned during that time? (c) Use Eq. (10.21) to calculate the work done by the torque. (d) What is the grinding wheel's kinetic energy when it is rotating at 1200 rev/min? Compare your answer to the result in part (c).

10.32 •• An electric motor consumes 9.00 kJ of electrical energy in 1.00 min. If one-third of this energy goes into heat and other forms of internal energy of the motor, with the rest going to the motor output, how much torque will this engine develop if you run it at 2500 rpm?

10.33 • (a) Compute the torque developed by an industrial motor whose output is 150 kW at an angular speed of 4000 rev/min. (b) A drum with negligible mass, 0.400 m in diameter, is attached to the motor shaft, and the power output of the motor is used to raise a weight hanging from a rope wrapped around the drum. How heavy a weight can the motor lift at constant speed? (c) At what constant speed will the weight rise?

10.34 •• An airplane propeller is 2.08 m in length (from tip to tip) and has a mass of 117 kg. When the airplane's engine is first started, it applies a constant torque of 1950 N · m to the propeller, which starts from rest. (a) What is the angular acceleration of the propeller? Model the propeller as a slender rod and see Table 9.2. (b) What is the propeller's angular speed after making 5.00 revolutions? (c) How much work is done by the engine during the first 5.00 revolutions? (d) What is the average power output of the engine during the first 5.00 revolutions? (e) What is the instantaneous power output of the motor at the instant that the propeller has turned through 5.00 revolutions?

Section 10.5 Angular Momentum

10.35 • A 2.00-kg rock has a horizontal velocity of magnitude 12.0 m/s when it is at point *P* in **Fig. E10.35**. (a) At this instant, what are the magnitude and direction of its angular momentum relative to point *O*? (b) If the only force acting on the rock is its weight, what is the rate of change (magnitude and direction) of its angular momentum at this instant?

Figure **E10.35**

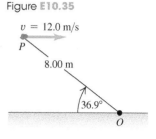

10.36 •• A woman with mass 50 kg is standing on the rim of a large disk that is rotating at 0.80 rev/s about an axis through its center. The disk has mass 110 kg and radius 4.0 m. Calculate the magnitude of the total angular momentum of the woman–disk system. (Assume that you can treat the woman as a point.)

10.37 •• Find the magnitude of the angular momentum of the second hand on a clock about an axis through the center of the clock face. The clock hand has a length of 15.0 cm and a mass of 6.00 g. Take the second hand to be a slender rod rotating with constant angular velocity about one end.

10.38 •• (a) Calculate the magnitude of the angular momentum of the earth in a circular orbit around the sun. Is it reasonable to model it as a particle? (b) Calculate the magnitude of the angular momentum of the earth due to its rotation around an axis through the north and south poles, modeling it as a uniform sphere. Consult Appendix E and the astronomical data in Appendix F.

10.39 •• CALC A hollow, thin-walled sphere of mass 12.0 kg and diameter 48.0 cm is rotating about an axle through its center. The angle (in radians) through which it turns as a function of time (in seconds) is given by $\theta(t) = At^2 + Bt^4$, where A has numerical value 1.50 and B has numerical value 1.10. (a) What are the units of the constants A and B? (b) At the time 3.00 s, find (i) the angular momentum of the sphere and (ii) the net torque on the sphere.

Section 10.6 Conservation of Angular Momentum

10.40 • CP A small block on a frictionless, horizontal surface has a mass of 0.0250 kg. It is attached to a massless cord passing through a hole in the surface (**Fig. E10.40**). The block is originally revolving at a distance of 0.300 m from the hole with an angular speed of 2.85 rad/s. The cord is then pulled from below, shortening the radius of the circle in which the block revolves to 0.150 m. Model the block as a particle. (a) Is the angular momentum of the block conserved? Why or why not? (b) What is the new angular speed? (c) Find the change in kinetic energy of the block. (d) How much work was done in pulling the cord?

Figure **E10.40**

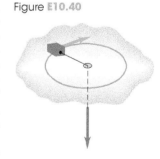

10.41 •• Under some circumstances, a star can collapse into an extremely dense object made mostly of neutrons and called a *neutron star*. The density of a neutron star is roughly 10^{14} times as great as that of ordinary solid matter. Suppose we represent the star as a uniform, solid, rigid sphere, both before and after the collapse. The star's initial radius was 7.0×10^5 km (comparable to our sun); its final radius is 16 km. If the original star rotated once in 30 days, find the angular speed of the neutron star.

10.42 •• A diver comes off a board with arms straight up and legs straight down, giving her a moment of inertia about her rotation axis of 18 kg · m². She then tucks into a small ball, decreasing this moment of inertia to 3.6 kg · m². While tucked, she makes two complete revolutions in 1.0 s. If she hadn't tucked at all, how many revolutions would she have made in the 1.5 s from board to water?

10.43 •• **The Spinning Figure** Figure E10.43
Skater. The outstretched hands and arms of a figure skater preparing for a spin can be considered a slender rod pivoting about an axis through its center (**Fig. E10.43**). When the skater's hands and arms are brought in and wrapped around his body to execute the spin, the hands and arms can be considered a thin-walled, hollow cylinder. His

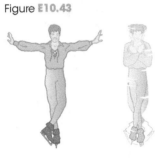

hands and arms have a combined mass of 8.0 kg. When outstretched, they span 1.8 m; when wrapped, they form a cylinder of radius 25 cm. The moment of inertia about the rotation axis of the remainder of his body is constant and equal to 0.40 kg · m². If his original angular speed is 0.40 rev/s, what is his final angular speed?

10.44 •• A solid wood door 1.00 m wide and 2.00 m high is hinged along one side and has a total mass of 40.0 kg. Initially open and at rest, the door is struck at its center by a handful of sticky mud with mass 0.500 kg, traveling perpendicular to the door at 12.0 m/s just before impact. Find the final angular speed of the door. Does the mud make a significant contribution to the moment of inertia?

10.45 •• A large wooden turntable in the shape of a flat uniform disk has a radius of 2.00 m and a total mass of 120 kg. The turntable is initially rotating at 3.00 rad/s about a vertical axis through its center. Suddenly, a 70.0-kg parachutist makes a soft landing on the turntable at a point near the outer edge. (a) Find the angular speed of the turntable after the parachutist lands. (Assume that you can treat the parachutist as a particle.) (b) Compute the kinetic energy of the system before and after the parachutist lands. Why are these kinetic energies not equal?

10.46 •• **Asteroid Collision!** Suppose that an asteroid traveling straight toward the center of the earth were to collide with our planet at the equator and bury itself just below the surface. What would have to be the mass of this asteroid, in terms of the earth's mass *M*, for the day to become 25.0% longer than it presently is as a result of the collision? Assume that the asteroid is very small compared to the earth and that the earth is uniform throughout.

10.47 •• A small 10.0-g bug stands at one end of a thin uniform bar that is initially at rest on a smooth horizontal table. The other end of the bar pivots about a nail driven into the table and can rotate freely, without friction. The bar has mass 50.0 g and is 100 cm in length. The bug jumps off in the horizontal direction, perpendicular to the bar, with a speed of 20.0 cm/s relative to the table. (a) What is the angular speed of the bar just after the frisky insect leaps? (b) What is the total kinetic energy of the system just after the bug leaps? (c) Where does this energy come from?

10.48 •• A thin uniform rod has a length of 0.500 m and is rotating in a circle on a frictionless table. The axis of rotation is perpendicular to the length of the rod at one end and is stationary. The rod has an angular velocity of 0.400 rad/s and a

moment of inertia about the axis of 3.00 × 10⁻³ kg · m². A bug initially standing on the rod at the axis of rotation decides to crawl out to the other end of the rod. When the bug has reached the end of the rod and sits there, its tangential speed is 0.160 m/s. The bug can be treated as a point mass. What is the mass of (a) the rod; (b) the bug?

10.49 •• A thin, uniform metal bar, 2.00 m long and weighing 90.0 N, is hanging vertically from the ceiling by a frictionless pivot. Suddenly it is struck 1.50 m below the ceiling by a small 3.00-kg ball, initially traveling horizontally at 10.0 m/s. The ball rebounds in the opposite direction with a speed of 6.00 m/s. (a) Find the angular speed of the bar just after the collision. (b) During the collision, why is the angular momentum conserved but not the linear momentum?

10.50 •• A uniform, 4.5-kg, square, solid wooden gate 1.5 m on each side hangs vertically from a frictionless pivot at the center of its upper edge. A 1.1-kg raven flying horizontally at 5.0 m/s flies into this door at its center and bounces back at 2.0 m/s in the opposite direction. (a) What is the angular speed of the gate just after it is struck by the unfortunate raven? (b) During the collision, why is the angular momentum conserved but not the linear momentum?

Section 10.7 Gyroscopes and Precession

10.51 •• The rotor (flywheel) of a toy gyroscope has mass 0.140 kg. Its moment of inertia about its axis is 1.20 × 10⁻⁴ kg · m². The mass of the frame is 0.0250 kg. The gyroscope is supported on a single pivot (**Fig. E10.51**) with its center of mass a horizontal distance of 4.00 cm from the pivot. The gyroscope is precessing in a horizontal plane at the rate of one revolution in 2.20 s. (a) Find the upward force exerted by the pivot. (b) Find the angular speed with which the rotor is spinning about its axis, expressed in rev/min. (c) Copy the diagram and draw vectors to show the angular momentum of the rotor and the torque acting on it.

Figure E10.51

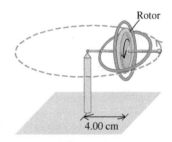

Rotor

4.00 cm

10.52 • **A Gyroscope on the Moon.** A certain gyroscope precesses at a rate of 0.50 rad/s when used on earth. If it were taken to a lunar base, where the acceleration due to gravity is 0.165*g*, what would be its precession rate?

10.53 • **Stabilization of the Hubble Space Telescope.** The Hubble Space Telescope is stabilized to within an angle of about 2-millionths of a degree by means of a series of gyroscopes that spin at 19,200 rpm. Although the structure of these gyroscopes is actually quite complex, we can model each of the gyroscopes as a thin-walled cylinder of mass 2.0 kg and diameter 5.0 cm, spinning about its central axis. How large a torque would it take to cause these gyroscopes to precess through an angle of 1.0 × 10⁻⁶ degree during a 5.0-hour exposure of a galaxy?

PROBLEMS

10.54 ⋯ A 50.0-kg grindstone is a solid disk 0.520 m in diameter. You press an ax down on the rim with a normal force of 160 N (**Fig. P10.54**). The coefficient of kinetic friction between the blade and the stone is 0.60, and there is a constant friction torque of 6.50 N · m between the axle of the stone and its bearings. (a) How much force must be applied tangentially at the end of a crank handle 0.500 m long to bring the stone from rest to 120 rev/min in 9.00 s? (b) After the grindstone attains an angular speed of 120 rev/min, what tangential force at the end of the handle is needed to maintain a constant angular speed of 120 rev/min? (c) How much time does it take the grindstone to come from 120 rev/min to rest if it is acted on by the axle friction alone?

Figure **P10.54**

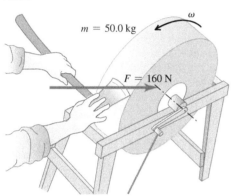

$m = 50.0$ kg

ω

$F = 160$ N

10.55 ⋯ A grindstone in the shape of a solid disk with diameter 0.520 m and a mass of 50.0 kg is rotating at 850 rev/min. You press an ax against the rim with a normal force of 160 N (Fig. P10.54), and the grindstone comes to rest in 7.50 s. Find the coefficient of friction between the ax and the grindstone. You can ignore friction in the bearings.

10.56 ⋯ A uniform, 8.40-kg, spherical shell 50.0 cm in diameter has four small 2.00-kg masses attached to its outer surface and equally spaced around it. This combination is spinning about an axis running through the center of the sphere and two of the small masses (**Fig. P10.56**). What friction torque is needed to reduce its angular speed from 75.0 rpm to 50.0 rpm in 30.0 s?

Figure **P10.56**

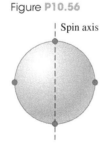

Spin axis

10.57 ⋯ A thin, uniform, 3.80-kg bar, 80.0 cm long, has very small 2.50-kg balls glued on at either end (**Fig. P10.57**). It is supported horizontally by a thin, horizontal, frictionless axle passing through its center and perpendicular to the bar. Suddenly the right-hand ball becomes detached and falls off, but the other ball remains glued to the bar. (a) Find the angular acceleration of the bar just after the ball falls off. (b) Will the angular acceleration remain constant as the bar continues to swing? If not, will it increase or decrease? (c) Find the angular velocity of the bar just as it swings through its vertical position.

Figure **P10.57**

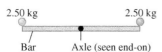

2.50 kg   2.50 kg

Bar   Axle (seen end-on)

10.58 ⋯ You are designing a simple elevator system for an old warehouse that is being converted to loft apartments. A 22,500-N elevator is to be accelerated upward by connecting it to a counterweight by means of a light (but strong!) cable passing over a solid uniform disk-shaped pulley. The cable does not slip where it is in contact with the surface of the pulley. There is no appreciable friction at the axle of the pulley, but its mass is 875 kg and it is 1.50 m in diameter. (a) What mass should the counterweight have so that it will accelerate the elevator upward through 6.75 m in the first 3.00 s, starting from rest? (b) What is the tension in the cable on each side of the pulley?

10.59 ⋯ The Atwood's Machine. **Figure P10.59** illustrates an Atwood's machine. Find the linear accelerations of blocks A and B, the angular acceleration of the wheel C, and the tension in each side of the cord if there is no slipping between the cord and the surface of the wheel. Let the masses of blocks A and B be 4.00 kg and 2.00 kg, respectively, the moment of inertia of the wheel about its axis be 0.220 kg · m², and the radius of the wheel be 0.120 m.

Figure **P10.59**

C

A

B

10.60 ⋯⋯ The mechanism shown in **Fig. P10.60** is used to raise a crate of supplies from a ship's hold. The crate has total mass 50 kg. A rope is wrapped around a wooden cylinder that turns on a metal axle. The cylinder has radius 0.25 m and moment of inertia $I = 2.9$ kg · m² about the axle.

Figure **P10.60**

0.12 m

F

The crate is suspended from the free end of the rope. One end of the axle pivots on frictionless bearings; a crank handle is attached to the other end. When the crank is turned, the end of the handle rotates about the axle in a vertical circle of radius 0.12 m, the cylinder turns, and the crate is raised. What magnitude of the force $\vec{F}$ applied tangentially to the rotating crank is required to raise the crate with an acceleration of 1.40 m/s²? (You can ignore the mass of the rope as well as the moments of inertia of the axle and the crank.)

10.61 ⋯ A large 16.0-kg roll of paper with radius $R = 18.0$ cm rests against the wall and is held in place by a bracket attached to a rod through the center of the roll (**Fig. P10.61**). The rod turns without friction in the bracket, and the moment of inertia of the paper and rod about the axis is 0.260 kg · m². The other end of the bracket is attached by a frictionless hinge to the wall such that the bracket makes an angle of 30.0° with the wall. The weight of the bracket is negligible. The coefficient of kinetic friction between the paper and the wall is $\mu_k = 0.25$. A constant vertical force $F = 60.0$ N is applied to the paper, and the paper unrolls. What is the magnitude of (a) the force that the rod exerts on the paper as it unrolls; (b) the angular acceleration of the roll?

Figure **P10.61**

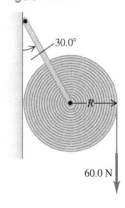

30.0°

R

60.0 N

10.62 ·· A block with mass $m = 5.00$ kg slides down a surface inclined 36.9° to the horizontal (**Fig. P10.62**). The coefficient of kinetic friction is 0.25. A string attached to the block is wrapped around a flywheel on a fixed axis at O. The flywheel has mass 25.0 kg and moment of inertia 0.500 kg·m² with respect to the axis of rotation.

Figure **P10.62**

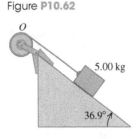

The string pulls without slipping at a perpendicular distance of 0.200 m from that axis. (a) What is the acceleration of the block down the plane? (b) What is the tension in the string?

10.63 ··· Two metal disks, one with radius $R_1 = 2.50$ cm and mass $M_1 = 0.80$ kg and the other with radius $R_2 = 5.00$ cm and mass $M_2 = 1.60$ kg, are welded together and mounted on a frictionless axis through their common center, as in Problem 9.77. (a) A light string is wrapped around the edge of the smaller disk, and a 1.50-kg block is suspended from the free end of the string. What is the magnitude of the downward acceleration of the block after it is released? (b) Repeat the calculation of part (a), this time with the string wrapped around the edge of the larger disk. In which case is the acceleration of the block greater? Does your answer make sense?

10.64 ·· A lawn roller in the form of a thin-walled, hollow cylinder with mass M is pulled horizontally with a constant horizontal force F applied by a handle attached to the axle. If it rolls without slipping, find the acceleration and the friction force.

10.65 · Two weights are connected by a very light, flexible cord that passes over an 80.0-N frictionless pulley of radius 0.300 m. The pulley is a solid uniform disk and is supported by a hook connected to the ceiling (**Fig. P10.65**). What force does the ceiling exert on the hook?

Figure **P10.65**

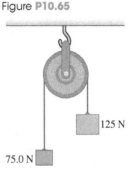

125 N

75.0 N

10.66 ·· You complain about fire safety to the landlord of your high-rise apartment building. He is willing to install an evacuation device if it is cheap and reliable, and he asks you to design it. Your proposal is to mount a large wheel (radius 0.400 m) on an axle at its center and wrap a long, light rope around the wheel, with the free end of the rope hanging just past the edge of the roof. Residents would evacuate to the roof and, one at a time, grasp the free end of the rope, step off the roof, and be lowered to the ground below. (Ignore friction at the axle.) You want a 90.0-kg person to descend with an acceleration of $g/4$. (a) If the wheel can be treated as a uniform disk, what mass must it have? (b) As the person descends, what is the tension in the rope?

10.67 · **The Yo-yo.** A yo-yo is made from two uniform disks, each with mass m and radius R, connected by a light axle of radius b. A light, thin string is wound several times around the axle and then held stationary while the yo-yo is released from rest, dropping as the string unwinds. Find the linear acceleration and angular acceleration of the yo-yo and the tension in the string.

10.68 ·· CP A thin-walled, hollow spherical shell of mass m and radius r starts from rest and rolls without slipping down a track (**Fig. P10.68**). Points A and B are on a circular part of the track

Figure **P10.68**

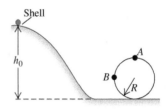

having radius R. The diameter of the shell is very small compared to h_0 and R, and the work done by rolling friction is negligible. (a) What is the minimum height h_0 for which this shell will make a complete loop-the-loop on the circular part of the track? (b) How hard does the track push on the shell at point B, which is at the same level as the center of the circle? (c) Suppose that the track had no friction and the shell was released from the same height h_0 you found in part (a). Would it make a complete loop-the-loop? How do you know? (d) In part (c), how hard does the track push on the shell at point A, the top of the circle? How hard did it push on the shell in part (a)?

10.69 ·· A basketball (which can be closely modeled as a hollow spherical shell) rolls down a mountainside into a valley and then up the opposite side, starting from rest at a height H_0 above the bottom. In **Fig. P10.69**, the rough part of the terrain prevents slipping while the smooth part has no friction. (a) How high, in terms of H_0, will the ball go up the other side? (b) Why doesn't the ball return to height H_0? Has it lost any of its original potential energy?

Figure **P10.69**

Rough

Smooth

H_0

10.70 ·· CP A solid uniform ball rolls without slipping up a hill (**Fig. P10.70**). At the top of the hill, it is moving horizontally, and then it goes over the vertical cliff. (a) How far from the foot of the cliff does the ball land, and how fast is it moving just before it lands? (b) Notice that when the balls lands, it has a greater translational speed than when it was at the bottom of the hill. Does this mean that the ball somehow gained energy? Explain!

Figure **P10.70**

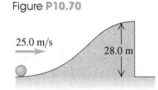

25.0 m/s

28.0 m

10.71 ·· **Rolling Stones.** A solid, uniform, spherical boulder starts from rest and rolls down a 50.0-m-high hill, as shown in **Fig. P10.71**. The top half of the hill is rough enough to cause the boulder to roll without slipping, but the lower half is covered with

Figure **P10.71**

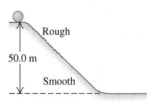

Rough

50.0 m

Smooth

ice and there is no friction. What is the translational speed of the boulder when it reaches the bottom of the hill?

10.72 ••• You are designing a system for moving aluminum cylinders from the ground to a loading dock. You use a sturdy wooden ramp that is 6.00 m long and inclined at 37.0° above the horizontal. Each cylinder is fitted with a light, frictionless yoke through its center, and a light (but strong) rope is attached to the yoke. Each cylinder is uniform and has mass 460 kg and radius 0.300 m. The cylinders are pulled up the ramp by applying a constant force $\vec{F}$ to the free end of the rope. $\vec{F}$ is parallel to the surface of the ramp and exerts no torque on the cylinder. The coefficient of static friction between the ramp surface and the cylinder is 0.120. (a) What is the largest magnitude $\vec{F}$ can have so that the cylinder still rolls without slipping as it moves up the ramp? (b) If the cylinder starts from rest at the bottom of the ramp and rolls without slipping as it moves up the ramp, what is the shortest time it can take the cylinder to reach the top of the ramp?

10.73 •• A 42.0-cm-diameter wheel, consisting of a rim and six spokes, is constructed from a thin, rigid plastic material having a linear mass density of 25.0 g/cm. This wheel is released from rest at the top of a hill 58.0 m high. (a) How fast is it rolling when it reaches the bottom of the hill? (b) How would your answer change if the linear mass density and the diameter of the wheel were each doubled?

10.74 ••• A uniform, 0.0300-kg rod of length 0.400 m rotates in a horizontal plane about a fixed axis through its center and perpendicular to the rod. Two small rings, each with mass 0.0200 kg, are mounted so that they can slide along the rod. They are initially held by catches at positions 0.0500 m on each side of the center of the rod, and the system is rotating at 48.0 rev/min. With no other changes in the system, the catches are released, and the rings slide outward along the rod and fly off at the ends. What is the angular speed (a) of the system at the instant when the rings reach the ends of the rod; (b) of the rod after the rings leave it?

10.75 • A uniform solid cylinder with mass M and radius $2R$ rests on a horizontal tabletop. A string is attached by a yoke to a frictionless axle through the center of the cylinder so that the cylinder can rotate about the axle. The string runs over a disk-shaped pulley with mass M and radius R that is mounted on a frictionless axle through its center. A block of mass M is suspended from the free end of the string (**Fig. P10.75**). The string doesn't slip over the pulley surface, and the cylinder rolls without slipping on the tabletop. Find the magnitude of the acceleration of the block after the system is released from rest.

Figure **P10.75**

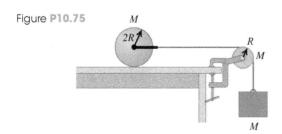

10.76 •• **Tarzan and Jane in the 21st Century.** Tarzan has foolishly gotten himself into another scrape with the animals and must be rescued once again by Jane. The 60.0-kg Jane starts from rest at a height of 5.00 m in the trees and swings down to the ground using a thin, but very rigid, 30.0-kg vine 8.00 m long.

She arrives just in time to snatch the 72.0-kg Tarzan from the jaws of an angry hippopotamus. What is Jane's (and the vine's) angular speed (a) just before she grabs Tarzan and (b) just after she grabs him? (c) How high will Tarzan and Jane go on their first swing after this daring rescue?

10.77 ••• A 5.00-kg ball is dropped from a height of 12.0 m above one end of a uniform bar that pivots at its center. The bar has mass 8.00 kg and is 4.00 m in length. At the other end of the bar sits another 5.00-kg ball, unattached to the bar. The dropped ball sticks to the bar after the collision. How high will the other ball go after the collision?

10.78 •• The solid wood door of a gymnasium is 1.00 m wide and 2.00 m high, has total mass 35.0 kg, and is hinged along one side. The door is open and at rest when a stray basketball hits the center of the door head-on, applying an average force of 1500 N to the door for 8.00 ms. Find the angular speed of the door after the impact. [*Hint:* Integrating Eq. (10.29) yields $\Delta L_z = \int_{t_1}^{t_2}(\Sigma\tau_z)dt = (\Sigma\tau_z)_{av}\,\Delta t$. The quantity $\int_{t_1}^{t_2}(\Sigma\tau_z)\,dt$ is called the angular impulse.]

10.79 •• A uniform rod of length L rests on a frictionless horizontal surface. The rod pivots about a fixed frictionless axis at one end. The rod is initially at rest. A bullet traveling parallel to the horizontal surface and perpendicular to the rod with speed v strikes the rod at its center and becomes embedded in it. The mass of the bullet is one-fourth the mass of the rod. (a) What is the final angular speed of the rod? (b) What is the ratio of the kinetic energy of the system after the collision to the kinetic energy of the bullet before the collision?

10.80 •• CP A large turntable with radius 6.00 m rotates about a fixed vertical axis, making one revolution in 8.00 s. The moment of inertia of the turntable about this axis is 1200 kg · m². You stand, barefooted, at the rim of the turntable and very slowly walk toward the center, along a radial line painted on the surface of the turntable. Your mass is 70.0 kg. Since the radius of the turntable is large, it is a good approximation to treat yourself as a point mass. Assume that you can maintain your balance by adjusting the positions of your feet. You find that you can reach a point 3.00 m from the center of the turntable before your feet begin to slip. What is the coefficient of static friction between the bottoms of your feet and the surface of the turntable?

10.81 •• In your job as a mechanical engineer you are designing a flywheel and clutch-plate system like the one in Example 10.11. Disk A is made of a lighter material than disk B, and the moment of inertia of disk A about the shaft is one-third that of disk B. The moment of inertia of the shaft is negligible. With the clutch disconnected, A is brought up to an angular speed ω_0; B is initially at rest. The accelerating torque is then removed from A, and A is coupled to B. (Ignore bearing friction.) The design specifications allow for a maximum of 2400 J of thermal energy to be developed when the connection is made. What can be the maximum value of the original kinetic energy of disk A so as not to exceed the maximum allowed value of the thermal energy?

10.82 •• A local ice hockey team has asked you to design an apparatus for measuring the speed of the hockey puck after a slap shot. Your design is a 2.00-m-long, uniform rod pivoted about one end so that it is free to rotate horizontally on the ice without friction. The 0.800-kg rod has a light basket at the other end to catch the 0.163-kg puck. The puck slides across the ice with velocity $\vec{v}$ (perpendicular to the rod), hits the basket, and is caught. After the collision, the rod rotates. If the rod makes one revolution every 0.736 s after the puck is caught, what was the puck's speed just before it hit the rod?

10.83 ••• You are designing a slide for a water park. In a sitting position, park guests slide a vertical distance h down the waterslide, which has negligible friction. When they reach the bottom of the slide, they grab a handle at the bottom end of a 6.00-m-long uniform pole. The pole hangs vertically, initially at rest. The upper end of the pole is pivoted about a stationary, frictionless axle. The pole with a person hanging on the end swings up through an angle of 72.0°, and then the person lets go of the pole and drops into a pool of water. Treat the person as a point mass. The pole's moment of inertia is given by $I = \frac{1}{3}ML^2$, where $L = 6.00$ m is the length of the pole and $M = 24.0$ kg is its mass. For a person of mass 70.0 kg, what must be the height h in order for the pole to have a maximum angle of swing of 72.0° after the collision?

10.84 •• **Neutron Star Glitches.** Occasionally, a rotating neutron star (see Exercise 10.41) undergoes a sudden and unexpected speedup called a *glitch*. One explanation is that a glitch occurs when the crust of the neutron star settles slightly, decreasing the moment of inertia about the rotation axis. A neutron star with angular speed $\omega_0 = 70.4$ rad/s underwent such a glitch in October 1975 that increased its angular speed to $\omega = \omega_0 + \Delta\omega$, where $\Delta\omega/\omega_0 = 2.01 \times 10^{-6}$. If the radius of the neutron star before the glitch was 11 km, by how much did its radius decrease in the starquake? Assume that the neutron star is a uniform sphere.

10.85 ••• A 500.0-g bird is flying horizontally at 2.25 m/s, not paying much attention, when it suddenly flies into a stationary vertical bar, hitting it 25.0 cm below the top (**Fig. P10.85**). The bar is uniform, 0.750 m long, has a mass of 1.50 kg, and is hinged at its base. The collision stuns the bird so that it just drops to the ground afterward (but soon recovers to fly happily away). What is the angular velocity of the bar (a) just after it is hit by the bird and (b) just as it reaches the ground?

Figure **P10.85**

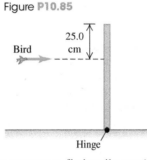

10.86 ••• **CP** A small block with mass 0.130 kg is attached to a string passing through a hole in a frictionless, horizontal surface (see Fig. E10.40). The block is originally revolving in a circle with a radius of 0.800 m about the hole with a tangential speed of 4.00 m/s. The string is then pulled slowly from below, shortening the radius of the circle in which the block revolves. The breaking strength of the string is 30.0 N. What is the radius of the circle when the string breaks?

10.87 • A 55-kg runner runs around the edge of a horizontal turntable mounted on a vertical, frictionless axis through its center. The runner's velocity relative to the earth has magnitude 2.8 m/s. The turntable is rotating in the opposite direction with an angular velocity of magnitude 0.20 rad/s relative to the earth. The radius of the turntable is 3.0 m, and its moment of inertia about the axis of rotation is 80 kg · m². Find the final angular velocity of the system if the runner comes to rest relative to the turntable. (You can model the runner as a particle.)

10.88 •• **DATA** The V6 engine in a 2014 Chevrolet Silverado 1500 pickup truck is reported to produce a maximum power of 285 hp at 5300 rpm and a maximum torque of 305 ft · lb at 3900 rpm. (a) Calculate the torque, in both ft · lb and N · m, at 5300 rpm. Is your answer in ft · lb smaller than the specified maximum value? (b) Calculate the power, in both horsepower and watts, at 3900 rpm. Is your answer in hp smaller than the specified maximum value? (c) The relationship between power in hp and torque in ft · lb

at a particular angular velocity in rpm is often written as hp = [torque (in ft · lb) × rpm]/c, where c is a constant. What is the numerical value of c? (d) The engine of a 2012 Chevrolet Camaro ZL1 is reported to produce 580 hp at 6000 rpm. What is the torque (in ft · lb) at 6000 rpm?

10.89 •• **DATA** You have one object of each of these shapes, all with mass 0.840 kg: a uniform solid cylinder, a thin-walled hollow cylinder, a uniform solid sphere, and a thin-walled hollow sphere. You release each object from rest at the same vertical height h above the bottom of a long wooden ramp that is inclined at 35.0° from the horizontal. Each object rolls without slipping down the ramp. You measure the time t that it takes each one to reach the bottom of the ramp; **Fig. P10.89** shows the results. (a) From the bar graphs, identify objects A through D by shape. (b) Which of objects A through D has the greatest total kinetic energy at the bottom of the ramp, or do all have the same kinetic energy? (c) Which of objects A through D has the greatest rotational kinetic energy $\frac{1}{2}I\omega^2$ at the bottom of the ramp, or do all have the same rotational kinetic energy? (d) What minimum coefficient of static friction is required for all four objects to roll without slipping?

Figure **P10.89**

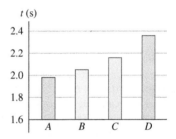

10.90 ••• **DATA** You are testing a small flywheel (radius 0.166 m) that will be used to store a small amount of energy. The flywheel is pivoted with low-friction bearings about a horizontal shaft through the flywheel's center. A thin, light cord is wrapped multiple times around the rim of the flywheel. Your lab has a device that can apply a specified horizontal force $\vec{F}$ to the free end of the cord. The device records both the magnitude of that force as a function of the horizontal distance the end of the cord has traveled and the time elapsed since the force was first applied. The flywheel is initially at rest. (a) You start with a test run to determine the flywheel's moment of inertia I. The magnitude F of the force is a constant 25.0 N, and the end of the rope moves 8.35 m in 2.00 s. What is I? (b) In a second test, the flywheel again starts from rest but the free end of the rope travels 6.00 m; **Fig. P10.90** shows the force magnitude F as a function of the distance d that the end of the rope has moved. What is the kinetic energy of the flywheel when $d = 6.00$ m? (c) What is the angular speed of the flywheel, in rev/min, when $d = 6.00$ m?

Figure **P10.90**

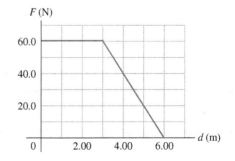

CHALLENGE PROBLEMS

10.91 ••• CP CALC A block with mass m is revolving with linear speed v_1 in a circle of radius r_1 on a frictionless horizontal surface (see Fig. E10.40). The string is slowly pulled from below until the radius of the circle in which the block is revolving is reduced to r_2. (a) Calculate the tension T in the string as a function of r, the distance of the block from the hole. Your answer will be in terms of the initial velocity v_1 and the radius r_1. (b) Use $W = \int_{r_1}^{r_2} \vec{T}(r) \cdot d\vec{r}$ to calculate the work done by $\vec{T}$ when r changes from r_1 to r_2. (c) Compare the results of part (b) to the change in the kinetic energy of the block.

10.92 ••• When an object is rolling without slipping, the rolling friction force is much less than the friction force when the object is sliding; a silver dollar will roll on its edge much farther than it will slide on its flat side (see Section 5.3). When an object is rolling without slipping on a horizontal surface, we can approximate the friction force to be zero, so that a_x and α_z are approximately zero and v_x and ω_z are approximately constant. Rolling without slipping means $v_x = r\omega_z$ and $a_x = r\alpha_z$. If an object is set in motion on a surface *without* these equalities, sliding (kinetic) friction will act on the object as it slips until rolling without slipping is established. A solid cylinder with mass M and radius R, rotating with angular speed ω_0 about an axis through its center, is set on a horizontal surface for which the kinetic friction coefficient is μ_k. (a) Draw a free-body diagram for the cylinder on the surface. Think carefully about the direction of the kinetic friction force on the cylinder. Calculate the accelerations a_x of the center of mass and α_z of rotation about the center of mass. (b) The cylinder is initially slipping completely, so initially $\omega_z = \omega_0$ but $v_x = 0$. Rolling without slipping sets in when $v_x = r\omega_z$. Calculate the *distance* the cylinder rolls before slipping stops. (c) Calculate the work done by the friction force on the cylinder as it moves from where it was set down to where it begins to roll without slipping.

10.93 ••• A demonstration gyroscope wheel is constructed by removing the tire from a bicycle wheel 0.650 m in diameter, wrapping lead wire around the rim, and taping it in place. The shaft projects 0.200 m at each side of the wheel, and a woman holds the ends of the shaft in her hands. The mass of the system is 8.00 kg; its entire mass may be assumed to be located at its rim. The shaft is horizontal, and the wheel is spinning about the shaft at 5.00 rev/s. Find the magnitude and direction of the force each hand exerts on the shaft (a) when the shaft is at rest; (b) when the shaft is rotating in a horizontal plane about its center at 0.050 rev/s; (c) when the shaft is rotating in a horizontal plane about its center at 0.300 rev/s. (d) At what rate must the shaft rotate in order that it may be supported at one end only?

BIO **HUMAN MOMENT OF INERTIA.** The moment of inertia of the human body about an axis through its center of mass is important in the application of biomechanics to sports such as diving and gymnastics. We can measure the body's moment of inertia in a particular position while a person remains in that position on a horizontal turntable, with the body's center of mass on the turntable's rotational axis. The turntable with the person on it is then accelerated from rest by a torque that is produced by using a rope wound around a pulley on the shaft of the turntable. From the measured tension in the rope and the angular acceleration, we can calculate the body's moment of inertia about an axis through its center of mass.

Overhead view of a female gymnast lying in somersault position atop a turntable

10.94 The moment of inertia of the empty turntable is 1.5 kg m². With a constant torque of 2.5 N · m, the turntable–person system takes 3.0 s to spin from rest to an angular speed of 1.0 rad/s. What is the person's moment of inertia about an axis through her center of mass? Ignore friction in the turntable axle. (a) 2.5 kg · m²; (b) 6.0 kg · m²; (c) 7.5 kg · m²; (d) 9.0 kg · m².

10.95 While the turntable is being accelerated, the person suddenly extends her legs. What happens to the turntable? (a) It suddenly speeds up; (b) it rotates with constant speed; (c) its acceleration decreases; (d) it suddenly stops rotating.

10.96 A doubling of the torque produces a greater angular acceleration. Which of the following would do this, assuming that the tension in the rope doesn't change? (a) Increasing the pulley diameter by a factor of $\sqrt{2}$; (b) increasing the pulley diameter by a factor of 2; (c) increasing the pulley diameter by a factor of 4; (d) decreasing the pulley diameter by a factor of $\sqrt{2}$.

10.97 If the body's center of mass were not placed on the rotational axis of the turntable, how would the person's measured moment of inertia compare to the moment of inertia for rotation about the center of mass? (a) The measured moment of inertia would be too large; (b) the measured moment of inertia would be too small; (c) the two moments of inertia would be the same; (d) it depends on where the body's center of mass is placed relative to the center of the turntable.

Answers

Chapter Opening Question ?

(iv) A tossed pin rotates around its center of mass (which is located toward its thick end). This is also the point at which the gravitational force acts on the pin, so this force exerts no torque on the pin. Hence the pin rotates with constant angular momentum, and its angular speed remains the same.

Test Your Understanding Questions

10.1 (ii) Force P acts along a vertical line, so the lever arm is the horizontal distance from A to the line of action. This is the horizontal component of distance L, which is $L\cos\theta$. Hence the magnitude of the torque is the product of the force magnitude P and the lever arm $L\cos\theta$, or $\tau = PL\cos\theta$.

10.2 (iii), (ii), (i) For the hanging object of mass m_2 to accelerate downward, the net force on it must be downward. Hence the magnitude m_2g of the downward weight force must be greater than the magnitude T_2 of the upward tension force. For the pulley to have a clockwise angular acceleration, the net torque on the pulley must be clockwise. Tension T_2 tends to rotate the pulley clockwise, while tension T_1 tends to rotate the pulley counterclockwise. Both tension forces have the same lever arm R, so there is a clockwise torque T_2R and a counterclockwise torque T_1R. For the net torque to be clockwise, T_2 must be greater than T_1. Hence $m_2g > T_2 > T_1$.

10.3 (a) (ii), (b) (i) If you redo the calculation of Example 10.6 with a hollow cylinder (moment of inertia $I_{cm} = MR^2$) instead of a solid cylinder (moment of inertia $I_{cm} = \frac{1}{2}MR^2$), you will find $a_{cm\text{-}y} = \frac{1}{2}g$ and $T = \frac{1}{2}Mg$ (instead of $a_{cm\text{-}y} = \frac{2}{3}g$ and $T = \frac{1}{3}Mg$ for a solid cylinder). Hence the acceleration is less but the tension is greater. You can come to the same conclusion without doing the calculation. The greater moment of inertia means that the hollow cylinder will rotate more slowly and hence will roll downward more slowly. To slow the downward motion, a greater upward tension force is needed to oppose the downward force of gravity.

10.4 (iii) You apply the same torque over the same angular displacement to both cylinders. Hence, by Eq. (10.21), you do the same amount of work to both cylinders and impart the same kinetic energy to both. (The one with the smaller moment of inertia ends up with a greater angular speed, but that isn't what we are asked. Compare Conceptual Example 6.5 in Section 6.2.)

10.5 (a) no, (b) yes As the ball goes around the circle, the magnitude of $\vec{p} = m\vec{v}$ remains the same (the speed is constant) but its direction changes, so the linear momentum vector isn't constant. But $\vec{L} = \vec{r} \times \vec{p}$ *is* constant: It has a constant magnitude (both the speed and the perpendicular distance from your hand to the ball are constant) and a constant direction (along the rotation axis, perpendicular to the plane of the ball's motion). The linear momentum changes because there is a net *force* $\vec{F}$ on the ball (toward the center of the circle). The angular momentum remains constant because there is no net *torque;* the vector $\vec{r}$ points from your hand to the ball and the force $\vec{F}$ on the ball is directed toward your hand, so the vector product $\vec{\tau} = \vec{r} \times \vec{F}$ is zero.

10.6 (i) In the absence of external torques, the earth's angular momentum $L_z = I\omega_z$ would remain constant. The melted ice would move from the poles toward the equator—that is, away from our planet's rotation axis—and the earth's moment of inertia I would increase slightly. Hence the angular velocity ω_z would decrease slightly and the day would be slightly longer.

10.7 (iii) Doubling the flywheel mass would double both its moment of inertia I and its weight w, so the ratio I/w would be unchanged. Equation (10.33) shows that the precession angular speed depends on this ratio, so there would be *no* effect on the value of Ω.

Bridging Problem

(a) $h = \dfrac{2R}{5}$ **(b)** $\frac{5}{7}$ of the speed it had just after the hit

This Roman aqueduct uses the principle of the arch to sustain the weight of the structure and the water it carries. Are the blocks that make up the arch being (i) compressed, (ii) stretched, (iii) a combination of these, or (iv) neither compressed nor stretched?

11 EQUILIBRIUM AND ELASTICITY

LEARNING GOALS

Looking forward at ...

11.1 The conditions that must be satisfied for a body or structure to be in equilibrium.

11.2 What the center of gravity of a body is and how it relates to the body's stability.

11.3 How to solve problems that involve rigid bodies in equilibrium.

11.4 How to analyze situations in which a body is deformed by tension, compression, pressure, or shear.

11.5 What happens when a body is stretched so much that it deforms or breaks.

Looking back at ...

4.2, 5.1 Newton's first law.

5.3 Static friction.

6.3, 7.2 Hooke's law for an ideal spring.

8.5 Center of mass.

10.2, 10.5 Torque, rotational dynamics, and angular momentum.

We've devoted a good deal of effort to understanding why and how bodies accelerate in response to the forces that act on them. But very often we're interested in making sure that bodies *don't* accelerate. Any building, from a multistory skyscraper to the humblest shed, must be designed so that it won't topple over. Similar concerns arise with a suspension bridge, a ladder leaning against a wall, or a crane hoisting a bucket full of concrete.

A body that can be modeled as a *particle* is in equilibrium whenever the vector sum of the forces acting on it is zero. But for the situations we've just described, that condition isn't enough. If forces act at different points on an extended body, an additional requirement must be satisfied to ensure that the body has no tendency to *rotate:* The sum of the *torques* about any point must be zero. This requirement is based on the principles of rotational dynamics developed in Chapter 10. We can compute the torque due to the weight of a body by using the concept of center of gravity, which we introduce in this chapter.

Idealized rigid bodies don't bend, stretch, or squash when forces act on them. But all real materials are *elastic* and do deform to some extent. Elastic properties of materials are tremendously important. You want the wings of an airplane to be able to bend a little, but you'd rather not have them break off. Tendons in your limbs need to stretch when you exercise, but they must return to their relaxed lengths when you stop. Many of the necessities of everyday life, from rubber bands to suspension bridges, depend on the elastic properties of materials. In this chapter we'll introduce the concepts of *stress, strain,* and *elastic modulus* and a simple principle called *Hooke's law,* which helps us predict what deformations will occur when forces are applied to a real (not perfectly rigid) body.

11.1 CONDITIONS FOR EQUILIBRIUM

We learned in Sections 4.2 and 5.1 that a particle is in *equilibrium*—that is, the particle does not accelerate—in an inertial frame of reference if the vector sum of all the forces acting on the particle is zero, $\sum \vec{F} = 0$. For an *extended* body, the equivalent statement is that the center of mass of the body has zero acceleration if the vector sum of all external forces acting on the body is zero, as discussed in Section 8.5. This is often called the **first condition for equilibrium:**

First condition for equilibrium:		
For the center of mass of a body at rest to remain at rest ...	$\sum \vec{F} = 0$ ·····• *... net external force* on the body must be *zero.*	(11.1)

A second condition for an extended body to be in equilibrium is that the body must have no tendency to *rotate.* A rigid body that, in an inertial frame, is not rotating about a certain point has zero angular momentum about that point. If it is not to start rotating about that point, the rate of change of angular momentum must *also* be zero. From the discussion in Section 10.5, particularly Eq. (10.29), this means that the sum of torques due to all the external forces acting on the body must be zero. A rigid body in equilibrium can't have any tendency to start rotating about *any* point, so the sum of external torques must be zero about any point. This is the **second condition for equilibrium:**

Second condition for equilibrium:		
For a nonrotating body to remain nonrotating ...	$\sum \vec{\tau} = 0$ ·····• *... net external torque* around *any point* on the body must be *zero.*	(11.2)

In this chapter we'll apply the first and second conditions for equilibrium to situations in which a rigid body is at rest (no translation or rotation). Such a body is said to be in **static equilibrium (Fig. 11.1).** But the same conditions apply to a rigid body in uniform *translational* motion (without rotation), such as an airplane in flight with constant speed, direction, and altitude. Such a body is in equilibrium but is not static.

TEST YOUR UNDERSTANDING OF SECTION 11.1 Which situation satisfies both the first and second conditions for equilibrium? (i) A seagull gliding at a constant angle below the horizontal and at a constant speed; (ii) an automobile crankshaft turning at an increasing angular speed in the engine of a parked car; (iii) a thrown baseball that does not rotate as it sails through the air. ▌

11.1 To be in static equilibrium, a body at rest must satisfy *both* conditions for equilibrium: It can have no tendency to accelerate as a whole or to start rotating.

(a) This body is in static equilibrium.

Equilibrium conditions:

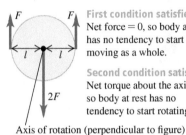

First condition satisfied: Net force = 0, so body at rest has no tendency to start moving as a whole.

Second condition satisfied: Net torque about the axis = 0, so body at rest has no tendency to start rotating.

Axis of rotation (perpendicular to figure)

(b) This body has no tendency to accelerate as a whole, but it has a tendency to start rotating.

First condition satisfied: Net force = 0, so body at rest has no tendency to start moving as a whole.

Second condition NOT satisfied: There is a net clockwise torque about the axis, so body at rest will start rotating clockwise.

(c) This body has a tendency to accelerate as a whole but no tendency to start rotating.

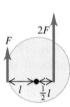

First condition NOT satisfied: There is a net upward force, so body at rest will start moving upward.

Second condition satisfied: Net torque about the axis = 0, so body at rest has no tendency to start rotating.

11.2 CENTER OF GRAVITY

In most equilibrium problems, one of the forces acting on the body is its weight. We need to be able to calculate the *torque* of this force. The weight doesn't act at a single point; it is distributed over the entire body. But we can always calculate the torque due to the body's weight by assuming that the entire force of gravity (weight) is concentrated at a point called the **center of gravity** (abbreviated "cg"). The acceleration due to gravity decreases with altitude; but if we can ignore this variation over the vertical dimension of the body, then the body's center of gravity is identical to its *center of mass* (abbreviated "cm"), which we defined in Section 8.5. We stated this result without proof in Section 10.2, and now we'll prove it.

First let's review the definition of the center of mass. For a collection of particles with masses $m_1, m_2, \ldots$ and coordinates $(x_1, y_1, z_1), (x_2, y_2, z_2), \ldots$, the coordinates $x_{cm}, y_{cm},$ and z_{cm} of the center of mass of the collection are

$$x_{cm} = \frac{m_1 x_1 + m_2 x_2 + m_3 x_3 + \cdots}{m_1 + m_2 + m_3 + \cdots} = \frac{\sum_i m_i x_i}{\sum_i m_i}$$

$$y_{cm} = \frac{m_1 y_1 + m_2 y_2 + m_3 y_3 + \cdots}{m_1 + m_2 + m_3 + \cdots} = \frac{\sum_i m_i y_i}{\sum_i m_i} \qquad \text{(center of mass)} \qquad (11.3)$$

$$z_{cm} = \frac{m_1 z_1 + m_2 z_2 + m_3 z_3 + \cdots}{m_1 + m_2 + m_3 + \cdots} = \frac{\sum_i m_i z_i}{\sum_i m_i}$$

Also, $x_{cm}, y_{cm},$ and z_{cm} are the components of the position vector $\vec{r}_{cm}$ of the center of mass, so Eqs. (11.3) are equivalent to the vector equation

Position vector of center of mass of a system of particles

Position vectors of individual particles

$$\vec{r}_{cm} = \frac{m_1 \vec{r}_1 + m_2 \vec{r}_2 + m_3 \vec{r}_3 + \cdots}{m_1 + m_2 + m_3 + \cdots} = \frac{\sum_i m_i \vec{r}_i}{\sum_i m_i} \qquad (11.4)$$

Masses of individual particles

Now consider the gravitational torque on a body of arbitrary shape (**Fig. 11.2**). We assume that the acceleration due to gravity $\vec{g}$ is the same at every point in the body. Every particle in the body experiences a gravitational force, and the total weight of the body is the vector sum of a large number of parallel forces. A typical particle has mass m_i and weight $\vec{w}_i = m_i \vec{g}$. If $\vec{r}_i$ is the position vector of this particle with respect to an arbitrary origin O, then the torque vector $\vec{\tau}_i$ of the weight $\vec{w}_i$ with respect to O is, from Eq. (10.3),

$$\vec{\tau}_i = \vec{r}_i \times \vec{w}_i = \vec{r}_i \times m_i \vec{g}$$

The *total* torque due to the gravitational forces on all the particles is

$$\vec{\tau} = \sum_i \vec{\tau}_i = \vec{r}_1 \times m_1 \vec{g} + \vec{r}_2 \times m_2 \vec{g} + \cdots$$

$$= (m_1 \vec{r}_1 + m_2 \vec{r}_2 + \cdots) \times \vec{g}$$

$$= \left(\sum_i m_i \vec{r}_i \right) \times \vec{g}$$

When we multiply and divide this by the total mass of the body,

$$M = m_1 + m_2 + \cdots = \sum_i m_i$$

we get

$$\vec{\tau} = \frac{m_1 \vec{r}_1 + m_2 \vec{r}_2 + \cdots}{m_1 + m_2 + \cdots} \times M\vec{g} = \frac{\sum_i m_i \vec{r}_i}{\sum_i m_i} \times M\vec{g}$$

11.2 The center of gravity (cg) and center of mass (cm) of an extended body.

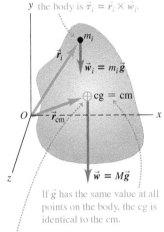

The gravitational torque about O on a particle of mass m_i within the body is $\vec{\tau}_i = \vec{r}_i \times \vec{w}_i$.

$\vec{w}_i = m_i \vec{g}$

cg = cm

$\vec{r}_{cm}$

$\vec{w} = M\vec{g}$

If $\vec{g}$ has the same value at all points on the body, the cg is identical to the cm.

The net gravitational torque about O on the entire body is the same as if all the weight acted at the cg: $\vec{\tau} = \vec{r}_{cm} \times \vec{w}$.

11.3 The acceleration due to gravity at the bottom of the 452-m-tall Petronas Towers in Malaysia is only 0.014% greater than at the top. The center of gravity of the towers is only about 2 cm below the center of mass.

11.4 Finding the center of gravity of an irregularly shaped body—in this case, a coffee mug.

Where is the center of gravity of this mug?

① Suspend the mug from any point. A vertical line extending down from the point of suspension passes through the center of gravity.

② Now suspend the mug from a different point. A vertical line extending down from this point intersects the first line at the center of gravity (which is inside the mug).

Center of gravity

The fraction in this equation is just the position vector $\vec{r}_{cm}$ of the center of mass, with components x_{cm}, y_{cm}, and z_{cm}, as given by Eq. (11.4), and $M\vec{g}$ is equal to the total weight $\vec{w}$ of the body. Thus

$$\vec{\tau} = \vec{r}_{cm} \times M\vec{g} = \vec{r}_{cm} \times \vec{w} \qquad (11.5)$$

The total gravitational torque, given by Eq. (11.5), is the same as though the total weight $\vec{w}$ were acting at the position $\vec{r}_{cm}$ of the center of mass, which we also call the *center of gravity*. **If $\vec{g}$ has the same value at all points on a body, its center of gravity is identical to its center of mass.** Note, however, that the center of mass is defined independently of any gravitational effect.

While the value of $\vec{g}$ varies somewhat with elevation, the variation is extremely slight (**Fig. 11.3**). We'll assume throughout this chapter that the center of gravity and center of mass are identical unless explicitly stated otherwise.

Finding and Using the Center of Gravity

We can often use symmetry considerations to locate the center of gravity of a body, just as we did for the center of mass. The center of gravity of a homogeneous sphere, cube, or rectangular plate is at its geometric center. The center of gravity of a right circular cylinder or cone is on its axis of symmetry.

For a body with a more complex shape, we can sometimes locate the center of gravity by thinking of the body as being made of symmetrical pieces. For example, we could approximate the human body as a collection of solid cylinders, with a sphere for the head. Then we can locate the center of gravity of the combination with Eqs. (11.3), letting m_1, m_2, . . . be the masses of the individual pieces and (x_1, y_1, z_1), (x_2, y_2, z_2), . . . be the coordinates of their centers of gravity.

When a body in rotational equilibrium and acted on by gravity is supported or suspended at a single point, the center of gravity is always at or directly above or below the point of suspension. If it were anywhere else, the weight would have a torque with respect to the point of suspension, and the body could not be in rotational equilibrium. **Figure 11.4** shows an application of this idea.

Using the same reasoning, we can see that a body supported at several points must have its center of gravity somewhere within the area bounded by the supports. This explains why a car can drive on a straight but slanted road if the slant angle is relatively small (**Fig. 11.5a**) but will tip over if the angle is too steep (Fig. 11.5b). The truck in Fig. 11.5c has a higher center of gravity than the car and will tip over on a shallower incline.

The lower the center of gravity and the larger the area of support, the harder it is to overturn a body. Four-legged animals such as deer and horses have a large area of support bounded by their legs; hence they are naturally stable and need only small feet or hooves. Animals that walk on two legs, such as humans and birds, need relatively large feet to give them a reasonable area of support. If a

11.5 In (a) the center of gravity is within the area bounded by the supports, and the car is in equilibrium. The car in (b) and the truck in (c) will tip over because their centers of gravity lie outside the area of support.

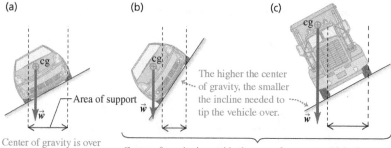

(a)

(b)

(c)

Area of support

The higher the center of gravity, the smaller the incline needed to tip the vehicle over.

Center of gravity is over the area of support: car is in equilibrium.

Center of gravity is outside the area of support: vehicle tips over.

two-legged animal holds its body approximately horizontal, like a chicken or the dinosaur *Tyrannosaurus rex,* it must perform a balancing act as it walks to keep its center of gravity over the foot that is on the ground. A chicken does this by moving its head; *T. rex* probably did it by moving its massive tail.

DEMO

EXAMPLE 11.1 WALKING THE PLANK

A uniform plank of length $L = 6.0$ m and mass $M = 90$ kg rests on sawhorses separated by $D = 1.5$ m and equidistant from the center of the plank. Cousin Throckmorton wants to stand on the right-hand end of the plank. If the plank is to remain at rest, how massive can Throckmorton be?

SOLUTION

IDENTIFY and SET UP: To just balance, Throckmorton's mass m must be such that the center of gravity of the plank–Throcky system is directly over the right-hand sawhorse (**Fig. 11.6**). We take the origin at C, the geometric center and center of gravity of the plank, and take the positive x-axis horizontally to the right. Then the centers of gravity of the plank and Throcky are at $x_P = 0$ and $x_T = L/2 = 3.0$ m, respectively, and the right-hand sawhorse is at

11.6 Our sketch for this problem.

$$L = 6.0\,\text{m}$$
$$D = 1.5\,\text{m} \quad \frac{L}{2} - \frac{D}{2}$$
$$M = 90\,\text{kg} \qquad cg \oplus \qquad m$$
$$C \quad S$$

$x_S = D/2$. We'll use Eqs. (11.3) to locate the center of gravity x_{cg} of the plank–Throcky system.

EXECUTE: From the first of Eqs. (11.3),

$$x_{cg} = \frac{M(0) + m(L/2)}{M + m} = \frac{m}{M + m} \frac{L}{2}$$

We set $x_{cg} = x_S$ and solve for m:

$$\frac{m}{M + m} \frac{L}{2} = \frac{D}{2}$$

$$mL = (M + m)D$$

$$m = M \frac{D}{L - D} = (90\,\text{kg}) \frac{1.5\,\text{m}}{6.0\,\text{m} - 1.5\,\text{m}} = 30\,\text{kg}$$

EVALUATE: As a check, let's repeat the calculation with the origin at the right-hand sawhorse. Now $x_S = 0$, $x_P = -D/2$, and $x_T = (L/2) - (D/2)$, and we require $x_{cg} = x_S = 0$:

$$x_{cg} = \frac{M(-D/2) + m[(L/2) - (D/2)]}{M + m} = 0$$

$$m = \frac{MD/2}{(L/2) - (D/2)} = M \frac{D}{L - D} = 30\,\text{kg}$$

The result doesn't depend on our choice of origin.

A 60-kg adult could stand only halfway between the right-hand sawhorse and the end of the plank. Can you see why?

TEST YOUR UNDERSTANDING OF SECTION 11.2 A rock is attached to the left end of a uniform meter stick that has the same mass as the rock. In order for the combination of rock and meter stick to balance atop the triangular object in **Fig. 11.7**, how far from the left end of the stick should the triangular object be placed? (i) Less than 0.25 m; (ii) 0.25 m; (iii) between 0.25 m and 0.50 m; (iv) 0.50 m; (v) more than 0.50 m. ∎

11.7 At what point will the meter stick with rock attached be in balance?

Rock, mass m Meter stick, mass m

11.3 SOLVING RIGID-BODY EQUILIBRIUM PROBLEMS

There are just two key conditions for rigid-body equilibrium: The vector sum of the forces on the body must be zero, and the sum of the torques about any point must be zero. To keep things simple, we'll restrict our attention to situations in which we can treat all forces as acting in a single plane, which we'll call the *xy*-plane. Then we need consider only the *x*- and *y*-components of force in Eq. (11.1), and in Eq. (11.2) we need consider only the *z*-components of torque (perpendicular to the plane). The first and second conditions for equilibrium are then

$$\sum F_x = 0 \quad \text{and} \quad \sum F_y = 0 \qquad \text{(first condition for equilibrium, forces in } xy\text{-plane)}$$

$$\sum \tau_z = 0 \qquad \text{(second condition for equilibrium, forces in } xy\text{-plane)}$$

(11.6)

CAUTION Choosing the reference point for calculating torques In equilibrium problems, the choice of reference point for calculating torques in $\sum \tau_z$ is completely arbitrary. But once you make your choice, you must use the *same* point to calculate *all* the torques on a body. Choose the point so as to simplify the calculations as much as possible. ∎

The challenge is to apply these simple conditions to specific problems. Problem-Solving Strategy 11.1 is very similar to the suggestions given in Section 5.1 for the equilibrium of a particle. You should compare it with Problem-Solving Strategy 10.1 (Section 10.2) for rotational dynamics problems.

PROBLEM-SOLVING STRATEGY 11.1 | **EQUILIBRIUM OF A RIGID BODY**

IDENTIFY *the relevant concepts:* The first and second conditions for equilibrium ($\sum F_x = 0$, $\sum F_y = 0$, and $\sum \tau_z = 0$) are applicable to any rigid body that is not accelerating in space and not rotating.

SET UP *the problem* using the following steps:
1. Sketch the physical situation and identify the body in equilibrium to be analyzed. Sketch the body accurately; do *not* represent it as a point. Include dimensions.
2. Draw a free-body diagram showing all forces acting *on* the body. Show the point on the body at which each force acts.
3. Choose coordinate axes and specify their direction. Specify a positive direction of rotation for torques. Represent forces in terms of their components with respect to the chosen axes.
4. Choose a reference point about which to compute torques. Choose wisely; you can eliminate from your torque equation

any force whose line of action goes through the point you choose. The body doesn't actually have to be pivoted about an axis through the reference point.

EXECUTE *the solution* as follows:
1. Write equations expressing the equilibrium conditions. Remember that $\sum F_x = 0$, $\sum F_y = 0$, and $\sum \tau_z = 0$ are *separate* equations. You can compute the torque of a force by finding the torque of each of its components separately, each with its appropriate lever arm and sign, and adding the results.
2. To obtain as many equations as you have unknowns, you may need to compute torques with respect to two or more reference points; choose them wisely, too.

EVALUATE *your answer:* Check your results by writing $\sum \tau_z = 0$ with respect to a different reference point. You should get the same answers.

EXAMPLE 11.2 | **LOCATING YOUR CENTER OF GRAVITY WHILE YOU WORK OUT**

The *plank* (**Fig. 11.8a**) is a great way to strengthen abdominal, back, and shoulder muscles. You can also use this exercise position to locate your center of gravity. Holding plank position with a scale under his toes and another under his forearms, one athlete measured that 66.0% of his weight was supported by his forearms and 34.0% by his toes. (That is, the total normal forces on his forearms and toes were $0.660w$ and $0.340w$, respectively, where w is the athlete's weight.) He is 1.80 m tall, and in plank position

the distance from his toes to the middle of his forearms is 1.53 m. How far from his toes is his center of gravity?

SOLUTION

IDENTIFY and SET UP: We can use the two conditions for equilibrium, Eqs. (11.6), for an athlete at rest. So both the net force and net torque on the athlete are zero. Figure 11.8b shows a free-body diagram, including x- and y-axes and our convention that counterclockwise torques are positive. The weight w acts at the center of gravity, which is between the two supports (as it must be; see Section 11.2). Our target variable is the distance L_{cg}, the lever arm of the weight with respect to the toes T, so it is wise to take torques with respect to T. The torque due to the weight is negative (it tends to cause a clockwise rotation around T), and the torque due to the upward normal force at the forearms F is positive (it tends to cause a counterclockwise rotation around T).

EXECUTE: The first condition for equilibrium is satisfied (Fig. 11.8b): $\sum F_x = 0$ because there are no x-components and $\sum F_y = 0$ because $0.340w + 0.660w + (-w) = 0$. We write the torque equation and solve for L_{cg}:

$$\sum \tau_R = 0.340w(0) - wL_{cg} + 0.660w(1.53 \text{ m}) = 0$$

$$L_{cg} = 1.01 \text{ m}$$

EVALUATE: The center of gravity is slightly below our athlete's navel (as it is for most people) and closer to his forearms than to his toes, which is why his forearms support most of his weight. You can check our result by writing the torque equation about the forearms F. You'll find that his center of gravity is 0.52 m from his forearms, or $(1.53 \text{ m}) - (0.52 \text{ m}) = 1.01$ m from his toes.

11.8 An athlete in plank position.

(a)

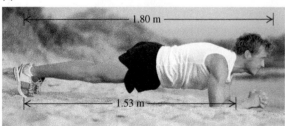

(b)

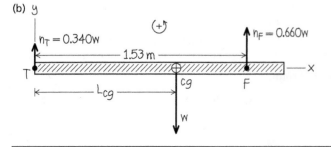

EXAMPLE 11.3 | WILL THE LADDER SLIP?

Sir Lancelot, who weighs 800 N, is assaulting a castle by climbing a uniform ladder that is 5.0 m long and weighs 180 N (**Fig. 11.9a**). The bottom of the ladder rests on a ledge and leans across the moat in equilibrium against a frictionless, vertical castle wall. The ladder makes an angle of 53.1° with the horizontal. Lancelot pauses one-third of the way up the ladder. (a) Find the normal and friction forces on the base of the ladder. (b) Find the minimum coefficient of static friction needed to prevent slipping at the base. (c) Find the magnitude and direction of the contact force on the base of the ladder.

SOLUTION

IDENTIFY and SET UP: The ladder–Lancelot system is stationary, so we can use the two conditions for equilibrium to solve part (a). In part (b), we need the relationship among the static friction force, coefficient of static friction, and normal force (see Section 5.3). In part (c), the contact force is the vector sum of the normal and friction forces acting at the base of the ladder, found in part (a). Figure 11.9b shows the free-body diagram, with x- and y-directions as shown and with counterclockwise torques taken to be positive. The ladder's center of gravity is at its geometric center. Lancelot's 800-N weight acts at a point one-third of the way up the ladder.

The wall exerts only a normal force n_1 on the top of the ladder. The forces on the base are an upward normal force n_2 and a static friction force f_s, which must point to the right to prevent slipping. The magnitudes n_2 and f_s are the target variables in part (a). From Eq. (5.4), these magnitudes are related by $f_s \leq \mu_s n_2$; the coefficient of static friction μ_s is the target variable in part (b).

EXECUTE: (a) From Eqs. (11.6), the first condition for equilibrium gives

$$\Sigma F_x = f_s + (-n_1) = 0$$
$$\Sigma F_y = n_2 + (-800 \text{ N}) + (-180 \text{ N}) = 0$$

These are two equations for the three unknowns n_1, n_2, and f_s. The second equation gives $n_2 = 980$ N. To obtain a third equation, we use the second condition for equilibrium. We take torques about point B, about which n_2 and f_s have no torque. The 53.1° angle creates a 3-4-5 right triangle, so from Fig. 11.9b the lever arm for the ladder's weight is 1.5 m, the lever arm for Lancelot's

weight is 1.0 m, and the lever arm for n_1 is 4.0 m. The torque equation for point B is then

$$\Sigma \tau_B = n_1 (4.0 \text{ m}) - (180 \text{ N})(1.5 \text{ m})$$
$$- (800 \text{ N})(1.0 \text{ m}) + n_2(0) + f_s(0) = 0$$

Solving for n_1, we get $n_1 = 268$ N. We substitute this into the $\Sigma F_x = 0$ equation and get $f_s = 268$ N.

(b) The static friction force f_s cannot exceed $\mu_s n_2$, so the *minimum* coefficient of static friction to prevent slipping is

$$(\mu_s)_{\min} = \frac{f_s}{n_2} = \frac{268 \text{ N}}{980 \text{ N}} = 0.27$$

(c) The components of the contact force $\vec{F}_B$ at the base are the static friction force f_s and the normal force n_2, so

$$\vec{F}_B = f_s \hat{\imath} + n_2 \hat{\jmath} = (268 \text{ N})\hat{\imath} + (980 \text{ N})\hat{\jmath}$$

The magnitude and direction of $\vec{F}_B$ (Fig. 11.9c) are

$$F_B = \sqrt{(268 \text{ N})^2 + (980 \text{ N})^2} = 1020 \text{ N}$$
$$\theta = \arctan \frac{980 \text{ N}}{268 \text{ N}} = 75°$$

EVALUATE: As Fig. 11.9c shows, the contact force $\vec{F}_B$ is *not* directed along the length of the ladder. Can you show that if $\vec{F}_B$ were directed along the ladder, there would be a net counterclockwise torque with respect to the top of the ladder, and equilibrium would be impossible?

As Lancelot climbs higher on the ladder, the lever arm and torque of his weight about B increase. This increases the values of n_1, f_s, and the required friction coefficient $(\mu_s)_{\min}$, so the ladder is more and more likely to slip as he climbs (see Exercise 11.10). A simple way to make slipping less likely is to use a larger ladder angle (say, 75° rather than 53.1°). This decreases the lever arms with respect to B of the weights of the ladder and Lancelot and increases the lever arm of n_1, all of which decrease the required friction force.

If we had assumed friction on the wall as well as on the floor, the problem would be impossible to solve by using the equilibrium conditions alone. (Try it!) The difficulty is that it's no longer adequate to treat the body as being perfectly rigid. Another problem of this kind is a four-legged table; there's no way to use the equilibrium conditions alone to find the force on each separate leg.

11.9 (a) Sir Lancelot pauses a third of the way up the ladder, fearing it will slip. (b) Free-body diagram for the system of Sir Lancelot and the ladder. (c) The contact force at B is the superposition of the normal force and the static friction force.

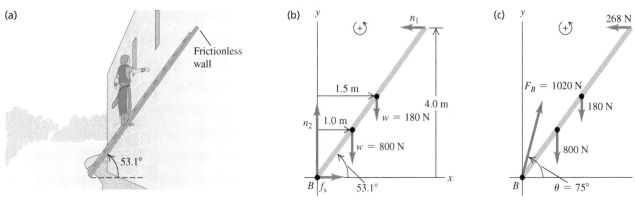

EXAMPLE 11.4 EQUILIBRIUM AND PUMPING IRON

Figure 11.10a shows a horizontal human arm lifting a dumbbell. The forearm is in equilibrium under the action of the weight $\vec{w}$ of the dumbbell, the tension $\vec{T}$ in the tendon connected to the biceps muscle, and the force $\vec{E}$ exerted on the forearm by the upper arm at the elbow joint. We ignore the weight of the forearm itself. (For clarity, in the drawing we've exaggerated the distance from the elbow to the point A where the tendon is attached.) Given the weight w and the angle θ between the tension force and the horizontal, find T and the two components of $\vec{E}$ (three unknown scalar quantities in all).

SOLUTION

IDENTIFY and SET UP: The system is at rest, so we use the conditions for equilibrium. We represent $\vec{T}$ and $\vec{E}$ in terms of their components (Fig. 11.10b). We guess that the directions of E_x and E_y are as shown; the signs of E_x and E_y as given by our solution will tell us the actual directions. Our target variables are T, E_x, and E_y.

EXECUTE: To find T, we take torques about the elbow joint so that the torque equation does not contain E_x, E_y, or T_x, then solve for T_y and hence T:

$$\sum \tau_{\text{elbow}} = Lw - DT_y = 0$$

$$T_y = \frac{Lw}{D} = T\sin\theta \quad \text{and} \quad T = \frac{Lw}{D\sin\theta}$$

To find E_x and E_y, we use the first conditions for equilibrium:

$$\sum F_x = T_x + (-E_x) = 0$$

$$E_x = T_x = T\cos\theta = \frac{Lw}{D\sin\theta}\cos\theta$$

$$= \frac{Lw}{D}\cot\theta = \frac{Lw}{D}\frac{D}{h} = \frac{Lw}{h}$$

$$\sum F_y = T_y + E_y + (-w) = 0$$

$$E_y = w - \frac{Lw}{D} = -\frac{(L-D)w}{D}$$

The negative sign for E_y tells us that it should actually point *down* in Fig. 11.10b.

EVALUATE: We can check our results for E_x and E_y by taking torques about points A and B, about both of which T has zero torque:

$$\sum \tau_A = (L-D)w + DE_y = 0 \quad \text{so} \quad E_y = -\frac{(L-D)w}{D}$$

$$\sum \tau_B = Lw - hE_x = 0 \quad \text{so} \quad E_x = \frac{Lw}{h}$$

As a realistic example, take $w = 200\,\text{N}$, $D = 0.050\,\text{m}$, $L = 0.30\,\text{m}$, and $\theta = 80°$, so that $h = D\tan\theta = (0.050\,\text{m})(5.67) = 0.28\,\text{m}$. Using our results for T, E_x, and E_y, we find

$$T = \frac{Lw}{D\sin\theta} = \frac{(0.30\,\text{m})(200\,\text{N})}{(0.050\,\text{m})(0.98)} = 1220\,\text{N}$$

$$E_y = -\frac{(L-D)w}{D} = -\frac{(0.30\,\text{m} - 0.050\,\text{m})(200\,\text{N})}{0.050\,\text{m}}$$

$$= -1000\,\text{N}$$

$$E_x = \frac{Lw}{h} = \frac{(0.30\,\text{m})(200\,\text{N})}{0.28\,\text{m}} = 210\,\text{N}$$

The magnitude of the force at the elbow is

$$E = \sqrt{E_x^2 + E_y^2} = 1020\,\text{N}$$

Note that T and E are *much* larger than the 200-N weight of the dumbbell. A forearm weighs only about 20 N, so it was reasonable to ignore its weight.

11.10 (a) The situation. (b) Our free-body diagram for the forearm. The weight of the forearm is ignored, and the distance D is greatly exaggerated for clarity.

(a)

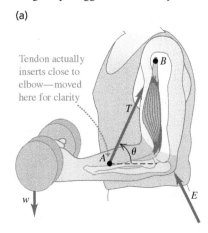

(b)

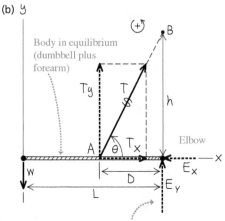

TEST YOUR UNDERSTANDING OF
SECTION 11.3 A metal advertising
sign (weight w) for a specialty shop is
suspended from the end of a horizontal
rod of length L and negligible mass
(**Fig. 11.11**). The rod is supported by a
cable at an angle θ from the horizontal
and by a hinge at point P. Rank the following force magnitudes in order from
greatest to smallest: (i) the weight w of
the sign; (ii) the tension in the cable;
(iii) the vertical component of force
exerted on the rod by the hinge at P. ▮

11.11 What are the tension in the diagonal cable and the vertical component of
force exerted by the hinge at P?

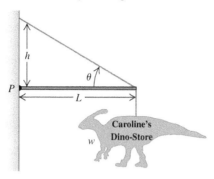

DATA *SPEAKS*

Rigid-Body Equilibrium

When students were given a problem
about the equilibrium of rigid bodies,
more than 24% gave an incorrect response. Common errors:

- Failing to include a plus or minus sign to
  account for the torque direction.
- Forgetting that if a force acts at the
  point about which you calculate
  torques, that force causes zero torque.

11.4 STRESS, STRAIN, AND ELASTIC MODULI

The rigid body is a useful idealized model, but the stretching, squeezing, and
twisting of real bodies when forces are applied are often too important to ignore.
Figure 11.12 shows three examples. We want to study the relationship between
the forces and deformations for each case.

You don't have to look far to find a deformable body; it's as plain as the nose
on your face (**Fig. 11.13**). If you grasp the tip of your nose between your index
finger and thumb, you'll find that the harder you pull your nose outward or push
it inward, the more it stretches or compresses. Likewise, the harder you squeeze
your index finger and thumb together, the more the tip of your nose compresses.
If you try to twist the tip of your nose, you'll get a greater amount of twist if you
apply stronger forces.

These observations illustrate a general rule. In each case you apply a **stress**
to your nose; the amount of stress is a measure of the forces causing the deformation, on a "force per unit area" basis. And in each case the stress causes a
deformation, or **strain.** More careful versions of the experiments with your nose
suggest that for relatively small stresses, the resulting strain is proportional to the
stress: The greater the deforming forces, the greater the resulting deformation.
This proportionality is called **Hooke's law,** and the ratio of stress to strain is
called the **elastic modulus:**

Measure of forces applied to deform a body

Hooke's law: $\dfrac{\text{Stress}}{\text{Strain}} = \text{Elastic modulus}$ Property of material of which body is made   (11.7)

Measure of how much deformation results from stress

11.12 Three types of stress. (a) Guitar
strings under *tensile stress*, being
stretched by forces acting at their ends.
(b) A diver under *bulk stress*, being
squeezed from all sides by forces due to
water pressure. (c) A ribbon under *shear
stress*, being deformed and eventually cut
by forces exerted by the scissors.

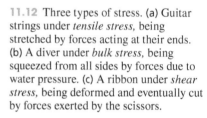

11.13 When you pinch your nose, the force per area that you apply to your nose is
called *stress*. The fractional change in the size of your nose (the change in size divided
by the initial size) is called *strain*. The deformation is *elastic* because your nose springs
back to its initial size when you stop pinching.

The value of the elastic modulus depends on what the body is made of but not its shape or size. If a material returns to its original state after the stress is removed, it is called **elastic;** Hooke's law is a special case of elastic behavior. If a material instead remains deformed after the stress is removed, it is called **plastic.** Here we'll consider elastic behavior only; we'll return to plastic behavior in Section 11.5.

We used one form of Hooke's law in Section 6.3: The elongation of an ideal spring is proportional to the stretching force. Remember that Hooke's "law" is not really a general law; it is valid over only a limited range of stresses. In Section 11.5 we'll see what happens beyond that limited range.

Tensile and Compressive Stress and Strain

The simplest elastic behavior to understand is the stretching of a bar, rod, or wire when its ends are pulled (Fig. 11.12a). **Figure 11.14** shows an object that initially has uniform cross-sectional area A and length l_0. We then apply forces of equal magnitude $F_\perp$ but opposite directions at the ends (this ensures that the object has no tendency to move left or right). We say that the object is in **tension.** We've already talked a lot about tension in ropes and strings; it's the same concept here. The subscript $\perp$ is a reminder that the forces act perpendicular to the cross section.

We define the **tensile stress** at the cross section as the ratio of the force $F_\perp$ to the cross-sectional area A:

$$\text{Tensile stress} = \frac{F_\perp}{A} \tag{11.8}$$

This is a *scalar* quantity because $F_\perp$ is the *magnitude* of the force. The SI unit of stress is the **pascal** (abbreviated Pa and named for the 17th-century French scientist and philosopher Blaise Pascal). Equation (11.8) shows that 1 pascal equals 1 newton per square meter (N/m^2):

$$1 \text{ pascal} = 1 \text{ Pa} = 1 \text{ N/m}^2$$

In the British system the most common unit of stress is the pound per square inch $(\text{lb/in.}^2 \text{ or psi})$. The conversion factors are

$$1 \text{ psi} = 6895 \text{ Pa} \quad \text{and} \quad 1 \text{ Pa} = 1.450 \times 10^{-4} \text{ psi}$$

The units of stress are the same as those of *pressure,* which we will encounter often in later chapters.

Under tension the object in Fig. 11.14 stretches to a length $l = l_0 + \Delta l$. The elongation Δl does not occur only at the ends; every part of the object stretches in the same proportion. The **tensile strain** of the object equals the fractional change in length, which is the ratio of the elongation Δl to the original length l_0:

$$\text{Tensile strain} = \frac{l - l_0}{l_0} = \frac{\Delta l}{l_0} \tag{11.9}$$

Tensile strain is stretch per unit length. It is a ratio of two lengths, always measured in the same units, and so is a pure (dimensionless) number with no units.

Experiment shows that for a sufficiently small tensile stress, stress and strain are proportional, as in Eq. (11.7). The corresponding elastic modulus is called **Young's modulus,** denoted by Y:

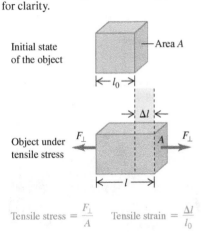

11.14 An object in tension. The net force on the object is zero, but the object deforms. The tensile stress (the ratio of the force to the cross-sectional area) produces a tensile strain (the elongation divided by the initial length). The elongation Δl is exaggerated for clarity.

Initial state of the object — Area A

l_0

Δl

Object under tensile stress $F_\perp$ $F_\perp$ A

l

$\text{Tensile stress} = \dfrac{F_\perp}{A} \qquad \text{Tensile strain} = \dfrac{\Delta l}{l_0}$

BIO Application Young's Modulus of a Tendon The anterior tibial tendon connects your foot to the large muscle that runs along the side of your shinbone. (You can feel this tendon at the front of your ankle.) Measurements show that this tendon has a Young's modulus of 1.2×10^9 Pa, much less than for the metals listed in Table 11.1. Hence this tendon stretches substantially (up to 2.5% of its length) in response to the stresses experienced in walking and running.

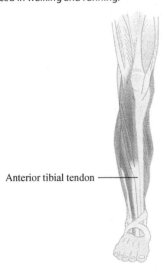

Anterior tibial tendon

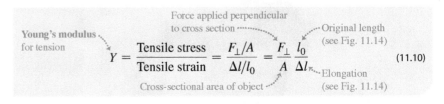

Young's modulus for tension
Force applied perpendicular to cross section
Original length (see Fig. 11.14)

$$Y = \frac{\text{Tensile stress}}{\text{Tensile strain}} = \frac{F_\perp/A}{\Delta l/l_0} = \frac{F_\perp}{A}\frac{l_0}{\Delta l} \tag{11.10}$$

Cross-sectional area of object
Elongation (see Fig. 11.14)

	TABLE 11.1	Approximate Elastic Moduli		
Material	**Young's Modulus, Y (Pa)**	**Bulk Modulus, B (Pa)**	**Shear Modulus, S (Pa)**
Aluminum	7.0×10^{10}	7.5×10^{10}	2.5×10^{10}
Brass	9.0×10^{10}	6.0×10^{10}	3.5×10^{10}
Copper	11×10^{10}	14×10^{10}	4.4×10^{10}
Iron	21×10^{10}	16×10^{10}	7.7×10^{10}
Lead	1.6×10^{10}	4.1×10^{10}	0.6×10^{10}
Nickel	21×10^{10}	17×10^{10}	7.8×10^{10}
Silicone rubber	0.001×10^{10}	0.2×10^{10}	0.0002×10^{10}
Steel	20×10^{10}	16×10^{10}	7.5×10^{10}
Tendon (typical)	0.12×10^{10}	—	—

Since strain is a pure number, the units of Young's modulus are the same as those of stress: force per unit area. **Table 11.1** lists some typical values. (This table also gives values of two other elastic moduli that we will discuss later in this chapter.) A material with a large value of Y is relatively unstretchable; a large stress is required for a given strain. For example, the value of Y for cast steel $(2 \times 10^{11}$ Pa) is much larger than that for a tendon $(1.2 \times 10^9$ Pa).

When the forces on the ends of a bar are pushes rather than pulls (**Fig. 11.15**), the bar is in **compression** and the stress is a **compressive stress.** The **compressive strain** of an object in compression is defined in the same way as the tensile strain, but Δl has the opposite direction. Hooke's law and Eq. (11.10) are valid for compression as well as tension if the compressive stress is not too great. For many materials, Young's modulus has the same value for both tensile and compressive stresses. Composite materials such as concrete and stone are an exception; they can withstand compressive stresses but fail under comparable tensile stresses. Stone was the primary building material used by ancient civilizations such as the Babylonians, Assyrians, and Romans, so their structures had to be designed to avoid tensile stresses. Hence they used arches in doorways and bridges, where the weight of the overlying material compresses the stones of the arch together and does not place them under tension.

In many situations, bodies can experience both tensile and compressive stresses at the same time. For example, a horizontal beam supported at each end sags under its own weight. As a result, the top of the beam is under compression while the bottom of the beam is under tension (**Fig. 11.16a**). To minimize the stress and hence the bending strain, the top and bottom of the beam are given a large cross-sectional area. There is neither compression nor tension along the centerline of the beam, so this part can have a small cross section; this helps keep the weight of the beam to a minimum and further helps reduce the stress. The result is an I-beam of the familiar shape used in building construction (Fig. 11.16b).

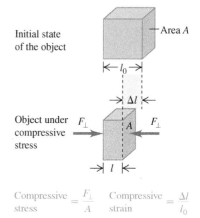

11.15 An object in compression. The compressive stress and compressive strain are defined in the same way as tensile stress and strain (see Fig. 11.14), except that Δl now denotes the distance that the object contracts.

$$\text{Compressive} \atop \text{stress} = \frac{F_\perp}{A} \qquad \text{Compressive} \atop \text{strain} = \frac{\Delta l}{l_0}$$

(a)

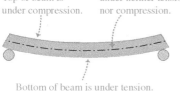

Top of beam is under compression.

Beam's centerline is under neither tension nor compression.

Bottom of beam is under tension.

(b)

The top and bottom of an I-beam are broad to minimize the compressive and tensile stresses.

The beam can be narrow near its centerline, which is under neither compression nor tension.

11.16 (a) A beam supported at both ends is under both compression and tension. (b) The cross-sectional shape of an I-beam minimizes both stress and weight.

EXAMPLE 11.5 TENSILE STRESS AND STRAIN

A steel rod 2.0 m long has a cross-sectional area of 0.30 cm². It is hung by one end from a support, and a 550-kg milling machine is hung from its other end. Determine the stress on the rod and the resulting strain and elongation.

SOLUTION

IDENTIFY, SET UP, and EXECUTE: The rod is under tension, so we can use Eq. (11.8) to find the tensile stress; Eq. (11.9), with the value of Young's modulus Y for steel from Table 11.1, to find the corresponding strain; and Eq. (11.10) to find the elongation Δl:

$$\text{Tensile stress} = \frac{F_\perp}{A} = \frac{(550\ \text{kg})(9.8\ \text{m/s}^2)}{3.0 \times 10^{-5}\ \text{m}^2} = 1.8 \times 10^8\ \text{Pa}$$

$$\text{Strain} = \frac{\Delta l}{l_0} = \frac{\text{Stress}}{Y} = \frac{1.8 \times 10^8\ \text{Pa}}{20 \times 10^{10}\ \text{Pa}} = 9.0 \times 10^{-4}$$

$$\text{Elongation} = \Delta l = (\text{Strain}) \times l_0$$
$$= (9.0 \times 10^{-4})(2.0\ \text{m}) = 0.0018\ \text{m} = 1.8\ \text{mm}$$

EVALUATE: This small elongation, resulting from a load of over half a ton, is a testament to the stiffness of steel. (We've ignored the relatively small stress due to the weight of the rod itself.)

BIO Application Bulk Stress on an Anglerfish The anglerfish (*Melanocetus johnsoni*) is found in oceans throughout the world at depths as great as 1000 m, where the pressure (that is, the bulk stress) is about 100 atmospheres. Anglerfish are able to withstand such stress because they have no internal air spaces, unlike fish found in the upper ocean, where pressures are lower. The largest anglerfish are about 12 cm (5 in.) long.

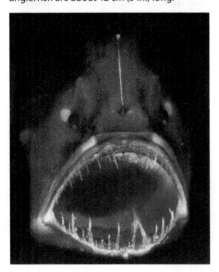

Bulk Stress and Strain

When a scuba diver plunges deep into the ocean, the water exerts nearly uniform pressure everywhere on his surface and squeezes him to a slightly smaller volume (see Fig. 11.12b). This is a different situation from the tensile and compressive stresses and strains we have discussed. The uniform pressure on all sides of the diver is a **bulk stress** (or **volume stress**), and the resulting deformation—a **bulk strain** (or **volume strain**)—is a change in his volume.

If an object is immersed in a fluid (liquid or gas) at rest, the fluid exerts a force on any part of the object's surface; this force is *perpendicular* to the surface. (If we tried to make the fluid exert a force parallel to the surface, the fluid would slip sideways to counteract the effort.) The force $F_\perp$ per unit area that the fluid exerts on an immersed object is called the **pressure** p in the fluid:

$$\text{Pressure in a fluid} \cdots\!\!\rightarrow p = \frac{F_\perp}{A} \begin{array}{l} \cdots\text{Force that fluid applies to} \\ \text{surface of an immersed object} \\ \cdots\text{Area over which force is exerted} \end{array} \quad (11.11)$$

Pressure has the same units as stress; commonly used units include 1 Pa ($= 1\ \text{N/m}^2$), 1 lb/in.² (1 psi), and 1 **atmosphere** (1 atm). One atmosphere is the approximate average pressure of the earth's atmosphere at sea level:

$$1\ \text{atmosphere} = 1\ \text{atm} = 1.013 \times 10^5\ \text{Pa} = 14.7\ \text{lb/in.}^2$$

CAUTION **Pressure vs. force** Unlike force, pressure has no intrinsic direction: The pressure on the surface of an immersed object is the same no matter how the surface is oriented. Hence pressure is a *scalar* quantity, not a vector quantity.

The pressure in a fluid increases with depth. For example, the pressure in the ocean increases by about 1 atm every 10 m. If an immersed object is relatively small, however, we can ignore these pressure differences for purposes of calculating bulk stress. We'll then treat the pressure as having the same value at all points on an immersed object's surface.

Pressure plays the role of stress in a volume deformation. The corresponding strain is the fractional change in volume (**Fig. 11.17**)—that is, the ratio of the volume change ΔV to the original volume V_0:

$$\text{Bulk (volume) strain} = \frac{\Delta V}{V_0} \quad (11.12)$$

Volume strain is the change in volume per unit volume. Like tensile or compressive strain, it is a pure number, without units.

When Hooke's law is obeyed, an increase in pressure (bulk stress) produces a *proportional* bulk strain (fractional change in volume). The corresponding elastic modulus (ratio of stress to strain) is called the **bulk modulus,** denoted by B. When the pressure on a body changes by a small amount Δp, from p_0 to $p_0 + \Delta p$, and the resulting bulk strain is $\Delta V/V_0$, Hooke's law takes the form

11.17 An object under bulk stress. Without the stress, the cube has volume V_0; when the stress is applied, the cube has a smaller volume V. The volume change ΔV is exaggerated for clarity.

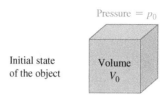

$$\underset{\substack{\text{Bulk modulus} \\ \text{for compression}}}{} B = \frac{\text{Bulk stress}}{\text{Bulk strain}} = -\frac{\Delta p}{\Delta V/V_0} \quad\underset{\substack{\text{Additional pressure} \\ \text{on object}}}{}$$

$$\underset{\substack{\text{Change in volume (see Fig. 11.17)}}}{} \qquad \underset{\substack{\text{Original volume} \\ \text{(see Fig. 11.17)}}}{} \tag{11.13}$$

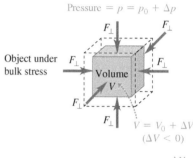

We include a minus sign in this equation because an *increase* of pressure always causes a *decrease* in volume. In other words, if Δp is positive, ΔV is negative. The bulk modulus B itself is a positive quantity.

For small pressure changes in a solid or a liquid, we consider B to be constant. The bulk modulus of a *gas,* however, depends on the initial pressure p_0. Table 11.1 includes values of B for several solid materials. Its units, force per unit area, are the same as those of pressure (and of tensile or compressive stress).

The reciprocal of the bulk modulus is called the **compressibility** and is denoted by k. From Eq. (11.13),

$$k = \frac{1}{B} = -\frac{\Delta V/V_0}{\Delta p} = -\frac{1}{V_0}\frac{\Delta V}{\Delta p} \quad \text{(compressibility)} \tag{11.14}$$

Compressibility is the fractional decrease in volume, $-\Delta V/V_0$, per unit increase Δp in pressure. The units of compressibility are those of *reciprocal pressure,* Pa^{-1} or atm^{-1}.

Table 11.2 lists the values of compressibility k for several liquids. For example, the compressibility of water is $46.4 \times 10^{-6}\,\text{atm}^{-1}$, which means that the volume of water decreases by 46.4 parts per million for each 1-atmosphere increase in pressure. Materials with small bulk modulus B and large compressibility k are easiest to compress.

Compressibilities

TABLE 11.2	of Liquids	
	Compressibility, k	
Liquid	$\textbf{Pa}^{-1}$	$\textbf{atm}^{-1}$
Carbon disulfide	93×10^{-11}	94×10^{-6}
Ethyl alcohol	110×10^{-11}	111×10^{-6}
Glycerine	21×10^{-11}	21×10^{-6}
Mercury	3.7×10^{-11}	3.8×10^{-6}
Water	45.8×10^{-11}	46.4×10^{-6}

EXAMPLE 11.6   BULK STRESS AND STRAIN

A hydraulic press contains $0.25\,\text{m}^3$ (250 L) of oil. Find the decrease in the volume of the oil when it is subjected to a pressure increase $\Delta p = 1.6 \times 10^7\,\text{Pa}$ (about 160 atm or 2300 psi). The bulk modulus of the oil is $B = 5.0 \times 10^9\,\text{Pa}$ (about 5.0×10^4 atm), and its compressibility is $k = 1/B = 20 \times 10^{-6}\,\text{atm}^{-1}$.

SOLUTION

IDENTIFY, SET UP, and EXECUTE: This example uses the ideas of bulk stress and strain. We are given both the bulk modulus and the compressibility, and our target variable is ΔV. Solving Eq. (11.13) for ΔV, we find

$$\Delta V = -\frac{V_0 \Delta p}{B} = -\frac{(0.25\,\text{m}^3)(1.6 \times 10^7\,\text{Pa})}{5.0 \times 10^9\,\text{Pa}}$$

$$= -8.0 \times 10^{-4}\,\text{m}^3 = -0.80\,\text{L}$$

Alternatively, we can use Eq. (11.14) with the approximate unit conversions given above:

$$\Delta V = -kV_0 \Delta p = -(20 \times 10^{-6}\,\text{atm}^{-1})(0.25\,\text{m}^3)(160\,\text{atm})$$

$$= -8.0 \times 10^{-4}\,\text{m}^3$$

EVALUATE: The negative value of ΔV means that the volume decreases when the pressure increases. The 160-atm pressure increase is large, but the *fractional* volume change is very small:

$$\frac{\Delta V}{V_0} = \frac{-8.0 \times 10^{-4}\,\text{m}^3}{0.25\,\text{m}^3} = -0.0032 \quad \text{or} \quad -0.32\%$$

11.18 An object under shear stress. Forces are applied tangent to opposite surfaces of the object (in contrast to the situation in Fig. 11.14, in which the forces act perpendicular to the surfaces). The deformation x is exaggerated for clarity.

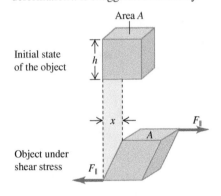

Area A

Initial state of the object

Object under shear stress

$$\text{Shear stress} = \frac{F_{\parallel}}{A} \qquad \text{Shear strain} = \frac{x}{h}$$

Shear Stress and Strain

The third kind of stress-strain situation is called *shear*. The ribbon in Fig. 11.12c is under **shear stress:** One part of the ribbon is being pushed up while an adjacent part is being pushed down, producing a deformation of the ribbon. **Figure 11.18** shows a body being deformed by a shear stress. In the figure, forces of equal magnitude but opposite direction act *tangent* to the surfaces of opposite ends of the object. We define the shear stress as the force $F_{\parallel}$ acting tangent to the surface divided by the area A on which it acts:

$$\text{Shear stress} = \frac{F_{\parallel}}{A} \qquad (11.15)$$

Shear stress, like the other two types of stress, is a force per unit area.

Figure 11.18 shows that one face of the object under shear stress is displaced by a distance x relative to the opposite face. We define **shear strain** as the ratio of the displacement x to the transverse dimension h:

$$\text{Shear strain} = \frac{x}{h} \qquad (11.16)$$

In real-life situations, x is typically much smaller than h. Like all strains, shear strain is a dimensionless number; it is a ratio of two lengths.

If the forces are small enough that Hooke's law is obeyed, the shear strain is *proportional* to the shear stress. The corresponding elastic modulus (ratio of shear stress to shear strain) is called the **shear modulus,** denoted by S:

Force applied tangent to surface of object

Transverse dimension (see Fig. 11.18)

$$\text{Shear modulus for shear} \quad S = \frac{\text{Shear stress}}{\text{Shear strain}} = \frac{F_{\parallel}/A}{x/h} = \frac{F_{\parallel}}{A}\frac{h}{x} \qquad (11.17)$$

Area over which force is exerted

Deformation (see Fig. 11.18)

Table 11.1 gives several values of shear modulus. For a given material, S is usually one-third to one-half as large as Young's modulus Y for tensile stress. Keep in mind that the concepts of shear stress, shear strain, and shear modulus apply to *solid* materials only. The reason is that *shear* refers to deforming an object that has a definite shape (see Fig. 11.18). This concept doesn't apply to gases and liquids, which do not have definite shapes.

EXAMPLE 11.7 | **SHEAR STRESS AND STRAIN**

Suppose the object in Fig. 11.18 is the brass base plate of an outdoor sculpture that experiences shear forces in an earthquake. The plate is 0.80 m square and 0.50 cm thick. What is the force exerted on each of its edges if the resulting displacement x is 0.16 mm?

SOLUTION

IDENTIFY and SET UP: This example uses the relationship among shear stress, shear strain, and shear modulus. Our target variable is the force $F_{\parallel}$ exerted parallel to each edge, as shown in Fig. 11.18. We'll find the shear strain from Eq. (11.16), the shear stress from Eq. (11.17), and $F_{\parallel}$ from Eq. (11.15). Table 11.1 gives the shear modulus of brass. In Fig. 11.18, h represents the 0.80-m length of each side of the plate. The area A in Eq. (11.15) is the product of the 0.80-m length and the 0.50-cm thickness.

EXECUTE: From Eq. (11.16),

$$\text{Shear strain} = \frac{x}{h} = \frac{1.6 \times 10^{-4}\ \text{m}}{0.80\ \text{m}} = 2.0 \times 10^{-4}$$

From Eq. (11.17),

$$\text{Shear stress} = (\text{Shear strain}) \times S$$
$$= (2.0 \times 10^{-4})(3.5 \times 10^{10}\ \text{Pa}) = 7.0 \times 10^{6}\ \text{Pa}$$

Finally, from Eq. (11.15),

$$F_{\parallel} = (\text{Shear stress}) \times A$$
$$= (7.0 \times 10^{6}\ \text{Pa})(0.80\ \text{m})(0.0050\ \text{m}) = 2.8 \times 10^{4}\ \text{N}$$

EVALUATE: The shear force supplied by the earthquake is more than 3 tons! The large shear modulus of brass makes it hard to deform. Further, the plate is relatively thick (0.50 cm), so the area A is relatively large and a substantial force $F_{\parallel}$ is needed to provide the necessary stress $F_{\parallel}/A$.

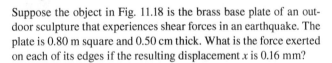

A copper rod of cross-sectional area 0.500 cm^2 and length 1.00 m is elongated by 2.00×10^{-2} mm, and a steel rod of the same cross-sectional area but 0.100 m in length is elongated by 2.00×10^{-3} mm. (a) Which rod has greater tensile *strain*? (i) The copper rod; (ii) the steel rod; (iii) the strain is the same for both. (b) Which rod is under greater tensile *stress*? (i) The copper rod; (ii) the steel rod; (iii) the stress is the same for both. ❚

11.5 ELASTICITY AND PLASTICITY

Hooke's law—the proportionality of stress and strain in elastic deformations—has a limited range of validity. In the preceding section we used phrases such as "if the forces are small enough that Hooke's law is obeyed." Just what *are* the limitations of Hooke's law? What's more, if you pull, squeeze, or twist *anything* hard enough, it will bend or break. Can we be more precise than that?

To address these questions, let's look at a graph of tensile stress as a function of tensile strain. **Figure 11.19** shows a typical graph of this kind for a metal such as copper or soft iron. The strain is shown as the *percent* elongation; the horizontal scale is not uniform beyond the first portion of the curve, up to a strain of less than 1%. The first portion is a straight line, indicating Hooke's law behavior with stress directly proportional to strain. This straight-line portion ends at point *a*; the stress at this point is called the *proportional limit*.

From *a* to *b*, stress and strain are no longer proportional, and Hooke's law is *not* obeyed. However, from *a* to *b* (and *O* to *a*), the behavior of the material is *elastic:* If the load is gradually removed starting at any point between *O* and *b*, the curve is retraced until the material returns to its original length. This elastic deformation is *reversible.*

Point *b*, the end of the elastic region, is called the *yield point;* the stress at the yield point is called the *elastic limit.* When we increase the stress beyond point *b*, the strain continues to increase. But if we remove the load at a point like *c* beyond the elastic limit, the material does *not* return to its original length. Instead, it follows the red line in Fig. 11.19. The material has deformed *irreversibly* and acquired a *permanent set.* This is the *plastic* behavior mentioned in Section 11.4.

Once the material has become plastic, a small additional stress produces a relatively large increase in strain, until a point *d* is reached at which *fracture* takes place. That's what happens if a steel guitar string in Fig. 11.12a is tightened too much: The string breaks at the fracture point. Steel is *brittle* because it breaks soon after reaching its elastic limit; other materials, such as soft iron, are *ductile*—they can be given a large permanent stretch without breaking. (The material depicted in Fig. 11.19 is ductile, since it can stretch by more than 30% before breaking.)

Unlike uniform materials such as metals, stretchable biological materials such as tendons and ligaments have no true plastic region. That's because these materials are made of a collection of microscopic fibers; when stressed beyond the elastic limit, the fibers tear apart from each other. (A torn ligament or tendon is one that has fractured in this way.)

If a material is still within its elastic region, something very curious can happen when it is stretched and then allowed to relax. **Figure 11.20** is a stress-strain curve for vulcanized rubber that has been stretched by more than seven times its original length. The stress is not proportional to the strain, but the behavior is elastic because when the load is removed, the material returns to its original length. However, the material follows *different* curves for increasing and decreasing stress. This is called *elastic hysteresis.* The work done by the material when it returns to its original shape is less than the work required to deform it; that's due to internal friction. Rubber with large elastic hysteresis is very useful for absorbing vibrations, such as in engine mounts and shock-absorber bushings for cars. Tendons display similar behavior.

11.19 Typical stress-strain diagram for a ductile metal under tension.

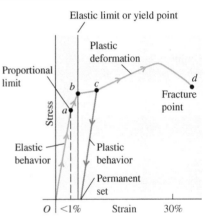

11.20 Typical stress-strain diagram for vulcanized rubber. The curves are different for increasing and decreasing stress, a phenomenon called elastic hysteresis.

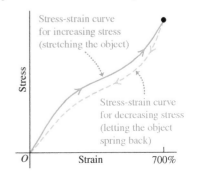

TABLE 11.3	Approximate Breaking Stresses

Material	Breaking Stress (Pa or N/m²)
Aluminum	2.2×10^8
Brass	4.7×10^8
Glass	10×10^8
Iron	3.0×10^8
Steel	$5{-}20 \times 10^8$
Tendon (typical)	1×10^8

The stress required to cause actual fracture of a material is called the *breaking stress,* the *ultimate strength,* or (for tensile stress) the *tensile strength.* Two materials, such as two types of steel, may have very similar elastic constants but vastly different breaking stresses. **Table 11.3** gives typical values of breaking stress for several materials in tension. Comparing Tables 11.1 and 11.3 shows that iron and steel are comparably *stiff* (they have almost the same value of Young's modulus), but steel is *stronger* (it has a larger breaking stress than does iron).

TEST YOUR UNDERSTANDING OF SECTION 11.5 While parking your car, you accidentally back into a steel post. You pull forward until the car no longer touches the post and then get out to inspect the damage. What does your rear bumper look like if the strain in the impact was (a) less than at the proportional limit; (b) greater than at the proportional limit but less than at the yield point; (c) greater than at the yield point but less than at the fracture point; and (d) greater than at the fracture point? ▮

CHAPTER **11** SUMMARY

SOLUTIONS TO ALL EXAMPLES

Conditions for equilibrium: For a rigid body to be in equilibrium, two conditions must be satisfied. First, the vector sum of forces must be zero. Second, the sum of torques about any point must be zero. The torque due to the weight of a body can be found by assuming the entire weight is concentrated at the center of gravity, which is at the same point as the center of mass if $\vec{g}$ has the same value at all points. (See Examples 11.1–11.4.)

$$\sum \vec{F} = 0 \qquad (11.1)$$

$$\sum \vec{\tau} = 0 \quad \text{about } any \text{ point} \qquad (11.2)$$

$$\vec{r}_{cm} = \frac{m_1\vec{r}_1 + m_2\vec{r}_2 + m_3\vec{r}_3 + \cdots}{m_1 + m_2 + m_3 + \cdots} \qquad (11.4)$$

Stress, strain, and Hooke's law: Hooke's law states that in elastic deformations, stress (force per unit area) is proportional to strain (fractional deformation). The proportionality constant is called the elastic modulus.

$$\frac{\text{Stress}}{\text{Strain}} = \text{Elastic modulus} \qquad (11.7)$$

Tensile and compressive stress: Tensile stress is tensile force per unit area, $F_\perp/A$. Tensile strain is fractional change in length, $\Delta l/l_0$. The elastic modulus for tension is called Young's modulus Y. Compressive stress and strain are defined in the same way. (See Example 11.5.)

$$Y = \frac{\text{Tensile stress}}{\text{Tensile strain}} = \frac{F_\perp/A}{\Delta l/l_0} = \frac{F_\perp}{A}\frac{l_0}{\Delta l} \qquad (11.10)$$

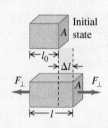

Bulk stress: Pressure in a fluid is force per unit area. Bulk stress is pressure change, Δp, and bulk strain is fractional volume change, $\Delta V/V_0$. The elastic modulus for compression is called the bulk modulus, B. Compressibility, k, is the reciprocal of bulk modulus: $k = 1/B$. (See Example 11.6.)

$$p = \frac{F_\perp}{A} \qquad (11.11)$$

$$B = \frac{\text{Bulk stress}}{\text{Bulk strain}} = -\frac{\Delta p}{\Delta V/V_0} \qquad (11.13)$$

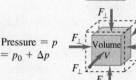

Shear stress: Shear stress is force per unit area, $F_\parallel/A$, for a force applied tangent to a surface. Shear strain is the displacement x of one side divided by the transverse dimension h. The elastic modulus for shear is called the shear modulus, S. (See Example 11.7.)

$$S = \frac{\text{Shear stress}}{\text{Shear strain}} = \frac{F_\parallel/A}{x/h} = \frac{F_\parallel}{A}\frac{h}{x} \quad (11.17)$$

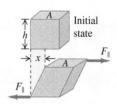

The limits of Hooke's law: The proportional limit is the maximum stress for which stress and strain are proportional. Beyond the proportional limit, Hooke's law is not valid. The elastic limit is the stress beyond which irreversible deformation occurs. The breaking stress, or ultimate strength, is the stress at which the material breaks.

BRIDGING PROBLEM IN EQUILIBRIUM AND UNDER STRESS

A horizontal, uniform, solid copper rod has an original length l_0, cross-sectional area A, Young's modulus Y, bulk modulus B, shear modulus S, and mass m. It is supported by a frictionless pivot at its right end and by a cable a distance $l_0/4$ from its left end (**Fig. 11.21**). Both pivot and cable are attached so that they exert their forces uniformly over the rod's cross section. The cable makes an angle θ with the rod and compresses it. (a) Find the tension in the cable. (b) Find the magnitude and direction of the force exerted by the pivot on the right end of the rod. How does this magnitude compare to the cable tension? How does this angle compare to θ? (c) Find the change in length of the rod due to the stresses exerted by the cable and pivot on the rod. (The length change is small compared to the original length l_0.) (d) By what factor would your answer in part (c) increase if the solid copper rod were twice as long but had the same cross-sectional area?

11.21 What are the forces on the rod? What are the stress and strain?

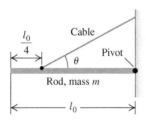

SOLUTION GUIDE

IDENTIFY and SET UP

1. Draw a free-body diagram for the rod. Be careful to place each force in the correct location.
2. List the unknown quantities, and decide which are the target variables.
3. What conditions must be met so that the rod remains at rest? What kind of stress (and resulting strain) is involved? Use your answers to select the appropriate equations.

EXECUTE

4. Use your equations to solve for the target variables. (*Hint:* You can make the solution easier by carefully choosing the point around which you calculate torques.)
5. Use trigonometry to decide whether the pivot force or the cable tension has the greater magnitude and whether the angle of the pivot force is greater than, less than, or equal to θ.

EVALUATE

6. Check whether your answers are reasonable. Which force, the cable tension or the pivot force, holds up more of the weight of the rod? Does this make sense?

Problems

For assigned homework and other learning materials, go to MasteringPhysics®.

•, ••, •••: Difficulty levels. CP: Cumulative problems incorporating material from earlier chapters. CALC: Problems requiring calculus. DATA: Problems involving real data, scientific evidence, experimental design, and/or statistical reasoning. BIO: Biosciences problems.

DISCUSSION QUESTIONS

Q11.1 Does a rigid object in uniform rotation about a fixed axis satisfy the first and second conditions for equilibrium? Why? Does it then follow that every particle in this object is in equilibrium? Explain.

Q11.2 (a) Is it possible for an object to be in translational equilibrium (the first condition) but *not* in rotational equilibrium (the second condition)? Illustrate your answer with a simple example. (b) Can an object be in rotational equilibrium yet *not* in translational equilibrium? Justify your answer with a simple example.

Q11.3 Car tires are sometimes "balanced" on a machine that pivots the tire and wheel about the center. Weights are placed around the wheel rim until it does not tip from the horizontal plane. Discuss this procedure in terms of the center of gravity.

Q11.4 Does the center of gravity of a solid body always lie within the material of the body? If not, give a counterexample.

Q11.5 In Section 11.2 we always assumed that the value of g was the same at all points on the body. This is *not* a good approximation if the dimensions of the body are great enough, because the value of g decreases with altitude. If this is taken into account, will the center of gravity of a long, vertical rod be above, below, or at its center of mass? Explain how this can be used to keep the long axis of an orbiting spacecraft pointed toward the earth. (This would be useful for a weather satellite that must always keep its camera lens trained on the earth.) The moon is not exactly spherical but is somewhat elongated. Explain why this same effect is responsible for keeping the same face of the moon pointed toward the earth at all times.

Q11.6 You are balancing a wrench by suspending it at a single point. Is the equilibrium stable, unstable, or neutral if the point is above, at, or below the wrench's center of gravity? In each case give the reasoning behind your answer. (For rotation, a rigid body is in *stable* equilibrium if a small rotation of the body produces a torque that tends to return the body to equilibrium; it is in *unstable* equilibrium if a small rotation produces a torque that tends to take the body farther from equilibrium; and it is in *neutral* equilibrium if a small rotation produces no torque.)

Q11.7 You can probably stand flatfooted on the floor and then rise up and balance on your tiptoes. Why are you unable do it if your toes are touching the wall of your room? (Try it!)

Q11.8 You freely pivot a horseshoe from a horizontal nail through one of its nail holes. You then hang a long string with a weight at its bottom from the same nail, so that the string hangs vertically in front of the horseshoe without touching it. How do you know that the horseshoe's center of gravity is along the line behind the string? How can you locate the center of gravity by repeating the process at another nail hole? Will the center of gravity be within the solid material of the horseshoe?

Q11.9 An object consists of a ball of weight W glued to the end of a uniform bar also of weight W. If you release it from rest, with the bar horizontal, what will its behavior be as it falls if air resistance is negligible? Will it (a) remain horizontal; (b) rotate about its center of gravity; (c) rotate about the ball; or (d) rotate so that the ball swings downward? Explain your reasoning.

Q11.10 Suppose that the object in Question 11.9 is released from rest with the bar tilted at 60° above the horizontal with the ball at the upper end. As it is falling, will it (a) rotate about its center of gravity until it is horizontal; (b) rotate about its center of gravity until it is vertical with the ball at the bottom; (c) rotate about the ball until it is vertical with the ball at the bottom; or (d) remain at 60° above the horizontal?

Q11.11 Why must a water skier moving with constant velocity lean backward? What determines how far back she must lean? Draw a free-body diagram for the water skier to justify your answers.

Q11.12 In pioneer days, when a Conestoga wagon was stuck in the mud, people would grasp the wheel spokes and try to turn the wheels, rather than simply pushing the wagon. Why?

Q11.13 The mighty Zimbo claims to have leg muscles so strong that he can stand flat on his feet and lean forward to pick up an apple on the floor with his teeth. Should you pay to see him perform, or do you have any suspicions about his claim? Why?

Q11.14 Why is it easier to hold a 10-kg dumbbell in your hand at your side than it is to hold it with your arm extended horizontally?

Q11.15 Certain features of a person, such as height and mass, are fixed (at least over relatively long periods of time). Are the following features also fixed? (a) location of the center of gravity of the body; (b) moment of inertia of the body about an axis through the person's center of mass. Explain your reasoning.

Q11.16 During pregnancy, women often develop back pains from leaning backward while walking. Why do they have to walk this way?

Q11.17 Why is a tapered water glass with a narrow base easier to tip over than a glass with straight sides? Does it matter whether the glass is full or empty?

Q11.18 When a tall, heavy refrigerator is pushed across a rough floor, what factors determine whether it slides or tips?

Q11.19 A uniform beam is suspended horizontally and attached to a wall by a small hinge (**Fig. Q11.19**). What are the directions (upward or downward, and to the left or the right) of the components of the force that the hinge exerts *on the beam*? Explain.

Figure Q11.19

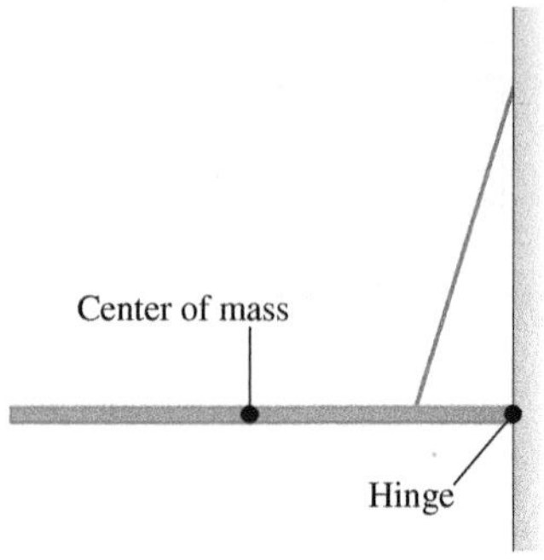

Center of mass

Hinge

Q11.20 If a metal wire has its length doubled and its diameter tripled, by what factor does its Young's modulus change?

Q11.21 A metal wire of diameter D stretches by 0.100 mm when supporting a weight W. If the same-length wire is used to support a weight three times as heavy, what would its diameter have to be (in terms of D) so it still stretches only 0.100 mm?

Q11.22 Compare the mechanical properties of a steel cable, made by twisting many thin wires together, with the properties of a solid steel rod of the same diameter. What advantages does each have?

Q11.23 The material in human bones and elephant bones is essentially the same, but an elephant has much thicker legs. Explain why, in terms of breaking stress.

Q11.24 There is a small but appreciable amount of elastic hysteresis in the large tendon at the back of a horse's leg. Explain how this can cause damage to the tendon if a horse runs too hard for too long a time.

Q11.25 When rubber mounting blocks are used to absorb machine vibrations through elastic hysteresis, as mentioned in Section 11.5, what becomes of the energy associated with the vibrations?

EXERCISES

Section 11.2 Center of Gravity

11.1 •• A 0.120-kg, 50.0-cm-long uniform bar has a small 0.055-kg mass glued to its left end and a small 0.110-kg mass glued to the other end. The two small masses can each be treated as point masses. You want to balance this system horizontally on a fulcrum placed just under its center of gravity. How far from the left end should the fulcrum be placed?

11.2 •• The center of gravity of a 5.00-kg irregular object is shown in **Fig. E11.2**. You need to move the center of gravity 2.20 cm to the left by gluing on a 1.50-kg mass, which will then be considered as part of the object. Where should the center of gravity of this additional mass be located?

Figure **E11.2**

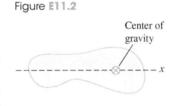

Center of gravity

11.3 • A uniform rod is 2.00 m long and has mass 1.80 kg. A 2.40-kg clamp is attached to the rod. How far should the center of gravity of the clamp be from the left-hand end of the rod in order for the center of gravity of the composite object to be 1.20 m from the left-hand end of the rod?

Section 11.3 Solving Rigid-Body Equilibrium Problems

11.4 • A uniform 300-N trapdoor in a floor is hinged at one side. Find the net upward force needed to begin to open it and the total force exerted on the door by the hinges (a) if the upward force is applied at the center and (b) if the upward force is applied at the center of the edge opposite the hinges.

11.5 •• **Raising a Ladder.** A ladder carried by a fire truck is 20.0 m long. The ladder weighs 3400 N and its center of gravity is at its center. The ladder is pivoted at one end (*A*) about a pin (**Fig. E11.5**); ignore the friction torque at the pin. The ladder is raised into position by a force applied by a hydraulic piston at *C*. Point *C* is 8.0 m from *A*, and the force $\vec{F}$ exerted by the piston makes an angle of 40° with the ladder. What magnitude must $\vec{F}$ have to just lift the ladder off the support bracket at *B*? Start with a free-body diagram of the ladder.

Figure **E11.5**

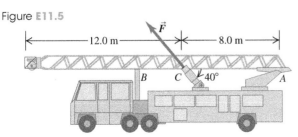

11.6 •• Two people are carrying a uniform wooden board that is 3.00 m long and weighs 160 N. If one person applies an upward force equal to 60 N at one end, at what point does the other person lift? Begin with a free-body diagram of the board.

11.7 •• Two people carry a heavy electric motor by placing it on a light board 2.00 m long. One person lifts at one end with a force of 400 N, and the other lifts the opposite end with a force of 600 N. (a) What is the weight of the motor, and where along the board is its center of gravity located? (b) Suppose the board is not light but weighs 200 N, with its center of gravity at its center, and the two people each exert the same forces as before. What is the weight of the motor in this case, and where is its center of gravity located?

11.8 •• A 60.0-cm, uniform, 50.0-N shelf is supported horizontally by two vertical wires attached to the sloping ceiling (**Fig. E11.8**). A very small 25.0-N tool is placed on the shelf midway between the points where the wires are attached to it. Find the tension in each wire. Begin by making a free-body diagram of the shelf.

Figure **E11.8**

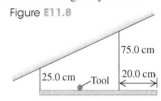

75.0 cm

25.0 cm Tool 20.0 cm

11.9 •• A 350-N, uniform, 1.50-m bar is suspended horizontally by two vertical cables at each end. Cable *A* can support a maximum tension of 500.0 N without breaking, and cable *B* can support up to 400.0 N. You want to place a small weight on this bar. (a) What is the heaviest weight you can put on without breaking either cable, and (b) where should you put this weight?

11.10 •• A uniform ladder 5.0 m long rests against a frictionless, vertical wall with its lower end 3.0 m from the wall. The ladder weighs 160 N. The coefficient of static friction between the foot of the ladder and the ground is 0.40. A man weighing 740 N climbs slowly up the ladder. Start by drawing a free-body diagram of the ladder. (a) What is the maximum friction force that the ground can exert on the ladder at its lower end? (b) What is the actual friction force when the man has climbed 1.0 m along the ladder? (c) How far along the ladder can the man climb before the ladder starts to slip?

11.11 • A diving board 3.00 m long is supported at a point 1.00 m from the end, and a diver weighing 500 N stands at the free end (**Fig. E11.11**). The diving board is of uniform cross section and weighs 280 N. Find (a) the force at the support point and (b) the force at the left-hand end.

Figure **E11.11**

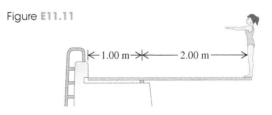

1.00 m 2.00 m

11.12 • A uniform aluminum beam 9.00 m long, weighing 300 N, rests symmetrically on two supports 5.00 m apart (**Fig. E11.12**). A boy weighing 600 N starts at point *A* and walks toward the right.

Figure **E11.12**

x

A *B*

(a) In the same diagram construct two graphs showing the upward forces F_A and F_B exerted on the beam at points A and B, as functions of the coordinate x of the boy. Let 1 cm = 100 N vertically, and 1 cm = 1.00 m horizontally. (b) From your diagram, how far beyond point B can the boy walk before the beam tips? (c) How far from the right end of the beam should support B be placed so that the boy can walk just to the end of the beam without causing it to tip?

11.13 • Find the tension T in each cable and the magnitude and direction of the force exerted on the strut by the pivot in each of the arrangements in **Fig. E11.13**. In each case let w be the weight of the suspended crate full of priceless art objects. The strut is uniform and also has weight w. Start each case with a free-body diagram of the strut.

Figure **E11.13**

(a)   (b)

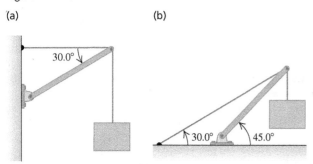

11.14 • The horizontal beam in **Fig. E11.14** weighs 190 N, and its center of gravity is at its center. Find (a) the tension in the cable and (b) the horizontal and vertical components of the force exerted on the beam at the wall.

Figure **E11.14**

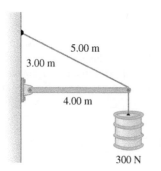

5.00 m
3.00 m
4.00 m
300 N

11.15 •• The boom shown in **Fig. E11.15** weighs 2600 N and is attached to a frictionless pivot at its lower end. It is not uniform; the distance of its center of gravity from the pivot is 35% of its length. Find (a) the tension in the guy wire and (b) the horizontal and vertical components of the force exerted on the boom at its lower end. Start with a free-body diagram of the boom.

Figure **E11.15**

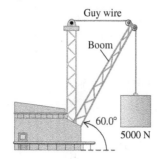

Guy wire
Boom
60.0°
5000 N

11.16 •• Suppose that you can lift no more than 650 N (around 150 lb) unaided. (a) How much can you lift using a 1.4-m-long wheelbarrow that weighs 80.0 N and whose center of gravity is 0.50 m from the center of the wheel (**Fig. E11.16**)? The center of gravity of the load carried in the wheelbarrow is also 0.50 m from the center of the wheel. (b) Where does the force come from to enable you to lift more than 650 N using the wheelbarrow?

Figure **E11.16**

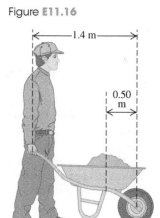

1.4 m
0.50 m

11.17 •• A 9.00-m-long uniform beam is hinged to a vertical wall and held horizontally by a 5.00-m-long cable attached to the wall 4.00 m above the hinge (**Fig. E11.17**). The metal of this cable has a test strength of 1.00 kN, which means that it will break if the tension in it exceeds that amount. (a) Draw a free-body diagram of the beam. (b) What is the heaviest beam that the cable can support in this configuration? (c) Find the horizontal and vertical components of the force the hinge exerts on the beam. Is the vertical component upward or downward?

Figure **E11.17**

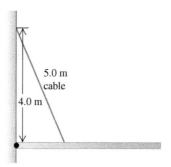

5.0 m
cable
4.0 m

11.18 •• A 15,000-N crane pivots around a friction-free axle at its base and is supported by a cable making a 25° angle with the crane (**Fig. E11.18**). The crane is 16 m long and is not uniform, its center of gravity being 7.0 m from the axle as measured along the crane. The cable is attached 3.0 m from the upper end of the crane. When the crane is raised to 55° above the horizontal holding an 11,000-N pallet of bricks by a 2.2-m, very light cord, find (a) the tension in the cable and (b) the horizontal and vertical components of the force that the axle exerts on the crane. Start with a free-body diagram of the crane.

Figure **E11.18**

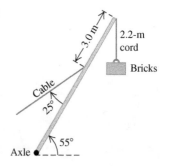

3.0 m
2.2-m cord
Bricks
Cable
25°
55°
Axle

11.19 •• A 3.00-m-long, 190-N, uniform rod at the zoo is held in a horizontal position by two ropes at its ends (**Fig. E11.19**). The left rope makes an angle of 150° with the rod, and the right rope makes an angle θ with the horizontal. A 90-N howler monkey (*Alouatta seniculus*) hangs motionless 0.50 m from the right end of the rod as he carefully studies you. Calculate the tensions in the two ropes and the angle θ. First make a free-body diagram of the rod.

Figure **E11.19**

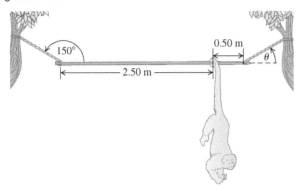

11.20 •• A nonuniform beam 4.50 m long and weighing 1.40 kN makes an angle of 25.0° below the horizontal. It is held in position by a frictionless pivot at its upper right end and by a cable 3.00 m farther down the beam and perpendicular to it (**Fig. E11.20**). The center of gravity of the beam is 2.00 m down the beam from the pivot. Lighting equipment exerts a 5.00-kN downward force on the lower left end of the beam. Find the tension T in the cable and the horizontal and vertical components of the force exerted on the beam by the pivot. Start by sketching a free-body diagram of the beam.

Figure **E11.20**

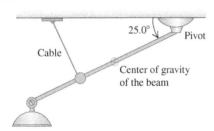

11.21 • **A Couple.** Two forces equal in magnitude and opposite in direction, acting on an object at two different points, form what is called a *couple*. Two antiparallel forces with equal magnitudes $F_1 = F_2 = 8.00$ N are applied to a rod as shown in **Fig. E11.21**. (a) What should the distance l between the forces be if they are to provide a net torque of 6.40 N·m about the left end of the rod? (b) Is the sense of this torque clockwise or counterclockwise? (c) Repeat parts (a) and (b) for a pivot at the point on the rod where $\vec{F}_2$ is applied.

Figure **E11.21**

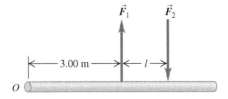

11.22 •• BIO **A Good Workout.** You are doing exercises on a Nautilus machine in a gym to strengthen your deltoid (shoulder) muscles. Your arms are raised vertically and can pivot around the shoulder joint, and you grasp the cable of the machine in your hand 64.0 cm from your shoulder joint. The deltoid muscle is attached to the humerus 15.0 cm from the shoulder joint and makes a 12.0° angle with that bone (**Fig. E11.22**). If you have set the tension in the cable of the machine to 36.0 N on each arm, what is the tension in each deltoid muscle if you simply hold your outstretched arms in place? (*Hint:* Start by making a clear free-body diagram of your arm.)

Figure **E11.22**

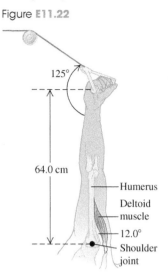

11.23 •• BIO **Neck Muscles.** A student bends her head at 40.0° from the vertical while intently reading her physics book, pivoting the head around the upper vertebra (point P in **Fig. E11.23**). Her head has a mass of 4.50 kg (which is typical), and its center of mass is 11.0 cm from the pivot point P. Her neck muscles are 1.50 cm from point P, as measured *perpendicular* to these muscles. The neck itself and the vertebrae are held vertical. (a) Draw a free-body diagram of the student's head. (b) Find the tension in her neck muscles.

Figure **E11.23**

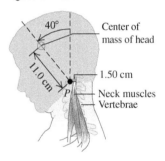

Section 11.4 Stress, Strain, and Elastic Moduli

11.24 • BIO **Biceps Muscle.** A relaxed biceps muscle requires a force of 25.0 N for an elongation of 3.0 cm; the same muscle under maximum tension requires a force of 500 N for the same elongation. Find Young's modulus for the muscle tissue under each of these conditions if the muscle is assumed to be a uniform cylinder with length 0.200 m and cross-sectional area 50.0 cm².

11.25 •• A circular steel wire 2.00 m long must stretch no more than 0.25 cm when a tensile force of 700 N is applied to each end of the wire. What minimum diameter is required for the wire?

11.26 •• Two circular rods, one steel and the other copper, are joined end to end. Each rod is 0.750 m long and 1.50 cm in diameter. The combination is subjected to a tensile force with magnitude 4000 N. For each rod, what are (a) the strain and (b) the elongation?

11.27 •• A metal rod that is 4.00 m long and 0.50 cm² in cross-sectional area is found to stretch 0.20 cm under a tension of 5000 N. What is Young's modulus for this metal?

11.28 •• **Stress on a Mountaineer's Rope.** A nylon rope used by mountaineers elongates 1.10 m under the weight of a 65.0-kg climber. If the rope is 45.0 m in length and 7.0 mm in diameter, what is Young's modulus for nylon?

11.29 •• In constructing a large mobile, an artist hangs an aluminum sphere of mass 6.0 kg from a vertical steel wire 0.50 m long and 2.5×10^{-3} cm² in cross-sectional area. On the bottom of the sphere he attaches a similar steel wire, from which he hangs a brass cube of mass 10.0 kg. For each wire, compute (a) the tensile strain and (b) the elongation.

11.30 •• A vertical, solid steel post 25 cm in diameter and 2.50 m long is required to support a load of 8000 kg. You can ignore the weight of the post. What are (a) the stress in the post; (b) the strain in the post; and (c) the change in the post's length when the load is applied?

11.31 •• BIO **Compression of Human Bone.** The bulk modulus for bone is 15 GPa. (a) If a diver-in-training is put into a pressurized suit, by how much would the pressure have to be raised (in atmospheres) above atmospheric pressure to compress her bones by 0.10% of their original volume? (b) Given that the pressure in the ocean increases by 1.0×10^4 Pa for every meter of depth below the surface, how deep would this diver have to go for her bones to compress by 0.10%? Does it seem that bone compression is a problem she needs to be concerned with when diving?

11.32 • A solid gold bar is pulled up from the hold of the sunken RMS *Titanic*. (a) What happens to its volume as it goes from the pressure at the ship to the lower pressure at the ocean's surface? (b) The pressure difference is proportional to the depth. How many times greater would the volume change have been had the ship been twice as deep? (c) The bulk modulus of lead is one-fourth that of gold. Find the ratio of the volume change of a solid lead bar to that of a gold bar of equal volume for the same pressure change.

11.33 • A specimen of oil having an initial volume of 600 cm³ is subjected to a pressure increase of 3.6×10^6 Pa, and the volume is found to decrease by 0.45 cm³. What is the bulk modulus of the material? The compressibility?

11.34 •• In the Challenger Deep of the Marianas Trench, the depth of seawater is 10.9 km and the pressure is 1.16×10^8 Pa (about 1.15×10^3 atm). (a) If a cubic meter of water is taken from the surface to this depth, what is the change in its volume? (Normal atmospheric pressure is about 1.0×10^5 Pa. Assume that k for seawater is the same as the freshwater value given in Table 11.2.) (b) What is the density of seawater at this depth? (At the surface, seawater has a density of 1.03×10^3 kg/m³.)

11.35 •• A copper cube measures 6.00 cm on each side. The bottom face is held in place by very strong glue to a flat horizontal surface, while a horizontal force F is applied to the upper face parallel to one of the edges. (Consult Table 11.1.) (a) Show that the glue exerts a force F on the bottom face that is equal in magnitude but opposite to the force on the top face. (b) How large must F be to cause the cube to deform by 0.250 mm? (c) If the same experiment were performed on a lead cube of the same size as the copper one, by what distance would it deform for the same force as in part (b)?

11.36 •• A square steel plate is 10.0 cm on a side and 0.500 cm thick. (a) Find the shear strain that results if a force of magnitude 9.0×10^5 N is applied to each of the four sides, parallel to the side. (b) Find the displacement x in centimeters.

11.37 • In lab tests on a 9.25-cm cube of a certain material, a force of 1375 N directed at 8.50° to the cube (**Fig. E11.37**) causes the cube to deform through an angle of 1.24°. What is the shear modulus of the material?

Figure **E11.37**

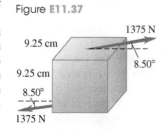

Section 11.5 Elasticity and Plasticity

11.38 •• A brass wire is to withstand a tensile force of 350 N without breaking. What minimum diameter must the wire have?

11.39 •• In a materials testing laboratory, a metal wire made from a new alloy is found to break when a tensile force of 90.8 N is applied perpendicular to each end. If the diameter of the wire is 1.84 mm, what is the breaking stress of the alloy?

11.40 • A 4.0-m-long steel wire has a cross-sectional area of 0.050 cm². Its proportional limit has a value of 0.0016 times its Young's modulus (see Table 11.1). Its breaking stress has a value of 0.0065 times its Young's modulus. The wire is fastened at its upper end and hangs vertically. (a) How great a weight can be hung from the wire without exceeding the proportional limit? (b) How much will the wire stretch under this load? (c) What is the maximum weight that the wire can support?

11.41 •• CP A steel cable with cross-sectional area 3.00 cm² has an elastic limit of 2.40×10^8 Pa. Find the maximum upward acceleration that can be given a 1200-kg elevator supported by the cable if the stress is not to exceed one-third of the elastic limit.

PROBLEMS

11.42 ••• A door 1.00 m wide and 2.00 m high weighs 330 N and is supported by two hinges, one 0.50 m from the top and the other 0.50 m from the bottom. Each hinge supports half the total weight of the door. Assuming that the door's center of gravity is at its center, find the horizontal components of force exerted on the door by each hinge.

11.43 ••• A box of negligible mass rests at the left end of a 2.00-m, 25.0-kg plank (**Fig. P11.43**). The width of the box is 75.0 cm, and sand is to be distributed uniformly throughout it. The center of gravity of the nonuniform plank is 50.0 cm from the right end. What mass of sand should be put into the box so that the plank balances horizontally on a fulcrum placed just below its midpoint?

Figure **P11.43**

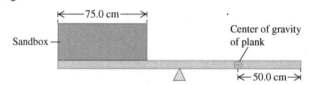

11.44 • Sir Lancelot rides slowly out of the castle at Camelot and onto the 12.0-m-long drawbridge that passes over the moat (**Fig. P11.44**). Unbeknownst to him, his enemies have partially severed the vertical cable holding up the front end of the bridge so that it will break under a tension of 5.80×10^3 N. The bridge has mass 200 kg and its center of gravity is at its center. Lancelot, his lance, his armor, and his horse together have a combined mass of 600 kg. Will the cable break before Lancelot reaches the end of the drawbridge? If so, how far from the castle end of the bridge will the center of gravity of the horse plus rider be when the cable breaks?

Figure **P11.44**

11.45 ••• **Mountain Climbing.** Mountaineers often use a rope to lower themselves down the face of a cliff (this is called *rappelling*). They do this with their body nearly horizontal and their feet pushing against the cliff (**Fig. P11.45**). Suppose that an 82.0-kg climber, who is 1.90 m tall and has a center of gravity 1.1 m from his feet, rappels down a vertical cliff with his body raised 35.0° above the horizontal. He holds the rope 1.40 m from his feet, and it makes a 25.0° angle with the cliff face. (a) What tension does his rope need to support? (b) Find the horizontal and vertical components of the force that the cliff face exerts on the climber's feet. (c) What minimum coefficient of static friction is needed to prevent the climber's feet from slipping on the cliff face if he has one foot at a time against the cliff?

Figure P11.45

11.46 •• A uniform, 8.0-m, 1150-kg beam is hinged to a wall and supported by a thin cable attached 2.0 m from the free end of the beam (**Fig. P11.46**). The beam is supported at an angle of 30.0° above the horizontal. (a) Draw a free-body diagram of the beam. (b) Find the tension in the cable. (c) How hard does the beam push inward on the wall?

Figure P11.46

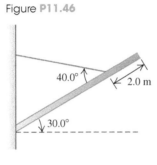

11.47 •• A uniform, 255-N rod that is 2.00 m long carries a 225-N weight at its right end and an unknown weight W toward the left end (**Fig. P11.47**). When W is placed 50.0 cm from the left end of the rod, the system just balances horizontally when the fulcrum is located 75.0 cm from the right end. (a) Find W. (b) If W is now moved 25.0 cm to the right, how far and in what direction must the fulcrum be moved to restore balance?

Figure P11.47

W   225 N

11.48 ••• A claw hammer is used to pull a nail out of a board (**Fig. P11.48**). The nail is at an angle of 60° to the board, and a force $\vec{F}_1$ of magnitude 400 N applied to the nail is required to pull it from the board. The hammer head contacts the board at point A, which is 0.080 m from where the nail enters the board. A horizontal force $\vec{F}_2$ is applied to the hammer handle at a distance of 0.300 m above the board. What magnitude of force $\vec{F}_2$ is required to apply the required 400-N force (F_1) to the nail? (Ignore the weight of the hammer.)

Figure P11.48

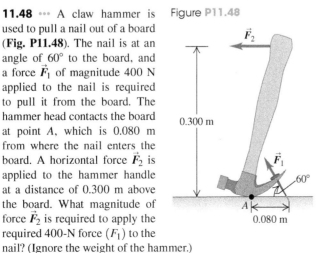

11.49 •• You open a restaurant and hope to entice customers by hanging out a sign (**Fig. P11.49**). The uniform horizontal beam supporting the sign is 1.50 m long, has a mass of 16.0 kg, and is hinged to the wall. The sign itself is uniform with a mass of 28.0 kg and overall length of 1.20 m. The two wires supporting the sign are each 32.0 cm long, are 90.0 cm apart, and are equally spaced from the middle of the sign. The cable supporting the beam is 2.00 m long. (a) What minimum tension must your cable be able to support without having your sign come crashing down? (b) What minimum vertical force must the hinge be able to support without pulling out of the wall?

Figure P11.49

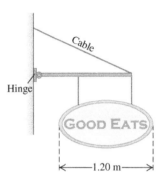

11.50 • End A of the bar AB in Fig. P11.50 rests on a frictionless horizontal surface, and end B is hinged. A horizontal force $\vec{F}$ of magnitude 220 N is exerted on end A. Ignore the weight of the bar. What are the horizontal and vertical components of the force exerted by the bar on the hinge at B?

Figure P11.50

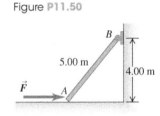

11.51 •• BIO **Supporting a Broken Leg.** A therapist tells a 74-kg patient with a broken leg that he must have his leg in a cast suspended horizontally. For minimum discomfort, the leg should be supported by a vertical strap attached at the center of mass of the leg–cast system (**Fig. P11.51**). To comply with these instructions, the patient consults a table of typical mass distributions and finds that both upper legs (thighs) together typically account for 21.5% of body weight and the center of mass of each thigh is 18.0 cm from the hip joint. The patient also reads that the two lower legs (including the feet) are 14.0% of body weight, with a center of mass 69.0 cm from the hip joint. The cast has a mass of 5.50 kg, and its center of mass is 78.0 cm from the hip joint. How far from the hip joint should the supporting strap be attached to the cast?

Figure P11.51

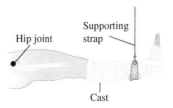

11.52 · A Truck on a Drawbridge. A loaded cement mixer drives onto an old drawbridge, where it stalls with its center of gravity three-quarters of the way across the span. The truck driver radios for help, sets the handbrake, and waits. Meanwhile, a boat approaches, so the drawbridge is raised by means of a cable attached to the end opposite the hinge (**Fig. P11.52**). The drawbridge is 40.0 m long and has a mass of 18,000 kg; its center of gravity is at its midpoint. The cement mixer, with driver, has mass 30,000 kg. When the drawbridge has been raised to an angle of 30° above the horizontal, the cable makes an angle of 70° with the surface of the bridge. (a) What is the tension T in the cable when the drawbridge is held in this position? (b) What are the horizontal and vertical components of the force the hinge exerts on the span?

Figure P11.52

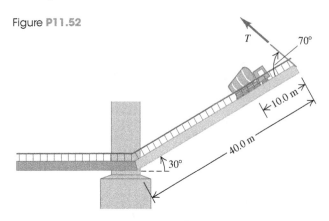

11.53 ·· BIO Leg Raises. In a simplified version of the musculature action in leg raises, the abdominal muscles pull on the femur (thigh bone) to raise the leg by pivoting it about one end (**Fig. P11.53**). When you are lying horizontally, these muscles make an angle of approximately 5° with the femur, and if you raise your legs, the muscles remain approximately horizontal, so the angle θ increases. Assume for simplicity that these muscles attach to the femur in only one place, 10 cm from the hip joint (although, in reality, the situation is more complicated). For a certain 80-kg person having a leg 90 cm long, the mass of the leg is 15 kg and its center of mass is 44 cm from his hip joint as measured along the leg. If the person raises his leg to 60° above the horizontal, the angle between the abdominal muscles and his femur would also be about 60°. (a) With his leg raised to 60°, find the tension in the abdominal muscle on each leg. Draw a free-body diagram. (b) When is the tension in this muscle greater: when the leg is raised to 60° or when the person just starts to raise it off the ground? Why? (Try this yourself.) (c) If the abdominal muscles attached to the femur were perfectly horizontal when a person was lying down, could the person raise his leg? Why or why not?

Figure P11.53

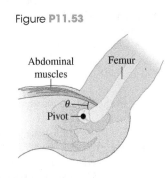

11.54 ·· BIO Pumping Iron. A 72.0-kg weightlifter doing arm raises holds a 7.50-kg weight. Her arm pivots around the elbow joint, starting 40.0° below the horizontal (**Fig. P11.54**). Biometric measurements have shown that, together, the forearms and the hands account for 6.00% of a person's weight. Since the

Figure P11.54

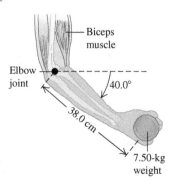

upper arm is held vertically, the biceps muscle always acts vertically and is attached to the bones of the forearm 5.50 cm from the elbow joint. The center of mass of this person's forearm–hand combination is 16.0 cm from the elbow joint, along the bones of the forearm, and she holds the weight 38.0 cm from her elbow joint. (a) Draw a free-body diagram of the forearm. (b) What force does the biceps muscle exert on the forearm? (c) Find the magnitude and direction of the force that the elbow joint exerts on the forearm. (d) As the weightlifter raises her arm toward a horizontal position, will the force in the biceps muscle increase, decrease, or stay the same? Why?

11.55 ·· BIO Back Pains During Pregnancy. Women often suffer from back pains during pregnancy. Model a woman (not including her fetus) as a uniform cylinder of diameter 30 cm and mass 60 kg. Model the fetus as a 10-kg sphere that is 25 cm in diameter and centered about 5 cm *outside* the front of the woman's body. (a) By how much does her pregnancy change the horizontal location of the woman's center of mass? (b) How does the change in part (a) affect the way the pregnant woman must stand and walk? In other words, what must she do to her posture to make up for her shifted center of mass? (c) Can you explain why she might have backaches?

11.56 · You are asked to design the decorative mobile shown in **Fig. P11.56**. The strings and rods have negligible weight, and the rods are to hang horizontally. (a) Draw a free-body diagram for each rod. (b) Find the weights of the balls A, B, and C. Find the tensions in the strings S_1, S_2, and S_3. (c) What can you say about the horizontal location of the mobile's center of gravity? Explain.

Figure P11.56

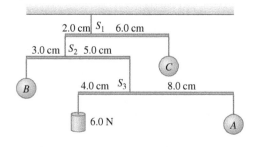

11.57 ·· A uniform, 7.5-m-long beam weighing 6490 N is hinged to a wall and supported by a thin cable attached 1.5 m from the free end of the beam. The cable runs between the beam and the wall and makes a 40° angle with the beam. What is the tension in the cable when the beam is at an angle of 30° above the horizontal?

11.58 •• CP A uniform drawbridge must be held at a 37° angle above the horizontal to allow ships to pass underneath. The drawbridge weighs 45,000 N and is 14.0 m long. A cable is connected 3.5 m from the hinge where the bridge pivots (measured along the bridge) and pulls horizontally on the bridge to hold it in place. (a) What is the tension in the cable? (b) Find the magnitude and direction of the force the hinge exerts on the bridge. (c) If the cable suddenly breaks, what is the magnitude of the angular acceleration of the drawbridge just after the cable breaks? (d) What is the angular speed of the drawbridge as it becomes horizontal?

11.59 •• BIO **Tendon-Stretching Exercises.** As part of an exercise program, a 75-kg person does toe raises in which he raises his entire body weight on the ball of one foot (**Fig. P11.59**). The Achilles tendon pulls straight upward on the heel bone of his foot. This tendon is 25 cm long and has a cross-sectional area of 78 mm² and a Young's modulus of 1470 MPa. (a) Draw a free-body diagram of the person's foot (everything below the ankle joint). Ignore the weight of the foot. (b) What force does the Achilles tendon exert on the heel during this exercise? Express your answer in newtons and in multiples of his weight. (c) By how many millimeters does the exercise stretch his Achilles tendon?

Figure **P11.59**

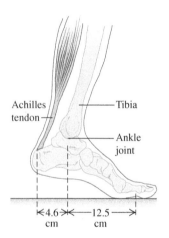

11.60 •• (a) In **Fig. P11.60** a 6.00-m-long, uniform beam is hanging from a point 1.00 m to the right of its center. The beam weighs 140 N and makes an angle of 30.0° with the vertical. At the right-hand end of the beam a 100.0-N weight is hung; an unknown weight w hangs at the left end. If the system is in equilibrium, what is w? You can ignore the thickness of the beam. (b) If the beam makes, instead, an angle of 45.0° with the vertical, what is w?

Figure **P11.60**

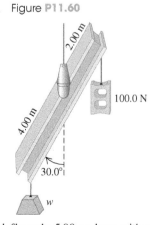

11.61 ••• A uniform, horizontal flagpole 5.00 m long with a weight of 200 N is hinged to a vertical wall at one end. A 600-N stuntwoman hangs from its other end. The flagpole is supported by a guy wire running from its outer end to a point on the wall directly above the pole. (a) If the tension in this wire is not to exceed 1000 N, what is the minimum height above the pole at

which it may be fastened to the wall? (b) If the flagpole remains horizontal, by how many newtons would the tension be increased if the wire were fastened 0.50 m below this point?

11.62 • A holiday decoration consists of two shiny glass spheres with masses 0.0240 kg and 0.0360 kg suspended from a uniform rod with mass 0.120 kg and length 1.00 m (**Fig. P11.62**). The rod is suspended from the ceiling by a vertical cord at each end, so that it is horizontal. Calculate the tension in each of the cords A through F.

Figure **P11.62**

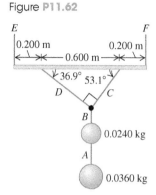

11.63 •• BIO **Downward-Facing Dog.** The yoga exercise "Downward-Facing Dog" requires stretching your hands straight out above your head and bending down to lean against the floor. This exercise is performed by a 750-N person as shown in **Fig. P11.63**. When he bends his body at the hip to a 90° angle between his legs and trunk, his legs, trunk, head, and arms have the dimensions indicated. Furthermore, his legs and feet weigh a total of 277 N, and their center of mass is 41 cm from his hip, measured along his legs. The person's trunk, head, and arms weigh 473 N, and their center of gravity is 65 cm from his hip, measured along the upper body. (a) Find the normal force that the floor exerts on each foot and on each hand, assuming that the person does not favor either hand or either foot. (b) Find the friction force on each foot and on each hand, assuming that it is the same on both feet and on both hands (but not necessarily the same on the feet as on the hands). [*Hint:* First treat his entire body as a system; then isolate his legs (or his upper body).]

Figure **P11.63**

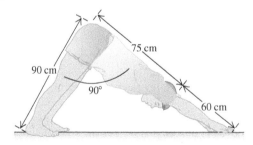

11.64 •• A uniform metal bar that is 8.00 m long and has mass 30.0 kg is attached at one end to the side of a building by a frictionless hinge. The bar is held at an angle of 64.0° above the horizontal by a thin, light cable that runs from the end of the bar opposite the hinge to a point on the wall that is above the hinge. The cable makes an angle of 37.0° with the bar. Your mass is 65.0 kg. You grab the bar near the hinge and hang beneath it, with your hands close together and your feet off the ground. To impress your friends, you intend to shift your hands slowly toward the top end of the bar. (a) If the cable breaks when its tension exceeds 455 N, how far from the upper end of the bar are you when the cable breaks? (b) Just before the cable breaks, what are the magnitude and direction of the resultant force that the hinge exerts on the bar?

11.65 • A worker wants to turn over a uniform, 1250-N, rectangular crate by pulling at 53.0° on one of its vertical sides (**Fig. P11.65**). The floor is rough enough to prevent the crate from slipping. (a) What pull is needed to just start the crate to tip? (b) How hard does the floor push upward on the crate? (c) Find the friction force on the crate. (d) What is the minimum coefficient of static friction needed to prevent the crate from slipping on the floor?

Figure P11.65

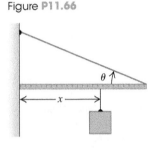

11.66 ••• One end of a uniform meter stick is placed against a vertical wall (**Fig. P11.66**). The other end is held by a lightweight cord that makes an angle θ with the stick. The coefficient of static friction between the end of the meter stick and the wall is 0.40. (a) What is the maximum value the angle θ can have if the stick is to remain in equilibrium? (b) Let the angle θ be 15°. A block of the same weight as the meter stick is suspended from the stick, as shown, at a distance x from the wall. What is the minimum value of x for which the stick will remain in equilibrium? (c) When $\theta = 15°$, how large must the coefficient of static friction be so that the block can be attached 10 cm from the left end of the stick without causing it to slip?

Figure P11.66

11.67 •• Two friends are carrying a 200-kg crate up a flight of stairs. The crate is 1.25 m long and 0.500 m high, and its center of gravity is at its center. The stairs make a 45.0° angle with respect to the floor. The crate also is carried at a 45.0° angle, so that its bottom side is parallel to the slope of the stairs (**Fig. P11.67**). If the force each person applies is vertical, what is the magnitude of each of these forces? Is it better to be the person above or below on the stairs?

Figure P11.67

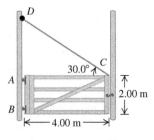

11.68 •• BIO **Forearm.** In the human arm, the forearm and hand pivot about the elbow joint. Consider a simplified model in which the biceps muscle is attached to the forearm 3.80 cm from the elbow joint. Assume that the person's hand and forearm together weigh 15.0 N and that their center of gravity is 15.0 cm from the elbow (not quite halfway to the hand). The forearm is held horizontally at a right angle to the upper arm, with the biceps muscle exerting its force perpendicular to the forearm. (a) Draw a free-body diagram for the forearm, and find the force exerted by the biceps when the hand is empty. (b) Now the person holds an 80.0-N weight in his hand, with the forearm still horizontal. Assume that the center of gravity of this weight is 33.0 cm from the elbow. Draw a free-body diagram for the forearm, and find the force now exerted by the biceps. Explain why the biceps muscle needs to be very strong. (c) Under the conditions of part (b), find the magnitude and direction of the force that the elbow joint exerts on the forearm. (d) While holding the 80.0-N weight, the person raises his forearm until it is at an angle of 53.0° above the horizontal. If the biceps muscle continues to exert its force perpendicular to the forearm, what is this force now? Has the force increased or decreased from its value in part (b)? Explain why this is so, and test your answer by doing this with your own arm.

11.69 •• BIO CALC Refer to the discussion of holding a dumbbell in Example 11.4 (Section 11.3). The maximum weight that can be held in this way is limited by the maximum allowable tendon tension T (determined by the strength of the tendons) and by the distance D from the elbow to where the tendon attaches to the forearm. (a) Let T_{max} represent the maximum value of the tendon tension. Use the results of Example 11.4 to express w_{max} (the maximum weight that can be held) in terms of T_{max}, L, D, and h. Your expression should *not* include the angle θ. (b) The tendons of different primates are attached to the forearm at different values of D. Calculate the derivative of w_{max} with respect to D, and determine whether the derivative is positive or negative. (c) A chimpanzee tendon is attached to the forearm at a point farther from the elbow than for humans. Use this to explain why chimpanzees have stronger arms than humans. (The disadvantage is that chimpanzees have less flexible arms than do humans.)

11.70 ••• In a city park a nonuniform wooden beam 4.00 m long is suspended horizontally by a light steel cable at each end. The cable at the left-hand end makes an angle of 30.0° with the vertical and has tension 620 N. The cable at the right-hand end of the beam makes an angle of 50.0° with the vertical. As an employee of the Parks and Recreation Department, you are asked to find the weight of the beam and the location of its center of gravity.

11.71 •• You are a summer intern for an architectural firm. An 8.00-m-long uniform steel rod is to be attached to a wall by a frictionless hinge at one end. The rod is to be held at 22.0° below the horizontal by a light cable that is attached to the end of the rod opposite the hinge. The cable makes an angle of 30.0° with the rod and is attached to the wall at a point above the hinge. The cable will break if its tension exceeds 650 N. (a) For what mass of the rod will the cable break? (b) If the rod has a mass that is 10.0 kg less than the value calculated in part (a), what are the magnitude and direction of the force that the hinge exerts on the rod?

11.72 •• You are trying to raise a bicycle wheel of mass m and radius R up over a curb of height h. To do this, you apply a horizontal force $\vec{F}$ (**Fig. P11.72**). What is the smallest magnitude of the force $\vec{F}$ that will succeed in raising the wheel onto the curb when the force is applied (a) at the center of the wheel and (b) at the top of the wheel? (c) In which case is less force required?

Figure P11.72

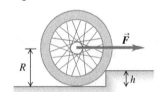

11.73 • **The Farmyard Gate.** A gate 4.00 m wide and 2.00 m high weighs 700 N. Its center of gravity is at its center, and it is hinged at A and B. To relieve the strain on the top hinge, a wire CD is connected as shown in **Fig. P11.73**. The tension in CD is increased until the horizontal force at hinge A is zero. What is (a) the tension in the wire CD; (b) the magnitude of the horizontal component of the force at hinge B; (c) the combined vertical force exerted by hinges A and B?

Figure P11.73

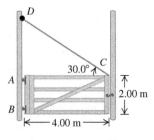

11.74 · If you put a uniform block at the edge of a table, the center of the block must be over the table for the block not to fall off. (a) If you stack two identical blocks at the table edge, the center of the top block must be over the bottom block, and the center of gravity of the two blocks together must be over the table. In terms of the length L of each block, what is the maximum overhang possible (**Fig. P11.74**)? (b) Repeat part (a) for three identical blocks and for four identical blocks. (c) Is it possible to make a stack of blocks such that the uppermost block is not directly over the table at all? How many blocks would it take to do this? (Try.)

Figure **P11.74**

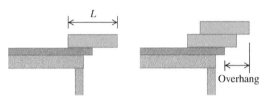

11.75 ··· Two uniform, 75.0-g marbles 2.00 cm in diameter are stacked as shown in **Fig. P11.75** in a container that is 3.00 cm wide. (a) Find the force that the container exerts on the marbles at the points of contact A, B, and C. (b) What force does each marble exert on the other?

Figure **P11.75**

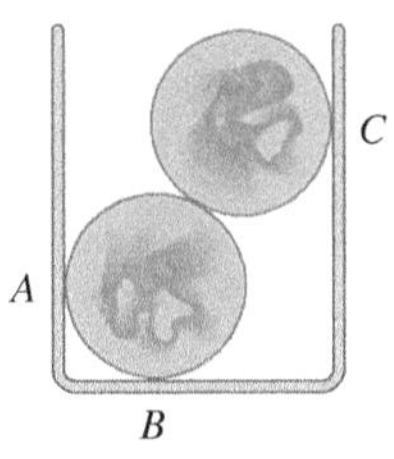

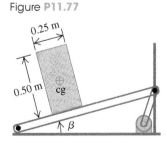

11.76 ·· Two identical, uniform beams weighing 260 N each are connected at one end by a frictionless hinge. A light horizontal crossbar attached at the midpoints of the beams maintains an angle of 53.0° between the beams. The beams are suspended from the ceiling by vertical wires such that they form a "V" (**Fig. P11.76**). (a) What force does the crossbar exert on each beam? (b) Is the crossbar under tension or compression? (c) What force (magnitude and direction) does the hinge at point A exert on each beam?

Figure **P11.76**

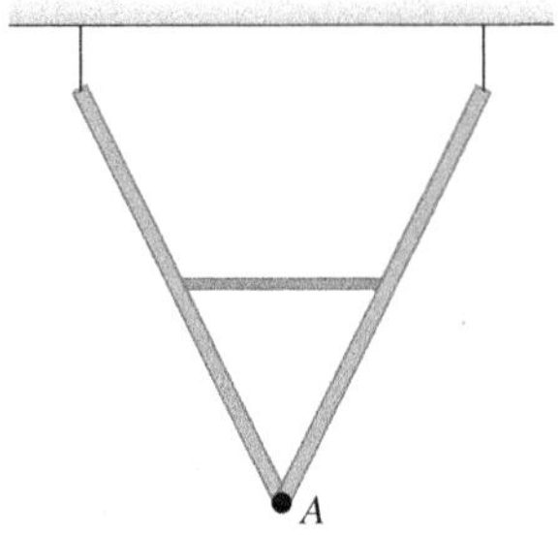

11.77 · An engineer is designing a conveyor system for loading hay bales into a wagon (**Fig. P11.77**). Each bale is 0.25 m wide, 0.50 m high, and 0.80 m long (the dimension perpendicular to the plane of the figure), with mass 30.0 kg. The center of gravity of each bale is at its geometrical center.

Figure **P11.77**

The coefficient of static friction between a bale and the conveyor belt is 0.60, and the belt moves with constant speed. (a) The angle β of the conveyor is slowly increased. At some critical angle a bale will tip (if it doesn't slip first), and at some different critical angle it will slip (if it doesn't tip first). Find the two critical angles and determine which happens at the smaller angle. (b) Would the outcome of part (a) be different if the coefficient of friction were 0.40?

11.78 · A weight W is supported by attaching it to a vertical uniform metal pole by a thin cord passing over a pulley having negligible mass and friction. The cord is attached to the pole 40.0 cm below the top and pulls horizontally on it (**Fig. P11.78**). The pole is pivoted about a hinge at its base, is 1.75 m tall, and weighs 55.0 N. A thin wire connects the top of the pole to a vertical wall. The nail that holds this wire to the wall will pull out if an *outward* force greater than 22.0 N acts on it. (a) What is the greatest weight W that can be supported this way without pulling out the nail? (b) What is the *magnitude* of the force that the hinge exerts on the pole?

Figure **P11.78**

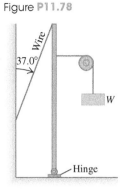

11.79 ·· A garage door is mounted on an overhead rail (**Fig. P11.79**). The wheels at A and B have rusted so that they do not roll, but rather slide along the track. The coefficient of kinetic friction is 0.52. The distance between the wheels is 2.00 m, and each is 0.50 m from the vertical sides of the door.

Figure **P11.79**

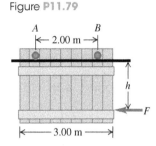

The door is uniform and weighs 950 N. It is pushed to the left at constant speed by a horizontal force $\vec{F}$. (a) If the distance h is 1.60 m, what is the vertical component of the force exerted on each wheel by the track? (b) Find the maximum value h can have without causing one wheel to leave the track.

11.80 ··· **Pyramid Builders.** Ancient pyramid builders are balancing a uniform rectangular slab of stone tipped at an angle θ above the horizontal using a rope (**Fig. P11.80**). The rope is held by five workers who share the force equally. (a) If $\theta = 20.0°$, what force does each worker exert on the rope? (b) As θ increases, does each worker have to exert more or less force than in part (a), assuming they do not change the angle of the rope? Why? (c) At what angle do the workers need to exert *no force* to balance the slab? What happens if θ exceeds this value?

Figure **P11.80**

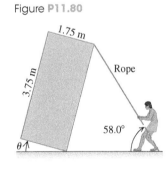

11.81 ··· **CP** A 12.0-kg mass, fastened to the end of an aluminum wire with an unstretched length of 0.70 m, is whirled in a vertical circle with a constant angular speed of 120 rev/min. The cross-sectional area of the wire is 0.014 cm². Calculate the elongation of the wire when the mass is (a) at the lowest point of the path and (b) at the highest point of its path.

11.82 ·· **Hooke's Law for a Wire.** A wire of length l_0 and cross-sectional area A supports a hanging weight W. (a) Show that if the wire obeys Eq. (11.7), it behaves like a spring of force constant AY/l_0, where Y is Young's modulus for the wire material. (b) What would the force constant be for a 75.0-cm length of 16-gauge (diameter = 1.291 mm) copper wire? See Table 11.1. (c) What would W have to be to stretch the wire in part (b) by 1.25 mm?

11.83 ••• A 1.05-m-long rod of negligible weight is supported at its ends by wires A and B of equal length (**Fig. P11.83**). The cross-sectional area of A is 2.00 mm^2 and that of B is 4.00 mm^2. Young's modulus for wire A is 1.80×10^{11} Pa; that for B is 1.20×10^{11} Pa. At what point along the rod should a weight w be suspended to produce (a) equal stresses in A and B and (b) equal strains in A and B?

Figure **P11.83**

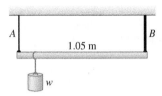

11.84 ••• CP An amusement park ride consists of airplane-shaped cars attached to steel rods (**Fig. P11.84**). Each rod has a length of 15.0 m and a cross-sectional area of 8.00 cm^2. (a) How much is each rod stretched when it is vertical and the ride is at rest? (Assume that each car plus two people seated in it has a total weight of 1900 N.) (b) When operating, the ride has a maximum angular speed of 12.0 rev/min. How much is the rod stretched then?

Figure **P11.84**

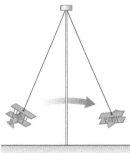

11.85 ••• CP BIO **Stress on the Shin Bone.** The compressive strength of our bones is important in everyday life. Young's modulus for bone is about 1.4×10^{10} Pa. Bone can take only about a 1.0% change in its length before fracturing. (a) What is the maximum force that can be applied to a bone whose minimum cross-sectional area is 3.0 cm^2? (This is approximately the cross-sectional area of a tibia, or shin bone, at its narrowest point.) (b) Estimate the maximum height from which a 70-kg man could jump and not fracture his tibia. Take the time between when he first touches the floor and when he has stopped to be 0.030 s, and assume that the stress on his two legs is distributed equally.

11.86 •• DATA You are to use a long, thin wire to build a pendulum in a science museum. The wire has an unstretched length of 22.0 m and a circular cross section of diameter 0.860 mm; it is made of an alloy that has a large breaking stress. One end of the wire will be attached to the ceiling, and a 9.50-kg metal sphere will be attached to the other end. As the pendulum swings back and forth, the wire's maximum angular displacement from the vertical will be 36.0°. You must determine the maximum amount the wire will stretch during this motion. So, before you attach the metal sphere, you suspend a test mass (mass m) from the wire's lower end. You then measure the increase in length Δl of the wire for several different test masses. **Figure P11.86**, a graph of Δl

Figure **P11.86**

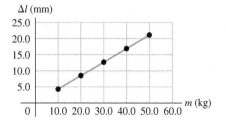

versus m, shows the results and the straight line that gives the best fit to the data. The equation for this line is $\Delta l = (0.422 \text{ mm/kg})m$. (a) Assume that $g = 9.80$ m/s^2, and use Fig. P11.86 to calculate Young's modulus Y for this wire. (b) You remove the test masses, attach the 9.50-kg sphere, and release the sphere from rest, with the wire displaced by 36.0°. Calculate the amount the wire will stretch as it swings through the vertical. Ignore air resistance.

11.87 •• DATA You need to measure the mass M of a 4.00-m-long bar. The bar has a square cross section but has some holes drilled along its length, so you suspect that its center of gravity isn't in the middle of the bar. The bar is too long for you to weigh on your scale. So, first you balance the bar on a knife-edge pivot and determine that the bar's center of gravity is 1.88 m from its left-hand end. You then place the bar on the pivot so that the point of support is 1.50 m from the left-hand end of the bar. Next you suspend a 2.00-kg mass (m_1) from the bar at a point 0.200 m from the left-hand end. Finally, you suspend a mass $m_2 = 1.00$ kg from the bar at a distance x from the left-hand end and adjust x so that the bar is balanced. You repeat this step for other values of m_2 and record each corresponding value of x. The table gives your results.

m_2 (kg)	1.00	1.50	2.00	2.50	3.00	4.00
x (m)	3.50	2.83	2.50	2.32	2.16	2.00

(a) Draw a free-body diagram for the bar when m_1 and m_2 are suspended from it. (b) Apply the static equilibrium equation $\Sigma \tau_z = 0$ with the axis at the location of the knife-edge pivot. Solve the equation for x as a function of m_2. (c) Plot x versus $1/m_2$. Use the slope of the best-fit straight line and the equation you derived in part (b) to calculate that bar's mass M. Use $g = 9.80$ m/s^2. (d) What is the y-intercept of the straight line that fits the data? Explain why it has this value.

11.88 ••• DATA You are a construction engineer working on the interior design of a retail store in a mall. A 2.00-m-long uniform bar of mass 8.50 kg is to be attached at one end to a wall, by means of a hinge that allows the bar to rotate freely with very little friction. The bar will be held in a horizontal position by a light cable from a point on the bar (a distance x from the hinge) to a point on the wall above the hinge. The cable makes an angle θ with the bar. The architect has proposed four possible ways to connect the cable and asked you to assess them:

Alternative	A	B	C	D
x (m)	2.00	1.50	0.75	0.50
θ (degrees)	30	60	37	75

(a) There is concern about the strength of the cable that will be required. Which set of x and θ values in the table produces the smallest tension in the cable? The greatest? (b) There is concern about the breaking strength of the sheetrock wall where the hinge will be attached. Which set of x and θ values produces the smallest horizontal component of the force the bar exerts on the hinge? The largest? (c) There is also concern about the required strength of the hinge and the strength of its attachment to the wall. Which set of x and θ values produces the smallest magnitude of the vertical component of the force the bar exerts on the hinge? The largest? (*Hint:* Does the direction of the vertical component of the force the hinge exerts on the bar depend on where along the bar the cable is attached?) (d) Is one of the alternatives given in the table preferable? Should any of the alternatives be avoided? Discuss.

CHALLENGE PROBLEMS

11.89 ••• Two ladders, 4.00 m and 3.00 m long, are hinged at point *A* and tied together by a horizontal rope 0.90 m above the floor (**Fig. P11.89**). The ladders weigh 480 N and 360 N, respectively, and the center of gravity of each is at its center. Assume that the floor is freshly waxed and frictionless. (a) Find the upward force at the bottom of each ladder. (b) Find the tension in the rope. (c) Find the magnitude of the force one ladder exerts on the other at point *A*. (d) If an 800-N painter stands at point *A*, find the tension in the horizontal rope.

Figure **P11.89**

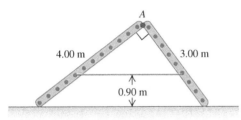

11.90 ••• **Knocking Over a Post.** One end of a post weighing 400 N and with height *h* rests on a rough horizontal surface with $\mu_s = 0.30$. The upper end is held by a rope fastened to the surface and making an angle of 36.9° with the post (**Fig. P11.90**). A horizontal force $\vec{F}$ is exerted on the post as shown. (a) If the force $\vec{F}$ is applied at the midpoint of the post, what is the largest value it can have without causing the post to slip? (b) How large can the force be without causing the post to slip if its point of application is $\frac{6}{10}$ of the way from the ground to the top of the post? (c) Show that if the point of application of the force is too high, the post cannot be made to slip, no matter how great the force. Find the critical height for the point of application.

Figure **P11.90**

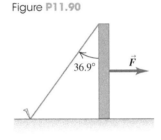

11.91 ••• CP An angler hangs a 4.50-kg fish from a vertical steel wire 1.50 m long and 5.00×10^{-3} cm^2 in cross-sectional area. The upper end of the wire is securely fastened to a support. (a) Calculate the amount the wire is stretched by the hanging fish. The angler now applies a varying force $\vec{F}$ at the lower end of the wire, pulling it very slowly downward by 0.500 mm from its equilibrium position. For this downward motion, calculate (b) the work done by gravity; (c) the work done by the force $\vec{F}$, (d) the work done by the force the wire exerts on the fish; and (e) the change in the elastic potential energy (the potential energy associated with the tensile stress in the wire). Compare the answers in parts (d) and (e).

BIO **TORQUES AND TUG-OF-WAR.** In a study of the biomechanics of the tug-of-war, a 2.0-m-tall, 80.0-kg competitor in the middle of the line is considered to be a rigid body leaning back at an angle of 30.0° to the vertical. The competitor is pulling on a rope that is held horizontal a distance of 1.5 m from his feet (as measured along the line of the body). At the moment shown in the figure, the man is stationary and the tension in the rope in front of him is $T_1 = 1160$ N. Since there is friction between the rope and his hands, the tension in the rope behind him, T_2, is not equal to T_1. His center of mass is halfway between his feet and the top of his head. The coefficient of static friction between his feet and the ground is 0.65.

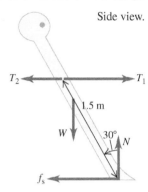

Side view.

11.92 What is tension T_2 in the rope behind him? (a) 590 N; (b) 650 N; (c) 860 N; (d) 1100 N.

11.93 If he leans slightly farther back (increasing the angle between his body and the vertical) but remains stationary in this new position, which of the following statements is true? Assume that the rope remains horizontal. (a) The difference between T_1 and T_2 will increase, balancing the increased torque about his feet that his weight produces when he leans farther back; (b) the difference between T_1 and T_2 will decrease, balancing the increased torque about his feet that his weight produces when he leans farther back; (c) neither T_1 nor T_2 will change, because no other forces are changing; (d) both T_1 and T_2 will change, but the difference between them will remain the same.

11.94 His body is again leaning back at 30.0° to the vertical, but now the height at which the rope is held above—but still parallel to—the ground is varied. The tension in the rope in front of the competitor (T_1) is measured as a function of the shortest distance between the rope and the ground (the holding height). Tension T_1 is found to decrease as the holding height increases. What could explain this observation? As the holding height increases, (a) the moment arm of the rope about his feet decreases due to the angle that his body makes with the vertical; (b) the moment arm of the weight about his feet decreases due to the angle that his body makes with the vertical; (c) a smaller tension in the rope is needed to produce a torque sufficient to balance the torque of the weight about his feet; (d) his center of mass moves down to compensate, so less tension in the rope is required to maintain equilibrium.

11.95 His body is leaning back at 30.0° to the vertical, but the coefficient of static friction between his feet and the ground is suddenly reduced to 0.50. What will happen? (a) His entire body will accelerate forward; (b) his feet will slip forward; (c) his feet will slip backward; (d) his feet will not slip.

Answers

Chapter Opening Question ?

(i) Each stone in the arch is under compression, not tension. This is because the forces on the stones tend to push them inward toward the center of the arch and thus squeeze them together. Compared to a solid supporting wall, a wall with arches is just as strong yet much more economical to build.

Test Your Understanding Questions

11.1 **(i)** Situation (i) satisfies both equilibrium conditions because the seagull has zero acceleration (so $\Sigma \vec{F} = 0$) and no tendency to start rotating (so $\Sigma \vec{\tau} = 0$). Situation (ii) satisfies the first condition because the crankshaft as a whole does not accelerate through space, but it does not satisfy the second condition; the crankshaft has an angular acceleration, so $\Sigma \vec{\tau}$ is not zero. Situation (iii) satisfies the second condition (there is no tendency to rotate) but not the first one; the baseball accelerates in its flight (due to gravity and air resistance), so $\Sigma \vec{F}$ is not zero.

11.2 **(ii)** In equilibrium, the center of gravity must be at the point of support. Since the rock and meter stick have the same mass and hence the same weight, the center of gravity of the system is midway between their respective centers. The center of gravity of the meter stick alone is 0.50 m from the left end (that is, at the middle of the meter stick), so the center of gravity of the combination of rock and meter stick is 0.25 m from the left end.

11.3 **(ii), (i), (iii)** This is the same situation described in Example 11.4, with the rod replacing the forearm, the hinge replacing the elbow, and the cable replacing the tendon. The only difference is that the cable attachment point is at the end of the rod, so the distances D and L are identical. From Example 11.4, the tension is

$$T = \frac{Lw}{L\sin\theta} = \frac{w}{\sin\theta}$$

Since $\sin\theta$ is less than 1, the tension T is greater than the weight w. The vertical component of the force exerted by the hinge is

$$E_y = -\frac{(L - L)w}{L} = 0$$

In this situation, the hinge exerts *no* vertical force. To see this, calculate torques around the right end of the horizontal rod: The only force that exerts a torque around this point is the vertical component of the hinge force, so this force component must be zero.

11.4 **(a) (iii), (b) (ii)** In (a), the copper rod has 10 times the elongation Δl of the steel rod, but it also has 10 times the original length l_0. Hence the tensile strain $\Delta l / l_0$ is the same for both rods. In (b), the stress is equal to Young's modulus Y multiplied by the strain. From Table 11.1, steel has a larger value of Y, so a greater stress is required to produce the same strain.

11.5 In (a) and (b), the bumper will have sprung back to its original shape (although the paint may be scratched). In (c), the bumper will have a permanent dent or deformation. In (d), the bumper will be torn or broken.

Bridging Problem

(a) $T = \dfrac{2mg}{3\sin\theta}$

(b) $F = \dfrac{2mg}{3\sin\theta}\sqrt{\cos^2\theta + \frac{1}{4}\sin^2\theta}, \quad \phi = \arctan\left(\frac{1}{2}\tan\theta\right)$

(c) $\Delta l = \dfrac{2mgl_0}{3AY\tan\theta}$ **(d)** 4

? The rings of Saturn are made of countless individual orbiting particles. Compared with a ring particle that orbits far from Saturn, does a ring particle close to Saturn orbit with (i) the same speed and greater acceleration; (ii) a faster speed and the same acceleration; (iii) a slower speed and the same acceleration; (iv) a faster speed and greater acceleration; or (v) none of these?

13 GRAVITATION

Some of the earliest investigations in physical science started with questions that people asked about the night sky. Why doesn't the moon fall to earth? Why do the planets move across the sky? Why doesn't the earth fly off into space rather than remaining in orbit around the sun? The study of gravitation provides the answers to these and many related questions.

As we remarked in Chapter 5, gravitation is one of the four classes of interactions found in nature, and it was the earliest of the four to be studied extensively. Newton discovered in the 17th century that the same interaction that makes an apple fall out of a tree also keeps the planets in their orbits around the sun. This was the beginning of *celestial mechanics,* the study of the dynamics of objects in space. Today, our knowledge of celestial mechanics allows us to determine how to put a satellite into any desired orbit around the earth or to choose just the right trajectory to send a spacecraft to another planet.

In this chapter you will learn the basic law that governs gravitational interactions. This law is *universal:* Gravity acts in the same fundamental way between the earth and your body, between the sun and a planet, and between a planet and one of its moons. We'll apply the law of gravitation to phenomena such as the variation of weight with altitude, the orbits of satellites around the earth, and the orbits of planets around the sun.

13.1 NEWTON'S LAW OF GRAVITATION

The gravitational attraction that's most familiar to you is your *weight,* the force that attracts you toward the earth. By studying the motions of the moon and planets, Newton discovered a fundamental **law of gravitation** that describes the gravitational attraction between *any* two bodies. Newton published this law in 1687 along with his three laws of motion. In modern language, it says

> **Every particle of matter in the universe attracts every other particle with a force that is directly proportional to the product of the masses of the particles and inversely proportional to the square of the distance between them.**

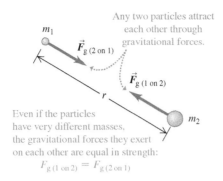

Any two particles attract each other through gravitational forces.

$\vec{F}_{g\,(2\text{ on }1)}$

$\vec{F}_{g\,(1\text{ on }2)}$

m_1

m_2

r

Even if the particles have very different masses, the gravitational forces they exert on each other are equal in strength:

$F_{g\,(1\text{ on }2)} = F_{g\,(2\text{ on }1)}$

13.1 The gravitational forces between two particles of masses m_1 and m_2.

Figure 13.1 depicts this law, which we can express as an equation:

Newton's **law of gravitation:**
Magnitude of attractive gravitational force between any two particles

Gravitational constant (same for any two particles)

Masses of particles

$$F_g = \frac{Gm_1m_2}{r^2} \qquad (13.1)$$

Distance between particles

The **gravitational constant** G in Eq. (13.1) is a fundamental physical constant that has the same value for *any* two particles. We'll see shortly what the value of G is and how this value is measured.

Equation (13.1) tells us that the gravitational force between two particles decreases with increasing distance r: If the distance is doubled, the force is only one-fourth as great, and so on. Although many of the stars in the night sky are far more massive than the sun, they are so far away that their gravitational force on the earth is negligibly small.

CAUTION **Don't confuse g and G** The symbols g and G are similar, but they represent two very different gravitational quantities. Lowercase g is the acceleration due to gravity, which relates the weight w of a body to its mass m: $w = mg$. The value of g is different at different locations on the earth's surface and on the surfaces of other planets. By contrast, capital G relates the gravitational force between any two bodies to their masses and the distance between them. We call G a *universal* constant because it has the same value for any two bodies, no matter where in space they are located. We'll soon see how the values of g and G are related. ▮

Gravitational forces always act along the line joining the two particles and form an action–reaction pair. Even when the masses of the particles are different, the two interaction forces have equal magnitude (Fig. 13.1). The attractive force that your body exerts on the earth has the same magnitude as the force that the earth exerts on you. When you fall from a diving board into a swimming pool, the entire earth rises up to meet you! (You don't notice this because the earth's mass is greater than yours by a factor of about 10^{23}. Hence the earth's acceleration is only 10^{-23} as great as yours.)

Gravitation and Spherically Symmetric Bodies

We have stated the law of gravitation in terms of the interaction between two *particles*. It turns out that the gravitational interaction of any two bodies having *spherically symmetric* mass distributions (such as solid spheres or spherical shells) is the same as though we concentrated all the mass of each at its center, as in **Fig. 13.2**. Thus, if we model the earth as a spherically symmetric body with mass m_E, the force it exerts on a particle or on a spherically symmetric body with mass m, at a distance r between centers, is

$$F_g = \frac{Gm_Em}{r^2} \qquad (13.2)$$

provided that the body lies outside the earth. A force of the same magnitude is exerted *on* the earth by the body. (We will prove these statements in Section 13.6.)

13.2 The gravitational effect *outside* any spherically symmetric mass distribution is the same as though all of the mass were concentrated at its center.

(a) The gravitational force between two spherically symmetric masses m_1 and m_2 ...

(b) ... is the same as if we concentrated all the mass of each sphere at the sphere's center.

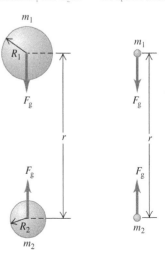

m_1

R_1

F_g

F_g

R_2

m_2

r

m_1

F_g

F_g

m_2

r

13.3 Spherical and nonspherical bodies: the planet Jupiter and one of Jupiter's small moons, Amalthea.

Jupiter's mass is very large (1.90×10^{27} kg), so the mutual gravitational attraction of its parts has pulled it into a nearly spherical shape.

100,000 km

100 km

Amalthea, one of Jupiter's small moons, has a relatively tiny mass (7.17×10^{18} kg, only about 3.8×10^{-9} the mass of Jupiter) and weak mutual gravitation, so it has an irregular shape.

At points *inside* the earth the situation is different. If we could drill a hole to the center of the earth and measure the gravitational force on a body at various depths, we would find that toward the center of the earth the force *decreases,* rather than increasing as $1/r^2$. As the body enters the interior of the earth (or other spherical body), some of the earth's mass is on the side of the body opposite from the center and pulls in the opposite direction. Exactly at the center, the earth's gravitational force on the body is zero.

Spherically symmetric bodies are an important case because moons, planets, and stars all tend to be spherical. Since all particles in a body gravitationally attract each other, the particles tend to move to minimize the distance between them. As a result, the body naturally tends to assume a spherical shape, just as a lump of clay forms into a sphere if you squeeze it with equal forces on all sides. This effect is greatly reduced in celestial bodies of low mass, since the gravitational attraction is less, and these bodies tend *not* to be spherical (**Fig. 13.3**).

Determining the Value of G

To determine the value of the gravitational constant G, we have to *measure* the gravitational force between two bodies of known masses m_1 and m_2 at a known distance r. The force is extremely small for bodies that are small enough to be brought into the laboratory, but it can be measured with an instrument called a *torsion balance,* which Sir Henry Cavendish used in 1798 to determine G.

Figure 13.4 shows a modern version of the Cavendish torsion balance. A light, rigid rod shaped like an inverted T is supported by a very thin, vertical quartz fiber. Two small spheres, each of mass m_1, are mounted at the ends of the horizontal arms of the T. When we bring two large spheres, each of mass m_2, to the positions shown, the attractive gravitational forces twist the T through a small angle. To measure this angle, we shine a beam of light on a mirror fastened to the T. The reflected beam strikes a scale, and as the T twists, the reflected beam moves along the scale.

After calibrating the Cavendish balance, we can measure gravitational forces and thus determine G. The presently accepted value is

$$G = 6.67384(80) \times 10^{-11} \text{ N} \cdot \text{m}^2/\text{kg}^2$$

To three significant figures, $G = 6.67 \times 10^{-11} \text{ N} \cdot \text{m}^2/\text{kg}^2$. Because $1 \text{ N} = 1 \text{ kg} \cdot \text{m/s}^2$, the units of G can also be expressed as $\text{m}^3/(\text{kg} \cdot \text{s}^2)$.

Gravitational forces combine vectorially. If each of two masses exerts a force on a third, the *total* force on the third mass is the vector sum of the individual forces of the first two. Example 13.3 makes use of this property, which is often called *superposition of forces* (see Section 4.1).

13.4 The principle of the Cavendish balance, used for determining the value of G. The angle of deflection has been exaggerated here for clarity.

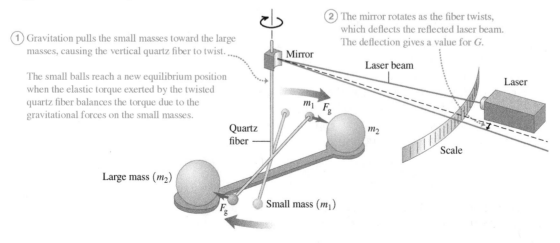

① Gravitation pulls the small masses toward the large masses, causing the vertical quartz fiber to twist.

The small balls reach a new equilibrium position when the elastic torque exerted by the twisted quartz fiber balances the torque due to the gravitational forces on the small masses.

② The mirror rotates as the fiber twists, which deflects the reflected laser beam. The deflection gives a value for G.

Mirror

Laser beam

Laser

m_1 F_g

m_2

Quartz fiber

Scale

Large mass (m_2)

F_g Small mass (m_1)

EXAMPLE 13.1   CALCULATING GRAVITATIONAL FORCE

The mass m_1 of one of the small spheres of a Cavendish balance is 0.0100 kg, the mass m_2 of the nearest large sphere is 0.500 kg, and the center-to-center distance between them is 0.0500 m. Find the gravitational force F_g on each sphere due to the other.

SOLUTION

IDENTIFY, SET UP, and EXECUTE: Because the spheres are spherically symmetric, we can calculate F_g by treating them as *particles* separated by 0.0500 m, as in Fig. 13.2. Each sphere experiences the same magnitude of force from the other sphere. We use Newton's

law of gravitation, Eq. (13.1), to determine F_g:

$$F_g = \frac{(6.67 \times 10^{-11} \text{ N} \cdot \text{m}^2/\text{kg}^2)(0.0100 \text{ kg})(0.500 \text{ kg})}{(0.0500 \text{ m})^2}$$

$$= 1.33 \times 10^{-10} \text{ N}$$

EVALUATE: It's remarkable that such a small force could be measured—or even detected—more than 200 years ago. Only a very massive object such as the earth exerts a gravitational force we can feel.

EXAMPLE 13.2   ACCELERATION DUE TO GRAVITATIONAL ATTRACTION

Suppose the two spheres in Example 13.1 are placed with their centers 0.0500 m apart at a point in space far removed from all other bodies. What is the magnitude of the acceleration of each, relative to an inertial system?

SOLUTION

IDENTIFY, SET UP, and EXECUTE: Each sphere exerts on the other a gravitational force of the same magnitude F_g, which we found in Example 13.1. We can ignore any other forces. The *acceleration* magnitudes a_1 and a_2 are different because the masses are different.

To determine these we'll use Newton's second law:

$$a_1 = \frac{F_g}{m_1} = \frac{1.33 \times 10^{-10} \text{ N}}{0.0100 \text{ kg}} = 1.33 \times 10^{-8} \text{ m/s}^2$$

$$a_2 = \frac{F_g}{m_2} = \frac{1.33 \times 10^{-10} \text{ N}}{0.500 \text{ kg}} = 2.66 \times 10^{-10} \text{ m/s}^2$$

EVALUATE: The larger sphere has 50 times the mass of the smaller one and hence has $\frac{1}{50}$ the acceleration. These accelerations are *not* constant; the gravitational forces increase as the spheres move toward each other.

EXAMPLE 13.3   SUPERPOSITION OF GRAVITATIONAL FORCES

Many stars belong to *systems* of two or more stars held together by their mutual gravitational attraction. **Figure 13.5** shows a three-star system at an instant when the stars are at the vertices of a 45° right triangle. Find the total gravitational force exerted on the small star by the two large ones.

SOLUTION

IDENTIFY, SET UP, and EXECUTE: We use the principle of superposition: The total force $\vec{F}$ on the small star is the vector sum of the forces $\vec{F}_1$ and $\vec{F}_2$ due to each large star, as Fig. 13.5 shows. We assume that the stars are spheres as in Fig. 13.2. We first calculate the magnitudes F_1 and F_2 from Eq. (13.1) and then compute the vector sum by using components:

$$F_1 = \frac{\left[\begin{array}{c}(6.67 \times 10^{-11} \text{ N} \cdot \text{m}^2/\text{kg}^2) \\ \times (8.00 \times 10^{30} \text{ kg})(1.00 \times 10^{30} \text{ kg})\end{array}\right]}{(2.00 \times 10^{12} \text{ m})^2 + (2.00 \times 10^{12} \text{ m})^2}$$

$$= 6.67 \times 10^{25} \text{ N}$$

$$F_2 = \frac{\left[\begin{array}{c}(6.67 \times 10^{-11} \text{ N} \cdot \text{m}^2/\text{kg}^2) \\ \times (8.00 \times 10^{30} \text{ kg})(1.00 \times 10^{30} \text{ kg})\end{array}\right]}{(2.00 \times 10^{12} \text{ m})^2}$$

$$= 1.33 \times 10^{26} \text{ N}$$

13.5 The total gravitational force on the small star (at O) is the vector sum of the forces exerted on it by the two larger stars. (For comparison, the mass of the sun—a rather ordinary star—is 1.99×10^{30} kg and the earth–sun distance is 1.50×10^{11} m.)

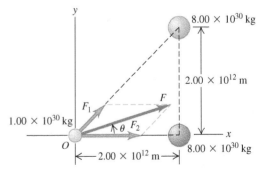

The x- and y-components of these forces are

$$F_{1x} = (6.67 \times 10^{25} \text{ N})(\cos 45°) = 4.72 \times 10^{25} \text{ N}$$

$$F_{1y} = (6.67 \times 10^{25} \text{ N})(\sin 45°) = 4.72 \times 10^{25} \text{ N}$$

$$F_{2x} = 1.33 \times 10^{26} \text{ N}$$

$$F_{2y} = 0$$

Continued

The components of the total force $\vec{F}$ on the small star are

$$F_x = F_{1x} + F_{2x} = 1.81 \times 10^{26} \text{ N}$$
$$F_y = F_{1y} + F_{2y} = 4.72 \times 10^{25} \text{ N}$$

The magnitude of $\vec{F}$ and its angle θ (see Fig. 13.5) are

$$F = \sqrt{F_x^2 + F_y^2} = \sqrt{(1.81 \times 10^{26} \text{ N})^2 + (4.72 \times 10^{25} \text{ N})^2}$$

$$= 1.87 \times 10^{26} \text{ N}$$

$$\theta = \arctan\frac{F_y}{F_x} = \arctan\frac{4.72 \times 10^{25} \text{ N}}{1.81 \times 10^{26} \text{ N}} = 14.6°$$

EVALUATE: While the force magnitude F is tremendous, the magnitude of the resulting acceleration is not: $a = F/m = (1.87 \times 10^{26} \text{ N})/(1.00 \times 10^{30} \text{ kg}) = 1.87 \times 10^{-4} \text{ m/s}^2$. Furthermore, the force $\vec{F}$ is *not* directed toward the center of mass of the two large stars.

DATA *SPEAKS*

Gravitation

When students were given a problem about superposition of gravitational forces, more than 60% gave an incorrect response. Common errors:

- Assuming that equal-mass objects *A* and *B* must exert equally strong gravitational attraction on an object *C* (which is not true when *A* and *B* are different distances from *C*).

- Neglecting to account for the vector nature of force. (To add two forces that point in different directions, you can't just add the force magnitudes.)

13.6 Our solar system is part of a spiral galaxy like this one, which contains roughly 10^{11} stars as well as gas, dust, and other matter. The entire assemblage is held together by the mutual gravitational attraction of all the matter in the galaxy.

Why Gravitational Forces Are Important

Comparing Examples 13.1 and 13.3 shows that gravitational forces are negligible between ordinary household-sized objects but very substantial between objects that are the size of stars. Indeed, gravitation is *the* most important force on the scale of planets, stars, and galaxies (**Fig. 13.6**). It is responsible for holding our earth together and for keeping the planets in orbit about the sun. The mutual gravitational attraction between different parts of the sun compresses material at the sun's core to very high densities and temperatures, making it possible for nuclear reactions to take place there. These reactions generate the sun's energy output, which makes it possible for life to exist on earth and for you to read these words.

The gravitational force is so important on the cosmic scale because it acts *at a distance*, without any direct contact between bodies. Electric and magnetic forces have this same remarkable property, but they are less important on astronomical scales because large accumulations of matter are electrically neutral; that is, they contain equal amounts of positive and negative charge. As a result, the electric and magnetic forces between stars or planets are very small or zero. The strong and weak interactions that we discussed in Section 5.5 also act at a distance, but their influence is negligible at distances much greater than the diameter of an atomic nucleus (about 10^{-14} m).

A useful way to describe forces that act at a distance is in terms of a *field*. One body sets up a disturbance or field at all points in space, and the force that acts on a second body at a particular point is its response to the first body's field at that point. There is a field associated with each force that acts at a distance, and so we refer to gravitational fields, electric fields, magnetic fields, and so on. We won't need the field concept for our study of gravitation in this chapter, so we won't discuss it further here. But in later chapters we'll find that the field concept is an extraordinarily powerful tool for describing electric and magnetic interactions.

TEST YOUR UNDERSTANDING OF SECTION 13.1 The planet Saturn has about 100 times the mass of the earth and is about 10 times farther from the sun than the earth is. Compared to the acceleration of the earth caused by the sun's gravitational pull, how great is the acceleration of Saturn due to the sun's gravitation? (i) 100 times greater; (ii) 10 times greater; (iii) the same; (iv) $\frac{1}{10}$ as great; (v) $\frac{1}{100}$ as great. ∎

13.2 WEIGHT

We defined the *weight* of a body in Section 4.4 as the attractive gravitational force exerted on it by the earth. We can now broaden our definition and say that *the weight of a body is the total gravitational force exerted on the body by all other bodies in the universe.* When the body is near the surface of the earth, we can ignore all other gravitational forces and consider the weight as just the earth's gravitational attraction. At the surface of the *moon* we consider a body's weight to be the gravitational attraction of the moon, and so on.

(MP)

PhET: Lunar Lander

If we again model the earth as a spherically symmetric body with radius R_E, the weight of a small body at the earth's surface (a distance R_E from its center) is

Gravitational constant · · · · · · · · · · · Mass of the earth

Weight of a body at
the earth's surface ...
... equals gravitational force
the earth exerts on body.
$$w = F_g = \frac{Gm_Em}{R_E^2}$$ Mass of body (13.3)

Radius of the earth

But we also know from Section 4.4 that the weight w of a body is the force that causes the acceleration g of free fall, so by Newton's second law, $w = mg$. Equating this with Eq. (13.3) and dividing by m, we find

Gravitational constant · · · · · · Mass of the earth

Acceleration due to gravity · · · · · · · ·
at the earth's surface
$$g = \frac{Gm_E}{R_E^2}$$ Radius of the earth (13.4)

The acceleration due to gravity g is independent of the mass m of the body because m doesn't appear in this equation. We already knew that, but we can now see how it follows from the law of gravitation.

We can *measure* all the quantities in Eq. (13.4) except for m_E, so this relationship allows us to compute the mass of the earth. Solving Eq. (13.4) for m_E and using $R_E = 6370$ km $= 6.37 \times 10^6$ m and $g = 9.80$ m/s², we find

$$m_E = \frac{gR_E^2}{G} = 5.96 \times 10^{24} \text{ kg}$$

This is very close to the currently accepted value of 5.972×10^{24} kg. Once Cavendish had measured G, he computed the mass of the earth in just this way.

At a point above the earth's surface a distance r from the center of the earth (a distance $r - R_E$ above the surface), the weight of a body is given by Eq. (13.3) with R_E replaced by r:

$$w = F_g = \frac{Gm_Em}{r^2}$$ (13.5)

The weight of a body decreases inversely with the square of its distance from the earth's center (**Fig. 13.7**). **Figure 13.8** shows how the weight varies with height above the earth for an astronaut who weighs 700 N at the earth's surface.

13.8 An astronaut who weighs 700 N at the earth's surface experiences less gravitational attraction when above the surface. The relevant distance r is from the astronaut to the *center* of the earth (*not* from the astronaut to the earth's surface).

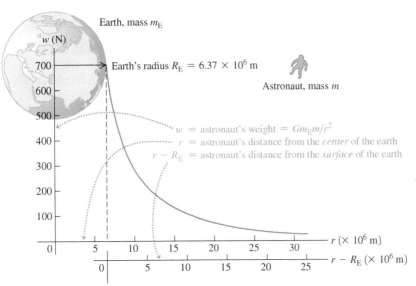

Application Walking and Running on the Moon You automatically transition from a walk to a run when the vertical force you exert on the ground—which, by Newton's third law, equals the vertical force the ground exerts on you—exceeds your weight. This transition from walking to running happens at much lower speeds on the moon, where objects weigh only 17% as much as on earth. Hence, the Apollo astronauts found themselves running even when moving relatively slowly during their moon "walks."

13.7 In an airliner at high altitude, you are farther from the center of the earth than when on the ground and hence weigh slightly less. Can you show that at an altitude of 10 km above the surface, you weigh 0.3% less than you do on the ground?

13.9 The density ρ of the earth decreases with increasing distance r from its center.

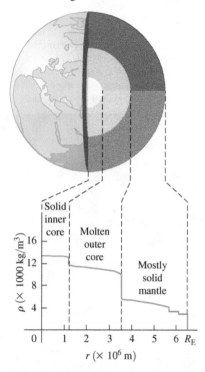

The *apparent* weight of a body on earth differs slightly from the earth's gravitational force because the earth rotates and is therefore not precisely an inertial frame of reference. We've ignored this relatively small effect in our discussion but will consider it carefully in Section 13.7.

While the earth is an approximately spherically symmetric distribution of mass, it is *not* uniform throughout its volume. To demonstrate this, let's first calculate the average *density*, or mass per unit volume, of the earth. If we assume a spherical earth, the volume is

$$V_{\text{E}} = \tfrac{4}{3}\pi R_{\text{E}}^3 = \tfrac{4}{3}\pi (6.37 \times 10^6 \text{ m})^3 = 1.08 \times 10^{21} \text{ m}^3$$

The average density ρ (the Greek letter rho) of the earth is the total mass divided by the total volume:

$$\rho = \frac{m_{\text{E}}}{V_{\text{E}}} = \frac{5.97 \times 10^{24} \text{ kg}}{1.08 \times 10^{21} \text{ m}^3}$$

$$= 5500 \text{ kg/m}^3 = 5.5 \text{ g/cm}^3$$

(Compare to the density of water, $1000 \text{ kg/m}^3 = 1.00 \text{ g/cm}^3$.) If the earth were uniform, rocks near the earth's surface would have this same density. In fact, the density of surface rocks is substantially lower, ranging from about 2000 kg/m^3 for sedimentary rocks to about 3300 kg/m^3 for basalt. So the earth *cannot* be uniform, and its interior must be much more dense than its surface in order that the *average* density be 5500 kg/m^3. According to geophysical models of the earth's interior, the maximum density at the center is about $13,000 \text{ kg/m}^3$. **Figure 13.9** is a graph of density as a function of distance from the center.

EXAMPLE 13.4 GRAVITY ON MARS

SOLUTION

A robotic lander with an earth weight of 3430 N is sent to Mars, which has radius $R_{\text{M}} = 3.39 \times 10^6$ m and mass $m_{\text{M}} = 6.42 \times 10^{23}$ kg (see Appendix F). Find the weight F_g of the lander on the Martian surface and the acceleration there due to gravity, g_{M}.

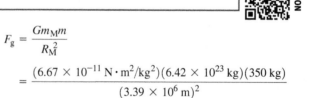

$$F_g = \frac{Gm_{\text{M}}m}{R_{\text{M}}^2}$$

$$= \frac{(6.67 \times 10^{-11} \text{ N} \cdot \text{m}^2/\text{kg}^2)(6.42 \times 10^{23} \text{ kg})(350 \text{ kg})}{(3.39 \times 10^6 \text{ m})^2}$$

$$= 1.30 \times 10^3 \text{ N}$$

SOLUTION

IDENTIFY and SET UP: To find F_g we use Eq. (13.3), replacing m_{E} and R_{E} with m_{M} and R_{M}. We determine the lander mass m from the lander's earth weight w and then find g_{M} from $F_g = mg_{\text{M}}$.

EXECUTE: The lander's earth weight is $w = mg$, so

$$m = \frac{w}{g} = \frac{3430 \text{ N}}{9.80 \text{ m/s}^2} = 350 \text{ kg}$$

The mass is the same no matter where the lander is. From Eq. (13.3), the lander's weight on Mars is

The acceleration due to gravity on Mars is

$$g_{\text{M}} = \frac{F_g}{m} = \frac{1.30 \times 10^3 \text{ N}}{350 \text{ kg}} = 3.7 \text{ m/s}^2$$

EVALUATE: Even though Mars has just 11% of the earth's mass (6.42×10^{23} kg versus 5.97×10^{24} kg), the acceleration due to gravity g_{M} (and hence an object's weight F_g) is roughly 40% as large as on earth. That's because g_{M} is also inversely proportional to the square of the planet's radius, and Mars has only 53% the radius of earth (3.39×10^6 m versus 6.37×10^6 m).

You can check our result for g_{M} by using Eq. (13.4), with appropriate replacements. Do you get the same answer?

TEST YOUR UNDERSTANDING OF SECTION 13.2 Rank the following hypothetical planets in order from highest to lowest value of g at the surface:
(i) mass = 2 times the mass of the earth, radius = 2 times the radius of the earth;
(ii) mass = 4 times the mass of the earth, radius = 4 times the radius of the earth;
(iii) mass = 4 times the mass of the earth, radius = 2 times the radius of the earth;
(iv) mass = 2 times the mass of the earth, radius = 4 times the radius of the earth. ▮

13.3 GRAVITATIONAL POTENTIAL ENERGY

When we first introduced gravitational potential energy in Section 7.1, we assumed that the earth's gravitational force on a body of mass m doesn't depend on the body's height. This led to the expression $U = mgy$. But Eq. (13.2), $F_g = Gm_E m/r^2$, shows that the gravitational force exerted by the earth (mass m_E) *does* in general depend on the distance r from the body to the earth's center. For problems in which a body can be far from the earth's surface, we need a more general expression for gravitational potential energy.

To find this expression, we follow the same steps as in Section 7.1. We consider a body of mass m outside the earth, and first compute the work W_{grav} done by the gravitational force when the body moves directly away from or toward the center of the earth from $r = r_1$ to $r = r_2$, as in **Fig. 13.10**. This work is given by

$$W_{grav} = \int_{r_1}^{r_2} F_r \, dr \tag{13.6}$$

where F_r is the radial component of the gravitational force $\vec{F}$—that is, the component in the direction *outward* from the center of the earth. Because $\vec{F}$ points directly *inward* toward the center of the earth, F_r is negative. It differs from Eq. (13.2), the magnitude of the gravitational force, by a minus sign:

$$F_r = -\frac{Gm_E m}{r^2} \tag{13.7}$$

Substituting Eq. (13.7) into Eq. (13.6), we see that W_{grav} is given by

$$W_{grav} = -Gm_E m \int_{r_1}^{r_2} \frac{dr}{r^2} = \frac{Gm_E m}{r_2} - \frac{Gm_E m}{r_1} \tag{13.8}$$

The path doesn't have to be a straight line; it could also be a curve like the one in Fig. 13.10. By an argument similar to that in Section 7.1, this work depends on only the initial and final values of r, not on the path taken. This also proves that the gravitational force is always *conservative*.

We now define the corresponding potential energy U so that $W_{grav} = U_1 - U_2$, as in Eq. (7.3). Comparing this with Eq. (13.8), we see that the appropriate definition for **gravitational potential energy** is

Gravitational constant ⋯⋯⋱   ⋰⋯⋯Mass of the earth
Gravitational ⋯⋯⋯⋱$U = -\dfrac{Gm_E m}{r}$ ⋯⋯Mass of body
potential energy ⋰   ⋯⋯Distance of body from
(general expression)   the earth's center $\tag{13.9}$

Figure 13.11 shows how the gravitational potential energy depends on the distance r between the body of mass m and the center of the earth. When the body moves away from the earth, r increases, the gravitational force does negative work, and U increases (i.e., becomes less negative). When the body "falls" toward earth, r decreases, the gravitational work is positive, and the potential energy decreases (i.e., becomes more negative).

You may be troubled by Eq. (13.9) because it states that gravitational potential energy is always negative. But in fact you've seen negative values of U before. In using the formula $U = mgy$ in Section 7.1, we found that U was negative whenever the body of mass m was at a value of y below the arbitrary height we chose to be $y = 0$—that is, whenever the body and the earth were closer together than some arbitrary distance. (See, for instance, Example 7.2 in Section 7.1.) In defining U by Eq. (13.9), we have chosen U to be zero when the body of mass m is infinitely far from the earth ($r = \infty$). As the body moves toward the earth, gravitational potential energy decreases and so becomes negative.

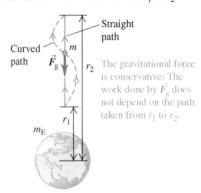

13.10 Calculating the work done on a body by the gravitational force as the body moves from radial coordinate r_1 to r_2.

13.11 A graph of the gravitational potential energy U for the system of the earth (mass m_E) and an astronaut (mass m) versus the astronaut's distance r from the center of the earth.

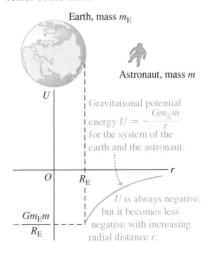

CAUTION Gravitational force vs. gravitational potential energy Don't confuse the expressions for gravitational force, Eq. (13.7), and gravitational potential energy, Eq. (13.9). The force F_r is proportional to $1/r^2$, while potential energy U is proportional to $1/r$. ∎

If we wanted, we could make $U = 0$ at the earth's surface, where $r = R_E$, by adding the quantity Gm_Em/R_E to Eq. (13.9). This would make U positive when $r > R_E$. We won't do this for two reasons: One, it would complicate the expression for U; two, the added term would not affect the *difference* in potential energy between any two points, which is the only physically significant quantity.

If the earth's gravitational force on a body is the only force that does work, then the total mechanical energy of the system of the earth and body is constant, or *conserved*. In the following example we'll use this principle to calculate **escape speed,** the speed required for a body to escape completely from a planet.

EXAMPLE 13.5 "FROM THE EARTH TO THE MOON"

In Jules Verne's 1865 story with this title, three men went to the moon in a shell fired from a giant cannon sunk in the earth in Florida. (a) Find the minimum muzzle speed needed to shoot a shell straight up to a height above the earth equal to the earth's radius R_E. (b) Find the minimum muzzle speed that would allow a shell to escape from the earth completely (the *escape speed*). Neglect air resistance, the earth's rotation, and the gravitational pull of the moon. The earth's radius and mass are $R_E = 6.37 \times 10^6$ m and $m_E = 5.97 \times 10^{24}$ kg.

SOLUTION

IDENTIFY and SET UP: Once the shell leaves the cannon muzzle, only the (conservative) gravitational force does work. Hence we can use conservation of mechanical energy to find the speed at which the shell must leave the muzzle so as to come to a halt (a) at two earth radii from the earth's center and (b) at an infinite distance from earth. The energy-conservation equation is $K_1 + U_1 = K_2 + U_2$, with U given by Eq. (13.9).

In **Fig. 13.12** point 1 is at $r_1 = R_E$, where the shell leaves the cannon with speed v_1 (the target variable). Point 2 is where the shell reaches its maximum height; in part (a) $r_2 = 2R_E$ (Fig. 13.12a), and

in part (b) $r_2 = \infty$ (Fig 13.12b). In both cases $v_2 = 0$ and $K_2 = 0$. Let m be the mass of the shell (with passengers).

EXECUTE: (a) We solve the energy-conservation equation for v_1:

$$K_1 + U_1 = K_2 + U_2$$

$$\tfrac{1}{2}mv_1^2 + \left(-\frac{Gm_Em}{R_E}\right) = 0 + \left(-\frac{Gm_Em}{2R_E}\right)$$

$$v_1 = \sqrt{\frac{Gm_E}{R_E}} = \sqrt{\frac{(6.67 \times 10^{-11}\,\text{N}\cdot\text{m}^2/\text{kg}^2)(5.97 \times 10^{24}\,\text{kg})}{6.37 \times 10^6\,\text{m}}}$$

$$= 7910\,\text{m/s}\ (= 28{,}500\,\text{km/h} = 17{,}700\,\text{mi/h})$$

(b) Now $r_2 = \infty$ so $U_2 = 0$ (see Fig. 13.11). Since $K_2 = 0$, the total mechanical energy $K_2 + U_2$ is zero in this case. Again we solve the energy-conservation equation for v_1:

$$\tfrac{1}{2}mv_1^2 + \left(-\frac{Gm_Em}{R_E}\right) = 0 + 0$$

$$v_1 = \sqrt{\frac{2Gm_E}{R_E}}$$

$$= \sqrt{\frac{2(6.67 \times 10^{-11}\,\text{N}\cdot\text{m}^2/\text{kg}^2)(5.97 \times 10^{24}\,\text{kg})}{6.37 \times 10^6\,\text{m}}}$$

$$= 1.12 \times 10^4\,\text{m/s}\ (= 40{,}200\,\text{km/h} = 25{,}000\,\text{mi/h})$$

EVALUATE: Our results don't depend on the mass of the shell or the direction of launch. A modern spacecraft launched from Florida must attain essentially the speed found in part (b) to escape the earth; however, before launch it's already moving at 410 m/s to the east because of the earth's rotation. Launching to the east takes advantage of this "free" contribution toward escape speed.

To generalize, the initial speed v_1 needed for a body to escape from the surface of a spherical body of mass M and radius R (ignoring air resistance) is $v_1 = \sqrt{2GM/R}$ (escape speed). This equation yields 5.03×10^3 m/s for Mars, 6.02×10^4 m/s for Jupiter, and 6.18×10^5 m/s for the sun.

13.12 Our sketches for this problem.

(a)

(b)

More on Gravitational Potential Energy

As a final note, let's show that when we are close to the earth's surface, Eq. (13.9) reduces to the familiar $U = mgy$ from Chapter 7. We first rewrite Eq. (13.8) as

$$W_{\text{grav}} = Gm_Em\frac{r_1 - r_2}{r_1 r_2}$$

If the body stays close to the earth, then in the denominator we may replace r_1 and r_2 by R_E, the earth's radius, so

$$W_{\text{grav}} = Gm_E m \frac{r_1 - r_2}{R_E^2}$$

According to Eq. (13.4), $g = Gm_E/R_E^2$, so

$$W_{\text{grav}} = mg(r_1 - r_2)$$

If we replace the r's by y's, this is just Eq. (7.1) for the work done by a constant gravitational force. In Section 7.1 we used this equation to derive Eq. (7.2), $U = mgy$, so we may consider Eq. (7.2) for gravitational potential energy to be a special case of the more general Eq. (13.9).

TEST YOUR UNDERSTANDING OF SECTION 13.3   If a planet has the same surface gravity as the earth (that is, the same value of g at the surface), what is its escape speed? (i) The same as the earth's; (ii) less than the earth's; (iii) greater than the earth's; (iv) any of these are possible. ∎

13.4 THE MOTION OF SATELLITES

Artificial satellites orbiting the earth are a familiar part of technology (**Fig. 13.13**). But how do they stay in orbit, and what determines the properties of their orbits? We can use Newton's laws and the law of gravitation to provide the answers. In the next section we'll analyze the motion of planets in the same way.

To begin, think back to the discussion of projectile motion in Section 3.3. In Example 3.6 a motorcycle rider rides horizontally off the edge of a cliff, launching himself into a parabolic path that ends on the flat ground at the base of the cliff. If he survives and repeats the experiment with increased launch speed, he will land farther from the starting point. We can imagine him launching himself with great enough speed that the earth's curvature becomes significant. As he falls, the earth curves away beneath him. If he is going fast enough, and if his launch point is high enough that he clears the mountaintops, he may be able to go right on around the earth without ever landing.

Figure 13.14 shows a variation on this theme. We launch a projectile from point A in the direction AB, tangent to the earth's surface. Trajectories 1 through 7 show the effect of increasing the initial speed. In trajectories 3 through 5 the projectile misses the earth and becomes a satellite. If there is no retarding force such

13.13 With a mass of approximately 4.5×10^5 kg and a width of over 108 m, the International Space Station is the largest satellite ever placed in orbit.

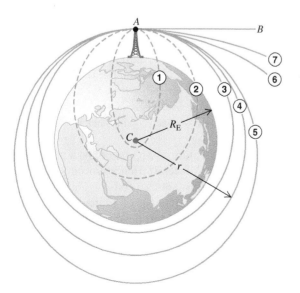

A projectile is launched from A toward B. Trajectories ① through ⑦ show the effect of increasing initial speed.

13.14 Trajectories of a projectile launched from a great height (ignoring air resistance). Orbits 1 and 2 would be completed as shown if the earth were a point mass at C. (This illustration is based on one in Isaac Newton's *Principia*.)

PhET: My Solar System

as air resistance, the projectile's speed when it returns to point *A* is the same as its initial speed and it repeats its motion indefinitely.

Trajectories 1 through 5 close on themselves and are called **closed orbits.** All closed orbits are ellipses or segments of ellipses; trajectory 4 is a circle, a special case of an ellipse. (We'll discuss the properties of an ellipse in Section 13.5.) Trajectories 6 and 7 are **open orbits.** For these paths the projectile never returns to its starting point but travels ever farther away from the earth.

Satellites: Circular Orbits

A *circular* orbit, like trajectory 4 in Fig. 13.14, is the simplest case. It is also an important case, since many artificial satellites have nearly circular orbits and the orbits of the planets around the sun are also fairly circular. The only force acting on a satellite in circular orbit around the earth is the earth's gravitational attraction, which is directed toward the center of the earth and hence toward the center of the orbit (**Fig. 13.15**). As we discussed in Section 5.4, this means that the satellite is in *uniform* circular motion and its speed is constant. The satellite isn't falling *toward* the earth; rather, it's constantly falling *around* the earth. In a circular orbit the speed is just right to keep the distance from the satellite to the center of the earth constant.

13.15 The force $\vec{F}_g$ due to the earth's gravitational attraction provides the centripetal acceleration that keeps a satellite in orbit. Compare to Fig. 5.28.

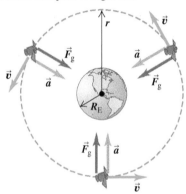

The satellite is in a circular orbit: Its acceleration $\vec{a}$ is always perpendicular to its velocity $\vec{v}$, so its speed v is constant.

Let's see how to find the constant speed v of a satellite in a circular orbit. The radius of the orbit is *r*, measured from the *center* of the earth; the acceleration of the satellite has magnitude $a_{\text{rad}} = v^2/r$ and is always directed toward the center of the circle. By the law of gravitation, the net force (gravitational force) on the satellite of mass *m* has magnitude $F_g = Gm_Em/r^2$ and is in the same direction as the acceleration. Newton's second law ($\sum \vec{F} = m\vec{a}$) then tells us that

$$\frac{Gm_Em}{r^2} = \frac{mv^2}{r}$$

Solving this for v, we find

Speed of satellite in a circular orbit around the earth

$$v = \sqrt{\frac{Gm_E}{r}}$$

Gravitational constant · · · · Mass of the earth · · · · Radius of orbit

(13.10)

This relationship shows that we can't choose the orbit radius *r* and the speed *v* independently; for a given radius *r*, the speed *v* for a circular orbit is determined.

The satellite's mass *m* doesn't appear in Eq. (13.10), which shows that the motion of a satellite does not depend on its mass. An astronaut on board an orbiting space station is herself a satellite of the earth, held by the earth's gravity in the same orbit as the station. The astronaut has the same velocity and acceleration as the station, so nothing is pushing her against the station's floor or walls. She is in a state of *apparent weightlessness,* as in a freely falling elevator; see the discussion following Example 5.9 in Section 5.2. (*True* weightlessness would occur only if the astronaut were infinitely far from any other masses, so that the gravitational force on her would be zero.) Indeed, every part of her body is apparently weightless; she feels nothing pushing her stomach against her intestines or her head against her shoulders (**Fig. 13.16**).

Apparent weightlessness is not just a feature of circular orbits; it occurs whenever gravity is the only force acting on a spacecraft. Hence it occurs for orbits of any shape, including open orbits such as trajectories 6 and 7 in Fig. 13.14.

We can derive a relationship between the radius *r* of a circular orbit and the period *T*, the time for one revolution. The speed *v* is the distance $2\pi r$ traveled in one revolution, divided by the period:

$$v = \frac{2\pi r}{T}$$

(13.11)

13.16 These astronauts are in a state of apparent weightlessness. Which are right side up and which are upside down?

We solve Eq. (13.11) for T and substitute v from Eq. (13.10):

$$\underset{\substack{\text{Period of a} \\ \text{circular orbit} \\ \text{around the earth}}}{} T = \frac{2\pi r}{v} = 2\pi r\sqrt{\frac{r}{Gm_E}} = \frac{2\pi r^{3/2}}{\sqrt{Gm_E}} \qquad (13.12)$$

Radius of orbit ⋯ · Orbital speed · Gravitational constant · Mass of the earth

Equations (13.10) and (13.12) show that larger orbits correspond to slower speeds and longer periods. As an example, the International Space Station (Fig. 13.13) orbits 6800 km from the center of the earth (400 km above the earth's surface) with an orbital speed of 7.7 km/s and an orbital period of 93 min. The moon orbits the earth in a much larger orbit of radius 384,000 km, and so has a much slower orbital speed (1.0 km/s) and a much longer orbital period (27.3 days).

It's interesting to compare Eq. (13.10) to the calculation of escape speed in Example 13.5. We see that the escape speed from a spherical body with radius R is $\sqrt{2}$ times greater than the speed of a satellite in a circular orbit at that radius. If our spacecraft is in circular orbit around *any* planet, we have to multiply our speed by a factor of $\sqrt{2}$ to escape to infinity, regardless of the planet's mass.

Since the speed v in a circular orbit is determined by Eq. (13.10) for a given orbit radius r, the total mechanical energy $E = K + U$ is determined as well. Using Eqs. (13.9) and (13.10), we have

$$E = K + U = \tfrac{1}{2}mv^2 + \left(-\frac{Gm_E m}{r}\right)$$

$$= \tfrac{1}{2}m\left(\frac{Gm_E}{r}\right) - \frac{Gm_E m}{r}$$

$$= -\frac{Gm_E m}{2r} \qquad \text{(circular orbit)} \qquad (13.13)$$

The total mechanical energy in a circular orbit is negative and equal to one-half the potential energy. Increasing the orbit radius r means increasing the mechanical energy (that is, making E less negative). If the satellite is in a relatively low orbit that encounters the outer fringes of earth's atmosphere, mechanical energy decreases due to negative work done by the force of air resistance; as a result, the orbit radius decreases until the satellite hits the ground or burns up in the atmosphere.

We have talked mostly about earth satellites, but we can apply the same analysis to the circular motion of *any* body under its gravitational attraction to a stationary body. **Figure 13.17** shows an example.

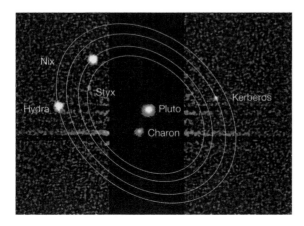

13.17 The dwarf planet Pluto is known to have at least five satellites. In accordance with Eqs. (13.10) and (13.12), the larger the satellite's orbit around Pluto, the slower the satellite's orbital speed and the longer its orbital period.

EXAMPLE 13.6   A SATELLITE ORBIT

You wish to put a 1000-kg satellite into a circular orbit 300 km above the earth's surface. (a) What speed, period, and radial acceleration will it have? (b) How much work must be done to the satellite to put it in orbit? (c) How much additional work would have to be done to make the satellite escape the earth? The earth's radius and mass are given in Example 13.5 (Section 13.3).

SOLUTION

IDENTIFY and SET UP: The satellite is in a circular orbit, so we can use the equations derived in this section. In part (a), we first find the radius r of the satellite's orbit from its altitude. We then calculate the speed v and period T from Eqs. (13.10) and (13.12) and the acceleration from $a_{rad} = v^2/r$. In parts (b) and (c), the work required is the difference between the initial and final mechanical energies, which for a circular orbit is given by Eq. (13.13).

EXECUTE: (a) The radius of the satellite's orbit is $r = 6370$ km + 300 km = 6670 km = 6.67×10^6 m. From Eq. (13.10), the orbital speed is

$$v = \sqrt{\frac{Gm_E}{r}} = \sqrt{\frac{(6.67 \times 10^{-11}\text{ N} \cdot \text{m}^2/\text{kg}^2)(5.97 \times 10^{24}\text{ kg})}{6.67 \times 10^6 \text{ m}}}$$

$$= 7730 \text{ m/s}$$

We find the orbital period from Eq. (13.12):

$$T = \frac{2\pi r}{v} = \frac{2\pi (6.67 \times 10^6 \text{ m})}{7730 \text{ m/s}} = 5420 \text{ s} = 90.4 \text{ min}$$

Finally, the radial acceleration is

$$a_{rad} = \frac{v^2}{r} = \frac{(7730 \text{ m/s})^2}{6.67 \times 10^6 \text{ m}} = 8.96 \text{ m/s}^2$$

This is the value of g at a height of 300 km above the earth's surface; it is about 10% less than the value of g at the surface.

(b) The work required is the difference between E_2, the total mechanical energy when the satellite is in orbit, and E_1, the total mechanical energy when the satellite was at rest on the launch pad. From Eq. (13.13), the energy in orbit is

$$E_2 = -\frac{Gm_E m}{2r}$$

$$= -\frac{(6.67 \times 10^{-11}\text{ N} \cdot \text{m}^2/\text{kg}^2)(5.97 \times 10^{24}\text{ kg})(1000 \text{ kg})}{2(6.67 \times 10^6 \text{ m})}$$

$$= -2.98 \times 10^{10} \text{ J}$$

The satellite's kinetic energy is zero on the launch pad ($r = R_E$), so

$$E_1 = K_1 + U_1 = 0 + \left(-\frac{Gm_E m}{R_E}\right)$$

$$= -\frac{(6.67 \times 10^{-11}\text{ N} \cdot \text{m}^2/\text{kg}^2)(5.97 \times 10^{24}\text{ kg})(1000 \text{ kg})}{6.37 \times 10^6 \text{ m}}$$

$$= -6.25 \times 10^{10} \text{ J}$$

Hence the work required is

$$W_{required} = E_2 - E_1 = (-2.98 \times 10^{10} \text{ J}) - (-6.25 \times 10^{10} \text{ J})$$

$$= 3.27 \times 10^{10} \text{ J}$$

(c) We saw in part (b) of Example 13.5 that the minimum total mechanical energy for a satellite to escape to infinity is zero. Here, the total mechanical energy in the circular orbit is $E_2 = -2.98 \times 10^{10}$ J; to increase this to zero, an amount of work equal to 2.98×10^{10} J would have to be done on the satellite, presumably by rocket engines attached to it.

EVALUATE: In part (b) we ignored the satellite's initial kinetic energy (while it was still on the launch pad) due to the rotation of the earth. How much difference does this make? (See Example 13.5 for useful data.)

TEST YOUR UNDERSTANDING OF SECTION 13.4   Your personal spacecraft is in a low-altitude circular orbit around the earth. Air resistance from the outer regions of the atmosphere does negative work on the spacecraft, causing the radius of the circular orbit to decrease slightly. Does the speed of the spacecraft (i) remain the same, (ii) increase, or (iii) decrease? ❙

13.5 KEPLER'S LAWS AND THE MOTION OF PLANETS

The name *planet* comes from a Greek word meaning "wanderer," and indeed the planets continuously change their positions in the sky relative to the background of stars. One of the great intellectual accomplishments of the 16th and 17th centuries was the threefold realization that the earth is also a planet, that all planets orbit the sun, and that the apparent motions of the planets as seen from the earth can be used to determine their orbits precisely.

The first and second of these ideas were published by Nicolaus Copernicus in Poland in 1543. The nature of planetary orbits was deduced between 1601 and 1619 by the German astronomer and mathematician Johannes Kepler, using precise data on apparent planetary motions compiled by his mentor, the Danish astronomer Tycho Brahe. By trial and error, Kepler discovered three empirical laws that accurately described the motions of the planets:

1. **Each planet moves in an elliptical orbit, with the sun at one focus of the ellipse.**
2. **A line from the sun to a given planet sweeps out equal areas in equal times.**
3. **The periods of the planets are proportional to the $\frac{3}{2}$ powers of the major axis lengths of their orbits.**

Kepler did not know *why* the planets moved in this way. Three generations later, when Newton turned his attention to the motion of the planets, he discovered that each of Kepler's laws can be *derived;* they are consequences of Newton's laws of motion and the law of gravitation. Let's see how each of Kepler's laws arises.

Kepler's First Law

First consider the elliptical orbits described in Kepler's first law. **Figure 13.18** shows the geometry of an ellipse. The longest dimension is the *major axis,* with half-length a; this half-length is called the **semi-major axis.** The sum of the distances from S to P and from S' to P is the same for all points on the curve. S and S' are the *foci* (plural of *focus*). The sun is at S (*not* at the center of the ellipse) and the planet is at P; we think of both as points because the size of each is very small in comparison to the distance between them. There is nothing at the other focus, S'.

The distance of each focus from the center of the ellipse is ea, where e is a dimensionless number between 0 and 1 called the **eccentricity.** If $e = 0$, the two foci coincide and the ellipse is a circle. The actual orbits of the planets are fairly circular; their eccentricities range from 0.007 for Venus to 0.206 for Mercury. (The earth's orbit has $e = 0.017$.) The point in the planet's orbit closest to the sun is the *perihelion,* and the point most distant is the *aphelion.*

Newton showed that for a body acted on by an attractive force proportional to $1/r^2$, the only possible closed orbits are a circle or an ellipse; he also showed that open orbits (trajectories 6 and 7 in Fig. 13.14) must be parabolas or hyperbolas. These results can be derived from Newton's laws and the law of gravitation, together with a lot more differential equations than we're ready for.

Kepler's Second Law

Figure 13.19 shows Kepler's second law. In a small time interval dt, the line from the sun S to the planet P turns through an angle $d\theta$. The area swept out is the colored triangle with height r, base length $r\, d\theta$, and area $dA = \frac{1}{2}r^2\, d\theta$ in Fig. 13.19b. The rate at which area is swept out, dA/dt, is called the *sector velocity:*

$$\frac{dA}{dt} = \tfrac{1}{2}r^2\frac{d\theta}{dt} \qquad (13.14)$$

The essence of Kepler's second law is that the sector velocity has the same value at all points in the orbit. When the planet is close to the sun, r is small and $d\theta/dt$ is large; when the planet is far from the sun, r is large and $d\theta/dt$ is small.

To see how Kepler's second law follows from Newton's laws, we express dA/dt in terms of the velocity vector $\vec{v}$ of the planet P. The component of $\vec{v}$ perpendicular to the radial line is $v_\perp = v \sin\phi$. From Fig. 13.19b the displacement along the direction of $v_\perp$ during time dt is $r\, d\theta$, so we also have $v_\perp = r\, d\theta/dt$. Using this relationship in Eq. (13.14), we find

$$\frac{dA}{dt} = \tfrac{1}{2}rv \sin\phi \qquad \text{(sector velocity)} \qquad (13.15)$$

13.18 Geometry of an ellipse. The sum of the distances SP and $S'P$ is the same for every point on the curve. The sizes of the sun (S) and planet (P) are exaggerated for clarity.

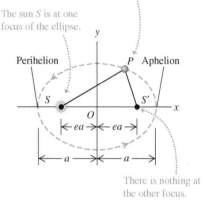

A planet P follows an elliptical orbit.

The sun S is at one focus of the ellipse.

There is nothing at the other focus.

13.19 (a) The planet (P) moves about the sun (S) in an elliptical orbit. (b) In a time dt the line SP sweeps out an area $dA = \frac{1}{2}(r\, d\theta)r = \frac{1}{2}r^2\, d\theta$. (c) The planet's speed varies so that the line SP sweeps out the same area A in a given time t regardless of the planet's position in its orbit.

(a)

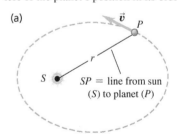

SP = line from sun (S) to planet (P)

(b)

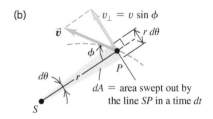

$v_\perp = v \sin\phi$

dA = area swept out by the line SP in a time dt

(c)

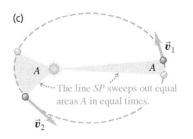

The line SP sweeps out equal areas A in equal times.

13.20 Because the gravitational force that the sun exerts on a planet produces zero torque around the sun, the planet's angular momentum around the sun remains constant.

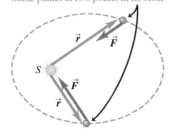

Same planet at two points in its orbit

- Gravitational force $\vec{F}$ on planet has different magnitudes at different points but is always opposite to vector $\vec{r}$ from sun S to planet.
- Hence $\vec{F}$ produces zero torque around sun.

BIO **Application Biological Hazards of Interplanetary Travel** A spacecraft sent from earth to another planet spends most of its journey coasting along an elliptical orbit with the sun at one focus. Rockets are used at only the start and end of the journey, and even the trip to a nearby planet like Mars takes several months. During its journey, the spacecraft is exposed to cosmic rays— radiation that emanates from elsewhere in our galaxy. (On earth we're shielded from this radiation by our planet's magnetic field, as we'll describe in Chapter 27.) This poses no problem for a robotic spacecraft but would be a severe medical hazard for astronauts undertaking such a voyage.

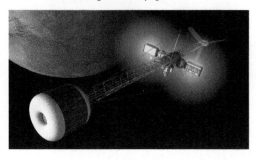

Now $rv \sin \phi$ is the magnitude of the vector product $\vec{r} \times \vec{v}$, which in turn is $1/m$ times the angular momentum $\vec{L} = \vec{r} \times m\vec{v}$ of the planet with respect to the sun. So we have

$$\frac{dA}{dt} = \frac{1}{2m}|\vec{r} \times m\vec{v}| = \frac{L}{2m} \qquad (13.16)$$

Thus Kepler's second law—that sector velocity is constant—means that angular momentum is constant!

It is easy to see why the angular momentum of the planet *must* be constant. According to Eq. (10.26), the rate of change of $\vec{L}$ equals the torque of the gravitational force $\vec{F}$ acting on the planet:

$$\frac{d\vec{L}}{dt} = \vec{\tau} = \vec{r} \times \vec{F}$$

In our situation, $\vec{r}$ is the vector from the sun to the planet, and the force $\vec{F}$ is directed from the planet to the sun (**Fig. 13.20**). So these vectors always lie along the same line, and their vector product $\vec{r} \times \vec{F}$ is zero. Hence $d\vec{L}/dt = \mathbf{0}$. This conclusion does not depend on the $1/r^2$ behavior of the force; angular momentum is conserved for *any* force that acts always along the line joining the particle to a fixed point. Such a force is called a *central force*. (Kepler's first and third laws are valid for a $1/r^2$ force *only*.)

Conservation of angular momentum also explains why the orbit lies in a plane. The vector $\vec{L} = \vec{r} \times m\vec{v}$ is always perpendicular to the plane of the vectors $\vec{r}$ and $\vec{v}$; since $\vec{L}$ is constant in magnitude *and* direction, $\vec{r}$ and $\vec{v}$ always lie in the same plane, which is just the plane of the planet's orbit.

Kepler's Third Law

We have already derived Kepler's third law for the particular case of circular orbits. Equation (13.12) shows that the period of a satellite or planet in a circular orbit is proportional to the $\frac{3}{2}$ power of the orbit radius. Newton was able to show that this same relationship holds for an *elliptical* orbit, with the orbit radius r replaced by the semi-major axis a:

$$T = \frac{2\pi a^{3/2}}{\sqrt{Gm_\text{S}}} \qquad \text{(elliptical orbit around the sun)} \qquad (13.17)$$

Since the planet orbits the sun, not the earth, we have replaced the earth's mass m_E in Eq. (13.12) with the sun's mass m_S. Note that the period does not depend on the eccentricity e. An asteroid in an elongated elliptical orbit with semi-major axis a will have the same orbital period as a planet in a circular orbit of radius a. The key difference is that the asteroid moves at different speeds at different points in its elliptical orbit (Fig. 13.19c), while the planet's speed is constant around its circular orbit.

CONCEPTUAL EXAMPLE 13.7 ORBITAL SPEEDS

At what point in an elliptical orbit (see Fig. 13.19) does a planet move the fastest? The slowest?

SOLUTION

Mechanical energy is conserved as a planet moves in its orbit. The planet's kinetic energy $K = \frac{1}{2}mv^2$ is maximum when the potential energy $U = -Gm_\text{S}m/r$ is minimum (that is, most negative; see Fig. 13.11), which occurs when the sun–planet distance r is a minimum. Hence the speed v is greatest at perihelion. Similarly, K is minimum when r is maximum, so the speed is slowest at aphelion.

Your intuition about falling bodies is helpful here. As the planet falls inward toward the sun, it picks up speed, and its speed is maximum when closest to the sun. The planet slows down as it moves away from the sun, and its speed is minimum at aphelion.

EXAMPLE 13.8   KEPLER'S THIRD LAW

The asteroid Pallas has an orbital period of 4.62 years and an orbital eccentricity of 0.233. Find the semi-major axis of its orbit.

SOLUTION

IDENTIFY and SET UP: We need Kepler's third law, which relates the period T and the semi-major axis a for an orbiting object (such as an asteroid). We use Eq. (13.17) to determine a; from Appendix F we have $m_S = 1.99 \times 10^{30}$ kg, and a conversion factor from Appendix E gives $T = (4.62 \text{ yr})(3.156 \times 10^7 \text{ s/yr}) = 1.46 \times 10^8$ s. Note that we don't need the value of the eccentricity.

EXECUTE: From Eq. (13.17), $a^{3/2} = [(Gm_S)^{1/2}T]/2\pi$. To solve for a, we raise both sides of this expression to the $\frac{2}{3}$ power and then substitute the values of G, m_S, and T:

$$a = \left(\frac{Gm_S T^2}{4\pi^2} \right)^{1/3} = 4.15 \times 10^{11} \text{ m}$$

(Plug in the numbers yourself to check.)

EVALUATE: Our result is intermediate between the semi-major axes of Mars and Jupiter (see Appendix F). Most known asteroids orbit in an "asteroid belt" between the orbits of these two planets.

EXAMPLE 13.9   COMET HALLEY

Comet Halley moves in an elongated elliptical orbit around the sun (**Fig. 13.21**). Its distances from the sun at perihelion and aphelion are 8.75×10^7 km and 5.26×10^9 km, respectively. Find the orbital semi-major axis, eccentricity, and period.

SOLUTION

IDENTIFY and SET UP: We are to find the semi-major axis a, eccentricity e, and orbital period T. We can use Fig. 13.18 to find a and e from the given perihelion and aphelion distances. Knowing a, we can find T from Kepler's third law, Eq. (13.17).

EXECUTE: From Fig. 13.18, the length $2a$ of the major axis equals the sum of the comet–sun distance at perihelion and the comet–sun distance at aphelion. Hence

$$a = \frac{(8.75 \times 10^7 \text{ km}) + (5.26 \times 10^9 \text{ km})}{2} = 2.67 \times 10^9 \text{ km}$$

Figure 13.18 also shows that the comet–sun distance at perihelion is $a - ea = a(1 - e)$. This distance is 8.75×10^7 km, so

$$e = 1 - \frac{8.75 \times 10^7 \text{ km}}{a} = 1 - \frac{8.75 \times 10^7 \text{ km}}{2.67 \times 10^9 \text{ km}} = 0.967$$

From Eq. (13.17), the period is

$$T = \frac{2\pi a^{3/2}}{\sqrt{Gm_S}} = \frac{2\pi (2.67 \times 10^{12} \text{ m})^{3/2}}{\sqrt{(6.67 \times 10^{-11} \text{ N} \cdot \text{m}^2/\text{kg}^2)(1.99 \times 10^{30} \text{ kg})}}$$

$$= 2.38 \times 10^9 \text{ s} = 75.5 \text{ years}$$

EVALUATE: The eccentricity is close to 1, so the orbit is very elongated (see Fig. 13.21a). Comet Halley was at perihelion in early 1986 (Fig. 13.21b); it will next reach perihelion one period later, in 2061.

13.21 (a) The orbit of Comet Halley. (b) Comet Halley as it appeared in 1986. At the heart of the comet is an icy body, called the nucleus, that is about 10 km across. When the comet's orbit carries it close to the sun, the heat of sunlight causes the nucleus to partially evaporate. The evaporated material forms the tail, which can be tens of millions of kilometers long.

(a)

(b)

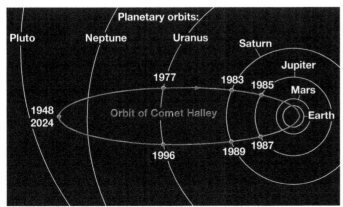

13.22 Both a star and its planet orbit about their common center of mass.

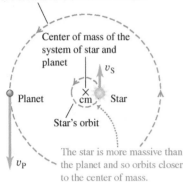

Planet's orbit around the center of mass

Center of mass of the system of star and planet

v_S

Planet

cm Star

Star's orbit

v_P

The star is more massive than the planet and so orbits closer to the center of mass.

The planet and star are always on opposite sides of the center of mass.

13.23 Calculating the gravitational potential energy of interaction between a point mass m outside a spherical shell and a ring on the surface of the shell of mass M.

(a) Geometry of the situation

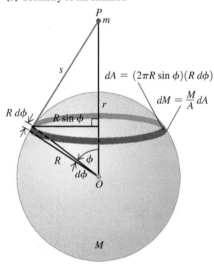

P
m

s

$dA = (2\pi R \sin \phi)(R\, d\phi)$

r

$dM = \dfrac{M}{A} dA$

$R\, d\phi$

$R \sin \phi$

R

ϕ

$d\phi$

O

M

(b) The distance s is the hypotenuse of a right triangle with sides $(r - R \cos \phi)$ and $R \sin \phi$.

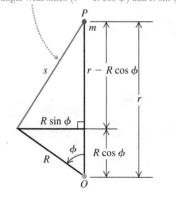

P
m

s

$r - R \cos \phi$

r

$R \sin \phi$

R

ϕ

$R \cos \phi$

O

Planetary Motions and the Center of Mass

We have assumed that as a planet or comet orbits the sun, the sun remains absolutely stationary. This can't be correct; because the sun exerts a gravitational force on the planet, the planet exerts a gravitational force on the sun of the same magnitude but opposite direction. In fact, *both* the sun and the planet orbit around their common center of mass (**Fig. 13.22**). We've made only a small error by ignoring this effect, however; the sun's mass is about 750 times the total mass of all the planets combined, so the center of mass of the solar system is not far from the center of the sun. Remarkably, astronomers have used this effect to detect the presence of planets orbiting other stars. Sensitive telescopes are able to detect the apparent "wobble" of a star as it orbits the common center of mass of the star and an unseen companion planet. (The planets are too faint to observe directly.) By analyzing these "wobbles," astronomers have discovered planets in orbit around hundreds of other stars.

The most remarkable result of Newton's analysis of planetary motion is that bodies in the heavens obey the *same* laws of motion as do bodies on the earth. This *Newtonian synthesis,* as it has come to be called, is one of the great unifying principles of science. It has had profound effects on the way that humanity looks at the universe—not as a realm of impenetrable mystery, but as a direct extension of our everyday world, subject to scientific study and calculation.

TEST YOUR UNDERSTANDING OF SECTION 13.5 The orbit of Comet X has a semi-major axis that is four times longer than the semi-major axis of Comet Y. What is the ratio of the orbital period of X to the orbital period of Y? (i) 2; (ii) 4; (iii) 8; (iv) 16; (v) 32; (vi) 64. ▐

13.6 SPHERICAL MASS DISTRIBUTIONS

We have stated without proof that the gravitational interaction between two spherically symmetric mass distributions is the same as though all the mass of each were concentrated at its center. Now we're ready to prove this statement. Newton searched for a proof for several years, and he delayed publication of the law of gravitation until he found one.

Rather than starting with two spherically symmetric masses, we'll tackle the simpler problem of a point mass m interacting with a thin spherical shell with total mass M. We'll show that when m is outside the sphere, the *potential energy* associated with this gravitational interaction is the same as though M were concentrated in a point at the center of the sphere. We learned in Section 7.4 that the force is the negative derivative of the potential energy, so the *force* on m is also the same as for a point mass M. Our result will also hold for *any* spherically symmetric mass distribution, which we can think of as being made of many concentric spherical shells.

A Point Mass Outside a Spherical Shell

We start by considering a ring on the surface of a shell (**Fig. 13.23a**), centered on the line from the center of the shell to m. We do this because all of the particles that make up the ring are the same distance s from the point mass m. From Eq. (13.9) the potential energy of interaction between the earth (mass m_E) and a point mass m, separated by a distance r, is $U = -Gm_E m/r$. From this expression, we see that the potential energy of interaction between the point mass m and a particle of mass m_i within the ring is

$$U_i = -\frac{Gmm_i}{s}$$

To find the potential energy dU of interaction between m and the entire ring of mass $dM = \Sigma_i m_i$, we sum this expression for U_i over all particles in the ring:

$$dU = \sum_i U_i = \sum_i \left(-\frac{Gmm_i}{s}\right) = -\frac{Gm}{s}\sum_i m_i = -\frac{Gm\,dM}{s} \quad (13.18)$$

To proceed, we need to know the mass dM of the ring. We can find this with the aid of a little geometry. The radius of the shell is R, so in terms of the angle ϕ shown in the figure, the radius of the ring is $R\sin\phi$, and its circumference is $2\pi R\sin\phi$. The width of the ring is $R\,d\phi$, and its area dA is approximately equal to its width times its circumference:

$$dA = 2\pi R^2 \sin\phi\,d\phi$$

The ratio of the ring mass dM to the total mass M of the shell is equal to the ratio of the area dA of the ring to the total area $A = 4\pi R^2$ of the shell:

$$\frac{dM}{M} = \frac{2\pi R^2 \sin\phi\,d\phi}{4\pi R^2} = \tfrac{1}{2}\sin\phi\,d\phi \quad (13.19)$$

Now we solve Eq. (13.19) for dM and substitute the result into Eq. (13.18) to find the potential energy of interaction between point mass m and the ring:

$$dU = -\frac{GMm\sin\phi\,d\phi}{2s} \quad (13.20)$$

The total potential energy of interaction between the point mass and the *shell* is the integral of Eq. (13.20) over the whole sphere as ϕ varies from 0 to π (*not* 2π!) and s varies from $r - R$ to $r + R$. To carry out the integration, we have to express the integrand in terms of a single variable; we choose s. To express ϕ and $d\phi$ in terms of s, we have to do a little more geometry. Figure 13.23b shows that s is the hypotenuse of a right triangle with sides $(r - R\cos\phi)$ and $R\sin\phi$, so the Pythagorean theorem gives

$$\begin{aligned} s^2 &= (r - R\cos\phi)^2 + (R\sin\phi)^2 \\ &= r^2 - 2rR\cos\phi + R^2 \end{aligned} \quad (13.21)$$

We take differentials of both sides:

$$2s\,ds = 2rR\sin\phi\,d\phi$$

Next we divide this by $2rR$ and substitute the result into Eq. (13.20):

$$dU = -\frac{GMm}{2s}\frac{s\,ds}{rR} = -\frac{GMm}{2rR}\,ds \quad (13.22)$$

We can now integrate Eq. (13.22), recalling that s varies from $r - R$ to $r + R$:

$$U = -\frac{GMm}{2rR}\int_{r-R}^{r+R} ds = -\frac{GMm}{2rR}\left[(r + R) - (r - R)\right] \quad (13.23)$$

Finally, we have

$$U = -\frac{GMm}{r} \qquad \text{(point mass } m \text{ outside spherical shell } M) \quad (13.24)$$

This is equal to the potential energy of two point masses m and M at a distance r. So we have proved that the gravitational potential energy of spherical shell M and point mass m at any distance r is the same as though they were point masses. Because the force is given by $F_r = -dU/dr$, the force is also the same.

The Gravitational Force Between Spherical Mass Distributions

Any spherically symmetric mass distribution can be thought of as a combination of concentric spherical shells. Because of the principle of superposition of forces, what is true of one shell is also true of the combination. So we have proved half of what we set out to prove: that the gravitational interaction between any spherically symmetric mass distribution and a point mass is the same as though all the mass of the spherically symmetric distribution were concentrated at its center.

The other half is to prove that *two* spherically symmetric mass distributions interact as though both were points. That's easier. In Fig. 13.23a the forces the two bodies exert on each other are an action–reaction pair, and they obey Newton's third law. So we have also proved that the force that m exerts *on* sphere M is the same as though M were a point. But now if we replace m with a spherically symmetric mass distribution centered at m's location, the resulting gravitational force on any part of M is the same as before, and so is the total force. This completes our proof.

A Point Mass Inside a Spherical Shell

We assumed at the beginning that the point mass m was outside the spherical shell, so our proof is valid only when m is outside a spherically symmetric mass distribution. When m is *inside* a spherical shell, the geometry is as shown in **Fig. 13.24**. The entire analysis goes just as before; Eqs. (13.18) through (13.22) are still valid. But when we get to Eq. (13.23), the limits of integration have to be changed to $R - r$ and $R + r$. We then have

$$U = -\frac{GMm}{2rR} \int_{R-r}^{R+r} ds = -\frac{GMm}{2rR}\left[(R + r) - (R - r)\right] \qquad (13.25)$$

and the final result is

$$U = -\frac{GMm}{R} \qquad \text{(point mass } m \text{ inside spherical shell } M\text{)} \qquad (13.26)$$

Compare this result to Eq. (13.24): Instead of having r, the distance between m and the center of M, in the denominator, we have R, the radius of the shell. This means that U in Eq. (13.26) doesn't depend on r and thus has the same value everywhere inside the shell. When m moves around inside the shell, no work is done on it, so the force on m at any point inside the shell must be zero.

More generally, at any point in the interior of any spherically symmetric mass distribution (not necessarily a shell), at a distance r from its center, the gravitational force on a point mass m is the same as though we removed all the mass at points farther than r from the center and concentrated all the remaining mass at the center.

13.24 When a point mass m is *inside* a uniform spherical shell of mass M, the potential energy is the same no matter where inside the shell the point mass is located. The force from the masses' mutual gravitational interaction is zero.

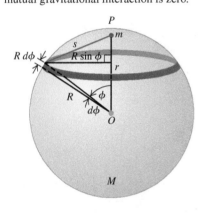

EXAMPLE 13.10 "JOURNEY TO THE CENTER OF THE EARTH"

Imagine that we drill a hole through the earth along a diameter and drop a mail pouch down the hole. Derive an expression for the gravitational force F_g on the pouch as a function of its distance from the earth's center. Assume that the earth's density is uniform (not a very realistic model; see Fig. 13.9).

SOLUTION

IDENTIFY and SET UP: From the discussion immediately above, the value of F_g at a distance r from the earth's center is determined by only the mass M within a spherical region of radius r

(**Fig. 13.25**). Hence F_g is the same as if all the mass within radius r were concentrated at the center of the earth. The mass of a uniform sphere is proportional to the volume of the sphere, which is $\frac{4}{3}\pi r^3$ for a sphere of arbitrary radius r and $\frac{4}{3}\pi R_E^3$ for the entire earth.

EXECUTE: The ratio of the mass M of the sphere of radius r to the mass m_E of the earth is

$$\frac{M}{m_E} = \frac{\frac{4}{3}\pi r^3}{\frac{4}{3}\pi R_E^3} = \frac{r^3}{R_E^3} \qquad \text{so} \qquad M = m_E\frac{r^3}{R_E^3}$$

13.25 A hole through the center of the earth (assumed to be uniform). When an object is a distance r from the center, only the mass inside a sphere of radius r exerts a net gravitational force on it.

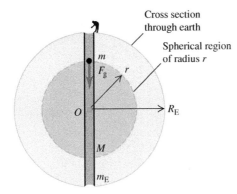

Cross section through earth

Spherical region of radius r

m

F_g

r

O

R_E

M

m_E

The magnitude of the gravitational force on m is then

$$F_g = \frac{GMm}{r^2} = \frac{Gm}{r^2}\left(m_E \frac{r^3}{R_E^3}\right) = \frac{Gm_E m}{R_E^3}r$$

EVALUATE: Inside this uniform-density sphere, F_g is *directly proportional* to the distance r from the center, rather than to $1/r^2$ as it is outside the sphere. At the surface $r = R_E$, we have $F_g = Gm_E m/R_E^2$, as we should. In the next chapter we'll learn how to compute the time it would take for the mail pouch to emerge on the other side of the earth.

TEST YOUR UNDERSTANDING OF SECTION 13.6 In the classic 1913 science-fiction novel *At the Earth's Core,* by Edgar Rice Burroughs, explorers discover that the earth is a hollow sphere and that an entire civilization lives on the inside of the sphere. Would it be possible to stand and walk on the inner surface of a hollow, nonrotating planet? ∎

13.7 APPARENT WEIGHT AND THE EARTH'S ROTATION

Because the earth rotates on its axis, it is not precisely an inertial frame of reference. For this reason the apparent weight of a body on earth is not precisely equal to the earth's gravitational attraction, which we will call the **true weight** $\vec{w}_0$ of the body. **Figure 13.26** is a cutaway view of the earth, showing three observers. Each one holds a spring scale with a body of mass m hanging from it. Each scale applies a tension force $\vec{F}$ to the body hanging from it, and the reading on each

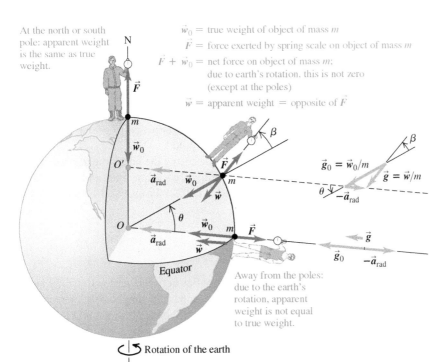

At the north or south pole: apparent weight is the same as true weight.

N

$\vec{w}_0$ = true weight of object of mass m

$\vec{F}$ = force exerted by spring scale on object of mass m

$\vec{F} + \vec{w}_0$ = net force on object of mass m; due to earth's rotation, this is not zero (except at the poles)

$\vec{w}$ = apparent weight = opposite of $\vec{F}$

$\vec{F}$

m

$\vec{w}_0$

O'

$\vec{a}_{rad}$

$\vec{w}_0$

β

$\vec{F}$

m

$\vec{w}$

$\vec{g}_0 = \vec{w}_0/m$

$\vec{g} = \vec{w}/m$

β

θ

$-\vec{a}_{rad}$

θ

O

$\vec{a}_{rad}$

$\vec{w}_0$

m

$\vec{F}$

$\vec{w}$

$\vec{g}$

$\vec{g}_0$

$-\vec{a}_{rad}$

Equator

Away from the poles: due to the earth's rotation, apparent weight is not equal to true weight.

Rotation of the earth

13.26 Except at the poles, the reading for an object being weighed on a scale (the *apparent weight*) is less than the gravitational force of attraction on the object (the *true weight*). The reason is that a net force is needed to provide a centripetal acceleration as the object rotates with the earth. For clarity, the illustration greatly exaggerates the angle β between the true and apparent weight vectors.

scale is the magnitude F of this force. If the observers are unaware of the earth's rotation, each one *thinks* that the scale reading equals the weight of the body because he thinks the body on his spring scale is in equilibrium. So each observer thinks that the tension $\vec{F}$ must be opposed by an equal and opposite force $\vec{w}$, which we call the **apparent weight.** But if the bodies are rotating with the earth, they are *not* precisely in equilibrium. Our problem is to find the relationship between the apparent weight $\vec{w}$ and the true weight $\vec{w}_0$.

If we assume that the earth is spherically symmetric, then the true weight $\vec{w}_0$ has magnitude $Gm_{\mathrm{E}}m/R_{\mathrm{E}}^2$, where m_{E} and R_{E} are the mass and radius of the earth. This value is the same for all points on the earth's surface. If the center of the earth can be taken as the origin of an inertial coordinate system, then the body at the north pole really *is* in equilibrium in an inertial system, and the reading on that observer's spring scale is equal to w_0. But the body at the equator is moving in a circle of radius R_{E} with speed v, and there must be a net inward force equal to the mass times the centripetal acceleration:

$$w_0 - F = \frac{mv^2}{R_{\mathrm{E}}}$$

So the magnitude of the apparent weight (equal to the magnitude of F) is

$$w = w_0 - \frac{mv^2}{R_{\mathrm{E}}} \qquad \left(\text{at the equator}\right) \qquad (13.27)$$

If the earth were not rotating, the body when released would have a free-fall acceleration $g_0 = w_0/m$. Since the earth *is* rotating, the falling body's actual acceleration relative to the observer at the equator is $g = w/m$. Dividing Eq. (13.27) by m and using these relationships, we find

$$g = g_0 - \frac{v^2}{R_{\mathrm{E}}} \qquad \left(\text{at the equator}\right)$$

To evaluate v^2/R_{E}, we note that in 86,164 s a point on the equator moves a distance equal to the earth's circumference, $2\pi R_{\mathrm{E}} = 2\pi(6.37 \times 10^6 \text{ m})$. (The solar day, 86,400 s, is $\frac{1}{365}$ longer than this because in one day the earth also completes $\frac{1}{365}$ of its orbit around the sun.) Thus we find

$$v = \frac{2\pi(6.37 \times 10^6 \text{ m})}{86,164 \text{ s}} = 465 \text{ m/s}$$

$$\frac{v^2}{R_{\mathrm{E}}} = \frac{(465 \text{ m/s})^2}{6.37 \times 10^6 \text{ m}} = 0.0339 \text{ m/s}^2$$

So for a spherically symmetric earth the acceleration due to gravity should be about 0.03 m/s^2 less at the equator than at the poles.

At locations intermediate between the equator and the poles, the true weight $\vec{w}_0$ and the centripetal acceleration are not along the same line, and we need to write a vector equation corresponding to Eq. (13.27). From Fig. 13.26 we see that the appropriate equation is

$$\vec{w} = \vec{w}_0 - m\vec{a}_{\mathrm{rad}} = m\vec{g}_0 - m\vec{a}_{\mathrm{rad}} \qquad (13.28)$$

The difference in the magnitudes of g and g_0 lies between zero and 0.0339 m/s^2. As Fig. 13.26 shows, the *direction* of the apparent weight differs from the direction toward the center of the earth by a small angle β, which is $0.1°$ or less.

Table 13.1 gives the values of g at several locations. In addition to moderate variations with latitude, there are small variations due to elevation, differences in local density, and the earth's deviation from perfect spherical symmetry.

Variations of g with Latitude and Elevation

TABLE 13.1			
Station	North Latitude	Elevation (m)	g (m/s^2)
Canal Zone	09°	0	9.78243
Jamaica	18°	0	9.78591
Bermuda	32°	0	9.79806
Denver, CO	40°	1638	9.79609
Pittsburgh, PA	40.5°	235	9.80118
Cambridge, MA	42°	0	9.80398
Greenland	70°	0	9.82534

Imagine a planet that has the same mass and radius as the earth but that makes 10 rotations during the time the earth makes one rotation. What would be the difference between the acceleration due to gravity at the planet's equator and the acceleration due to gravity at its poles? (i) 0.00339 m/s^2; (ii) 0.0339 m/s^2; (iii) 0.339 m/s^2; (iv) 3.39 m/s^2. ▮

13.8 BLACK HOLES

In 1916 Albert Einstein presented his general theory of relativity, which included a new concept of the nature of gravitation. In his theory, a massive object actually changes the geometry of the space around it. Other objects sense this altered geometry and respond by being attracted to the first object. The general theory of relativity is beyond our scope in this chapter, but we can look at one of its most startling predictions: the existence of **black holes,** objects whose gravitational influence is so great that nothing—not even light—can escape them. We can understand the basic idea of a black hole by using Newtonian principles.

The Escape Speed from a Star

Think first about the properties of our own sun. Its mass $M = 1.99 \times 10^{30}$ kg and radius $R = 6.96 \times 10^8$ m are much larger than those of any planet, but compared to other stars, our sun is not exceptionally massive. You can find the sun's average density ρ in the same way we found the average density of the earth in Section 13.2:

$$\rho = \frac{M}{V} = \frac{M}{\frac{4}{3}\pi R^3} = \frac{1.99 \times 10^{30} \text{ kg}}{\frac{4}{3}\pi(6.96 \times 10^8 \text{ m})^3} = 1410 \text{ kg/m}^3$$

The sun's temperatures range from 5800 K (about 5500°C or 10,000°F) at the surface up to 1.5×10^7 K (about 2.7×10^7°F) in the interior, so it surely contains no solids or liquids. Yet gravitational attraction pulls the sun's gas atoms together until the sun is, on average, 41% denser than water and about 1200 times as dense as the air we breathe.

Now think about the escape speed for a body at the surface of the sun. In Example 13.5 (Section 13.3) we found that the escape speed from the surface of a spherical mass M with radius R is $v = \sqrt{2GM/R}$. Substituting $M = \rho V = \rho\left(\frac{4}{3}\pi R^3\right)$ into the expression for escape speed gives

$$v = \sqrt{\frac{2GM}{R}} = \sqrt{\frac{8\pi G\rho}{3}}R \qquad (13.29)$$

Using either form of this equation, you can show that the escape speed for a body at the surface of our sun is $v = 6.18 \times 10^5$ m/s (about 2.2 million km/h, or 1.4 million mi/h). This value, roughly $\frac{1}{500}$ the speed of light in vacuum, is independent of the mass of the escaping body; it depends on only the mass and radius (or average density and radius) of the sun.

Now consider various stars with the same average density ρ and different radii R. Equation (13.29) shows that for a given value of density ρ, the escape speed v is directly proportional to R. In 1783 the Rev. John Mitchell, an amateur astronomer, noted that if a body with the same average density as the sun had about 500 times the radius of the sun, its escape speed would be greater than the speed of light in vacuum, c. With his statement that "all light emitted from such a body would be made to return toward it," Mitchell became the first person to suggest the existence of what we now call a black hole.

Black Holes, the Schwarzschild Radius, and the Event Horizon

The first expression for escape speed in Eq. (13.29) suggests that a body of mass M will act as a black hole if its radius R is less than or equal to a certain critical radius. How can we determine this critical radius? You might think that you can find the answer by simply setting $v = c$ in Eq. (13.29). As a matter of fact, this does give the correct result, but only because of two compensating errors. The kinetic energy of light is *not* $mc^2/2$, and the gravitational potential energy near a black hole is *not* given by Eq. (13.9). In 1916, Karl Schwarzschild used Einstein's general theory of relativity to derive an expression for the critical radius R_S, now called the **Schwarzschild radius.** The result turns out to be the same as though we had set $v = c$ in Eq. (13.29), so

$$c = \sqrt{\frac{2GM}{R_S}}$$

Solving for the Schwarzschild radius R_S, we find

$$\text{Schwarzschild radius} \cdots\!\!\rightarrow R_S = \frac{2GM}{c^2} \quad\begin{array}{l}\cdots\text{Gravitational constant}\\[2pt]\leftarrow\cdots\text{Mass of black hole}\\[2pt]\leftarrow\cdots\text{Speed of light in vacuum}\end{array} \qquad (13.30)$$

of a black hole

If a spherical, nonrotating body with mass M has a radius less than R_S, then *nothing* (not even light) can escape from the surface of the body, and the body is a black hole (**Fig. 13.27**). In this case, any other body within a distance R_S of the center of the black hole is trapped by the gravitational attraction of the black hole and cannot escape from it.

The surface of the sphere with radius R_S surrounding a black hole is called the **event horizon:** Since light can't escape from within that sphere, we can't see events occurring inside. All that an observer outside the event horizon can know about a black hole is its mass (from its gravitational effects on other bodies), its electric charge (from the electric forces it exerts on other charged bodies), and its angular momentum (because a rotating black hole tends to drag space—and everything in that space—around with it). All other information about the body is irretrievably lost when it collapses inside its event horizon.

13.27 (a) A body with a radius R greater than the Schwarzschild radius R_S. (b) If the body collapses to a radius smaller than R_S, it is a black hole with an escape speed greater than the speed of light. The surface of the sphere of radius R_S is called the event horizon of the black hole.

(a) When the radius R of a body is greater than the Schwarzschild radius R_S, light can escape from the surface of the body.

(b) If all the mass of the body lies inside radius R_S, the body is a black hole: No light can escape from it.

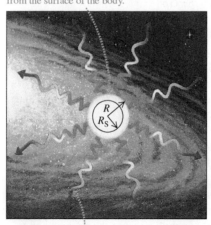

Gravity acting on the escaping light "red shifts" it to longer wavelengths.

EXAMPLE 13.11 BLACK HOLE CALCULATIONS

Astrophysical theory suggests that a burned-out star whose mass is at least three solar masses will collapse under its own gravity to form a black hole. If it does, what is the radius of its event horizon?

SOLUTION

IDENTIFY, SET UP, and EXECUTE: The radius in question is the Schwarzschild radius. We use Eq. (13.30) with a value of M equal to three solar masses, or $M = 3(1.99 \times 10^{30} \text{ kg}) = 6.0 \times 10^{30} \text{ kg}$:

$$R_S = \frac{2GM}{c^2} = \frac{2(6.67 \times 10^{-11} \text{ N} \cdot \text{m}^2/\text{kg}^2)(6.0 \times 10^{30} \text{ kg})}{(3.00 \times 10^8 \text{ m/s})^2}$$

$$= 8.9 \times 10^3 \text{ m} = 8.9 \text{ km} = 5.5 \text{ mi}$$

EVALUATE: The average density of such an object is

$$\rho = \frac{M}{\frac{4}{3}\pi R^3} = \frac{6.0 \times 10^{30} \text{ kg}}{\frac{4}{3}\pi(8.9 \times 10^3 \text{ m})^3} = 2.0 \times 10^{18} \text{ kg/m}^3$$

This is about 10^{15} times as great as the density of familiar matter on earth and is comparable to the densities of atomic nuclei. In fact, once the body collapses to a radius of R_S, nothing can prevent it from collapsing further. All of the mass ends up being crushed down to a single point called a *singularity* at the center of the event horizon. This point has zero volume and so has *infinite* density.

A Visit to a Black Hole

At points far from a black hole, its gravitational effects are the same as those of any normal body with the same mass. If the sun collapsed to form a black hole, the orbits of the planets would be unaffected. But things get dramatically different close to the black hole. If you decided to become a martyr for science and jump into a black hole, the friends you left behind would notice several odd effects as you moved toward the event horizon, most of them associated with effects of general relativity.

If you carried a radio transmitter to send back your comments on what was happening, your friends would have to retune their receiver continuously to lower and lower frequencies, an effect called the *gravitational red shift*. Consistent with this shift, they would observe that your clocks (electronic or biological) would appear to run more and more slowly, an effect called *time dilation*. In fact, during their lifetimes they would never see you make it to the event horizon.

In your frame of reference, you would make it to the event horizon in a rather short time but in a rather disquieting way. As you fell feet first into the black hole, the gravitational pull on your feet would be greater than that on your head, which would be slightly farther away from the black hole. The *differences* in gravitational force on different parts of your body would be great enough to stretch you along the direction toward the black hole and compress you perpendicular to it. These effects (called *tidal forces*) would rip you to atoms, and then rip your atoms apart, before you reached the event horizon.

Detecting Black Holes

If light cannot escape from a black hole and if black holes are as small as Example 13.11 suggests, how can we know that such things exist? The answer is that any gas or dust near the black hole tends to be pulled into an *accretion disk* that swirls around and into the black hole, rather like a whirlpool (**Fig. 13.28**, next page). Friction within the accretion disk's gas causes it to lose mechanical energy and spiral into the black hole; as it moves inward, it is compressed together. This causes heating of the gas, just as air compressed in a bicycle pump gets hotter. Temperatures in excess of 10^6 K can occur in the accretion disk, so hot that the disk emits not just visible light (as do bodies that are "red-hot" or "white-hot") but x rays. Astronomers look for these x rays (emitted by the gas material *before* it crosses the event horizon) to signal the presence of a black hole. Several promising candidates have been found, and astronomers now express considerable confidence in the existence of black holes.

13.28 In a *binary* star system, two stars orbit each other; in the special case shown here, one of the stars is a black hole. The black hole itself cannot be seen, but the x rays from its accretion disk can be detected.

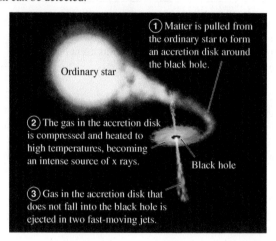

① Matter is pulled from the ordinary star to form an accretion disk around the black hole.

Ordinary star

② The gas in the accretion disk is compressed and heated to high temperatures, becoming an intense source of x rays.

Black hole

③ Gas in the accretion disk that does not fall into the black hole is ejected in two fast-moving jets.

13.29 This false-color image shows the motions of stars at the center of our galaxy over a 17-year period. Analysis of these orbits by using Kepler's third law indicates that the stars are moving about an unseen object that is some 4.1×10^6 times the mass of the sun. The scale bar indicates a length of 10^{14} m (670 times the distance from the earth to the sun).

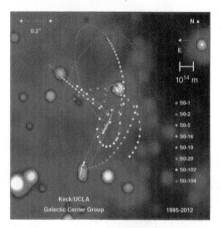

Black holes in binary star systems like the one depicted in Fig. 13.28 have masses a few times greater than the sun's mass. There is also mounting evidence for the existence of much larger *supermassive black holes*. One example lies at the center of our Milky Way galaxy, some 26,000 light-years from earth in the direction of the constellation Sagittarius. High-resolution images of the galactic center reveal stars moving at speeds greater than 1500 km/s about an unseen object that lies at the position of a source of radio waves called Sgr A* (**Fig. 13.29**). By analyzing these motions, astronomers can infer the period T and semi-major axis a of each star's orbit. The mass m_X of the unseen object can be calculated from Kepler's third law in the form given in Eq. (13.17), with the mass of the sun m_S replaced by m_X:

$$T = \frac{2\pi a^{3/2}}{\sqrt{Gm_X}} \qquad \text{so} \qquad m_X = \frac{4\pi^2 a^3}{GT^2}$$

The conclusion is that the mysterious dark object at the galactic center has a mass of 8.2×10^{36} kg, or 4.1 *million* times the mass of the sun. Yet observations with radio telescopes show that it has a radius no more than 4.4×10^{10} m, about one-third of the distance from the earth to the sun. These observations suggest that this massive, compact object is a black hole with a Schwarzschild radius of 1.1×10^{10} m. Astronomers hope to improve the resolution of their observations so that they can actually see the event horizon of this black hole.

Other lines of research suggest that even larger black holes, in excess of 10^9 times the mass of the sun, lie at the centers of other galaxies. Observational and theoretical studies of black holes of all sizes continue to be an exciting area of research in both physics and astronomy.

TEST YOUR UNDERSTANDING OF SECTION 13.8 If the sun somehow collapsed to form a black hole, what effect would this event have on the orbit of the earth? The orbit would (i) shrink; (ii) expand; (iii) remain the same size. ▮

Newton's law of gravitation: *Any* two particles with masses m_1 and m_2, a distance r apart, attract each other with forces inversely proportional to r^2. These forces form an action–reaction pair and obey Newton's third law. When two or more bodies exert gravitational forces on a particular body, the total gravitational force on that individual body is the vector sum of the forces exerted by the other bodies. The gravitational interaction between spherical mass distributions, such as planets or stars, is the same as if all the mass of each distribution were concentrated at the center. (See Examples 13.1–13.3 and 13.10.)

$$F_g = \frac{Gm_1m_2}{r^2} \qquad (13.1)$$

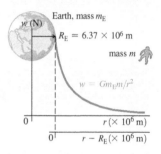

Gravitational force, weight, and gravitational potential energy: The weight w of a body is the total gravitational force exerted on it by all other bodies in the universe. Near the surface of the earth (mass m_E and radius R_E), the weight is essentially equal to the gravitational force of the earth alone. The gravitational potential energy U of two masses m and m_E separated by a distance r is inversely proportional to r. The potential energy is never positive; it is zero only when the two bodies are infinitely far apart. (See Examples 13.4 and 13.5.)

$$w = F_g = \frac{Gm_Em}{R_E^2} \qquad (13.3)$$

(weight at earth's surface)

$$g = \frac{Gm_E}{R_E^2} \qquad (13.4)$$

(acceleration due to gravity at earth's surface)

$$U = -\frac{Gm_Em}{r} \qquad (13.9)$$

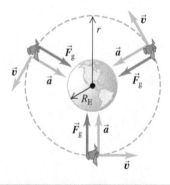

Earth, mass m_E

$R_E = 6.37 \times 10^6$ m

mass m

$w = Gm_Em/r^2$

$r\,(\times 10^6\ \mathrm{m})$

$r - R_E (\times 10^6\ \mathrm{m})$

Orbits: When a satellite moves in a circular orbit, the centripetal acceleration is provided by the gravitational attraction of the earth. Kepler's three laws describe the more general case: an elliptical orbit of a planet around the sun or a satellite around a planet. (See Examples 13.6–13.9.)

$$v = \sqrt{\frac{Gm_E}{r}} \qquad (13.10)$$

(speed in circular orbit)

$$T = \frac{2\pi r}{v} = 2\pi r\sqrt{\frac{r}{Gm_E}} = \frac{2\pi r^{3/2}}{\sqrt{Gm_E}}$$

(period in circular orbit) $\qquad (13.12)$

Black holes: If a nonrotating spherical mass distribution with total mass M has a radius less than its Schwarzschild radius R_S, it is called a black hole. The gravitational interaction prevents anything, including light, from escaping from within a sphere with radius R_S. (See Example 13.11.)

$$R_S = \frac{2GM}{c^2} \qquad (13.30)$$

(Schwarzschild radius)

If all of the body is inside its Schwarzschild radius $R_S = 2GM/c^2$, the body is a black hole.

BRIDGING PROBLEM SPEEDS IN AN ELLIPTICAL ORBIT

A comet orbits the sun (mass m_S) in an elliptical orbit of semi-major axis a and eccentricity e. (a) Find expressions for the speeds of the comet at perihelion and aphelion. (b) Evaluate these expressions for Comet Halley (see Example 13.9), and find the kinetic energy, gravitational potential energy, and total mechanical energy for this comet at perihelion and aphelion. Take the mass of Comet Halley to be 2.2×10^{14} kg.

SOLUTION GUIDE

IDENTIFY and SET UP

1. Sketch the situation; show all relevant dimensions. Label the perihelion and aphelion. (See Figure 13.18.)
2. List the unknown quantities, and identify the target variables.
3. Just as for a satellite orbiting the earth, the mechanical energy is conserved for a comet orbiting the sun. (Why?) What other quantity is conserved as the comet moves in its orbit? (*Hint:* See Section 13.5.)

EXECUTE

4. You'll need at least two equations that involve the two unknown speeds, and you'll need expressions for the sun–comet distances at perihelion and aphelion. (*Hint:* See Fig. 13.18.)
5. Solve the equations for your target variables. Compare your expressions: Which speed is lower? Does this make sense?
6. Use your expressions from step 5 to find the perihelion and aphelion speeds for Comet Halley. (*Hint:* See Appendix F.)
7. Use your results from step 6 to find the kinetic energy K, gravitational potential energy U, and total mechanical energy E for Comet Halley at perihelion and aphelion.

EVALUATE

8. Check whether your results from part (a) make sense for the special case of a circular orbit ($e = 0$).
9. In part (b), how do your calculated values of E at perihelion and aphelion compare? Does this make sense? What does it mean that E is negative?

Problems

For assigned homework and other learning materials, go to MasteringPhysics®. (MP)

•, ••, •••: Difficulty levels. CP: Cumulative problems incorporating material from earlier chapters. CALC: Problems requiring calculus.
DATA: Problems involving real data, scientific evidence, experimental design, and/or statistical reasoning. BIO: Biosciences problems.

DISCUSSION QUESTIONS

Q13.1 A student wrote: "The only reason an apple falls downward to meet the earth instead of the earth rising upward to meet the apple is that the earth is much more massive and so exerts a much greater pull." Please comment.

Q13.2 If all planets had the same average density, how would the acceleration due to gravity at the surface of a planet depend on its radius?

Q13.3 Is a pound of butter on the earth the same amount as a pound of butter on Mars? What about a kilogram of butter? Explain.

Q13.4 Example 13.2 (Section 13.1) shows that the acceleration of each sphere caused by the gravitational force is inversely proportional to the mass of that sphere. So why does the force of gravity give all masses the same acceleration when they are dropped near the surface of the earth?

Q13.5 When will you attract the sun more: today at noon, or tonight at midnight? Explain.

Q13.6 Since the moon is constantly attracted toward the earth by the gravitational interaction, why doesn't it crash into the earth?

Q13.7 A spaceship makes a circular orbit with period T around a star. If it were to orbit, at the same distance, a star with three times the mass of the original star, would the new period (in terms of T) be (a) $3T$, (b) $T\sqrt{3}$, (c) T, (d) $T/\sqrt{3}$, or (e) $T/3$?

Q13.8 A planet makes a circular orbit with period T around a star. If the planet were to orbit at the same distance around this star, but the planet had three times as much mass, what would the new period (in terms of T) be: (a) $3T$, (b) $T\sqrt{3}$, (c) T, (d) $T/\sqrt{3}$, or (e) $T/3$?

Q13.9 The sun pulls on the moon with a force that is more than twice the magnitude of the force with which the earth attracts the moon. Why, then, doesn't the sun take the moon away from the earth?

Q13.10 Which takes more fuel: a voyage from the earth to the moon or from the moon to the earth? Explain.

Q13.11 A planet is moving at constant speed in a circular orbit around a star. In one complete orbit, what is the net amount of work done on the planet by the star's gravitational force: positive, negative, or zero? What if the planet's orbit is an ellipse, so that the speed is not constant? Explain your answers.

Q13.12 Does the escape speed for an object at the earth's surface depend on the direction in which it is launched? Explain. Does your answer depend on whether or not you include the effects of air resistance?

Q13.13 If a projectile is fired straight up from the earth's surface, what would happen if the total mechanical energy (kinetic plus potential) is (a) less than zero, and (b) greater than zero? In each case, ignore air resistance and the gravitational effects of the sun, the moon, and the other planets.

Q13.14 Discuss whether this statement is correct: "In the absence of air resistance, the trajectory of a projectile thrown near the earth's surface is an *ellipse,* not a parabola."

Q13.15 The earth is closer to the sun in November than in May. In which of these months does it move faster in its orbit? Explain why.

Q13.16 A communications firm wants to place a satellite in orbit so that it is always directly above the earth's 45th parallel (latitude 45° north). This means that the plane of the orbit will not pass through the center of the earth. Is such an orbit possible? Why or why not?

Q13.17 At what point in an elliptical orbit is the acceleration maximum? At what point is it minimum? Justify your answers.

Q13.18 What would Kepler's third law be for circular orbits if an amendment to Newton's law of gravitation made the gravitational force inversely proportional to r^3? Would this change affect Kepler's other two laws? Explain.

Q13.19 In the elliptical orbit of Comet Halley shown in Fig. 13.21a, the sun's gravity is responsible for making the comet fall inward from aphelion to perihelion. But what is responsible for making the comet move from perihelion back outward to aphelion?

Q13.20 Many people believe that orbiting astronauts feel weightless because they are "beyond the pull of the earth's gravity." How far from the earth would a spacecraft have to travel to be truly beyond the earth's gravitational influence? If a spacecraft were really unaffected by the earth's gravity, would it remain in orbit? Explain. What is the real reason astronauts in orbit feel weightless?

Q13.21 As part of their training before going into orbit, astronauts ride in an airliner that is flown along the same parabolic trajectory as a freely falling projectile. Explain why this gives the same experience of apparent weightlessness as being in orbit.

EXERCISES

Section 13.1 Newton's Law of Gravitation

13.1 • What is the ratio of the gravitational pull of the sun on the moon to that of the earth on the moon? (Assume the distance of the moon from the sun can be approximated by the distance of the earth from the sun.) Use the data in Appendix F. Is it more accurate to say that the moon orbits the earth, or that the moon orbits the sun?

13.2 •• CP **Cavendish Experiment.** In the Cavendish balance apparatus shown in Fig. 13.4, suppose that $m_1 = 1.10$ kg, $m_2 = 25.0$ kg, and the rod connecting the m_1 pairs is 30.0 cm long. If, in each pair, m_1 and m_2 are 12.0 cm apart center to center, find (a) the net force and (b) the net torque (about the rotation axis) on the rotating part of the apparatus. (c) Does it seem that the torque in part (b) would be enough to easily rotate the rod? Suggest some ways to improve the sensitivity of this experiment.

13.3 • **Rendezvous in Space!** A couple of astronauts agree to rendezvous in space after hours. Their plan is to let gravity bring them together. One of them has a mass of 65 kg and the other a mass of 72 kg, and they start from rest 20.0 m apart. (a) Make a free-body diagram of each astronaut, and use it to find his or her initial acceleration. As a rough approximation, we can model the astronauts as uniform spheres. (b) If the astronauts' acceleration remained constant, how many days would they have to wait before reaching each other? (Careful! They *both* have acceleration toward each other.) (c) Would their acceleration, in fact, remain constant? If not, would it increase or decrease? Why?

13.4 •• Two uniform spheres, each with mass M and radius R, touch each other. What is the magnitude of their gravitational force of attraction?

13.5 • Two uniform spheres, each of mass 0.260 kg, are fixed at points A and B (**Fig. E13.5**). Find the magnitude and direction of the initial acceleration of a uniform sphere with mass 0.010 kg if released from rest at point P and acted on only by forces of gravitational attraction of the spheres at A and B.

Figure **E13.5**

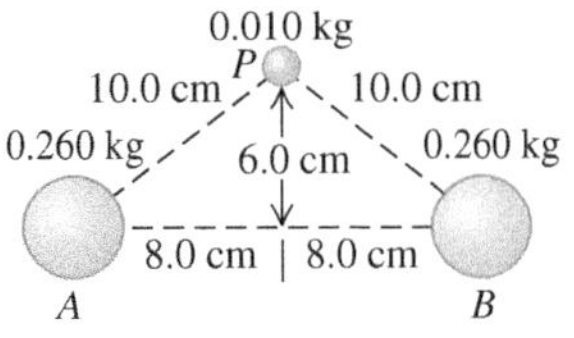

0.010 kg
P
10.0 cm   10.0 cm
0.260 kg   6.0 cm   0.260 kg
8.0 cm | 8.0 cm
A B

13.6 •• Find the magnitude and direction of the net gravitational force on mass A due to masses B and C in **Fig. E13.6**. Each mass is 2.00 kg.

Figure **E13.6**

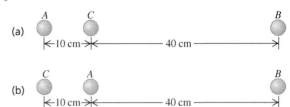

(a) A C B
       |←10 cm→|←————— 40 cm —————→|

(b) C A B
       |←10 cm→|←————— 40 cm —————→|

13.7 • A typical adult human has a mass of about 70 kg. (a) What force does a full moon exert on such a human when it is directly overhead with its center 378,000 km away? (b) Compare this force with the force exerted on the human by the earth.

13.8 •• An 8.00-kg point mass and a 12.0-kg point mass are held in place 50.0 cm apart. A particle of mass m is released from a point between the two masses 20.0 cm from the 8.00-kg mass along the line connecting the two fixed masses. Find the magnitude and direction of the acceleration of the particle.

13.9 •• A particle of mass $3m$ is located 1.00 m from a particle of mass m. (a) Where should you put a third mass M so that the net gravitational force on M due to the two masses is exactly zero? (b) Is the equilibrium of M at this point stable or unstable (i) for points along the line connecting m and $3m$, and (ii) for points along the line passing through M and perpendicular to the line connecting m and $3m$?

13.10 •• The point masses m and $2m$ lie along the x-axis, with m at the origin and $2m$ at $x = L$. A third point mass M is moved along the x-axis. (a) At what point is the net gravitational force on M due to the other two masses equal to zero? (b) Sketch the x-component of the net force on M due to m and $2m$, taking quantities to the right as positive. Include the regions $x < 0$, $0 < x < L$, and $x > L$. Be especially careful to show the behavior of the graph on either side of $x = 0$ and $x = L$.

Section 13.2 Weight

13.11 •• At what distance above the surface of the earth is the acceleration due to the earth's gravity 0.980 m/s^2 if the acceleration due to gravity at the surface has magnitude 9.80 m/s^2?

13.12 • The mass of Venus is 81.5% that of the earth, and its radius is 94.9% that of the earth. (a) Compute the acceleration due to gravity on the surface of Venus from these data. (b) If a rock weighs 75.0 N on earth, what would it weigh at the surface of Venus?

13.13 • Titania, the largest moon of the planet Uranus, has $\frac{1}{8}$ the radius of the earth and $\frac{1}{1700}$ the mass of the earth. (a) What is the acceleration due to gravity at the surface of Titania? (b) What is the average density of Titania? (This is less than the density of rock, which is one piece of evidence that Titania is made primarily of ice.)

13.14 • Rhea, one of Saturn's moons, has a radius of 764 km and an acceleration due to gravity of 0.265 m/s^2 at its surface. Calculate its mass and average density.

13.15 •• Calculate the earth's gravity force on a 75-kg astronaut who is repairing the Hubble Space Telescope 600 km above the earth's surface, and then compare this value with his weight at the earth's surface. In view of your result, explain why it is said that astronauts are weightless when they orbit the earth in a satellite such as a space shuttle. Is it because the gravitational pull of the earth is negligibly small?

Section 13.3 Gravitational Potential Energy

13.16 •• **Volcanoes on Io.** Jupiter's moon Io has active volcanoes (in fact, it is the most volcanically active body in the solar system) that eject material as high as 500 km (or even higher) above the surface. Io has a mass of 8.93×10^{22} kg and a radius of 1821 km. For this calculation, ignore any variation in gravity over the 500-km range of the debris. How high would this material go on earth if it were ejected with the same speed as on Io?

13.17 • Use the results of Example 13.5 (Section 13.3) to calculate the escape speed for a spacecraft (a) from the surface of Mars and (b) from the surface of Jupiter. Use the data in Appendix F. (c) Why is the escape speed for a spacecraft independent of the spacecraft's mass?

13.18 •• Ten days after it was launched toward Mars in December 1998, the *Mars Climate Orbiter* spacecraft (mass 629 kg) was 2.87×10^6 km from the earth and traveling at 1.20×10^4 km/h relative to the earth. At this time, what were (a) the spacecraft's kinetic energy relative to the earth and (b) the potential energy of the earth–spacecraft system?

13.19 •• A planet orbiting a distant star has radius 3.24×10^6 m. The escape speed for an object launched from this planet's surface is 7.65×10^3 m/s. What is the acceleration due to gravity at the surface of the planet?

Section 13.4 The Motion of Satellites

13.20 • An earth satellite moves in a circular orbit with an orbital speed of 6200 m/s. Find (a) the time of one revolution of the satellite; (b) the radial acceleration of the satellite in its orbit.

13.21 • For a satellite to be in a circular orbit 890 km above the surface of the earth, (a) what orbital speed must it be given, and (b) what is the period of the orbit (in hours)?

13.22 •• **Aura Mission.** On July 15, 2004, NASA launched the *Aura* spacecraft to study the earth's climate and atmosphere. This satellite was injected into an orbit 705 km above the earth's surface. Assume a circular orbit. (a) How many hours does it take this satellite to make one orbit? (b) How fast (in km/s) is the *Aura* spacecraft moving?

13.23 •• Two satellites are in circular orbits around a planet that has radius 9.00×10^6 m. One satellite has mass 68.0 kg, orbital radius 7.00×10^7 m, and orbital speed 4800 m/s. The second satellite has mass 84.0 kg and orbital radius 3.00×10^7 m. What is the orbital speed of this second satellite?

13.24 •• **International Space Station.** In its orbit each day, the International Space Station makes 15.65 revolutions around the earth. Assuming a circular orbit, how high is this satellite above the surface of the earth?

13.25 • Deimos, a moon of Mars, is about 12 km in diameter with mass 1.5×10^{15} kg. Suppose you are stranded alone on Deimos and want to play a one-person game of baseball. You would be the pitcher, and you would be the batter! (a) With what speed would you have to throw a baseball so that it would go into a circular orbit just above the surface and return to you so you could hit it? Do you think you could actually throw it at this speed? (b) How long (in hours) after throwing the ball should you be ready to hit it? Would this be an action-packed baseball game?

Section 13.5 Kepler's Laws and the Motion of Planets

13.26 •• **Planet Vulcan.** Suppose that a planet were discovered between the sun and Mercury, with a circular orbit of radius equal to $\frac{2}{3}$ of the average orbit radius of Mercury. What would be the orbital period of such a planet? (Such a planet was once postulated, in part to explain the precession of Mercury's orbit. It was even given the name Vulcan, although we now have no evidence that it actually exists. Mercury's precession has been explained by general relativity.)

13.27 •• The star Rho[1] Cancri is 57 light-years from the earth and has a mass 0.85 times that of our sun. A planet has been detected in a circular orbit around Rho[1] Cancri with an orbital radius equal to 0.11 times the radius of the earth's orbit around the sun. What are (a) the orbital speed and (b) the orbital period of the planet of Rho[1] Cancri?

13.28 •• In March 2006, two small satellites were discovered orbiting Pluto, one at a distance of 48,000 km and the other at 64,000 km. Pluto already was known to have a large satellite Charon, orbiting at 19,600 km with an orbital period of 6.39 days. Assuming that the satellites do not affect each other, find the orbital periods of the two small satellites *without* using the mass of Pluto.

13.29 • The dwarf planet Pluto has an elliptical orbit with a semi-major axis of 5.91×10^{12} m and eccentricity 0.249. (a) Calculate Pluto's orbital period. Express your answer in seconds and in earth years. (b) During Pluto's orbit around the sun, what are its closest and farthest distances from the sun?

13.30 •• **Hot Jupiters.** In 2004 astronomers reported the discovery of a large Jupiter-sized planet orbiting very close to the star HD 179949 (hence the term "hot Jupiter"). The orbit was just $\frac{1}{9}$ the distance of Mercury from our sun, and it takes the planet only 3.09 days to make one orbit (assumed to be circular). (a) What is the mass of the star? Express your answer in kilograms and as a multiple of our sun's mass. (b) How fast (in km/s) is this planet moving?

13.31 •• **Planets Beyond the Solar System.** On October 15, 2001, a planet was discovered orbiting around the star HD 68988. Its orbital distance was measured to be 10.5 million kilometers from the center of the star, and its orbital period was estimated at 6.3 days. What is the mass of HD 68988? Express your answer in kilograms and in terms of our sun's mass. (Consult Appendix F.)

Section 13.6 Spherical Mass Distributions

13.32 • A uniform, spherical, 1000.0-kg shell has a radius of 5.00 m. (a) Find the gravitational force this shell exerts on a 2.00-kg point mass placed at the following distances from the center of the shell: (i) 5.01 m, (ii) 4.99 m, (iii) 2.72 m. (b) Sketch a qualitative graph of the magnitude of the gravitational force this sphere exerts on a point mass m as a function of the distance r of m from the center of the sphere. Include the region from $r = 0$ to $r \rightarrow \infty$.

13.33 •• A uniform, solid, 1000.0-kg sphere has a radius of 5.00 m. (a) Find the gravitational force this sphere exerts on a 2.00-kg point mass placed at the following distances from the center of the sphere: (i) 5.01 m, (ii) 2.50 m. (b) Sketch a qualitative graph of the magnitude of the gravitational force this sphere exerts on a point mass m as a function of the distance r of m from the center of the sphere. Include the region from $r = 0$ to $r \rightarrow \infty$.

13.34 • CALC A thin, uniform rod has length L and mass M. A small uniform sphere of mass m is placed a distance x from one end of the rod, along the axis of the rod (**Fig. E13.34**). (a) Calculate the gravitational potential energy of the rod–sphere system. Take the potential energy to be zero when the rod and

Figure **E13.34**

sphere are infinitely far apart. Show that your answer reduces to the expected result when x is much larger than L. (*Hint:* Use the power series expansion for $\ln(1 + x)$ given in Appendix B.) (b) Use $F_x = -dU/dx$ to find the magnitude and direction of the gravitational force exerted on the sphere by the rod (see Section 7.4). Show that your answer reduces to the expected result when x is much larger than L.

13.35 • CALC Consider the ring-shaped body of **Fig. E13.35**. A particle with mass m is placed a distance x from the center of the ring, along the line through the center of the ring and perpendicular to its plane. (a) Calculate the gravitational potential energy U

Figure E13.35

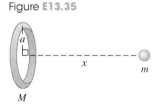

of this system. Take the potential energy to be zero when the two objects are far apart. (b) Show that your answer to part (a) reduces to the expected result when x is much larger than the radius a of the ring. (c) Use $F_x = -dU/dx$ to find the magnitude and direction of the force on the particle (see Section 7.4). (d) Show that your answer to part (c) reduces to the expected result when x is much larger than a. (e) What are the values of U and F_x when $x = 0$? Explain why these results make sense.

Section 13.7 Apparent Weight and the Earth's Rotation

13.36 •• **A Visit to Santa.** You decide to visit Santa Claus at the north pole to put in a good word about your splendid behavior throughout the year. While there, you notice that the elf Sneezy, when hanging from a rope, produces a tension of 395.0 N in the rope. If Sneezy hangs from a similar rope while delivering presents at the earth's equator, what will the tension in it be? (Recall that the earth is rotating about an axis through its north and south poles.) Consult Appendix F and start with a free-body diagram of Sneezy at the equator.

13.37 • The acceleration due to gravity at the north pole of Neptune is approximately 11.2 m/s². Neptune has mass 1.02×10^{26} kg and radius 2.46×10^4 km and rotates once around its axis in about 16 h. (a) What is the gravitational force on a 3.00-kg object at the north pole of Neptune? (b) What is the apparent weight of this same object at Neptune's equator? (Note that Neptune's "surface" is gaseous, not solid, so it is impossible to stand on it.)

Section 13.8 Black Holes

13.38 •• **Mini Black Holes.** Cosmologists have speculated that black holes the size of a proton could have formed during the early days of the Big Bang when the universe began. If we take the diameter of a proton to be 1.0×10^{-15} m, what would be the mass of a mini black hole?

13.39 •• **At the Galaxy's Core.** Astronomers have observed a small, massive object at the center of our Milky Way galaxy (see Section 13.8). A ring of material orbits this massive object; the ring has a diameter of about 15 light-years and an orbital speed of about 200 km/s. (a) Determine the mass of the object at the center of the Milky Way galaxy. Give your answer both in kilograms and in solar masses (one solar mass is the mass of the sun). (b) Observations of stars, as well as theories of the structure of stars, suggest that it is impossible for a single star to have a mass of more than about 50 solar masses. Can this massive object be a single, ordinary star? (c) Many astronomers believe that the massive object at the

center of the Milky Way galaxy is a black hole. If so, what must the Schwarzschild radius of this black hole be? Would a black hole of this size fit inside the earth's orbit around the sun?

13.40 • In 2005 astronomers announced the discovery of a large black hole in the galaxy Markarian 766 having clumps of matter orbiting around once every 27 hours and moving at 30,000 km/s. (a) How far are these clumps from the center of the black hole? (b) What is the mass of this black hole, assuming circular orbits? Express your answer in kilograms and as a multiple of our sun's mass. (c) What is the radius of its event horizon?

PROBLEMS

13.41 ••• Neutron stars, such as the one at the center of the Crab Nebula, have about the same mass as our sun but have a *much* smaller diameter. If you weigh 675 N on the earth, what would you weigh at the surface of a neutron star that has the same mass as our sun and a diameter of 20 km?

13.42 ••• Four identical masses of 8.00 kg each are placed at the corners of a square whose side length is 2.00 m. What is the net gravitational force (magnitude and direction) on one of the masses, due to the other three?

13.43 • Three uniform spheres are fixed at the positions shown in **Fig. P13.43**. (a) What are the magnitude and direction of the force on a 0.0150-kg particle placed at P? (b) If the spheres are in deep outer space and a 0.0150-kg particle is released from rest 300 m from the origin along a line 45° below the $-x$-axis, what will the particle's speed be when it reaches the origin?

Figure P13.43

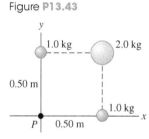

13.44 ••• CP **Exploring Europa.** There is strong evidence that Europa, a satellite of Jupiter, has a liquid ocean beneath its icy surface. Many scientists think we should land a vehicle there to search for life. Before launching it, we would want to test such a lander under the gravity conditions at the surface of Europa. One way to do this is to put the lander at the end of a rotating arm in an orbiting earth satellite. If the arm is 4.25 m long and pivots about one end, at what angular speed (in rpm) should it spin so that the acceleration of the lander is the same as the acceleration due to gravity at the surface of Europa? The mass of Europa is 4.80×10^{22} kg and its diameter is 3120 km.

13.45 •• A uniform sphere with mass 50.0 kg is held with its center at the origin, and a second uniform sphere with mass 80.0 kg is held with its center at the point $x = 0$, $y = 3.00$ m. (a) What are the magnitude and direction of the net gravitational force due to these objects on a third uniform sphere with mass 0.500 kg placed at the point $x = 4.00$ m, $y = 0$? (b) Where, other than infinitely far away, could the third sphere be placed such that the net gravitational force acting on it from the other two spheres is equal to zero?

13.46 •• **Mission to Titan.** On December 25, 2004, the *Huygens* probe separated from the *Cassini* spacecraft orbiting Saturn and began a 22-day journey to Saturn's giant moon Titan, on whose surface it landed. Besides the data in Appendix F, it is useful to know that Titan is 1.22×10^6 km from the center of Saturn and has a mass of 1.35×10^{23} kg and a diameter of 5150 km. At what distance from Titan should the gravitational pull of Titan just balance the gravitational pull of Saturn?

13.47 ••• CP An experiment is performed in deep space with two uniform spheres, one with mass 50.0 kg and the other with mass 100.0 kg. They have equal radii, $r = 0.20$ m. The spheres are released from rest with their centers 40.0 m apart. They accelerate toward each other because of their mutual gravitational attraction. You can ignore all gravitational forces other than that between the two spheres. (a) Explain why linear momentum is conserved. (b) When their centers are 20.0 m apart, find (i) the speed of each sphere and (ii) the magnitude of the relative velocity with which one sphere is approaching the other. (c) How far from the initial position of the center of the 50.0-kg sphere do the surfaces of the two spheres collide?

13.48 ••• At a certain instant, the earth, the moon, and a stationary 1250-kg spacecraft lie at the vertices of an equilateral triangle whose sides are 3.84×10^5 km in length. (a) Find the magnitude and direction of the net gravitational force exerted on the spacecraft by the earth and moon. State the direction as an angle measured from a line connecting the earth and the spacecraft. In a sketch, show the earth, the moon, the spacecraft, and the force vector. (b) What is the minimum amount of work that you would have to do to move the spacecraft to a point far from the earth and moon? Ignore any gravitational effects due to the other planets or the sun.

13.49 • **Geosynchronous Satellites.** Many satellites are moving in a circle in the earth's equatorial plane. They are at such a height above the earth's surface that they always remain above the same point. (a) Find the altitude of these satellites above the earth's surface. (Such an orbit is said to be *geosynchronous*.) (b) Explain, with a sketch, why the radio signals from these satellites cannot directly reach receivers on earth that are north of 81.3° N latitude.

13.50 •• CP **Submarines on Europa.** Some scientists are eager to send a remote-controlled submarine to Jupiter's moon Europa to search for life in its oceans below an icy crust. Europa's mass has been measured to be 4.80×10^{22} kg, its diameter is 3120 km, and it has no appreciable atmosphere. Assume that the layer of ice at the surface is not thick enough to exert substantial force on the water. If the windows of the submarine you are designing each have an area of 625 cm^2 and can stand a maximum inward force of 8750 N per window, what is the greatest depth to which this submarine can safely dive?

13.51 ••• What is the escape speed from a 300-km-diameter asteroid with a density of 2500 kg/m^3?

13.52 ••• A landing craft with mass 12,500 kg is in a circular orbit 5.75×10^5 m above the surface of a planet. The period of the orbit is 5800 s. The astronauts in the lander measure the diameter of the planet to be 9.60×10^6 m. The lander sets down at the north pole of the planet. What is the weight of an 85.6-kg astronaut as he steps out onto the planet's surface?

13.53 •• Planet X rotates in the same manner as the earth, around an axis through its north and south poles, and is perfectly spherical. An astronaut who weighs 943.0 N on the earth weighs 915.0 N at the north pole of Planet X and only 850.0 N at its equator. The distance from the north pole to the equator is 18,850 km, measured along the surface of Planet X. (a) How long is the day on Planet X? (b) If a 45,000-kg satellite is placed in a circular orbit 2000 km above the surface of Planet X, what will be its orbital period?

13.54 ••• (a) Suppose you are at the earth's equator and observe a satellite passing directly overhead and moving from west to east in the sky. Exactly 12.0 hours later, you again observe this satellite to be directly overhead. How far above the earth's surface is the satellite's orbit? (b) You observe another satellite directly overhead and traveling east to west. This satellite is again overhead in 12.0 hours. How far is this satellite's orbit above the surface of the earth?

13.55 •• CP An astronaut, whose mission is to go where no one has gone before, lands on a spherical planet in a distant galaxy. As she stands on the surface of the planet, she releases a small rock from rest and finds that it takes the rock 0.480 s to fall 1.90 m. If the radius of the planet is 8.60×10^7 m, what is the mass of the planet?

13.56 ••• CP Your starship, the *Aimless Wanderer*, lands on the mysterious planet Mongo. As chief scientist-engineer, you make the following measurements: A 2.50-kg stone thrown upward from the ground at 12.0 m/s returns to the ground in 4.80 s; the circumference of Mongo at the equator is 2.00×10^5 km; and there is no appreciable atmosphere on Mongo. The starship commander, Captain Confusion, asks for the following information: (a) What is the mass of Mongo? (b) If the *Aimless Wanderer* goes into a circular orbit 30,000 km above the surface of Mongo, how many hours will it take the ship to complete one orbit?

13.57 •• CP You are exploring a distant planet. When your spaceship is in a circular orbit at a distance of 630 km above the planet's surface, the ship's orbital speed is 4900 m/s. By observing the planet, you determine its radius to be 4.48×10^6 m. You then land on the surface and, at a place where the ground is level, launch a small projectile with initial speed 12.6 m/s at an angle of 30.8° above the horizontal. If resistance due to the planet's atmosphere is negligible, what is the horizontal range of the projectile?

13.58 •• The 0.100-kg sphere in Fig. P13.58 is released from rest at the position shown in the sketch, with its center 0.400 m from the center of the 5.00-kg mass. Assume that the only forces on the 0.100-kg sphere are the gravitational forces exerted by the other two spheres and that the 5.00-kg and 10.0-kg spheres are held in place at their initial positions. What is the speed of the 0.100-kg sphere when it has moved 0.400 m to the right from its initial position?

Figure **P13.58**

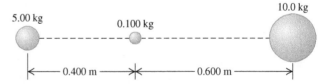

5.00 kg   0.100 kg   10.0 kg

|← 0.400 m →|← 0.600 m →|

13.59 ••• An unmanned spacecraft is in a circular orbit around the moon, observing the lunar surface from an altitude of 50.0 km (see Appendix F). To the dismay of scientists on earth, an electrical fault causes an on-board thruster to fire, decreasing the speed of the spacecraft by 20.0 m/s. If nothing is done to correct its orbit, with what speed (in km/h) will the spacecraft crash into the lunar surface?

13.60 ••• **Mass of a Comet.** On July 4, 2005, the NASA spacecraft *Deep Impact* fired a projectile onto the surface of Comet Tempel 1. This comet is about 9.0 km across. Observations of surface debris released by the impact showed that dust with a speed as low as 1.0 m/s was able to escape the comet. (a) Assuming a spherical shape, what is the mass of this comet? (*Hint:* See Example 13.5 in Section 13.3.) (b) How far from the comet's center will this debris be when it has lost (i) 90.0% of its initial kinetic energy at the surface and (ii) all of its kinetic energy at the surface?

13.61 • **Falling Hammer.** A hammer with mass m is dropped from rest from a height h above the earth's surface. This height is not necessarily small compared with the radius R_E of the earth. Ignoring air resistance, derive an expression for the speed v of the hammer when it reaches the earth's surface. Your expression should involve h, R_E, and m_E (the earth's mass).

13.62 · (a) Calculate how much work is required to launch a spacecraft of mass m from the surface of the earth (mass m_E, radius R_E) and place it in a circular *low earth orbit*—that is, an orbit whose altitude above the earth's surface is much less than R_E. (As an example, the International Space Station is in low earth orbit at an altitude of about 400 km, much less than $R_E = 6370$ km.) Ignore the kinetic energy that the spacecraft has on the ground due to the earth's rotation. (b) Calculate the minimum amount of additional work required to move the spacecraft from low earth orbit to a very great distance from the earth. Ignore the gravitational effects of the sun, the moon, and the other planets. (c) Justify the statement "In terms of energy, low earth orbit is halfway to the edge of the universe."

13.63 · **Binary Star—Equal Masses.** Two identical stars with mass M orbit around their center of mass. Each orbit is circular and has radius R, so that the two stars are always on opposite sides of the circle. (a) Find the gravitational force of one star on the other. (b) Find the orbital speed of each star and the period of the orbit. (c) How much energy would be required to separate the two stars to infinity?

13.64 ·· CP **Binary Star—Different Masses.** Two stars, with masses M_1 and M_2, are in circular orbits around their center of mass. The star with mass M_1 has an orbit of radius R_1; the star with mass M_2 has an orbit of radius R_2. (a) Show that the ratio of the orbital radii of the two stars equals the reciprocal of the ratio of their masses—that is, $R_1/R_2 = M_2/M_1$. (b) Explain why the two stars have the same orbital period, and show that the period T is given by $T = 2\pi(R_1 + R_2)^{3/2}/\sqrt{G(M_1 + M_2)}$. (c) The two stars in a certain binary star system move in circular orbits. The first star, Alpha, has an orbital speed of 36.0 km/s. The second star, Beta, has an orbital speed of 12.0 km/s. The orbital period is 137 d. What are the masses of each of the two stars? (d) One of the best candidates for a black hole is found in the binary system called A0620-0090. The two objects in the binary system are an orange star, V616 Monocerotis, and a compact object believed to be a black hole (see Fig. 13.28). The orbital period of A0620-0090 is 7.75 hours, the mass of V616 Monocerotis is estimated to be 0.67 times the mass of the sun, and the mass of the black hole is estimated to be 3.8 times the mass of the sun. Assuming that the orbits are circular, find the radius of each object's orbit and the orbital speed of each object. Compare these answers to the orbital radius and orbital speed of the earth in its orbit around the sun.

13.65 ··· Comets travel around the sun in elliptical orbits with large eccentricities. If a comet has speed 2.0×10^4 m/s when at a distance of 2.5×10^{11} m from the center of the sun, what is its speed when at a distance of 5.0×10^{10} m?

13.66 · The planet Uranus has a radius of 25,360 km and a surface acceleration due to gravity of 9.0 m/s^2 at its poles. Its moon Miranda (discovered by Kuiper in 1948) is in a circular orbit about Uranus at an altitude of 104,000 km above the planet's surface. Miranda has a mass of 6.6×10^{19} kg and a radius of 236 km. (a) Calculate the mass of Uranus from the given data. (b) Calculate the magnitude of Miranda's acceleration due to its orbital motion about Uranus. (c) Calculate the acceleration due to Miranda's gravity at the surface of Miranda. (d) Do the answers to parts (b) and (c) mean that an object released 1 m above Miranda's surface on the side toward Uranus will fall *up* relative to Miranda? Explain.

13.67 ··· CP Consider a spacecraft in an elliptical orbit around the earth. At the low point, or perigee, of its orbit, it is 400 km above the earth's surface; at the high point, or apogee, it is 4000 km above the earth's surface. (a) What is the period of the spacecraft's orbit? (b) Using conservation of angular momentum, find the ratio of the spacecraft's speed at perigee to its speed at apogee. (c) Using conservation of energy, find the speed at perigee and the speed at apogee. (d) It is necessary to have the spacecraft escape from the earth completely. If the spacecraft's rockets are fired at perigee, by how much would the speed have to be increased to achieve this? What if the rockets were fired at apogee? Which point in the orbit is more efficient to use?

13.68 ·· A rocket with mass 5.00×10^3 kg is in a circular orbit of radius 7.20×10^6 m around the earth. The rocket's engines fire for a period of time to increase that radius to 8.80×10^6 m, with the orbit again circular. (a) What is the change in the rocket's kinetic energy? Does the kinetic energy increase or decrease? (b) What is the change in the rocket's gravitational potential energy? Does the potential energy increase or decrease? (c) How much work is done by the rocket engines in changing the orbital radius?

13.69 ··· A 5000-kg spacecraft is in a circular orbit 2000 km above the surface of Mars. How much work must the spacecraft engines perform to move the spacecraft to a circular orbit that is 4000 km above the surface?

13.70 ·· A satellite with mass 848 kg is in a circular orbit with an orbital speed of 9640 m/s around the earth. What is the new orbital speed after friction from the earth's upper atmosphere has done -7.50×10^9 J of work on the satellite? Does the speed increase or decrease?

13.71 ··· CALC Planets are not uniform inside. Normally, they are densest at the center and have decreasing density outward toward the surface. Model a spherically symmetric planet, with the same radius as the earth, as having a density that decreases linearly with distance from the center. Let the density be 15.0×10^3 kg/m^3 at the center and 2.0×10^3 kg/m^3 at the surface. What is the acceleration due to gravity at the surface of this planet?

13.72 ·· One of the brightest comets of the 20th century was Comet Hyakutake, which passed close to the sun in early 1996. The orbital period of this comet is estimated to be about 30,000 years. Find the semi-major axis of this comet's orbit. Compare it to the average sun–Pluto distance and to the distance to Alpha Centauri, the nearest star to the sun, which is 4.3 light-years distant.

13.73 ··· CALC An object in the shape of a thin ring has radius a and mass M. A uniform sphere with mass m and radius R is placed with its center at a distance x to the right of the center of the ring, along a line through the center of the ring, and perpendicular to its plane (see Fig. E13.35). What is the gravitational force that the sphere exerts on the ring-shaped object? Show that your result reduces to the expected result when x is much larger than a.

13.74 ·· CALC A uniform wire with mass M and length L is bent into a semicircle. Find the magnitude and direction of the gravitational force this wire exerts on a point with mass m placed at the center of curvature of the semicircle.

13.75 · CALC A shaft is drilled from the surface to the center of the earth (see Fig. 13.25). As in Example 13.10 (Section 13.6), make the unrealistic assumption that the density of the earth is uniform. With this approximation, the gravitational force on an object with mass m, that is inside the earth at a distance r from the center, has magnitude $F_g = Gm_E mr/R_E^3$ (as shown in Example 13.10) and points toward the center of the earth. (a) Derive an expression for the gravitational potential energy $U(r)$ of the object–earth system as a function of the object's distance from the center of the earth. Take the potential energy to be zero when the object is at the center of the earth. (b) If an object is released in the shaft at the earth's surface, what speed will it have when it reaches the center of the earth?

13.76 •• DATA For each of the eight planets Mercury to Neptune, the semi-major axis a of their orbit and their orbital period T are as follows:

Planet	Semi-major Axis (10^6 km)	Orbital Period (days)
Mercury	57.9	88.0
Venus	108.2	224.7
Earth	149.6	365.2
Mars	227.9	687.0
Jupiter	778.3	4331
Saturn	1426.7	10,747
Uranus	2870.7	30,589
Neptune	4498.4	59,800

(a) Explain why these values, when plotted as T^2 versus a^3, fall close to a straight line. Which of Kepler's laws is being tested? However, the values of T^2 and a^3 cover such a wide range that this plot is not a very practical way to graph the data. (Try it.) Instead, plot $\log(T)$ (with T in seconds) versus $\log(a)$ (with a in meters). Explain why the data should also fall close to a straight line in such a plot. (b) According to Kepler's laws, what should be the slope of your $\log(T)$ versus $\log(a)$ graph in part (a)? Does your graph have this slope? (c) Using $G = 6.674 \times 10^{-11} \, \mathrm{N \cdot m^2/kg^2}$, calculate the mass of the sun from the y-intercept of your graph. How does your calculated value compare with the value given in Appendix F? (d) The only asteroid visible to the naked eye (and then only under ideal viewing conditions) is Vesta, which has an orbital period of 1325.4 days. What is the length of the semi-major axis of Vesta's orbit? Where does this place Vesta's orbit relative to the orbits of the eight major planets? Some scientists argue that Vesta should be called a minor planet rather than an asteroid.

13.77 •• DATA For a spherical planet with mass M, volume V, and radius R, derive an expression for the acceleration due to gravity at the planet's surface, g, in terms of the average density of the planet, $\rho = M/V$, and the planet's diameter, $D = 2R$. The table gives the values of D and g for the eight major planets:

Planet	D (km)	g (m/s²)
Mercury	4879	3.7
Venus	12,104	8.9
Earth	12,756	9.8
Mars	6792	3.7
Jupiter	142,984	23.1
Saturn	120,536	9.0
Uranus	51,118	8.7
Neptune	49,528	11.0

(a) Treat the planets as spheres. Your equation for g as a function of ρ and D shows that if the average density of the planets is constant, a graph of g versus D will be well represented by a straight line. Graph g as a function of D for the eight major planets. What does the graph tell you about the variation in average density? (b) Calculate the average density for each major planet. List the planets in order of decreasing density, and give the calculated average density of each. (c) The earth is not a uniform sphere and has greater density near its center. It is reasonable to assume this might be true for the other planets. Discuss the effect this nonuniformity has on your analysis. (d) If Saturn had the same average density as the earth, what would be the value of g at Saturn's surface?

13.78 ••• DATA For a planet in our solar system, assume that the axis of orbit is at the sun and is circular. Then the angular momentum about that axis due to the planet's orbital motion is $L = MvR$. (a) Derive an expression for L in terms of the planet's mass M, orbital radius R, and period T of the orbit. (b) Using Appendix F, calculate the magnitude of the orbital angular momentum for each of the eight major planets. (Assume a circular orbit.) Add these values to obtain the total angular momentum of the major planets due to their orbital motion. (All the major planets orbit in the same direction in close to the same plane, so adding the magnitudes to get the total is a reasonable approximation.) (c) The rotational period of the sun is 24.6 days. Using Appendix F, calculate the angular momentum the sun has due to the rotation about its axis. (Assume that the sun is a uniform sphere.) (d) How does the rotational angular momentum of the sun compare with the total orbital angular momentum of the planets? How does the mass of the sun compare with the total mass of the planets? The fact that the sun has most of the mass of the solar system but only a small fraction of its total angular momentum must be accounted for in models of how the solar system formed. (e) The sun has a density that decreases with distance from its center. Does this mean that your calculation in part (c) overestimates or underestimates the rotational angular momentum of the sun? Or doesn't the nonuniform density have any effect?

CHALLENGE PROBLEMS

13.79 ••• **Interplanetary Navigation.** The most efficient way to send a spacecraft from the earth to another planet is to use a *Hohmann transfer orbit* (**Fig. P13.79**). If the orbits of the departure and destination planets are circular, the Hohmann transfer orbit is an elliptical orbit whose perihelion and aphelion are tangent to the orbits of the two planets. The rockets are fired briefly at the departure planet to put the spacecraft into the transfer orbit; the spacecraft then coasts until it reaches the destination planet. The rockets are then fired again to put the spacecraft into the same orbit about the sun as the destination planet. (a) For a flight from earth to Mars, in what direction must the rockets be fired at the earth and at Mars: in the direction of motion or opposite the direction of motion? What about for a flight from Mars to the earth? (b) How long does a one-way trip from the earth to Mars take, between the firings of the rockets? (c) To reach Mars from the earth, the launch must be timed so that Mars will be at the right spot when the spacecraft reaches Mars's orbit around the sun. At launch, what must the angle between a sun–Mars line and a sun–earth line be? Use Appendix F.

Figure **P13.79**

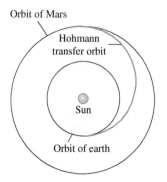

Orbit of Mars

Hohmann transfer orbit

Sun

Orbit of earth

13.80 ••• CP **Tidal Forces near a Black Hole.** An astronaut inside a spacecraft, which protects her from harmful radiation, is orbiting a black hole at a distance of 120 km from its center. The black hole is 5.00 times the mass of the sun and has a Schwarzschild radius of 15.0 km. The astronaut is positioned inside the spaceship such that one of her 0.030-kg ears is 6.0 cm farther from the black hole than the center of mass of the spacecraft and the other ear is 6.0 cm closer. (a) What is the tension between her ears? Would the astronaut find it difficult to keep from being torn apart by the gravitational forces? (Since her whole body orbits with the same angular velocity, one ear is moving too slowly for the radius of its orbit and the other is moving too fast. Hence her head must exert forces on her ears to keep them in their orbits.) (b) Is the center of gravity of her head at the same point as the center of mass? Explain.

13.81 ••• CALC Mass M is distributed uniformly over a disk of radius a. Find the gravitational force (magnitude and direction) between this disk-shaped mass and a particle with mass m located a distance x above the center of the disk (**Fig. P13.81**). Does your result reduce to the correct expression as x becomes very large? (*Hint:* Divide the disk into infinitesimally thin concentric rings, use the expression derived in Exercise 13.35 for the gravitational force due to each ring, and integrate to find the total force.)

Figure **P13.81**

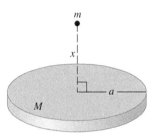

PASSAGE PROBLEMS

EXOPLANETS. As planets with a wide variety of properties are being discovered outside our solar system, astrobiologists are considering whether and how life could evolve on planets that might be very different from earth. One recently discovered extrasolar planet, or exoplanet, orbits a star whose mass is 0.70 times the mass of our sun. This planet has been found to have 2.3 times the earth's diameter and 7.9 times the earth's mass. For planets in this size range, computer models indicate a relationship between the planet's density and composition:

Density Compared with That of the Earth	Composition
2–3 times	Mostly iron
0.9–2 times	Iron core with a rock mantle
0.4–0.9 times	Iron core with a rock mantle and some lighter elements, such as (water) ice
< 0.4 times	Hydrogen and/or helium gas

Based on S. Seager et al., "Mass–Radius Relationships for Solid Exoplanets"; arXiv:0707.2895 [astro-ph].

13.82 Based on these data, what is the most likely composition of this planet? (a) Mostly iron; (b) iron and rock; (c) iron and rock with some lighter elements; (d) hydrogen and helium gases.

13.83 How many times the acceleration due to gravity g near the earth's surface is the acceleration due to gravity near the surface of this exoplanet? (a) About $0.29g$; (b) about $0.65g$; (c) about $1.5g$; (d) about $7.9g$.

13.84 Observations of this planet over time show that it is in a nearly circular orbit around its star and completes one orbit in only 9.5 days. How many times the orbital radius r of the earth around our sun is this exoplanet's orbital radius around its sun? Assume that the earth is also in a nearly circular orbit. (a) $0.026r$; (b) $0.078r$; (c) $0.70r$; (d) $2.3r$.

Answers

Chapter Opening Question ?

(iv) For a satellite a distance r from the center of its planet, the orbital speed is proportional to $\sqrt{1/r}$ and the acceleration due to gravity is proportional to $1/r^2$ (see Section 13.4). Hence a particle that orbits close to Saturn has a faster speed and a greater acceleration than one that orbits farther away.

Test Your Understanding Questions

13.1 (v) From Eq. (13.1), the gravitational force of the sun (mass m_1) on a planet (mass m_2) a distance r away has magnitude $F_g = Gm_1m_2/r^2$. Compared to the earth, Saturn has a value of r^2 that is $10^2 = 100$ times greater and a value of m_2 that is also 100 times greater. Hence the *force* that the sun exerts on Saturn has the same magnitude as the force that the sun exerts on earth. The *acceleration* of a planet equals the net force divided by the planet's mass: Since Saturn has 100 times more mass than the earth, its acceleration is $\frac{1}{100}$ as great as that of the earth.

13.2 (iii), (i), (ii), (iv) From Eq. (13.4), the acceleration due to gravity at the surface of a planet of mass m_P and radius R_P is $g_P = Gm_P/R_P^2$. That is, g_P is directly proportional to the planet's mass and inversely proportional to the square of its radius. It follows that compared to the value of g at the earth's surface, the value of g_P on each planet is (i) $2/2^2 = \frac{1}{2}$ as great; (ii) $4/4^2 = \frac{1}{4}$ as great; (iii) $4/2^2 = 1$ time as great—that is, the same as on earth; and (iv) $2/4^2 = \frac{1}{8}$ as great.

13.3 (iv) For a planet of mass m_P and radius R_P, the surface gravity is $g = Gm_P/R_P^2$ while the escape speed is $v_{esc} = \sqrt{2Gm_P/R_P}$. Comparing these two expressions, you get $v_{esc} = \sqrt{2gR_P}$. So even if a planet has the same value of g as the earth, its escape speed can be different, depending on how its radius R_P compares with the earth's radius. For the planet Saturn, for example, m_P is about 100 times the earth's mass and R_P is about 10 times the earth's radius. The value of g is different than on earth by a factor of $(100)/(10)^2 = 1$ (i.e., it is the same as on earth), while the escape speed is greater by a factor of $\sqrt{100}/10 = 3.2$.

13.4 (ii) Equation (13.10) shows that in a smaller-radius orbit, the spacecraft has a faster speed. The negative work done by air resistance decreases the *total* mechanical energy $E = K + U$; the kinetic energy K increases (becomes more positive), but the gravitational potential energy U decreases (becomes more negative) by a greater amount.

13.5 (iii) Equation (13.17) shows that the orbital period T is proportional to the $\frac{3}{2}$ power of the semi-major axis a. Hence the orbital period of Comet X is longer than that of Comet Y by a factor of $4^{3/2} = 8$.

13.6 No. Our analysis shows that there is *zero* gravitational force inside a hollow spherical shell. Hence visitors to the interior of a hollow planet would find themselves weightless, and they could not stand or walk on the planet's inner surface.

13.7 (iv) The discussion following Eq. (13.27) shows that the difference between the acceleration due to gravity at the equator and at the poles is v^2/R_E. Since this planet has the same radius and hence the same circumference as the earth, the speed v at its equator must be 10 times the speed at the earth's equator. Hence v^2/R_E is $10^2 = 100$ times greater than for the earth, or $100(0.0339 \text{ m/s}^2) = 3.39 \text{ m/s}^2$. The acceleration due to gravity at the poles is 9.80 m/s^2, while at the equator it is dramatically less, $9.80 \text{ m/s}^2 - 3.39 \text{ m/s}^2 = 6.41 \text{ m/s}^2$. You can show that if this planet were to rotate 17.0 times faster than the earth, the acceleration due to gravity at the equator would be *zero* and loose objects would fly off the equator's surface!

13.8 (iii) If the sun collapsed into a black hole (which, according to our understanding of stars, it cannot do), the sun would have a much smaller radius but the same mass. The sun's gravitational force on the earth doesn't depend on the sun's radius, so the earth's orbit would be unaffected.

Bridging Problem

(a) Perihelion: $v_P = \sqrt{\dfrac{Gm_S}{a}\dfrac{(1+e)}{(1-e)}}$

aphelion: $v_A = \sqrt{\dfrac{Gm_S}{a}\dfrac{(1-e)}{(1+e)}}$

(b) $v_P = 54.4$ km/s, $v_A = 0.913$ km/s; $K_P = 3.26 \times 10^{23}$ J,
$U_P = -3.31 \times 10^{23}$ J, $E_P = -5.47 \times 10^{21}$ J;
$K_A = 9.17 \times 10^{19}$ J, $U_A = -5.56 \times 10^{21}$ J,
$E_A = -5.47 \times 10^{21}$ J

14 PERIODIC MOTION

Many kinds of motion repeat themselves over and over: the vibration of a quartz crystal in a watch, the swinging pendulum of a grandfather clock, the sound vibrations produced by a clarinet or an organ pipe, and the back-and-forth motion of the pistons in a car engine. This kind of motion, called **periodic motion** or **oscillation,** is the subject of this chapter. Understanding periodic motion will be essential for our later study of waves, sound, alternating electric currents, and light.

A body that undergoes periodic motion always has a stable equilibrium position. When it is moved away from this position and released, a force or torque comes into play to pull it back toward equilibrium. But by the time it gets there, it has picked up some kinetic energy, so it overshoots, stopping somewhere on the other side, and is again pulled back toward equilibrium. Picture a ball rolling back and forth in a round bowl or a pendulum that swings back and forth past its straight-down position.

In this chapter we will concentrate on two simple examples of systems that can undergo periodic motions: spring-mass systems and pendulums. We will also study why oscillations often tend to die out with time and why some oscillations can build up to greater and greater displacements from equilibrium when periodically varying forces act.

14.1 DESCRIBING OSCILLATION

Figure 14.1 (next page) shows one of the simplest systems that can have periodic motion. A body with mass m rests on a frictionless horizontal guide system, such as a linear air track, so it can move along the x-axis only. The body is attached to a spring of negligible mass that can be either stretched or compressed. The left end of the spring is held fixed, and the right end is attached to the body. The spring force is the only horizontal force acting on the body; the vertical normal and gravitational forces always add to zero.

It's simplest to define our coordinate system so that the origin O is at the equilibrium position, where the spring is neither stretched nor compressed. Then x is

14.1 A system that can have periodic motion.

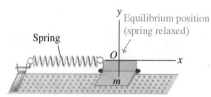

14.2 Model for periodic motion. When the body is displaced from its equilibrium position at $x = 0$, the spring exerts a restoring force back toward the equilibrium position.

(a)

$x > 0$: glider displaced to the right from the equilibrium position.

$F_x < 0$, so $a_x < 0$: stretched spring pulls glider toward equilibrium position.

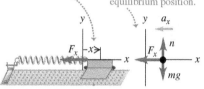

(b)

$x = 0$: The relaxed spring exerts no force on the glider, so the glider has zero acceleration.

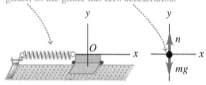

(c)

$x < 0$: glider displaced to the left from the equilibrium position.

$F_x > 0$, so $a_x > 0$: compressed spring pushes glider toward equilibrium position.

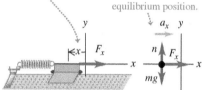

BIO Application Wing Frequencies
The ruby-throated hummingbird (*Archilochus colubris*) normally flaps its wings at about 50 Hz, producing the sound that gives hummingbirds their name. Insects can flap their wings at even faster rates, from 330 Hz for a house fly and 600 Hz for a mosquito to an amazing 1040 Hz for the tiny biting midge.

the x-component of the **displacement** of the body from equilibrium and is also the change in the length of the spring. The spring exerts a force on the body with x-component F_x, and the x-component of acceleration is $a_x = F_x/m$.

Figure 14.2 shows the body for three different displacements of the spring. Whenever the body is displaced from its equilibrium position, the spring force tends to restore it to the equilibrium position. We call a force with this character a **restoring force.** Oscillation can occur only when there is a restoring force tending to return the system to equilibrium.

Let's analyze how oscillation occurs in this system. If we displace the body to the right to $x = A$ and then let go, the net force and the acceleration are to the left (Fig. 14.2a). The speed increases as the body approaches the equilibrium position O. When the body is at O, the net force acting on it is zero (Fig. 14.2b), but because of its motion it *overshoots* the equilibrium position. On the other side of the equilibrium position the body is still moving to the left, but the net force and the acceleration are to the right (Fig. 14.2c); hence the speed decreases until the body comes to a stop. We will show later that with an ideal spring, the stopping point is at $x = -A$. The body then accelerates to the right, overshoots equilibrium again, and stops at the starting point $x = A$, ready to repeat the whole process. The body is oscillating! If there is no friction or other force to remove mechanical energy from the system, this motion repeats forever; the restoring force perpetually draws the body back toward the equilibrium position, only to have the body overshoot time after time.

In different situations the force may depend on the displacement x from equilibrium in different ways. But oscillation *always* occurs if the force is a *restoring* force that tends to return the system to equilibrium.

Amplitude, Period, Frequency, and Angular Frequency

Here are some terms that we'll use in discussing periodic motions of all kinds:

The **amplitude** of the motion, denoted by A, is the maximum magnitude of displacement from equilibrium—that is, the maximum value of $|x|$. It is always positive. If the spring in Fig. 14.2 is an ideal one, the total overall range of the motion is $2A$. The SI unit of A is the meter. A complete vibration, or **cycle,** is one complete round trip—say, from A to $-A$ and back to A, or from O to A, back through O to $-A$, and back to O. Note that motion from one side to the other (say, $-A$ to A) is a half-cycle, not a whole cycle.

The **period,** T, is the time to complete one cycle. It is always positive. The SI unit is the second, but it is sometimes expressed as "seconds per cycle."

The **frequency,** f, is the number of cycles in a unit of time. It is always positive. The SI unit of frequency is the *hertz,* named for the 19th-century German physicist Heinrich Hertz:

$$1 \text{ hertz} = 1 \text{ Hz} = 1 \text{ cycle/s} = 1 \text{ s}^{-1}$$

The **angular frequency,** ω, is 2π times the frequency:

$$\omega = 2\pi f$$

We'll learn shortly why ω is a useful quantity. It represents the rate of change of an angular quantity (not necessarily related to a rotational motion) that is always measured in radians, so its units are rad/s. Since f is in cycle/s, we may regard the number 2π as having units rad/cycle.

By definition, period and frequency are reciprocals of each other:

In periodic motion **frequency and period** are reciprocals of each other. $\cdots\cdots\!\!\rightarrow$ Period

$$f = \frac{1}{T} \qquad T = \frac{1}{f} \tag{14.1}$$

Frequency

Also, from the definition of ω,

Angular frequency related to frequency and period $\cdots\cdots\!\!\rightarrow$ Frequency

$$\omega = 2\pi f = \frac{2\pi}{T} \tag{14.2}$$

Period

EXAMPLE 14.1 PERIOD, FREQUENCY, AND ANGULAR FREQUENCY

An ultrasonic transducer used for medical diagnosis oscillates at $6.7 \text{ MHz} = 6.7 \times 10^6 \text{ Hz}$. How long does each oscillation take, and what is the angular frequency?

SOLUTION

IDENTIFY and SET UP: The target variables are the period T and the angular frequency ω. We can find these from the given frequency f in Eqs. (14.1) and (14.2).

EXECUTE: From Eqs. (14.1) and (14.2),

$$T = \frac{1}{f} = \frac{1}{6.7 \times 10^6 \text{ Hz}} = 1.5 \times 10^{-7} \text{ s} = 0.15 \ \mu\text{s}$$

$$\omega = 2\pi f = 2\pi (6.7 \times 10^6 \text{ Hz})$$
$$= (2\pi \text{ rad/cycle})(6.7 \times 10^6 \text{ cycle/s}) = 4.2 \times 10^7 \text{ rad/s}$$

EVALUATE: This is a very rapid vibration, with large f and ω and small T. A slow vibration has small f and ω and large T.

TEST YOUR UNDERSTANDING OF SECTION 14.1 A body like that shown in Fig. 14.2 oscillates back and forth. For each of the following values of the body's x-velocity v_x and x-acceleration a_x, state whether its displacement x is positive, negative, or zero. (a) $v_x > 0$ and $a_x > 0$; (b) $v_x > 0$ and $a_x < 0$; (c) $v_x < 0$ and $a_x > 0$; (d) $v_x < 0$ and $a_x < 0$; (e) $v_x = 0$ and $a_x < 0$; (f) $v_x > 0$ and $a_x = 0$. ▮

14.2 SIMPLE HARMONIC MOTION

The simplest kind of oscillation occurs when the restoring force F_x is *directly proportional* to the displacement from equilibrium x. This happens if the spring in Figs. 14.1 and 14.2 is an ideal one that obeys *Hooke's law* (see Section 6.3). The constant of proportionality between F_x and x is the force constant k. On either side of the equilibrium position, F_x and x always have opposite signs. In Section 6.3 we represented the force acting *on* a stretched ideal spring as $F_x = kx$. The x-component of force the spring exerts *on the body* is the negative of this, so

Restoring force exerted by an ideal spring $\cdots\cdots\!\!\rightarrow$ x-component of force

$$F_x = -kx \tag{14.3}$$

Displacement
Force constant of spring

This equation gives the correct magnitude and sign of the force, whether x is positive, negative, or zero (**Fig. 14.3**). The force constant k is always positive and has units of N/m (a useful alternative set of units is kg/s^2). We are assuming that there is no friction, so Eq. (14.3) gives the *net* force on the body.

14.3 An idealized spring exerts a restoring force that obeys Hooke's law, $F_x = -kx$. Oscillation with such a restoring force is called simple harmonic motion.

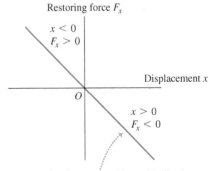

Restoring force F_x

$x < 0$
$F_x > 0$

Displacement x

O

$x > 0$
$F_x < 0$

The restoring force exerted by an idealized spring is directly proportional to the displacement (Hooke's law, $F_x = -kx$): the graph of F_x versus x is a straight line.

When the restoring force is directly proportional to the displacement from equilibrium, as given by Eq. (14.3), the oscillation is called **simple harmonic motion (SHM).** The acceleration $a_x = d^2x/dt^2 = F_x/m$ of a body in SHM is

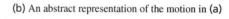

> **Equation for simple harmonic motion** $\quad a_x = \dfrac{d^2x}{dt^2} = -\dfrac{k}{m}x \qquad$ (14.4)
>
> *x*-component of acceleration ⋯ Force constant of restoring force
> Second derivative of displacement — Displacement — Mass of object

The minus sign means that, in SHM, the acceleration and displacement always have opposite signs. This acceleration is *not* constant, so don't even think of using the constant-acceleration equations from Chapter 2. We'll see shortly how to solve this equation to find the displacement x as a function of time. A body that undergoes simple harmonic motion is called a **harmonic oscillator.**

Why is simple harmonic motion important? Not all periodic motions are simple harmonic; in periodic motion in general, the restoring force depends on displacement in a more complicated way than in Eq. (14.3). But in many systems the restoring force is *approximately* proportional to displacement if the displacement is sufficiently small (**Fig. 14.4**). That is, if the amplitude is small enough, the oscillations of such systems are approximately simple harmonic and therefore approximately described by Eq. (14.4). Thus we can use SHM as an approximate model for many different periodic motions, such as the vibration of a tuning fork, the electric current in an alternating-current circuit, and the oscillations of atoms in molecules and solids.

Circular Motion and the Equations of SHM

To explore the properties of simple harmonic motion, we must express the displacement x of the oscillating body as a function of time, $x(t)$. The second derivative of this function, d^2x/dt^2, must be equal to $(-k/m)$ times the function itself, as required by Eq. (14.4). As we mentioned, the formulas for constant acceleration from Section 2.4 are no help because the acceleration changes constantly as the displacement x changes. Instead, we'll find $x(t)$ by noting that SHM is related to *uniform circular motion,* which we studied in Section 3.4.

Figure 14.5a shows a top view of a horizontal disk of radius A with a ball attached to its rim at point Q. The disk rotates with constant angular speed ω (measured in rad/s), so the ball moves in uniform circular motion. A horizontal

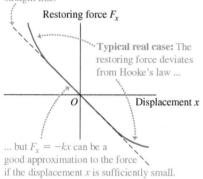

14.4 In most real oscillations Hooke's law applies provided the body doesn't move too far from equilibrium. In such a case small-amplitude oscillations are approximately simple harmonic.

Ideal case: The restoring force obeys Hooke's law ($F_x = -kx$), so the graph of F_x versus x is a straight line.

Restoring force F_x

Typical real case: The restoring force deviates from Hooke's law ...

O — Displacement x

... but $F_x = -kx$ can be a good approximation to the force if the displacement x is sufficiently small.

14.5 (a) Relating uniform circular motion and simple harmonic motion. (b) The ball's shadow moves exactly like a body oscillating on an ideal spring.

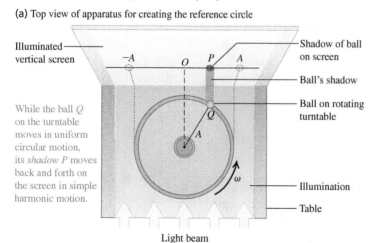

(a) Top view of apparatus for creating the reference circle

Illuminated vertical screen — $-A$ — O — P — A — Shadow of ball on screen

Ball's shadow

Ball on rotating turntable

While the ball Q on the turntable moves in uniform circular motion, its *shadow P* moves back and forth on the screen in simple harmonic motion.

ω — Illumination — Table

Light beam

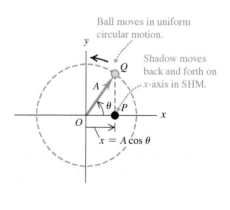

(b) An abstract representation of the motion in **(a)**

Ball moves in uniform circular motion.

Shadow moves back and forth on *x*-axis in SHM.

$x = A\cos\theta$

light beam casts a shadow of the ball on a screen. The shadow at point P oscillates back and forth as the ball moves in a circle. We then arrange a body attached to an ideal spring, like the combination shown in Figs. 14.1 and 14.2, so that the body oscillates parallel to the shadow. We will prove that the motions of the body and of the ball's shadow are *identical* if the amplitude of the body's oscillation is equal to the disk radius A, and if the angular frequency $2\pi f$ of the oscillating body is equal to the angular speed ω of the rotating disk. That is, *simple harmonic motion is the projection of uniform circular motion onto a diameter.*

We can verify this remarkable statement by finding the acceleration of the shadow at P and comparing it to the acceleration of a body undergoing SHM, given by Eq. (14.4). The circle in which the ball moves so that its projection matches the motion of the oscillating body is called the **reference circle;** we will call the point Q the *reference point.* We take the reference circle to lie in the xy-plane, with the origin O at the center of the circle (Fig. 14.5b). At time t the vector OQ from the origin to reference point Q makes an angle θ with the positive x-axis. As point Q moves around the reference circle with constant angular speed ω, vector OQ rotates with the same angular speed. Such a rotating vector is called a **phasor.** (This term was in use long before the invention of the *Star Trek* stun gun with a similar name.) We'll use phasors again when we study alternating-current circuits in Chapter 31 and the interference of light in Chapters 35 and 36.

The x-component of the phasor at time t is just the x-coordinate of the point Q:

$$x = A\cos\theta \qquad (14.5)$$

This is also the x-coordinate of the shadow P, which is the *projection* of Q onto the x-axis. Hence the x-velocity of the shadow P along the x-axis is equal to the x-component of the velocity vector of point Q (**Fig. 14.6a**), and the x-acceleration of P is equal to the x-component of the acceleration vector of Q (Fig. 14.6b). Since point Q is in uniform circular motion, its acceleration vector $\vec{a}_Q$ is always directed toward O. Furthermore, the magnitude of $\vec{a}_Q$ is constant and given by the angular speed squared times the radius of the circle (see Section 9.3):

$$a_Q = \omega^2 A \qquad (14.6)$$

Figure 14.6b shows that the x-component of $\vec{a}_Q$ is $a_x = -a_Q\cos\theta$. Combining this with Eqs. (14.5) and (14.6), we get that the acceleration of point P is

$$a_x = -a_Q\cos\theta = -\omega^2 A\cos\theta \qquad \text{or} \qquad (14.7)$$

$$a_x = -\omega^2 x \qquad (14.8)$$

The acceleration of point P is directly proportional to the displacement x and always has the opposite sign. These are precisely the hallmarks of simple harmonic motion.

Equation (14.8) is *exactly* the same as Eq. (14.4) for the acceleration of a harmonic oscillator, provided that the angular speed ω of the reference point Q is related to the force constant k and mass m of the oscillating body by

$$\omega^2 = \frac{k}{m} \qquad \text{or} \qquad \omega = \sqrt{\frac{k}{m}} \qquad (14.9)$$

We have been using the same symbol ω for the angular *speed* of the reference point Q and the angular *frequency* of the oscillating point P. The reason is that these quantities are equal! If point Q makes one complete revolution in time T, then point P goes through one complete cycle of oscillation in the same time; hence T is the period of the oscillation. During time T the point Q moves through

14.6 The (a) x-velocity and (b) x-acceleration of the ball's shadow P (see Fig. 14.5) are the x-components of the velocity and acceleration vectors, respectively, of the ball Q.

(a) Using the reference circle to determine the x-velocity of point P

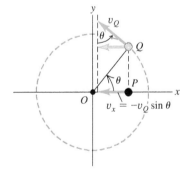

(b) Using the reference circle to determine the x-acceleration of point P

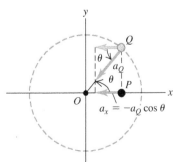

2π radians, so its angular speed is $\omega = 2\pi/T$. But this is the same as Eq. (14.2) for the angular frequency of the point P, which verifies our statement about the two interpretations of ω. This is why we introduced angular frequency in Section 14.1; this quantity makes the connection between oscillation and circular motion. So we reinterpret Eq. (14.9) as an expression for the angular frequency of simple harmonic motion:

$$\underset{\substack{\text{Angular frequency}\\ \text{for simple}\\ \text{harmonic motion}}}{} \omega = \sqrt{\frac{k \;\leftarrow\cdots\text{Force constant of restoring force}}{m \;\leftarrow\cdots\text{Mass of object}}} \qquad (14.10)$$

When you start a body oscillating in SHM, the value of ω is not yours to choose; it is predetermined by the values of k and m. The units of k are N/m or kg/s^2, so k/m is in $(\text{kg/s}^2)/\text{kg} = \text{s}^{-2}$. When we take the square root in Eq. (14.10), we get s^{-1}, or more properly rad/s because this is an *angular* frequency (recall that a radian is not a true unit).

According to Eqs. (14.1) and (14.2), the frequency f and period T are

$$\underset{\substack{\text{Frequency for}\\ \text{simple harmonic}\\ \text{motion}}}{} f = \frac{\overset{\text{Angular frequency}}{\omega}}{2\pi} = \frac{1}{2\pi}\sqrt{\frac{k \;\leftarrow\cdots\substack{\text{Force constant of}\\ \text{restoring force}}}{m \;\leftarrow\cdots\text{Mass of object}}} \qquad (14.11)$$

$$\underset{\substack{\text{Period for}\\ \text{simple harmonic}\\ \text{motion}}}{} T = \frac{1}{\underset{\text{Frequency}}{f}} = \frac{2\pi}{\underset{\text{Angular frequency}}{\omega}} = 2\pi\sqrt{\frac{m \;\leftarrow\cdots\text{Mass of object}}{k \;\leftarrow\cdots\substack{\text{Force constant of}\\ \text{restoring force}}}} \qquad (14.12)$$

We see from Eq. (14.12) that a larger mass m will have less acceleration and take a longer time for a complete cycle (**Fig. 14.7**). A stiffer spring (one with a larger force constant k) exerts a greater force at a given deformation x, causing greater acceleration and a shorter time T per cycle.

CAUTION Don't confuse frequency and angular frequency You can run into trouble if you don't make the distinction between frequency f and angular frequency $\omega = 2\pi f$. Frequency tells you how many cycles of oscillation occur per second, while angular frequency tells you how many radians per second this corresponds to on the reference circle. In solving problems, pay careful attention to whether the goal is to find f or ω. ▌

Period and Amplitude in SHM

Equations (14.11) and (14.12) show that the period and frequency of simple harmonic motion are completely determined by the mass m and the force constant k. *In simple harmonic motion the period and frequency do not depend on the amplitude A.* For given values of m and k, the time of one complete oscillation is the same whether the amplitude is large or small. Equation (14.3) shows why we should expect this. Larger A means that the body reaches larger values of $|x|$ and is subjected to larger restoring forces. This increases the average speed of the body over a complete cycle; this exactly compensates for having to travel a larger distance, so the same total time is involved.

The oscillations of a tuning fork are essentially simple harmonic motion, so it always vibrates with the same frequency, independent of amplitude. This is why a tuning fork can be used as a standard for musical pitch. If it were not for this characteristic of simple harmonic motion, it would be impossible to play most musical instruments in tune. If you encounter an oscillating body with a period that *does* depend on the amplitude, the oscillation is *not* simple harmonic motion.

14.7 The greater the mass m in a tuning fork's tines, the lower the frequency of oscillation $f = (1/2\pi)\sqrt{k/m}$ and the lower the pitch of the sound that the tuning fork produces.

Tines with large mass m:
low frequency $f = 128$ Hz

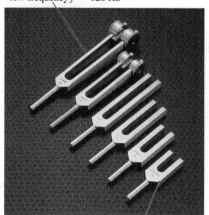

Tines with small mass m:
high frequency $f = 4096$ Hz

EXAMPLE 14.2   ANGULAR FREQUENCY, FREQUENCY, AND PERIOD IN SHM

A spring is mounted horizontally, with its left end fixed. A spring balance attached to the free end and pulled toward the right (**Fig. 14.8a**) indicates that the stretching force is proportional to the displacement, and a force of 6.0 N causes a displacement of 0.030 m. We replace the spring balance with a 0.50-kg glider, pull it 0.020 m to the right along a frictionless air track, and release it from rest (Fig. 14.8b). (a) Find the force constant k of the spring. (b) Find the angular frequency ω, frequency f, and period T of the resulting oscillation.

SOLUTION

IDENTIFY and SET UP: Because the spring force (equal in magnitude to the stretching force) is proportional to the displacement, the motion is simple harmonic. We find k from Hooke's law,

14.8 (a) The force exerted *on* the spring (shown by the vector F) has x-component $F_x = +6.0$ N. The force exerted *by* the spring has x-component $F_x = -6.0$ N. (b) A glider is attached to the same spring and allowed to oscillate.

(a)

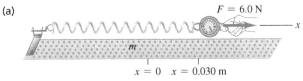

$x = 0$ $x = 0.030$ m

(b)

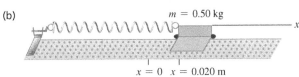

$x = 0$ $x = 0.020$ m

Eq. (14.3), and ω, f, and T from Eqs. (14.10), (14.11), and (14.12), respectively.

EXECUTE: (a) When $x = 0.030$ m, the force the spring exerts on the spring balance is $F_x = -6.0$ N. From Eq. (14.3),

$$k = -\frac{F_x}{x} = -\frac{-6.0 \text{ N}}{0.030 \text{ m}} = 200 \text{ N/m} = 200 \text{ kg/s}^2$$

(b) From Eq. (14.10), with $m = 0.50$ kg,

$$\omega = \sqrt{\frac{k}{m}} = \sqrt{\frac{200 \text{ kg/s}^2}{0.50 \text{ kg}}} = 20 \text{ rad/s}$$

$$f = \frac{\omega}{2\pi} = \frac{20 \text{ rad/s}}{2\pi \text{ rad/cycle}} = 3.2 \text{ cycle/s} = 3.2 \text{ Hz}$$

$$T = \frac{1}{f} = \frac{1}{3.2 \text{ cycle/s}} = 0.31 \text{ s}$$

EVALUATE: The amplitude of the oscillation is 0.020 m, the distance that we pulled the glider before releasing it. In SHM the angular frequency, frequency, and period are all independent of the amplitude. Note that a period is usually stated in "seconds" rather than "seconds per cycle."

Displacement, Velocity, and Acceleration in SHM

PhET: Motion in 2D

We still need to find the displacement x as a function of time for a harmonic oscillator. Equation (14.4) for a body in SHM along the x-axis is identical to Eq. (14.8) for the x-coordinate of the reference point in uniform circular motion with constant angular speed $\omega = \sqrt{k/m}$. Hence Eq. (14.5), $x = A\cos\theta$, describes the x-coordinate for both situations. If at $t = 0$ the phasor OQ makes an angle ϕ (the Greek letter phi) with the positive x-axis, then at any later time t this angle is $\theta = \omega t + \phi$. We substitute this into Eq. (14.5) to obtain

Displacement in simple harmonic motion as a function of time

Amplitude ⋯   Time ⋯ Phase angle

$$x = A\cos(\omega t + \phi) \tag{14.13}$$

Angular frequency $= \sqrt{k/m}$

Figure 14.9 shows a graph of Eq. (14.13) for the particular case $\phi = 0$. We could also have written Eq. (14.13) in terms of a sine function rather than a cosine by using the identity $\cos\alpha = \sin(\alpha + \pi/2)$. *In simple harmonic motion the displacement is a periodic, sinusoidal function of time.* There are many other periodic functions, but none so simple as a sine or cosine function.

The value of the cosine function is always between -1 and 1, so in Eq. (14.13), x is always between $-A$ and A. This confirms that A is the amplitude of the motion.

14.9 Graph of x versus t [see Eq. (14.13)] for simple harmonic motion. The case shown has $\phi = 0$.

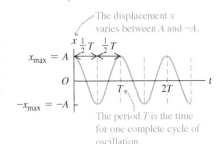

14.10 Variations of simple harmonic motion. All cases shown have $\phi = 0$ [see Eq. (14.13)].

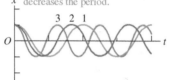

(a) Increasing m; same A and k

Mass m increases from curve 1 to 2 to 3. Increasing m alone increases the period.

(b) Increasing k; same A and m

Force constant k increases from curve 1 to 2 to 3. Increasing k alone decreases the period.

(c) Increasing A; same k and m

Amplitude A increases from curve 1 to 2 to 3. Changing A alone has no effect on the period.

14.11 Variations of simple harmonic motion: same m, k, and A but different phase angles ϕ.

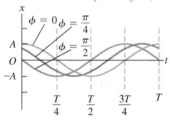

These three curves show SHM with the same period T and amplitude A but with different phase angles ϕ.

14.12 Graphs of (a) x versus t, (b) v_x versus t, and (c) a_x versus t for a body in SHM. For the motion depicted in these graphs, $\phi = \pi/3$.

(a) Displacement x as a function of time t

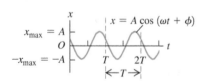

(b) Velocity v_x as a function of time t

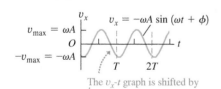

The v_x-t graph is shifted by $\frac{1}{4}$ cycle from the x-t graph.

(c) Acceleration a_x as a function of time t

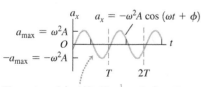

The a_x-t graph is shifted by $\frac{1}{4}$ cycle from the v_x-t graph and by $\frac{1}{2}$ cycle from the x-t graph.

The cosine function in Eq. (14.13) repeats itself whenever time t increases by one period T, or when $\omega t + \phi$ increases by 2π radians. Thus, if we start at time $t = 0$, the time T to complete one cycle is

$$\omega T = \sqrt{\frac{k}{m}}\,T = 2\pi \qquad \text{or} \qquad T = 2\pi\sqrt{\frac{m}{k}}$$

which is just Eq. (14.12). Changing either m or k changes the period T (**Figs. 14.10a** and 14.10b), but T does not depend on the amplitude A (Fig. 14.10c).

The constant ϕ in Eq. (14.13) is called the **phase angle.** It tells us at what point in the cycle the motion was at $t = 0$ (equivalent to where around the circle the point Q was at $t = 0$). We denote the displacement at $t = 0$ by x_0. Putting $t = 0$ and $x = x_0$ in Eq. (14.13), we get

$$x_0 = A\cos\phi \tag{14.14}$$

If $\phi = 0$, then $x_0 = A\cos 0 = A$, and the body starts at its maximum positive displacement. If $\phi = \pi$, then $x_0 = A\cos\pi = -A$, and the particle starts at its maximum *negative* displacement. If $\phi = \pi/2$, then $x_0 = A\cos(\pi/2) = 0$, and the particle is initially at the origin. **Figure 14.11** shows the displacement x versus time for three different phase angles.

We find the velocity v_x and acceleration a_x as functions of time for a harmonic oscillator by taking derivatives of Eq. (14.13) with respect to time:

$$v_x = \frac{dx}{dt} = -\omega A\sin(\omega t + \phi) \qquad \text{(velocity in SHM)} \tag{14.15}$$

$$a_x = \frac{dv_x}{dt} = \frac{d^2x}{dt^2} = -\omega^2 A\cos(\omega t + \phi) \qquad \text{(acceleration in SHM)} \tag{14.16}$$

The velocity v_x oscillates between $v_{max} = +\omega A$ and $-v_{max} = -\omega A$, and the acceleration a_x oscillates between $a_{max} = +\omega^2 A$ and $-a_{max} = -\omega^2 A$ (**Fig. 14.12**). Comparing Eq. (14.16) with Eq. (14.13) and recalling that $\omega^2 = k/m$ from Eq. (14.9), we see that

$$a_x = -\omega^2 x = -\frac{k}{m}x$$

which is just Eq. (14.4) for simple harmonic motion. This confirms that Eq. (14.13) for x as a function of time is correct.

We actually derived Eq. (14.16) earlier in a geometrical way by taking the x-component of the acceleration vector of the reference point Q. This was done in Fig. 14.6b and Eq. (14.7) (recall that $\theta = \omega t + \phi$). In the same way, we could have derived Eq. (14.15) by taking the x-component of the velocity vector of Q, as shown in Fig. 14.6b. We'll leave the details for you to work out.

Note that the sinusoidal graph of displacement versus time (Fig. 14.12a) is shifted by one-quarter period from the graph of velocity versus time (Fig. 14.12b) and by one-half period from the graph of acceleration versus time (Fig. 14.12c).

Figure 14.13 shows why this is so. When the body is passing through the equilibrium position so that $x = 0$, the velocity equals either v_{max} or $-v_{max}$ (depending on which way the body is moving) and the acceleration is zero. When the body is at either its most positive displacement, $x = +A$, or its most negative displacement, $x = -A$, the velocity is zero and the body is instantaneously at rest. At these points, the restoring force $F_x = -kx$ and the acceleration of the body have their maximum magnitudes. At $x = +A$ the acceleration is negative and equal to $-a_{max}$. At $x = -A$ the acceleration is positive: $a_x = +a_{max}$.

Here's how we can determine the amplitude A and phase angle ϕ for an oscillating body if we are given its initial displacement x_0 and initial velocity v_{0x}. The initial velocity v_{0x} is the velocity at time $t = 0$; putting $v_x = v_{0x}$ and $t = 0$ in Eq. (14.15), we find

$$v_{0x} = -\omega A \sin\phi \qquad (14.17)$$

To find ϕ, we divide Eq. (14.17) by Eq. (14.14). This eliminates A and gives an equation that we can solve for ϕ:

$$\frac{v_{0x}}{x_0} = \frac{-\omega A \sin\phi}{A \cos\phi} = -\omega \tan\phi$$

$$\phi = \arctan\left(-\frac{v_{0x}}{\omega x_0}\right) \qquad \text{(phase angle in SHM)} \qquad (14.18)$$

It is also easy to find the amplitude A if we are given x_0 and v_{0x}. We'll sketch the derivation, and you can fill in the details. Square Eq. (14.14); then divide Eq. (14.17) by ω, square it, and add to the square of Eq. (14.14). The right side will be $A^2(\sin^2\phi + \cos^2\phi)$, which is equal to A^2. The final result is

$$A = \sqrt{x_0^2 + \frac{v_{0x}^2}{\omega^2}} \qquad \text{(amplitude in SHM)} \qquad (14.19)$$

Note that when the body has both an initial displacement x_0 and a nonzero initial velocity v_{0x}, the amplitude A is *not* equal to the initial displacement. That's reasonable; if you start the body at a positive x_0 but give it a positive velocity v_{0x}, it will go *farther* than x_0 before it turns and comes back, and so $A > x_0$.

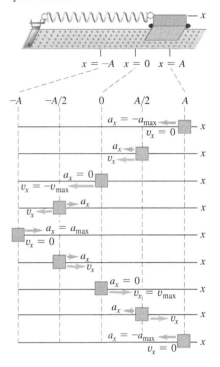

14.13 How x-velocity v_x and x-acceleration a_x vary during one cycle of SHM.

PROBLEM-SOLVING STRATEGY 14.1 | SIMPLE HARMONIC MOTION I: DESCRIBING MOTION

IDENTIFY *the relevant concepts:* An oscillating system undergoes simple harmonic motion (SHM) *only* if the restoring force is directly proportional to the displacement.

SET UP *the problem* using the following steps:
1. Identify the known and unknown quantities, and determine which are the target variables.
2. Distinguish between two kinds of quantities. *Properties of the system* include the mass m, the force constant k, and quantities derived from m and k, such as the period T, frequency f, and angular frequency ω. These are independent of *properties of the motion*, which describe how the system behaves when it is set into motion in a particular way; they include the amplitude A, maximum velocity v_{max}, and phase angle ϕ, and values of x, v_x, and a_x at particular times.
3. If necessary, define an x-axis as in Fig. 14.13, with the equilibrium position at $x = 0$.

EXECUTE *the solution* as follows:
1. Use the equations given in Sections 14.1 and 14.2 to solve for the target variables.
2. To find the values of x, v_x, and a_x at particular times, use Eqs. (14.13), (14.15), and (14.16), respectively. If both the initial displacement x_0 and initial velocity v_{0x} are given, determine ϕ and A from Eqs. (14.18) and (14.19). If the body has an initial positive displacement x_0 but zero initial velocity ($v_{0x} = 0$), then the amplitude is $A = x_0$ and the phase angle is $\phi = 0$. If it has an initial positive velocity v_{0x} but no initial displacement ($x_0 = 0$), the amplitude is $A = v_{0x}/\omega$ and the phase angle is $\phi = -\pi/2$. Express all phase angles in *radians*.

EVALUATE *your answer:* Make sure that your results are consistent. For example, suppose you used x_0 and v_{0x} to find general expressions for x and v_x at time t. If you substitute $t = 0$ into these expressions, you should get back the given values of x_0 and v_{0x}.

EXAMPLE 14.3 DESCRIBING SHM

We give the glider of Example 14.2 an initial displacement $x_0 = +0.015$ m and an initial velocity $v_{0x} = +0.40$ m/s. (a) Find the period, amplitude, and phase angle of the resulting motion. (b) Write equations for the displacement, velocity, and acceleration as functions of time.

SOLUTION

IDENTIFY and SET UP: As in Example 14.2, the oscillations are SHM. We use equations from this section and the given values $k = 200$ N/m, $m = 0.50$ kg, x_0, and v_{0x} to calculate the target variables A and ϕ and to obtain expressions for x, v_x, and a_x.

EXECUTE: (a) In SHM the period and angular frequency are *properties of the system* that depend on only k and m, not on the amplitude, and so are the same as in Example 14.2 ($T = 0.31$ s and $\omega = 20$ rad/s). From Eq. (14.19), the amplitude is

$$A = \sqrt{x_0^2 + \frac{v_{0x}^2}{\omega^2}} = \sqrt{(0.015\text{ m})^2 + \frac{(0.40\text{ m/s})^2}{(20\text{ rad/s})^2}} = 0.025\text{ m}$$

We use Eq. (14.18) to find the phase angle:

$$\phi = \arctan\left(-\frac{v_{0x}}{\omega x_0}\right)$$

$$= \arctan\left(-\frac{0.40\text{ m/s}}{(20\text{ rad/s})(0.015\text{ m})}\right) = -53° = -0.93\text{ rad}$$

(b) The displacement, velocity, and acceleration at any time are given by Eqs. (14.13), (14.15), and (14.16), respectively. We substitute the values of A, ω, and ϕ into these equations:

$$x = (0.025\text{ m})\cos[(20\text{ rad/s})t - 0.93\text{ rad}]$$

$$v_x = -(0.50\text{ m/s})\sin[(20\text{ rad/s})t - 0.93\text{ rad}]$$

$$a_x = -(10\text{ m/s}^2)\cos[(20\text{ rad/s})t - 0.93\text{ rad}]$$

EVALUATE: You can check the expressions for x and v_x by confirming that if you substitute $t = 0$, they yield $x = x_0 = 0.015$ m and $v_x = v_{0x} = 0.40$ m/s.

DATA *SPEAKS*

Oscillations and SHM

When students were given a problem about oscillations and SHM, more than 26% gave an incorrect response. Common errors:

- Forgetting that the period T is the time for one complete cycle of motion, *not* the time to travel between $x = -A$ and $x = +A$.

- Not using Eq. (14.18) to determine the phase angle ϕ.

PhET: Masses & Springs

TEST YOUR UNDERSTANDING OF SECTION 14.2 A glider is attached to a spring as shown in Fig. 14.13. If the glider is moved to $x = 0.10$ m and released from rest at time $t = 0$, it will oscillate with amplitude $A = 0.10$ m and phase angle $\phi = 0$. (a) Suppose instead that at $t = 0$ the glider is at $x = 0.10$ m and is moving to the right in Fig. 14.13. In this situation is the amplitude greater than, less than, or equal to 0.10 m? Is the phase angle greater than, less than, or equal to zero? (b) Suppose instead that at $t = 0$ the glider is at $x = 0.10$ m and is moving to the left in Fig. 14.13. In this situation is the amplitude greater than, less than, or equal to 0.10 m? Is the phase angle greater than, less than, or equal to zero? ∎

14.3 ENERGY IN SIMPLE HARMONIC MOTION

We can learn even more about simple harmonic motion by using energy considerations. The only horizontal force on the body in SHM in Figs. 14.2 and 14.13 is the conservative force exerted by an ideal spring. The vertical forces do no work, so the total mechanical energy of the system is *conserved*. We also assume that the mass of the spring itself is negligible.

The kinetic energy of the body is $K = \frac{1}{2}mv^2$ and the potential energy of the spring is $U = \frac{1}{2}kx^2$, just as in Section 7.2. There are no nonconservative forces that do work, so the total mechanical energy $E = K + U$ is conserved:

$$E = \tfrac{1}{2}mv_x^2 + \tfrac{1}{2}kx^2 = \text{constant} \qquad (14.20)$$

(Since the motion is one-dimensional, $v^2 = v_x^2$.)

The total mechanical energy E is also directly related to the amplitude A of the motion. When the body reaches the point $x = A$, its maximum displacement from equilibrium, it momentarily stops as it turns back toward the equilibrium position. That is, when $x = A$ (or $-A$), $v_x = 0$. At this point the energy is entirely potential, and $E = \frac{1}{2}kA^2$. Because E is constant, it is equal to $\frac{1}{2}kA^2$ at any other point. Combining this expression with Eq. (14.20), we get

Total mechanical energy in simple harmonic motion

$$E = \tfrac{1}{2}mv_x^2 + \tfrac{1}{2}kx^2 = \tfrac{1}{2}kA^2 = \text{constant} \qquad (14.21)$$

Mass — Force constant of restoring force
Velocity   Displacement   Amplitude

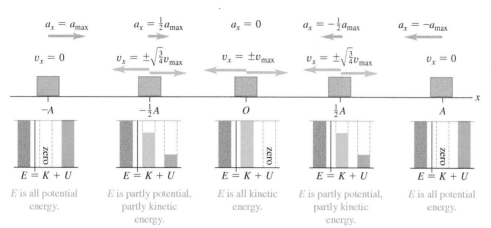

14.14 Graphs of E, K, and U versus displacement in SHM. The velocity of the body is *not* constant, so these images of the body at equally spaced positions are *not* equally spaced in time.

We can verify this equation by substituting x and v_x from Eqs. (14.13) and (14.15) and using $\omega^2 = k/m$ from Eq. (14.9):

$$E = \tfrac{1}{2}mv_x^2 + \tfrac{1}{2}kx^2 = \tfrac{1}{2}m[-\omega A \sin(\omega t + \phi)]^2 + \tfrac{1}{2}k[A\cos(\omega t + \phi)]^2$$

$$= \tfrac{1}{2}kA^2 \sin^2(\omega t + \phi) + \tfrac{1}{2}kA^2 \cos^2(\omega t + \phi) = \tfrac{1}{2}kA^2$$

(Recall that $\sin^2\alpha + \cos^2\alpha = 1$.) Hence our expressions for displacement and velocity in SHM are consistent with energy conservation, as they must be.

We can use Eq. (14.21) to solve for the velocity v_x of the body at a given displacement x:

$$v_x = \pm\sqrt{\frac{k}{m}}\,\sqrt{A^2 - x^2} \qquad (14.22)$$

The $\pm$ sign means that at a given value of x the body can be moving in either direction. For example, when $x = \pm A/2$,

$$v_x = \pm\sqrt{\frac{k}{m}}\,\sqrt{A^2 - \left(\pm\frac{A}{2}\right)^2} = \pm\sqrt{\frac{3}{4}}\,\sqrt{\frac{k}{m}}\,A$$

Equation (14.22) also shows that the *maximum* speed v_{max} occurs at $x = 0$. Using Eq. (14.10), $\omega = \sqrt{k/m}$, we find that

$$v_{max} = \sqrt{\frac{k}{m}}\,A = \omega A \qquad (14.23)$$

This agrees with Eq. (14.15): v_x oscillates between $-\omega A$ and $+\omega A$.

Interpreting *E*, *K*, and *U* in SHM

Figure 14.14 shows the energy quantities E, K, and U at $x = 0$, $x = \pm A/2$, and $x = \pm A$. **Figure 14.15** is a graphical display of Eq. (14.21); energy (kinetic, potential, and total) is plotted vertically and the coordinate x is plotted horizontally. The parabolic curve in Fig. 14.15a represents the potential energy $U = \tfrac{1}{2}kx^2$. The horizontal line represents the total mechanical energy E, which is constant and does not vary with x. At any value of x between $-A$ and A, the vertical distance from the x-axis to the parabola is U; since $E = K + U$, the remaining vertical distance up to the horizontal line is K. Figure 14.15b shows both K and U as functions of x. The horizontal line for E intersects the potential-energy curve at $x = -A$ and $x = A$, so at these points the energy is entirely potential, the kinetic energy is zero, and the body comes momentarily to rest before reversing

14.15 Kinetic energy K, potential energy U, and total mechanical energy E as functions of displacement for SHM. At each value of x the sum of the values of K and U equals the constant value of E. Can you show that the energy is half kinetic and half potential at $x = \pm\sqrt{\tfrac{1}{2}}A$?

(a) The potential energy U and total mechanical energy E for a body in SHM as a function of displacement x

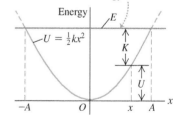

(b) The same graph as in **(a)**, showing kinetic energy K as well

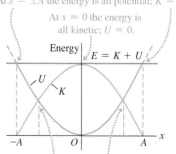

direction. As the body oscillates between $-A$ and A, the energy is continuously transformed from potential to kinetic and back again.

Figure 14.15a shows the connection between the amplitude A and the corresponding total mechanical energy $E = \frac{1}{2}kA^2$. If we tried to make x greater than A (or less than $-A$), U would be greater than E, and K would have to be negative. But K can never be negative, so x can't be greater than A or less than $-A$.

PROBLEM-SOLVING STRATEGY 14.2 | SIMPLE HARMONIC MOTION II: ENERGY

The SHM energy equation, Eq. (14.21), is a useful relationship among velocity, displacement, and total mechanical energy. If a problem requires you to relate displacement, velocity, and acceleration without reference to time, consider using Eq. (14.4) (from Newton's second law) or Eq. (14.21) (from energy conservation).

Because Eq. (14.21) involves x^2 and v_x^2, you must infer the *signs* of x and v_x from the situation. For instance, if the body is moving from the equilibrium position toward the point of greatest positive displacement, then x is positive and v_x is positive.

EXAMPLE 14.4 VELOCITY, ACCELERATION, AND ENERGY IN SHM

(a) Find the maximum and minimum velocities attained by the oscillating glider of Example 14.2. (b) Find the maximum and minimum accelerations. (c) Find the velocity v_x and acceleration a_x when the glider is halfway from its initial position to the equilibrium position $x = 0$. (d) Find the total energy, potential energy, and kinetic energy at this position.

SOLUTION

IDENTIFY and SET UP: The problem concerns properties of the motion at specified *positions*, not at specified *times*, so we can use the energy relationships of this section. Figure 14.13 shows our choice of x-axis. The maximum displacement from equilibrium is $A = 0.020$ m. We use Eqs. (14.22) and (14.4) to find v_x and a_x for a given x. We then use Eq. (14.21) for given x and v_x to find the total, potential, and kinetic energies E, U, and K.

EXECUTE: (a) From Eq. (14.22), the velocity v_x at any displacement x is

$$v_x = \pm \sqrt{\frac{k}{m}} \sqrt{A^2 - x^2}$$

The glider's maximum *speed* occurs when it is moving through $x = 0$:

$$v_{max} = \sqrt{\frac{k}{m}}\, A = \sqrt{\frac{200 \text{ N/m}}{0.50 \text{ kg}}}(0.020 \text{ m}) = 0.40 \text{ m/s}$$

Its maximum and minimum (most negative) *velocities* are $+0.40$ m/s and -0.40 m/s, which occur when it is moving through $x = 0$ to the right and left, respectively.

(b) From Eq. (14.4), $a_x = -(k/m)x$. The glider's maximum (most positive) acceleration occurs at the most negative value of x, $x = -A$:

$$a_{max} = -\frac{k}{m}(-A) = -\frac{200 \text{ N/m}}{0.50 \text{ kg}}(-0.020 \text{ m}) = 8.0 \text{ m/s}^2$$

The minimum (most negative) acceleration is $a_{min} = -8.0$ m/s^2, which occurs at $x = +A = +0.020$ m.

(c) The point halfway from $x = x_0 = A$ to $x = 0$ is $x = A/2 = 0.010$ m. From Eq. (14.22), at this point

$$v_x = -\sqrt{\frac{200 \text{ N/m}}{0.50 \text{ kg}}} \sqrt{(0.020 \text{ m})^2 - (0.010 \text{ m})^2}$$

$$= -0.35 \text{ m/s}$$

We choose the negative square root because the glider is moving from $x = A$ toward $x = 0$. From Eq. (14.4),

$$a_x = -\frac{200 \text{ N/m}}{0.50 \text{ kg}}(0.010 \text{ m}) = -4.0 \text{ m/s}^2$$

Figure 14.14 shows the conditions at $x = 0$, $\pm A/2$, and $\pm A$.

(d) The energies are

$$E = \tfrac{1}{2}kA^2 = \tfrac{1}{2}(200 \text{ N/m})(0.020 \text{ m})^2 = 0.040 \text{ J}$$

$$U = \tfrac{1}{2}kx^2 = \tfrac{1}{2}(200 \text{ N/m})(0.010 \text{ m})^2 = 0.010 \text{ J}$$

$$K = \tfrac{1}{2}mv_x^2 = \tfrac{1}{2}(0.50 \text{ kg})(-0.35 \text{ m/s})^2 = 0.030 \text{ J}$$

EVALUATE: At $x = A/2$, the total energy is one-fourth potential energy and three-fourths kinetic energy. You can confirm this by inspecting Fig. 14.15b.

EXAMPLE 14.5 **ENERGY AND MOMENTUM IN SHM**

A block of mass M attached to a horizontal spring with force constant k is moving in SHM with amplitude A_1. As the block passes through its equilibrium position, a lump of putty of mass m is dropped from a small height and sticks to it. (a) Find the new amplitude and period of the motion. (b) Repeat part (a) if the putty is dropped onto the block when it is at one end of its path.

SOLUTION

IDENTIFY and SET UP: The problem involves the motion at a given position, not a given time, so we can use energy methods. **Figure 14.16** shows our sketches. Before the putty falls, the mechanical energy of the block–spring system is constant. In part (a), the putty–block collision is completely inelastic: The horizontal component of momentum is conserved, kinetic energy decreases, and the amount of mass that's oscillating increases. After the collision, the mechanical energy remains constant at its new value. In part (b) the oscillating mass also increases, but the block isn't moving when the putty is added; there is effectively no collision at all, and no mechanical energy is lost. We find the amplitude A_2 after each collision from the final energy of the system by using Eq. (14.21) and conservation of momentum. The period T_2 after the collision is the same in both parts (a) and (b) because the final mass is the same; we find it by using Eq. (14.12).

EXECUTE: (a) Before the collision the total mechanical energy of the block and spring is $E_1 = \frac{1}{2}kA_1^2$. The block is at $x = 0$, so $U = 0$ and the energy is purely kinetic (Fig. 14.16a). If we let v_1 be the speed of the block at this point, then $E_1 = \frac{1}{2}kA_1^2 = \frac{1}{2}Mv_1^2$ and

$$v_1 = \sqrt{\frac{k}{M}}A_1$$

During the collision the x-component of momentum of the block–putty system is conserved. (Why?) Just before the collision this component is the sum of Mv_1 (for the block) and zero (for the putty). Just after the collision the block and putty move together with speed v_2, so their combined x-component of momentum is $(M + m)v_2$. From conservation of momentum,

$$Mv_1 + 0 = (M + m)v_2 \quad \text{so} \quad v_2 = \frac{M}{M + m}v_1$$

The collision lasts a very short time, so the block and putty are still at the equilibrium position just after the collision. The energy is still purely kinetic but is *less* than before the collision:

$$E_2 = \frac{1}{2}(M + m)v_2^2 = \frac{1}{2}\frac{M^2}{M + m}v_1^2$$

$$= \frac{M}{M + m}\left(\frac{1}{2}Mv_1^2\right) = \left(\frac{M}{M + m}\right)E_1$$

14.16 Our sketches for this problem.

(a)

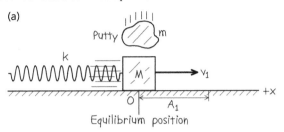

Equilibrium position

(b)

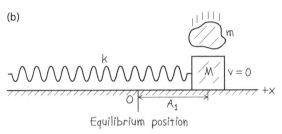

Equilibrium position

Since $E_2 = \frac{1}{2}kA_2^2$, where A_2 is the amplitude after the collision,

$$\frac{1}{2}kA_2^2 = \left(\frac{M}{M + m}\right)\frac{1}{2}kA_1^2$$

$$A_2 = A_1\sqrt{\frac{M}{M + m}}$$

From Eq. (14.12), the period of oscillation after the collision is

$$T_2 = 2\pi\sqrt{\frac{M + m}{k}}$$

(b) When the putty falls, the block is instantaneously at rest (Fig. 14.16b). The x-component of momentum is zero both before and after the collision. The block and putty have zero kinetic energy just before and just after the collision. The energy is all potential energy stored in the spring, so adding the putty has *no effect* on the mechanical energy. That is, $E_2 = E_1 = \frac{1}{2}kA_1^2$, and the amplitude is unchanged: $A_2 = A_1$. The period is again $T_2 = 2\pi\sqrt{(M + m)/k}$.

EVALUATE: Energy is lost in part (a) because the putty slides against the moving block during the collision, and energy is dissipated by kinetic friction. No energy is lost in part (b) because there is no sliding during the collision.

TEST YOUR UNDERSTANDING OF SECTION 14.3 (a) To double the total energy for a mass-spring system oscillating in SHM, by what factor must the amplitude increase? (i) 4; (ii) 2; (iii) $\sqrt{2} = 1.414$; (iv) $\sqrt[4]{2} = 1.189$. (b) By what factor will the frequency change due to this amplitude increase? (i) 4; (ii) 2; (iii) $\sqrt{2} = 1.414$; (iv) $\sqrt[4]{2} = 1.189$; (v) it does not change. ∎

14.17 A body attached to a hanging spring.

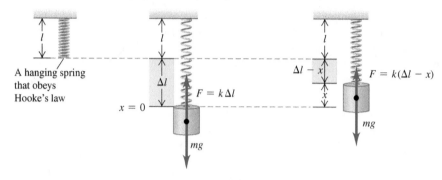

(a)

(b) A body is suspended from the spring. It is in equilibrium when the upward force exerted by the stretched spring equals the body's weight.

(c) If the body is displaced from equilibrium, the net force on the body is proportional to its displacement. The oscillations are SHM.

A hanging spring that obeys Hooke's law

$F = k \Delta l$

$x = 0$

mg

$\Delta l - x$

$F = k(\Delta l - x)$

mg

14.4 APPLICATIONS OF SIMPLE HARMONIC MOTION

So far, we've looked at a grand total of *one* situation in which simple harmonic motion (SHM) occurs: a body attached to an ideal horizontal spring. But SHM can occur in any system in which there is a restoring force that is directly proportional to the displacement from equilibrium, as given by Eq. (14.3), $F_x = -kx$. The restoring force originates in different ways in different situations, so we must find the force constant k for each case by examining the net force on the system. Once this is done, it's straightforward to find the angular frequency ω, frequency f, and period T; we just substitute the value of k into Eqs. (14.10), (14.11), and (14.12), respectively. Let's use these ideas to examine several examples of simple harmonic motion.

Vertical SHM

Suppose we hang a spring with force constant k (**Fig. 14.17a**) and suspend from it a body with mass m. Oscillations will now be vertical; will they still be SHM? In Fig. 14.17b the body hangs at rest, in equilibrium. In this position the spring is stretched an amount Δl just great enough that the spring's upward vertical force $k \Delta l$ on the body balances its weight mg:

$$k \Delta l = mg$$

Take $x = 0$ to be this equilibrium position and take the positive x-direction to be upward. When the body is a distance x *above* its equilibrium position (Fig. 14.17c), the extension of the spring is $\Delta l - x$. The upward force it exerts on the body is then $k(\Delta l - x)$, and the net x-component of force on the body is

$$F_{net} = k(\Delta l - x) + (-mg) = -kx$$

that is, a net downward force of magnitude kx. Similarly, when the body is *below* the equilibrium position, there is a net upward force with magnitude kx. In either case there is a restoring force with magnitude kx. If the body is set in vertical motion, it oscillates in SHM with the same angular frequency as though it were horizontal, $\omega = \sqrt{k/m}$. So vertical SHM doesn't differ in any essential way from horizontal SHM. The only real change is that the equilibrium position $x = 0$ no longer corresponds to the point at which the spring is unstretched. The same ideas hold if a body with weight mg is placed atop a compressible spring (**Fig. 14.18**) and compresses it a distance Δl.

14.18 If the weight mg compresses the spring a distance Δl, the force constant is $k = mg/\Delta l$ and the angular frequency for vertical SHM is $\omega = \sqrt{k/m}$—the same as if the body were suspended from the spring (see Fig. 14.17).

A body is placed atop the spring. It is in equilibrium when the upward force exerted by the compressed spring equals the body's weight.

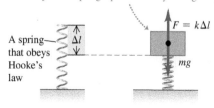

A spring that obeys Hooke's law

Δl

$F = k \Delta l$

mg

EXAMPLE 14.6 **VERTICAL SHM IN AN OLD CAR**

The shock absorbers in an old car with mass 1000 kg are completely worn out. When a 980-N person climbs slowly into the car at its center of gravity, the car sinks 2.8 cm. The car (with the person aboard) hits a bump, and the car starts oscillating up and down in SHM. Model the car and person as a single body on a single spring, and find the period and frequency of the oscillation.

SOLUTION

IDENTIFY and SET UP: The situation is like that shown in Fig. 14.18. The compression of the spring when the person's weight is added tells us the force constant, which we can use to find the period and frequency (the target variables).

EXECUTE: When the force increases by 980 N, the spring compresses an additional 0.028 m, and the x-coordinate of the car

changes by −0.028 m. Hence the effective force constant (including the effect of the entire suspension) is

$$k = -\frac{F_x}{x} = -\frac{980 \text{ N}}{-0.028 \text{ m}} = 3.5 \times 10^4 \text{ kg/s}^2$$

The person's mass is $w/g = (980 \text{ N})/(9.8 \text{ m/s}^2) = 100$ kg. The *total* oscillating mass is $m = 1000$ kg $+ 100$ kg $= 1100$ kg. The period T is

$$T = 2\pi\sqrt{\frac{m}{k}} = 2\pi\sqrt{\frac{1100 \text{ kg}}{3.5 \times 10^4 \text{ kg/s}^2}} = 1.11 \text{ s}$$

The frequency is $f = 1/T = 1/(1.11 \text{ s}) = 0.90$ Hz.

EVALUATE: A persistent oscillation with a period of about 1 second makes for a very unpleasant ride. The purpose of shock absorbers is to make such oscillations die out (see Section 14.7).

Angular SHM

A mechanical watch keeps time based on the oscillations of a balance wheel (**Fig. 14.19**). The wheel has a moment of inertia I about its axis. A coil spring exerts a restoring torque τ_z that is proportional to the angular displacement θ from the equilibrium position. We write $\tau_z = -\kappa\theta$, where κ (the Greek letter kappa) is a constant called the *torsion constant*. Using the rotational analog of Newton's second law for a rigid body, $\sum\tau_z = I\alpha_z = I\, d^2\theta/dt^2$, Eq. (10.7), we find

$$-\kappa\theta = I\alpha \qquad \text{or} \qquad \frac{d^2\theta}{dt^2} = -\frac{\kappa}{I}\theta$$

This equation is exactly the same as Eq. (14.4) for simple harmonic motion, with x replaced by θ and k/m replaced by κ/I. So we are dealing with a form of *angular* simple harmonic motion. The angular frequency ω and frequency f are given by Eqs. (14.10) and (14.11), respectively, with the same replacement:

14.19 The balance wheel of a mechanical watch. The spring exerts a restoring torque that is proportional to the angular displacement θ, so the motion is angular SHM.

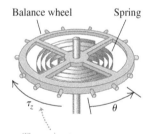

The spring torque τ_z opposes the angular displacement θ.

Angular simple harmonic motion
$$\underset{\text{Torsion constant divided by moment of inertia}}{\omega = \sqrt{\frac{\kappa}{I}} \quad \text{and} \quad f = \frac{1}{2\pi}\sqrt{\frac{\kappa}{I}}} \tag{14.24}$$

The angular displacement θ as a function of time is given by

$$\theta = \Theta\cos(\omega t + \phi)$$

where Θ (the capital Greek letter theta) plays the role of an angular amplitude.

It's a good thing that the motion of a balance wheel *is* simple harmonic. If it weren't, the frequency might depend on the amplitude, and the watch would run too fast or too slow as the spring ran down.

Vibrations of Molecules

The following discussion of the vibrations of molecules uses the binomial theorem. If you aren't familiar with this theorem, you should read about it in the appropriate section of a math textbook.

14.20 (a) Two atoms with centers separated by r. (b) Potential energy U and (c) force F_r in the van der Waals interaction.

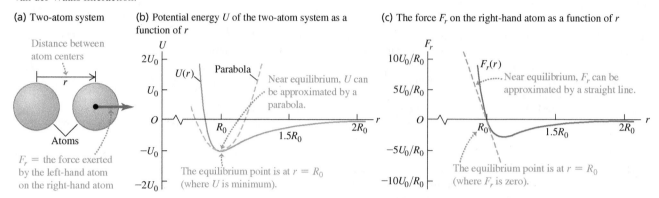

(a) Two-atom system

Distance between atom centers

r

Atoms

F_r = the force exerted by the left-hand atom on the right-hand atom

(b) Potential energy U of the two-atom system as a function of r

U

$2U_0$

$U(r)$ Parabola

U_0

Near equilibrium, U can be approximated by a parabola.

O R_0 $1.5R_0$ $2R_0$ r

$-U_0$ The equilibrium point is at $r = R_0$ (where U is minimum).

$-2U_0$

(c) The force F_r on the right-hand atom as a function of r

F_r

$10U_0/R_0$

$F_r(r)$ Near equilibrium, F_r can be approximated by a straight line.

$5U_0/R_0$

O R_0 $1.5R_0$ $2R_0$ r

$-5U_0/R_0$

The equilibrium point is at $r = R_0$ (where F_r is zero).

$-10U_0/R_0$

When two atoms are separated by a few atomic diameters, they can exert attractive forces on each other. But if the atoms are so close that their electron shells overlap, the atoms repel each other. Between these limits, there can be an equilibrium separation distance at which two atoms form a *molecule*. If these atoms are displaced slightly from equilibrium, they will oscillate.

Let's consider one type of interaction between atoms called the *van der Waals interaction*. Our immediate task here is to study oscillations, so we won't go into the details of how this interaction arises. Let the center of one atom be at the origin and let the center of the other atom be a distance r away (**Fig. 14.20a**); the equilibrium distance between centers is $r = R_0$. Experiment shows that the van der Waals interaction can be described by the potential-energy function

$$U = U_0\left[\left(\frac{R_0}{r}\right)^{12} - 2\left(\frac{R_0}{r}\right)^6\right] \quad (14.25)$$

where U_0 is a positive constant with units of joules. When the two atoms are very far apart, $U = 0$; when they are separated by the equilibrium distance $r = R_0$, $U = -U_0$. From Section 7.4, the force on the second atom is the negative derivative of Eq. (14.25):

$$F_r = -\frac{dU}{dr} = U_0\left[\frac{12R_0^{12}}{r^{13}} - 2\frac{6R_0^6}{r^7}\right] = 12\frac{U_0}{R_0}\left[\left(\frac{R_0}{r}\right)^{13} - \left(\frac{R_0}{r}\right)^7\right] \quad (14.26)$$

Figures 14.20b and 14.20c plot the potential energy and force, respectively. The force is positive for $r < R_0$ and negative for $r > R_0$, so it is a *restoring* force.

Let's examine the restoring force F_r in Eq. (14.26). We let x represent the displacement from equilibrium:

$$x = r - R_0 \quad \text{so} \quad r = R_0 + x$$

In terms of x, the force F_r in Eq. (14.26) becomes

$$F_r = 12\frac{U_0}{R_0}\left[\left(\frac{R_0}{R_0 + x}\right)^{13} - \left(\frac{R_0}{R_0 + x}\right)^7\right]$$

$$= 12\frac{U_0}{R_0}\left[\frac{1}{(1 + x/R_0)^{13}} - \frac{1}{(1 + x/R_0)^7}\right] \quad (14.27)$$

This looks nothing like Hooke's law, $F_x = -kx$, so we might be tempted to conclude that molecular oscillations cannot be SHM. But let us restrict ourselves to *small-amplitude* oscillations so that the absolute value of the displacement x is small in comparison to R_0 and the absolute value of the ratio x/R_0 is much less than 1. We can then simplify Eq. (14.27) by using the *binomial theorem:*

$$(1 + u)^n = 1 + nu + \frac{n(n-1)}{2!}u^2 + \frac{n(n-1)(n-2)}{3!}u^3 + \cdots \quad (14.28)$$

If $|u|$ is much less than 1, each successive term in Eq. (14.28) is much smaller than the one it follows, and we can safely approximate $(1 + u)^n$ by just the first two terms. In Eq. (14.27), u is replaced by x/R_0 and n equals -13 or -7, so

$$\frac{1}{(1 + x/R_0)^{13}} = (1 + x/R_0)^{-13} \approx 1 + (-13)\frac{x}{R_0}$$

$$\frac{1}{(1 + x/R_0)^{7}} = (1 + x/R_0)^{-7} \approx 1 + (-7)\frac{x}{R_0}$$

$$F_r \approx 12\frac{U_0}{R_0}\left[\left(1 + (-13)\frac{x}{R_0}\right) - \left(1 + (-7)\frac{x}{R_0}\right)\right] = -\left(\frac{72U_0}{R_0^2}\right)x \quad (14.29)$$

This is just Hooke's law, with force constant $k = 72U_0/R_0^2$. (Note that k has the correct units, J/m^2 or N/m.) So oscillations of molecules bound by the van der Waals interaction can be simple harmonic motion, provided that the amplitude is small in comparison to R_0 so that the approximation $|x/R_0| \ll 1$ used in the derivation of Eq. (14.29) is valid.

You can also use the binomial theorem to show that the potential energy U in Eq. (14.25) can be written as $U \approx \frac{1}{2}kx^2 + C$, where $C = -U_0$ and k is again equal to $72U_0/R_0^2$. Adding a constant to the potential-energy function has no effect on the physics, so the system of two atoms is fundamentally no different from a mass attached to a horizontal spring for which $U = \frac{1}{2}kx^2$.

EXAMPLE 14.7   MOLECULAR VIBRATION

Two argon atoms form the molecule Ar_2 as a result of a van der Waals interaction with $U_0 = 1.68 \times 10^{-21}$ J and $R_0 = 3.82 \times 10^{-10}$ m. Find the frequency of small oscillations of one Ar atom about its equilibrium position.

SOLUTION

IDENTIFY and SET UP: This is the situation shown in Fig. 14.20. Because the oscillations are small, we can use Eq. (14.29) to find the force constant k and Eq. (14.11) to find the frequency f of SHM.

EXECUTE: From Eq. (14.29),

$$k = \frac{72U_0}{R_0^2} = \frac{72(1.68 \times 10^{-21} \text{ J})}{(3.82 \times 10^{-10} \text{ m})^2} = 0.829 \text{ J/m}^2 = 0.829 \text{ N/m}$$

(This force constant is comparable to that of a loose toy spring like a Slinky™.) From Appendix D, the average atomic mass of argon is $(39.948 \text{ u})(1.66 \times 10^{-27} \text{ kg/1 u}) = 6.63 \times 10^{-26}$ kg.

From Eq. (14.11), if one atom is fixed and the other oscillates,

$$f = \frac{1}{2\pi}\sqrt{\frac{k}{m}} = \frac{1}{2\pi}\sqrt{\frac{0.829 \text{ N/m}}{6.63 \times 10^{-26} \text{ kg}}} = 5.63 \times 10^{11} \text{ Hz}$$

EVALUATE: Our answer for f isn't quite right. If no net external force acts on the molecule, its center of mass (halfway between the atoms) doesn't accelerate, so *both* atoms must oscillate with the same amplitude in opposite directions. It turns out that we can account for this by replacing m with $m/2$ in our expression for f. This makes f larger by a factor of $\sqrt{2}$, so the correct frequency is $f = \sqrt{2}(5.63 \times 10^{11} \text{ Hz}) = 7.96 \times 10^{11}$ Hz. What's more, on the atomic scale we must use *quantum mechanics* rather than Newtonian mechanics to describe motion; happily, quantum mechanics also yields $f = 7.96 \times 10^{11}$ Hz.

TEST YOUR UNDERSTANDING OF SECTION 14.4 A block attached to a hanging ideal spring oscillates up and down with a period of 10 s on earth. If you take the block and spring to Mars, where the acceleration due to gravity is only about 40% as large as on earth, what will be the new period of oscillation? (i) 10 s; (ii) more than 10 s; (iii) less than 10 s. ∎

14.21 The dynamics of a simple pendulum.

(a) A real pendulum

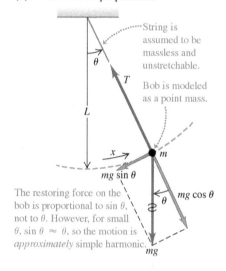

(b) An idealized simple pendulum

String is assumed to be massless and unstretchable.

Bob is modeled as a point mass.

The restoring force on the bob is proportional to $\sin\theta$, not to θ. However, for small θ, $\sin\theta \approx \theta$, so the motion is *approximately* simple harmonic.

14.22 For small angular displacements θ, the restoring force $F_\theta = -mg\sin\theta$ on a simple pendulum is approximately equal to $-mg\theta$; that is, it is approximately proportional to the displacement θ. Hence for small angles the oscillations are simple harmonic.

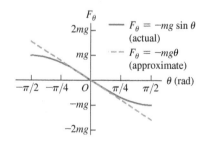

14.5 THE SIMPLE PENDULUM

A **simple pendulum** is an idealized model consisting of a point mass suspended by a massless, unstretchable string. When the point mass is pulled to one side of its straight-down equilibrium position and released, it oscillates about the equilibrium position. Familiar situations such as a wrecking ball on a crane's cable or a person on a swing (**Fig. 14.21a**) can be modeled as simple pendulums.

The path of the point mass (sometimes called a *pendulum bob*) is not a straight line but the arc of a circle with radius L equal to the length of the string (Fig. 14.21b). We use as our coordinate the distance x measured along the arc. If the motion is simple harmonic, the restoring force must be directly proportional to x or (because $x = L\theta$) to θ. Is it?

Figure 14.21b shows the radial and tangential components of the forces on the mass. The restoring force F_θ is the tangential component of the net force:

$$F_\theta = -mg\sin\theta \tag{14.30}$$

Gravity provides the restoring force F_θ; the tension T merely acts to make the point mass move in an arc. Since F_θ is proportional to $\sin\theta$, not to θ, the motion is *not* simple harmonic. However, if angle θ is *small*, $\sin\theta$ is very nearly equal to θ in radians (**Fig. 14.22**). (When $\theta = 0.1$ rad, about $6°$, $\sin\theta = 0.998$. That's only 0.2% different.) With this approximation, Eq. (14.30) becomes

$$F_\theta = -mg\theta = -mg\frac{x}{L} = -\frac{mg}{L}x \tag{14.31}$$

The restoring force is then proportional to the coordinate for small displacements, and the force constant is $k = mg/L$. From Eq. (14.10) the angular frequency ω of a simple pendulum with small amplitude is

Angular frequency of simple pendulum, small amplitude
$$\omega = \sqrt{\frac{k}{m}} = \sqrt{\frac{mg/L}{m}} = \sqrt{\frac{g}{L}} \tag{14.32}$$
Acceleration due to gravity · · · · Pendulum length
Pendulum mass (cancels)

The corresponding frequency and period relationships are

Frequency of simple pendulum, small amplitude
Angular frequency
$$f = \frac{\omega}{2\pi} = \frac{1}{2\pi}\sqrt{\frac{g}{L}} \tag{14.33}$$
Acceleration due to gravity · · · · Pendulum length

Period of simple pendulum, small amplitude
$$T = \frac{2\pi}{\omega} = \frac{1}{f} = 2\pi\sqrt{\frac{L}{g}} \tag{14.34}$$
Pendulum length
Angular frequency   Frequency
Acceleration due to gravity

These expressions don't involve the *mass* of the particle. That's because the gravitational restoring force is proportional to m, so the mass appears on *both* sides of $\sum\vec{F} = m\vec{a}$ and cancels out. (The same physics explains why bodies of different masses fall with the same acceleration in a vacuum.) For small oscillations, the period of a pendulum for a given value of g is determined entirely by its length.

Equations (14.32) through (14.34) tell us that a long pendulum (large L) has a longer period than a shorter one. Increasing g increases the restoring force, causing the frequency to increase and the period to decrease.

The motion of a pendulum is only *approximately* simple harmonic. When the maximum angular displacement Θ (amplitude) is not small, the departures from simple harmonic motion can be substantial. In general, the period T is given by

$$T = 2\pi\sqrt{\frac{L}{g}}\left(1 + \frac{1^2}{2^2}\sin^2\frac{\Theta}{2} + \frac{1^2\cdot 3^2}{2^2\cdot 4^2}\sin^4\frac{\Theta}{2} + \cdots\right) \tag{14.35}$$

We can compute T to any desired degree of precision by taking enough terms in the series. You can confirm that when $\Theta = 15°$, the true period is longer than that given by the approximate Eq. (14.34) by less than 0.5%.

A pendulum is a useful timekeeper because the period is *very nearly* independent of amplitude, provided that the amplitude is small. Thus, as a pendulum clock runs down and the amplitude of the swings decreases a little, the clock still keeps very nearly correct time.

EXAMPLE 14.8   A SIMPLE PENDULUM

Find the period and frequency of a simple pendulum 1.000 m long at a location where $g = 9.800 \text{ m/s}^2$.

SOLUTION

IDENTIFY and SET UP: This is a simple pendulum, so we can use Eq. (14.34) to determine the pendulum's period T from its length and Eq. (14.1) to find the frequency f from T.

EXECUTE: From Eqs. (14.34) and (14.1),

$$T = 2\pi \sqrt{\frac{L}{g}} = 2\pi \sqrt{\frac{1.000 \text{ m}}{9.800 \text{ m/s}^2}} = 2.007 \text{ s}$$

and

$$f = \frac{1}{T} = \frac{1}{2.007 \text{ s}} = 0.4983 \text{ Hz}$$

EVALUATE: The period is almost exactly 2 s. When the metric system was established, the second was *defined* as half the period of a 1-m simple pendulum. This was a poor standard, however, because the value of g varies from place to place. We discussed more modern time standards in Section 1.3.

TEST YOUR UNDERSTANDING OF SECTION 14.5   When a body oscillating on a horizontal spring passes through its equilibrium position, its acceleration is zero (see Fig. 14.2b). When the bob of an oscillating simple pendulum passes from left to right through its equilibrium position, is its acceleration (i) zero; (ii) to the left; (iii) to the right; (iv) upward; or (v) downward?

14.6 THE PHYSICAL PENDULUM

A **physical pendulum** is any *real* pendulum that uses an extended body, as contrasted to the idealized *simple* pendulum with all of its mass concentrated at a point. **Figure 14.23** shows a body of irregular shape pivoted so that it can turn without friction about an axis through point O. In equilibrium the center of gravity (cg) is directly below the pivot; in the position shown, the body is displaced from equilibrium by an angle θ, which we use as a coordinate for the system. The distance from O to the center of gravity is d, the moment of inertia of the body about the axis of rotation through O is I, and the total mass is m. When the body is displaced as shown, the weight mg causes a restoring torque

$$\tau_z = -(mg)(d\sin\theta) \tag{14.36}$$

The negative sign shows that the restoring torque is clockwise when the displacement is counterclockwise, and vice versa.

When the body is released, it oscillates about its equilibrium position. The motion is not simple harmonic because the torque τ_z is proportional to $\sin\theta$ rather than to θ itself. However, if θ is small, we can approximate $\sin\theta$ by θ in radians, just as we did in analyzing the simple pendulum. Then the motion is *approximately* simple harmonic. With this approximation,

$$\tau_z = -(mgd)\theta$$

From Section 10.2, the equation of motion is $\sum\tau_z = I\alpha_z$, so

$$-(mgd)\theta = I\alpha_z = I\frac{d^2\theta}{dt^2}$$

$$\frac{d^2\theta}{dt^2} = -\frac{mgd}{I}\theta \tag{14.37}$$

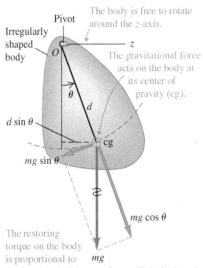

14.23 Dynamics of a physical pendulum.

The body is free to rotate around the z-axis.

The gravitational force acts on the body at its center of gravity (cg).

The restoring torque on the body is proportional to $\sin\theta$, not to θ. However, for small θ, $\sin\theta \approx \theta$, so the motion is *approximately* simple harmonic.

Comparing this with Eq. (14.4), we see that the role of (k/m) for the spring-mass system is played here by the quantity (mgd/I). Thus the angular frequency is

Angular frequency of physical pendulum, small amplitude

Mass ⋯ Acceleration due to gravity
$$\omega = \sqrt{\frac{mgd}{I}}$$ ⋯ Distance from rotation axis to center of gravity
Moment of inertia (14.38)

The frequency f is $1/2\pi$ times this, and the period T is $1/f$:

Period of physical pendulum, small amplitude

$$T = 2\pi\sqrt{\frac{I}{mgd}}$$ ⋯ Moment of inertia
⋯ Distance from rotation axis to center of gravity (14.39)
Mass ⋯ Acceleration due to gravity

Equation (14.39) is the basis of a common method for experimentally determining the moment of inertia of a body with a complicated shape. First locate the center of gravity by balancing the body. Then suspend the body so that it is free to oscillate about an axis, and measure the period T of small-amplitude oscillations. Finally, use Eq. (14.39) to calculate the moment of inertia I of the body about this axis from T, the body's mass m, and the distance d from the axis to the center of gravity (see Exercise 14.55). Biomechanics researchers use this method to find the moments of inertia of an animal's limbs. This information is important for analyzing how an animal walks, as we'll see in the second of the two following examples.

EXAMPLE 14.9 PHYSICAL PENDULUM VERSUS SIMPLE PENDULUM

If the body in Fig. 14.23 is a uniform rod with length L, pivoted at one end, what is the period of its motion as a pendulum?

SOLUTION

IDENTIFY and SET UP: Our target variable is the oscillation period T of a rod that acts as a physical pendulum. We find the rod's moment of inertia in Table 9.2, and then determine T from Eq. (14.39).

EXECUTE: The moment of inertia of a uniform rod about an axis through one end is $I = \frac{1}{3}ML^2$. The distance from the pivot to the rod's center of gravity is $d = L/2$. Then from Eq. (14.39),

$$T = 2\pi\sqrt{\frac{I}{mgd}} = 2\pi\sqrt{\frac{\frac{1}{3}ML^2}{MgL/2}} = 2\pi\sqrt{\frac{2L}{3g}}$$

EVALUATE: If the rod is a meter stick ($L = 1.00$ m) and $g = 9.80$ m/s², then

$$T = 2\pi\sqrt{\frac{2(1.00\text{ m})}{3(9.80\text{ m/s}^2)}} = 1.64\text{ s}$$

The period is smaller by a factor of $\sqrt{\frac{2}{3}} = 0.816$ than that of a simple pendulum of the same length (see Example 14.8). The rod's moment of inertia around one end, $I = \frac{1}{3}ML^2$, is one-third that of the simple pendulum, and the rod's cg is half as far from the pivot as that of the simple pendulum. You can show that, taken together in Eq. (14.39), these two differences account for the factor $\sqrt{\frac{2}{3}}$ by which the periods differ.

EXAMPLE 14.10 *TYRANNOSAURUS REX* AND THE PHYSICAL PENDULUM

All walking animals, including humans, have a natural walking pace—a number of steps per minute that is more comfortable than a faster or slower pace. Suppose that this pace corresponds to the oscillation of the leg as a physical pendulum. (a) How does this pace depend on the length L of the leg from hip to foot? Treat the leg as a uniform rod pivoted at the hip joint. (b) Fossil evidence shows that *T. rex*, a two-legged dinosaur that lived about 65 million years ago, had a leg length $L = 3.1$ m and a stride length $S = 4.0$ m (the distance from one footprint to the next print of the same foot; see **Fig. 14.24**). Estimate the walking speed of *T. rex*.

SOLUTION

IDENTIFY and SET UP: Our target variables are (a) the relationship between walking pace and leg length L and (b) the walking speed of *T. rex*. We treat the leg as a physical pendulum, with a period of oscillation as found in Example 14.9. We can find the walking speed from the period and the stride length.

EXECUTE: (a) From Example 14.9 the period of oscillation of the leg is $T = 2\pi\sqrt{2L/3g}$, which is proportional to $\sqrt{L}$. Each step

14.24 The walking speed of *Tyrannosaurus rex* can be estimated from leg length *L* and stride length *S*.

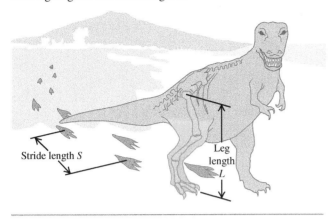

Stride length *S*

Leg length *L*

takes half of one period, so the walking pace (in steps per second) equals twice the oscillation frequency $f = 1/T$ and is proportional to $1/\sqrt{L}$. The longer the leg, the slower the pace.

(b) In our model, *T. rex* traveled one stride length *S* in a time

$$T = 2\pi\sqrt{\frac{2L}{3g}} = 2\pi\sqrt{\frac{2(3.1\text{ m})}{3(9.8\text{ m/s}^2)}} = 2.9\text{ s}$$

so its walking speed was

$$v = \frac{S}{T} = \frac{4.0\text{ m}}{2.9\text{ s}} = 1.4\text{ m/s} = 5.0\text{ km/h} = 3.1\text{ mi/h}$$

This is roughly the walking speed of an adult human.

EVALUATE: A uniform rod isn't a very good model for a leg. The legs of many animals, including both *T. rex* and humans, are tapered; there is more mass between hip and knee than between knee and foot. The center of mass is therefore less than $L/2$ from the hip; a reasonable guess would be about $L/4$. The moment of inertia is therefore *considerably* less than $ML^2/3$—say, $ML^2/15$. Use the analysis of Example 14.9 with these corrections; you'll get a shorter oscillation period and an even greater walking speed for *T. rex*.

TEST YOUR UNDERSTANDING OF SECTION 14.6 The center of gravity of a simple pendulum of mass *m* and length *L* is located at the pendulum bob, a distance *L* from the pivot point. The center of gravity of a uniform rod of the same mass *m* and length *2L* pivoted at one end is also a distance *L* from the pivot point. Compared to the period of the simple pendulum, is the period of this uniform rod (i) longer; (ii) shorter; or (iii) the same? ∎

14.7 DAMPED OSCILLATIONS

The idealized oscillating systems we have discussed so far are frictionless. There are no nonconservative forces, the total mechanical energy is constant, and a system set into motion continues oscillating forever with no decrease in amplitude.

Real-world systems always have some dissipative forces, however, and oscillations die out with time unless we replace the dissipated mechanical energy (**Fig. 14.25**). A mechanical pendulum clock continues to run because potential energy stored in the spring or a hanging weight system replaces the mechanical energy lost due to friction in the pivot and the gears. But eventually the spring runs down or the weights reach the bottom of their travel. Then no more energy is available, and the pendulum swings decrease in amplitude and stop.

The decrease in amplitude caused by dissipative forces is called **damping** (*not* "dampening"), and the corresponding motion is called **damped oscillation.** The simplest case is a simple harmonic oscillator with a frictional damping force that is directly proportional to the *velocity* of the oscillating body. This behavior occurs in friction involving viscous fluid flow, such as in shock absorbers or sliding between oil-lubricated surfaces. We then have an additional force on the body due to friction, $F_x = -bv_x$, where $v_x = dx/dt$ is the velocity and *b* is a constant that describes the strength of the damping force. The negative sign shows that the force is always opposite in direction to the velocity. The *net* force on the body is then

$$\sum F_x = -kx - bv_x \tag{14.40}$$

and Newton's second law for the system is

$$-kx - bv_x = ma_x \quad\text{or}\quad -kx - b\frac{dx}{dt} = m\frac{d^2x}{dt^2} \tag{14.41}$$

Equation (14.41) is a differential equation for *x*; it's the same as Eq. (14.4), the equation for the acceleration in SHM, but with the added term $-bdx/dt$. We won't

14.25 A swinging bell left to itself will eventually stop oscillating due to damping forces (air resistance and friction at the point of suspension).

go into how to solve this equation; we'll just present the solution. If the damping force is relatively small, the motion is described by

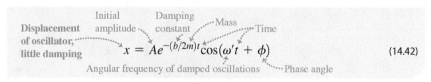

$$x = Ae^{-(b/2m)t}\cos(\omega't + \phi) \qquad (14.42)$$

The angular frequency of these damped oscillations is given by

$$\omega' = \sqrt{\frac{k}{m} - \frac{b^2}{4m^2}} \qquad (14.43)$$

You can verify that Eq. (14.42) is a solution of Eq. (14.41) by calculating the first and second derivatives of x, substituting them into Eq. (14.41), and checking whether the left and right sides are equal.

The motion described by Eq. (14.42) differs from the undamped case in two ways. First, the amplitude $Ae^{-(b/2m)t}$ is not constant but decreases with time because of the exponential factor $e^{-(b/2m)t}$. **Figure 14.26** is a graph of Eq. (14.42) for $\phi = 0$; the larger the value of b, the more quickly the amplitude decreases.

Second, the angular frequency ω', given by Eq. (14.43), is no longer equal to $\omega = \sqrt{k/m}$ but is somewhat smaller. It becomes zero when b becomes so large that

$$\frac{k}{m} - \frac{b^2}{4m^2} = 0 \qquad \text{or} \qquad b = 2\sqrt{km} \qquad (14.44)$$

When Eq. (14.44) is satisfied, the condition is called **critical damping.** The system no longer oscillates but returns to its equilibrium position without oscillation when it is displaced and released.

If b is greater than $2\sqrt{km}$, the condition is called **overdamping.** Again there is no oscillation, but the system returns to equilibrium more slowly than with critical damping. For the overdamped case the solutions of Eq. (14.41) have the form

$$x = C_1 e^{-a_1 t} + C_2 e^{-a_2 t}$$

where C_1 and C_2 are constants that depend on the initial conditions and a_1 and a_2 are constants determined by m, k, and b.

When b is less than the critical value, as in Eq. (14.42), the condition is called **underdamping.** The system oscillates with steadily decreasing amplitude.

In a vibrating tuning fork or guitar string, it is usually desirable to have as little damping as possible. By contrast, damping plays a beneficial role in the oscillations of an automobile's suspension system. The shock absorbers provide a velocity-dependent damping force so that when the car goes over a bump, it doesn't continue bouncing forever (**Fig. 14.27**). For optimal passenger comfort, the system should be critically damped or slightly underdamped. Too much damping would be counterproductive; if the suspension is overdamped and the car hits a second bump just after the first one, the springs in the suspension will still be compressed somewhat from the first bump and will not be able to fully absorb the impact.

Energy in Damped Oscillations

In damped oscillations the damping force is nonconservative; the mechanical energy of the system is not constant but decreases continuously, approaching zero after a long time. To derive an expression for the rate of change of energy, we first write an expression for the total mechanical energy E at any instant:

$$E = \tfrac{1}{2}mv_x^2 + \tfrac{1}{2}kx^2$$

14.26 Graph of displacement versus time for an oscillator with little damping [see Eq. (14.42)] and with phase angle $\phi = 0$. The curves are for two values of the damping constant b.

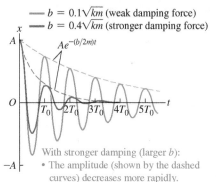

With stronger damping (larger b):
• The amplitude (shown by the dashed curves) decreases more rapidly.
• The period T increases (T_0 = period with zero damping).

14.27 An automobile shock absorber. The viscous fluid causes a damping force that depends on the relative velocity of the two ends of the unit.

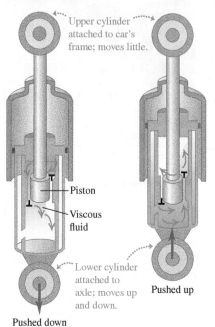

To find the rate of change of this quantity, we take its time derivative:

$$\frac{dE}{dt} = mv_x\frac{dv_x}{dt} + kx\frac{dx}{dt}$$

But $dv_x/dt = a_x$ and $dx/dt = v_x$, so

$$\frac{dE}{dt} = v_x(ma_x + kx)$$

From Eq. (14.41), $ma_x + kx = -b\,dx/dt = -bv_x$, so

$$\frac{dE}{dt} = v_x(-bv_x) = -bv_x^2 \qquad \text{(damped oscillations)} \qquad (14.45)$$

The right side of Eq. (14.45) is negative whenever the oscillating body is in motion, whether the x-velocity v_x is positive or negative. This shows that as the body moves, the energy decreases, though not at a uniform rate. The term $-bv_x^2 = (-bv_x)v_x$ (force times velocity) is the rate at which the damping force does (negative) work on the system (that is, the damping *power*). This equals the rate of change of the total mechanical energy of the system.

Similar behavior occurs in electric circuits containing inductance, capacitance, and resistance. There is a natural frequency of oscillation, and the resistance plays the role of the damping constant b. We will study these circuits in detail in Chapters 30 and 31.

TEST YOUR UNDERSTANDING OF SECTION 14.7 An airplane is flying in a straight line at a constant altitude. If a wind gust strikes and raises the nose of the airplane, the nose will bob up and down until the airplane eventually returns to its original attitude. Are these oscillations (i) undamped; (ii) underdamped; (iii) critically damped; or (iv) overdamped?

14.8 FORCED OSCILLATIONS AND RESONANCE

A damped oscillator left to itself will eventually stop moving. But we can maintain a constant-amplitude oscillation by applying a force that varies with time in a periodic way. As an example, consider your cousin Throckmorton on a playground swing. You can keep him swinging with constant amplitude by giving him a push once each cycle. We call this additional force a **driving force.**

Damped Oscillation with a Periodic Driving Force

If we apply a periodic driving force with angular frequency ω_d to a damped harmonic oscillator, the motion that results is called a **forced oscillation** or a *driven oscillation*. It is different from the motion that occurs when the system is simply displaced from equilibrium and then left alone, in which case the system oscillates with a **natural angular frequency** ω' determined by m, k, and b, as in Eq. (14.43). In a forced oscillation, however, the angular frequency with which the mass oscillates is equal to the driving angular frequency ω_d. This does *not* have to be equal to the natural angular frequency ω'. If you grab the ropes of Throckmorton's swing, you can force the swing to oscillate with any frequency you like.

Suppose we force the oscillator to vibrate with an angular frequency ω_d that is nearly *equal* to the angular frequency ω' it would have with no driving force. What happens? The oscillator is naturally disposed to oscillate at $\omega = \omega'$, so we expect the amplitude of the resulting oscillation to be larger than when the two frequencies are very different. Detailed analysis and experiment show that this is just what happens. The easiest case to analyze is a *sinusoidally* varying force—say, $F(t) = F_{max}\cos\omega_d t$. If we vary the frequency ω_d of the driving force, the amplitude

BIO Application Forced Oscillations This lady beetle (or "ladybug," family Coccinellidae) flies by means of a forced oscillation. Unlike the wings of birds, this insect's wings are extensions of its exoskeleton. Muscles attached to the inside of the exoskeleton apply a periodic driving force that deforms the exoskeleton rhythmically, causing the attached wings to beat up and down. The oscillation frequency of the wings and exoskeleton is the same as the frequency of the driving force.

14.28 Graph of the amplitude A of forced oscillation as a function of the angular frequency ω_d of the driving force. The horizontal axis shows the ratio of ω_d to the angular frequency $\omega = \sqrt{k/m}$ of an undamped oscillator. Each curve has a different value of the damping constant b.

Each curve shows the amplitude A for an oscillator subjected to a driving force at various angular frequencies ω_d. Successive curves from blue to gold represent successively greater damping.

A lightly damped oscillator exhibits a sharp resonance peak when ω_d is close to ω (the natural angular frequency of an undamped oscillator).

Stronger damping reduces and broadens the peak and shifts it to lower frequencies.

If $b \geq \sqrt{2km}$, the peak disappears completely.

$b = 0.2\sqrt{km}$
$b = 0.4\sqrt{km}$
$b = 0.7\sqrt{km}$
$b = 1.0\sqrt{km}$
$b = 2.0\sqrt{km}$

Driving frequency ω_d equals natural angular frequency ω of an undamped oscillator.

of the resulting forced oscillation varies in an interesting way (**Fig. 14.28**). When there is very little damping (small b), the amplitude goes through a sharp peak as the driving angular frequency ω_d nears the natural oscillation angular frequency ω'. When the damping is increased (larger b), the peak becomes broader and smaller in height and shifts toward lower frequencies.

Using more differential equations than we're ready for, we could find an expression for the amplitude A of the forced oscillation as a function of the driving angular frequency. Here is the result:

DEMO

Maximum value of driving force

Amplitude of a forced oscillator
$$A = \frac{F_{max}}{\sqrt{(k - m\omega_d^2)^2 + b^2\omega_d^2}}$$
Force constant of restoring force   Mass   Driving angular frequency   Damping constant

(14.46)

When $k - m\omega_d^2 = 0$, the first term under the radical is zero, so A has a maximum near $\omega_d = \sqrt{k/m}$. The height of the curve at this point is proportional to $1/b$; the less damping, the higher the peak. At the low-frequency extreme, when $\omega_d = 0$, we get $A = F_{max}/k$. This corresponds to a *constant* force F_{max} and a constant displacement $A = F_{max}/k$ from equilibrium, as we might expect.

Resonance and Its Consequences

The peaking of the amplitude at driving frequencies close to the natural frequency of the system is called **resonance.** Physics is full of examples of resonance; building up the oscillations of a child on a swing by pushing with a frequency equal to the swing's natural frequency is one. A vibrating rattle in a car that occurs only at a certain engine speed is another example. Inexpensive loudspeakers often have an annoying boom or buzz when a musical note coincides with the natural frequency of the speaker cone or housing. In Chapter 16 we will study examples of resonance that involve sound. Resonance also occurs in electric circuits, as we will see in Chapter 31; a tuned circuit in a radio receiver responds strongly to waves with frequencies near its natural frequency. This phenomenon lets us select one radio station and reject other stations.

Resonance in mechanical systems can be destructive. A company of soldiers once destroyed a bridge by marching across it in step; the frequency of their steps was close to a natural frequency of the bridge, and the resulting oscillation had large enough amplitude to tear the bridge apart. Ever since, marching soldiers have been ordered to break step before crossing a bridge. Some years ago,

BIO Application Canine Resonance Unlike humans, dogs have no sweat glands and so must pant in order to cool down. The frequency at which a dog pants is very close to the resonant frequency of its respiratory system. This causes the maximum amount of air inflow and outflow and so minimizes the effort that the dog must exert to cool itself.

vibrations of the engines of a particular type of airplane had just the right frequency to resonate with the natural frequencies of its wings. Large oscillations built up, and occasionally the wings fell off.

TEST YOUR UNDERSTANDING OF SECTION 14.8   When driven at a frequency near its natural frequency, an oscillator with very little damping has a much greater response than the same oscillator with more damping. When driven at a frequency that is much higher or lower than the natural frequency, which oscillator will have the greater response: (i) the one with very little damping or (ii) the one with more damping? ▮

CHAPTER 14 SUMMARY

SOLUTIONS TO ALL EXAMPLES

Periodic motion: Periodic motion is motion that repeats itself in a definite cycle. It occurs whenever a body has a stable equilibrium position and a restoring force that acts when the body is displaced from equilibrium. Period T is the time for one cycle. Frequency f is the number of cycles per unit time. Angular frequency ω is 2π times the frequency. (See Example 14.1.)

$$f = \frac{1}{T} \qquad T = \frac{1}{f} \qquad (14.1)$$

$$\omega = 2\pi f = \frac{2\pi}{T} \qquad (14.2)$$

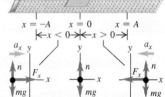

Simple harmonic motion: If the restoring force F_x in periodic motion is directly proportional to the displacement x, the motion is called simple harmonic motion (SHM). In many cases this condition is satisfied if the displacement from equilibrium is small. The angular frequency, frequency, and period in SHM do not depend on the amplitude but on only the mass m and force constant k. The displacement, velocity, and acceleration in SHM are sinusoidal functions of time; the amplitude A and phase angle ϕ of the oscillation are determined by the initial displacement and velocity of the body. (See Examples 14.2, 14.3, 14.6, and 14.7.)

$$F_x = -kx \qquad (14.3)$$

$$a_x = \frac{F_x}{m} = -\frac{k}{m}x \qquad (14.4)$$

$$\omega = \sqrt{\frac{k}{m}} \qquad (14.10)$$

$$f = \frac{\omega}{2\pi} = \frac{1}{2\pi}\sqrt{\frac{k}{m}} \qquad (14.11)$$

$$T = \frac{1}{f} = 2\pi\sqrt{\frac{m}{k}} \qquad (14.12)$$

$$x = A\cos(\omega t + \phi) \qquad (14.13)$$

Energy in simple harmonic motion: Energy is conserved in SHM. The total energy can be expressed in terms of the force constant k and amplitude A. (See Examples 14.4 and 14.5.)

$$E = \tfrac{1}{2}mv_x^2 + \tfrac{1}{2}kx^2 = \tfrac{1}{2}kA^2 = \text{constant} \qquad (14.21)$$

Angular simple harmonic motion: In angular SHM, the frequency and angular frequency are related to the moment of inertia I and the torsion constant κ.

$$\omega = \sqrt{\frac{\kappa}{I}} \quad \text{and}$$

$$f = \frac{1}{2\pi}\sqrt{\frac{\kappa}{I}} \qquad (14.24)$$

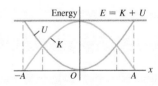

Balance wheel   Spring

Spring torque τ_z opposes angular displacement θ.

Simple pendulum: A simple pendulum consists of a point mass m at the end of a massless string of length L. Its motion is approximately simple harmonic for sufficiently small amplitude; the angular frequency, frequency, and period then depend on only g and L, not on the mass or amplitude. (See Example 14.8.)

$$\omega = \sqrt{\frac{g}{L}} \qquad (14.32)$$

$$f = \frac{\omega}{2\pi} = \frac{1}{2\pi}\sqrt{\frac{g}{L}} \qquad (14.33)$$

$$T = \frac{2\pi}{\omega} = \frac{1}{f} = 2\pi\sqrt{\frac{L}{g}} \qquad (14.34)$$

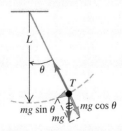

Physical pendulum: A physical pendulum is any body suspended from an axis of rotation. The angular frequency and period for small-amplitude oscillations are independent of amplitude but depend on the mass m, distance d from the axis of rotation to the center of gravity, and moment of inertia I about the axis. (See Examples 14.9 and 14.10.)

$$\omega = \sqrt{\frac{mgd}{I}} \quad (14.38)$$

$$T = 2\pi \sqrt{\frac{I}{mgd}} \quad (14.39)$$

Damped oscillations: When a force $F_x = -bv_x$ is added to a simple harmonic oscillator, the motion is called a damped oscillation. If $b < 2\sqrt{km}$ (called underdamping), the system oscillates with a decaying amplitude and an angular frequency ω' that is lower than it would be without damping. If $b = 2\sqrt{km}$ (called critical damping) or $b > 2\sqrt{km}$ (called overdamping), when the system is displaced it returns to equilibrium without oscillating.

$$x = Ae^{-(b/2m)t}\cos(\omega' t + \phi) \quad (14.42)$$

$$\omega' = \sqrt{\frac{k}{m} - \frac{b^2}{4m^2}} \quad (14.43)$$

Forced oscillations and resonance: When a sinusoidally varying driving force is added to a damped harmonic oscillator, the resulting motion is called a forced oscillation or driven oscillation. The amplitude is a function of the driving frequency ω_d and reaches a peak at a driving frequency close to the natural frequency of the system. This behavior is called resonance.

$$A = \frac{F_{max}}{\sqrt{(k - m\omega_d^2)^2 + b^2\omega_d^2}} \quad (14.46)$$

BRIDGING PROBLEM   OSCILLATING AND ROLLING

Two uniform, solid cylinders of radius R and total mass M are connected along their common axis by a short, light rod and rest on a horizontal tabletop (**Fig. 14.29**). A frictionless ring at the center of the rod is attached to a spring with force constant k; the other end of the spring is fixed. The cylinders are pulled to the left a distance x, stretching the spring, and then released from rest. Due to friction between the tabletop and the cylinders, the cylinders roll without slipping as they oscillate. Show that the motion of the center of mass of the cylinders is simple harmonic, and find its period.

14.29 Rolling cylinders attached to a spring.

SOLUTION GUIDE

IDENTIFY and SET UP

1. What condition must be satisfied for the motion of the center of mass of the cylinders to be simple harmonic?
2. Which equations should you use to describe the translational and rotational motions of the cylinders? Which equation should you use to describe the condition that the cylinders roll without slipping? (*Hint:* See Section 10.3.)
3. Sketch the situation and choose a coordinate system. List the unknown quantities and decide which is the target variable.

EXECUTE

4. Draw a free-body diagram for the cylinders when they are displaced a distance x from equilibrium.
5. Solve the equations to find an expression for the acceleration of the center of mass of the cylinders. What does this expression tell you?
6. Use your result from step 5 to find the period of oscillation of the center of mass of the cylinders.

EVALUATE

7. What would be the period of oscillation if there were no friction and the cylinders didn't roll? Is this period larger or smaller than your result from step 6? Is this reasonable?

Problems

•, ••, •••: Difficulty levels. CP: Cumulative problems incorporating material from earlier chapters. CALC: Problems requiring calculus.
DATA: Problems involving real data, scientific evidence, experimental design, and/or statistical reasoning. BIO: Biosciences problems.

DISCUSSION QUESTIONS

Q14.1 An object is moving with SHM of amplitude A on the end of a spring. If the amplitude is doubled, what happens to the total distance the object travels in one period? What happens to the period? What happens to the maximum speed of the object? Discuss how these answers are related.

Q14.2 Think of several examples in everyday life of motions that are, at least approximately, simple harmonic. In what respects does each differ from SHM?

Q14.3 Does a tuning fork or similar tuning instrument undergo SHM? Why is this a crucial question for musicians?

Q14.4 A box containing a pebble is attached to an ideal horizontal spring and is oscillating on a friction-free air table. When the box has reached its maximum distance from the equilibrium point, the pebble is suddenly lifted out vertically without disturbing the box. Will the following characteristics of the motion increase, decrease, or remain the same in the subsequent motion of the box? Justify each answer. (a) Frequency; (b) period; (c) amplitude; (d) the maximum kinetic energy of the box; (e) the maximum speed of the box.

Q14.5 If a uniform spring is cut in half, what is the force constant of each half? Justify your answer. How would the frequency of SHM using a half-spring differ from the frequency using the same mass and the entire spring?

Q14.6 A glider is attached to a fixed ideal spring and oscillates on a horizontal, friction-free air track. A coin rests atop the glider and oscillates with it. At what points in the motion is the friction force on the coin greatest? The least? Justify your answers.

Q14.7 Two identical gliders on an air track are connected by an ideal spring. Could such a system undergo SHM? Explain. How would the period compare with that of a single glider attached to a spring whose other end is rigidly attached to a stationary object? Explain.

Q14.8 You are captured by Martians, taken into their ship, and put to sleep. You awake some time later and find yourself locked in a small room with no windows. All the Martians have left you with is your digital watch, your school ring, and your long silver-chain necklace. Explain how you can determine whether you are still on earth or have been transported to Mars.

Q14.9 The system shown in Fig. 14.17 is mounted in an elevator. What happens to the period of the motion (does it increase, decrease, or remain the same) if the elevator (a) accelerates upward at 5.0 m/s^2; (b) moves upward at a steady 5.0 m/s; (c) accelerates downward at 5.0 m/s^2? Justify your answers.

Q14.10 If a pendulum has a period of 2.5 s on earth, what would be its period in a space station orbiting the earth? If a mass hung from a vertical spring has a period of 5.0 s on earth, what would its period be in the space station? Justify your answers.

Q14.11 A simple pendulum is mounted in an elevator. What happens to the period of the pendulum (does it increase, decrease, or remain the same) if the elevator (a) accelerates upward at 5.0 m/s^2; (b) moves upward at a steady 5.0 m/s; (c) accelerates downward at 5.0 m/s^2; (d) accelerates downward at 9.8 m/s^2? Justify your answers.

Q14.12 What should you do to the length of the string of a simple pendulum to (a) double its frequency; (b) double its period; (c) double its angular frequency?

Q14.13 If a pendulum clock is taken to a mountaintop, does it gain or lose time, assuming it is correct at a lower elevation? Explain.

Q14.14 When the amplitude of a simple pendulum increases, should its period increase or decrease? Give a qualitative argument; do not rely on Eq. (14.35). Is your argument also valid for a physical pendulum?

Q14.15 Why do short dogs (like Chihuahuas) walk with quicker strides than do tall dogs (like Great Danes)?

Q14.16 At what point in the motion of a simple pendulum is the string tension greatest? Least? In each case give the reasoning behind your answer.

Q14.17 Could a standard of time be based on the period of a certain standard pendulum? What advantages and disadvantages would such a standard have compared to the actual present-day standard discussed in Section 1.3?

Q14.18 For a simple pendulum, clearly distinguish between ω (the angular speed) and ω (the angular frequency). Which is constant and which is variable?

Q14.19 In designing structures in an earthquake-prone region, how should the natural frequencies of oscillation of a structure relate to typical earthquake frequencies? Why? Should the structure have a large or small amount of damping?

EXERCISES

Section 14.1 Describing Oscillation

14.1 • BIO (a) **Music.** When a person sings, his or her vocal cords vibrate in a repetitive pattern that has the same frequency as the note that is sung. If someone sings the note B flat, which has a frequency of 466 Hz, how much time does it take the person's vocal cords to vibrate through one complete cycle, and what is the angular frequency of the cords? (b) **Hearing.** When sound waves strike the eardrum, this membrane vibrates with the same frequency as the sound. The highest pitch that young humans can hear has a period of $50.0 \text{ } \mu s$. What are the frequency and angular frequency of the vibrating eardrum for this sound? (c) **Vision.** When light having vibrations with angular frequency ranging from 2.7×10^{15} rad/s to 4.7×10^{15} rad/s strikes the retina of the eye, it stimulates the receptor cells there and is perceived as visible light. What are the limits of the period and frequency of this light? (d) **Ultrasound.** High-frequency sound waves (ultrasound) are used to probe the interior of the body, much as x rays do. To detect small objects such as tumors, a frequency of around 5.0 MHz is used. What are the period and angular frequency of the molecular vibrations caused by this pulse of sound?

14.2 • If an object on a horizontal, frictionless surface is attached to a spring, displaced, and then released, it will oscillate. If it is displaced 0.120 m from its equilibrium position and released with zero initial speed, then after 0.800 s its displacement is found to be 0.120 m on the opposite side, and it has passed the equilibrium position once during this interval. Find (a) the amplitude; (b) the period; (c) the frequency.

14.3 • The tip of a tuning fork goes through 440 complete vibrations in 0.500 s. Find the angular frequency and the period of the motion.

14.4 • The displacement of an oscillating object as a function of time is shown in **Fig. E14.4**. What are (a) the frequency; (b) the amplitude; (c) the period; (d) the angular frequency of this motion?

Figure **E14.4**

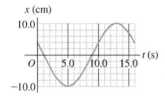

14.5 •• A machine part is undergoing SHM with a frequency of 4.00 Hz and amplitude 1.80 cm. How long does it take the part to go from $x = 0$ to $x = -1.80$ cm?

14.6 • BIO The wings of the blue-throated hummingbird (*Lampornis clemenciae*), which inhabits Mexico and the southwestern United States, beat at a rate of up to 900 times per minute. Calculate (a) the period of vibration of this bird's wings, (b) the frequency of the wings' vibration, and (c) the angular frequency of the bird's wing beats.

Section 14.2 Simple Harmonic Motion

14.7 • A 2.40-kg ball is attached to an unknown spring and allowed to oscillate. **Figure E14.7** shows a graph of the ball's position x as a function of time t. What are the oscillation's (a) period, (b) frequency, (c) angular frequency, and (d) amplitude? (e) What is the force constant of the spring?

Figure **E14.7**

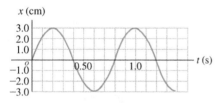

14.8 •• In a physics lab, you attach a 0.200-kg air-track glider to the end of an ideal spring of negligible mass and start it oscillating. The elapsed time from when the glider first moves through the equilibrium point to the second time it moves through that point is 2.60 s. Find the spring's force constant.

14.9 • When a body of unknown mass is attached to an ideal spring with force constant 120 N/m, it is found to vibrate with a frequency of 6.00 Hz. Find (a) the period of the motion; (b) the angular frequency; (c) the mass of the body.

14.10 • When a 0.750-kg mass oscillates on an ideal spring, the frequency is 1.75 Hz. What will the frequency be if 0.220 kg are (a) added to the original mass and (b) subtracted from the original mass? Try to solve this problem *without* finding the force constant of the spring.

14.11 •• An object is undergoing SHM with period 0.900 s and amplitude 0.320 m. At $t = 0$ the object is at $x = 0.320$ m and is instantaneously at rest. Calculate the time it takes the object to go (a) from $x = 0.320$ m to $x = 0.160$ m and (b) from $x = 0.160$ m to $x = 0$.

14.12 • A small block is attached to an ideal spring and is moving in SHM on a horizontal, frictionless surface. When the block is at $x = 0.280$ m, the acceleration of the block is -5.30 m/s². What is the frequency of the motion?

14.13 • A 2.00-kg, frictionless block is attached to an ideal spring with force constant 300 N/m. At $t = 0$ the spring is neither stretched nor compressed and the block is moving in the negative direction at 12.0 m/s. Find (a) the amplitude and (b) the phase angle. (c) Write an equation for the position as a function of time.

14.14 •• Repeat Exercise 14.13, but assume that at $t = 0$ the block has velocity -4.00 m/s and displacement $+0.200$ m.

14.15 • The point of the needle of a sewing machine moves in SHM along the x-axis with a frequency of 2.5 Hz. At $t = 0$ its position and velocity components are $+1.1$ cm and -15 cm/s, respectively. (a) Find the acceleration component of the needle at $t = 0$. (b) Write equations giving the position, velocity, and acceleration components of the point as a function of time.

14.16 •• A small block is attached to an ideal spring and is moving in SHM on a horizontal, frictionless surface. When the amplitude of the motion is 0.090 m, it takes the block 2.70 s to travel from $x = 0.090$ m to $x = -0.090$ m. If the amplitude is doubled, to 0.180 m, how long does it take the block to travel (a) from $x = 0.180$ m to $x = -0.180$ m and (b) from $x = 0.090$ m to $x = -0.090$ m?

14.17 • BIO **Weighing Astronauts.** This procedure has been used to "weigh" astronauts in space: A 42.5-kg chair is attached to a spring and allowed to oscillate. When it is empty, the chair takes 1.30 s to make one complete vibration. But with an astronaut sitting in it, with her feet off the floor, the chair takes 2.54 s for one cycle. What is the mass of the astronaut?

14.18 • A 0.400-kg object undergoing SHM has $a_x = -1.80$ m/s² when $x = 0.300$ m. What is the time for one oscillation?

14.19 • On a frictionless, horizontal air track, a glider oscillates at the end of an ideal spring of force constant 2.50 N/cm. The graph in **Fig. E14.19** shows the acceleration of the glider as a function of time. Find (a) the mass of the glider; (b) the maximum displacement of the glider from the equilibrium point; (c) the maximum force the spring exerts on the glider.

Figure **E14.19**

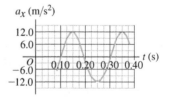

14.20 • A 0.500-kg mass on a spring has velocity as a function of time given by $v_x(t) = -(3.60 \text{ cm/s}) \sin[(4.71 \text{ rad/s})t - (\pi/2)]$. What are (a) the period; (b) the amplitude; (c) the maximum acceleration of the mass; (d) the force constant of the spring?

14.21 • A 1.50-kg mass on a spring has displacement as a function of time given by

$$x(t) = (7.40 \text{ cm}) \cos[(4.16 \text{ rad/s})t - 2.42]$$

Find (a) the time for one complete vibration; (b) the force constant of the spring; (c) the maximum speed of the mass; (d) the maximum force on the mass; (e) the position, speed, and acceleration of the mass at $t = 1.00$ s; (f) the force on the mass at that time.

14.22 • BIO **Weighing a Virus.** In February 2004, scientists at Purdue University used a highly sensitive technique to measure the mass of a vaccinia virus (the kind used in smallpox vaccine). The procedure involved measuring the frequency of oscillation of a tiny sliver of silicon (just 30 nm long) with a laser, first without the virus and then after the virus had attached itself to the silicon.

The difference in mass caused a change in the frequency. We can model such a process as a mass on a spring. (a) Show that the ratio of the frequency with the virus attached (f_{S+V}) to the frequency without the virus (f_S) is given by $f_{S+V}/f_S = 1/\sqrt{1 + (m_V/m_S)}$, where m_V is the mass of the virus and m_S is the mass of the silicon sliver. Notice that it is *not* necessary to know or measure the force constant of the spring. (b) In some data, the silicon sliver has a mass of 2.10×10^{-16} g and a frequency of 2.00×10^{15} Hz without the virus and 2.87×10^{14} Hz with the virus. What is the mass of the virus, in grams and in femtograms?

14.23 •• CALC **Jerk.** A guitar string vibrates at a frequency of 440 Hz. A point at its center moves in SHM with an amplitude of 3.0 mm and a phase angle of zero. (a) Write an equation for the position of the center of the string as a function of time. (b) What are the maximum values of the magnitudes of the velocity and acceleration of the center of the string? (c) The derivative of the acceleration with respect to time is a quantity called the *jerk*. Write an equation for the jerk of the center of the string as a function of time, and find the maximum value of the magnitude of the jerk.

Section 14.3 Energy in Simple Harmonic Motion

14.24 •• For the oscillating object in Fig. E14.4, what are (a) its maximum speed and (b) its maximum acceleration?

14.25 • A small block is attached to an ideal spring and is moving in SHM on a horizontal frictionless surface. The amplitude of the motion is 0.165 m. The maximum speed of the block is 3.90 m/s. What is the maximum magnitude of the acceleration of the block?

14.26 • A small block is attached to an ideal spring and is moving in SHM on a horizontal, frictionless surface. The amplitude of the motion is 0.250 m and the period is 3.20 s. What are the speed and acceleration of the block when $x = 0.160$ m?

14.27 • A 0.150-kg toy is undergoing SHM on the end of a horizontal spring with force constant $k = 300$ N/m. When the toy is 0.0120 m from its equilibrium position, it is observed to have a speed of 0.400 m/s. What are the toy's (a) total energy at any point of its motion; (b) amplitude of motion; (c) maximum speed during its motion?

14.28 •• A harmonic oscillator has angular frequency ω and amplitude A. (a) What are the magnitudes of the displacement and velocity when the elastic potential energy is equal to the kinetic energy? (Assume that $U = 0$ at equilibrium.) (b) How often does this occur in each cycle? What is the time between occurrences? (c) At an instant when the displacement is equal to $A/2$, what fraction of the total energy of the system is kinetic and what fraction is potential?

14.29 • A 0.500-kg glider, attached to the end of an ideal spring with force constant $k = 450$ N/m, undergoes SHM with an amplitude of 0.040 m. Compute (a) the maximum speed of the glider; (b) the speed of the glider when it is at $x = -0.015$ m; (c) the magnitude of the maximum acceleration of the glider; (d) the acceleration of the glider at $x = -0.015$ m; (e) the total mechanical energy of the glider at any point in its motion.

14.30 •• A cheerleader waves her pom-pom in SHM with an amplitude of 18.0 cm and a frequency of 0.850 Hz. Find (a) the maximum magnitude of the acceleration and of the velocity; (b) the acceleration and speed when the pom-pom's coordinate is $x = +9.0$ cm; (c) the time required to move from the equilibrium position directly to a point 12.0 cm away. (d) Which of the quantities asked for in parts (a), (b), and (c) can be found by using the energy approach used in Section 14.3, and which cannot? Explain.

14.31 • CP For the situation described in part (a) of Example 14.5, what should be the value of the putty mass m so that the amplitude after the collision is one-half the original amplitude? For this value of m, what fraction of the original mechanical energy is converted into thermal energy?

14.32 •• A block with mass $m = 0.300$ kg is attached to one end of an ideal spring and moves on a horizontal frictionless surface. The other end of the spring is attached to a wall. When the block is at $x = +0.240$ m, its acceleration is $a_x = -12.0$ m/s^2 and its velocity is $v_x = +4.00$ m/s. What are (a) the spring's force constant k; (b) the amplitude of the motion; (c) the maximum speed of the block during its motion; and (d) the maximum magnitude of the block's acceleration during its motion?

14.33 •• You are watching an object that is moving in SHM. When the object is displaced 0.600 m to the right of its equilibrium position, it has a velocity of 2.20 m/s to the right and an acceleration of 8.40 m/s^2 to the left. How much farther from this point will the object move before it stops momentarily and then starts to move back to the left?

14.34 • A 2.00-kg frictionless block is attached to an ideal spring with force constant 315 N/m. Initially the spring is neither stretched nor compressed, but the block is moving in the negative direction at 12.0 m/s. Find (a) the amplitude of the motion, (b) the block's maximum acceleration, and (c) the maximum force the spring exerts on the block.

14.35 • A 2.00-kg frictionless block attached to an ideal spring with force constant 315 N/m is undergoing simple harmonic motion. When the block has displacement +0.200 m, it is moving in the negative x-direction with a speed of 4.00 m/s. Find (a) the amplitude of the motion; (b) the block's maximum acceleration; and (c) the maximum force the spring exerts on the block.

14.36 •• A mass is oscillating with amplitude A at the end of a spring. How far (in terms of A) is this mass from the equilibrium position of the spring when the elastic potential energy equals the kinetic energy?

Section 14.4 Applications of Simple Harmonic Motion

14.37 • A 175-g glider on a horizontal, frictionless air track is attached to a fixed ideal spring with force constant 155 N/m. At the instant you make measurements on the glider, it is moving at 0.815 m/s and is 3.00 cm from its equilibrium point. Use *energy conservation* to find (a) the amplitude of the motion and (b) the maximum speed of the glider. (c) What is the angular frequency of the oscillations?

14.38 • A proud deep-sea fisherman hangs a 65.0-kg fish from an ideal spring having negligible mass. The fish stretches the spring 0.180 m. (a) Find the force constant of the spring. The fish is now pulled down 5.00 cm and released. (b) What is the period of oscillation of the fish? (c) What is the maximum speed it will reach?

14.39 • A thrill-seeking cat with mass 4.00 kg is attached by a harness to an ideal spring of negligible mass and oscillates vertically in SHM. The amplitude is 0.050 m, and at the highest point of the motion the spring has its natural unstretched length. Calculate the elastic potential energy of the spring (take it to be zero for the unstretched spring), the kinetic energy of the cat, the gravitational potential energy of the system relative to the lowest point of the motion, and the sum of these three energies when the cat is (a) at its highest point; (b) at its lowest point; (c) at its equilibrium position.

14.40 •• A uniform, solid metal disk of mass 6.50 kg and diameter 24.0 cm hangs in a horizontal plane, supported at its center by a vertical metal wire. You find that it requires a horizontal force of 4.23 N tangent to the rim of the disk to turn it by 3.34°, thus twisting the wire. You now remove this force and release the disk from rest. (a) What is the torsion constant for the metal wire? (b) What are the frequency and period of the torsional oscillations of the disk? (c) Write the equation of motion for $\theta(t)$ for the disk.

14.41 •• A certain alarm clock ticks four times each second, with each tick representing half a period. The balance wheel consists of a thin rim with radius 0.55 cm, connected to the balance shaft by thin spokes of negligible mass. The total mass of the balance wheel is 0.90 g. (a) What is the moment of inertia of the balance wheel about its shaft? (b) What is the torsion constant of the coil spring (Fig. 14.19)?

14.42 • A thin metal disk with mass 2.00×10^{-3} kg and radius 2.20 cm is attached at its center to a long fiber (**Fig. E14.42**). The disk, when twisted and released, oscillates with a period of 1.00 s. Find the torsion constant of the fiber.

Figure **E14.42**

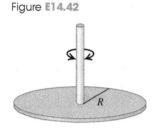

14.43 •• You want to find the moment of inertia of a complicated machine part about an axis through its center of mass. You suspend it from a wire along this axis. The wire has a torsion constant of 0.450 N · m/rad. You twist the part a small amount about this axis and let it go, timing 165 oscillations in 265 s. What is its moment of inertia?

14.44 •• CALC The balance wheel of a watch vibrates with an angular amplitude Θ, angular frequency ω, and phase angle $\phi = 0$. (a) Find expressions for the angular velocity $d\theta/dt$ and angular acceleration $d^2\theta/dt^2$ as functions of time. (b) Find the balance wheel's angular velocity and angular acceleration when its angular displacement is Θ, and when its angular displacement is $\Theta/2$ and θ is decreasing. (*Hint:* Sketch a graph of θ versus t.)

Section 14.5 The Simple Pendulum

14.45 •• You pull a simple pendulum 0.240 m long to the side through an angle of 3.50° and release it. (a) How much time does it take the pendulum bob to reach its highest speed? (b) How much time does it take if the pendulum is released at an angle of 1.75° instead of 3.50°?

14.46 • An 85.0-kg mountain climber plans to swing down, starting from rest, from a ledge using a light rope 6.50 m long. He holds one end of the rope, and the other end is tied higher up on a rock face. Since the ledge is not very far from the rock face, the rope makes a small angle with the vertical. At the lowest point of his swing, he plans to let go and drop a short distance to the ground. (a) How long after he begins his swing will the climber first reach his lowest point? (b) If he missed the first chance to drop off, how long after first beginning his swing will the climber reach his lowest point for the second time?

14.47 • A building in San Francisco has light fixtures consisting of small 2.35-kg bulbs with shades hanging from the ceiling at the end of light, thin cords 1.50 m long. If a minor earthquake occurs, how many swings per second will these fixtures make?

14.48 • **A Pendulum on Mars.** A certain simple pendulum has a period on the earth of 1.60 s. What is its period on the surface of Mars, where $g = 3.71$ m/s^2?

14.49 • After landing on an unfamiliar planet, a space explorer constructs a simple pendulum of length 50.0 cm. She finds that the pendulum makes 100 complete swings in 136 s. What is the value of g on this planet?

14.50 •• In the laboratory, a student studies a pendulum by graphing the angle θ that the string makes with the vertical as a function of time t, obtaining the graph shown in **Fig. E14.50**. (a) What are the period, frequency, angular frequency, and amplitude of the pendulum's motion? (b) How long is the pendulum? (c) Is it possible to determine the mass of the bob?

Figure **E14.50**

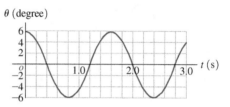

14.51 • A simple pendulum 2.00 m long swings through a maximum angle of 30.0° with the vertical. Calculate its period (a) assuming a small amplitude, and (b) using the first three terms of Eq. (14.35). (c) Which of the answers in parts (a) and (b) is more accurate? What is the percentage error of the less accurate answer compared with the more accurate one?

14.52 •• A small sphere with mass m is attached to a massless rod of length L that is pivoted at the top, forming a simple pendulum. The pendulum is pulled to one side so that the rod is at an angle θ from the vertical, and released from rest. (a) In a diagram, show the pendulum just after it is released. Draw vectors representing the *forces* acting on the small sphere and the *acceleration* of the sphere. Accuracy counts! At this point, what is the linear acceleration of the sphere? (b) Repeat part (a) for the instant when the pendulum rod is at an angle $\theta/2$ from the vertical. (c) Repeat part (a) for the instant when the pendulum rod is vertical. At this point, what is the linear speed of the sphere?

Section 14.6 The Physical Pendulum

14.53 • Two pendulums have the same dimensions (length L) and total mass (m). Pendulum A is a very small ball swinging at the end of a uniform massless bar. In pendulum B, half the mass is in the ball and half is in the uniform bar. Find the period of each pendulum for small oscillations. Which one takes longer for a swing?

14.54 •• We want to hang a thin hoop on a horizontal nail and have the hoop make one complete small-angle oscillation each 2.0 s. What must the hoop's radius be?

14.55 • A 1.80-kg connecting rod from a car engine is pivoted about a horizontal knife edge as shown in **Fig. E14.55**. The center of gravity of the rod was located by balancing and is 0.200 m from the pivot. When the rod is set into small-amplitude oscillation, it makes 100 complete swings in 120 s. Calculate the moment of inertia of the rod about the rotation axis through the pivot.

Figure **E14.55**

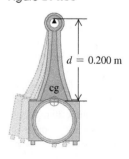

$d = 0.200$ m

cg

14.56 •• A 1.80-kg monkey wrench is pivoted 0.250 m from its center of mass and allowed to swing as a physical pendulum. The period for small-angle oscillations is 0.940 s. (a) What is the moment of inertia of the wrench about an axis through the pivot? (b) If the wrench is initially displaced 0.400 rad from its equilibrium position, what is the angular speed of the wrench as it passes through the equilibrium position?

14.57 •• The two pendulums shown in **Fig. E14.57** each consist of a uniform solid ball of mass M supported by a rigid massless rod, but the ball for pendulum A is very tiny while the ball for pendulum B is much larger. Find the period of each pendulum for small displacements. Which ball takes longer to complete a swing?

Figure E14.57

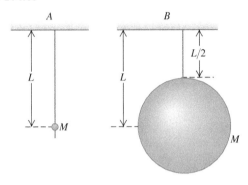

14.58 •• CP A holiday ornament in the shape of a hollow sphere with mass $M = 0.015$ kg and radius $R = 0.050$ m is hung from a tree limb by a small loop of wire attached to the surface of the sphere. If the ornament is displaced a small distance and released, it swings back and forth as a physical pendulum with negligible friction. Calculate its period. (*Hint:* Use the parallel-axis theorem to find the moment of inertia of the sphere about the pivot at the tree limb.)

Section 14.7 Damped Oscillations

14.59 • A 1.35-kg object is attached to a horizontal spring of force constant 2.5 N/cm. The object is started oscillating by pulling it 6.0 cm from its equilibrium position and releasing it so that it is free to oscillate on a frictionless horizontal air track. You observe that after eight cycles its maximum displacement from equilibrium is only 3.5 cm. (a) How much energy has this system lost to damping during these eight cycles? (b) Where did the "lost" energy go? Explain physically how the system could have lost energy.

14.60 •• A 50.0-g hard-boiled egg moves on the end of a spring with force constant $k = 25.0$ N/m. Its initial displacement is 0.300 m. A damping force $F_x = -bv_x$ acts on the egg, and the amplitude of the motion decreases to 0.100 m in 5.00 s. Calculate the magnitude of the damping constant b.

14.61 • An unhappy 0.300-kg rodent, moving on the end of a spring with force constant $k = 2.50$ N/m, is acted on by a damping force $F_x = -bv_x$. (a) If the constant b has the value 0.900 kg/s, what is the frequency of oscillation of the rodent? (b) For what value of the constant b will the motion be critically damped?

14.62 •• A mass is vibrating at the end of a spring of force constant 225 N/m. **Figure E14.62** shows a graph of its position x as a function of time t. (a) At what times is the mass not moving? (b) How much energy did this system originally contain? (c) How much energy did the system lose between $t = 1.0$ s and $t = 4.0$ s? Where did this energy go?

Figure E14.62

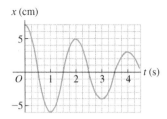

Section 14.8 Forced Oscillations and Resonance

14.63 • A sinusoidally varying driving force is applied to a damped harmonic oscillator of force constant k and mass m. If the damping constant has a value b_1, the amplitude is A_1 when the driving angular frequency equals $\sqrt{k/m}$. In terms of A_1, what is the amplitude for the same driving frequency and the same driving force amplitude F_{max}, if the damping constant is (a) $3b_1$ and (b) $b_1/2$?

PROBLEMS

14.64 ••• An object is undergoing SHM with period 0.300 s and amplitude 6.00 cm. At $t = 0$ the object is instantaneously at rest at $x = 6.00$ cm. Calculate the time it takes the object to go from $x = 6.00$ cm to $x = -1.50$ cm.

14.65 •• An object is undergoing SHM with period 1.200 s and amplitude 0.600 m. At $t = 0$ the object is at $x = 0$ and is moving in the negative x-direction. How far is the object from the equilibrium position when $t = 0.480$ s?

14.66 • Four passengers with combined mass 250 kg compress the springs of a car with worn-out shock absorbers by 4.00 cm when they get in. Model the car and passengers as a single body on a single ideal spring. If the loaded car has a period of vibration of 1.92 s, what is the period of vibration of the empty car?

14.67 •• At the end of a ride at a winter-theme amusement park, a sleigh with mass 250 kg (including two passengers) slides without friction along a horizontal, snow-covered surface. The sleigh hits one end of a light horizontal spring that obeys Hooke's law and has its other end attached to a wall. The sleigh latches onto the end of the spring and subsequently moves back and forth in SHM on the end of the spring until a braking mechanism is engaged, which brings the sleigh to rest. The frequency of the SHM is 0.225 Hz, and the amplitude is 0.950 m. (a) What was the speed of the sleigh just before it hit the end of the spring? (b) What is the maximum magnitude of the sleigh's acceleration during its SHM?

14.68 •• CP A block with mass M rests on a frictionless surface and is connected to a horizontal spring of force constant k. The other end of the spring is attached to a wall (**Fig. P14.68**). A second block with mass m rests on top of the first block. The coefficient of static friction between the blocks is μ_s. Find the *maximum* amplitude of oscillation such that the top block will not slip on the bottom block.

Figure P14.68

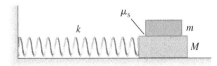

14.69 ••• A 1.50-kg, horizontal, uniform tray is attached to a vertical ideal spring of force constant 185 N/m and a 275-g metal ball is in the tray. The spring is below the tray, so it can oscillate up and down. The tray is then pushed down to point A, which is 15.0 cm below the equilibrium point, and released from rest. (a) How high above point A will the tray be when the metal ball leaves the tray? (*Hint:* This does *not* occur when the ball and tray reach their maximum speeds.)) (b) How much time elapses between releasing the system at point A and the ball leaving the tray? (c) How fast is the ball moving just as it leaves the tray?

14.70 • CP A 10.0-kg mass is traveling to the right with a speed of 2.00 m/s on a smooth horizontal surface when it collides with and sticks to a second 10.0-kg mass that is initially at rest but is attached to a light spring with force constant 170.0 N/m. (a) Find the frequency, amplitude, and period of the subsequent oscillations. (b) How long does it take the system to return the first time to the position it had immediately after the collision?

14.71 ••• An apple weighs 1.00 N. When you hang it from the end of a long spring of force constant 1.50 N/m and negligible mass, it bounces up and down in SHM. If you stop the bouncing and let the apple swing from side to side through a small angle, the frequency of this simple pendulum is half the bounce frequency. (Because the angle is small, the back-and-forth swings do not cause any appreciable change in the length of the spring.) What is the unstretched length of the spring (with the apple removed)?

14.72 ••• CP **SHM of a Floating Object.** An object with height h, mass M, and a uniform cross-sectional area A floats upright in a liquid with density ρ. (a) Calculate the vertical distance from the surface of the liquid to the bottom of the floating object at equilibrium. (b) A downward force with magnitude F is applied to the top of the object. At the new equilibrium position, how much farther below the surface of the liquid is the bottom of the object than it was in part (a)? (Assume that some of the object remains above the surface of the liquid.) (c) Your result in part (b) shows that if the force is suddenly removed, the object will oscillate up and down in SHM. Calculate the period of this motion in terms of the density ρ of the liquid, the mass M, and the cross-sectional area A of the object. You can ignore the damping due to fluid friction (see Section 14.7).

14.73 •• CP A square object of mass m is constructed of four identical uniform thin sticks, each of length L, attached together. This object is hung on a hook at its upper corner (**Fig. P14.73**). If it is rotated slightly to the left and then released, at what frequency will it swing back and forth?

Figure **P14.73**

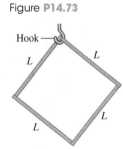

Hook

L L L L

14.74 ••• An object with mass 0.200 kg is acted on by an elastic restoring force with force constant 10.0 N/m. (a) Graph elastic potential energy U as a function of displacement x over a range of x from −0.300 m to +0.300 m. On your graph, let 1 cm = 0.05 J vertically and 1 cm = 0.05 m horizontally. The object is set into oscillation with an initial potential energy of 0.140 J and an initial kinetic energy of 0.060 J. Answer the following questions by referring to the graph. (b) What is the amplitude of oscillation? (c) What is the potential energy when the displacement is one-half the amplitude? (d) At what displacement are the kinetic and potential energies equal? (e) What is the value of the phase angle φ if the initial velocity is positive and the initial displacement is negative?

14.75 • CALC A 2.00-kg bucket containing 10.0 kg of water is hanging from a vertical ideal spring of force constant 450 N/m and oscillating up and down with an amplitude of 3.00 cm. Suddenly the bucket springs a leak in the bottom such that water drops out at a steady rate of 2.00 g/s. When the bucket is half full, find (a) the period of oscillation and (b) the rate at which the period is changing with respect to time. Is the period getting longer or shorter? (c) What is the shortest period this system can have?

14.76 •• A uniform beam is suspended horizontally by two identical vertical springs that are attached between the ceiling and each end of the beam. The beam has mass 225 kg, and a 175-kg sack of gravel sits on the middle of it. The beam is oscillating in SHM with an amplitude of 40.0 cm and a frequency of 0.600 cycle/s. (a) The sack falls off the beam when the beam has its maximum upward displacement. What are the frequency and amplitude of the subsequent SHM of the beam? (b) If the sack instead falls off when the beam has its maximum speed, repeat part (a).

14.77 •• A 5.00-kg partridge is suspended from a pear tree by an ideal spring of negligible mass. When the partridge is pulled down 0.100 m below its equilibrium position and released, it vibrates with a period of 4.20 s. (a) What is its speed as it passes through the equilibrium position? (b) What is its acceleration when it is 0.050 m above the equilibrium position? (c) When it is moving upward, how much time is required for it to move from a point 0.050 m below its equilibrium position to a point 0.050 m above it? (d) The motion of the partridge is stopped, and then it is removed from the spring. How much does the spring shorten?

14.78 •• A 0.0200-kg bolt moves with SHM that has an amplitude of 0.240 m and a period of 1.500 s. The displacement of the bolt is +0.240 m when t = 0. Compute (a) the displacement of the bolt when t = 0.500 s; (b) the magnitude and direction of the force acting on the bolt when t = 0.500 s; (c) the minimum time required for the bolt to move from its initial position to the point where x = −0.180 m; (d) the speed of the bolt when x = −0.180 m.

14.79 •• CP **SHM of a Butcher's Scale.** A spring of negligible mass and force constant k = 400 N/m is hung vertically, and a 0.200-kg pan is suspended from its lower end. A butcher drops a 2.2-kg steak onto the pan from a height of 0.40 m. The steak makes a totally inelastic collision with the pan and sets the system into vertical SHM. What are (a) the speed of the pan and steak immediately after the collision; (b) the amplitude of the subsequent motion; (c) the period of that motion?

14.80 •• A 40.0-N force stretches a vertical spring 0.250 m. (a) What mass must be suspended from the spring so that the system will oscillate with a period of 1.00 s? (b) If the amplitude of the motion is 0.050 m and the period is that specified in part (a), where is the object and in what direction is it moving 0.35 s after it has passed the equilibrium position, moving downward? (c) What force (magnitude and direction) does the spring exert on the object when it is 0.030 m below the equilibrium position, moving upward?

14.81 •• **Don't Miss the Boat.** While on a visit to Minnesota ("Land of 10,000 Lakes"), you sign up to take an excursion around one of the larger lakes. When you go to the dock where the 1500-kg boat is tied, you find that the boat is bobbing up and down in the waves, executing simple harmonic motion with amplitude 20 cm. The boat takes 3.5 s to make one complete up-and-down cycle. When the boat is at its highest point, its deck is at the same height as the stationary dock. As you watch the boat bob up and down, you (mass 60 kg) begin to feel a bit woozy, due in part to the previous night's dinner of lutefisk. As a result, you refuse to board the boat unless the level of the boat's deck is within 10 cm of the dock level. How much time do you have to board the boat comfortably during each cycle of up-and-down motion?

14.82 • CP An interesting, though highly impractical example of oscillation is the motion of an object dropped down a hole that extends from one side of the earth, through its center, to the other side. With the assumption (not realistic) that the earth is a sphere of uniform density, prove that the motion is simple harmonic and find the period. [*Note:* The gravitational force on the object as a function of the object's distance r from the center of the earth was derived in Example 13.10 (Section 13.6). The motion is simple harmonic if the acceleration a_x and the displacement from equilibrium x are related by Eq. (14.8), and the period is then $T = 2\pi/\omega$.]

14.83 ••• CP A rifle bullet with mass 8.00 g and initial horizontal velocity 280 m/s strikes and embeds itself in a block with mass 0.992 kg that rests on a frictionless surface and is attached to one end of an ideal spring. The other end of the spring is attached to the wall. The impact compresses the spring a maximum distance of 15.0 cm. After the impact, the block moves in SHM. Calculate the period of this motion.

14.84 ••• CP Two uniform solid spheres, each with mass $M = 0.800$ kg and radius $R = 0.0800$ m, are connected by a short, light rod that is along a diameter of each sphere and are at rest on a horizontal tabletop. A spring with force constant $k = 160$ N/m has one end attached to the wall and the other end attached to a frictionless ring that passes over the rod at the center of mass of the spheres, which is midway between the centers of the two spheres. The spheres are each pulled the same distance from the wall, stretching the spring, and released. There is sufficient friction between the tabletop and the spheres for the spheres to roll without slipping as they move back and forth on the end of the spring. Show that the motion of the center of mass of the spheres is simple harmonic and calculate the period.

14.85 • CP In **Fig. P14.85** the upper ball is released from rest, collides with the stationary lower ball, and sticks to it. The strings are both 50.0 cm long. The upper ball has mass 2.00 kg, and it is initially 10.0 cm higher than the lower ball, which has mass 3.00 kg. Find the frequency and maximum angular displacement of the motion after the collision.

Figure **P14.85**

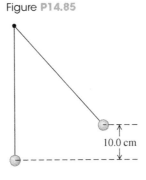

10.0 cm

14.86 •• **The Silently Ringing Bell.** A large, 34.0-kg bell is hung from a wooden beam so it can swing back and forth with negligible friction. The bell's center of mass is 0.60 m below the pivot. The bell's moment of inertia about an axis at the pivot is 18.0 kg·m². The clapper is a small, 1.8-kg mass attached to one end of a slender rod of length L and negligible mass. The other end of the rod is attached to the inside of the bell; the rod can swing freely about the same axis as the bell. What should be the length L of the clapper rod for the bell to ring silently—that is, for the period of oscillation for the bell to equal that of the clapper?

14.87 •• CALC A slender, uniform, metal rod with mass M is pivoted without friction about an axis through its midpoint and perpendicular to the rod. A horizontal spring with force constant k is attached to the lower end of the rod, with the other end of the spring attached to a rigid support. If the rod is displaced by a small angle Θ from the vertical (**Fig. P14.87**) and released, show that it moves in angular SHM and calculate the period. (*Hint:* Assume that the angle Θ is small enough for the approximations $\sin \Theta \approx \Theta$ and $\cos \Theta \approx 1$ to be valid. The motion is simple harmonic if $d^2\theta/dt^2 = -\omega^2\theta$, and the period is then $T = 2\pi/\omega$.)

Figure **P14.87**

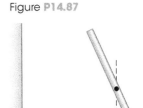

14.88 ••• Two identical thin rods, each with mass m and length L, are joined at right angles to form an L-shaped object. This object is balanced on top of a sharp edge (**Fig. P14.88**). If the L-shaped object is deflected slightly, it oscillates. Find the frequency of oscillation.

Figure **P14.88**

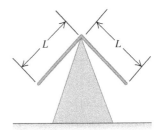

14.89 •• DATA A mass m is attached to a spring of force constant 75 N/m and allowed to oscillate. **Figure P14.89** shows a graph of its velocity component v_x as a function of time t. Find (a) the period, (b) the frequency, and (c) the angular frequency of this motion. (d) What is the amplitude (in cm), and at what times does the mass reach this position? (e) Find the maximum acceleration magnitude of the mass and the times at which it occurs. (f) What is the value of m?

Figure **P14.89** v_x (cm/s)

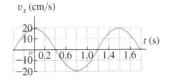

14.90 •• DATA You hang various masses m from the end of a vertical, 0.250-kg spring that obeys Hooke's law and is tapered, which means the diameter changes along the length of the spring. Since the mass of the spring is not negligible, you must replace m in the equation $T = 2\pi\sqrt{m/k}$ with $m + m_{eff}$, where m_{eff} is the effective mass of the oscillating spring. (See Challenge Problem 14.93.) You vary the mass m and measure the time for 10 complete oscillations, obtaining these data:

m (kg)	0.100	0.200	0.300	0.400	0.500
Time (s)	8.7	10.5	12.2	13.9	15.1

(a) Graph the square of the period T versus the mass suspended from the spring, and find the straight line of best fit. (b) From the slope of that line, determine the force constant of the spring. (c) From the vertical intercept of the line, determine the spring's effective mass. (d) What fraction is m_{eff} of the spring's mass? (e) If a 0.450-kg mass oscillates on the end of the spring, find its period, frequency, and angular frequency.

14.91 ••• DATA Experimenting with pendulums, you attach a light string to the ceiling and attach a small metal sphere to the lower end of the string. When you displace the sphere 2.00 m to the left, it nearly touches a vertical wall; with the string taut, you release the sphere from rest. The sphere swings back and forth as a simple pendulum, and you measure its period T. You repeat this act for strings of various lengths L, each time starting the motion with the sphere displaced 2.00 m to the left of the vertical position of the string. In each case the sphere's radius is very small compared with L. Your results are given in the table:

L (m)	12.00	10.00	8.00	6.00	5.00	4.00	3.00	2.50	2.30
T (s)	6.96	6.36	5.70	4.95	4.54	4.08	3.60	3.35	3.27

(a) For the five largest values of L, graph T^2 versus L. Explain why the data points fall close to a straight line. Does the slope of this line have the value you expected? (b) Add the remaining data to your graph. Explain why the data start to deviate from the straight-line fit as L decreases. To see this effect more clearly, plot T/T_0 versus L, where $T_0 = 2\pi\sqrt{L/g}$ and $g = 9.80$ m/s^2. (c) Use your graph of T/T_0 versus L to estimate the angular amplitude of the pendulum (in degrees) for which the equation $T = 2\pi\sqrt{L/g}$ is in error by 5%.

CHALLENGE PROBLEMS

14.92 ••• **The Effective Force Constant of Two Springs.** Two springs with the same unstretched length but different force constants k_1 and k_2 are attached to a block with mass m on a level, frictionless surface. Calculate the effective force constant k_{eff} in each of the three cases (a), (b), and (c) depicted in **Fig. P14.92**. (The effective force constant is defined by $\Sigma F_x = -k_{eff}x$.) (d) An object with mass m, suspended from a uniform spring with a force constant k, vibrates with a frequency f_1. When the spring is cut in half and the same object is suspended from one of the halves, the frequency is f_2. What is the ratio f_1/f_2?

Figure P14.92

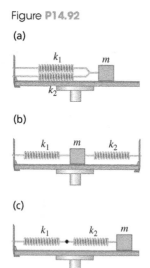

14.93 ••• CALC **A Spring with Mass.** The preceding problems in this chapter have assumed that the springs had negligible mass. But of course no spring is completely massless. To find the effect of the spring's mass, consider a spring with mass M, equilibrium length L_0, and spring constant k. When stretched or compressed to a length L, the potential energy is $\frac{1}{2}kx^2$, where $x = L - L_0$. (a) Consider a spring, as described above, that has one end fixed and the other end moving with speed v. Assume that the speed of points along the length of the spring varies linearly with distance l from the fixed end. Assume also that the

mass M of the spring is distributed uniformly along the length of the spring. Calculate the kinetic energy of the spring in terms of M and v. (*Hint:* Divide the spring into pieces of length dl; find the speed of each piece in terms of l, v, and L; find the mass of each piece in terms of dl, M, and L; and integrate from 0 to L. The result is *not* $\frac{1}{2}Mv^2$, since not all of the spring moves with the same speed.) (b) Take the time derivative of the conservation of energy equation, Eq. (14.21), for a mass m moving on the end of a *massless* spring. By comparing your results to Eq. (14.8), which defines ω, show that the angular frequency of oscillation is $\omega = \sqrt{k/m}$. (c) Apply the procedure of part (b) to obtain the angular frequency of oscillation ω of the spring considered in part (a). If the *effective mass* M' of the spring is defined by $\omega = \sqrt{k/M'}$, what is M' in terms of M?

PASSAGE PROBLEMS

BIO **"SEEING" SURFACES AT THE NANOSCALE.** One technique for making images of surfaces at the nanometer scale, including membranes and biomolecules, is dynamic atomic force microscopy. In this technique, a small tip is attached to a cantilever, which is a flexible, rectangular slab supported at one end, like a diving board. The cantilever vibrates, so the tip moves up and down in simple harmonic motion. In one operating mode, the resonant frequency for a cantilever with force constant $k = 1000$ N/m is 100 kHz. As the oscillating tip is brought within a few nanometers of the surface of a sample (as shown in the figure), it experiences an attractive force from the surface. For an oscillation with a small amplitude (typically, 0.050 nm), the force F that the sample surface exerts on the tip varies linearly with the displacement x of the tip, $|F| = k_{surf}x$, where k_{surf} is the effective force constant for this force. The net force on the tip is therefore $(k + k_{surf})x$, and the frequency of the oscillation changes slightly due to the interaction with the surface. Measurements of the frequency as the tip moves over different parts of the sample's surface can provide information about the sample.

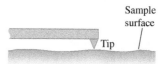

14.94 If we model the vibrating system as a mass on a spring, what is the mass necessary to achieve the desired resonant frequency when the tip is not interacting with the surface? (a) 25 ng; (b) 100 ng; (c) 2.5 μg; (d) 100 μg.

14.95 In the model of Problem 14.94, what is the mechanical energy of the vibration when the tip is not interacting with the surface? (a) 1.2×10^{-18} J; (b) 1.2×10^{-16} J; (c) 1.2×10^{-9} J; (d) 5.0×10^{-8} J.

14.96 By what percentage does the frequency of oscillation change if $k_{surf} = 5$ N/m? (a) 0.1%; (b) 0.2%; (c) 0.5%; (d) 1.0%.

Answers

Chapter Opening Question ?

(i) The back-and-forth motion of a leg during walking is like a physical pendulum, for which the oscillation period is $T = 2\pi\sqrt{I/mgd}$ [see Eq. (14.39)]. In this expression I is the moment of inertia of the pendulum, m is its mass, and d is the distance from the rotation axis to the pendulum center of mass. I is proportional to m, so the mass cancels out of this expression for T. Hence only the dimensions of the leg matter. (See Examples 14.9 and 14.10.)

Test Your Understanding Questions

14.1 **(a)** $x < 0$, **(b)** $x > 0$, **(c)** $x < 0$, **(d)** $x > 0$, **(e)** $x > 0$, **(f)** $x = 0$ Figure 14.2 shows that both the net x-component of force F_x and the x-acceleration a_x are positive when $x < 0$ (so the body is displaced to the left and the spring is compressed), while both F_x and a_x are negative when $x > 0$ (so the body is displaced to the right and the spring is stretched). Hence x and a_x always have *opposite* signs. This is true whether the object is moving to the right ($v_x > 0$), to the left ($v_x < 0$), or not at all ($v_x = 0$), since the force exerted by the spring depends on only whether it is compressed or stretched and by what distance. This explains the answers to (a) through (e). If the acceleration is zero as in (f), the net force must also be zero and so the spring must be relaxed; hence $x = 0$.

14.2 **(a)** $A > 0.10\,\text{m}$, $\phi < 0$; **(b)** $A > 0.10\,\text{m}$, $\phi > 0$ In both situations the initial ($t = 0$) x-velocity v_{0x} is nonzero, so from Eq. (14.19) the amplitude $A = \sqrt{x_0^2 + (v_{0x}^2/\omega^2)}$ is greater than the initial x-coordinate $x_0 = 0.10$ m. From Eq. (14.18) the phase angle is $\phi = \arctan(-v_{0x}/\omega x_0)$, which is positive if the quantity $-v_{0x}/\omega x_0$ (the argument of the arctangent function) is positive and negative if $-v_{0x}/\omega x_0$ is negative. In part (a) both x_0 and v_{0x} are positive, so $-v_{0x}/\omega x_0 < 0$ and $\phi < 0$. In part (b) x_0 is positive and v_{0x} is negative, so $-v_{0x}/\omega x_0 > 0$ and $\phi > 0$.

14.3 **(a)** (iii), **(b)** (v)   To increase the total energy $E = \frac{1}{2}kA^2$ by a factor of 2, the amplitude A must increase by a factor of $\sqrt{2}$. Because the motion is SHM, changing the amplitude has no effect on the frequency.

14.4 **(i)**   The oscillation period of a body of mass m attached to a hanging spring of force constant k is given by $T = 2\pi\sqrt{m/k}$, the same expression as for a body attached to a horizontal spring. Neither m nor k changes when the apparatus is taken to Mars, so the period is unchanged. The only difference is that in equilibrium, the spring will stretch a shorter distance on Mars than on earth due to the weaker gravity.

14.5 **(iv)**   Just as for an object oscillating on a spring, at the equilibrium position the *speed* of a pendulum bob is instantaneously not changing (this is where the speed is maximum, so its derivative at this time is zero). But the *direction* of motion is changing because the pendulum bob follows a circular path. Hence the bob must have a component of acceleration perpendicular to the path and toward the center of the circle (see Section 3.4). To cause this acceleration at the equilibrium position when the string is vertical, the upward tension force at this position must be greater than the weight of the bob. This causes a net upward force on the bob and an upward acceleration toward the center of the circular path.

14.6 **(i)**   The period of a physical pendulum is given by Eq. (14.39), $T = 2\pi\sqrt{I/mgd}$. The distance $d = L$ from the pivot to the center of gravity is the same for both the rod and the simple pendulum, as is the mass m. Thus for any displacement angle θ the same restoring torque acts on both the rod and the simple pendulum. However, the rod has a greater moment of inertia: $I_{rod} = \frac{1}{3}m(2L)^2 = \frac{4}{3}mL^2$ and $I_{simple} = mL^2$ (all the mass of the pendulum is a distance L from the pivot). Hence the rod has a longer period.

14.7 **(ii)**   The oscillations are underdamped with a decreasing amplitude on each cycle of oscillation, like those graphed in Fig. 14.26. If the oscillations were undamped, they would continue indefinitely with the same amplitude. If they were critically damped or overdamped, the nose would not bob up and down but would return smoothly to the original equilibrium attitude without overshooting.

14.8 **(i)**   Figure 14.28 shows that the curve of amplitude versus driving frequency moves upward at *all* frequencies as the value of the damping constant b is decreased. Hence for fixed values of k and m, the oscillator with the least damping (smallest value of b) will have the greatest response at any driving frequency.

Bridging Problem

$T = 2\pi\sqrt{3M/2k}$

APPENDIX A

THE INTERNATIONAL SYSTEM OF UNITS

The Système International d'Unités, abbreviated SI, is the system developed by the General Conference on Weights and Measures and adopted by nearly all the industrial nations of the world. The following material is adapted from the National Institute of Standards and Technology (**http://physics.nist.gov/cuu**).

Quantity	Name of unit	Symbol	
SI base units			
length	meter	m	
mass	kilogram	kg	
time	second	s	
electric current	ampere	A	
thermodynamic temperature	kelvin	K	
amount of substance	mole	mol	
luminous intensity	candela	cd	
SI derived units			**Equivalent units**
area	square meter	m^2	
volume	cubic meter	m^3	
frequency	hertz	Hz	s^{-1}
mass density (density)	kilogram per cubic meter	kg/m^3	
speed, velocity	meter per second	m/s	
angular velocity	radian per second	rad/s	
acceleration	meter per second squared	m/s^2	
angular acceleration	radian per second squared	rad/s^2	
force	newton	N	$kg \cdot m/s^2$
pressure (mechanical stress)	pascal	Pa	N/m^2
kinematic viscosity	square meter per second	m^2/s	
dynamic viscosity	newton-second per square meter	$N \cdot s/m^2$	
work, energy, quantity of heat	joule	J	$N \cdot m$
power	watt	W	J/s
quantity of electricity	coulomb	C	$A \cdot s$
potential difference, electromotive force	volt	V	$J/C, W/A$
electric field strength	volt per meter	V/m	N/C
electrical resistance	ohm	Ω	V/A
capacitance	farad	F	$A \cdot s/V$
magnetic flux	weber	Wb	$V \cdot s$
inductance	henry	H	$V \cdot s/A$
magnetic flux density	tesla	T	Wb/m^2
magnetic field strength	ampere per meter	A/m	
magnetomotive force	ampere	A	
luminous flux	lumen	lm	$cd \cdot sr$
luminance	candela per square meter	cd/m^2	
illuminance	lux	lx	lm/m^2
wave number	1 per meter	m^{-1}	
entropy	joule per kelvin	J/K	
specific heat capacity	joule per kilogram-kelvin	$J/kg \cdot K$	
thermal conductivity	watt per meter-kelvin	$W/m \cdot K$	

Quantity	Name of unit	Symbol	Equivalent units
radiant intensity	watt per steradian	W/sr	
activity (of a radioactive source)	becquerel	Bq	s^{-1}
radiation dose	gray	Gy	J/kg
radiation dose equivalent	sievert	Sv	J/kg
	SI supplementary units		
plane angle	radian	rad	
solid angle	steradian	sr	

Definitions of SI Units

meter (m) The *meter* is the length equal to the distance traveled by light, in vacuum, in a time of 1/299,792,458 second.

kilogram (kg) The *kilogram* is the unit of mass; it is equal to the mass of the international prototype of the kilogram. (The international prototype of the kilogram is a particular cylinder of platinum-iridium alloy that is preserved in a vault at Sévres, France, by the International Bureau of Weights and Measures.)

second (s) The *second* is the duration of 9,192,631,770 periods of the radiation corresponding to the transition between the two hyperfine levels of the ground state of the cesium-133 atom.

ampere (A) The *ampere* is that constant current that, if maintained in two straight parallel conductors of infinite length, of negligible circular cross section, and placed 1 meter apart in vacuum, would produce between these conductors a force equal to 2×10^{-7} newton per meter of length.

kelvin (K) The *kelvin,* unit of thermodynamic temperature, is the fraction 1/273.16 of the thermodynamic temperature of the triple point of water.

ohm (Ω) The *ohm* is the electric resistance between two points of a conductor when a constant difference of potential of 1 volt, applied between these two points, produces in this conductor a current of 1 ampere, this conductor not being the source of any electromotive force.

coulomb (C) The *coulomb* is the quantity of electricity transported in 1 second by a current of 1 ampere.

candela (cd) The *candela* is the luminous intensity, in a given direction, of a source that emits monochromatic radiation of frequency 540×10^{12} hertz and that has a radiant intensity in that direction of 1/683 watt per steradian.

mole (mol) The *mole* is the amount of substance of a system that contains as many elementary entities as there are carbon atoms in 0.012 kg of carbon 12. The elementary entities must be specified and may be atoms, molecules, ions, electrons, other particles, or specified groups of such particles.

newton (N) The *newton* is that force that gives to a mass of 1 kilogram an acceleration of 1 meter per second per second.

joule (J) The *joule* is the work done when the point of application of a constant force of 1 newton is displaced a distance of 1 meter in the direction of the force.

watt (W) The *watt* is the power that gives rise to the production of energy at the rate of 1 joule per second.

volt (V) The *volt* is the difference of electric potential between two points of a conducting wire carrying a constant current of 1 ampere, when the power dissipated between these points is equal to 1 watt.

weber (Wb) The *weber* is the magnetic flux that, linking a circuit of one turn, produces in it an electromotive force of 1 volt as it is reduced to zero at a uniform rate in 1 second.

lumen (lm) The *lumen* is the luminous flux emitted in a solid angle of 1 steradian by a uniform point source having an intensity of 1 candela.

farad (F) The *farad* is the capacitance of a capacitor between the plates of which there appears a difference of potential of 1 volt when it is charged by a quantity of electricity equal to 1 coulomb.

henry (H) The *henry* is the inductance of a closed circuit in which an electromotive force of 1 volt is produced when the electric current in the circuit varies uniformly at a rate of 1 ampere per second.

radian (rad) The *radian* is the plane angle between two radii of a circle that cut off on the circumference an arc equal in length to the radius.

steradian (sr) The *steradian* is the solid angle that, having its vertex in the center of a sphere, cuts off an area of the surface of the sphere equal to that of a square with sides of length equal to the radius of the sphere.

SI Prefixes To form the names of multiples and submultiples of SI units, apply the prefixes listed in Appendix F.

APPENDIX B

USEFUL MATHEMATICAL RELATIONS

Algebra

$$a^{-x} = \frac{1}{a^x} \qquad a^{(x+y)} = a^x a^y \qquad a^{(x-y)} = \frac{a^x}{a^y}$$

Logarithms: If $\log a = x$, then $a = 10^x$. $\quad \log a + \log b = \log(ab) \quad \log a - \log b = \log(a/b) \quad \log(a^n) = n\log a$

If $\ln a = x$, then $a = e^x$. $\quad \ln a + \ln b = \ln(ab) \quad \ln a - \ln b = \ln(a/b) \quad \ln(a^n) = n\ln a$

Quadratic formula: If $ax^2 + bx + c = 0$, $\quad x = \dfrac{-b \pm \sqrt{b^2 - 4ac}}{2a}$.

Binomial Theorem

$$(a + b)^n = a^n + na^{n-1}b + \frac{n(n-1)a^{n-2}b^2}{2!} + \frac{n(n-1)(n-2)a^{n-3}b^3}{3!} + \cdots$$

Trigonometry

In the right triangle ABC, $x^2 + y^2 = r^2$.

Definitions of the trigonometric functions:
$\sin\alpha = y/r \qquad \cos\alpha = x/r \qquad \tan\alpha = y/x$

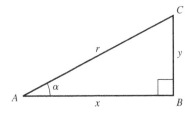

Identities:

$$\sin^2\alpha + \cos^2\alpha = 1 \qquad\qquad \tan\alpha = \frac{\sin\alpha}{\cos\alpha}$$

$$\sin 2\alpha = 2\sin\alpha\cos\alpha \qquad\qquad \cos 2\alpha = \cos^2\alpha - \sin^2\alpha = 2\cos^2\alpha - 1$$
$$= 1 - 2\sin^2\alpha$$

$$\sin\tfrac{1}{2}\alpha = \sqrt{\frac{1 - \cos\alpha}{2}} \qquad\qquad \cos\tfrac{1}{2}\alpha = \sqrt{\frac{1 + \cos\alpha}{2}}$$

$$\sin(-\alpha) = -\sin\alpha \qquad\qquad \sin(\alpha \pm \beta) = \sin\alpha\cos\beta \pm \cos\alpha\sin\beta$$

$$\cos(-\alpha) = \cos\alpha \qquad\qquad \cos(\alpha \pm \beta) = \cos\alpha\cos\beta \mp \sin\alpha\sin\beta$$

$$\sin(\alpha \pm \pi/2) = \pm\cos\alpha \qquad\qquad \sin\alpha + \sin\beta = 2\sin\tfrac{1}{2}(\alpha + \beta)\cos\tfrac{1}{2}(\alpha - \beta)$$

$$\cos(\alpha \pm \pi/2) = \mp\sin\alpha \qquad\qquad \cos\alpha + \cos\beta = 2\cos\tfrac{1}{2}(\alpha + \beta)\cos\tfrac{1}{2}(\alpha - \beta)$$

For *any* triangle $A'B'C'$ (not necessarily a right triangle) with sides a, b, and c and angles α, β, and γ:

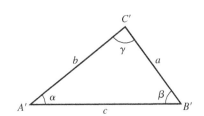

Law of sines: $\quad \dfrac{\sin\alpha}{a} = \dfrac{\sin\beta}{b} = \dfrac{\sin\gamma}{c}$

Law of cosines: $\quad c^2 = a^2 + b^2 - 2ab\cos\gamma$

Geometry

Circumference of circle of radius r: $\qquad C = 2\pi r$ $\qquad$ Surface area of sphere of radius r: $\qquad A = 4\pi r^2$

Area of circle of radius r: $\qquad A = \pi r^2$ $\qquad$ Volume of cylinder of radius r and height h: $\qquad V = \pi r^2 h$

Volume of sphere of radius r: $\qquad V = 4\pi r^3/3$

Calculus

Derivatives:

$$\frac{d}{dx}x^n = nx^{n-1}$$

$$\frac{d}{dx}\ln ax = \frac{1}{x}$$

$$\frac{d}{dx}e^{ax} = ae^{ax}$$

$$\frac{d}{dx}\sin ax = a\cos ax$$

$$\frac{d}{dx}\cos ax = -a\sin ax$$

Integrals:

$$\int x^n\,dx = \frac{x^{n+1}}{n+1} \quad (n \neq -1)$$

$$\int \frac{dx}{x} = \ln x$$

$$\int e^{ax}\,dx = \frac{1}{a}e^{ax}$$

$$\int \sin ax\,dx = -\frac{1}{a}\cos ax$$

$$\int \cos ax\,dx = \frac{1}{a}\sin ax$$

$$\int \frac{dx}{\sqrt{a^2 - x^2}} = \arcsin\frac{x}{a}$$

$$\int \frac{dx}{\sqrt{x^2 + a^2}} = \ln\left(x + \sqrt{x^2 + a^2}\right)$$

$$\int \frac{dx}{x^2 + a^2} = \frac{1}{a}\arctan\frac{x}{a}$$

$$\int \frac{dx}{(x^2 + a^2)^{3/2}} = \frac{1}{a^2}\frac{x}{\sqrt{x^2 + a^2}}$$

$$\int \frac{x\,dx}{(x^2 + a^2)^{3/2}} = -\frac{1}{\sqrt{x^2 + a^2}}$$

Power series (convergent for range of x shown):

$$(1 + x)^n = 1 + nx + \frac{n(n-1)x^2}{2!} + \frac{n(n-1)(n-2)}{3!}x^3$$
$$+ \cdots (|x| < 1)$$

$$\tan x = x + \frac{x^3}{3} + \frac{2x^5}{15} + \frac{17x^7}{315} + \cdots (|x| < \pi/2)$$

$$e^x = 1 + x + \frac{x^2}{2!} + \frac{x^3}{3!} + \cdots (\text{all } x)$$

$$\sin x = x - \frac{x^3}{3!} + \frac{x^5}{5!} - \frac{x^7}{7!} + \cdots (\text{all } x)$$

$$\ln(1 + x) = x - \frac{x^2}{2} + \frac{x^3}{3} - \frac{x^4}{4} + \cdots (|x| < 1)$$

$$\cos x = 1 - \frac{x^2}{2!} + \frac{x^4}{4!} - \frac{x^6}{6!} + \cdots (\text{all } x)$$

APPENDIX C

THE GREEK ALPHABET

Name	Capital	Lowercase	Name	Capital	Lowercase	Name	Capital	Lowercase
Alpha	A	α	Iota	I	ι	Rho	P	ρ
Beta	B	β	Kappa	K	κ	Sigma	Σ	σ
Gamma	Γ	γ	Lambda	Λ	λ	Tau	T	τ
Delta	Δ	δ	Mu	M	μ	Upsilon	Y	υ
Epsilon	E	ϵ	Nu	N	ν	Phi	Φ	ϕ
Zeta	Z	ζ	Xi	Ξ	ξ	Chi	X	χ
Eta	H	η	Omicron	O	o	Psi	Ψ	ψ
Theta	Θ	θ	Pi	Π	π	Omega	Ω	ω

APPENDIX D

Group	1	2	3	4	5	6	7	8	9	10	11	12	13	14	15	16	17	18
Period																		
1	1 **H** 1.008																	2 **He** 4.003
2	3 **Li** 6.941	4 **Be** 9.012											5 **B** 10.811	6 **C** 12.011	7 **N** 14.007	8 **O** 15.999	9 **F** 18.998	10 **Ne** 20.180
3	11 **Na** 22.990	12 **Mg** 24.305											13 **Al** 26.982	14 **Si** 28.086	15 **P** 30.974	16 **S** 32.065	17 **Cl** 35.453	18 **Ar** 39.948
4	19 **K** 39.098	20 **Ca** 40.078	21 **Sc** 44.956	22 **Ti** 47.867	23 **V** 50.942	24 **Cr** 51.996	25 **Mn** 54.938	26 **Fe** 55.845	27 **Co** 58.933	28 **Ni** 58.693	29 **Cu** 63.546	30 **Zn** 65.409	31 **Ga** 69.723	32 **Ge** 72.64	33 **As** 74.922	34 **Se** 78.96	35 **Br** 79.904	36 **Kr** 83.798
5	37 **Rb** 85.468	38 **Sr** 87.62	39 **Y** 88.906	40 **Zr** 91.224	41 **Nb** 92.906	42 **Mo** 95.94	43 **Tc** (98)	44 **Ru** 101.07	45 **Rh** 102.906	46 **Pd** 106.42	47 **Ag** 107.868	48 **Cd** 112.411	49 **In** 114.818	50 **Sn** 118.710	51 **Sb** 121.760	52 **Te** 127.60	53 **I** 126.904	54 **Xe** 131.293
6	55 **Cs** 132.905	56 **Ba** 137.327	71 **Lu** 174.967	72 **Hf** 178.49	73 **Ta** 180.948	74 **W** 183.84	75 **Re** 186.207	76 **Os** 190.23	77 **Ir** 192.217	78 **Pt** 195.078	79 **Au** 196.967	80 **Hg** 200.59	81 **Tl** 204.383	82 **Pb** 207.2	83 **Bi** 208.980	84 **Po** (209)	85 **At** (210)	86 **Rn** (222)
7	87 **Fr** (223)	88 **Ra** (226)	103 **Lr** (262)	104 **Rf** (261)	105 **Db** (262)	106 **Sg** (266)	107 **Bh** (270)	108 **Hs** (269)	109 **Mt** (278)	110 **Ds** (281)	111 **Rg** (281)	112 **Cn** (285)	113 **Uut** (284)	114 **Fl** (289)	115 **Uup** (288)	116 **Lv** (292)	117 **Uus** (294)	118 **Uuo** (294)

Lanthanoids

57 **La** 138.905	58 **Ce** 140.116	59 **Pr** 140.908	60 **Nd** 144.24	61 **Pm** (145)	62 **Sm** 150.36	63 **Eu** 151.964	64 **Gd** 157.25	65 **Tb** 158.925	66 **Dy** 162.500	67 **Ho** 164.930	68 **Er** 167.259	69 **Tm** 168.934	70 **Yb** 173.04

Actinoids

89 **Ac** (227)	90 **Th** (232)	91 **Pa** (231)	92 **U** (238)	93 **Np** (237)	94 **Pu** (244)	95 **Am** (243)	96 **Cm** (247)	97 **Bk** (247)	98 **Cf** (251)	99 **Es** (252)	100 **Fm** (257)	101 **Md** (258)	102 **No** (259)

For each element, the average atomic mass of the mixture of isotopes occurring in nature is shown. For elements having no stable isotope, the approximate atomic mass of the longest-lived isotope is shown in parentheses. All atomic masses are expressed in atomic mass units ($1 \text{ u} = 1.660538921(73) \times 10^{-27}$ kg), equivalent to grams per mole (g/mol).

APPENDIX E

UNIT CONVERSION FACTORS

Length
1 m = 100 cm = 1000 mm = $10^6 \mu$m = 10^9 nm
1 km = 1000 m = 0.6214 mi
1 m = 3.281 ft = 39.37 in.
1 cm = 0.3937 in.
1 in. = 2.540 cm
1 ft = 30.48 cm
1 yd = 91.44 cm
1 mi = 5280 ft = 1.609 km
1 Å = 10^{-10} m = 10^{-8} cm = 10^{-1} nm
1 nautical mile = 6080 ft
1 light-year = 9.461 × 10^{15} m

Area
1 cm^2 = 0.155 in.^{2}
1 m^2 = 10^4 cm^2 = 10.76 ft^2
1 in.^{2} = 6.452 cm^2
1 ft^2 = 144 in.^{2} = 0.0929 m^2

Volume
1 liter = 1000 cm^3 = 10^{-3} m^3 = 0.03531 ft^3 = 61.02 in.^{3}
1 ft^3 = 0.02832 m^3 = 28.32 liters = 7.477 gallons
1 gallon = 3.788 liters

Time
1 min = 60 s
1 h = 3600 s
1 d = 86,400 s
1 y = 365.24 d = 3.156 × 10^7 s

Angle
1 rad = 57.30° = 180°/π
1° = 0.01745 rad = π/180 rad
1 revolution = 360° = 2π rad
1 rev/min (rpm) = 0.1047 rad/s

Speed
1 m/s = 3.281 ft/s
1 ft/s = 0.3048 m/s
1 mi/min = 60 mi/h = 88 ft/s
1 km/h = 0.2778 m/s = 0.6214 mi/h
1 mi/h = 1.466 ft/s = 0.4470 m/s = 1.609 km/h
1 furlong/fortnight = 1.662 × 10^{-4} m/s

Acceleration
1 m/s^2 = 100 cm/s^2 = 3.281 ft/s^2
1 cm/s^2 = 0.01 m/s^2 = 0.03281 ft/s^2
1 ft/s^2 = 0.3048 m/s^2 = 30.48 cm/s^2
1 mi/h·s = 1.467 ft/s^2

Mass
1 kg = 10^3 g = 0.0685 slug
1 g = 6.85 × 10^{-5} slug
1 slug = 14.59 kg
1 u = 1.661 × 10^{-27} kg
1 kg has a weight of 2.205 lb when g = 9.80 m/s^2

Force
1 N = 10^5 dyn = 0.2248 lb
1 lb = 4.448 N = 4.448 × 10^5 dyn

Pressure
1 Pa = 1 N/m^2 = 1.450 × 10^{-4} lb/in.^{2} = 0.0209 lb/ft^2
1 bar = 10^5 Pa
1 lb/in.^{2} = 6895 Pa
1 lb/ft^2 = 47.88 Pa
1 atm = 1.013 × 10^5 Pa = 1.013 bar
        = 14.7 lb/in.^{2} = 2117 lb/ft^2
1 mm Hg = 1 torr = 133.3 Pa

Energy
1 J = 10^7 ergs = 0.239 cal
1 cal = 4.186 J (based on 15° calorie)
1 ft·lb = 1.356 J
1 Btu = 1055 J = 252 cal = 778 ft·lb
1 eV = 1.602 × 10^{-19} J
1 kWh = 3.600 × 10^6 J

Mass–Energy Equivalence
1 kg ↔ 8.988 × 10^{16} J
1 u ↔ 931.5 MeV
1 eV ↔ 1.074 × 10^{-9} u

Power
1 W = 1 J/s
1 hp = 746 W = 550 ft·lb/s
1 Btu/h = 0.293 W

APPENDIX F

NUMERICAL CONSTANTS

Fundamental Physical Constants*

Name	Symbol	Value
Speed of light in vacuum	c	2.99792458×10^8 m/s
Magnitude of charge of electron	e	$1.602176565(35) \times 10^{-19}$ C
Gravitational constant	G	$6.67384(80) \times 10^{-11}$ N·m²/kg²
Planck's constant	h	$6.62606957(29) \times 10^{-34}$ J·s
Boltzmann constant	k	$1.3806488(13) \times 10^{-23}$ J/K
Avogadro's number	N_A	$6.02214129(27) \times 10^{23}$ molecules/mol
Gas constant	R	$8.3144621(75)$ J/mol·K
Mass of electron	m_e	$9.10938291(40) \times 10^{-31}$ kg
Mass of proton	m_p	$1.672621777(74) \times 10^{-27}$ kg
Mass of neutron	m_n	$1.674927351(74) \times 10^{-27}$ kg
Magnetic constant	μ_0	$4\pi \times 10^{-7}$ Wb/A·m
Electric constant	$\epsilon_0 = 1/\mu_0 c^2$	$8.854187817... \times 10^{-12}$ C²/N·m²
	$1/4\pi\epsilon_0$	$8.987551787... \times 10^9$ N·m²/C²

Other Useful Constants*

Mechanical equivalent of heat		4.186 J/cal (15° calorie)
Standard atmospheric pressure	1 atm	1.01325×10^5 Pa
Absolute zero	0 K	$-273.15°$C
Electron volt	1 eV	$1.602176565(35) \times 10^{-19}$ J
Atomic mass unit	1 u	$1.660538921(73) \times 10^{-27}$ kg
Electron rest energy	$m_e c^2$	$0.510998928(11)$ MeV
Volume of ideal gas (0°C and 1 atm)		$22.413968(20)$ liter/mol
Acceleration due to gravity (standard)	g	9.80665 m/s²

*Source: National Institute of Standards and Technology (**http://physics.nist.gov/cuu**). Numbers in parentheses show the uncertainty in the final digits of the main number; for example, the number 1.6454(21) means 1.6454 ± 0.0021. Values shown without uncertainties are exact.

Body	Mass (kg)	Radius (m)	Orbit radius (m)	Orbital period
Sun	1.99×10^{30}	6.96×10^{8}	—	—
Moon	7.35×10^{22}	1.74×10^{6}	3.84×10^{8}	27.3 d
Mercury	3.30×10^{23}	2.44×10^{6}	5.79×10^{10}	88.0 d
Venus	4.87×10^{24}	6.05×10^{6}	1.08×10^{11}	224.7 d
Earth	5.97×10^{24}	6.37×10^{6}	1.50×10^{11}	365.3 d
Mars	6.42×10^{23}	3.39×10^{6}	2.28×10^{11}	687.0 d
Jupiter	1.90×10^{27}	6.99×10^{7}	7.78×10^{11}	11.86 y
Saturn	5.68×10^{26}	5.82×10^{7}	1.43×10^{12}	29.45 y
Uranus	8.68×10^{25}	2.54×10^{7}	2.87×10^{12}	84.02 y
Neptune	1.02×10^{26}	2.46×10^{7}	4.50×10^{12}	164.8 y
Pluto[‡]	1.31×10^{22}	1.15×10^{6}	5.91×10^{12}	247.9 y

[†]Source: NASA (**http://solarsystem.nasa.gov/planets/**). For each body, "radius" is its average radius and "orbit radius" is its average distance from the sun or (for the moon) from the earth.

[‡]In August 2006, the International Astronomical Union reclassified Pluto and similar small objects that orbit the sun as "dwarf planets."

Prefixes for Powers of 10

Power of ten	Prefix	Abbreviation	Pronunciation
10^{-24}	yocto-	y	*yoc*-toe
10^{-21}	zepto-	z	*zep*-toe
10^{-18}	atto-	a	*at*-toe
10^{-15}	femto-	f	*fem*-toe
10^{-12}	pico-	p	*pee*-koe
10^{-9}	nano-	n	*nan*-oe
10^{-6}	micro-	μ	*my*-crow
10^{-3}	milli-	m	*mil*-i
10^{-2}	centi-	c	*cen*-ti
10^{3}	kilo-	k	*kil*-oe
10^{6}	mega-	M	*meg*-a
10^{9}	giga-	G	*jig*-a or *gig*-a
10^{12}	tera-	T	*ter*-a
10^{15}	peta-	P	*pet*-a
10^{18}	exa-	E	*ex*-a
10^{21}	zetta-	Z	*zet*-a
10^{24}	yotta-	Y	*yot*-a

Examples:

1 femtometer = 1 fm = 10^{-15} m   1 millivolt = 1 mV = 10^{-3} V

1 picosecond = 1 ps = 10^{-12} s   1 kilopascal = 1 kPa = 10^{3} Pa

1 nanocoulomb = 1 nC = 10^{-9} C   1 megawatt = 1 MW = 10^{6} W

1 microkelvin = 1 μK = 10^{-6} K   1 gigahertz = 1 GHz = 10^{9} Hz

ANSWERS TO ODD-NUMBERED PROBLEMS

Chapter 1

1.1 a) 1.61 km b) 3.28×10^3 ft
1.3 1.02 ns
1.5 5.36 L
1.7 31.7 y
1.9 a) 23.4 km/L b) 1.4 tanks
1.11 9.0 cm
1.13 4.2×10^{-12} cm^3, 1.3×10^{-5} mm^2
1.15 0.45%
1.17 a) no b) no c) no d) no e) no
1.19 $\approx 4 \times 10^8$
1.21 $\approx$ \$70 million
1.23 2×10^5
1.25 7.8 km, 38° north of east
1.27 $A_x = 0, A_y = -8.00$ m, $B_x = 7.50$ m,
    $B_y = 13.0$ cm, $C_x = -10.9$ cm,
    $C_y = -5.07$ cm, $D_x = -7.99$ m, $D_y = 6.02$ m
1.29 a) -6.00 m b) 11.3 m
1.31 a) 9.01 m, 33.7° b) 9.01 m, 33.7°
    c) 22.3 m, 250° d) 22.3 m, 70.3°
1.33 2.81 km, 38.5° north of west
1.35 a) 2.48 cm, 18.4° b) 4.09 cm, 83.7°
    c) 4.09 cm, 264°
1.37 $\vec{A} = -(8.00 \text{ m})\hat{j}$,
    $\vec{B} = (7.50 \text{ m})\hat{i} + (+13.0 \text{ m})\hat{j}$,
    $\vec{C} = (-10.9 \text{ m})\hat{i} + (-5.07 \text{ m})\hat{j}$,
    $\vec{D} = (-7.99 \text{ m})\hat{i} + (6.02 \text{ m})\hat{j}$
1.39 a) $\vec{A} = (1.23 \text{ m})\hat{i} + (3.38 \text{ m})\hat{j}$,
    $\vec{B} = (-2.08 \text{ m})\hat{i} + (-1.20 \text{ m})\hat{j}$
    b) $\vec{C} = (12.0 \text{ m})\hat{i} + (14.9 \text{ m})\hat{j}$
    c) 19.2 m, 51.2°
1.41 a) $A = 5.38, B = 4.36$
    b) $-5.00\hat{i} + 2.00\hat{j} + 7.00\hat{k}$
    c) 8.83, yes
1.43 a) -104 m^2 b) -148 m^2 c) 40.6 m^2
1.45 a) 165° b) 28° c) 90°
1.47 a) $(-63.9 \text{ m}^2)\hat{k}$ b) $(63.9 \text{ m}^2)\hat{k}$
1.49 a) 5.51 g/cm^3
    b) 1.1×10^6 g/cm^3
    c) 4.7×10^{14} g/cm^3
1.51 a) 1.64×10^4 km b) $2.57 r_E$
1.53 a) 2200 g b) 2.1 m
1.55 a) (2.8 ± 0.3) cm^3 b) 170 ± 20
1.57 $\approx 6 \times 10^{27}$
1.59 179 N, 358 N, 45.8° east of north, or 393 N,
    786 N, 45.8° south of east
1.61 144 m, 41° south of west
1.63 7.55 N
1.65 60.9 km, 33.0° south of west
1.67 28.8 m, 11.4° north of east
1.69 71.9 m, 64.1° north of west
1.71 160 N, 13° below horizontal
1.73 a) 818 m, 15.8° west of south
1.75 18.6° east of south, 29.6 m
1.77 28.2 m
1.79 124°
1.81 156 m^2
1.83 28.0 m
1.85 $C_x = -8.0, C_y = -6.1$
1.87 D, F, B, C, A, E
1.89 b) (i) 0.9857 AU (ii) 1.3820 AU
    (iii) 1.695 AU c) 54.6°
1.91 a) 76.2 ly b) 129°
1.93 choice (a)

Chapter 2

2.1 25.0 m
2.3 55 min
2.5 a) 0.312 m/s b) 1.56 m/s
2.7 a) 12.0 m/s b) (i) 0 (ii) 15.0 m/s
    (iii) 12.0 m/s c) 13.3 m/s
2.9 a) 2.33 m/s, 2.33 m/s
    b) 2.33 m/s, 0.33 m/s
2.11 6.7 m/s, 6.7 m/s, 0, -40.0 m/s, -40.0 m/s,
    -40.0 m/s, 0
2.13 a) no b) (i) 12.8 m/s^2 (ii) 3.50 m/s^2
    (iii) 0.718 m/s^2
2.15 a) 2.00 cm/s, 50.0 cm, -0.125 cm/s^2
    b) 16.0 s c) 32.0 s
    d) 6.20 s, 1.23 cm/s;
    25.8 s, -1.23 cm/s; 36.4 s, -2.55 cm/s
2.17 a) 0.500 m/s^2 b) 0, 1.00 m/s^2
2.19 a) 8.33 m/s b) 1.11 m/s^2
2.21 a) 675 m/s^2 b) 0.0667 s
2.23 1.70 m
2.25 0.38 m
2.27 a) 3.1×10^6 m/s^2 = 3.2×10^5 g
    b) 1.6 ms c) no
2.29 a) (i) 5.59 m/s^2 (ii) 7.74 m/s^2
    b) (i) 179 m (ii) 1.28×10^4 m
2.31 a) 0, 6.3 m/s^2, -11.2 m/s^2
    b) 100 m, 230 m, 320 m
2.33 2.69 m/s
2.35 a) 2.94 m/s b) 0.600 s
2.37 1.67 s
2.39 a) 33.5 m b) 15.8 m/s
2.41 a) $t = \sqrt{2d/g}$ b) 0.190 s
2.43 a) 646 m b) 16.4 s, 112 m/s
2.45 a) 249 m/s^2 b) 25.4 c) 101 m
    d) no (if a is constant)
2.47 0.0868 m/s^2
2.49 37.6 m/s
2.51 a) 467 m b) 110 m/s
2.53 a) $x = (0.25 \text{ m/s}^3)t^3 - (0.010 \text{ m/s}^4)t^4$,
    $v_x = (0.75 \text{ m/s}^3)t^2 - (0.040 \text{ m/s}^4)t^3$
    b) 39.1 m/s
2.55 a) 10.0 m b) (i) 8.33 m/s (ii) 9.09 m/s
    (iii) 9.52 m/s
2.57 250 km
2.59 a) 197 m/s b) 169 m/s
2.61 a) 92.0 m b) 92.0 m
2.63 67 m
2.65 a) 7.56 s b) 37.2 m
    c) 25.7 m/s (car), 15.9 m/s (truck)
2.67 a) 15.9 s b) 393 m c) 29.5 m/s
2.69 a) -4.00 m/s b) 12.0 m/s
2.71 a) $2.64H$ b) $2.64T$
2.73 a) 6.69 m/s b) 4.49 m c) 1.42 s
2.75 a) 3.3 s b) $9H$
2.77 6.75 s
2.79 a) 380 m b) 184 m
2.81 a) 0.625 m/s^3 b) 107 m
2.83 a) car A b) 2.27 s, 5.73 s c) 1.00 s, 4.33 s
    d) 2.67 s
2.85 a) 0.0510 s^2/m b) lower than c) no
2.87 4.8
2.89 a) 8.3 m/s b) (i) 0.411 m (ii) 1.15 km
    c) 9.8 m/s d) 4.9 m/s
2.91 choice (b)

Chapter 3

3.1 a) 1.4 m/s, -1.3 m/s b) 1.9 m/s, 317°
3.3 a) 7.1 cm/s, 45°
    b) 5.0 cm/s, 90°; 7.1 cm/s, 45°; 11 cm/s, 27°
3.5 b) -8.67 m/s^2, -2.33 m/s^2
    c) 8.98 m/s^2, 195°
3.7 b) $\vec{v} = \alpha\hat{i} - 2\beta t\hat{j}, \vec{a} = -2\beta\hat{j}$
    c) 5.4 m/s, 297°; 2.4 m/s^2, 270°
    d) speeding up and turning right
3.9 a) 1.13 m b) 0.528 m
    c) $v_x = 1.10$ m/s, $v_y = -4.70$ m/s, 4.83 m/s,
    76.8° below the horizontal
3.11 2.57 m
3.13 a) 24.1 m/s b) 31.0 m/s
3.15 1.28 m/s^2
3.17 a) 0.683 s, 2.99 s
    b) 24.0 m/s, 11.3 m/s; 24.0 m/s, -11.3 m/s
    c) 30.0 m/s, 36.9° below the horizontal
3.19 a) 1.5 m b) -0.89 m/s
3.21 a) 13.6 m b) 34.6 m/s c) 103 m
3.23 a) 0.034 m/s^2 = 0.0034g b) 1.4 h
3.25 120 m/s^2, 270 mph
3.27 a) 2.57 m/s^2 upward
    b) 2.57 m/s^2 downward
    c) 14.7 s
3.29 a) 32.9 m/s b) 27.7 m/s^2 c) 35.5 rpm
3.31 a) 14 s b) 70 s
3.33 0.36 m/s, 52.5° south of west
3.35 a) 4.7 m/s, 25° south of east b) 120 s
    c) 240 m
3.37 a) 24° west of south b) 5.5 h
3.39 a) $A = 0, B = 2.00$ m/s^2,
    $C = 50.0$ m, $D = 0.500$ m/s^3
    b) $\vec{a} = (4.00 \text{ m/s}^2)\hat{i}, \vec{v} = 0$
    c) $v_x = 40.0$ m/s, $v_y = 150$ m/s, 155 m/s
    d) $\vec{r} = (200 \text{ m})\hat{i} + (550 \text{ m})\hat{j}$
3.41 $2b/3c$
3.43 a) 128 m b) 315 m
3.45 31 m/s
3.47 274 m
3.49 795 m
3.51 33.7 m
3.53 a) 42.8 m/s b) 42.0 m
3.55 a) 16.6 m/s
    b) 10.9 m/s, 40.5° below the horizontal
3.57 a) 1.50 m/s b) 4.66 m
3.59 a) 6.91 m c) no
3.61 a) 4.25 m/s b) 10.6 m
3.63 a) 17.8 m/s b) in the river, 28.4 m
    horizontally from his launch point
3.65 a) 49.5 m/s b) 50 m
3.67 a) 81.6 m b) 245 m
    c) in the cart
3.69 a) 13.3 m/s b) 3.8 m
3.71 a) 44.7 km/h, 26.6° west of south
    b) 10.5° north of west
3.73 7.39 m/s, 12.4° north of east
3.75 3.01 m/s, 33.7° north of east
3.77 a) graph R^2 versus h b) 16.4 m/s
    c) 23.8 m
3.79 70.5°
3.81 5.15 s
3.83 choice (b)
3.85 choice (c)

Chapter 4

4.1 494 N, 31.8°
4.3 3.15 N
4.5 a) −8.10 N, 3.00 N b) 8.64 N
4.7 46.7 N, opposite to the motion of the skater
4.9 21.8 kg
4.11 a) 3.12 m, 3.12 m/s b) 21.9 m, 6.24 m/s
4.13 a) 45.0 N, between 2.0 s and 4.0 s
      b) between 2.0 s and 4.0 s c) 0 s, 6.0 s
4.15 a) $A = 100$ N, $B = 12.5$ N/s²
      b) (i) 21.6 N, 2.70 m/s² (ii) 134 N, 16.8 m/s²
      c) 26.6 m/s²
4.17 2940 N
4.19 a) 4.49 kg b) 4.49 kg, 8.13 N
4.21 825 N, blocks
4.23 50 N
4.25 b) yes
4.27 a) yes b) no
4.29 b) 142 N
4.31 2.58 s
4.33 a) 17 N, 90° clockwise from the $+x$-axis
      b) 840 N
4.35 a) 4.85 m/s b) 16.2 m/s² upward
      c) 1470 N upward (on him), 2360 N downward
      (on ground)
4.37 a) 153 N
4.39 a) 2.50 m/s² b) 10.0 N
      c) to the right, $F > T$ d) 25.0 N
4.41 a) 4.4 m b) 300 m/s
      c) (i) 2.7×10^4 N (ii) 9.0×10^3 N
4.43 b) 0.049 N c) $410mg$
4.45 a) 0.603 m/s², upward
      b) 1.26 m/s², downward
4.47 a) 7.79 m/s b) 50.6 m/s² upward
      c) $F_{\text{ground}} - mg$ upward, 4530 N upward,
      $6.16mg$
4.49 a) 4.34 kg b) 5.30 kg
4.51 7.78 m
4.53 a) largest: Ferrari; smallest: Alpha Romeo and
      Honda Civic b) largest: Ferrari; smallest:
      Volvo c) 7.5 kN, smaller d) zero
4.55 b) 26 kg, 8.3 m/s²
4.57 choice (d)
4.59 choice (a)

Chapter 5

5.1 a) 25.0 N b) 50.0 N
5.3 a) 990 N, 735 N b) 926 N
5.5 48°
5.7 a) $T_A = 0.732w$, $T_B = 0.897w$, $T_C = w$
     b) $T_A = 2.73w$, $T_B = 3.35w$, $T_C = w$
5.9 a) 574 N b) 607 N
5.11 a) 1.10×10^8 N b) $5w$ c) 8.4 s
5.13 a) 4610 m/s² = $470g$
      b) 9.70×10^5 N = $471w$ c) 0.0187 s
5.15 b) 2.96 m/s² c) 191 N; greater than; less than
5.17 b) 3.75 m/s² c) 2.48 kg
      d) $T <$ weight of the hanging block
5.19 a) 0.832 m/s² b) 17.3 s
5.21 a) 3.4 m/s c) $2.2w$
5.23 a) 14.0 m b) 18.0 m/s
5.25 50°
5.27 a) 33 N b) 3.1 m
5.29 a) μ_s: 0.710; μ_k: 0.472 b) 258 N
      c) (i) 51.8 N (ii) 4.97 m/s²
5.31 a) 18.3 m/s² b) 2.29 m/s²
5.33 a) 57.1 N b) 146 N up the ramp
5.35 a) 52.5 m b) 16.0 m/s
5.37 a) $\mu_k(m_A + m_B)g$ b) $\mu_k m_A g$

5.39 a) 0.218 m/s b) 11.7 N
5.41 a) $\dfrac{\mu_k mg}{\cos\theta - \mu_k \sin\theta}$ b) $1/\tan\theta$
5.43 b) 8.2 m/s
5.45 a) 61.8 N b) 30.4 N
5.47 3.66 s
5.49 a) 21.0°, no b) 11,800 N (car), 23,600 N (truck)
5.51 6200 N (horizontal cable), 1410 N (upper cable)
5.53 a) 1.5 rev/min b) 0.92 rev/min
5.55 a) 38.3 m/s = 138 km/h b) 3580 N
5.57 2.42 m/s
5.59 a) 1.73 m/s² c) 0.0115 N upward
      d) 0.0098 N
5.61 a) rope making 60° angle b) 6400 N
5.63 $T_B = 4960$ N, $T_C = 1200$ N
5.65 a) 470 N b) 163 N
5.67 762 N
5.69 a) (i) −3.80 m/s (ii) 24.6 m/s b) 4.36 m
      c) 2.45 s
5.71 a) 11.4 N b) 2.57 kg
5.73 12.3 m/s
5.75 1.78 m/s
5.77 a) $m_1(\sin\alpha + \mu_k \cos\alpha)$
      b) $m_1(\sin\alpha - \mu_k \cos\alpha)$
      c) $m_1(\sin\alpha - \mu_s \cos\alpha) \le m_2 \le$
      $m_1(\sin\alpha + \mu_s \cos\alpha)$
5.79 a) 1.44 N b) 1.80 N
5.81 920 N
5.83 a) 88.0 N northward b) 78 N southward
5.85 a) 294 N (18.0-cm wire), 152 N, 152 N
      b) 40.0 N
5.87 3.0 N
5.89 a) 12.9 kg b) $T_{AB} = 47.2$ N, $T_{BC} = 101$ N
5.91 $a_1 = \dfrac{2m_2 g}{4m_1 + m_2}$, $a_2 = \dfrac{m_2 g}{4m_1 + m_2}$
5.93 1.46 m above the floor
5.95 g/μ_s
5.97 b) 0.452
5.99 0.34
5.101 b) 8.8 N c) 31.0 N d) 1.54 m/s²
5.103 $v = (2mg/k)\left[\frac{1}{2} + e^{-(k/m)t}\right]$
5.105 b) 0.28 c) no
5.107 a) 81.1° b) no
       c) The bead rides at the bottom of the hoop.
5.109 a) 0.371 b) 0.290
       c) yes, same slope, less-negative intercept
5.111 a) 5/8 in. b) 23.9 kN c) 3.57 kN, smaller
       d) larger; accurate
5.113 $F = (M + m)g \tan\alpha$
5.115 $\cos^2\beta$
5.117 choice (b)

Chapter 6

6.1 a) 3.60 J b) −0.900 J c) 0 d) 0 e) 2.70 J
6.3 a) 74 N b) 333 J c) −330 J d) 0,0 e) 0
6.5 a) −1750 J b) no
6.7 a) (i) 9.00 J (ii) −9.00 J
     b) (i) 0 (ii) 9.00 J (iii) −9.00 J (iv) 0
     c) zero for each block
6.9 a) (i) 0 (ii) 0 b) (i) 0 (ii) −25.1 J
6.11 a) 374 J b) −333 J c) 0 d) 41 J
      e) 352 J
6.13 −572 J
6.15 a) 120 J b) −108 J c) 24.3 J
6.17 a) 36,000 J b) 4
6.19 a) 1.0×10^{16} J b) 2.4 times
6.21 a) 43.2 m/s b) 101 m/s
6.23 $\sqrt{2gh(1 + \mu_k/\tan\alpha)}$

6.25 48.0 N
6.27 a) 4.48 m/s b) 3.61 m/s
6.29 a) 4.96 m/s b) 1.43 m/s²; 4.96 m/s, same
6.31 a) $v_0^2/2\mu_k g$ b) (i) $\frac{1}{2}$ (ii) 4 (iii) 2
6.33 a) 40.0 N/m b) 0.456 N
6.35 b) 13.1 cm (bottom), 14.1 cm (middle),
      15.2 cm (top)
6.37 a) 2.83 m/s b) 3.46 m/s
6.39 8.5 cm
6.41 a) 1.76 b) 0.666 m/s
6.43 a) 4.0 J b) 0 c) −1.0 J d) 3.0 J
      e) −1.0 J
6.45 a) 2.83 m/s b) 2.40 m/s
6.47 a) 0.0565 m b) no, 0.57 J
6.49 8.17 m/s
6.51 360,000 J; 100 m/s
6.53 $(3.9 \times 10^{13})P$
6.55 745 W ≈ 1 hp
6.57 a) 84.6/min b) 22.7/min
6.59 29.6 kW
6.61 0.20 W
6.63 a) 608 J b) −395 J c) 0 d) −189 J
      e) 24 J f) 1.5 m/s
6.65 a) 5.62 J (20.0-N block), 3.38 J (12.0-N
      block) b) 2.58 J (20.0-N block), 1.54 J
      (12.0-N block)
6.67 a) 1.8 m/s = 4.0 mi/h
      b) 180 m/s² ≈ 18g, 900 N
6.69 a) 5.11 m b) 0.304 c) 10.3 m
6.71 a) 0.074 N b) 4.7 N c) 0.22 J
6.73 6.3×10^4 N/m
6.75 1.1 m
6.77 a) 2.39 m/s b) 9.42 m/s, away from the wall
6.79 a) 0.600 m b) 1.50 m/s
6.81 0.786
6.83 1.3 m
6.85 a) 1.10×10^5 J b) 1.30×10^5 J
      c) 3.99 kW
6.87 3.6 h
6.89 a) 1.26×10^5 J b) 1.46 W
6.91 b) $v^2 = -\dfrac{k}{m}d^2 + 2d\left[\dfrac{k}{m}(0.400 \text{ m}) - \mu_k g\right]$
      c) 1.29 m/s, 0.204 m d) 12.0 N/m, 0.800
6.93 a) $Mv^2/6$ b) 6.1 m/s c) 3.9 m/s
      d) 0.40 J, 0.60 J
6.95 choice (a)
6.97 choice (d)

Chapter 7

7.1 a) 6.6×10^5 J b) -7.7×10^5 J
7.3 a) 610 N b) (i) 0 (ii) 550 J
7.5 a) 24.0 m/s b) 24.0 m/s c) part (b)
7.7 a) 2.0 m/s b) $9.8/10^{-7}$ J, 2.0 J/kg c) 200 m,
     63 m/s d) 5.9 J/kg e) in its tensed legs
7.9 a) (i) 0 (ii) 0.98 J b) 2.8 m/s
     c) Only gravity is constant. d) 5.1 N
7.11 −5400 J
7.13 a) 660 J b) −118 J c) 353 J d) 190 J
      e) 3.16 m/s², 6.16 m/s, 190 J
7.15 a) 52.0 J b) 3.25 J
7.17 a) (i) $4U_0$ (ii) $U_0/4$
      b) (i) $x_0\sqrt{2}$ (ii) $x_0/\sqrt{2}$
7.19 a) 5.48 cm b) 3.92 cm
7.21 a) 6.32 cm b) 12 cm
7.23 a) 3.03 m/s, as it leaves the spring
      b) 95.9 m/s², when the spring has its maximum
      compression
7.25 a) 4.46×10^5 N/m b) 0.128 m
7.27 a) −5.4 J b) −5.4 J c) −10.8 J
      d) nonconservative

7.29 a) 8.16 m/s b) 766 J
7.31 1.29 N, $+x$-direction
7.33 130 m/s^2, 132° counterclockwise from
      the $+x$-axis
7.35 a) $F(r) = (12a/r^{13}) - (6b/r^7)$
      b) $(2a/b)^{1/6}$, yes c) $b^2/4a$
      d) $a = 6.67 \times 10^{-138}$ J·m^{12},
         $b = 6.41 \times 10^{-78}$ J·m^6
7.37 a) zero (gravel), 637 N (box) b) 2.99 m/s
7.39 0.41
7.41 a) 16.0 m/s b) 11,500 N
7.43 a) 20.0 m along the rough bottom b) -78.4 J
7.45 a) 22.2 m/s b) 16.4 m c) no
7.47 0.602 m
7.49 15.5 m/s
7.51 4.4 m/s
7.53 a) 7.00 m/s b) 8.82 N
7.55 48.2°
7.57 a) 0.392 b) -0.83 J
7.59 a) $U(x) = \frac{1}{2}\alpha x^2 + \frac{1}{3}\beta x^3$ b) 7.85 m/s
7.61 a) $\alpha/(x + x_0)$ b) 3.27 m/s
7.63 7.01 m/s
7.65 a) 0.747 m/s b) 0.931 m/s
7.67 a) 0.480 m/s b) 0.566 m/s
7.69 a) 3.87 m/s b) 0.10 m
7.71 0.456 N
7.73 119 J
7.75 a) -50.6 J b) -67.5 J c) nonconservative
7.77 a) 57.0 m b) 16.5 m
      c) negative work done by air resistance
7.79 a) yes b) 0.14 J d) -1.0 m, 0, 1.0 m
      e) positive: -1.5 m $< x < -1.0$ m and
         $0 < x < 1.0$ m; negative: -1.0 m $< x < 0$
         and 1.0 m $< x < 1.5$ m f) -0.55 m, 0.12 J
7.81 choice (c)
7.83 choice (b)

Chapter 8

8.1   a) 1.20×10^5 kg·m/s
      b) (i) 60.0 m/s (ii) 26.8 m/s
8.3   a) -30 kg·m/s, -55 kg·m/s
      b) 0, 52 kg·m/s c) 0, -3.0 kg·m/s
8.5   a) 22.5 kg·m/s, to the left b) 838 J
8.7   562 N, not significant
8.9   a) 10.8 m/s, to the right
      b) 0.750 m/s, to the left
8.11 a) 500 N/s^2 b) 5810 N·s c) 2.70 m/s
8.13 a) 2.50 N·s, in the direction of the force
      b) (i) 6.25 m/s, to the right (ii) 3.75 m/s,
         to the right
8.15 0.593 kg·m/s
8.17 0.87 kg·m/s, in the same direction as the bullet
      is traveling
8.19 a) 6.79 m/s b) 55.2 J
8.21 a) 0.790 m/s b) -0.0023 J
8.23 1.97 m/s
8.25 a) 0.0559 m/s b) 0.0313 m/s
8.27 a) 7.20 m/s, 38.0° from Rebecca's original
      direction b) -680 J
8.29 a) 4.3 m/s c) 4.3 m/s
8.31 a) A: 29.3 m/s; B: 20.7 m/s b) 19.6%
8.33 a) 0.846 m/s b) 2.10 J
8.35 a) -1.4×10^{-6} km/h, no
      b) -6.7×10^{-8} km/h, no
8.37 5.9 m/s, 58° north of east
8.39 5.46 m/s, 36.0° south of east
8.41 19.5 m/s (car), 21.9 m/s (truck)
8.43 a) 2.93 cm b) 866 J c) 1.73 J
8.45 13.6 N

8.47 a) 3.00 J; 0.500 m/s for both
      b) A: -1.00 m/s; B: 1.00 m/s
8.49 a) $v_1/3$ b) $K_1/9$ c) 10
8.51 (0.0444 m, 0.0556 m)
8.53 2520 km
8.55 0.700 m to the right and 0.700 m upward
8.57 0.73 m/s
8.59 $F_x = -(1.50$ N/s$)t$, $F_y = 0.25$ N, $F_z = 0$
8.61 a) 0.053 kg b) 5.19 N
8.63 a) 7.2×10^{-66} b) 0.223
8.65 a) -1.14 N·s, 0.330 N·s
      b) 0.04 m/s, 1.8 m/s
8.67 a) 5.21 J, -0.0833 m/s
      b) -2.17 m/s (A), 0.333 m/s (B)
8.69 a) 1.75 m/s, 0.260 m/s b) -0.092 J
8.71 0.946 m
8.73 1.8 m
8.75 a) $a_A = 162$ m/s^2, $a_B = 54.0$ m/s^2
      b) $v_A = 5.23$ m/s, $v_B = 1.74$ m/s
8.77 12 m/s (SUV), 21 m/s (sedan)
8.79 a) 2.60 m/s b) 325 m/s
8.81 a) 5.3 m/s b) 5.7 m
8.83 53.7°
8.85 a) 0.0781 b) 248 J c) 0.441 J
8.87 a) 9.35 m/s b) 3.29 m/s
8.89 1.61×10^{-22} kg·m/s, to the left
8.91 1.33 m
8.93 0.400 m/s
8.95 250 J
8.97 a) 71.6 m/s (0.28-kg piece),
      14.3 m/s (1.40-kg piece) b) 347 m
8.99 a) yes b) no, decreases by 4800 J
8.101 a) maximum: C, minimum: B
      b) 69 N/m c) 0.12 m
8.103 a) $g/3$ b) 14.7 m c) 29.4 g
8.105 0, $4a/3\pi$
8.107 choice (b)
8.109 choice (b)

Chapter 9

9.1   a) 0.600 rad, 34.4° b) 6.27 cm c) 1.05 m
9.3   a) rad/s, rad/s^3 b) (i) 0 (ii) 15.0 rad/s^2
      c) 9.50 rad
9.5   a) $\omega_z = \gamma + 3\beta t^2$ b) 0.400 rad/s
      c) 1.30 rad/s, 0.700 rad/s
9.7   a) $\pi/4$ rad, 2.00 rad/s, -0.139 rad/s^3
      b) 0 c) 19.5 rad/s, 9.36 rad/s
9.9   a) 2.00 rad/s b) 4.38 rad
9.11 a) 24.0 s b) 68.8 rev
9.13 3.00 rad/s
9.15 a) 300 rpm b) 75.0 s, 312 rev
9.17 9.00 rev
9.19 a) 1.99×10^{-7} rad/s
      b) 7.27×10^{-5} rad/s c) 2.98×10^4 m/s
      d) 463 m/s e) 0.0337 m/s^2, 0
9.21 a) 15.1 m/s^2 b) 15.1 m/s
9.23 a) 0.180 m/s^2, 0, 0.180 m/s^2
      b) 0.180 m/s^2, 0.377 m/s^2, 0.418 m/s^2
      c) 0.180 m/s^2, 0.754 m/s^2, 0.775 m/s^2
9.25 0.107 m, no
9.27 a) 0.831 m/s b) 109 m/s^2
9.29 a) (i) 0.469 kg·m^2 (ii) 0.117 kg·m^2 (iii) 0
      b) (i) 0.0433 kg·m^2 (ii) 0.0722 kg·m^2
      c) (i) 0.0288 kg·m^2 (ii) 0.0144 kg·m^2
9.31 a) 1.93 kg·m^2 b) 6.53 kg·m^2
      c) 1.15 kg·m^2
9.33 0.193 kg·m^2
9.35 8.52 kg·m^2
9.37 6.49 m/s
9.39 0.600 kg·m^2

9.41 7.35×10^4 J
9.43 a) 0.673 m b) 45.5%
9.45 46.5 kg
9.47 a) f^5 b) 6.37×10^8 J
9.49 an axis that is parallel to a diameter and is
      0.516R from the center
9.51 $M(a^2 + b^2)/3$
9.53 $\frac{1}{2}MR^2$
9.55 a) $\gamma L^2/2$ b) $ML^2/2$ c) $ML^2/6$
9.57 7.68 m
9.59 a) 0.600 m/s^3 b) $\alpha = (2.40$ rad/s$^3)t$
      c) 3.54 s d) 17.7 rad
9.61 13.8 rad/s^2
9.63 a) 1.70 m/s b) 94.2 rad/s
9.65 2.99 cm
9.67 a) 7.36 m b) 327 m/s^2
9.69 4.65 kg·m^2
9.71 a) -0.882 J b) 5.42 rad/s c) 5.42 m/s
      d) 5.42 m/s compared to 4.43 m/s
9.73 1.46 m/s
9.75 $\sqrt{\dfrac{2gd(m_B - \mu_k m_A)}{m_A + m_B + I/R^2}}$
9.77 a) 2.25×10^{-3} kg·m^2 b) 3.40 m/s
      c) 4.95 m/s
9.79 13.9 m
9.81 a) 1.05 rad/s b) 5.0 J c) 78.5 J d) 6.4%
9.85 a) 55.3 kg b) 0.804 kg·m^2
9.87 a) 4.0 rev, no b) 15 rad/s c) 9.5 rad/s
9.89 a) yes b) 3.15 m/s c) 0.348 kg·m^2
      d) 36.4 N
9.91 a) $s(\theta) = r_0\theta + \dfrac{\beta}{2}\theta^2$
      b) $\theta(t) = \dfrac{1}{\beta}\left(\sqrt{r_0^2 + 2\beta vt} - r_0\right)$
      c) $\omega_z(t) = \dfrac{v}{\sqrt{r_0^2 + 2\beta vt}}$,
         $\alpha_z(t) = -\dfrac{\beta v^2}{(r_0^2 + 2\beta vt)^{3/2}}$, no
      d) 25.0 mm, 0.247 μm/rad, 2.13×10^4 rev
9.93 choice (d)
9.95 choice (d)

Chapter 10

10.1 a) 40.0 N·m, out of the page
      b) 34.6 N·m, out of the page
      c) 20.0 N·m, out of the page
      d) 17.3 N·m, into the page e) 0 f) 0
10.3 2.50 N·m, out of the page
10.5 b) $-\hat{k}$ c) $(-1.05$ N·m$)\hat{k}$
10.7 a) 2.56 N·m
      b) 4.25 N·m, perpendicular to handle
10.9 8.38 N·m
10.11 a) 14.8 rad/s^2 b) 1.52 s
10.13 a) 7.5 N (at book on table), 18.2 N (at hanging
      book) b) 0.16 kg·m^2
10.15 0.255 kg·m^2
10.17 a) 1.56 m/s b) 5.35 J
      c) (i) 3.12 m/s to the right (ii) 0
      (iii) 2.21 m/s at 45° below the horizontal
      d) (i) 1.56 m/s to the right (ii) 1.56 m/s to
      the left (iii) 1.56 m/s downward
10.19 a) $\frac{1}{3}$ b) $\frac{2}{7}$ c) $\frac{2}{5}$ d) $\frac{5}{13}$
10.21 a) 0.613 b) no c) no slipping
10.23 14.0 m
10.25 a) 3.76 m b) 8.58 m/s
10.27 a) 67.9 rad/s b) 8.35 J
10.29 a) 0.309 rad/s b) 100 J c) 6.67 W
10.31 a) 0.704 N·m b) 157 rad c) 111 J
      d) 111 J

10.33 a) 358 N·m   b) 1790 N   c) 83.8 m/s
10.35 a) 115 kg·m²/s into the page
    b) 125 kg·m²/s² out of the page
10.37 4.71×10^{-6} kg·m²/s
10.39 a) A: rad/s²; B: rad/s⁴
    b) (i) 59.0 kg·m²/s   (ii) 56.1 N·m
10.41 4600 rad/s
10.43 1.14 rev/s
10.45 a) 1.38 rad/s   b) 1080 J, 495 J
10.47 a) 0.120 rad/s   b) 3.20×10^{-4} J
    c) work done by the bug
10.49 a) 5.88 rad/s
10.51 a) 1.62 N   b) 1800 rev/min
10.53 2.4×10^{-12} N·m
10.55 0.483
10.57 a) 16.3 rad/s²   b) no, decrease
    c) 5.70 rad/s
10.59 0.921 m/s², 7.68 rad/s², 35.5 N (at A),
    21.4 N (at B)
10.61 a) 293 N   b) 16.2 rad/s²
10.63 a) 2.88 m/s²   b) 6.13 m/s²
10.65 270 N
10.67 $a = \dfrac{2g}{2 + (R/b)^2}$, $\alpha = \dfrac{2g}{2b + R^2/b}$,
    $T = \dfrac{2mg}{2(b/R)^2 + 1}$
10.69 a) $3H_0/5$
10.71 29.0 m/s
10.73 a) 26.0 m/s   b) no change
10.75 $g/3$
10.77 1.87 m
10.79 a) $\frac{6}{19}v/L$ b) $\frac{3}{19}$
10.81 3200 J
10.83 5.41 m
10.85 a) 2.00 rad/s   b) 6.58 rad/s
10.87 0.776 rad/s
10.89 a) A: solid sphere, B: solid cylinder,
    C: hollow sphere, D: hollow cylinder
    b) same   c) D d) 0.350
10.91 a) $mv_1^2 r_1^2/r^3$ b) $\dfrac{mv_1^2}{2}r_1^2\left(\dfrac{1}{r_2^2} - \dfrac{1}{r_1^2}\right)$
    c) same
10.93 a) 39.2 N upward, 39.2 N upward
    b) 60.0 N upward, 18.4 N upward   c) 165 N
    upward, 86.2 N downward   d) 0.0940 rev/s
10.95 choice (c)
10.97 choice (a)

Chapter 11

11.1   29.8 cm
11.3   1.35 m
11.5   6.6 kN
11.7   a) 1000 N, 0.800 m from end where 600-N
    force is applied   b) 800 N, 0.75 m from end
    where 600-N force is applied
11.9   a) 550 N   b) 0.614 m from A
11.11 a) 1920 N   b) 1140 N
11.13 a) $T = 2.60w$; $3.28w$, $37.6°$
    b) $T = 4.10w$; $5.39w$, $48.8°$
11.15 a) 3410 N   b) 3410 N, 7600 N
11.17 b) 533 N   c) 600 N, 267 N; downward
11.19 220 N (left), 255 N (right), 42°
11.21 a) 0.800 m   b) clockwise
    c) 0.800 m, clockwise
11.23 a) 208 N
11.25 1.9 mm
11.27 2.0×10^{11} Pa
11.29 a) 3.1×10^{-3} (upper), 2.0×10^{-3} (lower)
    b) 1.6 mm (upper), 1.0 mm (lower)
11.31 a) 150 atm   b) 1.5 km, no

11.33 4.8×10^9 Pa, 2.1×10^{-10} Pa⁻¹
11.35 b) 6.6×10^5 N   c) 1.8 mm
11.37 7.36×10^6 Pa
11.39 3.41×10^7 Pa
11.41 10.2 m/s²
11.43 20.0 kg
11.45 a) 525 N   b) 222 N, 328 N   c) 1.48
11.47 a) 140 N   b) 6 cm to the right
11.49 a) 409 N   b) 161 N
11.51 49.9 cm
11.53 a) 370 N   b) when he starts to raise his leg
    c) no
11.55 a) 3 cm   b) lean backward
11.57 5500 N
11.59 b) 2000 N = 2.72mg c) 4.4 mm
11.61 a) 4.90 m   b) 60 N
11.63 a) 175 N at each hand, 200 N at each foot
    b) 91 N at each hand and at each foot
11.65 a) 1150 N   b) 1940 N   c) 918 N   d) 0.473
11.67 590 N (person above), 1370 N (person below);
    person above
11.69 a) $\dfrac{T_{max}hD}{L\sqrt{h^2 + D^2}}$
    b) $\dfrac{T_{max}h}{L\sqrt{h^2 + D^2}}\left(1 - \dfrac{D^2}{h^2 + D^2}\right)$, positive
11.71 a) 71.5 kg
    b) 380 N, 25.2° above the horizontal
11.73 a) 375 N   b) 325 N   c) 512 N
11.75 a) 0.424 N (A), 1.47 N (B), 0.424 N (C)
    b) 0.848 N
11.77 a) 27° to tip, 31° to slip, tips first
    b) 27° to tip, 22° to slip, slips first
11.79 a) 80 N (A), 870 N (B)   b) 1.92 m
11.81 a) 1.0 cm   b) 0.86 cm
11.83 a) 0.70 m from A b) 0.60 m from A
11.85 a) 4.2×10^4 N   b) 65 m
11.87 b) $x = 1.50$ m $+ \dfrac{(1.30\ \text{m})m_1 - (0.38\ \text{m})M}{m_2}$
    c) 1.59 kg   d) 1.50 m
11.89 a) 391 N (4.00-m ladder), 449 N (3.00-m ladder)
    b) 322 N   c) 334 N   d) 937 N
11.91 a) 0.66 mm   b) 0.022 J   c) 8.35×10^{-3} J
    d) -3.04×10^{-2} J   e) 3.04×10^{-2} J
11.93 choice (a)
11.95 choice (d)

Chapter 12

12.1   no (41.8 N)
12.3   7020 kg/m³; yes
12.5   1.6
12.7   61.6 N
12.9   a) 1.86×10^6 Pa   b) 184 m
12.11 0.581 m
12.13 a) 1.90×10^4 Pa
    b) causes additional force on their walls
12.15 2.8 m
12.17 6.0×10^4 Pa
12.19 2.27×10^5 N
12.21 a) 636 Pa   b) (i) 1170 Pa   (ii) 1170 Pa
12.23 10.9
12.25 a) 2.19×10^7 N   b) 2.17×10^7 N
    c) 5.79×10^8 N
12.27 0.122 m
12.29 6.43×10^{-4} m³, 2.78×10^3 kg/m³
12.31 10.5 N
12.33 a) 116 Pa   b) 921 Pa
    c) 0.822 kg, 822 kg/m³
12.35 1640 kg/m³
12.37 9.6 m/s
12.39 a) 17.0 m/s   b) 0.317 m

12.41 28.4 m/s
12.43 1.47×10^5 Pa
12.45 2.03×10^4 Pa
12.47 2.25×10^5 Pa
12.49 $1.19D$
12.51 a) $(p_0 - p)\pi D^2/4$ b) 776 N
12.53 a) 5.9×10^5 N   b) 1.8×10^5 N
12.55 2.61×10^4 N·m
12.57 0.964 cm, rise
12.59 a) 1470 Pa   b) 13.9 cm
12.61 a) 0.0500 m³   b) 10.0 kg
12.63 9.8×10^6 kg, yes
12.65 a) 0.30   b) 0.70
12.67 a) 8.27×10^3 m³   b) 83.8 kN
12.69 a) 16.5 cm   b) 1.75 m
12.71 a) 5.07 m/s, 1.28   b) 32.4 min, 2.08
12.73 a) 53.9 N   b) 31.0 m/s²
12.75 a) $1 - \dfrac{\rho_B}{\rho_L}$ b) $\left(\dfrac{\rho_L - \rho_B}{\rho_L - \rho_w}\right)L$ c) 4.60 cm
12.77 a) $2\sqrt{h(H - h)}$ b) h
12.79 5.47 m
12.81 a) 0.200 m³/s   b) 6.97×10^4 Pa
12.83 $3h_1$
12.85 b) no
12.87 a) 2.5×10^{-4} m²/Pa (slope), 16 m²
    (intercept)   b) 8.2 m, 800 kg/m³
12.89 choice (b)
12.91 choice (a)

Chapter 13

13.1   a) 2.18
13.3   a) 1.2×10^{-11} m/s²   b) 15 days
    c) no, increase
13.5 2.1×10^{-9} m/s², downward
13.7   a) 2.4×10^{-3} N
    b) $F_{moon}/F_{earth} = 3.5 \times 10^{-6}$
13.9   a) 0.634 m from $3m$
    b) (i) unstable   (ii) stable
13.11 1.38×10^7 m
13.13 a) 0.37 m/s²   b) 1700 kg/m³
13.15 610 N, 735 N (on earth), astronaut and satellite
    have same acceleration; no
13.17 a) 5030 m/s   b) 60,200 m/s
13.19 9.03 m/s²
13.21 a) 7410 m/s   b) 1.71 h
13.23 7330 m/s
13.25 a) 4.1 m/s = 9.1 mph, yes   b) 2.6 h
13.27 a) 82,700 m/s   b) 14.5 days
13.29 a) 7.84×10^9 s = 248 y
    b) 4.44×10^{12} m, 7.38×10^{12} m
13.31 2.3×10^{30} kg = $1.2M_S$
13.33 a) (i) 5.31×10^{-9} N   (ii) 2.67×10^{-9} N
13.35 a) $-\dfrac{GmM}{\sqrt{x^2 + a^2}}$ b) $-GmM/x$
    c) $\dfrac{GmMx}{(x^2 + a^2)^{3/2}}$, toward the ring   d) GmM/x^2
    e) $U = -GmM/a$, $F_x = 0$
13.37 a) 33.7 N   b) 32.8 N
13.39 a) 4.3×10^{37} kg = $(2.1 \times 10^7)M_S$ b) no
    c) 6.32×10^{10} m, yes
13.41 9.16×10^{13} N
13.43 a) 9.67×10^{-12} N, at 45° above $+x$-axis
    b) 3.02×10^{-5} m/s
13.45 a) 2.00×10^{-10} N, 161° above $+x$-axis
    b) $x = 0$, $y = 1.32$ m
13.47 b) (i) 1.49×10^{-5} m/s (50.0-kg sphere),
    7.46×10^{-6} m/s (100.0-kg sphere)
    (ii) 2.24×10^{-5} m/s
    c) 26.6 m
13.49 a) 3.59×10^7 m

13.51 177 m/s

13.53 a) 7.36 h   b) 2.47 h

13.55 1.83×10^{27} kg

13.57 22.8 m

13.59 6060 km/h

13.61 $v = \sqrt{\dfrac{2Gm_{E}h}{R_{E}(R_{E}+h)}}$

13.63 a) $GM^2/4R^2$
  b) $v = \sqrt{GM/4R},\ T = 4\pi\sqrt{R^3/GM}$
  c) $GM^2/4R$

13.65 6.8×10^4 m/s

13.67 a) 7900 m/s   b) 1.53
  c) 8430 m/s (perigee), 5510 m/s (apogee)
  d) 2420 m/s; 3250 m/s; perigee

13.69 5.38×10^9 J

13.71 9.34 m/s²

13.73 $GmMx/(a^2 + x^2)^{3/2}$

13.75 a) $U(r) = \dfrac{Gm_{E}m}{2R_{E}^{3}}r^2$ b) 7.91×10^3 m/s

13.77 a) It is considerable and shows no apparent pattern.
  b) Earth (5500 kg/m³), Mercury (5400 kg/m³), Venus (5300 kg/m³), Mars (3900 kg/m³), Neptune (1600 kg/m³), Uranus (1200 kg/m³), Jupiter (1200 kg/m³), Saturn (530 kg/m³)
  c) no effect   d) 93 m/s²

13.79 a) opposite; opposite   b) 259 days
  c) 44.1°

13.81 $\dfrac{2GMm}{a^2}\left(1 - \dfrac{x}{\sqrt{a^2 + x^2}}\right)$

13.83 choice (c)

Chapter 14

14.1 a) 2.15 ms, 2930 rad/s
  b) 2.00×10^4 Hz, 1.26×10^5 rad/s
  c) 1.3×10^{-15} s $\le T \le 2.3 \times 10^{-15}$ s, 4.3×10^{14} Hz $\le f \le 7.5 \times 10^{14}$ Hz
  d) 2.0×10^{-7} s, 3.1×10^7 rad/s

14.3 5530 rad/s, 1.14 ms

14.5 0.0625 s

14.7 a) 0.80 s   b) 1.25 Hz   c) 7.85 rad/s
  d) 3.0 cm   e) 148 N/m

14.9 a) 0.167 s   b) 37.7 rad/s   c) 0.0844 kg

14.11 a) 0.150 s   b) 0.0750 s

14.13 a) 0.98 m   b) $\pi/2$ rad
  c) $x = (-0.98\text{ m})\sin[(12.2\text{ rad/s})t]$

14.15 a) -2.71 m/s²   b) $x = (1.46\text{ cm}) \times \cos[(15.7\text{ rad/s})t + 0.715\text{ rad}]$,
  $v_x = (-22.9\text{ cm/s}) \times \sin[(15.7\text{ rad/s})t + 0.715\text{ rad}]$,
  $a_x = (-359\text{ cm/s}^2) \times \cos[(15.7\text{ rad/s})t + 0.715\text{ rad}]$

14.17 120 kg

14.19 a) 0.253 kg   b) 1.21 cm   c) 3.03 N

14.21 a) 1.51 s   b) 26.0 N/m
  c) 30.8 cm/s   d) 1.92 N
  e) -0.0125 m, 30.4 cm/s, 0.216 m/s²
  f) 0.324 N

14.23 a) $x = (0.0030\text{ m})\cos[(2760\text{ rad/s})t]$
  b) 8.3 m/s, 2.3×10^4 m/s²
  c) $da_x/dt = (6.3 \times 10^7\text{ m/s}^3) \times \sin[(2760\text{ rad/s})t]$, 6.3×10^7 m/s³

14.25 92.2 m/s²

14.27 a) 0.0336 J   b) 0.0150 m   c) 0.669 m/s

14.29 a) 1.20 m/s   b) 1.11 m/s   c) 36 m/s²
  d) 13.5 m/s²   e) 0.36 J

14.31 $3M; \frac{3}{4}$

14.33 0.240 m

14.35 a) 0.376 m   b) 59.3 m/s²   c) 119 N

14.37 a) 4.06 cm   b) 1.21 m/s   c) 29.8 rad/s

14.39 a) 0, 0, 3.92 J, 3.92 J   b) 3.92 J, 0, 0, 3.92 J
  c) 0.98 J, 0.98 J, 1.96 J, 3.92 J

14.41 a) 2.7×10^{-8} kg·m²
  b) 4.3×10^{-6} N·m/rad

14.43 0.0294 kg·m²

14.45 a) 0.25 s   b) 0.25 s

14.47 0.407 swing per second

14.49 10.7 m/s²

14.51 a) 2.84 s   b) 2.89 s   c) 2.89 s; -2%

14.53 $A: 2\pi\sqrt{\dfrac{L}{g}},\ B: \dfrac{2\sqrt{2}}{3}\left(2\pi\sqrt{\dfrac{L}{g}}\right)$; pendulum A

14.55 0.129 kg·m²

14.57 $A: 2\pi\sqrt{\dfrac{L}{g}},\ B: \sqrt{\dfrac{11}{10}}\left(2\pi\sqrt{\dfrac{L}{g}}\right)$, pendulum B

14.59 a) 0.30 J

14.61 a) 0.393 Hz   b) 1.73 kg/s

14.63 a) $A_1/3$ b) $2A_1$

14.65 0.353 m

14.67 a) 1.34 m/s   b) 1.90 m/s²

14.69 a) 24.4 cm   b) 0.221 s   c) 1.19 m/s

14.71 2.00 m

14.73 $0.921\left(\dfrac{1}{2\pi}\sqrt{\dfrac{g}{L}}\right)$

14.75 a) 0.784 s   b) -1.12×10^{-4} s per s; shorter
  c) 0.419 s

14.77 a) 0.150 m/s   b) 0.112 m/s² downward
  c) 0.700 s   d) 4.38 m

14.79 a) 2.6 m/s   b) 0.21 m   c) 0.49 s

14.81 1.17 s

14.83 0.421 s

14.85 0.705 Hz, 14.5°

14.87 $2\pi\sqrt{\dfrac{M}{3k}}$

14.89 a) 1.60 s   b) 0.625 Hz   c) 3.93 rad/s
  d) 5.1 cm; 0.4 s, 1.2 s, 1.8 s
  e) 79 cm/s²; 0.4 s, 1.2 s, 1.8 s   f) 4.9 kg

14.91 b) The angular amplitude increases as L decreases.   c) about 53°

14.93 a) $Mv^2/6$ c) $\omega = \sqrt{3k/M},\ M' = M/3$

14.95 choice (a)

Chapter 15

15.1 a) 0.439 m, 1.28 ms   b) 0.219 m

15.3 220 m/s = 800 km/h

15.5 a) 1.7 cm to 17 m
  b) 4.3×10^{14} Hz to 7.5×10^{14} Hz
  c) 1.5 cm   d) 6.4 cm

15.7 a) 25.0 Hz, 0.0400 s, 19.6 rad/m
  b) $y(x, t) = (0.0700\text{ m}) \times \cos[(19.6\text{ m}^{-1})x + (157\text{ rad/s})t]$
  c) 4.95 cm   d) 0.0050 s

15.9 a) yes   b) yes   c) no
  d) $v_y = \omega A\cos(kx + \omega t)$, $a_y = -\omega^2 A\sin(kx + \omega t)$

15.11 a) 4 mm   b) 0.040 s   c) 0.14 m, 3.6 m/s
  d) 0.24 m, 6.0 m/s   e) no

15.13 b) $+x$-direction

15.15 a) 17.5 m/s   b) 0.146 m
  c) both would increase by a factor of $\sqrt{2}$

15.17 0.337 kg

15.19 a) 9.53 N   b) 20.8 m/s

15.21 a) 10.0 m/s   b) 0.250 m
  c) $y(x, t) = (3.00\text{ cm}) \times \cos[(8.00\pi\text{ rad/m})x - (80.0\pi\text{ rad/s})t]$
  d) 1890 m/s²   e) yes

15.23 4.10 mm

15.25 a) 95 km   b) 0.25 μW/m²   c) 110 kW

15.27 a) 0.050 W/m²   b) 22 kJ

15.29 9.48×10^{27} W

15.37 a) $(1.33\text{ m})n,\ n = 0, 1, 2, \ldots$
  b) $(1.33\ m)\left(n + \tfrac{1}{2}\right),\ n = 0, 1, 2, \ldots$

15.39 a) 96.0 m/s   b) 461 N
  c) 1.13 m/s, 4.26 m/s²

15.41 b) 2.80 cm   c) 277 cm
  d) 185 cm, 7.96 Hz, 0.126 s, 1470 cm/s
  e) 280 cm/s
  f) $y(x, t) = (5.60\text{ cm}) \times \sin[(0.0906\text{ rad/cm})x]\sin[(133\text{ rad/s})t]$

15.43 4.0 m, 2.0 m, 1.33 m

15.45 a) 45.0 cm   b) no

15.47 a) 311 m/s   b) 246 Hz   c) 245 Hz, 1.40 m

15.49 a) 20.0 Hz, 126 rad/s, 3.49 rad/m
  b) $y(x, t) = (2.50 \times 10^{-3}\text{ m}) \times \cos[(3.49\text{ rad/m})x - (126\text{ rad/s})t]$
  c) $y(0, t) = (2.50 \times 10^{-3}\text{ m})\cos[(126\text{ rad/s})t]$
  d) $y(1.35\text{ m}, t) = (2.50 \times 10^{-3}\text{ m}) \times \cos[(126\text{ rad/s})t - 3\pi/2\text{ rad}]$
  e) 0.315 m/s   f) -2.50×10^{-3} m, 0

15.51 $\dfrac{7L}{2}\sqrt{\dfrac{\mu_1}{F}}$ b) no

15.53 a) 62.1 m

15.55 13.7 Hz, 25.0 m

15.57 1.83 m

15.59 361 Hz (copper), 488 Hz (aluminum)

15.61 a) 18.8 cm   b) 0.0169 kg

15.63 a) 7.07 cm   b) 0.400 kW

15.65 $(0.800\text{ Hz})n,\ n = 1, 2, 3, \ldots$

15.67 a) 2.22 g   b) 2.24×10^4 m/s²

15.69 233 N

15.71 1780 kg/m³

15.73 a) 148 N   b) 26%

15.75 c) 47.5 Hz   d) 138 g

15.77 a) 392 N   b) 392 N + (7.70 N/m)x
  c) 3.89 s

15.79 choice (b)

Chapter 16

16.1 a) 0.344 m   b) 1.2×10^{-5} m
  c) 6.9 m, 50 Hz

16.3 a) 7.78 Pa   b) 77.8 Pa   c) 778 Pa

16.5 a) 90 m   b) 102 kHz   c) 1.4 cm
  d) 4.4 mm to 8.8 mm   e) 6.2 MHz

16.7 90.8 m

16.9 81.4°C

16.11 0.16 s

16.13 a) 5.5×10^{-15} J   b) 0.074 mm/s

16.15 15.0 cm

16.17 a) 4.14 Pa   b) 0.0208 W/m²   c) 103 dB

16.19 a) 4.4×10^{-12} W/m²   b) 6.4 dB
  c) 5.8×10^{-11} m

16.21 14.0 dB

16.23 a) 2.0×10^{-7} W/m²   b) 6.0 m
  c) 290 m   d) yes, no

16.25 a) fundamental: 0.60 m; 0, 1.20 m; first overtone: 0.30 m, 0.90 m; 0, 0.60 m, 1.20 m; second overtone: 0.20 m, 0.60 m, 1.00 m; 0, 0.40 m, 0.80 m, 1.20 m
  b) fundamental: 0; 1.20 m; first overtone: 0, 0.80 m; 0.40 m, 1.20 m; second overtone: 0, 0.48 m, 0.96 m; 0.24 m, 0.72 m, 1.20 m

16.27 506 Hz, 1517 Hz, 2529 Hz

16.29 a) 35.2 Hz   b) 17.6 Hz

16.31 a) 614 Hz   b) 1230 Hz

16.33 a) 137 Hz, 0.50 m   b) 137 Hz, 2.51 m

16.35 a) 172 Hz   b) 86 Hz

16.37 0.125 m

16.39 a) $(820\text{ Hz})n,\ n = 1, 2, 3, \ldots$
  b) $(410\text{ Hz})(2n + 1),\ n = 0, 1, 2, \ldots$

16.41 a) 433 Hz   b) loosen

16.43 1.3 Hz

16.45 780 m/s
16.47 a) 375 Hz b) 371 Hz c) 4 Hz
16.49 a) 0.25 m/s b) 0.91 m
16.51 19.8 m/s
16.53 a) 1910 Hz b) 0.188 m
16.55 a) 7.02 m/s, toward b) 1404 Hz
16.57 a) 36.0° b) 2.94 s
16.59 a) 1.00 b) 8.00
       c) 4.73×10^{-8} m = 47.3 nm
16.61 flute harmonic $3n$ resonates with string
       harmonic $4n$, $n = 1, 3, 5, \ldots$
16.63 a) stopped b) 7th and 9th c) 0.439 m
16.65 a) 0.026 m, 0.53 m, 1.27 m, 2.71 m, 9.01 m
       b) 0.26 m, 0.86 m, 1.84 m, 4.34 m c) 86 Hz
16.67 a) 0.0823 m b) 120 Hz
16.69 b) 2.0 m/s
16.71 a) 38 Hz b) no
16.73 a) 375 m/s b) 1.39 c) 0.8 cm
16.75 d) 9.69 cm/s, 667 m/s²
16.77 choice (b)
16.79 choice (a)
16.81 choice (b)

Chapter 17

17.1   a) −81.0°F b) 134.1°F c) 88.0°F
17.3   a) 27.2 C° b) −55.6 C°
17.5   a) −18.0 F° b) −10.0 C°
17.7   0.964 atm
17.9   a) −282°C b) no, 47,600 Pa
17.11 0.39 m
17.13 1.9014 cm; 1.8964 cm
17.15 49.4°C
17.17 1.7×10^{-5} (C°)⁻¹
17.19 a) 1.431 cm² b) 1.436 cm²
17.21 a) 6.0 mm b) -1.0×10^8 Pa
17.23 555 kJ
17.25 23 min
17.27 240 J/kg · K
17.29 0.526 C°
17.31 45.2 C°
17.33 0.0613 C°
17.35 a) 215 J/kg·K b) water c) too small
17.37 0.114 kg
17.39 27.5°C
17.41 150°C
17.43 7.6 min
17.45 54.5 kJ, 13.0 kcal, 51.7 Btu
17.47 357 m/s
17.49 3.45 L
17.51 5.05×10^{15} kg
17.53 0.0674 kg
17.55 190 g
17.57 a) 222 K/m b) 10.7 W c) 73.3°C
17.59 a) −0.86C° b) 24 W/m²
17.61 4.0×10^{-3} W/m·C°
17.63 105.5°C
17.65 a) 21 kW b) 6.4 kW
17.67 15 W
17.69 2.1 cm²
17.71 35.0°C
17.73 a) 35.1°M b) 39.6 C°
17.75 69.4°C
17.77 23.0 cm (first rod), 7.0 cm (second rod)
17.79 b) 1.9×10^8 Pa
17.81 a) 87°C b) −80°C
17.83 460 s
17.85 a) 83.6 J b) 1.86 J/mol·K
       c) 5.60 J/mol·K
17.87 a) 4.20×10^7 J b) 10.7 C° c) 30.0 C°
17.89 a) 0.60 kg b) 0.80 bottle/h
17.91 3.4×10^5 J/kg

17.93 a) no b) 0.0°C, 0.156 kg
17.95 a) 86.1°C
       b) no ice, 0.130 kg liquid water, no steam
17.97 a) 100°C
       b) 0.0214 kg steam, 0.219 kg liquid water
17.99 a) 93.9 W b) 1.35
17.101 2.9
17.103 a) 59.8°C b) 42.7°C c) 8.40 W
17.105 c) 170 h d) 1.5×10^{10} s ≈ 500 y, no
17.107 5.82 g
17.109 a) 1.04 kW b) 87.1 W c) 1.13 kW
       d) 28 g e) 1.1 bottles
17.111 a) 3.00×10^4 J/kg b) 1.00×10^3 J/kg·K
       (liquid), 1.33×10^3 J/kg·K (solid)
17.113 A: 216 W/m·K, B: 130 W/m·K
17.115 a) $H = \dfrac{(T_2 - T_1) 2\pi k L}{\ln(b/a)}$

       b) $T = T_2 - \dfrac{(T_2 - T_1)\ln(r/a)}{\ln(b/a)}$

       d) 73°C e) 49 W
17.117 choice (a)
17.119 choice (a)

Chapter 18

18.1   a) 0.122 mol b) 14,700 Pa, 0.145 atm
18.3   0.100 atm
18.5   a) 0.0136 kg/m³, 67.6 kg/m³, 5.39 kg/m³
       b) $0.011\rho_E$, $56\rho_E$, $4.5\rho_E$
18.7   503°C
18.9   19.7 kPa
18.11 0.159 L
18.13 $0.0508V$
18.15 a) 70.2°C b) yes
18.17 850 m
18.19 a) 6.95×10^{-16} kg b) 2.32×10^{-13} kg/m³
18.21 55.6 mol, 3.35×10^{25} molecules
18.23 a) 2.20×10^6 molecules
       b) 2.44×10^{19} molecules
18.25 6.4×10^{-6} m
18.27 a) 5.83×10^7 J b) 242 m/s
18.29 (d) must be true; the others could be true.
18.31 a) 1.93×10^6 m/s, no b) 7.3×10^{10} K
18.33 a) 6.21×10^{-21} J b) 2.34×10^5 m²/s²
       c) 484 m/s d) 2.57×10^{-23} kg·m/s
       e) 1.24×10^{-19} N f) 1.24×10^{-17} Pa
       g) 8.17×10^{21} molecules
       h) 2.45×10^{22} molecules
18.35 3800°C
18.37 a) 1870 J b) 1120 J
18.39 a) 741 J/kg·K, $c_w = 5.65 c_{N_2}$
       b) 5.65 kg; 4850 L
18.41 a) 337 m/s b) 380 m/s c) 412 m/s
18.43 a) 610 Pa b) 22.12 MPa
18.45 18.0 cm³, $V_{20°C} = 0.32 V_{cp}$
18.47 a) 11.8 kPa b) 0.566 L
18.49 272°C
18.51 0.195 kg
18.53 a) −179°C b) 1.2×10^{26} molecules/m³
       c) $\rho_T = 4.8\rho_e$
18.55 1.92 atm
18.57 a) 30.7 cylinders b) 8420 N c) 7800 N
18.59 a) 26.2 m/s b) 16.1 m/s, 5.44 m/s c) 1.74 m
18.61 $\approx 5 \times 10^{27}$ atoms
18.63 a) A b) B c) 4250°C d) B
18.65 a) 6.00×10^3 Pa b) 32.8 m/s
18.67 a) 4.65×10^{-26} kg b) 6.11×10^{-21} J
       c) 2.04×10^{24} molecules d) 12.5 kJ
18.69 a) r_2 c) $r_1 = \dfrac{R_0}{2^{1/6}}$, $r_2 = R_0, 2^{-1/6}$ d) U_0
18.71 a) $2R = 16.6$ J/mol·K b) less than

18.73 b) 1.40×10^5 K (N₂), 1.01×10^4 K (H₂)
       c) 6370 K (N₂), 459 K (H₂)
18.75 $3kT/m$, same
18.77 b) 0.0421N c) $(2.94 \times 10^{-21})N$
       d) 0.0297N, $(2.08 \times 10^{-21})N$
       e) 0.0595N, $(4.15 \times 10^{-21})N$
18.79 a) $p_0 + \dfrac{mg}{\pi r^2}$ b) $-\left(\dfrac{y}{h}\right)(p_0 \pi r^2 + mg)$

       c) $\dfrac{1}{2\pi}\sqrt{\dfrac{g}{h}\left(1 + \dfrac{p_0 \pi r^2}{mg}\right)}$, no
18.81 a) 42.6% b) 3 km c) 1 km
18.83 a) 4.5×10^{11} m
       b) 703 m/s, 6.4×10^8 s (≈20 y)
       c) 1.4×10^{-14} Pa
       d) 650 m/s, $v_H > v_{esc}$, evaporate
       f) 2×10^5 K, $>3T_{sun}$, no
18.85 choice (a)
18.87 choice (c)

Chapter 19

19.1   b) 1330 J
19.3   b) −6180 J
19.5   a) 1.04 atm
19.7   a) $(p_1 - p_2)(V_2 - V_1)$
       b) negative of work done in reverse direction
19.9   a) 34.7 kJ b) 80.4 kJ c) no
19.11 a) 278 K, at a b) 0; 162 J c) 53 J
19.13 a) $T_a = 535$ K, $T_b = 9350$ K, $T_c = 15,000$ K
       b) 21 kJ done by gas c) 36 kJ
19.15 a) 0 b) $T_b = 2T_a$ c) $U_b = U_a + 700$ J
19.17 b) 208 J c) on the piston d) 712 J
       e) 920 J f) 208 J
19.19 a) 948 K b) 900 K
19.21 $\frac{2}{5}$
19.23 a) 747 J b) 1.30
19.25 a) −605 J b) 0 c) yes, 605 J, liberate
19.27 a) 476 kPa b) −10.6 kJ c) 1.59, heated
19.29 b) 314 J c) −314 J
19.31 11.6°C
19.33 a) increase b) 4.8 kJ
19.35 a) 0.681 mol b) 0.0333 m³
       c) 2.23 kJ d) 0
19.37 a) 45.0 J b) liberate, 65.0 J c) 23.0 J, 22.0 J
19.39 a) the same b) 4.0 kJ, absorb c) 8.0 kJ
19.41 b) −2460 J
19.43 a) 0.80 L b) 305 K, 1220 K, 1220 K
       c) ab: 76 J, into the gas
       ca: −107 J, out of the gas
       bc: 56 J, into the gas
       d) ab: 76 J, increased
       bc: 0, no change
       ca: −76 J, decreased
19.45 a) 837°C b) 11.5 kJ c) 40.3 kJ d) 42.4 kJ
19.47 b) 6.00 L, 2.5×10^4 Pa, 75.0 K
       c) 95 J d) heat it at constant volume
19.49 b) 11.9 C°
19.51 a) 0.168 m b) 196°C c) 70.1 kJ
19.53 a) $Q = 450$ J, $\Delta U = 0$
       b) $Q = 0$, $\Delta U = -450$ J
       c) $Q = 1125$ J, $\Delta U = 675$ J
19.55 a) $W = 738$ J, $Q = 2590$ J, $\Delta U = 1850$ J
       b) $W = 0$, $Q = -1850$ J, $\Delta U = -1850$ J
       c) $\Delta U = 0$
19.57 a) $W = -187$ J, $Q = -654$ J, $\Delta U = -467$ J
       b) $W = 113$ J, $Q = 0$, $\Delta U = -113$ J
       c) $W = 0$, $Q = 580$ J, $\Delta U = 580$ J
19.59 a) a: adiabatic, b: isochoric, c: isobaric
       b) 28.0°C c) a: −30.0 J, a: 0, a: 20.0 J
       d) a
       e) a: decrease, b: stay the same, c: increase

19.61 b) -300 J, out of the gas
19.63 choice (c)
19.65 choice (d)

Chapter 20

20.1 a) 6500 J   b) 34%
20.3 a) 23%   b) 12,400 J   c) 0.350 g
 d) 222 kW = 298 hp
20.5 a) 12.3 atm   b) 5470 J, ca c) 3723 J, bc
 d) 1747 J   e) 31.9%
20.7 a) 58%   b) 1.4%
20.9 a) 14.8 kJ   b) 45.8 kJ
20.11 1.2 h
20.13 a) 215 J   b) 378 K   c) 39.0%
20.15 a) 38 kJ   b) 590°C
20.17 a) 492 J   b) 212 W   c) 5.4
20.19 44.5 hp
20.21 a) 429 J/K   b) -393 J/K   c) 36 J/K
20.23 a) irreversible   b) 1250 J/K
20.25 -6.31 J/K
20.27 a) 6.05×10^3 J/K
 b) about five times greater for vaporization
20.29 a) no   b) 18.3 J/K   c) 18.3 J/K
20.31 10.0 J/K
20.33 a) 121 J   b) 3800 cycles
20.35 a) 90.2 J   b) 320 J   c) 45°C   d) 0
 e) 263 g
20.37 -5.8 J/K, decrease
20.39 b) absorbed: bc; rejected: ab and ca
 c) $T_a = T_b = 241$ K, $T_c = 481$ K
 d) 610 J, 610 J   e) 8.7%
20.41 a) 21.0 kJ (enters), 16.6 kJ (leaves)
 b) 4.4 kJ, 21%   c) $e = 0.31e_{max}$
20.43 a) 7.0%   b) 3.0 MW; 2.8 MW
 c) 6×10^5 kg/h = 6×10^5 L/h
20.45 a) 1: 2.00 atm, 4.00 L; 2: 2.00 atm, 6.00 L;
 3: 1.11 atm, 6.00 L; 4: 1.67 atm, 4.00 L
 b) $1 \rightarrow 2$: 1422 J, 405 J; $2' \rightarrow 3$: -1355 J, 0;
 $3 \rightarrow 4$: -274 J, -274 J; $4 \rightarrow 1$: 339 J, 0
 c) 131 J   d) 7.44%; $e = 0.168e_C$
20.47 $1 - T_C/T_H$, same
20.49 a) 122 J, -78 J   b) 5.10×10^{-4} m³
 c) b: 2.32 MPa, 4.81×10^{-5} m³, 771 K
 c: 4.01 MPa, 4.81×10^{-5} m³, 1332 K
 d: 0.147 MPa, 5.10×10^{-4} m³, 518 K
 d) 61.1%, 77.5%
20.51 6.23
20.55 a) A: 28.9%, B: 38.3%, C: 53.8%, D: 24.4%
 b) C   c) $B > D > A$
20.57 a) 4.83%   b) 4.83%   c) 6.25%
 d) $e = \dfrac{0.80T_d - 200}{12T_d - 2700}$, 6.67%
20.59 choice (b)
20.61 choice (d)

Chapter 21

21.1 a) 2.00×10^{10} b) 8.59×10^{-13}
21.3 3.4×10^{18} m/s² (proton),
 6.3×10^{21} m/s² (electron)
21.5 1.3 nC
21.7 3.7 km
21.9 a) 0.742 μC   b) 0.371 μC, 1.48 μC
21.11 a) 2.21×10^4 m/s²
21.13 $+0.750$ nC
21.15 1.8×10^{-4} N, in the $+x$-direction
21.17 $x = -0.144$ m
21.19 2.58 μN, in the $-y$-direction
21.21 a) 8.80×10^{-9} N, attractive
 b) 8.22×10^{-8} N; about 10 times larger than
 the bonding force

21.23 a) 4.40×10^{-16} N   b) 2.63×10^{11} m/s²
 c) 2.63×10^5 m/s
21.25 a) 3.30×10^6 N/C, to the left   b) 14.2 ns
 c) 1.80×10^3 N/C, to the right
21.27 a) -21.9μC   b) 1.02×10^{-7} N/C
21.29 a) 364 N/C   b) no; 2.73 μm, downward
21.31 1.79×10^6 m/s
21.33 a) $-\hat{j}$ b) $\dfrac{\sqrt{2}}{2}\hat{i} + \dfrac{\sqrt{2}}{2}\hat{j}$
 c) $-0.39\hat{i} + 0.92\hat{j}$
21.35 a) 633 km/s   b) 15.9 km/s
21.37 a) 0
 b) for $|x| < a$: $E_x = -\dfrac{q}{\pi\epsilon_0}\dfrac{ax}{(x^2 - a^2)^2}$;
 for $x > a$: $E_x = \dfrac{q}{2\pi\epsilon_0}\dfrac{x^2 + a^2}{(x^2 - a^2)^2}$;
 for $x < -a$: $E_x = -\dfrac{q}{2\pi\epsilon_0}\dfrac{x^2 + a^2}{(x^2 - a^2)^2}$
21.39 a) (i) 574 N/C, $+x$-direction   (ii) 268 N/C,
 $-x$-direction   (iii) 404 N/C, $-x$-direction
 b) (i) 9.20×10^{-17} N, $-x$-direction
 (ii) 4.30×10^{-17} N, $+x$-direction
 (iii) 6.48×10^{-17} N, $+x$-direction
21.41 1.04×10^7 N/C, toward the -2.00-μC charge
21.43 a) 8740 N/C, to the right
 b) 6540 N/C, to the right
 c) 1.40×10^{-15} N, to the right
21.45 1.73×10^{-8} N, toward the point midway
 between the electrons
21.47 a) $E_x = E_y = E = 0$ b) $E_x = 2660$ N/C,
 $E_y = 0, E = 2660$ N/C, $+x$-direction
 c) $E_x = 129$ N/C, $E_y = -510$ N/C,
 $E = 526$ N/C, 284° counterclockwise from
 the $+x$-axis   d) $E_x = 0, E_y = 1380$ N/C,
 $E = 1380$ N/C, $+y$-direction
21.49 a) 1.14×10^5 N/C, toward the center of the
 disk   b) 8.92×10^4 N/C, toward the center
 of the disk
 c) 1.46×10^5 N/C, toward the charge
21.51 a) $(7.0$ N/C$)\hat{i}$ b) $(1.75 \times 10^{-5}$ N$)\hat{i}$
21.53 a) 1.4×10^{-11} C·m, from q_1 toward q_2
 b) 860 N/C
21.55 a) $\vec{p}$ aligned in the same or the opposite
 direction as $\vec{E}$
 b) stable: $\vec{p}$ aligned in the same direction as $\vec{E}$;
 unstable: $\vec{p}$ aligned in the opposite direction
21.57 a) 1680 N, from the $+5.00$-μC charge toward
 the -5.00-μC charge   b) 22.3 N·m, clockwise
21.59 $\dfrac{Q^2}{8\pi\epsilon_0L^2}(1 + 2\sqrt{2})$, away from the center
 of the square
21.61 a) 8.63×10^{-5} N, -5.52×10^{-5} N
 b) 1.02×10^{-4} N, 32.6° below the $+x$-axis
21.63 b) 2.80 μC   c) 39.5°
21.65 3.41×10^4 N/C, to the left
21.67 between the charges, 0.24 m from the 0.500-nC
 charge
21.69 at $x = d/3, q = -4Q/9$
21.71 a) $\dfrac{6q^2}{4\pi\epsilon_0L^2}$, away from the vacant corner
 b) $\dfrac{3q^2}{4\pi\epsilon_0L^2}\left(\sqrt{2} + \dfrac{1}{2}\right)$, toward the center of
 the square
21.73 a) 6.0×10^{23} b) 4.1×10^{-31} N (gravitational), 510 kN (electric)
 c) yes (electric), no (gravitational)
21.75 2190 km/s
21.77 a) $\dfrac{mv_0^2 \sin^2\alpha}{2eE}$ b) $\dfrac{mv_0^2 \sin^2 2\alpha}{eE}$
 d) h_{max}: 0.418 m, d: 2.89 m

21.79 a) $E_x = \dfrac{Q}{4\pi\epsilon_0a}\left(\dfrac{1}{x-a} - \dfrac{1}{x}\right), E_y = 0$
 b) $\dfrac{qQ}{4\pi\epsilon_0a}\left(\dfrac{1}{r} - \dfrac{1}{r+a}\right)\hat{i}$
21.81 a) -7.99 nC   b) -24.0 nC
21.83 a) 1.56 N/C, $+x$-direction   c) smaller
 d) 4.7%
21.85 $E_x = E_y = \dfrac{Q}{2\pi^2\epsilon_0a^2}$
21.87 a) 6.25×10^4 N/C, 225° counterclockwise
 from an axis pointing to the right at point P
 b) 1.00×10^{-14} N, opposite the electric field
 direction
21.89 a) 1.15×10^6 N/C, to the left
 b) 1.58×10^5 N/C, to the left
 c) 1.58×10^5 N/C, to the right
21.91 a) $\pi(R_2^2 - R_1^2)\sigma$
 b) $\dfrac{\sigma}{2\epsilon_0}\left(\dfrac{1}{\sqrt{(R_1/x)^2 + 1}} - \dfrac{1}{\sqrt{(R_2/x)^2 + 1}}\right)\dfrac{|x|}{x}\hat{i}$
 c) $\dfrac{\sigma}{2\epsilon_0}\left(\dfrac{1}{R_1} - \dfrac{1}{R_2}\right)x\hat{i}; x \ll R_1$
 d) $\dfrac{1}{2\pi}\sqrt{\dfrac{q\sigma}{2\epsilon_0m}\left(\dfrac{1}{R_1} - \dfrac{1}{R_2}\right)}$
21.93 a) $q_1 = 8.00 \mu$C, $q_2 = 3.00 \mu$C   b) 7.49 N,
 in the $-x$-direction   c) $x = 0.248$ m
21.95 b) $q_1 < 0, q_2 > 0$ c) 0.843 μC   d) 56.2 N
21.97 a) $\dfrac{Q}{2\pi\epsilon_0L}\left(\dfrac{1}{2x+a} - \dfrac{1}{2L+2x+a}\right)$
21.99 choice (c)
21.101 choice (b)

Chapter 22

22.1 a) 1.8 N·m²/C   b) no   c) (i) 0°   (ii) 90°
22.3 a) 3.53×10^5 N·m²/C   b) 3.13 μC
22.5 $\pi r^2 E$
22.7 0.977 N·m²/C, inward
22.9 a) 0   b) 1.22×10^8 N/C, radially inward
 c) 3.64×10^7 N/C, radially inward
22.11 a) 1.17×10^5 N·m²/C   b) no change
22.13 0.0810 N
22.15 1.35×10^{10}
22.17 a) 6.47×10^5 N/C, $+y$-direction
 b) 7.2×10^4 N/C, $-y$-direction
22.19 a) 5.73 μC/m²   b) 6.47×10^5 N/C
 c) -5.65×10^4 N·m²/C
22.21 a) 0.260 μC/m³   b) 1960 N/C
22.23 a) 6.56×10^{-21} J   b) 1.20×10^5 m/s
22.25 a) 6.00 nC   b) -1.00 nC
22.27 σ/ϵ_0 (between), 0 (outside)
22.29 a) $2\pi R\sigma$ b) $\dfrac{\sigma R}{\epsilon_0 r}$ c) $\dfrac{\lambda}{2\pi\epsilon_0 r}$
22.31 1.16 km/s
22.33 10.2°
22.35 a) 750 N·m²/C   b) 0
 c) 577 N/C, $+x$-direction
 d) within and outside
22.37 a) -0.598 nC   b) within and outside
22.39 a) $\dfrac{\lambda}{2\pi\epsilon_0 r}$, radially outward
 b) $\dfrac{\lambda}{2\pi\epsilon_0 r}$, radially outward
 d) $-\lambda$ (inner), $+\lambda$ (outer)
22.41 a) $\dfrac{\rho r}{2\epsilon_0}$ b) $\dfrac{\lambda}{2\pi\epsilon_0 r}$
 c) They are equal.

22.43 a) $r < R$: 0; $R < r < 2R$: $\dfrac{1}{4\pi\epsilon_0}\dfrac{Q}{r^2}$, radially outward; $r > 2R$: $\dfrac{1}{4\pi\epsilon_0}\dfrac{2Q}{r^2}$, radially outward

22.45 a) (i) 0 (ii) 0 (iii) $\dfrac{q}{2\pi\epsilon_0 r^2}$, radially outward
(iv) 0 (v) $\dfrac{3q}{2\pi\epsilon_0 r^2}$, radially outward
b) (i) 0 (ii) $+2q$ (iii) $-2q$ (iv) $+6q$

22.47 a) $\dfrac{qQ}{4\pi\epsilon_0 r^2}$, toward the center of the shell b) 0

22.49 a) $\dfrac{\alpha}{2\epsilon_0}\left(1 - \dfrac{a^2}{r^2}\right)$ b) $q = +2\pi\alpha a^2$, $E = \dfrac{\alpha}{2\epsilon_0}$

22.51 $R/2$

22.53 c) $\dfrac{Qr}{4\pi\epsilon_0 R^3}\left(4 - \dfrac{3r}{R}\right)$ e) $2R/3$, $\dfrac{Q}{3\pi\epsilon_0 R^2}$

22.55 b) $|x| > d$ (outside the slab): $\dfrac{\rho_0 d}{3\epsilon_0}\dfrac{x}{|x|}\hat{i}$;
$|x| < d$ (inside the slab): $\dfrac{\rho_0 x^3}{3\epsilon_0 d^2}\hat{i}$

22.57 b) $\dfrac{\rho\vec{b}}{3\epsilon_0}$

22.59 a) uniform line of charge: A; uniformly charged sphere: B b) $\lambda = 1.50 \times 10^{-7}$ C/m, $\rho = 2.81 \times 10^{-3}$ C/m³

22.61 (i) 377 N/C (ii) 653 N/C (iii) 274 N/C
(iv) 0

22.63 choice (a)

22.65 choice (b)

Chapter 23

23.1 -0.356 J

23.3 3.46×10^{-13} J $= 2.16$ MeV

23.5 a) 12.5 m/s b) 0.323 m

23.7 1.94×10^{-5} N

23.9 a) 13.6 km/s; very long after release
b) 2.45×10^{17} m/s²; just after release

23.11 $-q/2$

23.13 7.42 m/s, faster

23.15 a) 0 b) 0.750 mJ c) -2.06 mJ

23.17 a) 0 b) -175 kV c) -0.875 J

23.19 a) -737 V b) -704 V c) 8.2×10^{-8} J

23.21 b) $V = \dfrac{q}{4\pi\epsilon_0}\left(\dfrac{1}{|x|} - \dfrac{2}{|x - a|}\right)$
c) $x = -a, a/3$ e) $V = \dfrac{q}{4\pi\epsilon_0 x}$

23.23 a) b b) 800 V/m c) -48.0 μJ

23.25 a) (i) 180 V (ii) -270 V (iii) -450 V
b) 719 V, inner shell

23.27 a) oscillatory b) 1.67×10^7 m/s

23.29 150 m/s

23.31 a) 94.9 nC/m b) no, less c) 0

23.33 a) 78.2 kV b) 0

23.35 0.474 J

23.37 a) 8.00 kV/m b) 19.2 μN c) 0.864 μJ
d) -0.864 μJ

23.39 -760 V

23.41 a) (i) $V = \dfrac{q}{4\pi\epsilon_0}\left(\dfrac{1}{r_a} - \dfrac{1}{r_b}\right)$
(ii) $V = \dfrac{q}{4\pi\epsilon_0}\left(\dfrac{1}{r} - \dfrac{1}{r_b}\right)$ (iii) $V = 0$
d) 0 e) $E = \dfrac{q - Q}{4\pi\epsilon_0 r^2}$

23.43 a) $E_x = -Ay + 2Bx$, $E_y = -Ax - C$, $E_z = 0$
b) $x = -C/A$, $y = -2BC/A^2$, any value of z

23.45 a) 0.762 nC

23.47 a) -0.360 μJ b) $x = 0.074$ m

23.49 4.2×10^6 V

23.51 a) 4.79 MeV, 7.66×10^{-13} J
b) 5.17×10^{-14} m

23.53 a) -21.5 μJ b) -2.83 kV c) 35.4 kV/m

23.55 a) 7.85×10^4 V/m$^{4/3}$
b) $E_x(x) = -(1.05 \times 10^5$ V/m$^{4/3})x^{1/3}$
c) 3.13×10^{-15} N, toward the anode

23.57 $-\dfrac{1.46q^2}{\pi\epsilon_0 d}$

23.59 47.8 V

23.61 a) (i) $V = (\lambda/2\pi\epsilon_0)\ln(b/a)$
(ii) $V = (\lambda/2\pi\epsilon_0)\ln(b/r)$ (iii) $V = 0$
d) $(\lambda/2\pi\epsilon_0)\ln(b/a)$

23.63 a) 1.76×10^{-16} N, downward
b) 1.93×10^{14} m/s², downward c) 0.822 cm
d) 15.3° e) 3.29 cm

23.65 a) 97.1 kV/m b) 30.3 pC

23.67 $\dfrac{3}{5}\left(\dfrac{Q^2}{4\pi\epsilon_0 R}\right)$

23.69 360 kV

23.71 a) 50.0 g: 216 m/s², 12.7 m/s; 150.0 g:
7.20 m/s², 4.24 m/s

23.73 a) $\dfrac{Q}{4\pi\epsilon_0 a}\ln\left(\dfrac{x + a}{x}\right)$
b) $\dfrac{Q}{4\pi\epsilon_0 a}\ln\left(\dfrac{a + \sqrt{a^2 + y^2}}{y}\right)$
c) (a): $\dfrac{Q}{4\pi\epsilon_0 x}$, (b): $\dfrac{Q}{4\pi\epsilon_0 y}$

23.75 a) $\frac{1}{3}$ b) 3

23.77 a) 7580 km/s b) 7260 km/s
c) 2.3×10^9 K; 6.4×10^9 K

23.79 a) $A = -6.0$ V/m², $B = -4.0$ V/m³,
$C = -2.0$ V/m⁶, $D = 10$ V, $l = 2.0$, $m = 3.0$,
$n = 6.0$
b) (0, 0, 0): 10.0 V, 0; (0.50 m, 0.50 m, 0.50 m):
8.0 V, 6.7 V/m; (1.00 m, 1.00 m, 1.00 m):
-2.0 V, 21 V/m

23.81 c) 4.79×10^{-19} C (drop 1), 1.59×10^{-19} C
(drop 2), 8.09×10^{-19} C (drop 3),
3.23×10^{-19} C (drop 4)
d) 3 (drop 1), 5 (drop 3), 2 (drop 4)
e) 1.60×10^{-19} C (drop 1), 1.59×10^{-19} C
(drop 2), 1.62×10^{-19} C (drops 3 and 4);
1.61×10^{-19} C

23.83 1.01×10^{-12} m, 1.11×10^{-13} m,
2.54×10^{-14} m

23.85 choice (b)

Chapter 24

24.1 a) 10.0 kV b) 22.6 cm² c) 8.00 pF

24.3 a) 604 V b) 90.8 cm² c) 1840 kV/m
d) 16.3 μC/m²

24.5 a) 120 μC b) 60 μC c) 480 μC

24.7 a) 1.05 mm b) 84.0 V

24.9 a) 4.35 pF b) 2.30 V

24.11 a) 15.0 pF b) 3.09 cm c) 31.2 kN/C

24.13 a) 17.5 cm b) 25.5 nC

24.15 a) series b) 5000

24.17 a) $Q_1 = Q_2 = 22.4$ μC, $Q_3 = 44.8$ μC,
$Q_4 = 67.2$ μC b) $V_1 = V_2 = 5.6$ V,
$V_3 = 11.2$ V, $V_4 = 16.8$ V c) 11.2 V

24.19 a) $Q_1 = 156$ μC, $Q_2 = 260$ μC
b) $V_1 = V_2 = 52.0$ V

24.21 a) 19.3 nF b) 482 nC c) 162 nC
d) 25 V

24.23 0.0283 J/m³

24.25 a) 90.0 pF b) 0.0152 m³ c) 4.5 kV
d) 1.80 μJ

24.27 a) $U_p = 4U_s$ b) $Q_p = 2Q_s$ c) $E_p = 2E_s$

24.29 a) 24.2 μC b) $Q_{35} = 7.7$ μC,
$Q_{75} = 16.5$ μC c) 2.66 mJ
d) $U_{35} = 0.85$ mJ, $U_{75} = 1.81$ mJ e) 220 V

24.31 a) 1.60 nC b) 8.05

24.33 a) 3.60 mJ (before), 13.5 mJ (after)
b) 9.9 mJ, increase

24.35 a) 0.620 μC/m² b) 1.28

24.37 0.0135 m²

24.39 a) 6.3 μC b) 6.3 μC c) none

24.41 a) 10.1 V b) 2.25

24.43 a) $\dfrac{Q}{\epsilon_0 AK}$ b) $\dfrac{Qd}{\epsilon_0 AK}$ c) $K\dfrac{\epsilon_0 A}{d} = KC_0$

24.45 a) 421 J b) 0.054 F

24.47 a) 0.531 pF b) 0.224 mm

24.49 a) 0.0160 C b) 533 V c) 4.26 J d) 2.14 J

24.51 a) 158 μJ b) 72.1 μJ

24.53 a) 2.5 μF
b) $Q_1 = 550$ μC, $Q_2 = 370$ μC, $Q_3 = Q_4 = $
180 μC, $Q_5 = 550$ μC; $V_1 = 65$ V, $V_2 = 87$ V,
$V_3 = V_4 = 43$ V, $V_5 = 65$ V

24.55 $C_2 = 6.00$ μF, $C_3 = 4.50$ μF

24.57 a) 76 μC b) 1.4 mJ c) 11 V d) 1.3 mJ

24.59 a) 2.3 μF
b) $Q_1 = 970$ μC, $Q_2 = 640$ μC c) 47 V

24.61 a) 3.91 b) 22.8 V

24.63 1.67 μF

24.65 0.185 μJ

24.67 b) 2.38 nF

24.69 a) $C_1 = 6.00$ μF, $C_2 = 3.00$ μF
b) same charge; C_2 stores more energy
c) C_1 stores more charge and energy

24.71 a) first (connected) b) 144 cm²
c) disconnected

24.73 choice (c)

24.75 choice (a)

Chapter 25

25.1 1.0 C

25.3 a) 3.12×10^{19} b) 1.51×10^6 A/m²
c) 0.111 mm/s
d) both (b) and (c) would increase

25.5 a) 110 min b) 440 min c) $v_d \propto 1/d^2$

25.7 a) 330 C b) 41 A

25.9 9.0 μA

25.11 a) 1.06×10^{-5} $\Omega \cdot$m b) 0.00105 (C°)⁻¹

25.13 a) 0.206 mV b) 0.176 mV

25.15 a) 1.21 V/m b) 0.0145 Ω c) 0.182 V

25.17 0.125 Ω

25.19 a) 4.67×10^{-8} Ω b) 6.72×10^{-4} Ω

25.21 a) 11 A b) 3.1 V c) 0.28 Ω

25.23 a) 99.54 Ω b) 0.0158 Ω

25.25 a) 27.4 V b) 12.3 MJ

25.27 a) 0 b) 5.0 V c) 5.0 V

25.29 3.08 V, 0.067 Ω, 1.80 Ω

25.31 a) 1.41 A, clockwise b) 13.7 V c) -1.0 V

25.33 a) 0.471 A, counterclockwise b) 15.2 V

25.35 a) 144 Ω b) 240 Ω
c) 100 W: 0.833 A; 60 W: 0.500 A

25.37 a) 29.8 W b) 0.248 A

25.39 a) 3.1 W b) 7.2 W c) 4.1 W

25.41 a) 300 W b) 0.90 J

25.43 a) 2.6 MJ b) 0.063 L c) 1.6 h

25.45 12.3%

25.47 a) 24.0 W b) 4.0 W c) 20.0 W

25.49 a) 1.55×10^{-12} s

25.51 a) 3.65×10^{-8} $\Omega \cdot$m b) 172 A
c) 2.58 mm/s

25.53 0.060 Ω

25.55 a) 2.5 mA   b) 21.4 μV/m   c) 85.5 μV/m
  d) 0.180 mV

25.57 a) 80 C°   b) no

25.59 a) $\dfrac{\rho h}{\pi r_1 r_2}$

25.61 a) 0.36 Ω b) 8.94 V

25.63 a) 1.0 kΩ b) 100 V   c) 10 W

25.65 a) $78.90   b) $140.27

25.67 a) $I_A\left(1 + \dfrac{R_A}{r + R}\right)$ b) 0.0429 Ω

25.69 a) 171 $\mu\Omega$ b) 176 μV/m
  c) left: 54.7 $\mu\Omega$; right: 116 $\mu\Omega$

25.71 a) 204 V   b) 199 J

25.73 6.67 V

25.75 b) no   c) yes   d) 9.40 W   e) 4.12 W

25.77 a) $R = \dfrac{\rho_0 L}{A}\left(1 - \dfrac{1}{e}\right), I = \dfrac{V_0 A}{\rho_0 L\left(1 - \dfrac{1}{e}\right)}$

  b) $E(x) = \dfrac{V_0 e^{-x/L}}{L\left(1 - \dfrac{1}{e}\right)}$

  c) $V(x) = \dfrac{V_0\left(e^{-x/L} - \dfrac{1}{e}\right)}{1 - \dfrac{1}{e}}$

25.79 choice (c)

25.81 choice (d)

Chapter 26

26.1 $3R/4$

26.3 22.5 W

26.5 a) 3.50 A   b) 4.50 A   c) 3.15 A
  d) 3.25 A

26.7 0.769 A

26.9 a) 8.80 Ω b) 3.18 A   c) 3.18 A
  d) $V_{1.60} = 5.09$ V, $V_{2.40} = 7.63$ V,
  $V_{4.80} = 15.3$ V   e) $P_{1.60} = 16.2$ W,
  $P_{2.40} = 24.3$ W, $P_{4.80} = 48.5$ W   f) greatest

26.11 a) $I_1 = 8.00$ A, $I_3 = 12.0$ A   b) 84.0 V

26.13 5.00 Ω; $I_{3.00} = 8.00$ A, $I_{4.00} = 9.00$ A,
  $I_{6.00} = 4.00$ A, $I_{12.0} = 3.00$ A

26.15 a) $I_1 = 1.50$ A, $I_2 = I_3 = I_4 = 0.500$ A
  b) $P_1 = 10.1$ W, $P_2 = P_3 = P_4 = 1.12$ W;
  bulb R_1 c) $I_1 = 1.33$ A, $I_2 = I_3 = 0.667$ A
  d) $P_1 = 8.00$ W, $P_2 = P_3 = 2.00$ W
  e) brighter: R_2 and R_3; less bright: R_1

26.17 18.0 V, 3.00 A

26.19 1010 s

26.21 a) 0.100 A   b) $P_{400} = 4.0$ W, $P_{800} = 8.0$ W
  c) 12.0 W   d) $I_{400} = 0.300$ A, $I_{800} = 0.150$ A
  e) $P_{400} = 36.0$ W, $P_{800} = 18.0$ W
  f) 54.0 W   g) series: 800-Ω bulb;
  parallel: 400-Ω bulb   h) parallel

26.23 a) 20.0 Ω b) A_2: 4.00 A; A_3: 12.0 A;
  A_4: 14.0 A; A_5: 8.00 A

26.25 a) 2.00 A   b) 5.00 Ω c) 42.0 V   d) 3.50 A

26.27 a) 8.00 A   b) $\mathscr{E}_1 = 36.0$ V, $\mathscr{E}_2 = 54.0$ V
  c) 9.00 Ω

26.29 a) 1.60 A (top), 1.40 A (middle),
  0.20 A (bottom)   b) 10.4 V

26.31 a) 36.4 V   b) 0.500 A

26.33 a) 2.14 V, a b) 0.050 A, 0; down

26.35 a) 0.641 Ω b) 975 Ω

26.37 a) 17.9 V   b) 22.7 V   c) 21.4%

26.39 a) 0.849 μF   b) 2.89 s

26.41 a) 0   b) 245 V   c) 0   d) 32.7 mA
  e) (a): 245 V; (b): 0; (c): 1.13 mC; (d): 0

26.43 a) 4.21 ms   b) 0.125 A

26.45 192 μC

26.47 13.6 A

26.49 a) 0.937 A   b) 0.606 A

26.51 a) 165 μC   b) 463 Ω c) 12.6 ms

26.53 900 W

26.55 a) 2.2 A, 4.4 V, 9.7 W
  b) 16.3 W; more brightly

26.57 a) +0.22 V   b) 0.464 A

26.59 $I_1 = 0.848$ A, $I_2 = 2.14$ A, $I_3 = 0.171$ A

26.61 $I_{2.00} = 5.21$ A, $I_{4.00} = 1.11$ A,
  $I_{5.00} = 6.32$ A

26.63 a) 109 V; no   b) 13.5 s

26.65 a) 186 V, upper terminal positive
  b) 3.00 A, upward   c) 20.0 Ω

26.67 a) -12.0 V   b) 1.71 A   c) 4.21 Ω

26.69 a) $P_1 + P_2$ b) $\dfrac{P_1 P_2}{P_1 + P_2}$

26.71 a) 1.35 W   b) 8.31 ms   c) 0.337 W

26.73 a) 114 V   b) 263 V   c) 266 V

26.75 a) 18.0 V   b) a c) 6.00 V
  d) both decrease by 36.0 μC

26.77 a) $V_{224} = 24.8$ V, $V_{589} = 65.2$ V
  b) 3840 Ω c) 62.6 V   d) no

26.79 1.7 MΩ, 3.1 μF

26.81 a) -1.23 ms (slope), 79.5 μC (y-intercept)
  b) 247 Ω, 15.9 V   c) 1.22 ms   d) 11.9 V

26.85 b) 4   c) 3.2 MΩ, 4.0×10^{-3}
  d) 3.4×10^{-4} e) 0.88

26.87 choice (d)

Chapter 27

27.1 a) $(-6.68 \times 10^{-4}\,\text{N})\hat{k}$
  b) $(6.68 \times 10^{-4}\,\text{N})\hat{\imath} + (7.27 \times 10^{-4}\,\text{N})\hat{\jmath}$

27.3 a) positive   b) 0.0505 N

27.5 9490 km/s

27.7 a) $B_x = -0.175$ T, $B_z = -0.256$ T   b) B_y
  c) 0; 90°

27.9 a) 1.46 T, in the xz-plane at 40° from the
  $+x$-axis toward the $-z$-axis
  b) 7.47×10^{-16} N, in the xz-plane at 50° from
  the $-x$-axis toward the $-z$-axis

27.11 a) 3.05 mWb   b) 1.83 mWb   c) 0

27.13 -0.78 mWb

27.15 a) 0.160 mT, into the page   b) 0.111 μs

27.17 7.93×10^{-10} N, toward the south

27.19 a) 2.84×10^6 m/s, negative   b) yes   c) same

27.21 a) 835 km/s   b) 26.2 ns   c) 7.27 kV

27.23 0.838 mT

27.25 a) $(1.60 \times 10^{-14}\,\text{N})\hat{\jmath}$ b) yes
  c) helix; no   d) 1.40 cm

27.27 a) 7900 N/C, $\hat{\imath}$ b) 7900 N/C, $\hat{\imath}$

27.29 0.0445 T, out of the page

27.31 a) 4.92 km/s   b) 9.96×10^{-26} kg

27.33 2.0 cm

27.35 0.724 N, 63.4° below the current direction in
  the upper wire segment

27.37 a) 817 V   b) 113 m/s^2

27.39 a) a b) 3.21 kg

27.41 b) $F_{cd} = 1.20$ N   c) 0.420 N $\cdot$ m

27.43 a) A_2 b) 290 rad/s^2

27.45 a) $-NIAB\hat{\imath}$, 0   b) 0, $-NIAB$ c) $+NIAB\hat{\imath}$, 0
  d) 0, $+NIAB$

27.47 a) 1.13 A   b) 3.69 A   c) 98.2 V   d) 362 W

27.49 a) 4.7 mm/s
  b) $+4.5 \times 10^{-3}$ V/m, $+z$-direction
  c) 53 μV

27.51 a) $-\dfrac{F_2}{qv_1}\hat{\jmath}$ b) $F_2/\sqrt{2}$

27.53 a) 8.3×10^6 m/s   b) 0.14 T

27.55 3.45 T, perpendicular to the coin's initial
  velocity

27.57 a) -3.89 μC
  b) $(7.60 \times 10^{14}\,\text{m/s}^2)\hat{\imath} + (5.70 \times 10^{14}\,\text{m/s}^2)\hat{\jmath}$
  c) 2.90 cm   d) 2.88×10^7 Hz
  e) $(0.0290\,\text{m}, 0, 0.874\,\text{m})$

27.59 1.6 mm

27.61 $\dfrac{Mg\tan\theta}{LB}$, right to left

27.63 a) 8.46 mT   b) 27.2 cm   c) 2.2 cm; yes

27.65 a) ILB, to the right   b) $\dfrac{v^2 m}{2ILB}$ c) 1960 km

27.67 1.97 N, 68.3° clockwise from the left-hand
  segment

27.69 0.024 T, $+y$-direction

27.71 a) $F_{PQ} = 0$; $F_{RP} = 12.0$ N, into the page;
  $F_{QR} = 12.0$ N, out of the page
  b) 0   c) $\tau_{PQ} = \tau_{RP} = 0$; $\tau_{QR} = 3.60$ N $\cdot$ m
  d) 3.60 N $\cdot$ m; yes   e) out

27.73 $-(0.444\,\text{N})\hat{\jmath}$

27.75 b) left: $(B_0 LI/2)\hat{\imath}$; top: $-IB_0 L\hat{\jmath}$; right:
  $-(B_0 LI/2)\hat{\imath}$; bottom: 0   c) $-IB_0 L\hat{\jmath}$

27.77 a) $-IA\,\hat{k}$ b) $B_x = \dfrac{3D}{IA}, B_y = \dfrac{4D}{IA}, B_z = -\dfrac{12D}{IA}$

27.79 a) 1.85×10^{-28} kg   c) 1.20 kV
  d) 8.32×10^5 m/s

27.81 a) 5.14 m   b) 1.72 μs   c) 6.08 mm
  d) 3.05 cm

27.83 choice (c)

27.85 choice (a)

Chapter 28

28.1 a) $-(19.2\,\mu\text{T})\hat{k}$ b) 0   c) $(19.2\,\mu\text{T})\hat{\imath}$
  d) $(6.79\,\mu\text{T})\hat{\imath}$

28.3 a) 60.0 nT, out of the page at A and B
  b) 0.120 μT, out of the page   c) 0

28.5 a) 0   b) $-(1.31\,\mu\text{T})\hat{k}$ c) $-(0.462\,\mu\text{T})\hat{k}$
  d) $(1.31\,\mu\text{T})\hat{\jmath}$

28.7 $(97.5\,\text{nT})\hat{k}$

28.9 a) 0.440 μT, out of the page
  b) 16.7 nT, out of the page   c) 0

28.11 a) $(50.0\,\text{pT})\hat{\jmath}$ b) $-(50.0\,\text{pT})\hat{\imath}$
  c) $-(17.7\,\text{pT})(\hat{\imath} - \hat{\jmath})$ d) 0

28.13 17.6 μT, into the page

28.15 a) 0.8 mT   b) 40 μT (20 times larger)

28.17 250 μA

28.19 a) 10.0 A   b) at all points directly above the
  wire   c) at all points directly east of the wire

28.21 a) $-(0.10\,\mu\text{T})\hat{\imath}$ b) 2.19 μT, at 46.8° from
  the $+x$-axis to the $+z$-axis   c) $(7.9\,\mu\text{T})\hat{\imath}$

28.23 a) 0   b) 6.67 μT, toward the top of the page
  c) 7.54 μT, to the left

28.25 a) 0   b) 0   c) 0.40 mT, to the left

28.27 a) P: 41 μT, into the page; Q: 25 μT, out of the
  page   b) P: 9.0 μT, out of the page;
  Q: 9.0 μT, into the page

28.29 a) 6.00 μN; repulsive   b) 24.0 μN

28.31 46 μN/m; repulsive; no

28.33 0.38 μA

28.35 $\dfrac{\mu_0 |I_1 - I_2|}{4R}$; 0

28.37 a) 25.1 μT   b) 503 μT; no

28.39 18.0 A, counterclockwise

28.41 a) 305 A   b) -3.83×10^{-4} T $\cdot$ m

28.43 a) $\mu_0 I/2\pi r$ b) 0

28.45 a) 2.83 mT   b) 35.0 μT; no

28.47 a) 1790 turns per meter   b) 63.0 m

28.49 a) 3.72 MA   b) 249 kA   c) 237 A

28.51 1.11 mT

28.53 a) (i) 1.13 mT (ii) 4.68 MA/m (iii) 5.88 T

28.55 a) 1.00 μT, into the page b) $(74.9\ \text{nN})\hat{j}$

28.57 a) in the plane of the wires, between them, 0.300 m from the 75.0-A wire

b) in the plane of the wires, 0.200 m from the 25.0-A wire and 0.600 m from the 75.0-A wire

28.59 a) 5.7×10^{12} m/s^2, away from the wire

b) 32.5 N/C, away from the wire c) no

28.61 a) 81 A b) 2.4×10^{-3} N/m

28.63 a) 2.00 A, out of the page

b) 2.13 μT, upward c) 2.06 μT

28.65 23.2 A

28.67 a) $\dfrac{\mu_0 N I a^2}{2} \times$

$$\left\{ \frac{1}{\left[(x+a/2)^2+a^2\right]^{3/2}} + \frac{1}{\left[(x-a/2)^2+a^2\right]^{3/2}} \right\}$$

c) $\left(\dfrac{4}{5}\right)^{3/2} \dfrac{\mu_0 N I}{a}$ d) 20.2 mT e) 0, 0

28.69 a) $\dfrac{3I}{2\pi R^3}$ b) (i) $B = \dfrac{\mu_0 I r^2}{2\pi R^3}$ (ii) $B = \dfrac{\mu_0 I}{2\pi r}$

28.71 b) $B = \dfrac{\mu_0 I_0}{2\pi r}$ c) $\dfrac{I_0 r^2}{a^2}\left(2 - \dfrac{r^2}{a^2}\right)$

d) $B = \dfrac{\mu_0 I_0 r}{2\pi a^2}\left(2 - \dfrac{r^2}{a^2}\right)$

28.73 a) $B = \mu_0 I n/2$, $+x$-direction

b) $B = \mu_0 I n/2$, $-x$-direction

28.75 a) $I_0 = 2\pi b\delta(1 - e^{-a/\delta})$, 81.5 A b) $\dfrac{\mu_0 I_0}{2\pi r}$

c) $\left(\dfrac{e^{r/\delta}-1}{e^{a/\delta}-1}\right)I_0$ d) $\dfrac{\mu_0 I}{2\pi r}\left(\dfrac{e^{r/\delta}-1}{e^{a/\delta}-1}\right)$

e) $r = \delta$: 175 μT; $r = a$: 326 μT; $r = 2a$: 163 μT

28.77 a) no c) 65 A, 1.2 cm

28.79 b) $\dfrac{1}{2g}\left(\dfrac{\mu_0 Q_0^2}{4\pi \lambda R C d}\right)^2$

28.81 choice (b)

28.83 choice (c)

Chapter 29

29.1 a) 17.1 mV b) 28.5 mA

29.3 a) $Q = NBA/R$ c) no

29.5 a) 34 V b) counterclockwise

29.7 a) $\mu_0 i/2\pi r$, into the page b) $\dfrac{\mu_0 i}{2\pi r} L\, dr$

c) $\dfrac{\mu_0 i L}{2\pi} \ln(b/a)$ d) $\dfrac{\mu_0 L}{2\pi} \ln(b/a)\dfrac{di}{dt}$

e) 0.506 μV

29.9 a) 5.44 mV b) clockwise

29.11 a) bAv b) clockwise

c) bAv, counterclockwise

29.13 10.4 rad/s

29.15 a) counterclockwise b) clockwise

c) no induced current

29.17 a) C: counterclockwise; A: clockwise

b) toward the wire

29.19 a) a to b b) b to a c) b to a

29.21 a) clockwise b) no induced current

c) counterclockwise

29.23 13.2 mA, counterclockwise

29.25 a) 0.675 V b) b c) 2.25 V/m, b to a

d) b e) (i) 0 (ii) 0

29.27 46.2 m/s = 103 mph; no

29.29 a) 3.00 V b) b to a

c) 0.800 N, to the right d) 6.00 W for each

29.31 a) counterclockwise b) 42.4 mW

29.33 35.0 m/s, to the right

29.35 a) 0.225 A, clockwise b) 0

c) 0.225 A, counterclockwise

29.37 a) $\pi r_1^2 \dfrac{dB}{dt}$ b) $\dfrac{r_1}{2}\dfrac{dB}{dt}$ c) $\dfrac{R^2}{2r_2}\dfrac{dB}{dt}$ e) $\dfrac{\pi R^2}{4}\dfrac{dB}{dt}$

f) $\pi R^2 \dfrac{dB}{dt}$ g) $\pi R^2 \dfrac{dB}{dt}$

29.39 9.21 A/s

29.41 0.950 mV

29.43 a) 0.599 nC b) 6.00 mA c) 6.00 mA

29.45 a) inside: $B = 0$, $\vec{M} = -(0.103\ \text{MA/m})\hat{i}$; outside: $\vec{B} = (0.130\ \text{T})\hat{i}$, $M = 0$

b) inside and outside: $\vec{B} = (0.260\ T)\hat{i}$, $M = 0$

29.47 a) 3.7 A b) 1.33 mA c) counterclockwise

29.49 16.2 μV

29.51 a) $\dfrac{\mu_0 I a b v}{2\pi r(r+a)}$ b) clockwise

29.53 a) 17.9 mV b) a to b

29.55 $\mu_0 I W / 4\pi$

29.57 a) $\dfrac{\mu_0 I v}{2\pi} \ln(1 + L/d)$ b) a c) 0

29.59 a) 0.165 V b) 0.165 V c) 0; 0.0412 V

29.61 a) $B^2 L^2 v / R$

29.63 $a: \dfrac{qr}{2}\dfrac{dB}{dt}$, to the left; $b: \dfrac{qr}{2}\dfrac{dB}{dt}$, toward the top of the page; c: 0

29.65 5.0 s

29.67 a) 0.3071 s^{-1} b) 3.69 T c) a d) 2.26 s

29.69 a) a to b b) $\dfrac{Rmg\tan\phi}{L^2 B^2 \cos\phi}$ c) $\dfrac{mg\tan\phi}{LB}$

d) $\dfrac{Rm^2g^2\tan^2\phi}{L^2 B^2}$ e) $\dfrac{Rm^2g^2\tan^2\phi}{L^2 B^2}$; same

29.71 choice (c)

29.73 choice (c)

Chapter 30

30.1 a) 0.270 V; yes b) 0.270 V

30.3 6.32 μH

30.5 a) 1.96 H b) 7.11 mWb

30.7 a) 1940 b) 800 A/s

30.9 a) 0.250 H b) 0.450 mWb

30.11 a) 4.68 mV b) a

30.13 a) 1000 b) 2.09 Ω

30.15 b) 0.111 μH

30.17 2850

30.19 a) 0.161 T b) 10.3 kJ/m^3 c) 0.129 J

d) 40.2 μH

30.21 91.7 J

30.23 a) 2.40 A/s b) 0.800 A/s c) 0.413 A

d) 0.750 A

30.25 a) 17.3 μs b) 30.7 μs

30.27 a) 0.250 A b) 0.137 A c) 32.9 V; c

d) 0.462 ms

30.29 15.3 V

30.31 a) 443 nC b) 358 nC

30.33 a) 25.0 mH b) 90.0 nC c) 0.540 μJ

d) 6.58 mA

30.35 a) 105 rad/s, 59.6 ms b) 0.720 mC

c) 4.32 mJ d) -0.542 mC

e) -0.050 A, counterclockwise

f) $U_C = 2.45$ mJ, $U_L = 1.87$ mJ

30.37 a) 7.50 μC b) 15.9 kHz c) 21.2 mJ

30.39 a) 298 rad/s b) 83.8 Ω

30.41 a) 8.76 kHz b) 1.35 ms c) 2420 Ω

30.43 a) 0.288 μH b) 14.2 μV

30.45 20 km/s; about 30 times smaller

30.47 a) $\dfrac{\mu_0 i}{2\pi r}$ b) $\dfrac{\mu_0 i^2 l}{4\pi r}\, dr$ c) $\dfrac{\mu_0 i^2 l}{4\pi} \ln(b/a)$

d) $\dfrac{\mu_0 l}{2\pi} \ln(b/a)$

30.49 a) 5.00 H b) 31.7 m; no

30.51 222 μF, 9.31 μH

30.53 a) 0.896 mJ b) 0.691 A; 0

30.55 a) 24.0 mV b) 1.55 mA c) 72.1 nJ

d) 5.20 μC, 18.0 nJ

30.57 a) 0, 20.0 V b) 0.267 A, 0 c) 0.147 A, 9.0 V

30.59 a) $A_1 = A_4 = 0.800$ A, $A_2 = A_3 = 0$; $V_1 = 40.0$ V, $V_2 = V_3 = V_4 = V_5 = 0$

b) $A_1 = 0.480$ A, $A_2 = 0.160$ A, $A_3 = 0.320$ A, $A_4 = 0$; $V_1 = 24.0$ V, $V_2 = 0$, $V_3 = V_4 = V_5 = 16.0$ V c) 192 μC

30.61 a) 60.0 V b) a c) 60.0 V d) c

e) -96.0 V f) b g) 156 V h) d

30.63 a) 0; $v_{ac} = 0$, $v_{cb} = 36.0$ V

b) 0.180 A, $v_{ac} = 9.0$ V, $v_{cb} = 27.0$ V

c) $i_0 = (0.180\ \text{A})(1 - e^{-t/(0.020\ \text{s})})$, $v_{ac} = (9.0\ \text{V})(1 - e^{-t/(0.020\ \text{s})})$, $v_{cb} = (9.0\ \text{V})(3.00 + e^{-t/(0.020\ \text{s})})$

30.65 a) $A_1 = A_4 = 0.455$ A, $A_2 = A_3 = 0$

b) $A_1 = 0.585$ A, $A_2 = 0.320$ A, $A_3 = 0.160$ A, $A_4 = 0.107$ A

30.67 a) $v_L = \dfrac{\epsilon}{R + R_L}(R_L + Re^{-(R+R_L)t/L})$

b) 50.0 V c) 30.0 V; 3.00 A d) 6.67 Ω

e) 40.0 mH

30.69 b) 5.0 Ω, 8.5 H c) 1.7 kJ; 2.0 kW

30.71 a) $i_1 = \dfrac{\epsilon}{R_1}(1 - e^{-R_1 t/L})$, $i_2 = \dfrac{\epsilon}{R_2}e^{-t/R_2 C}$, $q_2 = \epsilon C(1 - e^{-t/R_2 C})$

b) $i_1 = 0$, $i_2 = 9.60$ mA

c) $i_1 = 1.92$ A, $i_2 = 0$; $t \gg L/R_1$ and $t \gg R_2 C$

d) 1.6 ms e) 9.4 mA f) 0.22 s

30.73 choice (b)

30.75 choice (c)

Chapter 31

31.1 1.06 A

31.3 a) 31.8 V b) 0

31.5 a) 90°; lead b) 193 Hz

31.7 13.3 μF

31.9 a) 1510 Ω b) 0.239 H c) 497 Ω

d) 16.6 μF

31.11 a) $(12.5\ \text{V}) \cos[(480\ \text{rad/s})t]$ b) 7.17 V

31.13 a) $i = (0.0253\ \text{A}) \cos[(720\ \text{rad/s})t]$

b) 180 Ω

c) $v_L = -(4.56\ \text{V}) \sin[(720\ \text{rad/s})t]$

31.15 a) 601 Ω b) 49.9 mA c) -70.6°; lag

d) $V_R = 9.98$ V, $V_L = 4.99$ V, $V_C = 33.3$ V

31.17 50.0 V

31.19 a) 40.0 W b) 0.167 A c) 720 Ω

31.21 b) 76.7 V

31.23 a) 45.8°, 0.697 b) 344 Ω c) 155 V

d) 48.6 W e) 48.6 W f) 0 g) 0

31.25 a) 0.302 b) 0.370 W

c) 0.370 W (resistor), 0, 0

31.27 a) 113 Hz; 15.0 mA b) 7.61 mA; lag

31.29 a) 150 V b) $V_R = 150$ V, $V_L = V_C = 1290$ V c) 37.5 W

31.31 a) 1.00 b) 75.0 W c) 75.0 W

31.33 a) 945 rad/s b) 70.6 Ω

c) $V_L = V_C = 450$ V, $V_R = 120$ V

31.35 a) 10 b) 2.40 A c) 28.8 W d) 500 Ω

31.37 0.124 H

31.39 230 Ω

31.41 3.59×10^7 rad/s

31.43 a) inductor b) 0.133 H

31.45 a) 0.831 b) 161 W

31.47 $\dfrac{V_{\text{out}}}{V_{\text{s}}} = \sqrt{\dfrac{R^2 + \omega^2 L^2}{R^2 + \left(\omega L - \dfrac{1}{\omega C}\right)^2}}$

31.51 a) 102 Ω b) 0.882 A c) 270 V

31.53 a) V_R = 48.6 V, V_L = 155 V, V_C = 243 V, $-60.9°$
  b) V_R = 100 V, V_L = V_C = 400 V, 0°
  c) V_R = 48.6 V, V_L = 243 V, V_C = 155 V, $+60.9°$

31.55 b) 5770 rad/s c) 2.40 A d) 2.40 A
  e) 0.139 A f) 0.139 A

31.57 a) ω = 28,800 rad/s so ϕ = 60°
  b) P_R = 0.375 W, P_L = P_C = 0; 0.100 A

31.59 a) 0.750 A b) 160 Ω c) 341 Ω, 619 Ω
  d) 341 Ω

31.61 a) $\dfrac{V}{R}$ b) $\dfrac{V}{R}\sqrt{\dfrac{L}{C}}$ c) $\dfrac{V}{R}\sqrt{\dfrac{L}{C}}$ d) $\dfrac{1}{2}L\dfrac{V^2}{R^2}$
  e) $\dfrac{1}{2}L\dfrac{V^2}{R^2}$

31.63 a) 20.6 Ω b) 105 μF c) 699 W

31.65 20.0 Ω, 0.18 H

31.67 a) $\frac{1}{2}V_R I$ b) 0 c) 0

31.69 choice (b)

31.71 choice (d)

Chapter 32

32.1 a) 1.28 s b) 8.15×10^{13} km

32.3 13.3 nT, +y-direction

32.5 3.0×10^{18} Hz, 3.3×10^{-19} s,
  6.3×10^{10} rad/s

32.7 a) 6.94×10^{14} Hz b) 375 V/m
  c) $E(x, t) = (375 \text{ V/m}) \times$
  $\cos[(1.45 \times 10^7 \text{ rad/m})x$
  $\qquad - (4.36 \times 10^{15} \text{ rad/s})t]$,
  $B(x, t) = (1.25 \,\mu\text{T}) \times$
  $\cos[(1.45 \times 10^7 \text{ rad/m})x$
  $\qquad - (4.36 \times 10^{15} \text{ rad/s})t]$

32.9 a) (i) 60 kHz (ii) 6.0×10^{13} Hz
  (iii) 6.0×10^{16} Hz
  b) (i) 4.62×10^{-14} m = 4.62×10^{-5} nm
  (ii) 508 m = 5.08×10^{11} nm

32.11 a) +y-direction b) 0.149 mm
  c) $\vec{B} = (1.03 \text{ mT}) \cos[(4.22 \times 10^4 \text{ rad/m})y$
  $\qquad - (1.265 \times 10^{13} \text{ rad/s})t]\hat{\imath}$

32.13 a) 361 m b) 0.0174 rad/m
  c) 5.22×10^6 rad/s d) 0.0144 V/m

32.15 a) 0.381 μm b) 0.526 μm
  c) 1.38 d) 1.90

32.17 a) 330 W/m² b) 500 V/m, 1.7 μT

32.19 2.5×10^{25} W

32.21 a) 0.24 mW b) 17.4 V/m

32.23 12.0 V/m, 40.0 nT

32.25 850 kW

32.27 a) 0.18 mW b) 274 V/m, 0.913 μT
  c) 0.18 mJ/s d) 0.010 W/cm²

32.29 a) 637 W/m² b) 693 V/m, 2.31 μT
  c) 2.12 μJ/m³

32.31 a) 30.5 cm b) 2.46 GHz c) 2.11 GHz

32.33 a) 0.375 mJ b) 4.08 mPa c) 604 nm,
  3.70×10^{14} Hz d) 30.3 kV/m, 101 μT

32.35 a) 6.02×10^{-9} W/m² b) 2.13×10^{-3} N/C,
  7.10×10^{-12} T c) 1.20×10^{-18} N; no

32.37 a) at r = R: 64 MW/m², 0.21 Pa; at r = $R/2$:
  260 MW/m², 0.85 Pa b) no

32.39 3.89×10^{-13} rad/s²

32.41 a) $\rho I/\pi a^2$, in the direction of the current
  b) $\mu_0 I/2\pi a$, counterclockwise if the current is
  out of the page

32.41 c) $\dfrac{\rho I^2}{2\pi^2 a^3}$, radially inward d) $\dfrac{\rho I^2}{\pi a^2} = I^2 R$

32.43 a) 1.363 m b) 10.90 m

32.45 a) 9.75×10^{-15} W/m²
  b) 2.71 μV/m, 9.03×10^{-15} T, 67.3 ms
  c) 3.25×10^{-23} Pa d) 0.190 m

32.47 a) $\dfrac{4\rho G\pi MR^3}{3r^2}$ b) $\dfrac{LR^2}{4cr^2}$ c) 0.19 μm; no

32.49 b) 3.00×10^8 m/s

32.51 b) 1.39×10^{-11} c) 2.54×10^{-8}

32.53 c) 66.0 μm

32.55 choice (d)

Chapter 33

33.1 39.4°

33.3 a) 2.04×10^8 m/s b) 442 nm

33.5 a) 1.55 b) 550 nm

33.7 a) 47.5° b) 66.0°

33.9 2.51×10^8 m/s

33.11 a) 2.34 b) 82°

33.13 71.8°

33.15 a) 51.3° b) 33.6°

33.17 a) 58.1° b) 22.8°

33.19 1.77

33.21 a) 48.9° b) 28.7°

33.23 0.6°

33.25 0.375I_0

33.27 a) A: $I_0/2$, B: 0.125I_0, C: 0.0938I_0 b) 0

33.29 a) 1.40 b) 35.5°

33.31 $\arccos\left(\dfrac{\cos\theta}{\sqrt{2}}\right)$

33.33 6.38 W/cm²

33.35 a) 0.364I b) 2.70I

33.37 a) 46.7° b) 13.4°

33.39 72.1°

33.41 1.28

33.43 3.52×10^4

33.45 1.84

33.47 a) 48.6° b) 48.6°

33.49 39.1°

33.51 b) 0.23°; about the same

33.53 b) 38.9° c) 5.0°

33.55 23.3°

33.57 a) A: 1.46, carbon tetrachloride; B: 1.33, water;
  C: 1.63, carbon disulfide; D: 1.50, benzene
  b) A: 2.13, B: 1.77, C: 2.66, D: 2.25
  c) all: 5.09×10^{14} Hz

33.59 a) 35° b) I_0 = 10 W/m², I_p = 20 W/m²

33.61 a) $\Delta = 2\theta_a{}^A - 6\arcsin\left(\dfrac{\sin\theta_a{}^A}{n}\right) + 2\pi$
  b) $\theta_2 = \arccos\sqrt{\dfrac{n^2 - 1}{8}}$
  c) violet: θ_2 = 71.55°, Δ = 233.2°
  red: θ_2 = 71.94°, Δ = 230.1°; violet

33.63 choice (d)

Chapter 34

34.1 39.2 cm to the right of the mirror, 4.85 cm

34.3 9.0 cm; tip of the lead

34.5 b) 33.0 cm to the left of the vertex, 1.20 cm,
  inverted, real

34.7 0.213 mm

34.9 18.0 cm from the vertex; 0.50 cm, erect, virtual

34.11 a) $+4.00$
  b) 48.0 cm to the right of the mirror; virtual

34.13 a) concave b) f = 2.50 cm, R = 5.00 cm

34.15 a) 10.0 cm to the left of the shell vertex, 2.20 mm

34.15 b) 4.29 cm to the right of the shell vertex,
  0.944 mm

34.17 2.67 cm

34.19 3.30 m

34.21 a) at the center of the bowl, 1.33 b) no

34.23 39.5 cm

34.25 8.35 cm to the left of the vertex, 0.326 mm;
  erect

34.27 a) 107 cm to the right of the lens, 17.8 mm;
  real; inverted b) the same

34.29 71.2 cm to the right of the lens; -2.97

34.31 3.69 cm; 2.82 cm to the left of the lens

34.33 1.67

34.35 a) 18.6 mm b) 19 mm from the cornea
  c) 0.61 cm; real; inverted

34.37 a) 36.0 cm to the right of the lens b) 180 cm
  to the left of the lens c) 7.20 cm to the left of
  the lens d) 13.8 cm to the left of the lens

34.39 26.3 cm from the lens, 12.4 mm; erect;
  same side

34.41 a) 200 cm to the right of the first lens, 4.80 cm
  b) 150 cm to the right of the second lens,
  7.20 cm

34.43 a) 53.0 cm b) real c) 2.50 mm; inverted

34.45 10.2 m

34.47 8.69 cm; no

34.49 a) $f/11$ b) $1/480$ s = 2.1 ms

34.51 a) 80.0 cm b) 76.9 cm

34.53 49.4 cm, 2.02 diopters

34.55 -1.37 diopters

34.57 a) 6.06 cm b) 4.12 mm

34.59 a) 8.37 mm b) 21.4 c) -297

34.61 a) -6.33 b) 1.90 cm c) 0.127 rad

34.63 a) 0.661 m b) 59.1

34.65 7.20 m/s

34.67 a) 20.0 cm b) 39.0 cm

34.69 51 m/s

34.71 a) 1.49 cm

34.73 b) 2.4 cm; -0.133

34.75 2.00

34.77 a) converging, 52.5 cm from the lens
  b) converging, 17.5 cm from the lens

34.79 converging, $+50.2$ cm

34.81 a) 58.7 cm, converging b) 4.48 mm; virtual

34.83 a) 6.48 mm b) no, behind the retina
  c) 19.3 mm from the cornea; in front of the retina

34.85 10.6 cm

34.87 a) 0.24 m b) 0.24 m

34.89 b) first image: (i) 51.3 cm to the right of the
  lens (ii) real (iii) inverted
  second image: (i) 51.3 cm to the right of
  the lens (ii) real (iii) erect

34.91 -26.7 cm

34.93 7.06 cm to the left of the spherical mirror
  vertex, 0.177 cm tall; 13.3 cm to the left of the
  spherical mirror vertex, 0.111 cm tall

34.95 134 cm to the left of the object

34.97 4.17 diopters

34.99 a) 30.9 cm b) 29.2 cm

34.101 d) 36.0 cm, 21.6 cm; d = 1.2 cm

34.103 a) -16.6 cm b) 20.0 cm to the right

34.105 a) $4f$

34.107 b) 1.74 cm

34.109 choice (d)

34.111 choice (b)

Chapter 35

35.1 a) 14 cm, 48 cm, 82 cm, 116 cm, 150 cm
  b) 31 cm, 65 cm, 99 cm, 133 cm

35.3 0.75 m, 2.00 m, 3.25 m, 4.50 m, 5.75 m,
  7.00 m, 8.25 m

35.5 a) 2.0 m b) constructively
   c) 1.0 m, destructively
35.7 1.14 mm
35.9 0.83 mm
35.11 a) 39 b) $\pm 73.3°$
35.13 12.6 cm
35.15 1200 nm
35.17 a) $0.750I_0$ b) 80 nm
35.19 1670 rad
35.21 a) 4.52 rad b) $0.404I_0$
35.23 114 nm
35.25 $0.0234°$
35.27 a) 55.6 nm
   b) (i) 2180 nm (ii) 11.0 wavelengths
35.29 a) 514 nm; green b) 603 nm; orange
35.31 0.11 μm
35.33 0.570 mm
35.35 1.57
35.37 a) 96.0 nm b) no, no
35.39 a) 1.58 mm (green), 1.72 mm (orange)
   b) 3.45 mm (violet), 4.74 mm (green),
   5.16 mm (orange) c) 9.57 μm
35.41 1.730
35.43 761 m, 219 m, 90.1 m, 20.0 m
35.45 $6.8 \times 10^{-5}\ (\text{C}°)^{-1}$
35.47 1.33 μm
35.49 600 nm, 467 nm; no
35.51 a) 1.54 b) $\pm 15.0°$
35.53 a) 50 MHz b) 237.0 m
35.55 14.0
35.57 choice (d)
35.59 choice (c)

Chapter 36

36.1 506 nm
36.3 a) 226 b) $\pm 83.0°$
36.5 9.07 m
36.7 a) 63.8 cm
   b) $\pm 22.1°, \pm 34.3°, \pm 48.8°, \pm 70.1°$
36.9 $\pm 16.0°, \pm 33.4°, \pm 55.6°$
36.11 a) 10.9 mm b) 5.4 mm
36.13 a) 580 nm b) 0.128
36.15 a) 6.75 nm b) 2.43 μW/m^2
36.17 a) 668 nm b) $(9.36 \times 10^{-5})I_0$
36.19 a) 3 b) 2
36.21 a) $0.0627°, 0.125°$ b) $0.249I_0, 0.0256I_0$
36.23 a) 4830 lines/cm b) 4; $\pm 37.7°, \pm 66.5°$
36.25 a) 4790 slits/cm b) $19.1°, 40.8°$ c) no
36.27 a) yes b) 13.3 nm
36.29 a) 467 nm b) $27.8°$
36.31 a) 17,500 b) yes
   c) (i) 587.8170 nm (ii) 587.7834 nm
   (iii) 587.7834 nm $< \lambda <$ 587.8170 nm
36.33 2752 slits/cm
36.35 0.232 nm
36.37 92 cm
36.39 1.88 m
36.41 220 m
36.43 a) 73 m (Hubble), 1100 km (Arecibo)
   b) 1600 km
36.45 1.45 m
36.47 30.2 μm
36.49 a) 78 b) $\pm 80.8°$ c) 555 μW/m^2
36.51 1.68
36.53 b) 4.49 rad, 7.73 rad c) 3.14 rad, 6.28 rad,
   9.42 rad; no d) $4.78°, 6.84°, 9.59°$
36.55 -0.033 mm; decrease
36.57 360 nm
36.59 second
36.61 1.40
36.63 a) 1.03 mm b) 0.148 mm

36.65 a) 12.1 μm b) 10.4 cm, 15.2 cm
36.69 choice (d)
36.71 choice (a)

Chapter 37

37.1 bolt A
37.3 $0.867c$; no
37.5 a) $0.998c$ b) 126 m
37.7 1.12 h, in the spacecraft
37.9 92.5 m
37.11 a) 0.66 km b) 49 μs; 15 km c) 0.45 km
37.13 a) 3570 m b) 90.0 μs c) 89.2 μs
37.15 a) $0.806c$ b) $0.974c$ c) $0.997c$
37.17 a) toward b) $0.385c$
37.19 $0.784c$
37.21 $0.611c$
37.23 a) $0.159c$ b) \$172 million
37.25 $0.220c$; toward you
37.27 $3.06p_0$
37.29 a) $0.866c$ b) $0.608c$
37.31 a) $0.866c$ b) $0.986c$
37.33 a) 0.450 nJ b) 1.94×10^{-18} kg$\cdot$m/s
   c) $0.968c$
37.35 a) 1110 kg b) 52.1 cm
37.37 a) 0.867 nJ b) 0.270 nJ c) 0.452
37.39 a) 5.34 pJ (nonrel), 5.65 pJ (rel), 1.06
   b) 67.8 pJ (nonrel), 331 pJ (rel), 4.88
37.41 a) 2.06 MV b) 0.330 pJ = 2.06 MeV
37.43 a) $\Delta = 8.42 \times 10^{-6}$ b) 34.0 GeV
37.45 $0.700c$
37.47 42.5 y
37.49 a) $\Delta = 9 \times 10^{-9}$ b) $7000m$
37.51 5.01 ns, clock on plane
37.53 0.168 MeV
37.55 a) 1.08×10^{14} J b) 2.70×10^{19} W
   c) 1.10×10^{10} kg
37.57 a) $0.999929c$ b) $-0.9965c$ c) (i) 42.4 MeV
   (a), 5.60 MeV (b) (ii) 15.7 MeV (a) and (b)
37.59 $0.357c$; receding
37.61 154 km/h
37.63 2.04×10^{-13} N
37.65 a) 2.6×10^{-8} s b) 0.97
37.67 a) 2.0×10^{-18} kg b) 4.0×10^4 m/s^2
37.69 a) 2494 MeV b) 2.526 times
   c) 987.4 MeV, twice as much
37.71 choice (c)
37.73 choice (b)

Chapter 38

38.1 5.77×10^{14} Hz, 1.28×10^{-27} kg$\cdot$m/s,
   3.84×10^{-19} J = 2.40 eV
38.3 a) 5.00×10^{14} Hz b) 1.13×10^{19} photons/s
   c) no
38.5 a) 2.47×10^{-19} J = 1.54 eV
   b) 804 nm; infrared
38.7 249 km/s
38.9 2.14 eV
38.11 a) 264 nm b) 4.70 eV, same
38.13 0.311 nm; same
38.15 1.13 keV
38.17 0.0714 nm; $180°$
38.19 a) 4.39×10^{-4} nm b) 0.04294 nm
   c) 300 eV, loss d) 300 eV
38.21 $51.0°$
38.23 1.19×10^{-27} kg$\cdot$m/s, 1.96×10^{-29} kg$\cdot$m/s
38.25 16.6 fs
38.27 a) 5.07 mJ b) 11.3 W
   c) 1.49×10^{16} photons/s
38.29 a) 6.99×10^{-24} kg$\cdot$m/s b) 705 eV
38.31 6.28×10^{-24} kg$\cdot$m/s, $59.4°$

38.33 a) 5×10^{-33} m b) $(4 \times 10^{-9})°$ c) 0.1 mm
38.35 a) 319 eV; 1.06×10^7 m/s b) 3.89 nm
38.37 a) V_0 versus $1/\lambda$; 1.23×10^{-6} V$\cdot$m (slope),
   -4.76 V (y-intercept) b) 6.58×10^{-34} J$\cdot$s,
   4.76 eV c) 260 nm d) 84.0 nm
38.39 a) 2.40 pm (slope), 5.21 pm (y-intercept)
   b) 2.40 pm c) 5.21 pm
38.41 choice (c)
38.43 choice (a)
38.45 choice (b)

Chapter 39

39.1 a) 0.155 nm b) 8.46×10^{-14} m
39.3 a) 2.37×10^{-24} kg$\cdot$m/s
   b) 3.08×10^{-18} J = 19.3 eV
39.5 4.36 km/s
39.7 a) 62.0 nm (photon), 0.274 nm (electron)
   b) 4.96 eV (photon), 2.41×10^{-5} eV (electron)
   c) ≈ 250 nm, electron
39.9 3.90×10^{-34} m, no
39.11 a) 0.0607 V b) 248 eV c) 20.5 μm
39.13 0.432 eV
39.15 a) $2.07°, 4.14°$ b) 1.81 cm
39.17 a) 5.82×10^{-13} J = 3.63 MeV
   b) 5.82×10^{-13} J = 3.63 MeV
   c) 1.32×10^7 m/s
39.19 3.16×10^{-34} kg$\cdot$m^2/s
39.21 a) -218 eV; 16 times b) 218 eV; 16 times
   c) 7.60 nm d) $\frac{1}{4}$ hydrogen radius
39.23 a) 2.18×10^6 m/s, 1.09×10^6 m/s,
   7.27×10^5 m/s b) 1.53×10^{-16} s,
   1.22×10^{-15} s, 4.13×10^{-15} s c) 8.2×10^6
39.25 a) 20 eV b) 3 eV, 5 eV, 8 eV, 10 eV, 15 eV,
   18 eV c) photo will not be absorbed
   d) 3 eV $< \phi <$ 5 eV
39.27 a) -17.50 eV, -4.38 eV, -1.95 eV, -1.10 eV,
   -0.71 eV b) 378 nm
39.29 a) -5.08 eV b) -5.64 eV
39.31 5.32×10^{21} photons/s
39.33 4.00×10^{17} photons/s
39.35 a) 1.2×10^{-33} b) 3.5×10^{-17}
   c) 5.9×10^{-9}
39.37 a) 2060 K b) 1410 nm
39.39 1.06 mm; microwave
39.41 a) $1.77T$ b) 0.58
39.43 a) 1.9×10^{10} W/m^2 b) 20 nm; no
   c) 6510 km = $0.0093R_{\text{sun}}$ d) sun; 39
39.45 a) 1.6×10^4 m/s b) 2.3×10^{-4} m
39.47 not valid
39.49 6.34×10^{-14} eV
39.51 a) 1.69×10^{-28} kg b) -2.53 keV
   c) 0.655 nm
39.53 a) 12.1 eV b) 3; 103 nm, 122 nm, 657 nm
39.55 a) 0.90 eV
39.57 a) 5×10^{49} photons/s b) 30,000
39.59 29,800 K
39.61 a) $I(f) = \dfrac{2\pi h f^5}{c^3(e^{hf/kT} - 1)}$
39.63 a) 12 eV b) 0.15 mV; 7.3 km/s
   c) 0.082 μV; 4.0 m/s
39.65 a) no b) 2.52 V
39.67 a) $E = c\sqrt{2mK}$ b) photon
39.69 b) $\Delta = \dfrac{m^2c^2\lambda^2}{2h^2}$
   c) $v = (1 - 8.50 \times 10^{-8})c$, $\Delta = 8.50 \times 10^{-8}$
39.71 a) $\dfrac{h}{mc\sqrt{15}}$
   b) (i) 1.53 MeV, 6.26×10^{-13} m
   (ii) 2810 MeV, 3.41×10^{-16} m

39.73 a) 1.1×10^{-20} kg·m/s b) 19 MeV
   c) $|U_{Coul}| = 0.015K$; no
39.75 a) 1.1×10^{-35} m/s b) 2.3×10^{27} y; no
39.77 20.9°
39.79 a) 248 eV b) 0.0603 eV
39.81 a) $F = -\dfrac{A|x|}{x}$, where $x \neq 0$

   b) $E = \dfrac{3}{2}\left(\dfrac{\hbar^2 A^2}{m}\right)^{1/3}$
39.83 a) 3 b) 11.44 nm c) 60.5 eV
39.85 a) Antares b) Polaris and α Centauri B
   c) α Centauri B
39.89 choice (a)
39.91 choice (a)

Chapter 40

40.1 $\Psi(x, t) = Ae^{-i(4.27 \times 10^{10}\, \text{m}^{-1})x}e^{-i(1.05 \times 10^{17}\, \text{s}^{-1})t}$
40.3 a) $8\pi/k$ b) $4\omega/k$; same
40.5 a) $\lambda/4, 3\lambda/4, 5\lambda/4, \ldots$ b) $0, \lambda/2, 3\lambda/2, \ldots$
40.7 no
40.9 a) 1.6×10^{-67} J b) 1.3×10^{-33} m/s;
   1.0×10^{33} s c) 4.9×10^{-67} J d) no
40.11 0.166 nm
40.13 0.61 nm
40.15 b) no; no c) $\sqrt{2}b$
40.17 a) $0, L/2, L$ b) $L/4, 3L/4$ c) yes
40.19 a) 6.0×10^{-10} m (twice the width of the box),
   1.1×10^{-24} kg·m/s b) 3.0×10^{-10} m (same
   as the width of the box), 2.2×10^{-24} kg·m/s
   c) 2.0×10^{-10} m (2/3 the width of the box),
   3.3×10^{-24} kg·m/s
40.21 3.43×10^{-10} m
40.23 1.38 μm
40.25 22 fm
40.27 a) 0.0013 b) 10^{-143}
40.29 a) 4.4×10^{-8} b) 4.2×10^{-4}
40.31 $1/\sqrt{2}$
40.33 1.11×10^{-33} J = 6.93×10^{-15} eV,
   2.22×10^{-33} J = 1.39×10^{-14} eV; no
40.35 a) 0.21 eV b) 5900 N/m
40.37 111 nm
40.39 $(2n + 1)\dfrac{\hbar}{2}$, increases with n
40.41 a) 5.89×10^{-3} eV b) 106 μm c) 0.0118 eV
40.43 a) $|\Psi(x, t)|^2 = \dfrac{2}{L}\left[1 - \cos\left(\dfrac{4\pi^2 \hbar t}{mL^2}\right)\right]$

   b) $\dfrac{4\pi^2 \hbar}{mL^2}$
40.45 $B = \left(\dfrac{k_1 - k_2}{k_1 + k_2}\right)A, C = \left(\dfrac{2k_2}{k_1 + k_2}\right)A$
40.47 a) 19.2 μm b) 11.5 μm
40.49 a) $(2/L)dx$ b) 0 c) $(2/L)dx$
40.51 a) 0.818 b) 0.500 c) yes
40.55 a) $A = C, B\sin kL + A\cos kL = De^{-\kappa L}$,
   where $k = \dfrac{\sqrt{2mE}}{\hbar}$
   b) $kB = \kappa C, kB\cos kL - kA\sin kL = -\kappa De^{-\kappa L}$
40.57 6.63×10^{-34} J = 4.14×10^{-15} eV,
   1.33×10^{-33} J = 8.30×10^{-15} eV, no
40.59 b) 134 eV
40.61 a) 3, 4 b) 0.90 nm c) 890 nm
40.63 22 eV, 56 eV, 110 eV
40.65 a) $x = \pm\sqrt{2E/k'}$ c) underestimate
40.67 choice (c)
40.69 choice (a)

Chapter 41

41.1 a) 1 b) 3
41.3 3.51 nm

41.5 $(2, 2, 1)$: $x = L/2, y = L/2$; $(2, 1, 1)$: $x = L/2$;
   $(1, 1, 1)$: none
41.7 a) 0 b) $\sqrt{12}\hbar$, 3.65×10^{-34} kg·m²/s
   c) $3\hbar$, 3.16×10^{-34} kg·m²/s
   d) $\frac{1}{2}\hbar$, 5.27×10^{-35} kg·m²/s e) $\frac{1}{6}$
41.9 4
41.11 4
41.13 $1.414\hbar$, $19.49\hbar$, $199.5\hbar$; as n increases, the
   maximum L gets closer to $n\hbar$.
41.15 a) 18 b) $m_l = -4$, 153.4°
   c) $m_l = +4$, 26.6°
41.19 a) 0.468 T b) 3
41.21 a) 9 b) 3.47×10^{-5} eV c) 2.78×10^{-4} eV
41.23 a) 2.5×10^{30} rad/s
   b) 2.5×10^{13} m/s; not valid since $v > c$
41.25 1.68×10^{-4} eV; $m_s = +\frac{1}{2}$
41.27 $n = 1, l = 0, m_l = 0, m_s = \pm\frac{1}{2}$: 2 states;
   $n = 2, l = 0, m_l = 0, m_s = \pm\frac{1}{2}$: 2 states;
   $n = 2, l = 1, m_l = 0, \pm1, m_s = \pm\frac{1}{2}$: 6 states
41.29 a) $1s^2 2s^2$ b) magnesium; $1s^2 2s^2 2p^6 3s^2$
   c) calcium, $1s^2 2s^2 2p^6 3s^2 3p^6 4s^2$
41.31 4.18 eV
41.33 a) $1s^2 2s^2 2p$ b) -30.6 eV
   c) $1s^2 2s^2 2p^6 3s^2 3p$ d) -13.6 eV
41.35 a) -13.6 eV b) -3.4 eV
41.37 a) 8.95×10^{17} Hz, 3.71 keV, 3.35×10^{-10} m
   b) 1.68×10^{18} Hz, 6.96 keV, 1.79×10^{-10} m
   c) 5.48×10^{18} Hz, 22.7 keV, 5.47×10^{-11} m
41.39 $3E_{1,1,1}$
41.41 a) $\frac{1}{64} = 0.0156$ b) 7.50×10^{-4}
   c) 2.06×10^{-3}
41.43 a) 0.500 b) 0.409
41.45 a) $E = \hbar\left[(n_x + n_y + 1)\omega_1^2 + \left(n_z + \frac{1}{2}\right)\omega_2^2\right]$,
   with n_x, n_y, n_z nonnegative integers
   b) $\hbar\left(\omega_1^2 + \frac{1}{2}\omega_2^2\right), \hbar\left(\omega_1^2 + \frac{3}{2}\omega_2^2\right)$ c) 1
41.47 b) $n = 5$ shell
41.49 a) $2a$ b) 0.238
41.51 $4a$; same
41.53 a) $(\theta_L)_{max} = \arccos\left(-\sqrt{1 - 1/n}\right)$
41.55 3.00 T
41.57 a) $0.99999978 = 1 - 2.2 \times 10^{-7}$
   b) 0.9978 c) 0.978
41.59 a) 4, 20 b) $1s^4 2s^4 2p^3$
41.61 a) 122 nm b) 1.52 pm; increase
41.63 a) 0.188 nm, 0.250 nm
   b) 0.0471 nm, 0.0624 nm
41.65 a) Li: 5.391 eV; Na: 5.139 eV; K: 4.341 eV;
   Rb: 4.177 eV; Cs: 3.894 eV; Fr: 3.9 eV
   b) Li: 3; 2; Na: 11; 3; K: 19; 4; Rb: 37; 5;
   Cs: 55; 6; Fr: 87; 7
   c) Li: 1.26; Na: 1.84; K: 2.26; Rb: 2.77;
   Cs: 3.21; Fr: 3.8 d) increase
41.67 a) 2.84×10^{10} Hz/T b) 9.41×10^{-24} J/T
   c) 1.78×10^{11} Hz/T; 2.03
41.69 a) 3.02×10^{-11} m, 3.83×10^6 m/s
   b) 83.5 eV c) -166.9 eV d) 83.4 eV
41.71 choice (b)
41.73 choice (d)

Chapter 42

42.1 277 nm; ultraviolet
42.3 40.8 μm
42.5 5.65×10^{-13} m
42.7 2440 MHz; 0.123 m; yes
42.9 a) 1.03×10^{12} rad/s
   b) 66.3 m/s (C), 49.8 m/s (O) c) 6.10 ps
42.11 a) 7.49×10^{-3} eV b) 166 μm
42.13 30.27 N/m
42.15 2170 kg/m³
42.17 a) 1.12 eV

42.19 1.20×10^6
42.21 1.5×10^{22} states per electron volt
42.23 a) $0.0233R$ b) $0.00767 = 0.767\%$
   c) no, motion of the ions
42.25 $0.312 = 31.2\%$
42.27 0.20 eV below the bottom of the conduction
   band
42.29 a) (i) 0.0204 mA (ii) -0.0196 mA
   (iii) 26.8 mA (iv) -0.491 mA
   b) yes, where -1.0 mV $< V < +1.0$ mV
42.31 a) 5.56 mA b) -5.18 mA, -3.77 mA
42.33 a) 977 N/m b) 1.25×10^{14} Hz
42.35 a) 3.8×10^{-29} C·m b) 1.3×10^{-19} C
   c) 0.81 d) 0.058, much less
42.37 a) 0.96 nm b) 1.8 nm
42.39 b) (i) 2.95 (ii) 4.73 (iii) 7.57 (iv) 0.838
   (v) 5.69×10^{-9}
42.41 a) 1.146 cm, 2.291 cm
   b) 1.171 cm, 2.341 cm; 0.025 cm $(2 \rightarrow 1)$,
   0.050 cm $(1 \rightarrow 0)$
42.43 0.274 eV; much less
42.45 a) 4.24×10^{-47} kg·m²
   b) (i) 4.30 μm (ii) 4.28 μm (iii) 4.40 μm
42.47 2.03 eV
42.49 a) $2/a^3$ b) 4.7 eV
42.51 a) 0.445 eV (slope), 1.80 eV (y-intercept)
   b) 5170 K, 1.80 eV
42.53 a) 3.81×10^{10} Pa = 3.76×10^5 atm
42.55 a) 1.67×10^{33} m⁻³ b) yes
   c) 6.66×10^{35} m⁻³ d) no
42.57 choice (b)

Chapter 43

43.1 a) 14 p, 14 n b) 37 p, 48 n c) 81 p, 124 n
43.3 0.533 T
43.5 a) 76.21 MeV
   b) 76.68 MeV; 0.6%; greater accuracy for $^{62}_{28}$Ni
43.7 a) 92.16 MeV b) 7.680 MeV/nucleon
   c) 0.8245%
43.9 a) 1.32 MeV b) 1.13×10^7 m/s
43.11 $^{86}_{36}$K: 8.73 MeV/nucleon;
   $^{180}_{73}$Ta: 8.08 MeV/nucleon; yes
43.13 a) $^{235}_{92}$U b) $^{24}_{12}$Mg c) $^{15}_{7}$N
43.15 156 keV
43.17 a) 0.836 MeV b) 0.700 MeV
43.19 5.01×10^4 y
43.21 a) 4.92×10^{-18} s⁻¹ b) 2990 kg
   c) 1.24×10^5 decays/s
43.23 a) 163 decays/min b) 0.435 decay/min
43.25 a) 0.421 decay/s b) 11.4 pCi
43.27 2.80 days
43.29 a) 2.02×10^{15}
   b) 1.01×10^{15}; 3.78×10^{11} decays/s
   c) 2.53×10^{14}; 9.45×10^{10} decays/s
43.31 a) 1.2 mJ b) 10 mrem, 10 mrad, 7.5 mJ
   c) 6.2
43.33 500 rad, 2000 rem, 5.0 J/kg
43.35 a) 1.75 kGy, 1.75 kSv, 175 krem, 385 J
   b) 1.75 kGy, 2.625 kSv, 262.5 krem, 385 J
43.37 a) 9.32 rad, 9.32 rem
43.39 a) 0.497 mJ b) 0.0828 rem
43.41 a) $Z = 3, A = 7$ b) 7.152 MeV
   c) 1.4 MeV
43.43 a) 173.3 MeV b) 4.42×10^{23} MeV/g
43.45 a) $Z = 5, A = 10$ b) absorbed; 2.79 MeV
43.47 a) 4.7×10^4 J/g b) 8.2×10^{10} J/g
   c) 4.3×10^{11} J/g d) 7600 y
43.49 a) 4.14 MeV b) 7.75 MeV/nucleon, about
   half the binding energy per nucleon
43.51 a) $^{90}_{39}$Y b) 25% c) 112 y

43.53 a) $^{25}_{13}$Al will decay into $^{25}_{12}$Mg.
       b) β^+ or electron capture   c) 3.255 MeV (β^+), 4.277 MeV (electron capture)

43.55 a) $^{14}_6$C → e$^-$ + $^{14}_7$N + $\bar{v}_e$ b) 0.156 MeV
       c) 13.5 kg; 3400 decays/s
       d) 530 MeV/s = 8.5×10^{-11} J/s
       e) 36 μGy, 3.6 mrad, 36 μSv, 3.6 mrem

43.57 1.03×10^{-3} u; yes

43.59 a) 5.0×10^4 b) $10^{-15,000}$

43.61 29.2%

43.63 a) 0.96 μJ/s   b) 0.48 mrad/s   c) 0.34 mrem
       d) 6.9 days

43.65 1.0×10^4 y

43.67 a) 0.48 MeV
       b) 3.270 MeV = 5.239×10^{-13} J
       c) 3.155×10^{-11} J/mol, more than a million times larger

43.69 a) 1.16 h   b) 1.20×10^8 c) 1.81×10^6

43.71 4.59×10^{-5} g/h

43.73 choice (a)

43.75 choice (d)

43.77 choice (b)

Chapter 44

44.1   a) 69 MeV, 1.7×10^{22} Hz, 18 fm; gamma ray

44.3   a) 32 MeV

44.5 9.26×10^6 m/s

44.7 7.2×10^{19} J; 70%

44.9   a) 1.18 T   b) 3.42 MeV, 1.81×10^7 m/s

44.11 a) 30.6 GeV   b) 8.0 GeV

44.13 a) $0.999999559c$ b) 3.83×10^8 rad/s (nonrel), 3.59×10^5 rad/s (rel)

44.15 a) 3200 GeV   b) 38.7 GeV

44.17 a) π^0, π^+ b) 219.1 MeV

44.19 1.63×10^{-25} kg; 97.2

44.21 116 MeV

44.23 (b) and (d)

44.25 (c) and (d)

44.27 a) 0, 1, -1, 0   b) 0, 0, 0, 1   c) $-e$, 1, 0, 0
       d) $-e$, 0, 0, -1

44.29 a) $u\bar{s}$ b) $\bar{d}\,\bar{d}\,\bar{s}$ c) uss

44.31 a) 3.28×10^7 m/s   b) 1590 Mly

44.33 a) 1.08×10^5 km/s   b) 1.46

44.35 -0.783 MeV; endoergic

44.37 966 nm

44.39 a) $\pi^- \to \mu^- + v \to e^- + 3v$; an electron and neutrinos   b) 139 MeV   c) 2.24×10^{10}
       d) 50 Sv, 5.0 krem

44.41 2.494 GeV

44.43 a) 0, $+e$, 1, $L_e = L_\mu = L_\tau = 0$, K$^+$
       b) 0, $-e$, 0, $L_e = L_\mu = L_\tau = 0$, π^-
       c) -1, 0, 0, $L_e = L_\mu = L_\tau = 0$, antineutron ($\bar{\text{n}}$)
       d) 0, $+e$, 0, $L_\mu = -1$, $L_e = L_\tau = 0$, μ^+

44.45 7.5×10^{-23} s

44.47 a) 0.70 rad   b) 0.70 rem, 7 times, 2%; no

44.49 b) $R/R_0 = 0.574$ c) speeding up at 300 My, slowing down at 13.1 Gy

44.51 230 MeV, 12.5° below the $+x$-axis

44.53 a) all are much less; no   b) 37.5 cm
       c) 0.42 MeV   d) 3.8×10^7 rad/s

44.55 a) $Q = -1$, $S = -3$; yes
       b) Δ: ddd, udd, uud, uuu, Σ^*: dds, uds, uus, Ξ^*: dss, uss, Ω^-: sss

44.57 choice (d)

44.59 choice (c)

CREDITS

Chapter 36 Opener: Tomatito/Shutterstock; 36.2ab: Pearson; 36.6: Pearson; 36.9b: Richard Megna/Fundamental Photographs; 36.11: Roger A. Freedman; 36.12d: Pearson; 36.17: Dr.OGA/Shutterstock; 36.18a: National Solar Observatory; 36.18b: Science Source; Appl. p. 1200: Tek Image/Science Source; 36.20b: Estate of Bertram Eugene Warren; 36.24: SPL/Science Source; 36.26: Pearson; 36.27abc: Pearson; Appl. p. 1206: National Radio Astronomy Observatory; Appl. p. 1207: Michal Ninger/Shutterstock; 36.3: Paul Silverman/Fundamental Photographs; Summ. p. 1210: Pearson; P36.90: NASA

Chapter 37 Opener: Brookhaven National Laboratory; 37.4: Adimas/Fotolia; 37.7: John F. Kennedy Space Center/NASA; Appl. p. 1228: Getty Images; 37.11: Science Source; Appl. p. 1234: bikeriderlondon/Shutterstock; 37.18: Science Source; 37.19: John F. Kennedy Space Center/NASA; Appl. p. 1242: Imaginechina/AP Images; 37.25: Matt Cooper/Shutterstock

Chapter 38 Opener: Photolibrary/Getty Images; 38.2a: U.S. Air Force; 38.2b: Bill Corwin; Appl. p. 1260: National Cancer Institute; 38.9: Jupiterimages/Getty Images; Appl. p. 1263: Gianluca Padovani/E+/Getty Images; 38.14a: Lawrence Berkeley National Laboratory; 38.16: Pearson; Appl. p. 1270: glenda/Shutterstock; P38.44 (table): Source: http://physics.nist.gov/PhysRefData/Xcom/html/xcom1.html

Chapter 39 Opener: Eye of Science/Science Source; 39.1: American Institute of Physics/Emilio Segre Visual Archives; 39.4: Education Development Center; 39.6: Scimat/Science Source; 39.8: Ted Kinsman/Science Source; Appl. p. 1286: NASA; 39.9: Kitt Peak National Observatory; 39.10: American Institute of Physics/Emilio Segre Visual Archives; p. 1288 (quote): Source: Ernest Rutherford quoted in Ratcliffe, J. A. (1938). "Forty Years of Physics." In Needham, J., Pagel, W. *Background to Modern Science*. Cambridge University Press, p. 61; 39.15: Boyer/Roger Viollet/Getty Images; 39.19b: Andrew Lambert Photography/Science Source; Appl. p. 1293: Louise Murray/Science Source; 39.31: Ambio-Royal Swedish Academy of Sciences; Appl. p. 1305 (a): Piotr Krzeslak/Shutterstock; Appl. p. 1305 (b): Africa Studio/Shutterstock; Appl. p. 1305 (c): Kletr/Shutterstock; Appl. p. 1306 (top): NASA Images; 39.34b: From Huggins, *Physics I*, © 1968 by W.A. Benjamin, Inc. Reprinted by permission of Addison Wesley Longman; 39.36: NASA; PP39.88–91: Source: "Whole-Cell Imaging at Nanometer Resolutions Using Fast and Slow Focused Helium Ions," Xiao Chen et al., *Biophysical Journal*, Oct. 5, 2011; 101(7): 1788–1793

Chapter 40 Opener: Dmitri Talapin; 40.1: JGI/Blend Images/Age Fotostock; 40.2: Bettmann/Corbis; 40.4: Churchill Archives Centre; 40.17: Media Services/NASA; Appl. p. 1342: Dr. Mark J. Winter/Science Source; 40.21b: Hewlett-Packard Laboratories/Science Source

Chapter 41 Opener (left): Fundamental Photographs; Opener (right): Syda Productions/Fotolia; 41.7: NASA; 41.11ab: National Optical Astronomy Observatories; Appl. p. 1381: Creativemarc/Fotolia; 41.19a: National Radio Astronomy Observatory; 41.20: Courtesy AIP Emilio Segre Visual Archives; 41.22: Felipe Oliveira/Brazil/Fotolia; Appl. p. 1389: SPL/Science Source; Appl. p. 1393 (top): Andrea Danti/Getty Images; Appl. p. 1393 (bottom): Science Source; PP41.70–73: Source: G. Günter et al., "Observing the Dynamics of Dipole-Mediated Energy Transport by Interaction Enhanced Imaging." *Science*, Nov. 2013, 342(6161): 954–956. http://www.physi.uni-heidelberg.de/Forschung/QD/datafiles/publications/2013_Guenter.pdf

Chapter 42 Opener: JPL/NASA; Appl. p. 1410: Alfred Pasieka/Science Source; 42.9: Roger A. Freedman; Appl. p. 1414: Marshall Space Flight Center/NASA; 42.17: Mondadori/Contributor/Getty Images; Appl. p. 1430: Andy Crump/Science Source; 42.36: full image/Fotolia; P42.42: NASA

Chapter 43 Opener: Newscom; Appl. p. 1442: National Science Foundation; T43.2 Source: G. Audi, A. H. Wapstra, and C. Thibault, *Nuclear Physics* A729, 337 (2003); 43.1b: Science Source; Appl. p. 1446: Steve Gschmeissner & Carol Upton/Science Source; 43.6: Lloyd Cluff/Encyclopedia/Corbis; Appl. p. 1463: f11photo/Fotolia; 43.10: Science Source; Appl. p. 1468: Argonne National Laboratory; 43.17: National Optical Astronomy Observatory; 43.18: LLNL/Science Source; Summ. p. 1473: Science Source

Chapter 44 Opener: ESA and The Hubble Heritage Team (STScI/AURA)/NASA; 44.1: Ernest Orlando Lawrence Berkeley National Laboratory; 44.3a: Ernest Orlando Lawrence Berkeley National Laboratory; Appl. p. 1484: Susan Landau; Appl. p. 1486: Mark Kostich/E+/Getty Images; 44.7ab: CERN/European Organization for Nuclear Research; 44.8: CERN/European Organization for Nuclear Research; 44.9: Roger A. Freedman via Mark R. Lowenstine; p. 1497 (quote): From *Finnegans Wake* by James Joyce quoted in J. Joyce (1982) [1939]. *Finnegans Wake*. Penguin Books. p. 383. ISBN 0-14-006286-6; 44.15: ICRR Institute for Cosmic Ray Research; 44.16ab: NASA; 44.20: NASA; Appl. p. 1509: Natursports/Shutterstock; 44.23: National Optical Astronomy Observatories; 44.24: European Space; Summ. p. 1518: National Optical Astronomy Observatories

INDEX

NOTE: Page numbers followed by f indicate figures; those followed by t indicate tables.